World Car Catalogue
1971

ISBN 910714-03-7

Published in the United States of America in 1971

by

HERALD BOOKS

Bronxville, New York

WORLD CAR CATALOGUE

PUBLISHED ANNUALLY BY
THE AUTOMOBILE CLUB OF ITALY

Edited by
L'EDITRICE DELL'AUTOMOBILE LEA

HERALD BOOKS, BRONXVILLE, NEW YORK

Cover picture

Lancia Fulvia 1.6 HF « Stratos »
coachwork by Bertone

Contributors and correspondents

Gianfilippo Elti di Rodeano
Anatolij Gudimov (USSR)
Alan Langley (Great Britain)
Jan P. Norbye (USA)
Gianni Rogliatti
Hilmar Schmitt (Germany)
Luis M. Varela (South America)
Kazimierz Wolff-Zdzienicki (Poland)
Jack K. Yamaguchi (Japan)

Language consultant

Jean Gribble

Editorial offices

L'Editrice dell'Automobile,
Viale Regina Margherita 279, 00198 Roma

Black-and-white illustrations, composition and binding

Arnoldo Mondadori Editore,
Verona, Italy

Colour illustrations and printing

L'Editrice dell'Automobile LEA
Rome, Italy

SUMMARY

Editor's note

The technical information presented in this annual publication has been collected by means of questionnaires sent out to all the motor manufacturers. Though, in a few cases, the incompleteness of their replies has made it necessary to use other reliable sources, the technical information supplied should, for the most part, be taken as official. For a precise interpretation of the figures relating to performance, the following factors should be borne in mind. Firstly, that DIN and CUNA standards for measuring horsepower vary from SAE. It should be noted for general guidance that 100 max horsepower expressed in SAE would be expressed in a DIN or CUNA figure lower than 100. Exactly how much lower varies considerably, though rarely more than 20 percent, and therefore no precise conversion factor can be applied. Secondly, the horsepower for cars manufactured by English-speaking countries represents a slightly higher power than the horsepower of cars made by other countries (1.0139:1). Thirdly, fuel consumption, indicated by figures that are inevitably approximative, is calculated for a medium load and at a cruising speed of about 60 percent of the car's maximum speed on a varied run.

The technical information is grouped in basic descriptions relative to the fundamental models, and similar models differing only in price and in some characteristics refer back to these basic descriptions.

Often the same car may be available with engines that vary both in engine capacity and in power. These different engines appear under "Variations" at the foot of the 'basic' descriptions and are also available for the models which refer back to these descriptions, except when otherwise specified. American production has been organised in a different manner.

The "Optional Acessories" which are shown immediately above the "Varations" (if there are any) are also valid for all the models that refer back to the 'basic' description, except when otherwise specified (some accessories may become 'standard', or not be available or others may be added, but this is always specified).

The prices expressed in sterling are prices before purchase tax.

The prices indicated for American cars are for models equipped with the lowest power standard engine (normally a 4- or 6-cylinder engine). The extra price shown at the foot refers to the higher power standard engine or engines available.

When prices are shown in the currency of the country of origin, these have a merely indicative value for anyone wishing to import the car into another country.

The technical and photographic coverage includes about 900 models at present in production. In general the following have been excluded: 1) those of little importance or visually very little different from others already illustrated and 2) models which, built or assembled outside the country of origin, are on the whole a repetition, even if bearing another name, of the characteristics of a car presented as part of the maker's standard range.

World automobile production

The American Auto Industry and the US Market 1970-71

by Jan P. Norbye

"Can Detroit sell in the U.S. Market?" *Marketing/Communications*, a leading voice in America's advertising world, ran this provocative headline in the number that went on sale just as the 1971 cars appeared in the dealers' showrooms. The question is based on deep problems within the automobile industry. Has Detroit been building the wrong cars, selling them the wrong way, to the wrong people, for the wrong reasons?

The facts confirm that in fact something is wrong. Nationwide sales of imported cars reached 17 percent at the end of the 1970 model year and in California, a trend-setting state, accounted for almost 35 percent of the market. Something happened out there, in the market place, while much of Detroit was unimaginatively pursuing its establish-

ed policy of creating status-symbol cars with built-in obsolescence. At the same time, the auto industry has had to contend with two underlying factors: specific safety and emission standards dictated by the Government, and the end of the American public's love affair with the automobile.

The automobile remains just as necessary as ever to the life of the nation but the types of cars people are buying now are very different from the cars they bought five years ago. Table 1 on page 19 shows the evolution of new car-buying habits. January through September figures are given for 1970 in view of the General Motors strike which began on 15 September.

Don't be misled by the drop in compact sales since 1965. Compacts were down be-

low five percent two years ago, but have bounced back. On the other hand, the loss in popularity of the full-size cars has been gradual and steady, year after year.

What has made smaller, lower-priced cars so popular in the U.S.? The reasons are not hard to find. Traffic congestion, continually getting worse, works in favor of small cars. They are easier to maneuver and park. The state of the national economy — inflation and recession at the same time — has switched buying decisions to less expensive and usually smaller cars. Moreover, the growth in suburban population has led to increased multi-car ownership, which in most cases means adding one small car to the household.

During the five years 1966-70 Detroit saw

The American Motors "Sciabola Bizzarrini" with a 6,500 cc rear engine developing 340 hp.

the sales of imported cars double, while yet another damaging factor to the industry began to take effect. The profit margin began to shrink. Smaller cars have lower prices and the net profit per unit is considerably smaller. As the gross goes, so goes the profit. Oldsmobile, for instance, must sell about 160 Cutlasses to make the same profit as on 100 Delta 88s. There are two further factors that contribute to darken the profit picture:

1. Reduced volume of production increases unit cost (this is true of all sizes of cars).

2. Labor costs are going up drastically, as are certain raw material prices, contributing to an increase in unit cost.

What is the industry doing to cut its costs? It is discontinuing superfluous models (particularly convertibles); eliminating the annual model change on a given car line, such as the Pinto and Vega; increasing commonality of parts between different makes and models; and applying more automation in manufacture and assembly.

In a situation where General Motors has 49.7 percent of the market, Ford Motor Company 27.96 percent, Chrysler 18.21 percent and American Motors 4.07 percent (the remaining 0.06 percent is Checker Motors Corporation), it does not make sense for Chrysler to offer more models than Ford. Yet Chrysler had 111 models in 1970, against Ford's 88. This year, for the first time, the situation is approaching parity, with 87 Chrysler models to 78 from Ford. Standardization among cars of similar size from different divisions has been increasing

for years at General Motors. Fisher Body now builds nine basic bodies with enough variations to produce 132 models, ranging from the small Vega to the giant Cadillac limousine.

It is true this may result in excessive and obvious duplication. But here is how it's done: generally the basic body is designed for a 3-year production run with minor annual "facelifts" involving fenders, door panels, grilles and tail panels, but not the structural members of the body. The parts that do not change are called "under body" and the term is applied to both unit-construction bodies and bodies supported on separate frames. The longer a company can use the tooling for the same underbody, and the more units of that underbody it can turn out in a given time, the higher its profits. At General Motors one basic body may be used by no less than four of its five car divisions. See table 2 on page 19.

Such methods severely restrict styling freedom, of course. GM styling is a separate division which maintains separate studios for each make of car. While the corporate directors of styling have access to all the studios, stylists in the individual car divisions do not. For instance, the men of the Oldsmobile studio cannot come and look inside the Buick studio, and vice versa. Advanced studies are in the corporate hands of GM Styling, and the divisional studios are mainly restricted to making variations on a theme, consistent with the styling specialities of each, so as to assure evolutionary and not revolutionary changes.

Recent examples indicate that the produc-

tion cycle for a basic underbody can profitably be cut from 3 years to 2 by spreading body commonality to more divisions and more models. The advantage of more frequent basic changes seems clear: it provides the sales organisation with a *newer* product, which has always been found to stimulate public interest and increase turnover. The impressive number of different basic bodies within General Motors is shown in the table 2 on page 19. It is significant to keep in mind that the B, C and D bodies have a certain degree of commonality; also that the G body is almost identical with the A body behind the windshield base.

Here it should be pointed out that at Chrysler, there is a great deal of commonality between the B and E bodies (see table 3, page 19). At Ford, bodies 2 and 3 share many underbody, components (see table 4, page 19). But at Ford there is a clear need for improved rationalization. To have eight separate bodies to build 88 different models compares unfavorably with the GM situation. In a year or two, Ford will probably merge bodies 2 and 5, which means discontinuing the unit-construction body of the intermediate size, so the Torino, for instance, can have the same chassis and underbody as the Thunderbird. At the same time, we can expect Ford to merge bodies 3 and 4. This one new body will be smaller than the present body 3 and larger than body 4. Thus sporty cars will be reduced to compact size (following GM's lead with the Camaro and Firebird) while the subcompacts will be upgraded in typical Ford fashion.

At American Motors there are four bodies for five models but rationalization and commonality are further advanced than would appear from this. Though the Gremlin and the Hornet are the only ones to share a body (Body 1), Bodies 2, 3 and 4, used by Matador, Javelin and Ambassador respectively, have extensive commonality. Suspension, brakes, and drive train units are interchangeable to some degree among all models. Which brings us one step further. Commonality does not stop with the bodywork. It involves the engine and chassis, too.

Pontiac, Oldsmobile and Buick use Chevrolet sixes in their intermediaries. But each division still manufactures its own V-8 engines. Chevrolet, Buick and Pontiac all have 350 cubic-inch V-8s. Chevrolet, Pontiac, Buick and Oldsmobile build different 400, 454 and 455 cubic-inch V-8s. Cadillac alone builds 472 and 500 cubic-inch V-8s.

What will happen? Probably one division will be given responsibility for one engine size and supply its engines to the other divisions as required. At some future date, perhaps, all 350 cubic-inch V-8s will come from Pontiac, all 400 V-8s from Chevrolet, and all 455 V-8s from Oldsmobile! Such standardization has long been applied to chassis components, and this trend is increasing. Chevrolet has responsibility for all front suspensions. Brakes are assigned to Buick. Oldsmobile dictates casting techniques and controls rear axles. In the newest automatic transmission built by Chevrolet and Buick, the only difference is in the mountings. Steering gears are supplied by the Saginaw Division of General Motors to the different car divisions' requirements, and will probably be the next target of standardization. The steering linkages have been made uniform on all B and C body 1971 models.

As early as 1966 GM and Ford leaders had really decided to go into the small car business. Chrysler's management had no vision of coming disasters and ignored the question. American Motors had financial troubles and clearly was in no position to study, design, test and develop an entirely new kind of product. Today, Chrysler is still groping for answers and keeps making decisions of questionable merit. American Motors has found compromises that promise success. But the creation of the practical American-built small economy car was left to GM and Ford.

Both giants have overseas branches with many years of experience with small cars, most of which have originated on Detroit's drawing boards. But they never dared to manufacture them in America. It's futile but very interesting to speculate on what would have happened if Ford had decided to build the Cardinal in the U.S., as the intention was as far back as 1962. The whole program was cancelled at the last moment, and the prototype was handed over to Ford of Germany who began producing it as the Taunus 12M. It was never imported into America. Had it been built as an American car, Ford might have won a larger share of the small car market much earlier. From 1967 to 1970 Ford tried half-heartedly to participate in the small car boom with the Cortina while studies for a domestic small car were renewed.

Several parallel programs were instituted. One resulted in the Maverick. That was a practical solution, using a maximum of off-the-shelf parts. Concurrently Ford was toying with a smaller car project, known as the G-car. It had VW exterior dimensions and was powered by a transversely positioned in-line four-cylinder water-cooled engine in the rear. The chassis configuration was discarded, but the G-car body was adopted for a new project code-named Phoenix, using a front engine and live rear axle. This was the basis for the Pinto. It is not an adaptation of the Escort or the Cortina, but a car of similar size aimed at the American driver, and American driving conditions. Yet it has no commonality of parts with other U.S. Fords. The prototype was to have conventional engineering and use certain existing components from Ford's overseas branches, such as engines and transmissions. The overall vehicle size was dictated by Ford management's desire to compete directly with the Volkswagen. Design goals were to match VW price, performance and economy while adding space, style, and flair. Ford also sought to match the ride and handling of the Opel Kadett, the quietness of the Toyota Corolla, and the seating comfort of the Fiat 124.

The result is a surprisingly sensible package. To get the low silhouette dictated by styling, Ford had to lower the seats below European standards of comfort. Headroom is ample, but short people have a problem seeing out. Only one body style was designed for the Pinto — a two-door sedan. The standard power unit in the Pinto is the 1600 cc Cortina engine, built at Dagenham. This decision cut both development time for the car and tooling costs, since production capacity for another new engine in American Ford plants just did not exist. The optional engine is a two-liter version of the new single-overhead-

Left, a diagrammatic view of the Chevrolet Vega 2300 Coupé; above, a detail of the front suspension.

camshaft Ford Taunus power unit, built in Germany.

Over at General Motors, the Chevrolet engineers started with a clean sheet in designing the Vega. It was understood that no Nova, Camaro or Chevelle parts were to be used, or even any Opel or Vauxhall components. Nevertheless, the Vega is conventional in most respects. It does not have front wheel drive; it does not have a rear engine. It's as different from the Corvair as a car can be, in fact, and that distinction must have been a consciously pursued design objective. The 2.3-liter engine is an in-line water-cooled four, but that's all it has in common with the 2.5-liter four-cylinder which used to be listed as an economy option in the Nova catalogue. The Nova four is a slow-running pushrod-OMV job, while the Vega has a radical aluminium-block engine with a belt-driven single overhead camshaft. It is about 50 pounds lighter than the cast-iron Nova unit.

The great news inside the Vega engine is that it has no cylinder liners. The pistons have a cast-iron coating, which gives the same surface compatibility as would have been obtained with untreated aluminium pistons and cast-iron liners, and the block alloy is a special high-silicon development that has been four years in the making and thoroughly tested. The cylinder head is iron, because die-casting technology has not yet been developed to a point where Chevrolet feels justified in trying it out on a complex thing like a head, full of ports and coolant passages and plug holes and camshaft bearings. It is an entirely new design, and if it borrows from anything, it is from the

Vauxhall Victor rather than the now defunct sohc Pontiac Six.

The Vega engine was designed and well into the testing stage before the vehicle was even on the drawing board. Fiat 124 sedans and rebuilt Opels were among the cars used for testing the engine and it is no coincidence that the Vega two-door sedan bears a strong likeness to the Fiat 124 sport coupé. The chassis, however, is strictly Chevrolet in its origin and execution. Coil springs are used all around, and the suspension geometry is patterned on the successful Camaro.

What about the third mini-compact, the Gremlin by American Motors? Introduced in February 1970, Gremlin production for the first model year was scheduled for only 20,000. Public demand was higher than expected, and over 28,000 had been built when the production line closed down at the end of July. By the end of 1971 model year, annual Gremlin output is expected to reach at least 50,000. What sort of car is the Gremlin? It's a weird mixture with a touch of brilliance. The company could not afford to develop a new concept, far less to tool up for production of an all-new small car. It decided to use as many Hornet components as possible on a shortened wheelbase, and for sales appeal to rely on clever styling rather than a sensible package. The Hornet replaced the Rambler American a year ago and is a truly contemporary subcompact with a small success story behind it already. From the front bumper to the windshield there is no difference between the Hornet and the Gremlin. This means that Gremlin buyers find themselves with a

six and a long hood, one unnecessary and the other impractical for a mini-compact.

As late as August 21, 1968, Chrysler Corporation thought it would be well enough represented in the small car field if it merely imported the Sunbeam Arrow and Simca 1100. But as the market potential continued to grow, Chrysler started its 25-car project. It was not to be an all-new car, but a subcompact using a shortened Valiant underbody, and Valiant chassis, drive train components, and engine.

As more details of the Pinto and the Vega leaked out, Chrysler began to realize it was on the wrong track with the 25-car. The car would be too big compared with its rivals, and unsuited for the market conditions in other ways. The 25-car project was scrapped in June 1970, only three months before the Pinto and the Vega were to go on sale, and replaced by plans for a smaller car, code-named R-429. The R-car is to be built in the U.S. but will be powered by British and French engines. The standard power unit will be a 1,500 cc four-cylinder job manufactured in a new engine plant near Coventry. The optional engine will be a two-liter V-6 destined for a future Simca, to be built by Chrysler-France at Poissy. Two versions of the R-429, one for Plymouth, and the other for Dodge, are planned to go into production in January, 1972.

While the new-product emphasis has been placed entirely on small cars, the bigger models have remained in production. A look at the model-by-model bestseller list is not only illuminating in terms of overall trends but also sheds some light on the value of newness and styling.

TOP TWENTY IN US MARKET

Model	Pos. 1968	Pos. 1969	Pos. 6 mo. '70	Pos. July '70
Impala	1	1	1	1
Galaxie/LTD	2	2	2	2
Chevelle	4	4	3	3
Maverick	—	21	4	4
Buick (full size)	6	3	5	5
Valiant	22	22	12	6
Nova	15	8	8	7
F-85	11	11	9	8
Torino	3	7	6	9
Dart	18	18	15	10
Tempest	7	10	13	11
Skylark	16	15	14	12
Camaro	14	18	17	13
Pontiac (full size)	5	6	7	14
Monte Carlo	—	—	22	15
Mustang	8	9	18	16
Cadillac	19	13	16	17
Belvedere	13	16	20	18
Fury	10	12	10	19
Oldsmobile (full size)	9	5	11	20

Chevrolet leads Ford by about 20 percent in the full-size car market. This proportion has been almost constant over the past three years. But only a year ago, Mustang was outselling the Camaro at the rate of 1.5 to one. This situation was reversed in 1970. The table also shows the near-disastrous drop in Pontiac sales and the surprisingly strong showing by Buick. The striking recoveries made by Valiant and Dart overshadow the strange inconsistencies of the Belvedere. The fall in demand for the Torino (which replaced the Fairlane) is perhaps best explained by the sudden appearance of the Maverick.

In the imported car field, the recent situation has been fairly stable, but when seen over a five-year period it becomes clear that significant changes have occurred:

TOP TEN IMPORTS 1966-1970

Make	1966	1967	1968	1969	1970
Volkswagen	1	1	1	1	1
Toyota	8	5	3	2	2
Opel	2	2	2	3	3
Datsun	4	3	4	4	4
Volvo	3	4	5	6	5
Fiat	11	11	6	5	6
Mercedes-Benz	7	7	7	7	7
Renault	10	8	9	10	8
BMW	23	19	14	14	9
Porsche	16	16	15	15	10

The national Highway Safety Bureau has announced the Federal safety standards to take effect between 1971 and 1975:
- Car seats to protect from side impacts by Jan. 1, 1973.
- The car to be rendered inoperable unless safety belts are worn by occupant by Jan. 1, 1972.
- Special restraints to be available for pregnant women by March 1, 1973.
- Inflatable or pop-up types of head restraints.
- Side and rear windows not to pop out by July 1, 1973.
- Non-collapsible car roofs by Jan. 1, 1973.
- A barrier or fire wall to prevent fuel spillage into vehicle interior, possibly by Sept. 1973.
- Energy absorption for lateral intrusions, possibly by Sept. 1974.
- Regulation of exterior protrusions and ornamental add ons to protect pedestrians, perhaps as early as July 1, 1972.

- Greatly upgraded interior impact protection standards for 20 mph protection by Jan. 1, 1974.
- Passive restraint devices (air bags, or similar), postponed from Jan. 1, 1973 to July 1, 1973.
- Safety performance and dimensions for wheels, tentatively for May 1, 1973.
- Maximum limit on carbon monoxide content permissible in the passenger compartment over a period of time, perhaps by Oct. 1, 1972.
- An emergency warning device in cars to warn other vehicles of a stopped vehicle, possibly by Jan. 1, 1972.
- A series of standards covering the handling characteristics of new vehicles — sometime between Jan. 1972 and Aug. 1975.
- Arm and leg reach limits, seat location and access to controls, possibly by July 1, 1974.
- Rear field of view standards (possibly through periscopes) hopefully by July 1, 1973.

Detroit's efforts to eliminate the automobile as a factor in air pollution have also been prodded by Federal and state (notably California) legislation. Most '71 engines are designed to operate efficiently on 91 octane, low-lead-content, regular-grade fuels. The industry claims this will:
a) greatly reduce exhaust particulate emissions.
b) reduce hydrocarbon exhaust emissions.
c) enhance durability of advanced exhaust emission control systems such as catalysts and thermal reactors.
d) increase durability of exhaust gas recir-

culation systems being developed for control of oxides of nitrogen. Catalytic converters and/or thermal reactors (afterburners) with or without partial exhaust gas recirculation may be necessary to meet future emission laws.

General Motors president Edward N. Cole has said that by the fall of 1972, GM will begin "phasing in" its advanced, more sophisticated control systems on a nationwide basis, and plans to have these new systems on all GM North American cars by the fall of 1974 when the 1975 models are introduced.

General Motors says its laboratory expenditure will be pushed up this year by more work on pollution control. In 1970 GM spent $51.2-million on emission research; this year it will spend $70.2-million.

Advocates of steam and electric power tend to assume that the gasoline-fueled piston-type internal combustion engine cannot be made pollution free. Wait a minute! Do we know for a fact that steam cars and electric cars will be pollution free? Not at all. Whenever energy is converted from one form to another, there is a risk that the process will be incomplete, which leaves pollutant by-products. The industry continues to work on the assumption that the reciprocating-piston gasoline-burning internal combustion engine can be "cleaned up" but is not disregarding any possibility. The gas turbine is a strong contender. Detroit Diesel Division of General Motors will begin series production of industrial gas turbines suitable for motor truck application during

1971, and GM top management, who gave the go-ahead order, naturally assumes that GMC and Chevrolet will order these turbines for installation in certain types of truck.

Ford disclosed in June 1970 that industrial gas turbine production will begin in August 1971, initially for stationary purposes, and subsequently for use in trucks and buses. But Chrysler, who have more experience of building turbine-powered passenger cars than any other American company, say production is a long way off.

Recently the Wankel engine has come back into the headlines. Last November 10th, GM signed a $50 million contract with Curtiss-Wright, NSU and Wankel GmbH for rights to manufacture and sell Wankel engines. Ford has also moved closer to the Wankel engine. Ford has several working agreements with Toyo Kogyo of Japan, one of the pioneer licensees of the Wankel engine, and a leader in research and development. NSU has disclosed that Chrysler Corp. has expressed an interest in the Wankel engine.

Yet Detroit all but rejected the rotating combustion engine four years ago, when emission tests gave very discouraging results. Since then a lot of work has been done to "clean up" the Wankel engine, and it has been demonstrated that the Wankel engine has no inherent air-pollution problems. Its potential, we can now conclude, is at least as good as that of the ordinary piston engine. On equal terms in this respect, the Wankel engine still has an important advantage. For, if afterburners and catalytic converters are going to be needed for V-8 piston engines,

there will be a space problem. Not so with the Wankel engine, since it is so much smaller. The rotating combustion engine, and the additional clean-air hardware, can be accommodated inside the existing "package". But there is a third advantage to the Wankel engine, which is the most intriguing from a point of view of economy. Due to its simplicity of design and construction, it may be possible to assemble it in a fully automated plant.

The potential reduction in labor costs is enormously high, and coupled with material savings made possible by the Wankel engine's small bulk and low weight, the financial aspects of the case make the rotating combustion engine extremely attractive for mass production. And there's still a full year left for development work before the design must be frozen so that tooling orders can go out in time for production to start with Job One, 1975 (model year)!

What will happen next? Auto executives have been forecasting an 8.5-million car year for the industry (not including imports). Now some spokesmen for Detroit think it could be a bigger year.

Sales could go beyond 10 million, one company official said. Why this sudden optimism?

There are three main reasons. Savings accounts are swelling with all the money that the stock market failed to attract in 1970. That constitutes a substantial reserve. Why should it be used for new car purchases? There is an enormaus latent demand. Car buying decisions have been postponed in the

1. How American Car Buying has Changed in Five Years

Percent of Market	1965	1970	Change (percent)
Sub-Compacts (Maverick, etc.)	0	4.8	+ 4.8
Compacts (Valiant, etc.)	10.4	8.6	− 1.8
Sporty Compacts (Camaro, etc.)	7.0	7.5	+ 0.5
Intermediates (Torino, etc.)	21.9	22.7	+ 0.8
Full-size Cars (Impala, etc.)	50.5	35.9	− 14.6
Specialty Cars (Riviera, etc.)	1.4	4.1	+ 2.7
Luxury Cars (Cadillac, etc.)	2.7	2.8	+ 0.1
Imports	6.1	13.6	+ 7.5
TOTAL	100.0	100.0	

The Pontiac Ventura II Coupé, available with 145 and 200 hp engines.

hope of better times, while the scrappage rate has remained constant. The recent GM strike had an effect on the latent demand, too.

America's driver-age population is increasing. That means many young people will be buying their first car in 1971.

Finally, economists look for an upsurge in business activity and an easing of interest rates. That will also stimulate the demand for new cars.

1971 could be a new record year.

2. Basic Body Sharing at General Motors

	Chevrolet	Pontiac	Oldsmobile	Buick	Cadillac
A-body	Chevelle	Le Mans GTO	F-85 Cutlass	Skylark	
B-body	Bel Air Impala Caprice	Catalina	Delta 88	Le Sabre Centurion	
C-body		Bonneville Grand Ville	98 Series	Electra 225	Sixty Special Sedan de Ville
D-body					Fleetwood 75
E-body			Toronado	Riviera	Eldorado
F-body	Camaro	Firebird			
G-body	Monte Carlo	Grand Prix			
H-body	Vega				
X-body	Nova	Ventura II			

N.B. There are no plans at the moment to extend use of the H-body to other divisions. However, Olds may build an economy car based on a shortened F-body.

3. Basic Body Sharing at Chrysler Corporation

	Plymouth	Dodge	Chrysler
A-body	Valiant Duster	Dart Demon	
B-body	Satellite Road Runner GTX	Coronet Charger	
C-body	Fury	Polara Monaco	Newport 300 New Yorker Imperial
E-body	Barracuda	Challenger	

4. Basic Body Sharing at Ford Motor Company

	Ford	Mercury	Lincoln
Body 1	Custom Galaxie LTD	Monterey Marquis	
Body 2	Torino	Montego Cyclone	
Body 3	Mustang	Cougar	
Body 4	Maverick	Comet	
Body 5	Thunderbird		
Body 6	Pinto		
Body 7			Continental
Body 8			Mark III

The British Motor Industry

by L.J.K. Setright

Smug though they commonly are in their self-analysis, the British curse themselves in their despair; and the somewhat foetid air breathed by the British motor industry in particular has this year been loud with uncommonly desperate imprecations. No longer can *sad patience, too near neighbour to despair*, afford an example to be followed in the best British tradition of muddling through and winning the last battle; the industry's predicament is altogether too shocking. Some of the blame lies with weak and ineffectual sales techniques and technicians, some with insensitive managements who habitually resort to speech to disguise their thoughts, and some with an

artificial enfeeblement of the intellect among the designers of the cars upon which the nation's economy so much depends; but most of all the blame lies with a greedy and irresponsible labour force whose resemblance to the Gadarene swine is more than a little uncanny. Industrial unrest, given expression in a wild sequence of unofficial strikes, has crippled the industry this year. Very often the strike has been one involving just a few men, but they have been men in key trades in the components industry or have occupied some similarly crucial position in the machinery of car production: indeed the whole pattern looks efficiently planned, and only the naïve pre-

tend not to see in it the workings of a revolutionary and perhaps exotic political agency.

Everybody knows the consequences of this anarchy. The managing director of British Leyland's Austin-Morris division, Mr George Turnbull (whose initials are to be seen on many small British saloons), warned his workers in November that if production were to be hampered by more incessant strikes the division could not stay in business. In the past financial year Austin-Morris have in fact had to pay out an extra £21 million for labour and materials, but strike action lost them 700,000 vehicles. It is scarcely remarkable that the Leyland group's finances are in a bad state. After pre-tax profits amounting to £40.4 million in 1969, they are expected to make a £1 million loss in 1970.

Even this pales in comparison with the £11 million loss suffered by Chrysler UK (the quondam Rootes Group), 6,000 of whose workers are nevertheless demanding a 40% pay rise. Small wonder that Chrysler's other and more docile European subsidiary, Simca, is being encouraged to develop its British market. Then there are 46,000 of Ford's men demanding an equally extravagant ransom; while troubles which beset Vauxhall (*alias* General Motors) earlier in the year set the firm back so far that production has only just recovered to the levels of April 1969. Lotus pre-tax profits for the half-year are only 28% of what they were for the corresponding half-year in 1969, though there are fields in Norfolk full of unsold cars bearing silent testimony to the higher production achieved this year. Ford and Leyland's Jaguar/Daimler division have also produced more in the first nine months of 1970 than they did in the same

The Ford Escort Mexico 1600 GT during a speed test.

months of 1969; but in general production is down, as well as sales. Left-wingers are saying that if there had been no strikes there would have been lay-offs instead, economic depression and credit squeezes having weakened the market anyway. It is true that the 10 million man-days lost this year through strikes are only half as many as those lost through industrial accidents, while "sickness" accounted for no less than 400 million; but strikes are less consistent and predictable, and relatively more expensive.

Desperate ills call for desperate remedies. It may be unfortunate, though, that the American tendency for company doctors to specify surgery rather than prophylaxis is being copied in Britain. With so much of our industry under American domination it is not surprising, at any rate: there have been suggestions that Chrysler will decide on prompt euthanasia for the old Rootes Group, even though the Avenger saloons are now selling very well. The sudden and inept closing of British Leyland's competitions department showed a disturbed state of mind there as well, making some of Mr Turnbull's warnings more menacing than ominous. And there may yet come a time when shall all regret the stunning series of "mergers" that produced BLMC and put so many of our eggs at risk with one basket.

Meanwhile the foreigners made hay while the sun of our exceptional summer shone for them. Imports rose from 10% of new registrations to over 13%, with Volkswagen, Renault and Fiat dominating the lists. At the beginning of the year Fiat were understandably suffering from a lack of production – they too have had labour troubles of no mean importance – but from their

Above, the Ford Cortina 1300 4-door saloon; below, the Cortina 1600 GXL 4-door saloon and, right, a diagrammatic view of the Cortina 1300 4-door saloon.

shaky start they have recovered bravely to oust Renault from second place in the September figures, while at the top of the list VW's share of the imports market has dropped to 2.52%, well below its 3.32% average for the first nine months of 1970. Volvo are doing well in fourth place, proving that the British do not buy foreign cars only for sprightliness or engineering unorthodoxy.

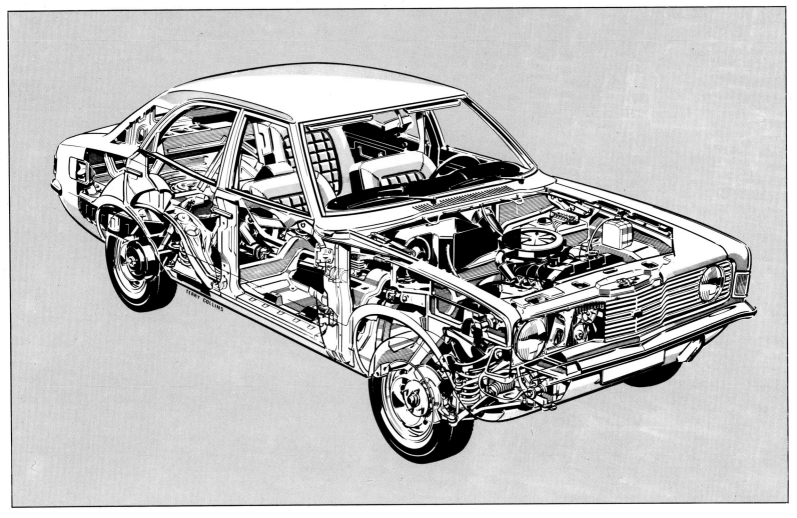

Orthodoxy is my doxy, as Bishop William Warburton explained to Lord Sandwich a couple of centuries ago, *heteroday is another man's doxy*. It was a very English remark, epitomising the mental sloth and ingrained prejudice of the British car-buyer. Only when they think things are going well do British manufacturers dare to introduce anything iconoclastic; so 1970 has not been a stimulating year at the technical level. Rolls-Royce, those archetypes of excellent conservatism, have done nothing to help: we have in the past fifty years grown used to the idea that even if they cannot get their designs right first time they are the world's best development engineers, but the RB 111 aero-engine fiasco and its attendant financial collapse left even that theory overthrown, and all we are left with is the knowledge that no other company could hope to have its losses covered by the Government to the tune of £40 million. Rolls-Royce cars inspire just as much doubt: instead of being given dynamometer figures we were always told that their engines' power output was "enough" – but after changing from GM Hydramatic to Chrysler Torqueflite transmission in order to improve the performance of the Silver Shadow, Rolls-Royce have

quietly increased the engine size from 6.2 litres to 6.9. "Enough" may have been true, but would "barely enough" have been more honest?

In such a situation, what is there left upon which one can rely? The only answer appears to be inflation – not only in the monetary sense, but also in the spatial. Rolls-Royce's engine is not the only one to be growing larger: Ford have now decided for us that the typical family four-seater, as exemplified by their Cortina, will have a 1.6 or 2-litre engine, where only a little while ago 1.6 litres would have been thought the maximum. Ford have for some time excelled in telling the public what it ought to buy instead of asking what it wants, with such remarkable success as may be observed in the welcomes accorded the Capri and the earlier Cortinas. Now the Cortina appears in a third guise, looking much bigger overall despite being exactly the same length as before, feeling bigger, and proving heavier. The more grandiose specification is partly justified by the elimination of the Corsair from the Ford range, partly by the availability of a new pair of overhead-camshaft engines that were going to be built anyway. The product

of Ford's newly cultivated close liaison between their English and German branches, these modestly-rated four-cylinder engines are destined to serve in American-built compact cars as well as in Ford and Taunus machinery built in Europe. American pollution laws have encouraged the evolution of larger and more slothful engines than we had grown accustomed to – in fairness, the extra capacity of the Silver Shadow's engine is thus explained – and the purblind retention of an anachronistic 70 mph speed limit throughout Britain continues to encourage the evolution of cars built to accelerate easily to about the legal speed and then get out of breath. Every offering from all our major manufacturers reveals the same character; Ford's Cortina is only singled out because it is new and interesting.

The most amazing thing about it is the new shape, so scarcely distinguishable from what Vauxhall gave us some time ago that Ford must surely be paying GM a licence fee for it. The kicked-up waistline over the rear wheel arches is a nuisance to folk in the back seat who, as a result, suffer attenuation of the view, in addition to being short of headroom already (the new Cortina is lower than the old); but this must

Three views of the Ford GT 70. Above, a diagrammatic view, right a front three-quarters view and below seen in profile.

be presumed to matter less to Ford than the importance of adopting a given styling feature in as many models of their range as possible. The same trend can be noted in some of the latest American Fords, though Taunus will have none of it. Another stylistic feature is the reversion to a more bulbous style in place of the very rectilinear one that had been all the rage here for a few years: this does wonders for polychromatic paints, and Ford know the importance of their cars looking pretty — the average customer can see much more clearly than he can think.

Styling features may be the most remarkable in the new Cortina, but they are not the most important. Observe the reduced height (2.7 in lower), the wheelbase lengthened by 3½ in and the width enlarged by 2 in and then marvel at a track increased by 5 inches! It is a tremendous increase (one

that other manufacturers are likely to emulate), and the car's stability and looks both benefit. In fact the Cortina is a very well-behaved car, making it the more interesting in embodying double-wishbone front suspension instead of the MacPherson strut system that Ford themselves pioneered so many years ago. If the car is still bad in some details (in particular, the development of the draughtless ventilation system took a wrong turning) it is nevertheless good in most, and a fair improvement on its predecessors.

The same could be said of sundry new offerings from British Leyland. The Toledo that will replace the superannuated Herald is an unremarkable front-engined live-axled family box of modest pretensions, devoid alike of vices and character. It still bears an engine derived from the original Herald's, one that is blessed with strength

and stamina, and the whole car is so indescribably humdrum as to echo Bishop Warburton faithfully: yet, dated though it be, it is more of the 'seventies than the old Herald, which is something over which to rejoice, I dare say. As for its stablemate the Triumph 1500, this too is an amorphous anonymous saloon which replaces the 1300 and is likewise endowed with front-wheel-drive and yet another version of the same old engine. It is a general-purpose trap, whereas the old 1300 was a bijou town carriage, and it is not hard to see where Triumph will be sticking the chromium embellishments next year...

What Triumph will do with their new model, the Stag, is anybody's guess. Sell it, most probably, for it is cleverly designed to fill a vacancy in the market for a stylish if not beautiful fast tourer. It is emphatically not a sports car — not until its power

steering is made more feeling, anyway – but it cruises quite happily at up to 110 mph and is comfortable for two. It is uncomfortable for four, but nowadays what isn't? So it will sell; but not in large numbers, for the complexities of its cast iron cylinder block defy the skills of what passes for a British ironfounding trade, just as the dimensions and shapes of the valves and ports will defy any attempts to tune the new V8 engine to higher power outputs. In fact it is not so new, being but a redesign of that original V8 upon the half of which the four-cylinder engine built by Triumph for SAAB was based. You can date it pretty accurately by its retention of chain drive for the overhead camshafts: the cogged belt was not then an item of proven reliability.

Better endowed with performance, handling and accommodation, the new 2½ litre

pursuits. The Range Rover is the only new car from Britain this year to have anything technically exceptional about it; but in the light of what we have said earlier, it is sufficiently revolutionary to show that for Rover (at least in the case of Land Rovers) things had been going fairly well. The Range Rover makes use of the same very light 3½ litre V8 that has figured in the Rover 3.5 and 3500 cars for some time, detuned and recarburetted so as to run on any petrol and on any gradient. Four-wheel drive at all times (not using the Ferguson type employed by Jensen) gives this new Rover outstanding traction to match the high performance assured by the engine, and a surprisingly effective suspension system ensures that ride and handling are up to the same unexpectedly high standards. Both axles are carried on radius-arm systems and both have 8 inches of working travel, coil-sprung and controlled at the rear by a Boge Hydromat road-pumped self-levelling strut. It is this last item which allows the suspension to be designed for comfort and handling, without worrying about the effects of the 1,500 lb payload which is carried almost entirely by the rear axle. In sum, this go-anywhere car (and it is fit for anywhere, having the mobility and the smartness) is quite brilliant, full of admirable details, and adaptable to an incomparable variety of duties. It is fair to rank it one of the three most outstanding cars to be introduced anywhere in the world in 1970.

Marcos Mantis also has a Triumph engine and transmission, originating in the TR6 PI sports car. The welded tubular chassis frame, while by no means a scientific space frame, is robust enough to serve, and the body behind the engine bulkhead is a one-piece glass-reinforced plastics moulding that is rather nicely made, even through the complete car its pretty hideous. The Mantis is just what many keen family motorists in Britain have been wanting, even if few of them wanted it to look as it does.

Just as extraordinary, though it does not demand such intellectual effort to appreciate it, is the Range Rover, a new all-terrain vehicle to take the place of the old established Land Rover and if possible extend its appeal into those relatively wealthy corners of the market where off-highway vehicles are bought for recreation and leisure

Apart from these few new models, there have been several cases of existing ones being improved or restyled. Sometimes, as in the

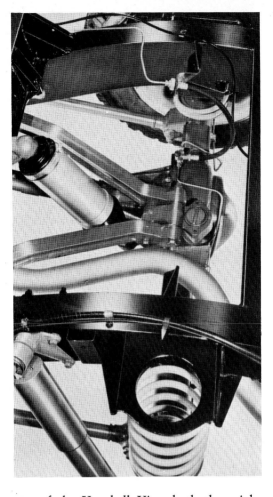

Left, the front end and profile of the Marcos Mantis. Above, the rear suspension of the Range Rover and a three-quarters rear view of the car.

case of the Vauxhall Viva, both these jobs have been done: the new Viva has shed the GM look that Ford have just acquired, and its once notorious ride has been significantly improved. The Triumph Spitfire has been given a Michelotti Stag look, along with a revised rear springing arrangement which quite transforms the handling and makes this economical little sportster splendidly agile. The Austin Maxi has had rectified the few faults upon which so many journalists commented so adversely and perhaps unfairly, and is now as good as it should have been at its inception; while the new 1.75 litre version of it is even better. The attractive, fast and sure-footed Reliant Scimitar GTE may now be bought with Borg-Warner automatic transmission, which suits it well and works more satisfactorily than the Ford gearbox. Marcos have gone further and got rid of the Ford engine (the same 3 litre V6) as well, substituting in their rakish two-seater the Volvo in-line six-cylinder engine with automatic transmission. Thus they eliminate an unreliable engine, probably save money as well (Volvo engines are cheap, even cheaper than Ford), and have the advantage of an engine whose exhaust toxicity is within the limits set by American legislation.

How much good it will do them remains to be seen. With America brooding over a trade-protection bill aimed at proscribing the importation of foreign cars, the possibility that we shall be freed from their mischievous constraints is revived. The British motor industry is pathetically dependent on the American market, and BLMC in particular would be very hard hit if the bill became law — as would Volkswagen and sundry Japanese. The obvious recourse of the Japanese would be to the European market, doubtless to the dismay of the indigenous manufacturers; and the probable entry of Britain into the European Common Market would certainly give Leyland an opportunity to recover — always supposing they had anything suitable for European tastes. At any rate it is certain that they and all our other makers (a few specialists apart) will be working hard to exploit all European possibilities.

Much has been made of the problems that will face Britain in the event of joining the Common Market, but in terms of motor industry competition the Community's other members may be more troubled. A couple of dozen continental firms may have to squabble and scratch for a little share of the pickings in Britain; but Britain will be free to offer its wares to a far larger potential clientèle in Europe. Nor will the attempt wait upon the threatened fortification of transatlantic trade barriers: there cannot be much hope for future profit from an America in which the conscience-stricken expiation of former sins prompts its inhabitants to condemn the motor car as we know it to extinction. If the pollution scare in the USA proceeds at its present tubercular gallop, the Americans will soon be left with nothing but rockets and horses — and no doubt there are plans for purifying the exhaust discharges of these, too. Even if the British motor industry succeeds in putting its own house in order — in which it will need more help than any government in power has yet been brave enough to offer — it is likely to feel confused for some considerable time...

The Italian Motor Industry in 1970

by Eraldo Sculati

For the Italian motor industry 1970 was a year that, even with a touch of optimism, could only be called a period of consolidation. The chief negative factors are the low level of industrial production and the failure to provide adequate housing facilities in the large industrial towns. On the positive side, there is the progress made in the construction of motorways: over ten million motor vehicles, with an average of 5.3 inhabitants per vehicle, have 3,784 kilometres of motorway at their disposal and another 1,319 km are well under way, while yet another 1,294 km are shortly to be begun.

The total number of miles travelled on motorways rose by 15% in 1970 and was accompanied by a comparable increase in the consumption of petrol, which topped 8.55 million tons. Nearly 25 million foreign tourists visited Italy.

The Italian motor industry, both the private sector (the Fiat Group) and the partially state-controlled sector (the Alfa Romeo Group), ran up against a serious problem; it did not succeed in raising production. Fiat produced one million, six hundred thousand motor vehicles, about 80% of its production potential. Alfa Romeo had trouble in matching last year's production figures of 107,000 motor vehicles. The causes of this situation are to be found in the long drawn out negotiations between employers and trade unions on the application of the provisions of the new three-year labour contract for the light engineering trades which came into force on 1 January 1970 and on the consequent long period of trade union agitation.

The development of the Italian motor industry has not been simply a matter of investment; to a large degree it has depended on the evolution of this crisis whose history was in brief the following: on 1 January 1970, once the light engineering contract had been signed, management was faced by the problem of offsetting the rise in the cost of labour in terms of productivity. In other words, how to produce more without increasing the number of persons on the payroll in order to compensate for higher wages and salaries. For 1970 – according to studies carried out by IRI – this increase was 22.5% and, at the end of the contract's three year period of validity, it will reach 40%. These figures are confirmed by experts of the Fiat Group.

These increases include different items, such as regional compensation, the cost of living sliding scale, length of service increases and so on. For management it was a question of making improvements in organisation, renewing plant, making technological alterations to the product, ensuring a uniform work load and so on, in order to achieve full utilisation of productive capacity and to achieve a balance between wage commitments and productivity. There were two means for reaching these objectives: an increase in investment and technological progress. Both required long-term planning

The Alfa Romeo Montreal, the prestige car of the Milan factory.

Above and below, the Pininfarina-bodied Alfa Romeo 33 Spider Prototipo Speciale.

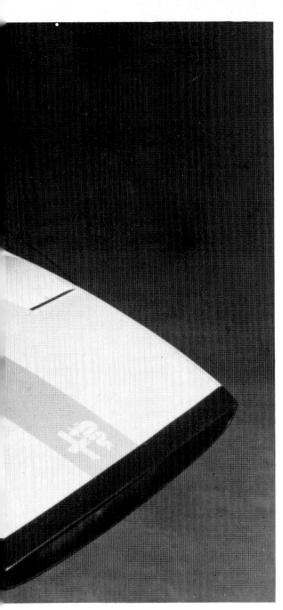

Above, the front end and facia of the Ferrari 365 GTC4 Coupé. Below, a profile of the same car with coachwork by Pininfarina.

and freedom from agitation – or at any rate a truce: in other words a planned evolution of relations with trade unions that would guarantee tranquil working conditions. This fundamental objective was not reached at any point during the year.

Bargaining at company level began in February and March when the firms were busy reorganising their production. There was no lack of meetings: in fact, by the end of the year no less than 300 company agreements had been reached. But the basic differences were not ironed out. The problem that lies at the heart of this divergence is the accusation levelled by the trade unions against the firms: that, by cutting down job times, they have stepped up the rhythm of work to increase productivity and thus re-absorbed the increased costs resulting from the national labour contract by demanding a faster rhythm from their workers.

In short, it was a matter of establishing the maximum limit of the "individual saturation point". The expression needs some explanation: simply put, it could be explained as follows. A man working on an assembly line must carry out a certain number of movements in a certain period of time: the time period is decided by the speed of the assembly belt. These movements take on a constant frequency which, if it is too rapid, reaches the limit of fatigue. Likewise, each man uses a certain proportion of his strength to carry out the movements involved in the work that he has been assigned to. If the material to be shifted is heavier and the movements are more far-reaching and more taxing, the work becomes more burdensome and the limit of fatigue is reached earlier than for another man who is not so heavily taxed physically. Different jobs can be compared by assigning differently

proportioned times, so that each man's work limit is kept below the level of physiological fatigue.

If 100 is taken as the maximum limit of human working potentiality, the average rhythm established by management ranged between 80% and 85%. The trade unions demanded for their members a "70% saturation", and declared that above this point began the phase of the "exploitation of the worker", who lost, in terms of physical strain, what he had gained with the wage increases laid down in the new contract. A 70% saturation meant a fall in productivity; the increased costs could only by met by means of investments and technological progress as mentioned earlier, that is to say over a long-term period, with budget losses and sacrificing possibilities of auto-financing and therefore investment. The firms' managements tried to hold out for an "80% saturation". This resistance led to a fresh wave of agitation and strengthened the trade union leader's conviction of the need for a shift in the balance of power in the factories. This is what has been held to be the fundamental problem.

But there have been others: the reduction of hours of work in accordance with contractual regulations, the elimination of piece work in the sense of separating wages from the measuring rod of productivity, by-passing every form of incentive; the negotiation of a fixed, guaranteed wage, independent of the rhythm of work and criterion of efficiency; the reorganisation of the work categories, reducing the number of grades and eliminating the lower ones, with the final aim of equal privileges for factory hands and office staff. The trade unions recognised the need for an increase in productivity but felt that the goal must be reached gradually, along the long-term path of investment and technological progress, and without increasing the speed of the assembly lines. Alfa Romeo was particularly hard hit by agitations. This fact has led to a psychologically difficult situation in the firm, facing the employees – or at least the majority of them – with a battle of conscience between their loyalty to the firm and to their work and the need to improve their conditions under the stimulus of family demands.

In this regard, Sig. Petrilli, president of IRI (the group to which Alfa Romeo belongs) stated:

"What we are chiefly concerned about is not so much the continual increase in the cost of work as the concentration of the increases in the moment when the labour contract is renewed, the hammering we took during the 'hot autumn' of 1969. Can we absorb these blows? Frankly I hardly feel able to say we can in 1970. They can only

be absorbed to the extent that we succeed in rediscovering peace within the company; to the degree in which trade union relations can develop and to the degree in which calm working conditions in our firms can be guaranteed". The goal of peace within the company has partially been achieved in the firms belonging to the Fiat Group, but to a far lesser degree in Alfa Romeo.

Last year decentralisation towards the South took a more concrete step forward. The aim is always the same: to increase production. Instead of increasing the size of the existing factories by shifting labour from the South to the North with all the re-settlement problems this involves, to build new factories in the South; to bring the work

to where the men are and not to move the men to where the work is. For the three-year period 1970-72, the investments of the Fiat Group in the South, in line with a programme approved by the ministerial commission for "planned negotiation", amount to a figure in the region of 250 billion lire. More than 19,000 persons will be employed in the new plants and this will mean employment for at least as many unskilled persons. Three factories are being built at Bari, one at Lecce and another at Brindisi, and work has begun on others at Cassino, Termoli, Sulmona and Vasto. At Termini Imerese, the Sicilfiat factory is nearing completion and will have an annual productive capacity of 50,000 motor vehicles.

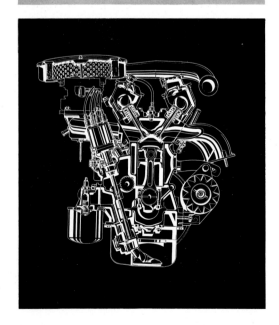

On this page, the Fiat 124 Special T and its dohc engine. Opposite: above, the Fiat 130 Coupé and a detail of the automatic gearbox used on the 124 and 125; below, the 125 Special Berlina.

In all, in 1972, Fiat will have a potential production of 300,000 cars per year in the South, that is to say the same number as Alfa Sud.

Within the framework of IRI investments in the motor industry in the South, Alfa Sud takes the foremost place. The president of Alfa Romeo in Milan, who is also president of Alfa Sud in Naples, recently illustrated the position of Alfa Sud at the end of 1970:

"Alfa Romeo had for some time been active in the South in the light engineering industry for the manufacture of industrial vehicles and aviation engines. Today the company's programmes are more extensive, with the construction of the new Alfa Sud factory at Pomigliano d'Arco. In fact, on 17 January 1968 'Industria Napoletana Costruzione Autoveicoli Alfa Romeo Alfasud S.p.A.' was founded in Naples.

"The foundation stone of the factory was laid on 29 April 1968 and the completion of the building, all plans regarding the car, the testing of prototypes and the beginning of production was planned to take no more than four years. Labour requirements, including those employed on the sales network, will reach 15,000 units. Alfa Sud will distribute wages amounting to about 45 billion

lire a year and is expected to promote the development of unskilled activities in sectors connected with the motor industry. The plant covers an area of 400,000 square meters and the volume of the building is 4,560,000 cubic meters. The car that will come off the new production lines has been being tested for some time now on the Alfa Romeo experimental track at Balocco, and also on the road, and is now in the final stage of preparation. It offers every guarantee from the technical and aesthetic point of view.

"It is expected that production will reach a thousand units a day when it is fully under way. This rhythm, which will coincide with maximum employment, will be reached in 1973, but as I have already said, the first vehicles will be coming out of Pomigliano by next year". The plans for Alfa Romeo in Milan, again for 1973, foresee a development in production that will bring total figures up to 250,000 motor vehicles a year. So, taken together, the two Alfas in the South and the North, will be producing over half a million motor vehicles a year.

In the autumn of last year, in an interview granted to a journalist, the Managing Director of Innocenti, Mario Fusaia, confirmed that

IRI would be acquiring a holding in Innocenti. However, as far as the motor industry is concerned, he pointed out that Innocenti and Alfa Romeo production could be dovetailed: in fact the Alfa Romeo range of models could be complemented by the Innocenti cars whose engine capacity does not exceed 1,100 cc. Sig. Fusaia then added that the possibility of an agreement should not be excluded, again for the motoring sector, that would see the direct collaboration of British Leyland, Alfa Romeo and Innocenti: this would mean the presence of a large complex in both European and world markets. It was reiterated that the aim of the operation was to increase the potential of Innocenti by means of collaboration with a giant like IRI, for the smaller firm, in view of its characteristics and needs, could find only in IRI a really valid partner.

After Sig. Fusaia's declarations, it was learned from Alfa Romeo sources that the negotiations between the two companies, which had been going on for some time, were still far from a conclusion due to the numerous difficulties inherent in an agreement of this nature. Speaking on this question the president of IRI, Sig. Petrilli, stated: "We are interested. We are examining the possibilities of such developments".

At Fiat, as has already been mentioned, the situation was not so tense. Here is what its president, Gianni Agnelli, had to say about the general trends over the year:

"We have been touched by various aspects. First of all our position on the Italian market has been hit by the fact that we cannot satisfy demand. Imports, which had never risen above 10% of sales, settled down at about 25%. It is a well-known fact that

when you sell a car you gain a customer. We have therefore irretrievably lost some customers.

"At the same time we have lost ground abroad because there too we have not been able to sell enough cars. Our production should at present be about two million units per year and instead we did not reach 1,600,000 motor vehicles.

"Finally our production potential at Turin has fallen by about 5-6% as a result of the national labour contract. Another of the effects of this contract has been, given the possibilities employees have been offered, to bring absenteeism up to 15%, when for a decade it has never been above 5%. This year we have lost 30 million working hours from absenteeism and five million from strikes. Yet our product is still competitive. The drama is that we cannot produce enough".

Besides expansion in the South, Fiat has managed to expand abroad. In 1970, 440,000 cars were produced abroad under Fiat licence or by firms in which Fiat has a holding. On the Italian market, again as a result of inadequate production and the consequent import of foreign cars, Fiat's share fell to a low it had never before touched, 63%.

Fiat participation in the holding that controls Citroën reached 49%. To this regard Sig. Agnelli stated that: "An investment of 25 billion lire has given us a foothold in a firm with 500,000 customers and a technology that is – I do not want to say better – much more advanced than ours and complementary to it". The plant built by Fiat at Togliattigrad on the Volga on behalf of the Soviet Union has already begun pro-

duction. It will reach its full rhythm in 1972 with a daily production of two thousand cars derived from the Fiat 124 and suited to the needs of the Soviet market.

Let us now turn to the most important novelties presented during the year by the principal Italian makers.

At the Geneva Motor Show last March, Alfa Romeo presented its prestige car, the Montreal. This is a "grand touring" car with a large engine capacity; its 2.6 litre engine is derived from racing experience and is built of light alloy. It has four camshafts, injection fuel feed, electronic ignition, a Porsche gearbox and coachwork by Bertone. The Montreal takes its name from the Canadian town where its first version was on show at the 1967 World Fair.

At the Turin Motor Show we saw the new range of Giulias (dual braking circuit, hung pedals, alternator in place of dynamo, etc.) and a new model, the 1300 Super: this has the engine of the GT 1300 Junior mounted on the slightly improved body of the 1300 TI.

Autobianchi (Fiat Group) is concentrating on three models: the A 111, the Miniprimula A 112 and the Giardiniera. In 1970 the A 111 was renovated, the design of the bumpers was changed, the headlamps were improved, the gear lever, the dashboard box and the new ventilation and heating system were placed more rationally and a new type of upholstery was used.

The Dino Ferrari (Fiat Group) underwent radical evolution on the basis of recent rac-

Above, the Lamborghini Urraco and below the V8 engine. Right, the Lancia Flavia Coupé 1600 HF 2ª Serie.

ing experience in its engine, gearbox and suspension. Both the chassis and the brakes were completely renewed. There is a newly designed steering wheel on an anti-shock steering column, more room inside, improved sound-proofing, ventilation and heating. The controls have been rearranged.

There has been no important novelty in the Fiat range, simply updating and interesting innovations. The 130 had its power increased: the compression ratio moved up from 8.3 to 9, the carburettors from 42 to 45 mm and the power was raised from 144 to 155 hp (DIN), partly due to a new design of the outlet manifold. A 900 cc engine was mounted on the 850 Familiare. The 124 and 125 family saloons now have modernised mechanics, front ends, tails and internal finishings. Originally there were four models of these saloons: the 124 (60 hp DIN, 140

km/h), the 124 Special (70 hp DIN, 150 km/h), the 125 (90 hp DIN, 160 km/h) and the 125 Special (100 hp DIN, 170 km/h). Now a fifth has been added to the range – the 124 Special T. This saloon has the same body as the 124 Special, the twin-shaft engine of the 1,438 cc 124 Coupé but with slightly less power. In addition, the 124 Special, the 125 and the 125 Special are now available with automatic gearbox and hydraulic torque convertor.

Innocenti has presented the third series of its Minis: the MK3. The doors no longer have sliding windows, but the usual up and down type with a deflector. There are push-button door handles. Ventilation has been improved, there is a new steering wheel, the accelerator pedal is wider to make it easier to "heel and toe", and the seating is more comfortable. The performance remains un-

changed at 135 km/h. The Mini Cooper too has become the MK3 with new more sporting seating but again with unvaried performance (150 km/h). The Mini Matic version of this little car with automatic transmission has also been introduced into Italy: you change gear either by stepping on the accelerator or by using the gear lever (without using the clutch). It has a 46 hp engine, a maximum speed of 78 mph and weighs 1,444 lbs, and normal fuel consumption is 38.7 m/imp pt, 32.2 m/US pt. A new car, inspired by the IM3 and the J4 was also presented by Innocenti – the J5. Compared with the two earlier models, the mechanical parts have been improved while the coachwork has been even more radically modified. Externally it has a new front end and inside a newly designed facia, reclining backrests, a jointed steering column with anti-theft device, new wheel rims and so on. A servo brake has also been added.

At the 1970 Geneva Motor Show, Lamborghini presented a new model with coach-work by Bertone, the Jarama Coupé, a de luxe grand touring car with clean, modern lines. The car is made for two but with a little good will another two can be tucked in behind. The absolute novelty of the Turin Show, on the other hand, offers four commodious seats. This is the Urraco P 250 with a centrally placed 2 ½ litre V8 engine mounted transversally. This car, too, has a Bertone designed body.

Lancia (Fiat Group) stepped up the power of its Fulvia range, presenting the second series which shows noteworthy technical improvements and new suspension that gives much better road holding. The new Fulvia coupés have larger-section tyres. There are also practical improvements: a five-speed gearbox and dual circuit braking system. The careful study and application of a series of elements that improve preventive and protective safety, tried out during a testing rally, give the second series Fulvias the air of a completely new range of models.

Racing activities in the early part of the year did not give fans much to cheer about. As the year went by, however, things gradually improved and in the second half the Ferraris regained their mastery both of the Formula 1, beating the Lotus, its chief rival, in the last Grand Prix, and of the sports prototype category, beating the Porsches in the last race of the season in South Africa. In rallies, the Lancia Fulvias ran extremely well winning many victories, of which one of the last was the most important, the Rally of Great Britain. Alfa Romeo which had been doing very well in the sports prototype class also finished the season in glory by winning the European Cup for touring cars.

The Motor Industry of Japan

by Jack K. Yamaguchi

The emergence of Japan as a major world economic power is now universally acknowledged, initially with admiration, then inevitably with awe and fears. The young motor industry has been a spearhead in the extraordinary growth of Japanese power, devouring the healthy home market demand as well as vigorously pushing export programs. The government's restraints on trade and investment have kept major foreign economic powers away from our shores, and protected the motor industry in its fledgling days. All this is changing now. 1970 was probably the toughest year the industry has gone through. There were signs of recessions in the general economic situation, and suddenly those home market buyers who had displayed such unsatiable hunger for personalized wheeled transport were a bit more cautious when parting with their yen.

Higher compulsory insurance premiums at mid-year, and public outcries over automobile safety and air pollution did not help domestic sales, either. By October 1970, even the mighty Toyota had to adjust its production target by some 100,000 vehicles (including commercial vehicles). Others suffered more serious drawbacks. The growth rate in home sales was now a mere 8.1 per cent over the previous year, as compared with the original forecast of 14 per cent. For the first time in two decades, it was under 10 per cent. Fortunately, thriving exports hiked up the overall production growth to over 13 per cent.

Explosive expansion is clearly a thing of the past, and the government has released its forecast for 1971, in which it prophesies a total passenger car production of 3,620,000 vehicles, as compared with 3,230,000 in 1970, or an increase of 12 per cent.

As of April 1971, the Japanese motor industry is relaxing restrictions on foreign investors, although the Ministry of International Trade and Industry still controls any affliations and capital participation. The American Big Three seem to have chosen their respective partners, or targets. The Mitsubishi-Chrysler pact is already bearing its first tangible fruits, with the Galant range being marketed through Dodge outlets in the U.S.A. under the name of Colt. Negotiations between Ford and Toyo Kogyo (Mazda), and GM and Isuzu are still in progress at the time of writing, and no concrete agreements have been reached.

Again the government is determined to prevent outright take-overs by the Americans at all costs, and may restrict capital participation to a maximum of 35 per cent, or even less. Toyota now has Daihatsu and Hino in its group, although the latter has long ceased passenger car production. Suzuki may join the group at the most opportune time, although it is riding quite high financially. It is believed that Nissan will sever its relationship with Isuzu, if and when GM sinks dollars in the latter's coffer. Isuzu is currently undertaking part production of Nissan's small car, the Cherry. This should bring Nissan and Fuji Heavy Industries,

The twin-cylinder 2-stroke Daihatsu Fellow Max with front wheel drive.

fastback coupé, is also one of the new crop of speciality cars, although it is perhaps more closely related to the basic saloon theme. The GTO, which unashamedly sports a Pontiac-like grille, is powered by an "export" size 1.6 litre sohc inline four, which ensures good performance. As with the Celica, there is one version which is given a highly tuned twin cam engine mated to a special 5-speed gearbox. Obviously you must offer twin cammers, if your pride-and-joy is to carry sufficient sporting appeal and prestige. Nissan really goes to the limit by offering a detuned version of the race-bred dohc 24-valve six in a domestic model of the 240Z sports car and the Skyline GT-R hardtop coupé. Back to the Galant, which started with a single 4-door saloon body style, but now has no less than four different bodies; 4-door saloon, estate wagon, notch-back hardtop and the GTO fastback. That's proliferation.

Above, the Honda Vamos. Top right the Mitsubishi Colt Galant GTO and bottom right a diagrammatic view of the Nissan Cherry.

makers of Subaru cars and also undertaking a part production of the Nissan range, even closer. The two companies also have common interests in aerospace spheres.

Honda is still going at it alone. It still holds the leading position in the lucrative 360 cc class, although it is now being chased very hard, and its ambitious 1300 range has not fared too well in penetrating the fiercely competitive popular car class.

Intense commercial rivalry between the nine manufacturers who all want to win the largest possible market slices has led to the greatest proliferation of models we have known. This is particularly true of Toyota and Nissan, who between them hold 78 per cent of the over-360 cc market in Japan. Earlier in 1970, Toyota updated the Corona, which supplemented the senior Mark II range. The new Corona is a thoroughly conventional front-engined, rear wheel drive car, which inherited many components from the older model as well as borrowing some, including its sohc iron four, from the Mark II, and is clothed in a roomier sheet metal body.

The Corona was initially available in 4-door saloon and estate car versions, and powered by either a pushrod 1.5 litre or a sohc 1.6 litre four. The home market Mark II was then upgraded to 1.7, but the Corona still ate up a large chunk of the Mark II share. That was, however, a well calculated

risk for Toyota. The Corona range has since been joined by a pillarless hardtop version, and the sohc engine now comes in 1.7 litre capacity only. The Corona for the U.S.A. market even boasts a 1.9 litre Mark II engine to make it competitive against such new rivals as the Pinto and the Vega.

And for the 1971 season, Toyota has introduced two brand new models, the Carina saloon and the Celica hardtop coupé, both using the same power train and chassis but featuring entirely different body shells. Again the Carina overlaps the Corona in size, performance and price range. In fact, it utilizes some of the Corona body panels. Its engine is, however, all new, and features cross-flow hemispherical combustion chambers and 5-main crankshaft. Toyota did not opt for the fashionable overhead camshaft but chose a pushrod-and-rocker system. The engine comes in two sizes, 1.4 and 1.6. The Celica is to the Carina what the Mustang is to the Falcon, or the Capri to the Cortina. It is the first speciality car to appear from the Japanese industry, and will undoubtedly be followed by many others. It is a stylish 2 plus 2, and the top of this "pony car" range even has a twin cam 1600 four, based on the pushrod lower half. Both the Carina and the Celica are very roadworthy, brisk performers, and already showing signs of commercial success.

Mitsubishi's Galant variation, the GTO

Toyota's Corolla has gone through the first major model change since its introduction. The new Corolla is slightly larger and roomier, and is more refined in its interior appointments. As before, it is powered by the familiar 1.2 litre ohv "slant" four, but the latest addition to the range features a 1.4 litre version of the Carina/Celica "upright" four. The Corolla is now Toyota's star merchandise in the U.S.A. market, in which it is offered with a new 1600 cc engine, again of Carina/Celica parentage. Escalation in the displacement war is likely to continue, for Nissan is preparing a 1400 version of the Datsun (Sunny) 1200. Likewise, Nissan's 510 (Bluebird) range now includes 1400 (to replace the basic 1300), 1600 and new 1800 models.

Technically, the most interesting car of the year was the Nissan Cherry front wheel drive saloon. It closely follows the popular European small car theme, in that a transversely placed four inline engine drives the front wheels. All the wheels are independently sprung by McPherson struts at the front and trailing arms at the hind end. There are two engines available for the Cherry, a former Datsun 1000 three-main 58 hp four and a tuned 1200 5-bearing unit rated at 80 hp for the high performance X-1 model. Nissan also introduced two pillarless hardtops last year, the Laurel 2000, which is a variation of the Datsun 1800 saloon, and the Skyline hardtop. Both were received quite well on the home market. The Skyline 2000 GT-R hardtop, which has a shorter wheelbase than the saloon version it replaced, should continue to dominate the local touring car racing scene.

Another successful new range is Toyo

Above, the Suzuki Fronte 71 and, top right, the engine of the SSS version. Below, the Toyota Carina 1600 and below right the Toyota Celica GT.

Kogyo's Mazda Capella. The Capella saloon and coupé are available either with Wankel rotary engine or 1500/1600 sohc four. Toyo Kogyo must have mixed feelings about the Capella sales figures, in which Wankel-powered versions are outselling piston-engined cars! This latest product from the Hiroshima factory has completely wiped out any

doubts and scepticism about this unique power unit.

It is indeed a credit to Toyo Kogyo's technical resourcefulness, but on the other hand, piston engines could bring in more profits (the rotary still suffers from higher component costs. For example, a complete set of rotor seals for the twin rotor engine costs

engine capacity under 360 cc, have been subjected to as much, or even more, civic and legislative pressures, but they continued to prosper. Many privileges they had enjoyed are slowly but surely being taken away. A special and easier-to-obtain driving license has been dropped, and one must now struggle with the controls of a large 2-litre saloon (usually with a 3-speed column change gearbox, and non-servo brakes and steering) to win a much coveted driving permit. There have been talks in official quarters of limiting the top speed of the 360 cc vehicle to less than 90 km/h (there is an unofficial agreement among the 360 manufacturers to hold it under 120 km/h now).

Yet, 1970 registration statistics showed an increase of 11.5 per cent over the previous year for 360 cc vehicles as a whole and an amazing 26.7 per cent increase for 360 passenger car sales.

This class is also reflecting the pattern of larger cars. No factory could now be assured of a comfortable position in the sales chart, if it were to offer one model only. Honda was quick to realize this, and went into a proliferation program with typical zeal. In addition to the 360 saloon (also a 600 for export), it now offers the new Z 2 plus 2 coupé, and a streetcum-off-road vehicle called the Vamos Honda, which is based on a commercial 360 chassis with its aircooled twin immediately ahead of a de Dion axle. Honda is also preparing another separate 360 model, code-named "611", which by all indications will be a 2-seater with 4-cylinder

as much as US$ 30, compared to a few dollars' worth for normal piston rings.) A new Wankel car that had reached the prototype stage but then headed for the rocks was the 360 cc Carol Rotary. The car could not win the necessary certification on the grounds that the 360 cc single chamber capacity did not correspond to the piston engine's equivalent displacement.

Toyo Kogyo has been joined by two more licensees of the basic NSU-Wankel patent, Nissan and Suzuki, the latter developing rotary engines for motor cycle application. Toyota is also considering the Wankel, and has expressed its willingness to use the rotary if its research and experiments prove favourable.

Light automobiles, or vehicles with an

360 cc engine! In this catalogue, you will also see two entirely new 360 cars, the Daihatsu Fellow Max and the Suzuki Fronte 71. The tendency of this extraordinary class of the home market shows that there is remarkably, little owner loyality to fixed brands. Whenever a factory brings out a new model, its sales soar up. Only a few months later, the same factory may slip down the sales ladder if its rival comes up with a yet newer car.

Another interesting phenomenon in this class is a crop of hot 360's. Honda, Suzuki and Fuji (Subaru) offer micro sizzlers powered by 36 hp engines—over 100 hp per litre! Honda's latest "GS" Z coupé even boasts 5-speed crash gearbox, servo-assisted disc brakes and pressure limiting valve to the rear drums. Last year, the horsepower king of the mini pack, the Mitsubishi Minica GSS (38 hp), was toppled from its throne by the Daihatsu Max SS which hit a magic 40 hp. Naturally a highly tuned 2-stroke twin has a narrow power band, and is quite noisy, but provides great fun for younger drivers. With micro cars with this performance, there is bound to be racing and competition. 360 cc racing is indeed becoming quite popular in Japan.

Big time motor racing has come to a temporary halt in Japan. The premier racing event in our calendar, the Japanese Grand Prix for Group 7 cars, was cancelled in 1970, due mainly to the untimely retirement of the Nissan racing team, which had successfully campaigned a fleet of R382 quadcam V12-engined cars in the previous year. Toyota went on developing the latest Group 7 car which is powered by a turbo-charged dohc 5 litre V8 which is reputed to produce over 800 hp. A few examples of the Toyota monster appeared in a demonstration run dur-

ing the season, but there was no race to run it in.

Toyota claims that its primary objective in completing the car was to make it all Japanese or as Japanese as possible, thereby testing and improving components made by its subsidiary accessory makers.

Mr. Kawamata, the head of Nissan, cited more urgent research and development projects on safety and emission control, the latter being of top priority order as the reason for his racing team's retirement. Indeed, Mr. Kawamata was most active in this context, and bought patents on an American developed Freon vapour engine, as well as licensing rights on the NSU Wankel rotary. In the Tokyo Motor Show, Nissan displayed a prototype of an electric runabout, which looked more practical than anything else we had seen, and a gas turbine that was intended for

Opposite, from top to bottom, the Mazda RX500 with a twin rotor central Wankel engine, the Nissan "Personal GT2" with front-wheel drive and the Toyota EX7 with V8 engine. Above, the Toyota Group 7.

larger commercial vehicles. Toyota is equally hard at work. Its electronic safety and emission controls are indeed impressive, the most notable feature being a Doppler-activated air bag system. Isuzu is now offering a Bosch electronic fuel injection system on the exotic 117 coupé, and Honda will soon have mechanical injection on the 1300. Both claim reduced pollution from the engines.

Daihatsu is already selling a limited number of electric 3- and 4-wheelers. Their latest approach is a hybrid vehicle with a 2-stroke engine driving the front wheels in open areas, and an electric motor driving the rear wheels in densely populated areas. The government is also riding the electric wagon by setting official specifications for a 1975 city car, which include a top speed of 80 km/h, a range of 180-200 km and a vehicle weight of 2 tons to haul three to five occupants. Actual development and construction of the government electric will be delegated to the industry with funds from the national coffer.

1970 STATISTICS

Table 1 - Domestic passenger car registrations (cars with engine capacity over 360 cc)

TOYOTA	706,960	(42.7%)
NISSAN	587,590	(35.5%)
TOYO KOGYO	149,046	(9.0%)
MITSUBISHI	88,323	(5.3%)
HONDA	47,326	(2.8%)
FUJI HEAVY INDUSTRIES	28,187	(1.7%)
ISUZU	19,095	(1.2%)
DAIHATSU	13,554	(0.8%)
OTHERS	13	
IMPORTS	16,810	(1.0%)
TOTAL	1,656,904	

Table 2 - Domestic passenger car registrations, 360 cc light cars

HONDA	205,736	(28.7%)
SUZUKI	142,969	(19.9%)
DAIHATSU	129,168	(18.0%)
MITSUBISHI	125,249	(17.5%)
FUJI HEAVY INDUSTRIES	109,306	(15.2%)
TOYO KOGYO	4,663	(0.7%)
OTHERS	7	
TOTAL	717,098	

Table 3 - Domestic registrations by size and type of cars

LARGE (over 2 litres)	2,252	(0.1%)
MEDIUM (2 litre)	135,932	(5.8%)
SMALL (1.5 - 2 litre)	716,723	(30.4%)
POPULAR (1 - 1.4 litre)	780,504	(33.1%)
SPORTS CAR	4,684	(0.2%)
LIGHT (360 cc)	717,098	(30.4%)

Note: typical examples, large car - Toyota Century, Nissan, President — medium car - Toyota Crown — small car - Datsun 1600, Toyota Corona — popular - Toyota Corolla, Datsun 1200.

Table 4 - Passenger car production, home sales and exports of leading three exporters

	production	home sales	export
TOYOTA	1,068,321	706,960	350,590
NISSAN	899,008	587,589	267,197
TOYO KOGYO	220,581	153,762	59,302

The 1970-71 Car Market in Federal Germany

by Hilmar Schmitt

Packed with events for the German motor industry: that is how the 1970-1971 period might be defined. Just look back on the new models and series of models already presented by four makers (Ford, Opel, Volkswagen and Audi-NSU), and forward to further novelties from Audi-NSU, Daimler-Benz and perhaps from Opel and BMW, too - novelties that are likely to be launched in the autumn; consider the price increases, some of them sharp, stagnation in exports, the new Highway Code that comes into force on 1 March 1971 and the new insurance premiums, in force from 1 January 1971, with increases up to 22%. In the first half of 1970 production and sales of German cars were 10% higher than in the corresponding period in 1969, but then came a drop that made the final increase barely 5%, so the German motor industry certainly is not booming and will have to make even greater efforts to remain on a competitive level. This hometruth is underlined by the success, in some cases remarkable success, that one or two foreign makes are having in Germany with new models that seem particularly suited to this market (the home industry offers no cars with an engine capacity below 1,000 cc and only a few models — not many of them interesting — below 1½ litres).

In this connexion it seems rather odd that a spokesman for BMW should have declared not so long ago that the market for smaller-engined cars could happily be left "to the others", particularly as BMW itself now intends to build a factory in Austria in collaboration with the Austrian Steyr-Daimler-Puch AG for the production of a 1.2 litre BMW. Problems connected with production policy seem to be arising more or less everywhere. For instance, experts of the Adam Opel AG forecast that the new Manta will not find enough purchasers in the ranks of present Kadett owners because the difference in price is too great; they feel that the Ascona 16 might become a direct competitor of the Rekord and that the chances of the Manta in competition with the Ford Capri are not good enough to justify hopes that it will steal the scene from the Ford as the "family sports car".

There are problems for Volkswagen, too, that dealers in particular will be faced by: the VW 411 E and the K 70 are in direct competition and the situation is further complicated by the Audi 100, which has the same engine capacity and is produced by a factory belonging to the same group. Production doesn't seem to have suffered, seeing that in 1970 the sales of Audi NSU Auto Union AG, an associate of Volkswagen, for the first time reached a total of two billion marks and it improved its position inside the group.

Mercedes-Benz remains unchanged. Apart from the up-powering of one or two models with 3.5 litre engines when the so-called "new generation" was presented in 1968, nothing has been done to attempt to win fresh customers for this make. Above all, the "little Mercedes" has not been introduced and probably it will never appear. For the autumn Motor Shows, a 4-litre coupé and a roadster are expected. These cars, however, will merely complete the range — and in a rather costly manner.

While we are on the subject of new cars, it must not be forgotten that there are rumours that NSU will be presenting a coupé with a Wankel 3-rotor engine and this car is raising high expectations. The twin-rotor engine of the Ro 80 is still not troublefree, it is true, and pessimists forecast that this model will be extinct by the spring of 1971. But now the might of the Volkswagen Group and above all the experience of the famous Audi engioneers is buttressing the efforts of the formerly tiny NSU.

Two more news items: BMW will probably do something to freshen up its 1800/2000 saloons, last revised and improved in 1968, and Opel are likely to modify the Kadett (the Manta chassis might even be used), first of all to bring it more into line with the Manta and Ascona and secondly to strengthen the final and weakest link in the long chain of Opel models and to bring the Kadett up to the level of the rest of the cars made by the firm.

Ford do not seem to have any worries, but appearances could be misleading. This factory, with its impressive production programme and infinite variations and countless optionals has now lauched on a very competitive market — perhaps under pressure from the parent company — some medium-powered cars that have not everywhere met with a favourable reception. Four years ago Ford introduced a series of models that did not answer the needs of the European market and was saved only by the success of the Capri. It now remains to be seen whether, in the near future, too, the Capri can keep the Ford standard bravely flying, though in the long run it will not be easy for Ford to rely on a single winner.

In a consideration of the problems facing some makes, Porsche and VW-Porsche are rather a case apart, for these two companies are an élite continuing to produce high-class sports cars.

After the analysis of the worries and anxieties of the single companies, let us move on to the pleasanter aspects and more favour-

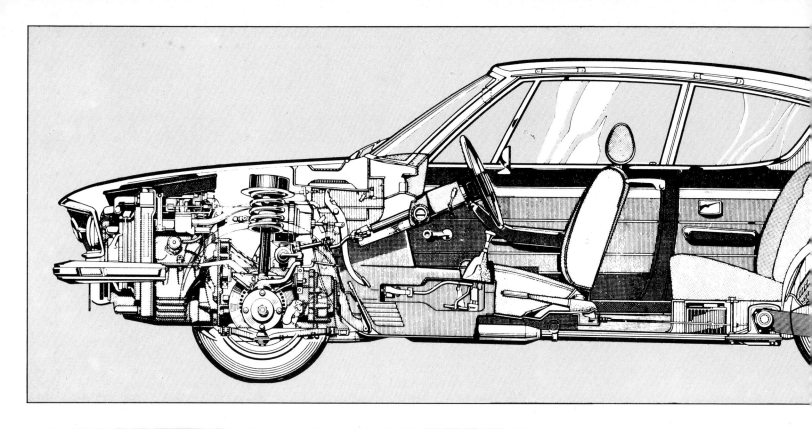

Above, a diagrammatic view of the Audi 100 Coupé S and below, the front axle assembly. Right, two views of the BMW Touring 2000 TII.

able prospects – taken as a whole – of the German motor industry.

Audi-NSU is at present the most "international" firm, holding the patent for the rotating piston engine which took the name of its inventor, Felix Wankel. Twenty-one firms, foreign and German, have to date obtained licences of exploit it. Curtiss-Wright was the first licencee (21 November 1958), Suzuki is for the moment the latest (November 1970) and General Motors (10 November 1970) is the one that to date has made the greatest stir, spending no less than 50 million dollars for the right to exploit and develop the Wankel engine.

Volkswagen clearly does not intend to stand by and merely look on at its associate's activities. It intends to remain a focus point of attention not only with the aid of the K 70 , designed by NSU, withdrawn in the spring of 1969 just before its official presentation and temporarily shelved, but also with a new project, the "safe car".

The K 70 has complex history. It was designed as "little sister" for the Ro 80 and as a link between the small NSU models and the large and costly Ro 80. Its conventional configuration – front four in-line water-cooled engine – is essentially a repetition of good old NSU traditions. Even if the 75 and 80 bhp is above the usual Volkswagen limits, the K 70 certainly isn't the miraculous machine it was thought to be during its lengthy 18 month long gestation period. There were many who did not forgive Volkswagen for giving up such an interesting car

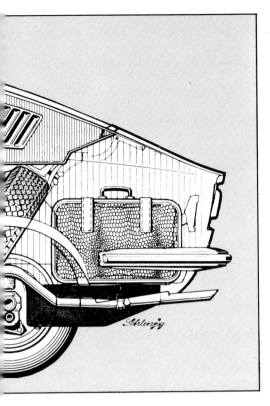

will be able to bring it to a successful conclusion and this is probably why Ernst Fiala has been appointed to head the department. This Berliner is the leading figure in the study of safety in cars and his experience with Daimler-Benz and BMW, together with his job in the same field with the German Motor Manufacturers Association, seems to ensure that he will be busily engaged in making decided improvements to the safety element in cars of European characteristics and dimensions. The 20,000 persons killed and the 550,000 injured on the roads of the Federal Republic in 1970 demand a moment's thought at this point.

Needless to say, the Beetle will live on. How, is what it would be interesting to know, for – for the first time since the standard models of the early years moved on from the old mechanical brakes to the new hydraulic brakes — the Beetle family has been split up. The younger branch, the 1,200 cc engined 1302 and 1302S, has a much-improved chassis and the body too is different from the rest of the family with more room inside and a larger boot.

The "safe car" and the new "Beetles" are in strict relation to one of Volkswagen's vital problems – the American market. Today as yesterday, every fourth VW is destined for the USA and the realisation that sales were dropping in the autumn of 1970 (they fell by about a third in September) caused anxiety. In the summer of 1970, before the annual general meeting, Herr Lotz revealed that, of the two million motor vehicles produced by Volkswagen and its associated companies, too few were sold on non-American and particularly European markets. Volkswagen built 17.7% of the cars produced in Europe but its share of sales on this market was only 12.7%. It is this gap that is worrying the Wolfsburg management, even if a slight improvement has been noted (in 1968 VW's share was only 9.8%), which is however largely to be attributed to the home market's large capacity for absorption up to the middle of 1970.

If the "Beetle" is top of the list of foreign cars imported into the USA, the Opel Kadett lies third. It is therefore clear that some German makes rely to a certain extent –

with a chassis that, compared with the standard VW, could be considered exceptional. Some people even supposed that a touch of envy of the engineers of the "little" NSU had played an inglorious part. Now that the K 70 is on the market, it convinces the experts without arousing their whole-hearted enthusiasm. It should not be forgotten that the K 70 upsets everything that had been accepted by Volkswagen as established dogma in car designing: rear engine, air-cooling, to say nothing of rear driving wheels. In the K 70, which bears the VW badge on its radiator grille, everything is just the opposite. Volkswagen have modified nothing from the K 70 prototype designed in 1968 but rather in their advertising they emphasise that "only the excellent workmanship and the vast sales service network" belong to Volkswagen.

A taste for risk at Volkswagen, the motor company that has always been chided with quite the opposite? The new management headed by Kurt Lotz has found its feet: it wants to show it is not merely capable of building "Beetles", and there is an important development project for a safe car that would keep its passengers from being seriously injured even after crashing into a fixed object at 50 mph. To tell the truth, other Eureopean firms, too, have similar projects in hand and VW's claim to have been first in the field stirred up a storm in the German motor industry. However, it seems certain that Volkswagen, backed up by its 3000-strong research and development department,

and the tendency seems to be increasing – on the American market. Of the roughly 18 billion marks that car exports bring in (15% of the export total figure and second place in value among German exports), almost 5 billion comes from the American market, only a fifth less than the value of car exports to other Common Market countries.

It cannot be denied that in recent years there has been rather unilateral production, which could be worrying, and at the same time the German motor industry is finding harsher competition on the home market. Here are some figures: in 1970 exports stagnated with two million motor vehicles sold abroad. Following favourable trends on the home market in the first half of 1970, production rose to 3.5 million units, while exports fell from 56% to barely 53% of the total. The home market had to, and will have to, absorb a larger and larger number of cars, but there is no certainty it will be able to in the future.

In accordance with the general upward trend, there have been some increases in car prices. In the autumn of 1970 Opel and Daimler-Benz were the first to raise their prices. Shortly afterwards Porsche announced slight markings up and on that occasion a distinction was made between the six-cylinder VW-Porsche 914/6 and the 911 T Coupé, the least costly of the Porsche range. Last December Audi-NSU and Ford announced a 6% increase. Volkswagen, which at the start of 1970 followed the example of the

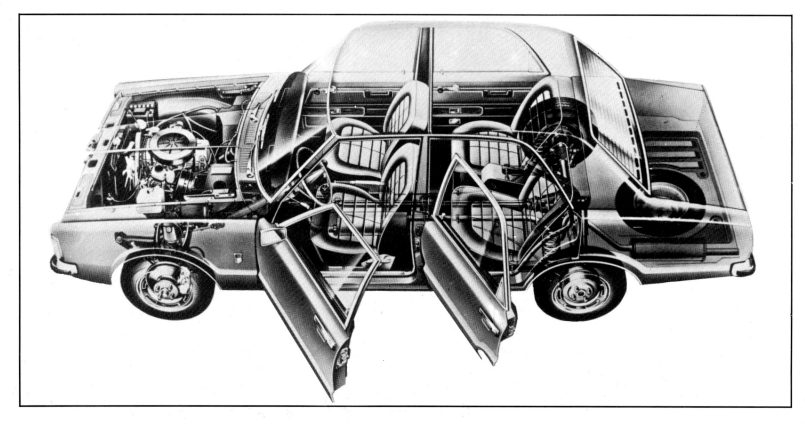

On the opposite page, the Ford Taunus engine in section and a diagrammatic view of the Taunus 4-door Limousine. Right, the profile and below a diagrammatic view of the Opel Manta.

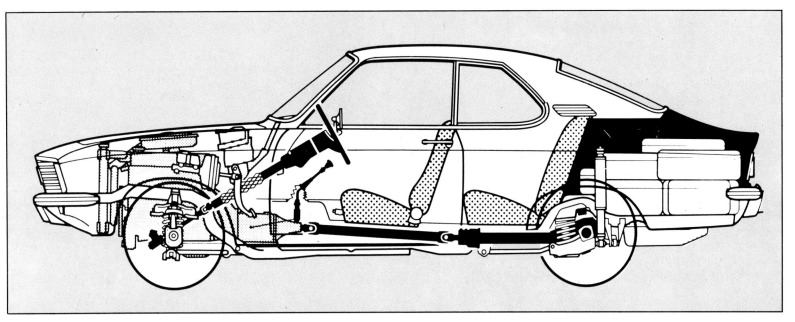

other makes, though raising its prices by only 3.5%, was obliged to announce another slight alteration in order to be able to guarantee once again a 26% dividend for its shareholders in spite of a marked rise in costs. If the sharp rise in insurance premiums is taken into consideration – the fourth in six years – it seems reasonable to doubt whether the home market can expand very much.

The German public's preference in some cases for foreign makes therefore becomes very important. In 1969 376,000 foreign cars were registered, about 20% of the new cars in circulation. In 1970, with about 470,000 foreign cars in about 2 million new registrations, last year's quota was easily exceeded. And when towards the end of 1970 an easing-off in sales was noticed for most of the German makes (except BMW, Mercedes and Audi-NSU), this did not affect any foreign makes except Fiat.

The revaluation of the mark carried out by the new government formed of Social Democrats and Liberals allowed importers to sell their cars at favourable prices. They made good use of this fact throughout the year, following a wise prices policy, that is to say echoing the increases and fixing new prices in line with the market situation in that they were already high enough not to have to be raised any further. Almost every foreign make selling on the German market launched some models at "bargain prices". Then there were the prices fixed by German makers for low-powered cars: many young people buying a new car for the first time have no choice but an imported car. Given a German's loyalty to the make he has chosen, a factor that should not be underestimated, this first step may be followed by many others if the make chosen gives the customer the chance to move on to higher-powered cars.

German motor engineering, which is famed for being loyal to its principles but often boring and bereft of ideas, is changing and is trying to make itself a new image. Opel, notorious for following a policy independent of General Motors and considered by Germans to be a German firm, is an example of this change. Its "grandparents' cars", once slightly despised, are on the way out and are being followed by powerful saloons with complex chassis, the Kapitan, Admiral, and Diplomat and finally the Manta, a production car with sporting overtones, which combines good handling with reliability and has engines that ensure rapid acceleration. The principle of rationality in making cars is to a large extent realised in the Opel Manta. A new front axle and an improved rear axle that has reached perfection contribute to form a chassis that is well up to the engine's performance. This is true of the Ascona, too. The K 70 has similar virtues: compact, functional with slight front and rear protruberances, it stands out in favour of front wheel drive, which has been rather neglected in Germany.

The most costly novelty presented on the German market in the autumn of 1970, the Audi Coupé 100, also has front-wheel drive. This model, too, is a curiosity, for it was exhibited at the 1969 Frankfurt Motor Show but the first cars were sent out to the concessionnaires nearly a year later. Typical difficulties that the German motor industry must face due to suppliers' delays and numerous slight alterations to the 115 hp Coupé delayed its delivery. That delays of this nature due to faulty planning do nothing to win customers' hearts is proved by the letters that can be read every day in the press, and not a few potential purchasers of the Audi Coupé have bought other makes. The German motor industry has perhaps for the first time produced a car that is a happy compromise between a saloon and a coupé body with a sporting air, for it will hold four comfortably.

The new Ford models have already been mentioned. The large use of sheet metal, the American cut of the front end and the return to a traditional configuration with front engine and rear-wheel drive clearly show the direct influence of the parent company. Only the new engines – four in-line with overhead cams – are really interesting and worthy of being called successful if compared with the new engines – again straight fours – of the Opel Manta and Ascona. In fact 72 and 88 bhp DIN are produced by a 1.6 engine capacity in the Ford and 68 and 80 bhp DIN in the Opels. So, these two rivals are facing the market.

This brief technical review, which could be extended to the models expected to be launched, shows how the German motor industry is wavering between low-priced cars that perfectly answer the needs of the larger public and costly prestige models like the Mercedes, Audi Coupé, six-cylinder BMW, VW-Porsche and Porsche and also the VW

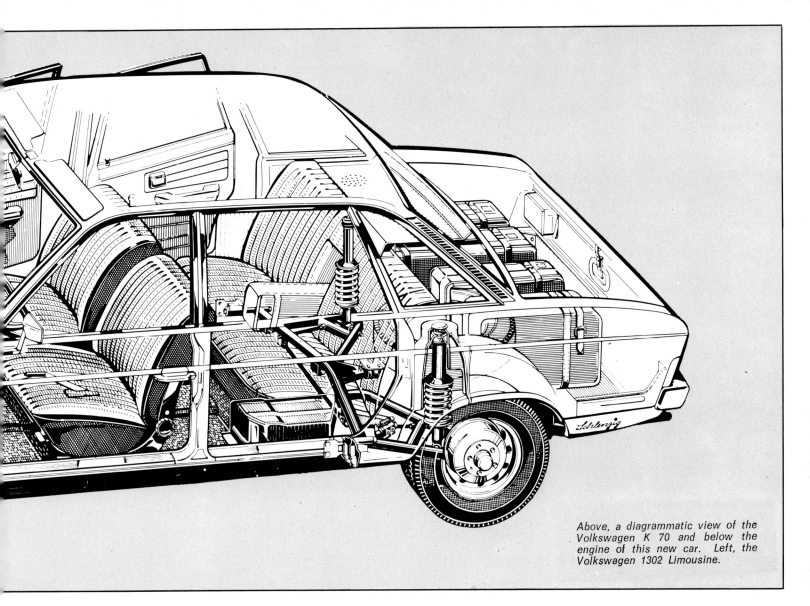

Above, a diagrammatic view of the Volkswagen K 70 and below the engine of this new car. Left, the Volkswagen 1302 Limousine.

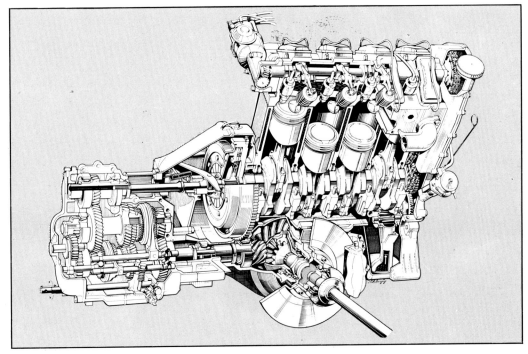

K 70 in its class. Federal Germany is and must remain one of the great producers of cars both for export and for the home market. Obstacles have appeared on the path to success, and no one is willing to breathe a word about Japanese expansion on the world market, let alone bring the problem out into the open.

Before concluding, let us remember two events: Ford has been active in Germany for 40 years. It began quietly with the Model A and in 1970 built over 700,000 passenger cars at Cologne on the Rhine and at Genk in Belgium. To celebrate this anniversary it has launched the 34 variations of the new Taunus series and – almost at the same time – it celebrated the 250 thousandth Capri to leave its production lines in 21 months.

NSU has set up a less spectacular record: it has built its millionth car, a Ro 80. The letters Ro – rotary piston engine – are now a synonym of the motor engineering of the future.

The Fiat-Citroën Agreement in the Context of the French Motor Industry

by Paul Frère

In France there are four of the fourteen European makes that produce over fifty thousand cars a year. Only two of them, however, are still completely French – Renault and Peugeot. Of the other two, Simca has changed the firm's official name to Chrysler France, becoming more declaredly one with Chrysler America which holds a controlling interest in its stock, while Citroën is bound by commercial and technical agreements to Fiat, which holds 26% of its capital.

As a matter of fact, Fiat's intervention in Citroën is much more far-reaching than would appear from this percentage. Before the agreements were concluded in 1968, Michelin, which has controlled Citroën since 1934, held 53% of its capital, a controlling interest since – quite apart from other considerations – the remaining shares were split up among a large number of small shareholders. In 1968 Fiat acquired 15% of the Citroën capital from Michelin (the maximum permitted at that moment by the French government), creating together with Michelin a holding in which Fiat underwrote the part of the capital it had purchased from Michelin and Michelin underwrote the rest of the capital with the remainder of the Citroën shares it held, that is to say 38%. Thus, control of this French make passed from Michelin to the Michelin-Fiat holding. Then, at the beginning of 1970, again with the consent of the French government, Fiat acquired part of the Michelin participation in the holding and thus brought its own participation up to 49% of the capital. However within the holding, whose decisions are law for Citroën, Michelin still has the deciding voice in spite of the increased Fiat participation.

In fact, however, the agreement between Michelin and Fiat may be taken as interpreting Michelin's desire to free itself of the effective management of the motor manufacturing company while retaining an interest in it; it has in effect chosen to entrust the management to a company that has greater experience in this field, one that has clearly shown that it has the necessary competence. And so Michelin can enjoy all the advantages springing from the trading and technical collaboration between two great industrial concerns. And to this regard it should be pointed out that the advantages are not merely the ones deriving from production on a larger scale and from the rationalisation of distribution, but are also specific. Commercially speaking, Fiat offers Citroën huge advantages, while the latter has an extremely advanced technical sector that Citroën's marketing organisation was not in a position to exploit fully, unlike Fiat. In this context we do not have to stretch our imaginations to foresee a car placed on the market one day with the Lancia badge, Citroën hydropneumatic suspension and the variable power-assisted steering that has recently been mounted on the Maserati-engined Citroën SM. Just as it is possible to imagine

The Alpine Berlinette 1600 S Tour de France which dominated the 1971 Monte Carlo Rally.

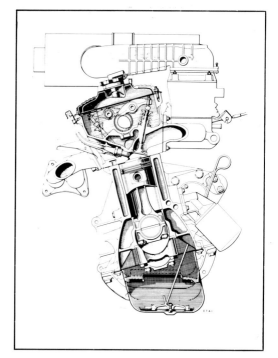

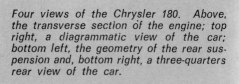

Four views of the Chrysler 180. Above, the transverse section of the engine; top right, a diagrammatic view of the car; bottom left, the geometry of the rear suspension and, bottom right, a three-quarters rear view of the car.

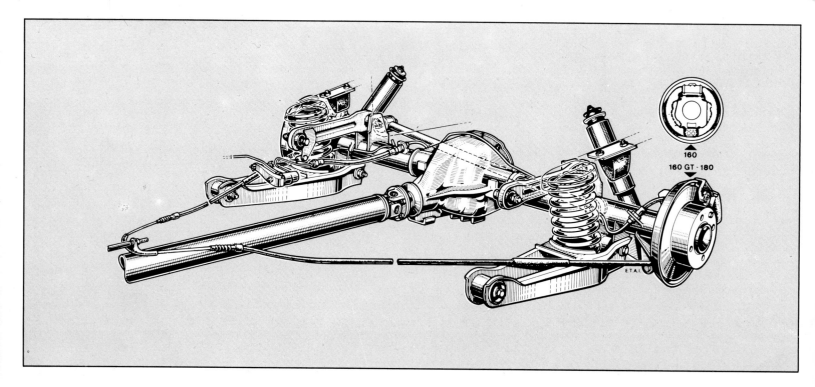

160

160 GT · 180

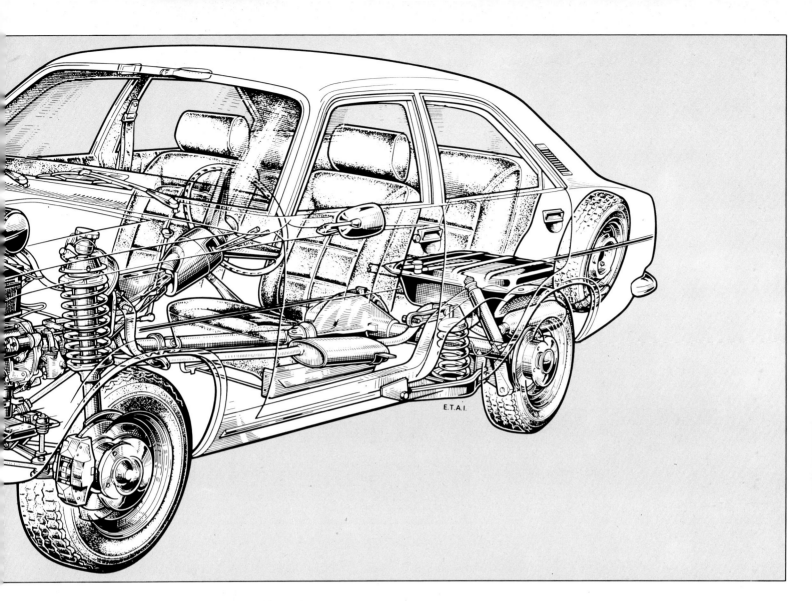

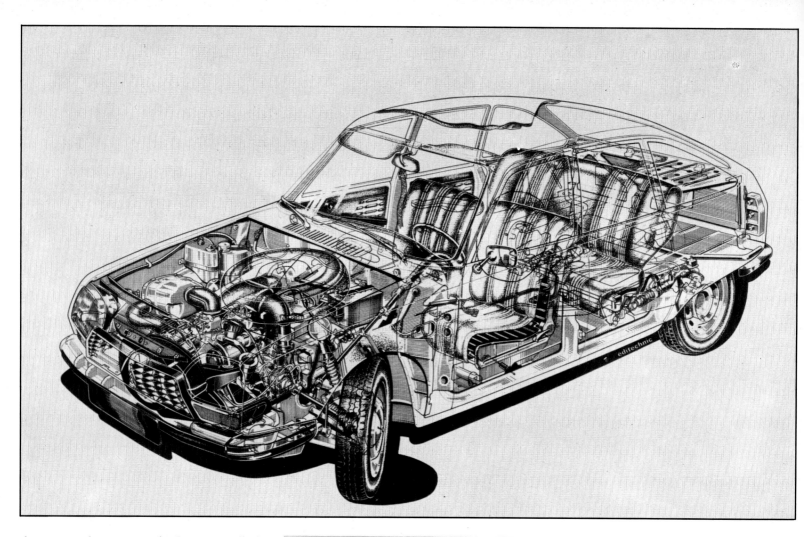

that a medium-powered Citroën will be brought out with the engine of the Fiat 125 – or one derived from it – and at any rate much more modern and efficient than the current D series. Perhaps on the level of mechanical simplification and production, too, Citroën has something to learn from Fiat.

For that matter, even well before the agreements with Fiat were signed, Citroën had been looking for collaboration on a European level and had shown an interest in the NSU-Wankel rotary piston engine, creating together with NSU a company called Co-motor registered in Geneva in which each of them held 50% of the stock. The aim of this agreement was to speed up the development of the rotary piston engine and to design engines that could be common to future Citroën and NSU models. It is quite possible that some of the results of this collaboration may be seen in a couple of years when a car derived from the recent Citroën GS is produced with a Franco-German engine. For their part the Fiat engineers, whose first opinion of the Wankel engine had not been positive, now seem to be changing their minds, probably influenced by the projected American anti-pollution laws

which are likely to lead to legislation in Europe in the same field. The second thoughts that Fiat has had about the Wankel engine are not an isolated example: many firms have reconsidered, including General Motors which recently acquired the NSU-Wankel patents for the huge sum of fifty million dollars.

Within the framework of the Citroën-Fiat agreements, the mutual advantage to the two firms resulting from the distribution of Auto-

bianchi cars by the Citroën marketing organisation in certain Common Market countries (France, Belgium and Holland) must not be forgotten.

For its closely-woven sales and servicing network the Primulas and the A 111 are just the medium-powered cars Citroën needed and they even subscribe to the "Citroën religion", thanks to their front-wheel drive, and thus suit the tastes of the traditional customers of the French make.

Even the little A 112 is a useful addition to the Citroën sales programme since, although a station wagon (even if a de luxe one) it is completely different from the Citroën models in this category, thanks to the compactness of its lines and its decidedly sporting temperament. For its part, Fiat has managed to find a really efficient marketing organisation for Autobianchi cars.

It has been claimed that at the origin of the Fiat acquisition of Citroën capital lay the fact that the French company was labouring under financial difficulties. Even though not denying the existence of these difficulties, (due partly to the decision not to go ahead in 1967 with the production of a new model which was ready and for which all the production investment had already been made), the then president of Citroën, Pierre Bercot, stated that Citroën could have managed quite well alone. What is certain is that, due to the lack of a homogenous production programme (there were no intermediate models between the little two-cylinder 2CV and Ami 6 – 425 and 602 cc – and the D series – 2,000 and 2,200 cc –) and the limited success of the ugly Ami 6, which did not even have the 2 CV's excuse that it was functional, Citroën production has in recent years failed

to follow the general upward trend and is still today feeling the effect of this. Though production has risen in absolute terms, Citroën's share in the French production of cars has gone on dropping steadily: from 22.2% of the entire French production in the period July 1967 to June 1968 it fell to 20.5% in June 1969 and to 19.4% in June 1970.

It is likely that this tendency will be modified by the GS whose size, performance and comfort thanks to its hydropneumatic suspension make it a car in the medium bracket in spite of an engine capacity of little more than 1000 cc.

But more than passing financial difficulties, it seems that the association with Fiat is due to the fact that Citroën, with a production of 450,000 cars a year plus about 100,000 industrial vehicles (including Berliets), is one of that category of average-sized motor manufacturers who are finding it difficult to survive alone. Compared with the price at which, for competitive reasons, the product must be sold, tooling costs are so high today that millions of cars of the same model just have to be built, and in a short period of time so that the model does not lose its sales appeal. This is the only chance of writing off

the cost of the assembly lines. But the problem does not only concern the final stage of manufacturing a car, for this economic principle is repeated at each production stage. Component suppliers, in fact, can quote a lower price for a very large order, since it is only if they are sure of intense production that they in their turn can share out the costs of amortisation over a large number of parts, and the price they must demand has its influence on the final selling price to the public.

Much the same has happened to Simca which has recently been renamed Chrysler France. In this case, too, an annual production just below 400,000 cars manufactured in three principal models was not enough to guarantee sufficient profits, and for several years Simca's share of total French production had been falling, even if only slightly. The merging of Simca with the Chrysler Group, which had been the chief shareholder ever since Fiat had let a part of its controlling interest go to Chrysler, was just as easy to foresee as the Rootes merger.

However, in the case of the ex-Simca, unlike the Citroën-Fiat association, the effective control of the firm passed to Chrysler which has a majority interest in the capital (although

20% still belongs to Fiat), while at Citroën Michelin with its 51% of the shares still has the deciding voice. In the case of Simca, it could be called a take-over, while in Citroën's case it is no more that an agreement for industrial and commercial collaboration and it is only within the limits of this agreement that Fiat can act without asking Michelin for the green light.

As was said at the beginning of this article, the only truly French firms that remain are Renault, whose entire capital is underwritten by the state, and Peugeot. With a production that in 1970 reached a million passenger cars, plus 140,000 industrial vehicles made as either Renault or Saviem vehicles, Renault's share of total French production is about 42-43%, while Peugeot, controlled by the Banque Jordan with a large number of shares held by the Peugeot family, produces almost 21% of the cars produced in France, and this percentage tends to increase. In 1970 nearly half a million passenger cars came out of the Sochaux factory, besides about 50-60 thousand industrial vehicles. Thus Peugeot too is one of the medium-sized firms whose survival is arduous in the industrial world of today. But Peugeot has the advantage of being part of a closely-knit group which also contains some large steel works, so that it manages to procure its raw materials at a

favourable price. Yet even this firm, even though it is not very outgoing, is moving towards agreements and, seeing that the first steps that some years ago led it to a cautious collaboration with Citroën were not successful due to the very closed policy that Citroën was following at that time, about four years ago it moved closer to Renault. In this case, there were no financial operations, but only agreements to collaborate in the technical and commercial fields. One of the aims of the technical collaboration was the design of a new V6 engine with an engine capacity of 2,500-2,600 cc, which is expected to be mounted in a few years on models produced by both makes.

More exports, less imports

For the first time, the financial year 1969-70 saw the French motor manufacturing industry export more than 50% of its production, no less 54%, a figure that was partly due to the devaluation of the French franc during 1969. But even if devaluation stimulated exports in this period, it was not a determining factor in the general trend that has developed over several years, in as much as the fall in production during the 1967-68 financial year was caused by labour troubles which paralysed industry during May and June 1968.

Imports, on the other hand, followed a more irregular trend with an increase of 43.9% from 1967 to 1968, a further 42.5% rise from 1968 to 1969, and then a definite drop of 22.8% in the financial year 1969-70 when the ratio between car exports and imports (including industrial vehicles) returned to very near the 1967 level, that is to say four vehicles exported for every one imported.

Period	Production	Exports	Imports	Ratio Exports to Imports
1.7.66-30.6.67	1,680,500	772,882 = 46%	99.191	4.1 : 1
1.7.67-30.6.68	1,787,161	729,266 = 40.6%	142,748	3.06 : 1
1.7.68-30.6.68	2,110,669	1,006,092 = 47.5%	203,469	2.84 : 1
1.7.69-30.6.70	2,316,631	1,252,294 = 54%	157,159	4 : 1

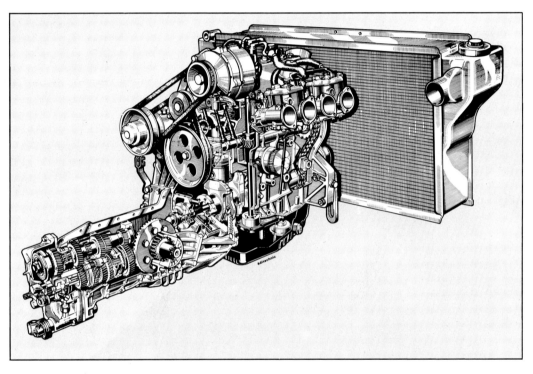

On the opposite page: top, the Renault 6 (1100) and the Renault 12 Break. Left, the engine of the Renault 12 Gordini; below, the front disc brake; and above, the tail light of the Renault 16 TL.

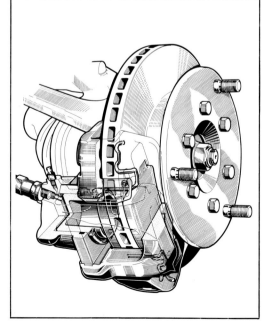

Obviously, the sharp fall in imports from the 1968-69 period to the 1969-70 period was caused by factors extraneous to the industry itself. The steady rise in imports over the year 1967-69 reflects the progressive lowering of tariff barriers between the countries of the Common Market, making it possible to sell certain foreign cars in France at extremely competitive prices. At the beginning of 1969, for instance, a Fiat 125 cost no more than a Peugeot 404, a much less modern car, and the Fiat 125 Special was offered at a lower list price than the Renault 16 TS. During the last financial year (July 1969 - June 1970) labour troubles in Italy caused delivery terms to be lengthened, while in Germany the revaluation of the mark was reflected in the list prices of German cars sold in France. So, since Italy and Germany are the two countries that export most cars to France, the fall in imports is easily explained and also the rise in the sales of home-produced cars.

Make	Production	Rise or fall compared with earlier period
Alpine	880 (485)	+ 82%
Citroën	447,001 (431,893)	+ 3.5%
Chrysler-France (Simca)	398,220 (375,574)	+ 6%
Peugeot	483,309 (427,895)	+ 11.3%
Matra-Simca	1,621 (1,996)	— 18.5%
Renault	985,541 (872,539)	+ 11.3%

Special bodies
Illustrations and technical information

De Tomaso Pantera GT

TECHNICAL INFORMATION

Rear 4-stroke engine, 8 cylinders Vee-slanted at 90°, engine capacity 351.7 cu in, 5,763 cu cm, 10.7 compression ratio, max power (DIN) 310 hp at 5,400 rpm, 53.8 hp/l specific power, cast iron cylinder block, cast iron cylinder head, 5 crankshaft bearings, 1 4-barrel carburettor, water-cooled; rear driving wheels, 5-speed fully synchronized mechanical gearbox, limited slip final drive; backbone chassis; independent suspension, telescopic dampers; rack-and-pinion steering gear; 12 V electrical equipment; wheel base 98.43 in, 2,500 mm, front track 57.01 in, 1,448 mm, rear track 57.99 in, 1,473 mm, overall length 167.01 in, 4,242 mm, overall width 67.01 in, 1,702 mm, overall height 43.39 in, 1,102 mm.

Alfa Romeo 1750 Spider Veloce

TECHNICAL INFORMATION

Front 4-stroke engine, 4 cylinders in line, engine capacity 108.6 cu in, 1,779 cu cm, 9 compression ratio, max power (SAE) 132 hp at 5,500 rpm, 74.2 hp/l specific power, 2 Weber 40 DCOE 32 horizontal twin barrel carburettors, water-cooled; rear driving wheels, 5-speed fully synchronized mechanical gearbox, central gear lever; integral chassis; independent front suspension, rigid axle and telescopic dampers rear suspension; recirculating ball or worm and roller steering gear; disc brakes, servo; 12 V electrical equipment. (For further technical information see Alfa Romeo 1750 Spider Veloce, p. 235).

Alfa Romeo 33 Prototipo Speciale

TECHNICAL INFORMATION

Rear 4-stroke engine, 8 cylinders Vee-slanted at 90°, engine capacity 121.7 cu in, 1,995 cu cm, 10 compression ratio, max power (DIN) 245 hp at 8,800 rpm, 122.8 hp/l specific power, light alloy cylinder block with wet liners, light alloy cylinder head with hemispherical combustion chambers, 5 crankshaft bearings, carburation by injection in inlet pipes, water-cooled; rear driving wheels, 6-speed fully synchronized mechanical gearbox, central gear lever; tubular frame; independent suspension, telescopic dampers; rack-and-pinion steering gear; disc brakes; 12 V electrical equipment; wheel base 92.52 in, 2,350 mm, front track 53.15 in, 1,350 mm, rear track 56.89 in, 1,445 mm, overall length 159.84 in, 4,060 mm, overall width 71.06 in, 1,805 mm, overall height 38.58 in, 980 mm.

Ferrari 365 GTB 4 Berlinetta

TECHNICAL INFORMATION

Front 4-stroke engine, 12 cylinders Vee-slanted at 60°, engine capacity 267.9 cu in, 4,390 cu cm, 8.8 compression ratio, max power (DIN) 352 hp at 7,500 rpm, 80.2 hp/l specific power, light alloy cylinder block, light alloy cylinder head with hemispherical combustion chambers, 7 crankshaft bearings, 6 Weber 40 DCN-20 downdraught twin barrel carburettors, water-cooled; rear driving wheels, 5-speed fully synchronized mechanical gearbox, central gear lever, limited slip final drive; tubular frame; independent suspension, telescopic dampers; worm and roller steering gear; disc brakes, servo; 12 V electrical equipment. (For further technical information see Ferrari 365 GTB 4 Berlinetta, p. 239).

Ferrari 365 GTS 4 Spider

TECHNICAL INFORMATION

Front 4-stroke engine, 12 cylinders Vee-slanted at 60°, engine capacity 267.9 cu in, 4,390 cu cm, 8.8 compression ratio, max power (DIN) 352 hp at 7,500 rpm, 80.2 hp/l specific power, light alloy cylinder block, light alloy cylinder head with hemispherical combustion chambers, 7 crank-shaft bearings, 6 Weber 40 DCN-20 downdraught twin barrel carburettors, water-cooled; rear driving wheels, 5-speed fully synchronized mechanical gearbox, central gear lever, limited slip final drive; tubular frame; independent suspension, telescopic dampers; worm and roller steering gear; disc brakes, servo; 12 V electrical equipment. (For further technical information see Ferrari 365 GTB 4 Berlinetta, p. 239).

Ferrari 512 S Berlinetta Speciale

TECHNICAL INFORMATION

Rear 4-stroke engine, 12 cylinders Vee-slanted at 60°, engine capacity 304.7 cu in, 4,994 cu cm, 11 compression ratio, max power 550 hp at 8,000 rpm, 110.1 hp/l specific power, light alloy cylinder block, light alloy cylinder head with hemispherical combustion chambers, 7 crankshaft bearings, carburation by injection in inlet pipes, water-cooled; rear driving wheels, 5-speed fully synchronized mechanical gearbox, central gear lever, limited slip final drive; tubular frame; independent suspension, telescopic dampers; disc brakes; 12 V electrical equipment; wheel base 94.49 in, 2,400 mm, front track 59.76 in, 1,518 mm, rear track 59.49 in, 1,511 mm, overall length 183.07 in, 4,650 mm, overall width 77.36 in, 1,965 mm, overall height 38.66 in, 982 mm.

Ferrari "PF Modulo"

TECHNICAL INFORMATION

Rear 4-stroke engine, 12 cylinders Vee-slanted at 60°, engine capacity 304.7 cu in, 4,994 cu cm, 11 compression ratio, max power 550 hp at 8,000 rpm, 110.1 hp/l specific power, light alloy cylinder block, light alloy cylinder head with flat-bottomed combustion chambers, 7 crankshaft bearings, Lucas indirect injection system, water-cooled; rear driving wheels, 5-speed fully synchronized mechanical gearbox, limited slip final drive; tubular frame; independent suspension, telescopic dampers; disc brakes, dual circuit; 12 V electrical equipment; wheel base 94.49 in, 2,400 mm, front track 59.76 in, 1,518 mm, rear track 59.49 in, 1,511 mm, overall length 176.38 in, 4,480 mm, overall width 80.63 in, 2,048 mm, overall height 32.83 in, 834 mm.

Fiat 124 Sport Spider 1600

TECHNICAL INFORMATION

Front 4-stroke engine, 4 cylinders in line, engine capacity 98.1 cu in, 1,608 cu cm, 9.8 compression ratio, max power (DIN) 110 hp at 6,400 rpm, 68.4 hp/l specific power, cast iron cylinder block, light alloy cylinder head, 5 crankshaft bearings, 2 Weber 40 IDF or Solex C 40 PII 6 downdraught twin barrel carburettors, water-cooled; rear driving wheels, 5-speed fully synchronized mechanical gearbox, central gear lever; integral chassis; independent front suspension, rigid axle and telescopic dampers rear suspension; worm and roller steering gear; disc brakes, servo; 12 V electrical equipment. (For further technical information see Fiat 124 Sport Spider 1600, p. 245).

Fiat Dino Spider 2400

TECHNICAL INFORMATION

Front 4-stroke engine, 6 cylinders Vee-slanted at 65°, engine capacity 147.5 cu in, 2,418 cu cm, 9 compression ratio, max power (DIN) 180 hp at 6,600 rpm, 74.4 hp/l specific power, cast iron cylinder block, light alloy cylinder head with hemispherical combustion chambers, 4 crankshaft bearings, 3 Weber 40 DCNF 6 downdraught twin barrel carburettors, water-cooled; rear driving wheels, 5-speed fully synchronized mechanical gearbox, central gear lever, limited slip final drive; integral chassis; independent suspension, telescopic dampers; worm and roller steering gear; disc brakes, servo; 12 V electrical equipment. (For further technical information see Fiat Dino Spider 2400, p: 247).

Lancia Flavia Coupé 2000

TECHNICAL INFORMATION

Front 4-stroke engine, 4 cylinders horizontally opposed, engine capacity 121.5 cu in, 1,991 cu cm, 9 compression ratio, max power (SAE) 131 hp at 5,400 rpm, 65.8 hp/l specific power, light alloy cylinder block with wet liners, light alloy cylinder head with hemispherical combustion chambers, 3 crankshaft bearings, 1 Solex C 34 EIES downdraught twin barrel carburettor, water-cooled; front driving wheels, 4-speed mechanical gearbox, central gear lever; integral chassis; front suspension independent, rear suspension rigid axle and telescopic dampers; worm and roller steering gear; disc brakes, servo; 12 V electrical equipment. (For further technical information see Lancia Flavia Coupé 2000, p. 259).

Peugeot 504 Coupé

TECHNICAL INFORMATION

Front 4-stroke engine, 4 cylinders in line slanted at 45°, engine capacity 120.3 cu in, 1,971 cu cm, 8.3 compression ratio, max power (SAE) 110 hp at 5,600 rpm, 55.8 hp/l specific power, cast iron cylinder block with wet liners, light alloy cylinder head with hemispherical combustion chambers, 5 crankshaft bearings, carburation by injection in inlet pipes, water-cooled; rear driving wheels, 4-speed mechanical gearbox, central gear lever; integral chassis; independent suspension, telescopic dampers; rack-and-pinion steering gear; disc brakes, servo; 12 V electrical equipment. (For further technical information see Peugeot 504 Coupé, p. 119).

BERTONE

ITALY

Lancia Fulvia 1.6 HF "Stratos"

TECHNICAL INFORMATION

Rear 4-stroke engine, 4 cylinders Vee-slanted at 12°35', engine capacity 96.7 cu in, 1,584 cu cm, 10.5 compression ratio, max power (DIN) 114 hp at 6,000 rpm, 72 hp/l specific power, cast iron cylinder block, light alloy cylinder head with hemispherical combustion chambers, 3 crankshaft bearings, 2 Solex C 42 DDHF horizontal twin barrel carburettors, water-cooled; rear driving wheels, 5-speed fully synchronized mechanical gearbox, central gear lever; integral chassis; independent suspension, telescopic dampers; disc brakes; 12 V electrical equipment; wheel base 87.40 in, 2,220 mm, front track 52.87 in, 1,343 mm, rear track 57.40 in, 1,458 mm, overall length 140.94 in, 3,580 mm, overall width 73.62 in, 1,870 mm, overall height 33.07 in, 840 mm. (For further technical information see Lancia Fulvia Coupé 1600 HF 2ª Serie, p. 257, bearing in mind that performance and consumption may be affected by different weight and aerodynamics).

Autobianchi A 112 "Torpedo"

TECHNICAL INFORMATION

Front 4-stroke engine, 4 cylinders in line, engine capacity 55.1 cu in, 903 cu cm, 9 compression ratio, max power (DIN) 44 hp at 5,600 rpm, 48.7 hp/l specific power, cast iron cylinder block, light alloy cylinder head, 3 crankshaft bearings, 1 Weber 32 IBA downdraught carburettor, water-cooled; front driving wheels, 4-speed fully synchronized mechanical gearbox; integral chassis; independent suspension, telescopic dampers; rack-and-pinion steering gear; front disc brakes, rear drum; 12 V electrical equipment. (For further technical information see Autobianchi A 112 Berlina, p. 236, bearing in mind that performance and consumption may be affected by different weight and aerodynamics).

FRANCIS LOMBARDI

Volkswagen 1600 Super Sport

TECHNICAL INFORMATION

Rear 4-stroke engine, 4 cylinders horizontally opposed, engine capacity 96.7 cu in, 1,584 cu cm, max power (SAE) 85 hp at 5,500 rpm, 53.7 hp/l specific power, cast iron cylinder block with light alloy fins, light alloy cylinder head, 4 crankshaft bearings, air-cooled; rear driving wheels, 4-speed fully synchronized mechanical gearbox, central gear lever; backbone platform; independent suspension, telescopic dampers; worm and roller steering gear; front disc brakes, rear drum, dual circuit; 12 V electrical equipment; overall length 154.72 in, 3,930 mm, overall width 64.96 in, 1,650 mm, overall height 44.29 in, 1,125 mm.

ITAL DESIGN

Volkswagen-Porsche 914/6 "Tapiro"

TECHNICAL INFORMATION

Rear 4-stroke engine, 6 cylinders horizontally opposed, engine capacity 146.4 cu in, 2,400 cu cm, 10 compression ratio, max power (DIN) 220 hp at 7,200 rpm, 91.7 hp/l specific power, cylinder block with cast iron liners and light alloy fins, light alloy cylinder head, 8 crankshaft bearings, 2 downdraught 3-barrel carburettors; rear driving wheels, 5-speed fully synchronized mechanical gearbox, central gear lever; integral chassis; independent suspension, telescopic dampers; rack-and-pinion steering gear; disc brakes; 12 V electrical equipment; wheel base 96.46 in, 2,450 mm, front track 54.33 in, 1,380 mm, rear track 57.48 in, 1,460 mm, overall length 159.84 in, 4,060 mm, overall width 69.29 in, 1,760 mm, overall height 43.70 in, 1,110 mm.

MORETTI

Fiat 128 Coupé

TECHNICAL INFORMATION

Front 4-stroke engine, 4 cylinders in line, engine capacity 68.1 cu in, 1,116 cu cm, 8.8 compression ratio, max power (DIN) 55 hp at 6,000 rpm, 49.3 hp/l specific power, cast iron cylinder block, light alloy cylinder head, 5 crankshaft bearings, 1 Weber 32 ICEV or Solex C 32 DISA downdraught carburettor, water-cooled; front driving wheels, 4-speed fully synchronized mechanical gearbox, central gear lever; integral chassis; independent suspension, telescopic dampers; rack-and-pinion steering gear; front disc brakes, rear drum, dual circuit; 12 V electrical equipment; wheel base 96.38 in, 2,448 mm, front track 51.50 in, 1,308 mm, rear track 51.42 in, 1,306 mm, overall length 165.35 in, 4,200 mm, overall width 63.39 in, 1,610 mm, overall height 50.39 in, 1,280 mm.

ITALY

Lancia Flavia 2000 Berlinetta

TECHNICAL INFORMATION

Rear (tuned) 4-stroke engine, 4 cylinders horizontally opposed, engine capacity about 122 cu in, 2,000 cu cm, max power (DIN) 130 hp at 5,000 rpm, light alloy cylinder block, light alloy cylinder head with hemispherical combustion chambers, 3 crankshaft bearings, water-cooled; rear driving wheels, mechanical gearbox; backbone chassis; independent suspension, telescopic dampers; 12 V electrical equipment.

ITALY

VIGNALE

Studio City Car

TECHNICAL INFORMATION

Rear engine; rear driving wheels, mechanical gearbox; integral chassis; independent suspension; wheel base 76.38 in, 1,940 mm, front track 46.46 in, 1,180 mm, rear track 46.89 in, 1,191 mm, overall length 130.71 in, 3,320 mm, overall width 57.48 in, 1,460 mm, overall height 50.39 in, 1,280 mm.

ITALY

ZAGATO

Nart

TECHNICAL INFORMATION

Rear engine, 8 cylinders Vee-slanted at 90°, engine capacity 488.2 cu in, 8,000 cu cm, cast iron cylinder block, cast iron cylinder head, 5 crankshaft bearings, 1 Rochester downdraught 4-barrel carburettor; rear driving wheels, automatic gearbox; independent suspension, telescopic dampers; recirculating ball steering gear; front disc brakes, rear drum, servo; 12 V electrical equipment; wheel base 123.03 in, 3,125 mm, overall length 209.45 in, 5,320 mm, overall width 74.02 in, 1,880 mm, overall height 50.98 in, 1,295 mm.

The major competitions

The Return of the Ferraris

by Giovanni Lurani

The 1970 season saw exceptional vitality in motor racing at the highest level in Grand Prix races for Formula 1 monocoques (maximum engine capacity 3,000 cc, commercial fuel, atmospheric fuel feed, minimum weight 530 kg). Let us briefly examine one or two aspects of this sport.

Technically speaking, the season was a very interesting and significant one. First of all it should be noted with pleasure that remarkable progress was made in performance, for, on nearly all the tracks over which championship Grand Prix races were run, lap and distance records were broken when the races were run under normal conditions. This is the clearest possible proof that on the whole Formula 1 cars were faster than in 1969.

Progress is therefore clearly being made. It remains to be seen whether the progress is in the right direction and this is a matter of opinion, particularly in the context of the safety of the cars and their reliability.

With these general observations in mind, we can add that 1970 saw the complete disappearance of the four-wheel drive cars that had made their debut in 1969 and had looked like being the final solution of the problem posed by the transmission of power to the wheels and its utilisation on the road. The four-wheel drive cars, apart from engineering and constructional complications, losses of relative power and high costs, demonstrated that, in order to exploit them fully, they needed to be driven by someone very familiar with their querks, since they require a totally different driving technique from normal racing cars. These difficulties of adaptation came to light particularly on the European-type mixed circuits, more than at Indianapolis where these cars had been successful.

The eclipse of four-wheel drive was thus due mainly to the drawbacks already mentioned, which seemed to be inherent to the cars but also to a new external factor – the remarkable progress made in racing tyres.

The tyre war unleashed between Goodyear and Firestone for the United States and Dunlop for Great Britain, with the French Michelin playing the part of independent combatant, led to a marked evolution in tyres which

more and more are becoming prime factors in Grand Prix racing.

Tyre sections that border on the absurd, new mixtures, new designs, untried structures, and so on, have helped to make tyres seem the decisive elements in the way competitions went. Whoever managed to pick the right type of type for the track, for the road surface, the temperature, the atmospheric conditions, even the driving style of the man

Monza: the complex equipment of the mechanics looking after the F 1 cars.

at the wheel, and knew how to adapt the geometry of the car's suspension to the particular characteristics of the tyre chosen, had the trump cards in his hand. Today these gigantic tyres, tubeless to make them lighter, often burst or puncture easily due to the warping of the rims, and the consequences of incidents of this nature can be extremely serious.

While admitting that the new racing tyres give exceptional, almost incredible performance, it is hard to say whether this progress is really useful, whether we are moving in the right direction and whether the experience gained can be transferred to normal production cars as is hoped. Dunlop, in fact, seem to have been asking themselves this question, and have decided to give up Formula 1 racing in future and they may be followed by Firestone.

This is why we feel that the moment has come for the people who make motor racing regulations to wake up to the exaggerations that are to be noted in tyre sections and to draw the right conclusions.

Just think that the delicacy of use of present tyres reaches the point that the tyre has to reach a certain temperature beneath which the mixture does not give maximum performance.

1970 also saw the return to the forefront of 12-cylinder engines, which since 1968 had been regularly beaten and at times downright humiliated by the unbeatable Ford-Cosworth V8 engine. It was natural to expect that sooner or later the greater relative power to be obtained from these engines would become decisive. The Ferrari engine or "boxer" type as it is called and also the redesigned Matra and the remade B.R.M., all twelves, have decreed the eclipse of the 8-cylinder Ford-Cosworth, more than 70 of which were built.

The Ferrari engine, daring in its reduced number of main bearings which require crankshafts made out of very special material, asserted its mastery and, after two years in which the red Italian cars had not been able to win a single Grand Prix, had its revenge. An examination of the 1970 results makes it seem possible that a new period of Italian predominance may have begun, even if there is no doubt that the other makes will use all the means at their disposal to challenge them.

The thirteen races qualifying for the World Championship were as usual divided into two series: the first composed of seven Grand Prix (up to the end of July) and the second consisting of six Grand Prix from August to October. Six of the first series were won by three different marques all using 8-cylinder Ford Cosworth engines and only one by the 12-cylinder B.R.M. engine.

In the second series of six Grand Prix, only two were won with 8-cylinder Ford engines and no less than four by the 12-cylinder Ferraris. A total, then, of seven wins for the 8-cylinder engines and five for the twelves but, given the general trend of the season and the final events, it would seem to be safe to assume that the 12-cylinder engine in general and the famous Ferrari "boxer" in particular have gained definite supremacy over the eights, which could only hold their own when pushed to the limit. If there had not been some strokes of bad luck rather than technical difficulties, the French, the American and probably the Dutch and German Grand Prix might very well have been won by the 12-cylinder cars. They should certainly sweep everything before them in the future unless there is some miraculous Voronoff treatment to improve the Ford-Cosworth engine and bring the 8-cylinder Alfa Romeo up to the top line.

The 1970 season, besides the general technical progress and the development in tyres already mentioned, thus saw decided progress for the 12-cylinder B.R.M. engine, which won one Grand Prix and was leading in another until very close to the end, for the 12-cylinder Matra (leading most of the time in one Grand Prix and always well to the fore) and finally for the 12-cylinder Ferrari engine which won four times and took four second

Left above. Rindt with his wife Nina and Colin Chapman. Below, Jackie Ickx, with Clay Regazzoni on his heels in the Austrian GP. Above and below, two views of the 1970 Italian GP: the Ferrari 312 at a pit stop during testing and the winner, Clay Regazzoni.

Above, François Cévert and Pedro Rodriguez in the Canadian GP; below, Rodriguez' car during a pit stop for refuelling in the United States GP. Right, two moments of the Mexican GP; above, the start and, below, Surtees trailed by Oliver.

places, leading the field in an authoritative manner on several other occasions.

Besides the dazzling Ferrari recovery, the 1970 season was marked by one or two other important technical facts. First and foremost the return of Alfa Romeo (even if not with its own chassis), once in the years between 1924 and 1951 one of the most frequent stars of the most famous Grand Prix. Alfa "lent" McLaren its 3-litre V8 engine, the tipo 33-3 which originated as the power unit for proto-types and turned out to be powerful enough to make a good showing against the renowned British eights. One may be allowed to hope that Alfa Romeo, busily engaged as it is in the preparation of 3-litre prototypes for long-distance races and probably also tempted to try the path of the twelve instead of eight-cylinder engine, will ally itself with Ferrari, at least as far as the engine is concerned, in the World Championship Grand Prix.

Structurally speaking the 1970 Grand Prix cars are nothing more than the logical out-come of the 1969 plans. All the marques competing in the major races now have monocoque or semi-monocoque bodies and the wedge-shape aerodynamic theme has been exploited to a greater or lesser extent.

Besides the real makers – that is to say the marques that build not only the chassis but also the engines and gearboxes, the complete car, like B.R.M., Ferrari and Matra – and besides the assembly men like Lotus, Brabham and McLaren, 1970 saw the arrival of new chassis makers such as

but March's frames, though good, appear to be nothing out of the ordinary.

The De Tomaso firm presented some interesting classical solutions designed by Dallara, using light alloy diecast elements that increase chassis rigidity.

With the aim of reducing the weight of the car and getting down as close as possible to the minimum limit proposed by the C.S.I. (out of touch with technical reality), almost all the makers have made the engine a resistant part of the structure. But this solution, even though daring and intelligent, is not completely convincing for the likelihood cannot be entirely excluded that a certain amount of strain may be transmitted to the engine itself, the degree and nature of which cannot be fully known, causing slight internal distorsion that will negatively influence the output and reliability of the power unit.

From the point of view of numbers of entries it can be claimed that Formula 1 racing is enjoying increasing popularity. In one of the 1969 competitions (the French Grand Prix) only 13 cars faced the starter's flag. In 1970 there were nearly thirty lined up at the start and qualification heats that were both tough and selective were often needed to reduce the number of starters in a drastic fashion. This is proof that the sport is flourishing.

On the human side the season was marred by the disappearance from the narrow ranks of the great drivers of three outstanding figures. Bruce McLaren, Piers Courage and Jochen Rindt were in fact killed either while testing or racing. For the first time in the history of motor racing the Drivers' World Championship was awarded posthumously, to the memory of Jochen Rindt who had won it with an impressive series of five victories and was well worthy of this honour.

the Englishmen Surtees, Tyrrell and March and the Italians De Tomaso and Bellasi.

The greatest progress in chassis construction was once again achieved by Colin Chapman with his Lotus 72 which, thanks to its designer's brilliant innovations has shown itself to be without doubt the most competitive of the new structures, even if its fragility has been criticised.

The Lotus which, like many Sports and Prototype cars, has side-mounted radiators has improved weight distribution and aerodynamics and the wedge shape is exploited to the full with a triplane air-foil that is most effective. The suspension, too, of the Lotus 72 is very advanced with torsion bars and centralised brakes. Surtees' chassis and Tyrrell's in particular seem to be excellent

Prototypes

Illustrations and technical information

Fiat Abarth 1000 "Biposto Corsa"

TECHNICAL INFORMATION

ENGINE rear, 4 stroke; cylinders: 4, in line; bore and stroke: 2.56 x 2.91 in, 65 x 74 mm; engine capacity: 59.9 cu in, 982 cu cm; compression ratio: 12; max power: 120 hp at 8,200 rpm; specific power: 122 hp/l; cylinder block: cast iron; cylinder head: light alloy, hemispherical combustion chambers; crankshaft bearings: 3; valves: 2 per cylinder, Vee-slanted; camshafts: 2, overhead; lubrication: gear pump, dry sump; lubricating system capacity: 15.8 imp pt, 19 US pt, 9 l; carburation: 2 Weber twin barrel carburettors; fuel feed: electric pump; cooling system: water.

TRANSMISSION driving wheels: rear; clutch: single dry plate; gearbox: mechanical; gears: 5 + reverse; gear lever: central; final drive: hypoid bevel, limited slip; tyres: 4.25/9.50 x 13 front, 4.75/11.50 x 13 rear.

PERFORMANCE max speed: 137 mph, 220 km/h.

CHASSIS tubular trellis frame; front suspension: independent, wishbones, coil springs, telescopic dampers; rear suspension: independent, trailing radius arms, coil springs, telescopic dampers.

STEERING rack-and-pinion.

BRAKES disc, dual circuit.

ELECTRICAL EQUIPMENT voltage: 12 V; ignition distributor: Marelli.

DIMENSIONS AND WEIGHT wheel base: 76.77 in, 1,950 mm; front track: 50.39 in, 1,280 mm; rear track: 51.18 in, 1,300 mm; overall length: 132.28 in, 3,360 mm; overall width: 62.60 in, 1,590 mm; dry weight: 882 lb, 400 kg; fuel tank capacity: 15.4 imp gal, 18.5 US gal, 70 l.

BODY sports in plastic material.

DATA REGARDING CAR

Keeping up the tradition of its small racing cars derived from production models, Abarth has built this little racing two-seater for categories up to 1,000 cc. It has the performance of a racing car and is an excellent car for anyone intending to take up motor racing seriously to cut his teeth on. The price of course is considerable, for the moment you get into the field of racing true and proper everything is refined and extremely expensive, from the materials to the long hours needed to build the car. This two-seater is sold at Lit. 7,800,000.

Fiat Abarth 2000

TECHNICAL INFORMATION

ENGINE rear, 4 stroke; cylinders: 4, in line; bore and stroke: 3.46 x 3.15 in, 88 x 80 mm; engine capacity: 118.7 cu in, 1,946 cu cm; compression ratio: 11.5; max power: 250 hp at 8,000 rpm; specific power: 129 hp/l; cylinder block: light alloy; cylinder head: light alloy, hemispherical combustion chambers; crankshaft bearings: 5; valves: 4 per cylinder, Vee-slanted; camshafts: 2, overhead; lubrication: gear pump, dry sump; lubricating system capacity: 21.1 imp pt, 25.4 US pt, 12 l; carburation: 2 Weber twin barrel carburettors; fuel feed: electric pump; cooling system: water.

TRANSMISSION driving wheels: rear; clutch: dry multiplates; gearbox: mechanical; gears: 5 + reverse; gear lever: central; final drive: hypoid bevel, limited slip; tyres: 4.50/11.60 x 13 front, 5.50/13.60 x 13 rear.

PERFORMANCE max speed: 155 mph, 250 km/h.

CHASSIS tubular trellis frame; front suspension: independent, wishbones, coil springs, telescopic dampers; rear suspension: independent, trailing radius arms, coil springs, telescopic dampers.

STEERING rack-and-pinion.

BRAKES disc, dual circuit.

ELECTRICAL EQUIPMENT voltage: 12 V; ignition distributor: Marelli.

DIMENSIONS AND WEIGHT wheel base: 82.09 in, 2,085 mm; front track: 55.31 in, 1,405 mm; rear track: 56.50 in, 1,435 mm; overall length: 149.61 in, 3,800 mm; overall width: 70.08 in, 1,780 mm; dry weight: 1,169 lb, 530 kg; fuel tank capacity: 22 imp gal, 26.4 US gal, 100 l (2 separate tanks).

BODY sports in plastic material.

DATA REGARDING CAR

The Fiat Abarth 2000 sports prototype has a good deal in common with the well-known 2000 sports car, twenty-five of which were built, that proved to be the most successful car in its class. Naturally there is a difference in the weight and the prototype has some special characteristics and heightened performance. The price, Lit. 11,000,000 is not excessively high for a racing car that is built with special techniques from the first piece to the last.

Fiat Abarth 3000

TECHNICAL INFORMATION

ENGINE rear, 4 stroke; cylinders: 8, Vee-slanted at 90°; bore and stroke: 3.46 x 2.40 in, 88 x 61 mm; engine capacity: 181.1 cu in, 2,968 cu cm; compression ratio: 12; max power: 365 hp at 8,400 rpm; specific power: 122 hp/l; cylinder block: light alloy; cylinder head: light alloy, hemispherical combustion chambers; valves: 2 per cylinder, Vee-slanted; camshafts: 2 per cylinder block, overhead; lubrication: gear pump; lubricating system capacity: 21.1 imp pt, 25.4 US pt, 12 l; carburation: Lucas indirect injection system; cooling system: water.

TRANSMISSION driving wheels: rear; clutch: dry multi-plates; gearbox: mechanical; gears: 5 + reverse; gear lever: central; final drive: hypoid bevel, limited slip; tyres: 4.50/11.60 x 13 front, 5.50/15 x 13 rear.

PERFORMANCE max speed: 177 mph, 285 km/h.

CHASSIS tubular trellis frame; front suspension: independent, wishbones, coil springs, telescopic dampers; rear suspension: independent, trailing radius arms, coil springs, telescopic dampers.

STEERING rack-and-pinion.

BRAKES disc, dual circuit.

ELECTRICAL EQUIPMENT voltage: 12 V; ignition distributor: Dinoplex, electronically controlled.

DIMENSIONS AND WEIGHT wheel base: 82.68 in, 2,100 mm; front track: 55.31 in, 1,405 mm; rear track: 57.87 in, 1,470 mm; overall length: 137.80 in, 3,500 mm; overall width: 74.02 in, 1,880 mm; dry weight: 1,356 lb, 615 kg; fuel tank capacity: 26.4 imp gal, 31.7 US gal, 120 l (2 separate tanks).

BODY sports in plastic material.

DATA REGARDING CAR

The new Abarth prototype with an eight-cylinder engine is derived from the firm's earlier experiences and represents an interesting addition to their range. The car will be ready for the 1971 racing season which will see the three-litre prototypes battling once more against the five-litre sports, while in 1972 the engine capacity will be limited to three litres. This racing prototype costs Lit. 19,000,000.

33-3

TECHNICAL INFORMATION

ENGINE rear, 4 stroke; cylinders: 8, Vee-slanted at 90°; bore and stroke: 3.39 x 2.54 in, 86 x 64.4 mm; engine capacity: 182.6 cu in, 2,993 cu cm; compression ratio: 11.3; max power: 420 hp at 9,300 rpm; specific power: 140 hp/l; cylinder block: light alloy; cylinder head: light alloy, hemispherical combustion chambers; crankshaft bearings: 5; valves: 4 per cylinder, overhead, Vee-slanted; camshafts: 2 per cylinder block, overhead; lubrication: gear pump, dry sump; lubricating system capacity: 24.6 imp pt, 29.6 US pt, 14 l; carburation: Lucas indirect injection system; fuel feed: 2 electric pumps; cooling system: water.

TRANSMISSION driving wheels: rear; clutch: dry multi-plates; gearbox: mechanical; gears: 6 + reverse; gear lever: side; final drive: hypoid bevel, limited slip; tyres: 10 x 13 front, 15 x 15 rear.

PERFORMANCE max speed: 199 mph, 320 km/h.

CHASSIS box-type light alloy sheet bearing body containing flexible fuel tanks; front suspension: independent, wishbones, coil springs, telescopic dampers; rear suspension: independent, wishbones, trailing radius arms, coil springs, telescopic dampers.

STEERING rack-and-pinion.

BRAKES disc, dual circuit, front and rear compensator.

ELECTRICAL EQUIPMENT voltage: 12 V; ignition distributor: Marelli.

DIMENSIONS AND WEIGHT wheel base: 91.34 in, 2,320 mm; front track: 55.51 in, 1,410 mm; rear track: 55.12 in, 1,400 mm; overall length: 143.31 in, 3,640 mm; overall width: 74.80 in, 1,900 mm; dry weight: 1,345 lb, 610 kg; fuel tank capacity: 26.4 imp gal, 31.7 US gal, 120 l (2 separate tanks).

BODY sports in plastic material.

DATA REGARDING CAR

The Alfa Romeo racing cars were improved during the 1970 season and their weight reduced and they will be appearing in a renovated form in 1971 races, even if the traditional lines and characteristics are retained. An interesting detail is the use of titanium for many parts of the chassis and the modifications to the coachwork to bring it in line with the changes in the regulations.

2 J

TECHNICAL INFORMATION

ENGINE rear, 4 stroke; cylinders: 8, Vee-slanted at 90°; engine capacity: 488.2 cu in, 8,000 cu cm; compression ratio: 10; max power: 650 hp; specific power: 81 hp/l; cilinder block: light alloy; cylinder head: light alloy, wedge-shaped combustion chambers; crankshaft bearings: 5; valves: 2 per cylinder, overhead, parallel; camshafts: 1, in crankcase; lubrication: gear pump, dry sump; lubricating system capacity: 26.4 imp pt, 31.7 US pt, 15 l; carburation: Lucas indirect injection system; fuel feed: 2 electric pumps; cooling system: aircooled.

TRANSMISSION driving wheels: rear; gearbox: automatic, hydraulic torque convertor with 2 or 3 ratios; selector lever: side; final drive: hypoid bevel, limited slip; tyres: 13.90 x 15 front, 17 x 17 rear.

PERFORMANCE max speed: 217 mph, 350 km/h.

CHASSIS integral, honeycomb light alloy panels, sealed peripherically; 2 aspirators in lower part of coachwork driven by 2-cylinder engine; front suspension: independent, wishbones, coil springs, telescopic dampers; rear suspension: independent, wishbones, trailing radius arms, coil springs, telescopic dampers.

STEERING rack-and-pinion.

BRAKES disc, dual circuit.

ELECTRICAL EQUIPMENT voltage: 12 V; ignition distributor: Delco.

DIMENSIONS AND WEIGHT wheel base: 95.08 in, 2,415 mm; front track: 59.88 in, 1,521 mm; rear track: 54.92 in, 1,395 mm; overall length: 145.67 in, 3,700 mm; overall width: 78.74 in, 2,000 mm; dry weight: 1,510 lb, 685 kg; fuel tank capacity: 26.4 imp gal, 31.7 US gal, 120 l (2 separate tanks).

BODY sports in plastic material.

DATA REGARDING CAR

One of the most curious cars ever to appear on a racing circuit and certainly the most debated, Jim Hall's latest Chaparral is one of a series of cars designed and built by the Texas millionaire with great skill and originality. He first astonished by using an automatic gearbox for racing and then by applying a mobile aileron: in the present version the Chaparral has an aspirator which increases its stability by making it cling to the ground like a suction pad.

CHEVROLET

USA

Corvette

TECHNICAL INFORMATION

ENGINE front, 4 stroke; cylinders: 8, Vee-slanted at 90°; bore and stroke: 4.25 x 3.76 in, 108 x 95.5 mm; engine capacity: 427 cu in, 6,998 cu cm; compression ratio: 11; max power: 440 hp at 5,800 rpm; specific power: 63 hp/l; cylinder block: cast iron; cylinder head: cast iron, flat-bottomed combustion chambers; crankshaft bearings: 5; valves: 2 per cylinder, in line, camshafts: 1, in crankcase; lubrication: gear pump; lubricating system capacity: 11.8 imp pt, 14.2 US pt, 6.7 l; carburation: 1 4-barrel carburettor; fuel feed: 2 electric pumps; cooling system: water.

TRANSMISSION driving wheels: rear; clutch: single dry plate; gearbox: mechanical; gears: 4 + reverse; gear lever: central; final drive: hypoid bevel, limited slip; tyres: 4.50/11.60 x 15 front, 5.75/13.50 x 15 rear.

PERFORMANCE max speed: 146 mph, 235 km/h.

CHASSIS box-type ladder frame; front suspension: independent, wishbones, coil springs, anti-roll bar, telescopic dampers; rear suspension: independent, wishbones, semi-axle as upper arm, transverse semi-elliptic leafsprings, trailing radius arms, anti-roll bar, telescopic dampers.

STEERING recirculating ball.

BRAKES disc, dual circuit, servo.

ELECTRICAL EQUIPMENT voltage: 12 V; ignition distributor: Delco.

DIMENSIONS AND WEIGHT wheel base: 98.03 in, 2,490 mm; front track: 58.27 in, 1,480 mm; rear track: 59.06 in, 1,500 mm; overall length: 182.28 in, 4,630 mm; overall width: 69.29 in, 1,760 mm; dry weight: 2,844 lb, 1,290 kg; fuel tank capacity: 26.4 imp gal, 31.7 US gal, 120 l.

BODY coupé in plastic material.

DATA REGARDING CAR

The Chevrolet Corvette is one of the very few American production cars to be raced in European competitions, including the 24 Heures du Mans. Of a greater weight and size than is common in racing in Europe, the Corvette is a worthy competitor thanks to its enormous seven-litre engine which gives it exceptional acceleration and a very high top speed.
This is one of the few racing cars still using the traditional configuration of front engine and rear driving wheels. It is available not only with the racing-type gearbox with four speeds and close ratios but also with an automatic gearbox.

B 16

TECHNICAL INFORMATION

ENGINE rear, 4 stroke; cylinder: 4, in line; bore and stroke: 3.35 x 3.07 in, 85.05 x 77.9 mm; engine capacity: 108.1 cu in, 1,771 cu cm; compression ratio: 10.5; max power: 240 hp at 8,500 rpm; specific power: 134 hp/l; cylinder block: cast iron; cylinder head: light alloy, flat-bottomed combustion chambers; crankshaft bearings: 5; valves: 4 per cylinder, overhead, vertical; camshafts: 2, overhead; lubrication: gear pump, dry sump; lubricating system capacity: 15.8 imp pt, 19 US pt, 9 l; carburation: Lucas indirect injection system; fuel feed: 2 electric pumps; cooling system: water.

TRANSMISSION driving wheels: rear; clutch: 2 dry plates; gearbox: mechanical; gears: 5 + reverse; gear lever: side; final drive: hypoid bevel, limited slip; tyres: 4.30/11.50 x 13 front, 5.30/13.50 x 15 rear.

PERFORMANCE max speed: 168 mph, 270 km/h.

CHASSIS integral; front suspension: independent, wishbones, coil springs, telescopic dampers; rear suspension: independent, wishbones, trailing radius arms, coil springs, telescopic dampers.

STEERING rack-and-pinion.

BRAKES disc, dual circuit.

ELECTRICAL EQUIPMENT voltage: 12 V; ignition distributor: Lucas.

DIMENSIONS AND WEIGHT wheel base: 92.99 in, 2,362 mm; front track: 51.97 in, 1,320 mm; rear track: 51.97 in, 1,320 mm; overall length: 149.61 in, 3,800 mm; overall width: 65.98 in, 1,676 mm; dry weight: 1,213 lb, 550 kg; fuel tank capacity: 20 imp gal, 24 US gal, 91 l.

BODY coupé.

DATA REGARDING CAR

Chevron is a fairly new and relatively small make, a typical enterprise in England where firms of this type are more successful than in most countries. The B 16 won the European Makers Cup for cars up to two litre engine capacity in 1970 and is remarkable for the way it lends itself to various types of engine. In fact, besides the Cosworth-engined version (the most successful of the various solutions), a BMW engine and also a Mazda rotating piston engine have also been adopted.

312 P

TECHNICAL INFORMATION

ENGINE rear, 4 stroke; clylinders: 12, horizontally, opposed; bore and stroke: 3.09 x 2.03 in, 78.5 x 51.5 mm; engine capacity: 182.5 cu in, 2,991 cu cm; compression ratio: 11.5; max power: 450 hp at 10,800 rpm; specific power: hp/l 150; cylinder block: light alloy; cylinder head: light alloy, flat-bottomed combustion chambers; crankshaft bearings: 7; valves: 4 per cylinder, overhead, vertical; camshafts: 2 per cylinder block, overhead; lubrication: gear pump, dry sump; lubricating system capacity: 26.4 imp pt, 31.7 US pt, 15 l; carburation: Lucas indirect injection system; fuel feed: 2 electric pumps; cooling system: water.

TRANSMISSION driving wheels: rear; clutch: dry multiplates; gearbox: mechanical; gears: 5 + reverse; gear lever: side; final drive: hypoid bevel, limited slip; tyres: 9/22 x 13 front, 13/26 x 15 rear.

PERFORMANCE max speed: 186 mph, 300 km/h.

CHASSIS tubular and sheet frame; front suspension: independent, wishbones, coil springs, telescopic dampers; rear suspension: independent, wishbones, trailing radius arms, coil springs, telescopic dampers.

STEERING rack-and-pinion.

BRAKES disc, internal radial fins, dual circuit.

ELECTRICAL EQUIPMENT voltage: 12 V; ignition distributor: Dinoplex Marelli, electronically-controlled.

DIMENSIONS AND WEIGHT wheel base: 87.40 in, 2,220 mm; front track: 56.10 in, 1,425 mm; rear track: 55.12 in, 1,400 mm; overall length: 137.80 in, 3,500 mm; overall width: 74.02 in, 1,880 mm; dry weight: 1,290 lb, 585 kg; fuel tank capacity: 26.4 imp gal, 31.7 US gal, 120 l (2 separate tank).

BODY sports in plastic material.

DATA REGARDING CAR

The Ferrari three-litre prototype was built towards the end of 1970 with the aim of preparing it for racing in the 1971 season against the three-litre and also the five-litre cars with no weight limit, but with a view to the new regulations for 1972 which limit the engine capacity to three litres for sports car prototypes. It is largely derived from the Ferrari single seater which did so well in 1970 when it won four races at the of the season.

512

TECHNICAL INFORMATION

ENGINE rear, 4 stroke; cylinders: 12, Vee-slanted at 60°; bore and stroke: 3.43 x 2.76 in, 87 x 70 mm; engine capacity: 304.7 cu in, 4,993 cu cm; compression ratio: 11; max power: 600 hp at 8,500 rpm; specific power: 120 hp/l; cylinder block: light alloy; cylinder head: light alloy, flat-bottomed combustion chambers; crankshaft bearings: 7; valves: 4 per cylinder, vertical; camshafts: 2 per cylinder block, overhead; lubrication: gear pump, dry sump; lubricating system capacity: 31.7 imp pt, 38.1 US pt, 18 l; carburation: Lucas indirect injection system; fuel feed: 2 electric pumps; cooling system: water.

TRANSMISSION driving wheels: rear; clutch: dry multi-plates; gearbox: mechanical; gears: 5 + reverse; gear lever: side; final drive: hypoid bevel, limited slip; tyres: 4.50/10.50 x 15 front, 6.00/14.50 x 15 rear.

PERFORMANCE max speed: 217 mph, 350 km/h.

CHASSIS tubular frame with box-type light alloy sheets; front suspension: independent, wishbones, coil springs, telescopic dampers; rear suspension: independent, wishbones, trailing radius arms, coil springs, telescopic dampers.

STEERING rack-and-pinion.

BRAKES disc, dual circuit.

ELECTRICAL EQUIPMENT voltage: 12 V; ignition distributor: Marelli.

DIMENSIONS AND WEIGHT wheel base: 94.49 in, 2,400 mm; front track: 59.76 in, 1,518 mm; rear track: 59.49 in, 1,511 mm; overall length: 159.84 in, 4,060 mm; overall width: 78.74 in, 2,000 mm; dry weight: 1,764 lb, 800 kg; fuel tank capacity: 30.8 imp gal, 37 US gal, 140 l (2 separate tanks).

BODY coupé in plastic material.

DATA REGARDING CAR

The 1970 racing season did not bring many successes for the Ferrari 512 but it allowed the car to be more carefully prepared and modified. In particular, the weight was reduced and the power increased. However, the alteration of the regulations has meant that the makers will no longer use these cars for the works team in 1971 but will leave them in the hands of private owners.

3-litre XR 37

TECHNICAL INFORMATION

ENGINE rear, 4 stroke; cylinders: 8, Vee-slanted at 90°; bore and stroke: 3.50 x 2.37 in, 88.9 x 60.3 mm; engine capacity: 182.7 cu in, 2,994 cu cm; compression ratio: 11; max power: 300 hp at 7,500 rpm; specific power: 100 hp/l; cylinder block: light alloy; cylinder head: light alloy, flat-bottomed combustion chambers; crankshaft bearings: 5; valves: 2 per cylinder, in line; camshafts: 1 per cylinder block; lubrication: gear pump, dry sump; lubricating system capacity: 29.9 imp pt, 35.9 US pt, 17 l; carburation: Lucas indirect injection system; fuel feed: 2 electric pumps; cooling system: water.

TRANSMISSION driving wheels: rear; clutch: 2 dry plates; gearbox: mechanical; gears: 5 + reverse; gear lever: side; final drive: hypoid bevel, limited slip; tyres: 4.75/11.30 x 15 front, 6.00/13.50 x 15 rear.

PERFORMANCE max speed: 174 mph, 280 km/h.

CHASSIS light alloy integral body; front suspension: independent, wishbones, coil springs, telescopic dampers; rear suspension: independent, wishbones, coil springs, telescopic dampers.

STEERING rack-and-pinion.

BRAKES disc, dual circuit.

ELECTRICAL EQUIPMENT voltage: 12 V; ignition distributor: Lucas.

DIMENSIONS AN DWEIGHT wheel base: 94.02 in, 2,388 mm; front track: 54.61 in, 1,387 mm; rear track: 54.61 in, 1,387 mm; overall length: 158.50 in, 4,026 mm; overall width: 70.98 in, 1,803 mm; dry weight: 1,775 lb, 805 kg; fuel tank capacity: 25.3 imp gal, 30.4 US gal, 115 l.

BODY sports in plastic material.

DATA REGARDING CAR

The Healey prototype marks the return to motor racing of a British make created by the keenness and enthusiasm of Donald Healey, the racing driver. After a period of inactivity the firm, which is now managed by the founder's sons, is preparing to launch a series of sports cars. The prototype, which ran in the Le Mans 24 Heures allowed certain technical solutions to be tried out and reminded the public of a familiar name. The Repco Brabham engine is mounted centrally, the gearbox is Hewland, and Girling brakes and Dunlop tyres are used.

S&M Special 2

TECHNICAL INFORMATION

ENGINE front, 4 stroke; cylinders: 4, Vee-slanted; bore and stroke: 3.24 x 2.95 in, 82.4 x 75 mm; engine capacity: 97.6 cu in, 1,599 cu cm; compression ratio: 11.5; max power: 162 hp at 7,200 rpm; specific power: 101 hp/l; cylinder block: cast iron; cylinder head: light alloy, hemispherical combustion chambers; crankshaft bearings: 3; valves: 2 per cylinder, slanted; camshafts: 2, overhead; lubrication: gear pump; lubricating system capacity: 8.8 imp pt, 10.6 US pt, 5 l (9.9 imp pt, 11.8 US pt, 5.6 l with oilcooler); carburation: 2 Weber twin barrel carburettors; fuel feed: mechanical pump, controlled by electric engine; cooling system: water.

TRANSMISSION driving wheels: front; clutch: single dry pate; gearbox: mechanical; gears: 5 + reverse; gear lever: central; final drive: hypoid bevel; tyres: 4.75/10.00 x 13.

PERFORMANCE max speed: 143 mph, 230 km/h.

CHASSIS sheet platform with tubular reinforcements; front suspension: independent, wishbones, transverse upper leaf-spring, telescopic dampers; rear suspension: rigid axle, semi-elliptic leafsprings, telescopic dampers.

STEERING worm and roller.

BRAKES disc, rear compensator.

ELECTRICAL EQUIPMENT voltage: 12 V; ignition distributor: Marelli.

DIMENSIONS AND WEIGHT wheel base: 91.73 in, 2,330 mm; front track: 51.18 in, 1,300 mm; rear track: 50.39 in, 1,280 mm; overall length: 64.17 in, 1,630 mm; dry weight: 1,367 lb, 620 kg; fuel tank capacity: 19.8 imp gal, 23.8 US gal, 90 l.

BODY sports.

DATA REGARDING CAR

The first version of this curious Lancia prototype was built in 1969 by Cesare Fiorio, racing manager of the Lancia team, and by Claudio Maglioli who drives for the team. Their purpose was to try out the possibilities offered by a car built economically, that is to say using a production car with modified coachwork and tuned mechanical elements. In view of the fine results obtained, a second prototype was built in 1970 and will be used again in 1971. At the end of last season this car achieved some interesting successes including an outright first in the Coppa Iglesias and second place in the Occhieppo-Graglia and Catania-Etna hill climbs.

JS I

TECHNICAL INFORMATION

ENGINE rear, 4 stroke; cylinders: 4, in line; bore and stroke: 3.37 x 3.06 in, 85.6 x 77.6 mm; engine capacity: 109 cu in, 1,786 cu cm; compression ratio: 10; max power: 240 hp at 8,500 rpm; specific power: 135 hp/l; cylinder block: cast iron; cylinder head: light alloy, hemispherical combustion chambers; crankshaft bearings: 5; valves: 4 per cylinder, overhead, slanted; camshafts: 2, overhead; lubrication: gear pump, dry sump; lubricating system capacity: 17.6 imp pt, 21.1 US pt, 10 l; carburation: Lucas indirect injection system; fuel feed: electric pump; cooling system: water.

TRANSMISSION driving wheels: rear; clutch: 2 dry plates; gearbox: Hewland mechanical; gears: 5 + reverse; gear lever: central; final drive: hypoid bevel, limited slip; tyres: 8.5/21 x 13 front, 10.5/28 x 13 rear.

PERFORMANCE max speed: 168 mph, 270 km/h.

CHASSIS tubular frame with sheet reinforcements; front suspension: independent, wishbones, coil springs, telescopic dampers; rear suspension: independent, wishbones, coil springs, telescopic dampers, anti-roll compensating system.

STEERING rack-and-pinion.

BRAKES disc, dual circuit.

ELECTRICAL EQUIPMENT voltage: 12 V; ignition distributor: Lucas, electronically-controlled.

DIMENSIONS AND WEIGHT wheel base: 90.55 in, 2,300 mm; front track: 54.33 in, 1,380 mm; rear track: 53.54 in, 1,360 mm; overall length: 155.51 in, 3,950 mm; overall width: 66.14 in, 1,680 mm; dry weight: 1,323 lb, 600 kg; fuel tank capacity: 20.9 imp gal, 25.1 US gal, 95 l.

BODY coupé in plastic material.

DATA REGARDING CAR

The racing prototype built by the French driver Guy Lgier as the basis of a limited production of high-performance touring cars gears the initials JS in memory of his close friend, the racing driver Jo Schlesser, who died so tragically. The car has been entered for a large number of races, driven by its maker and has been honourably placed in its class. The commercial version has an engine with a larger engine capacity but is not so highly tuned. In both cases Ford engines are used, a four-cylinder Ford Cosworth for racing and a 2,500 cc V6 for production cars.

T 210

TECHNICAL INFORMATION

ENGINE rear, 4 stroke; cylinders: 4, in line; bore and stroke: 3.35 x 3.07 in, 85.05 x 77.9 mm; engine capacity: 108.1 cu in, 1,771 cu cm; compression ratio: 10.5; max power: 250 hp at 8,500 rpm; specific power: 140 hp/l; cylinder block: cast iron; cylinder head: light alloy, flat-bottomed combustion chambers; crankshaft bearings: 5; valves: 4 per cylinder, overhead, vertical; camshafts: 2, overhead; lubrication: gear pump, dry sump; lubricating system capacity: 15.8 imp pt, 19 US pt, 9 l; carburation: Lucas indirect injection system; fuel feed: 2 electric pumps; cooling system: water.

TRANSMISSION driving wheels: rear; clutch: 2 dry plates; gearbox: mechanical; gears: 5 + reverse; gear lever: side; final drive: hypoid bevel, limited slip; tyres 4.80/10.20 x 13 front, 5.90/13.80 x 13 rear.

PERFORMANCE max speed: 171 mph, 275 km/h.

CHASSIS light alloy integral body; front suspension: independent, wishbones, coil springs, telescopic dampers; rear suspension: independent, wishbones, trailing radius arms, coil springs, telescopic dampers.

STEERING rack-and-pinion.

BRAKES disc, dual circuit.

ELECTRICAL EQUIPMENT voltage: 12 V; ignition distributor: Lucas.

DIMENSIONS AND WEIGHT wheel base: 84.84 in, 2,155 mm; front track: 51.97 in, 1,320 mm; rear track: 51.97 in, 1,320 mm; overall length: 135.83 in, 3,450 mm; overall width: 65.75 in, 1,670 mm; dry weight: 1,213 lb, 550 kg; fuel tank capacity: 19.8 imp gal, 23.8 US gal, 90 l.

BODY sports in plastic material.

DATA REGARDING CAR

When the Lola T 210 was designed, the needs of a particular sector of motor racing-young drivers-were borne in mind, and so the car is simple even if very competitive (in fact it was only one point behind the Chevron which won the European Championship for cars up to two litres). Like the Chevron, the Lola mounts a Cosworth engine and a Hewland gearbox.

M 660

TECHNICAL INFORMATION

ENGINE rear, 4 stroke; cylinders: 12, Vee-slanted at 60°; bore and stroke: 3.14 x 1.97 in, 79.7 x 50 mm; engine capacity: 183 cu in, 2,999 cu cm; compression ratio: 11; max power: 450 hp at 9,500 rpm; specific power: 150 hp/l; cylinder block: light alloy; cylinder head: light alloy, flat-bottomed combustion chambers; valves: 4 per cylinder, vertical; camshafts: 2 per cylinder block, overhead; lubrication: gear pump, dry sump, lubricating system capacity: 26.4 imp pt, 31.7 US pt, 15 l; carburation: Lucas indirect injection system; cooling system: water.

TRANSMISSION driving wheels: rear; clutch: dry multiplates; gearbox: mechanical; gears: 5 + reverse; gear lever: side; final drive: hypoid bevel, limited slip; tyres: 4.50/10.60 x 15 front, 5.50/15.30 x 15 rear.

PERFORMANCE max speed: 199 mph, 320 km/h.

CHASSIS integral body, front trellis frame and engine at rear acting as frame element; front suspension: independent, wishbones, coil springs, telescopic dampers; rear suspension: independent, trailing radius arms, coil springs, telescopic dampers.

STEERING rack-and-pinion.

BRAKES disc, dual circuit.

ELECTRICAL EQUIPMENT voltage: 12 V; ignition distributor: electronic system.

DIMENSIONS AND WEIGHT wheel base: 98.43 in, 2,500 mm; front track: 59.06 in, 1,500 mm; rear trac: 59.06 in, 1,500 mm; overall length: 165.35 in, 4,200 mm; overall width: 76.38 in, 1,940 mm; dry weight: 1,389 lb, 630 kg; fuel tank capacity: 26.4 imp gal, 31.7 US gal, 120 l (2 separate tanks).

BODY sports in plastic material.

DATA REGARDING CAR

The latest version of the three-litre prototype built by Matra is a proof of the constant refinement that is the outcome of the experience gained in racing. The name Matra is now coupled with that of Simca due to commercial agreements. These cars have had their ups and downs during their development, partly due to the fact that they were raced against the big five-litre cars when their preparation was still being completed. They finished the 1970 season in glory by winning the Tour de France.

908/03

TECHNICAL INFORMATION

ENGINE rear, 4 stroke; cylinders: 8, horizontally, opposed; bore and stroke: 3.35 x 2.60 in, 85 x 66 mm; engine capacity: 182.9 cu in, 2,997 cu cm; compression ratio: 10.4; max power: 360 hp at 8,500 rpm; specific power: 120 hp/l; cylinder block: light alloy; cylinder head: light alloy, hemispherical combustion chambers; crankshaft bearings: 5; valves: 2 per cylinder, Vee-slanted; camshafts: 2 per cylinder block, overhead; lubrication: gear pump, dry sump; lubricating system capacity: 35.2 imp pt, 42.3 US pt, 20 l; carburation: Bosch indirect injection system; fuel feed: 2 electric pumps; cooling system: aircooled.

TRANSMISSION driving wheels: rear; clutch: dry multiplates; gearbox: mechanical; gears: 5 + reverse; gear lever: side; final drive: hypoid bevel, limited slip; tyres: 4.50/10.85 x 13 front, 5.50/15.30 x 13 rear.

PERFORMANCE max speed: 174 mph, 280 km/h.

CHASSIS light alloy trellis frame; front suspension: independent, wishbones, torsion bars, telescopic dampers; rear suspension: independent, torsion bars, trailing radius arms, telescopic dampers.

STEERING rack-and-pinion.

BRAKES disc, internal radial fins, dual circuit.

ELECTRICAL EQUIPMENT voltage: 12 V; ignition distributors, 2 Bosch.

DIMENSIONS AND WEIGHT wheel base: 90.55 in, 2,300 mm; front track: 59.65 in, 1,515 mm; rear track: 59.06 in, 1,500 mm; overall length: 137.80 in, 3,500 mm; overall width: 73.23 in, 1,860 mm; dry weight: 1,301 lb, 590 kg; fuel tank capacity: 26 imp gal, 31.2 US gal, 118 l.

BODY sports in plastic material.

DATA REGARDING CAR

The Porsche 908/03, which is without doubt the most sensational car of recent years, was built and tested in record time for a particular race, the Targa Florio, and it was run with equal success on the Nürburgring circuit. Breaking completely with tradition, even the slightest superfluous weight has been eliminated, such as headlamps and so on. The driver sits between the front wheels and the gearbox is between the engine and the final drive.

917

TECHNICAL INFORMATION

ENGINE rear, 4 stroke; cylinders: 12, horizontally, opposed; bore and stroke: 3.39 x 2.77 in, 86 x 70.4 mm; engine capacity: 299.4 cu in, 4,907 cu cm; compression ratio: 10.5; max power: 600 hp at 8,500 rpm; specific power: 123 hp/l; cylinder block: light alloy; cylinder head: light alloy, hemispherical combustion chambers; crankshaft bearings: 8; valves: 2 per cylinder, overhead, slanted; camshafts: 2 per cylinder block, overhead; lubrication: gear pump, dry sump; lubricating system capacity: 45.8 imp pt, 55 US pt, 26 l; carburation: Bosch indirect injection system; fuel feed: 2 electric pumps; cooling system: aircooled.

TRANSMISSION driving wheels: rear; clutch: dry multiplates; gearbox: mechanical; gears: 5 + reverse; gear lever: side; final drive: hypoid bevel, limited slip; tyres: 4.25/10.20 x 15 front, 12.5/26 x 15 rear.

PERFORMANCE max speed: 224 mph, 360 km/h.

CHASSIS tubular trellis frame (to which body is stucked); front suspension: independent, wishbones, coil springs, telescopic dampers; rear suspension: independent, wishbones, trailing radius arms, coil springs, telescopic dampers.

STEERING rack-and-pinion.

BRAKES disc, dual circuit, compensator.

ELECTRICAL EQUIPMENT voltage: 12 V; ignition distributors: 2 Bosch.

DIMENSIONS AND WEIGHT wheel base: 90.55 in, 2,300 mm; front track: 60.08 in, 1,526 mm; rear track: 60.35 in, 1,533 mm; overall length: 168.90 in, 4,290 mm; overall width: 80.04 in, 2,033 mm; dry weight: 1,764 lb, 800 kg; fuel tank capacity: 29.7 imp gal, 35.6 US gal, 135 l (2 separate tanks).

BODY coupé in plastic material.

DATA REGARDING CAR

In 1970 the Porsche 917 with its new five-litre engine swept everything before it in the sports car classes. A refined and even more powerful version of the same car is destined to take part in 1971 races driven by the men of the Gulf and Martini teams as well as some private drivers. An open and much lighter version will run in the Can Am races next season.

Europe

Models now in production
Illustrations and technical information

STEYR-PUCH   AUSTRIA

500 S

PRICE EX WORKS: 29,700 schillings.

ENGINE rear, 4 stroke: cylinders: 2, horizontally opposed; bore and stroke: 2.76 x 2.52 in, 70 x 64 mm; engine capacity: 30.1 cu in, 493 cu cm; compression ratio: 6.7; max power (DIN) 19.8 hp at 5,000 rpm; max torque (DIN): 25 lb ft, 3.4 kg m at 3,200 rpm; max engine rpm: 5,000; specific power: 40.2 hp/l; cylinder block: cast iron; cylinder head: light alloy, hemispherical combustion chambers; crankshaft bearings: 3; valves: 2 per cylinder, overhead, Vee-slanted, push-rods and rockers; camshafts: 1, central, lower; lubrication: gear pump, full flow filter, oil cooler; lubricating system capacity: 3 imp pt, 3.6 US pt, 1.7 l; carburation: 1 Solex 40 PID downdraught carburettor; fuel feed: mechanical pump; cooling system: air cooled.

TRANSMISSION driving wheels: rear; clutch: single dry plate; gearbox: mechanical; gears: 4 + reverse; silent claw coupling gears; gearbox ratios: I 3.700, II 2.067, III 1.300, IV 0.875, rev 5.140; gear lever: central; final drive: spiral bevel; axle ratio: 5.125; tyres: 125 x 12.

PERFORMANCE max speeds: 16 mph, 25 km/h in 1st gear; 28 mph, 45 km/h in 2nd gear; 45 mph, 72 km/h in 3rd gear; 65 mph, 105 km/h in 4th gear; power-weight ratio: 57.8 lb/hp, 26.2 kg/hp; carrying capacity: 706 lb, 320 kg; speed in top at 1,000 rpm: 13.3 mph, 21.4 km/h; fuel consumption: 56.5 m/imp gal, 47 m/US gal, 5 l x 100 km.

CHASSIS integral; front suspension: independent, wishbones, transverse leafspring lower arms, telescopic dampers; rear suspension: independent, swinging trailing radius arms, coil springs, telescopic dampers.

STEERING screw and sector; turns of steering wheel lock to lock: 2.80.

BRAKES drum; lining area: front 33.5 sq in, 216 sq cm, rear 33.5 sq in, 216 sq cm, total 67 sq in, 432 sq cm.

ELECTRICAL EQUIPMENT voltage: 12 V; battery: 32 Ah; generator type: dynamo, 230 W; ignition distributor: Bosch; headlamps: 2.

DIMENSIONS AND WEIGHT wheel base: 72.44 in, 1,840 mm; front track: 44.13 in, 1,121 mm; rear track: 44.68 in, 1,135 mm; overall length: 116.93 in, 2,970 mm; overall width: 51.97 in, 1,320 mm; overall height: 53.94 in, 1,370 mm; ground clearance: 5.71 in, 145 mm; dry weight: 1,147 lb, 520 kg; turning circle (between walls): 28.2 ft, 8.6 m; fuel tank capacity: 4.8 imp gal, 5.8 US gal, 22 l.

BODY saloon/sedan; doors: 2; seats: 4; front seats: separate.

PRACTICAL INSTRUCTIONS fuel: 100 oct petrol; engine sump oil: 3.2 imp pt, 3.8 US pt, 1.8 l, SAE 20W-40, change every 1,600 miles, 2,500 km; gearbox and final drive oil: 1.9 imp pt, 2.3 US pt, 1.1 l, SAE 90, change every 18,600 miles, 30,000 km; greasing: every 1,600 miles, 2,500 km, 2 points; sparking plug type: 225°; tappet clearances: inlet 0.006 in, 0,15 mm, exhaust 0.006 in, 0.15 mm; normal tyre pressure: front 21 psi, 1.5 atm, rear 27 psi, 1.9 atm.

VARIATIONS

ENGINE max power (DIN) 16 hp at 4,600 rpm, max torque (DIN) 24 lb ft, 3.3 kg m at 2,800 rpm, max engine rpm 5,000, specific power 32.5 hp/l.
PERFORMANCE max speed 59 mph, 95 km/h, fuel consumption 62.7 m/imp gal, 52.3 m/US gal, 4.5 l x 100 km.

ŠKODA   CZECHOSLOVAKIA

100 Saloon

PRICE IN GB: £ 511.

ENGINE rear, 4 stroke; cylinders: 4, slanted 30° to right, in line; bore and stroke: 2.68 x 2.68 in, 68 x 68 mm; engine capacity: 54.2 cu in, 988 cu cm; compression ratio: 8.3; max power (SAE): 48 hp at 4,750 rpm; max torque (SAE): 54 lb ft, 7.5 kg m at 3,000 rpm; max engine rpm: 6,000; specific power: 48.6 hp/l; cylinder block: light alloy, wet liners; cylinder head: cast iron; crankshaft bearings: 3; valves: 2 per cylinder, overhead, in line, push-rods and rockers; camshafts: 1, side; lubrication: gear pump, cartridge on by-pass; lubricating system capacity: 7 imp pt, 8.5 US pt, 4 l; carburation: 1 Jikov 32 BS 3170 downdraught carburettor; fuel feed: mechanical pump; cooling system: water; cooling system capacity: 10.6 imp pt, 12.7 US pt, 6 l.

TRANSMISSION driving wheels: rear; clutch: single dry plate, hydraulically controlled; gearbox: mechanical; gears:

STEYR-PUCH 500 S

ŠKODA 110 R Coupé

TATRA T2-603

+ reverse; synchromesh gears: I, II, III, IV; gearbox ratios: I 3.800, II 2.120, III 1.410, IV 0.960, rev 3.270; gear lever: central; final drive: spiral bevel; axle ratio: 4.444; width of rims: 4.5''; tyres: 155 x 14.

PERFORMANCE max speeds: 22 mph, 35 km/h in 1st gear; 37 mph, 60 km/h in 2nd gear; 56 mph, 90 km/h in 3rd gear; 78 mph, 125 km/h in 4th gear; power-weight ratio: 35.5 lb/hp, 16.1 kg/hp; carrying capacity: 827 lb, 375 kg; max gradient in 1st gear: 30%; acceleration: 0-50 mph (0-80 km/h) 16 sec; speed in top at 1,000 rpm: 15.5 mph, 25 km/h; fuel consumption: 37.2 m/imp gal, 30.9 m/US gal, 7.6 l x 100 km.

CHASSIS integral; front suspension: independent, wishbones, coil springs, anti-roll bar, telescopic dampers; rear suspension: independent, swinging semi-axles, swinging longitudinal leading arms, coil springs, telescopic dampers.

STEERING screw and nut; turns of steering wheel lock to lock: 2.50.

BRAKES front disc, rear drum; lining area: front 11.8 sq in, 76 sq cm, rear 59.7 sq in, 385 sq cm, total 71.5 sq in, 461 sq cm.

ELECTRICAL EQUIPMENT voltage: 12 V; battery: 35 Ah; generator type: dynamo, 300 W; ignition distributor: Pal; headlamps: 2.

DIMENSIONS AND WEIGHT wheel base: 94.49 in, 2,400 mm; front track: 50.39 in, 1,280 mm; rear track: 49.21 in, 1,250 mm; overall length: 163.58 in, 4,155 mm; overall width: 63.78 in, 1,620 mm; overall height: 54.33 in, 1,380 mm; ground clearance: 6.89 in, 175 mm; dry weight: 1,709 lb, 775 kg; distribution of weight: 41% front axle, 59% rear axle; turning circle (between walls): 33.5 ft, 10.2 m; fuel tank capacity: 7 imp gal, 8.4 US gal, 32 l.

BODY saloon/sedan; doors: 4; seats: 4-5; front seats: separate.

PRACTICAL INSTRUCTIONS fuel: 84 oct petrol; engine sump oil: 7 imp pt, 8.5 US pt, 4 l, SAE 20W-30, change every 3,100 miles, 5,000 km; gearbox and final drive oil: 4.4 imp pt, 5.3 US pt, 2.5 l, SAE 80, change every 12,400 miles, 20,000 km; greasing: every 6,200 miles, 10,000 km, 4 points; tappet clearances (hot): inlet 0.006 in, 0.15 mm, exhaust 0.008 in, 0.20 mm; valve timing: inlet opens 14°30' before tdc and closes 45°30' after bdc, exhaust opens 40° before bdc and closes 13° after tdc; normal tyre pressure: front 17 psi, 1.2 atm, rear 23 psi, 1.6 atm.

100 L Saloon

See 100 Saloon, except for:

PRICE IN GB: £ 542.

PERFORMANCE power-weight ratio: 36.2 lb/hp, 16.4 kg/hp.

DIMENSIONS AND WEIGHT dry weight: 1,742 lb, 790 kg.

110 L Saloon

See 100 Saloon, except for:

PRICE IN GB: £ 565.

ENGINE bore and stroke: 2.83 x 2.68 in, 72 x 68 mm; engine capacity: 67.5 cu in, 1,107 cu cm; compression ratio: 8.8; max power (SAE): 53 hp at 5,000 rpm; max torque (SAE): 62 lb ft, 8.6 kg m at 3,200 rpm; max engine rpm: 5,800; specific power: 47.9 hp/l; carburation: 1 Jikov 32 BS 3171 downdraught carburettor; cooling system capacity: 12 imp pt, 14.4 US pt, 6.8 l.

PERFORMANCE max speeds: 22 mph, 35 km/h in 1st gear; 40 mph, 65 km/h in 2nd gear; 62 mph, 100 km/h in 3rd gear; 84 mph, 135 km/h in 4th gear; power-weight ratio: 33.1 lb/hp, 15 kg/hp; acceleration: 0-50 mph (0-80 km/h) 15 sec; fuel consumption: 35.3 m/imp gal, 29.4 m/US gal, 8 l x 100 km.

DIMENSIONS AND WEIGHT dry weight: 1,753 lb, 795 kg.

PRACTICAL INSTRUCTIONS valve timing: inlet opens 14°30' before tdc and closes 45°30' after bdc, exhaust opens 49°30' before bdc and closes 10°30' after tdc.

110 LS Saloon

See 110 L Saloon, except for:

PRICE: —

ENGINE compression ratio: 9.5; max power (SAE): 62 hp at 5,500 rpm; max torque (SAE): 64 lb ft, 8.8 kg m at

STEYR-PUCH 500 S

ŠKODA 110 R Coupé

TATRA T2-603

3,500 rpm; specific power: 56 hp/l; carburation: 1 Jikov 32 DDSR downdraught twin barrel carburettor.

PERFORMANCE max speed: 90 mph, 145 km/h; power-weight ratio: 28 lb/hp, 12.7 kg/hp; fuel consumption: 33.2 m/imp gal, 27.7 m/US gal, 8.5 l x 100 km.

DIMENSIONS AND WEIGHT overall height: 52.76 in, 1,340 mm; dry weight: 1,742 lb, 790 kg.

110 R Coupé

See 110 LS Saloon, except for:

PRICE: —

ENGINE lubrication: oil cooler.

PERFORMANCE power-weight ratio: 30 lb/hp, 13.5 kg/hp.

ELECTRICAL EQUIPMENT generator type: alternator, 490 W.

DIMENSIONS AND WEIGHT dry weight: 1,841 lb, 835 kg.

BODY coupé; doors: 2; seats: 2 + 2.

TATRA   **CZECHOSLOVAKIA**

T2-603

PRICE: —

ENGINE rear, 4 stroke; cylinders: 8, Vee-slanted at 90°; bore and stroke: 2.95 x 2.76 in, 75 x 70 mm; engine capacity: 150.8 cu in, 2,472 cu cm; compression ratio: 8.2; max power (DIN): 105 hp at 4,800 rpm; max torque (DIN): 123 lb ft, 17 kg m at 4,000 rpm; max engine rpm: 5,000; specific power: 42.5 hp/l; cylinder block: light alloy; cylinder head: light alloy; crankshaft bearings: 5; valves: 2 per cylinder, overhead, push-rods and rockers; camshafts: 1, at centre of Vee; lubrication: gear pump, full flow filter, twin oil cooler; lubricating system capacity: 11.4 imp pt, 13.7 US pt, 6.5 l; carburation: 2 Jikov 30 SSOP downdraught twin barrel carburettors; fuel feed: mechanical pump; cooling system: air cooled.

TRANSMISSION driving wheels: rear; clutch: single dry plate, hydraulically controlled; gearbox: mechanical; gears: 4 + reverse; synchromesh gears: I, II, III, IV; gearbox ratios: I 3.545, II 2.265, III 1.450, IV 0.960, rev 3.428; gear lever: steering column; final drive: spiral bevel; axle ratio: 4.100; tyres: 6.70 x 15.

PERFORMANCE max speeds: 27 mph, 43 km/h in 1st gear; 42 mph, 67 km/h in 2nd gear; 65 mph, 105 km/h in 3rd gear; 99 mph, 160 km/h in 4th gear; power-weight ratio: 30.9 lb/hp, 14 kg/hp; carrying capacity: 992 lb, 450 kg; max gradient in 1st gear: 33.8%; acceleration: 0-50 mph (0-80 km/h) 11 sec; speed in top at 1,000 rpm: 19.9 mph, 32 km/h; fuel consumption: 22.6 m/imp gal, 18.8 m/US gal, 12.5 l x 100 km.

CHASSIS integral; front suspension: independent, twin swinging longitudinal trailing arms, coil springs, anti-roll bar, telescopic dampers; rear suspension: independent, swinging semi-axles, swinging longitudinal trailing arms, coil springs, telescopic dampers.

STEERING rack-and-pinion.

BRAKES disc, servo.

ELECTRICAL EQUIPMENT voltage: 12 V; battery: 82 Ah; generator type: dynamo, 300 W; ignition distributor: Pal-Magneton; headlamps: 4; fog lamps: 2.

DIMENSIONS AND WEIGHT wheel base: 108.27 in, 2,750 mm; front track: 58.46 in, 1,485 mm; rear track: 55.12 in, 1,400 mm; overall length: 196.65 in, 4,995 mm; overall width: 74.61 in, 1,895 mm; overall height: 60.24 in, 1,530 mm; ground clearance: 7.87 in, 200 mm; dry weight: 3,241 lb, 1,470 kg; distribution of weight: 48% front axle, 52% rear axle; turning circle (between walls): 36.1 ft, 11 m; fuel tank capacity: 13.2 imp gal, 15.8 US gal, 60 l.

BODY saloon/sedan; doors: 4; seats: 6; front seats: separate.

PRACTICAL INSTRUCTIONS fuel: 84 oct petrol; engine sump oil: 7 imp pt, 8.5 US pt, 4 l, SAE 20W-30, change every 2,500 miles, 4,000 km; gearbox and final drive oil: 5.8 imp pt, 7 US pt, 3.3 l, SAE 90, change every 9,900 miles, 16,000 km; tappet clearances: inlet 0.004 in, 0.10 mm, exhaust 0.008 in, 0.20 mm; valve timing: inlet opens 10° before tdc and closes 30° after bdc, exhaust opens 25° before bdc and closes 6° after tdc; normal tyre pressure: front 27 psi, 1.9 atm, rear 33 psi, 2.3 atm.

ALPINE   FRANCE

Berlinette 85 Tour de France

PRICE EX WORKS: 21,960 francs.

ENGINE rear, 4 stroke; cylinders: 4; bore and stroke: 2.87 x 3.03 in, 73 x 77 mm; engine capacity: 78.7 cu in, 1,289 cu cm; compression ratio: 9; max power (SAE): 81 hp at 5,900 rpm; max torque (SAE): 76 lb ft, 10.5 kg m at 3,500 rpm; max engine rpm: 6,500; specific power: 62.8 hp/l; cylinder block: cast iron; cylinder head: light alloy; crankshaft bearings: 5; valves: 2 per cylinder, overhead, in line, push-rods and rockers; camshafts: 1, side; lubrication: gear pump; lubricating system capacity: 4.4 imp pt, 5.3 US pt, 2.5 l; carburation: 1 Weber 32 DIR downdraught twin barrel carburettor; fuel feed: mechanical pump; cooling system: liquid, sealed circuit, front supplementary radiator, electric automatic fan; cooling system capacity: 15.8 imp pt, 19 US pt, 9 l.

TRANSMISSION driving wheels: rear; clutch: single dry plate; gearbox: mechanical; gears: 4 + reverse; synchromesh gears: I, II, III, IV; gearbox ratios: I 3.610, II 2.250, III 1.480, IV 1.030, rev 3.080; gear lever: central; final drive: hypoid bevel; axle ratio: 3.890; tyres: 145 x 15.

PERFORMANCE max speeds: 33 mph, 53 km/h in 1st gear; 53 mph, 85 km/h in 2nd gear; 81 mph, 130 km/h in 3rd gear; 112 mph, 180 km/h in 4th gear; power-weight ratio: 17 lb/hp, 7.7 kg/hp; carrying capacity: 353 lb, 160 kg; acceleration: standing ¼ mile 17.2 sec; speed in top at 1,000 rpm: 17.8 mph, 28.7 km/h; fuel consumption: 31.4 m/imp gal, 26.1 m/US gal, 9 l x 100 km.

CHASSIS integral, central steel backbone; front suspension: independent, wishbones, rubber elements, coil springs, anti-roll bar, telescopic dampers; rear suspension: independent, swinging semi-axles, trailing radius arms, coil springs, 4 telescopic dampers.

STEERING rack-and-pinion; turns of steering wheel lock to lock: 3.20.

BRAKES disc (diameter 10.24 in, 260 mm), dual circuit; area rubbed by linings: total 342.9 sq in, 2,212 sq cm.

ELECTRICAL EQUIPMENT voltage: 12 V; battery: 55 Ah; generator type: alternator, 30 A; ignition distributor: Ducellier; headlamps: 4, iodine long-distance lights.

DIMENSIONS AND WEIGHT wheel base: 82.68 in, 2,100 mm; front track: 51.02 in, 1,296 mm; rear track: 50.20 in, 1,275 mm; overall length: 151.57 in, 3,850 mm; overall width: 59.84 in, 1,520 mm; overall height: 44.49 in, 1,130 mm; ground clearance: 5.91 in, 150 mm; dry weight: 1,378 lb, 625 kg; distribution of weight: 40% front axle, 60% rear axle; turning circle (between walls): 32.8 ft, 10 m; fuel tank capacity: 8.4 imp gal, 10 US gal, 38 l.

BODY coupé in plastic material; doors: 2; seats: 2.

PRACTICAL INSTRUCTIONS fuel: 98 oct petrol; engine sump oil: 4.4 imp pt, 5.3 US pt, 2.5 l, SAE 10W-30, change every 1,600 miles, 2,500 km; gearbox and final drive oil: 4.4 imp pt, 5.3 US pt, 2.5 l, SAE 80 EP, change every 6,200 miles, 10,000 km; greasing: every 1,600 miles, 2,500 km, 1 point; tappet clearances: inlet 0.008 in, 0.20 mm, exhaust 0.010 in, 0.25 mm; normal tyre pressure: front 20 psi, 1.4 atm, rear 28 psi, 2 atm.

OPTIONAL ACCESSORIES engine sump oil 8.8 imp pt, 10.6 US pt, 5 l; electric pump; limited slip final drive; 5-speed mechanical gearbox (I 3.610, II 2.360, III 1.690, IV 1.290, V 1.030, rev 3.080), 3.780 axle ratio; 165 x 13 tyres; servo brake; fuel tank capacity 16.7 imp gal, 20.1 US gal, 76 l.

Berlinette 1300 G Tour de France

See Berlinette 85 Tour de France, except for:

PRICE EX WORKS: 28,760 francs.

ENGINE bore and stroke: 2.93 x 2.83 in, 74.5 x 72 mm; engine capacity: 76.6 cu in, 1,255 cu cm; compression ratio: 10.5; max power (SAE): 103 hp at 6,750 rpm; max torque (SAE): 86 lb ft, 11.9 kg m at 5,000 rpm; max engine rpm: 7,000; specific power: 82.1 hp/l; cylinder head: hemispherical combustion chambers; lubrication: oil cooler; carburation: 2 Weber 40 DCOE horizontal twin barrel carburettors.

TRANSMISSION gears: 5 + reverse; synchromesh gears: I, II, III, IV, V; gearbox ratios: I 3.610, II 2.360, III 1.690, IV 1.290, V 1.030, rev 3.080; axle ratio: 4.125; tyres: 155 x 15 rear.

PERFORMANCE max speed: 127 mph, 205 km/h; power-weight ratio: 13.5 lb/hp, 6.1 kg/hp; fuel consumption: 28.2 m/imp gal, 23.5 m/US gal, 10 l x 100 km.

OPTIONAL ACCESSORIES 3.780 3.890 4.370 axle ratios; 5-speed mechanical gearbox not available.

ALPINE Berlinette 1600 S Tour de France

CG 1200 S Spider

CHRYSLER FRANCE Simca 1000 GL

Berlinette 1300 S Tour de France

See Berlinette 85 Tour de France, except for:

PRICE EX WORKS: 32,400 francs.

ENGINE bore and stroke: 2.98 x 2.83 in, 75.7 x 72 mm; engine capacity: 79.1 cu in, 1,296 cu cm; compression ratio: 12; max power (SAE): 132 hp at 7,200 rpm; max torque (SAE): 90 lb ft, 12.4 kg m at 4,500 rpm; max engine rpm: 7,500; specific power: 101.9 hp/l; cylinder head: hemispherical combustion chambers; lubrication: oil cooler; lubricating system capacity: 7.9 imp pt, 9.5 US pt, 4.5 l; carburation: 2 Weber 40 DCOE horizontal twin barrel carburettors.

TRANSMISSION gears: 5 + reverse; synchromesh gears: I, II, III, IV, V; gearbox ratios: I 3.610, II 2.360, III 1.690, IV 1.290, V 1.030, rev 3.080; axle ratio: 4.125; tyres: 155 x 15 rear.

PERFORMANCE max speed: 134 mph, 215 km/h; power-weight ratio: 10.4 lb/hp, 4.7 kg/hp; fuel consumption: 25. m/imp gal, 21.4 m/US gal, 11 l x 100 km.

OPTIONAL ACCESSORIES 3.780 3.890 4.370 axle ratios; large engine sump and 5-speed mechanical gearbox not available.

Berlinette 1600 S Tour de France

See Berlinette 85 Tour de France, except for:

PRICE EX WORKS: 30,840 francs.

ENGINE bore and stroke: 3.03 x 3.31 in, 77 x 84 mm; engine capacity: 95.5 cu in, 1,565 cu cm; compression ratio: 10.2; max power (SAE): 138 hp at 6,000 rpm; max torque (SAE): 107 lb ft, 14.7 kg m at 5,000 rpm; max engine rpm: 6,500; specific power: 88.2 hp/l; lubricating system capacity: imp pt, 8.5 US pt, 4 l; carburation: 1 Weber 45 DCOE horizontal twin barrel carburettor.

TRANSMISSION gears: 5 + reverse; synchromesh gears: I, II, III, IV, V; gearbox ratios: I 3.610, II 2.360, III 1.690, IV 1.290, V 1.030, rev 3.080; axle ratio: 3.370; tyres: 155 x 15 rear.

PERFORMANCE max speed: 134 mph, 215 km/h; power-weight ratio: 10.1 lb/hp, 4.6 kg/hp; acceleration: standing ¼ mile 15.4 sec; speed in top at 1,000 rpm: 21.1 mph, 33.9 km/h; fuel consumption: 25.7 m/imp gal, 21.4 m/US gal, 11 l x 100 km.

DIMENSIONS AND WEIGHT dry weight: 1,400 lb, 635 kg.

OPTIONAL ACCESSORIES larger engine sump and 5-speed mechanical gearbox not available.

CG   FRANCE

1200 S Coupé

PRICE EX WORKS: 23,400 francs.

ENGINE rear, 4 stroke; cylinders: 4, slanted at 15°, in line; bore and stroke: 2.91 x 2.76 in, 74 x 70 mm; engine capacity: 73.5 cu in, 1,204 cu cm; compression ratio: 9.4; max power (DIN): 85 hp at 6,200 rpm; max torque (DIN): 78 lb ft, 10.7 kg m at 4,800 rpm; max engine rpm: 6,500; specific power: 70.6 hp/l; cylinder block: cast iron; cylinder head: light alloy; crankshaft bearings: 5; valves: 2 per cylinder, overhead, push-rods and rockers; camshafts: 1, side; lubrication: gear pump, full flow filter; lubricating system capacity: 7 imp pt, 8.5 US pt, 4 l; carburation: 2 Solex C 35 PHH 5 horizontal twin barrel carburettors; fuel feed: mechanical pump; cooling system: water, electric thermostatic fan; cooling system capacity: 19.4 imp pt, 23.3 US pt, 11 l.

TRANSMISSION driving wheels: rear; clutch: single dry plate (diaphragm), hydraulically controlled; gearbox: mechanical; gears: 4 + reverse; synchromesh gears: I, II, III, IV; gearbox ratios: I 3.546, II 2.119, III 1.408, IV 0.963, rev 3.436; gear lever: central; final drive: hypoid bevel; axle ratio: 3.888; width of rims: 4.5''; tyres: 145 x 13 front, 155 x 13 rear.

PERFORMANCE max speeds: 34 mph, 54 km/h in 1st gear; 53 mph, 85 km/h in 2nd gear; 76 mph, 122 km/h in 3rd gear; 117 mph, 188 km/h in 4th gear; power-weight ratio: 17.2 lb/hp, 7.8 kg/hp; carrying capacity: 397 lb, 180 kg; acceleration: standing ¼ mile 17.2 sec; speed in top at 1,000 rpm: 17.8 mph, 28.6 km/h; fuel consumption: 31.4 m/imp gal, 26.1 m/US gal, 9 l x 100 km.

CHASSIS integral, tubular reinforced platform; front suspension: independent, wishbones, transverse leafspring lower arms, anti-roll bar, telescopic dampers; rear suspension: independent, semi-trailing arms, coil springs, anti-roll bar, telescopic dampers.

ALPINE Berlinette 1600 S Tour de France

CG 1200 S Coupé

CHRYSLER FRANCE Simca 1000 GL

STEERING rack-and-pinion; turns of steering wheel lock to lock: 4.25.

BRAKES disc (diameter 8.70 in, 221 mm), dual circuit, servo; area rubbed by linings: front 140.2 sq in, 904 sq cm, rear 140.2 sq in, 904 sq cm, total 280.4 sq in, 1,808 sq cm.

ELECTRICAL EQUIPMENT voltage: 12 V; battery: 40 Ah; generator type: alternator, 340 W; ignition distributor: Ducellier; headlamps: 4; fog lamps: 2.

DIMENSIONS AND WEIGHT wheel base: 87.40 in, 2,220 mm; front track: 49.21 in, 1,250 mm; rear track: 48.58 in, 1,234 mm; overall length: 158.27 in, 4,020 mm; overall width: 60.63 in, 1,540 mm; overall height: 46.46 in, 1,180 mm; ground clearance: 4.92 in, 125 mm; dry weight: 1,455 lb, 660 kg; turning circle (between walls): 34.1 ft, 10.4 m; fuel tank capacity: 11.7 imp gal, 14 US gal, 53 l.

BODY coupé in plastic material; doors: 2; seats: 2.

PRACTICAL INSTRUCTIONS fuel: 98-100 oct petrol; engine sump oil: 7 imp pt, 8.5 US pt, 4 l, SAE 20W-40, change every 3,700 miles, 6,000 km; gearbox and final drive oil: 3.2 imp pt, 3.8 US pt, 1.8 l, SAE 90 EP, change every 6,200 miles, 10,000 km; greasing: none; tappet clearances (hot): inlet 0.014 in, 0.35 mm, exhaust 0.016 in, 0.40 mm; normal tyre pressure: front 23 psi, 1.6 atm, rear 30 psi, 2.1 atm.

OPTIONAL ACCESSORIES light alloy wheels.

1200 S Spider

See 1200 S Coupé, except for:

PRICE EX WORKS: 23,950 francs.

BODY convertible.

OPTIONAL ACCESSORIES hardtop.

CHRYSLER FRANCE   FRANCE

Sim'4

PRICE EX WORKS: 7,695 francs.

ENGINE rear, 4 stroke; cylinders: 4, slanted at 15°, in line; bore and stroke: 2.68 x 2.11 in, 68 x 53.5 mm; engine capacity: 47.4 cu in, 777 cu cm; compression ratio: 9.2; max power (DIN): 33 hp at 6,000 rpm; max torque (DIN): 36 lb ft, 4.9 kg m at 2,600 rpm; max engine rpm: 6,000; specific power: 42.5 hp/l; cylinder block: cast iron; cylinder head: light alloy; crankshaft bearings: 5; valves: 2 per cylinder, overhead, in line, push-rods and rockers; camshafts: 1, side; lubrication: gear pump, centrifugal filter; lubricating system capacity: 5.3 imp pt, 6.3 US pt, 3 l; carburation: 1 Weber 32 ICR-12 downdraught carburettor; fuel feed: mechanical pump; cooling system: water; cooling system capacity: 9.7 imp pt, 11.6 US pt, 5.5 l.

TRANSMISSION driving wheels: rear; clutch: single dry plate, hydraulically controlled; gearbox: mechanical; gears: 4 + reverse; synchromesh gears: I, II, III, IV; gearbox ratios: I 3.546, II 2.118, III 1.408, IV 0.963, rev 3.436; gear lever: central; final drive: hypoid bevel; axle ratio: 5.375; width of rims: 4''; tyres: 5.60 x 12.

PERFORMANCE max speeds: 19 mph, 30 km/h in 1st gear; 34 mph, 55 km/h in 2nd gear; 52 mph, 83 km/h in 3rd gear; 75 mph, 121 km/h in 4th gear; power-weight ratio: 51.2 lb/hp, 23.2 kg/hp; carrying capacity: 882 lb, 400 kg; speed in top at 1,000 rpm: 12.5 mph, 20.1 km/h; fuel consumption: 44.1 m/imp gal, 36.8 m/US gal, 6.4 l x 100 km.

CHASSIS integral; front suspension: independent, wishbones, transverse leafspring lower arms, anti-roll bar, telescopic dampers; rear suspension: independent, semi-trailing arms, coil springs, telescopic dampers.

STEERING rack-and-pinion; turns of steering wheel lock to lock: 3.17.

BRAKES drum; lining area: front 45 sq in, 290 sq cm, rear 39.4 sq in, 254 sq cm, total 84.4 sq in, 544 sq cm.

ELECTRICAL EQUIPMENT voltage: 12 V; battery: 40 Ah; generator type: dynamo, 240 W; ignition distributor: Ducellier; headlamps: 2.

DIMENSIONS AND WEIGHT wheel base: 87.40 in, 2,220 mm; front track: 49.21 in, 1,250 mm; rear track: 50.39 in, 1,280 mm; overall length: 149.49 in, 3,797 mm; overall width: 58.46 in, 1,485 mm; overall height: 54.96 in, 1,396 mm; ground clearance: 5.51 in, 140 mm; dry weight: 1,687 lb, 765 kg; turning circle (between walls): 31.2 ft, 9.5 m; fuel tank capacity: 7.9 imp gal, 9.5 US gal, 36 l.

SIM' 4

BODY saloon/sedan; doors: 4; seats: 5; front seats: separate.

PRACTICAL INSTRUCTIONS fuel: 98 oct petrol; engine sump oil: 5.3 imp pt, 6.3 US pt, 3 l, SAE 20W-40, change every 3,100 miles, 5,000 km; gearbox and final drive oil: 3.2 imp pt, 3.8 US pt, 1.8 l, SAE 90 EP, change every 6,200 miles, 10,000 km; greasing: none; normal tyre pressure: front 16 psi, 1.1 atm, rear 24 psi, 1.7 atm.

OPTIONAL ACCESSORIES back seat folding down to luggage table.

Simca 1000

See Sim'4, except for:

PRICE IN GB: £ 534.
PRICE EX WORKS: 7,995 francs.

ENGINE bore and stroke: 2.68 x 2.56 in, 68 x 65 mm; engine capacity: 57.6 cu in, 944 cu cm; compression ratio: 9.4; max power (DIN): 44 hp at 6,000 rpm; max torque (DIN): 48 lb ft, 6.6 kg m at 2,800 rpm; specific power: 46.6 hp/l.

TRANSMISSION axle ratio: 4.375; tyres: 145 x 13.

PERFORMANCE max speeds: 24 mph, 38 km/h in 1st gear; 40 mph, 64 km/h in 2nd gear; 60 mph, 96 km/h in 3rd gear; 87 mph, 140 km/h in 4th gear; power-weight ratio: 39 lb/hp, 17.7 kg/hp; speed in top at 1,000 rpm: 15 mph, 24.1 km/h.

DIMENSIONS AND WEIGHT dry weight: 1,720 lb, 780 kg.

PRACTICAL INSTRUCTIONS tappet clearances (hot): inlet 0.014 in, 0.35 mm, exhaust 0.016 in, 0.40 mm; valve timing: inlet opens 16°30' before tdc and closes 58° after bdc, exhaust opens 60°30' before bdc and closes 14° after tdc; normal tyre pressure: front 20 psi, 1.4 atm, rear 27 psi, 1.9 atm.

OPTIONAL ACCESSORIES Ferodo 3-speed semi-automatic gearbox, hydraulic torque convertor (I 2.532, II 1.524, III 0.765, rev 3.436), max ratio of convertor at stall 2, possible manual selection, central selector lever; back seat folding down to luggage table.

Simca 1000 GL

See Simca 1000, except for:

PRICE IN GB: £ 572.
PRICE EX WORKS: 8,745 francs.

BODY luxury equipment.

Simca 1000 Special

See Sim'4, except for:

PRICE IN GB: £ 625.
PRICE EX WORKS: 9,515 francs.

ENGINE bore and stroke: 2.91 x 2.56 in, 74 x 65 mm; engine capacity: 68.2 cu in, 1,118 cu cm; compression ratio: 9.6; max power (DIN): 53 hp at 5,800 rpm; max torque (DIN): 62 lb ft, 8.5 kg m at 2,800 rpm; max engine rpm: 6,000; specific power: 47.4 hp/l; carburation: 1 Weber 32 ICR-3 downdraught carburettor.

TRANSMISSION axle ratio: 4.111; tyres: 145 x 13.

PERFORMANCE max speeds: 25 mph, 41 km/h in 1st gear; 42 mph, 68 km/h in 2nd gear; 64 mph, 103 km/h in 3rd gear; 91 mph, 147 km/h in 4th gear; power-weight ratio: 33.3 lb/hp, 15.1 kg/hp; speed in top at 1,000 rpm: 16.1 mph, 25.9 km/h; fuel consumption: 37.7 m/imp gal, 31.4 m/US gal, 7.5 l x 100 km.

BRAKES front disc (diameter 9.21 in, 234 mm), rear drum; area rubbed by linings: front 161.9 sq in, 1,044 sq cm, rear 73.8 sq in, 476 sq cm, total 235.7 sq in, 1,520 sq cm.

ELECTRICAL EQUIPMENT headlamps: 2; fog lamps: 2, iodine.

DIMENSIONS AND WEIGHT dry weight: 1,760 lb, 798 kg.

PRACTICAL INSTRUCTIONS tappet clearances (hot): inlet 0.014 in, 0.35 mm, exhaust 0.016 in, 0.40 mm; valve timing: inlet opens 16°30' before tdc and closes 58° after bdc, exhaust opens 60°30' before bdc and closes 14° after tdc.

OPTIONAL ACCESSORIES none.

CHRYSLER FRANCE Simca 1000 Rallye

CHRYSLER FRANCE 4-door Simca 1100 GLS Berline

CHRYSLER FRANCE Simca 1100 Special Berline

Simca 1000 Rallye

See Simca 1000 Special, except for:

PRICE EX WORKS: 8,995 francs.

2-door Simca 1100 LS Berline (5 CV)

PRICE EX WORKS: 9,595 francs.

ENGINE front, transverse, 4 stroke; cylinders: 4, slanted at 41°, in line; bore and stroke: 2.68 x 2.56 in, 68 x 65 mm; engine capacity: 57.6 cu in, 944 cu cm; compression ratio 9.4; max power (DIN): 48 hp at 6,000 rpm; max torque (DIN): 49 lb ft, 6.7 kg m at 3,200 rpm; max engine rpm 6,000; specific power: 50.8 hp/l; cylinder block: cast iron cylinder head: light alloy; crankshaft bearings: 5; valves 2 per cylinder, overhead, push-rods and rockers; camshafts 1, side; lubrication: gear pump, full flow filter; lubricating system capacity: 5.3 imp pt, 6.3 US pt, 3 l; carburation 1 Solex 32 BISA downdraught carburettor; fuel feed: mechanical pump; cooling system: water, electric thermostatic fan; cooling system capacity: 10.6 imp pt, 12.7 US pt, 6 l

TRANSMISSION driving wheels: front; clutch: single dry plate (diaphragm), hydraulically controlled; gearbox: mechanical; gears: 4 + reverse; synchromesh gears: I, II, III, IV; gearbox ratios: I 3.906, II 2.315, III 1.524, IV 1.080, rev 3.773; gear lever: central; final drive: cylindrical gears; axle ratio: 4.062; width of rims: 4.5''; tyres: 145 x 13.

PERFORMANCE max speeds: 23 mph, 37 km/h in 1st gear; 39 mph, 62 km/h in 2nd gear; 58 mph, 94 km/h in 3rd gear; 84 mph, 135 km/h in 4th gear; power-weight ratio: 40.3 lb/hp, 18.3 kg/hp; carrying capacity: 882 lb, 400 kg; speed in top at 1,000 rpm: 13.7 mph, 22 km/h; fuel consumption: 44.1 m/imp gal, 36.8 m/US gal, 6.4 l x 100 km.

CHASSIS integral; front suspension: independent, wishbones, longitudinal torsion bars, anti-roll bar, telescopic dampers; rear suspension: independent, longitudinal trailing arms, transverse torsion bars, anti-roll bar, telescopic dampers.

STEERING rack-and-pinion; turns of steering wheel lock to lock: 3.25.

BRAKES front disc (diameter 9.21 in, 234 mm), rear drum, rear compensator; area rubbed by linings: front 161.9 sq in, 1,044 sq cm, rear 73.8 sq in, 476 sq cm, total 235.7 sq in, 1,520 sq cm.

ELECTRICAL EQUIPMENT voltage: 12 V; battery: 40 Ah; generator type: alternator, 330 W; ignition distributor: Ducellier; headlamps: 2.

DIMENSIONS AND WEIGHT wheel base: 99.21 in, 2,520 mm; front track: 53.82 in, 1,367 mm; rear track: 51.57 in, 1,310 mm; overall length: 155.28 in, 3,944 mm; overall width: 62.52 in, 1,588 mm; overall height: 57.40 in, 1,458 mm; ground clearance: 4.72 in, 120 mm; dry weight: 1,940 lb, 880 kg; turning circle (between walls): 35.4 ft, 10.8 m; fuel tank capacity: 9.2 imp gal, 11.1 US gal, 42 l.

BODY saloon/sedan; doors: 2 + 1; seats: 5; front seats: separate; details: back seat folding down to luggage table.

PRACTICAL INSTRUCTIONS fuel: 98 oct petrol; engine sump oil: 5.3 imp pt, 6.3 US pt, 3 l, SAE 20W-40, change every 3,100 miles, 5,000 km; gearbox and final drive oil: 3.2 imp pt, 3.8 US pt, 1.8 l, SAE 90 EP, change every 6,200 miles, 10,000 km; greasing: none; normal tyre pressure: front 24 psi, 1.7 atm, rear 26 psi, 1.8 atm.

4-door Simca 1100 LS Berline (5 CV)

See 2-door Simca 1100 LS Berline (5 CV), except for:

PRICE EX WORKS: 9,995 francs.

PERFORMANCE power-weight ratio: 41.2 lb/hp, 18.7 kg/hp.

DIMENSIONS AND WEIGHT dry weight: 1,985 lb, 900 kg.

BODY doors: 4 + 1.

2-door Simca 1100 LS Berline

See 2-door Simca 1100 LS Berline (5 CV), except for:

PRICE IN GB: £ 625.
PRICE EX WORKS: 9,995 francs.

ENGINE bore and stroke: 2.91 x 2.56 in, 74 x 65 mm; engine capacity: 68.2 cu in, 1,118 cu cm; compression ratio: 9.6; max power (DIN): 60 hp at 6,000 rpm; max torque (DIN): 69 lb ft, 9.5 kg m at 3,200 rpm; specific power: 53.7 hp/l.

TRANSMISSION axle ratio: 3.937.

CHRYSLER FRANCE Simca 1000 Rallye

CHRYSLER FRANCE 4-door Simca 1100 GLS Berline

CHRYSLER FRANCE 2-door Simca 1100 Special Berline

PERFORMANCE max speeds: 25 mph, 40 km/h in 1st gear; 42 mph, 68 km/h in 2nd gear; 64 mph, 103 km/h in 3rd gear; 87 mph, 140 km/h in 4th gear; power-weight ratio: 32.6 lb/hp, 14.8 kg/hp; speed in top at 1,000 rpm: 15 mph, 24.1 km/h; fuel consumption: 38.7 m/imp gal, 32.2 m/US gal, 7.3 l x 100 km.

DIMENSIONS AND WEIGHT dry weight: 1,958 lb, 888 kg.

OPTIONAL ACCESSORIES Ferodo 3-speed semi-automatic gearbox, hydraulic torque convertor (I 2.469, II 1.650, III 1.080, rev 3.774), max ratio of convertor at stall 2, possible manual selection, central selector lever, max speeds (I) 40 mph, 64 km/h, (II) 59 mph, 95 km/h, (III) 87 mph, 140 km/h; servo brake.

4-door Simca 1100 LS Berline

See 2-door Simca 1100 LS Berline, except for:

PRICE EX WORKS: 10,295 francs.

PERFORMANCE power-weight ratio: 33.1 lb/hp, 15 kg/hp.

DIMENSIONS AND WEIGHT dry weight: 1,985 lb, 900 kg.

BODY doors: 4 + 1.

4-door Simca 1100 GLS Berline

See 4-door Simca 1100 LS Berline, except for:

PRICE IN GB: £ 687.
PRICE EX WORKS: 11,195 francs.

BRAKES servo.

OPTIONAL ACCESSORIES semi-automatic gearbox and electrically-heated rear window.

4-door Simca 1100 LS Break

See 2-door Simca 1100 LS Berline, except for:

PRICE EX WORKS: 10,995 francs.

TRANSMISSION tyres: 155 x 13.

PERFORMANCE power-weight ratio: 34.8 lb/hp, 15.8 kg/hp; carrying capacity: 992 lb, 450 kg.

DIMENSIONS AND WEIGHT overall length: 154.33 in, 3,920 mm; overall height: 55.83 in, 1,418 mm; dry weight: 2,095 lb, 950 kg.

BODY estate car/station wagon; doors: 4 + 1.

4-door Simca 1100 GLS Break

See 4-door Simca 1100 LS Break, except for:

PRICE IN GB: £ 687.
PRICE EX WORKS: 11,895 francs.

BRAKES servo.

OPTIONAL ACCESSORIES semi-automatic gearbox and electrically-heated rear window.

2-door Simca 1100 Special Berline

See 2-door Simca 1100 LS Berline (5 CV), except for:

PRICE IN GB: £ 763.
PRICE IN USA: $ 1,875.

ENGINE bore and stroke: 2.91 x 2.76 in, 74 x 70 mm; engine capacity: 73.5 cu in, 1,204 cu cm; compression ratio: 9.5; max power (DIN): 76.5 hp at 6,000 rpm; max torque (DIN): 72 lb ft, 10 kg m at 4,000 rpm; specific power: 63.5 hp/l; carburation: 2 Weber 36 DCNF downdraught twin barrel carburettors.

TRANSMISSION axle ratio: 3.704; width of rims: 4.5''.

PERFORMANCE max speeds: 27 mph, 43 km/h in 1st gear; 45 mph, 72 km/h in 2nd gear; 68 mph, 109 km/h in 3rd gear; 96 mph, 154 km/h in 4th gear; power-weight ratio: 26.2 lb/hp, 11.9 kg/hp; speed in top at 1,000 rpm: 15.9 mph, 25.6 km/h; fuel consumption: 35.3 m/imp gal, 29.4 m/US gal, 8 l x 100 km.

BRAKES servo.

ELECTRICAL EQUIPMENT fog lamps: 2, iodine.

DIMENSIONS AND WEIGHT front track: 54.37 in, 1,381 mm; rear track: 52.13 in, 1,324 mm; dry weight: 2,002 lb, 908 kg.

4-door Simca 1100 Special Berline

See 2-door Simca 1100 Special Berline, except for:

PRICE IN GB: £ 794.
PRICE IN USA: $ 1,960.

PERFORMANCE power-weight ratio: 26.5 kg/hp, 12 kg/hp.

DIMENSIONS AND WEIGHT dry weight: 2,029 lb, 920 kg.

BODY doors: 4 + 1.

Simca 1200 S Coupé

PRICE IN GB: £ 1,220.
PRICE EX WORKS: 17,195 francs.

ENGINE rear, 4 stroke; cylinders: 4, slanted at 15°, in line; bore and stroke: 2.91 x 2.76 in. 74 x 70 mm; engine capacity: 73.5 cu in, 1,204 cu cm; compression ratio: 9.4; max power (DIN): 84 hp at 6,200 rpm; max torque (DIN): 78 lb ft, 10.7 kg m at 4,800 rpm; max engine rpm: 6,400; specific power: 69.8 hp/l; cylinder block: cast iron; cylinder head: light alloy; crankshaft bearings: 5; valves: 2 per cylinder, overhead, in line, push-rods and rockers; camshafts: 1, side; lubrication: gear pump, full flow filter; lubricating system capacity: 7 imp pt, 8.5 US pt, 4 l; carburation: 2 Solex 36 PHH 12 horizontal twin barrel carburettors; fuel feed: mechanical pump; cooling system: water, electric thermostatic fan; cooling system capacity: 19.4 imp pt, 23.3 US pt, 11 l.

TRANSMISSION driving wheels: rear; clutch: single dry plate (diaphragm), hydraulically controlled; gearbox: mechanical; gears: 4 + reverse; synchromesh gears: I, II, III, IV; gearbox ratios: I 3.546, II 2.119, III 1.478, IV 0.963, rev 3.436; gear lever: central; final drive: hypoid bevel; axle ratio: 3.888; width of rims: 4.5''; tyres: 145 x 13.

PERFORMANCE max speeds: 30 mph, 48 km/h in 1st gear; 50 mph, 80 km/h in 2nd gear; 75 mph, 121 km/h in 3rd gear; 110 mph, 177 km/h in 4th gear; power-weight ratio: 23.8 lb/hp, 10.8 kg/hp; carrying capacity: 706 lb, 320 kg; speed in top at 1,000 rpm: 17.1 mph, 27.6 km/h; fuel consumption: 37.2 m/imp gal, 30.9 m/US gal, 7.6 l x 100 km.

CHASSIS integral; front suspension: independent, wishbones, transverse leafspring lower arms, anti-roll bar, telescopic dampers; rear suspension: independent, semi-trailing arms, coil springs, telescopic dampers.

STEERING rack-and-pinion; turns of steering wheel lock to lock: 3.25.

BRAKES disc (diameter 8.70 in, 221 mm), dual circuit, servo; area rubbed by linings: front 140.2 sq in, 904 sq cm, rear 140.2 sq in, 904 sq cm, total 280.4 sq in, 1,808 sq cm.

ELECTRICAL EQUIPMENT voltage: 12 V; battery: 40 Ah; generator type: alternator, 330 W; ignition distributor: Ducellier; headlamps: 2; fog lamps: 2, iodine.

DIMENSIONS AND WEIGHT wheel base: 87.87 in, 2,232 mm; front track: 49.09 in, 1,247 mm; rear track: 49.80 in, 1,265 mm; overall length: 157.36 in, 3,997 mm; overall width: 60.04 in, 1,525 mm; overall height: 50 in, 1,270 mm; ground clearance: 4.92 in, 125 mm; dry weight: 2,007 lb, 910 kg; distribution of weight: 39.1% front axle, 60.9% rear axle; turning circle (between walls): 34.1 ft, 10.4 m; fuel tank capacity: 11.7 imp gal, 14 US gal, 53 l.

BODY coupé; doors: 2; seats: 2 + 2; front seats: separate, reclining backrests.

PRACTICAL INSTRUCTIONS fuel: 98-100 oct petrol; engine sump oil: 7 imp pt, 8.5 US pt, 4 l, SAE 20W-40, change every 3,100 miles, 5,000 km; gearbox and final drive oil: 3.2 imp pt, 3.8 US pt, 1.8 l, SAE 90 EP, change every 12,400 miles, 20,000 km; greasing: none; sparking plug type: 240°; tappet clearances (hot): inlet 0.014 in, 0.35 mm, exhaust 0.016 in, 0.40 mm; normal tyre pressure: front 20 psi, 1.4 atm, rear 27 psi, 1.9 atm.

OPTIONAL ACCESSORIES light alloy wheels; 155 x 13 tyres; electrically-heated rear window.

Simca 1301 Berline

PRICE IN GB: £ 802.
PRICE EX WORKS: 10,845 francs.

ENGINE front, 4 stroke; cylinders: 4, vertical, in line; bore and stroke: 2.91 x 2.95 in, 74 x 75 mm; engine capacity: 78.7 cu in, 1,290 cu cm; compression ratio: 8.6-8.8; max power (DIN): 54 hp at 5,200 rpm; max torque (DIN): 67 lb ft, 9.2 kg m at 2,600 rpm; max engine rpm: 5,300; specific power: 41.9 hp/l; cylinder block: cast iron; cylinder head: light alloy; crankshaft bearings: 5; valves: 2 per cylinder, overhead, push-rods and rockers; camshafts: 1, side; lubrication: gear pump, centrifugal filter; lubricating

CHRYSLER FRANCE Simca 1200 S Coupé

CHRYSLER FRANCE 1301 Special Berline

CHRYSLER FRANCE Chrysler 180

system capacity: 7 imp pt, 8.5 US pt, 4 l; carburation: 1 Weber 32 ICB 3 downdraught carburettor; fuel feed: mechanical pump; cooling system: water; cooling system capacity: 11.4 imp pt, 13.7 US pt, 6.5 l.

TRANSMISSION driving wheels: rear; clutch: single dry plate; gearbox: mechanical; gears: 4 + reverse; synchromesh gears: I, II, III, IV; gearbox ratios: I 3.546, II 2.141, III 1.383, IV 1, rev 3.390; gear lever: steering column; final drive: hypoid bevel; axle ratio: 4.444; width of rims: 4''; tyres: 165 x 13.

PERFORMANCE max speeds: 22 mph, 36 km/h in 1st gear; 39 mph, 62 km/h in 2nd gear; 59 mph, 95 km/h in 3rd gear; 82 mph, 132 km/h in 4th gear; power-weight ratio: 40.8 lb/hp, 18.5 kg/hp; carrying capacity: 882 lb, 400 kg; speed in direct drive at 1,000 rpm: 15.5 mph, 25 km/h; fuel consumption: 39.2 m/imp gal, 32.7 m/US gal, 7.2 l x 100 km.

CHASSIS integral; front suspension: independent, wishbones, lower trailing links, coil springs/telescopic dampers; rear suspension: rigid axle, trailing lower radius arms, upper torque arms, transverse linkage bar, coil springs/telescopic dampers.

STEERING worm and roller; turns of steering wheel lock to lock: 4.

BRAKES front disc (diameter 10.04 in, 255 mm), rear drum, rear compensator; area rubbed by linings: front 189.8 sq in, 1,224 sq cm, rear 111.6 sq in, 720 sq cm, total 301.4 sq in, 1,944 sq cm.

ELECTRICAL EQUIPMENT voltage: 12 V; battery: 40 Ah; generator type: dynamo, 350 W; ignition distributor: Ducellier; headlamps: 2.

DIMENSIONS AND WEIGHT wheel base: 99.21 in, 2,520 mm; front track: 52.05 in, 1,322 mm; rear track: 51.18 in, 1,300 mm; overall length: 175.47 in, 4,457 mm; overall width: 62.20 in, 1,580 mm; overall height: 55.91 in, 1,420 mm; ground clearance: 4.72 in, 120 mm; dry weight: 2,205 lb, 1,000 kg; distribution of weight: 52% front axle, 48% rear axle; turning circle (between walls): 34.1 ft, 10.4 m; fuel tank capacity: 12.1 imp gal, 14.5 US gal, 55 l.

BODY saloon/sedan; doors: 4; seats: 5-6; front seats: separate.

PRACTICAL INSTRUCTIONS fuel: 98-100 oct petrol; engine sump oil: 7 imp pt, 8.5 US pt, 4 l, SAE 20W-40, change every 3,100 miles, 5,000 km; gearbox oil: 2.8 imp pt, 3.4 US pt, 1.6 l, SAE 90 EP, change every 12,400 miles, 20,000 km; final drive oil: 1.9 imp pt, 2.3 US pt, 1.1 l, SAE 90 EP, change every 12,400 miles, 20,000 km; greasing: every 6,200 miles, 10,000 km, 4 points; tappet clearances (hot): inlet 0.010 in, 0.25 mm, exhaust 0.010 in, 0.25 mm; valve timing: inlet opens 12° before tdc and closes 60° after bdc, exhaust opens 52° before bdc and closes 20° after tdc; normal tyre pressure: front 23 psi, 1.6 atm, rear 24 psi, 1.7 atm.

OPTIONAL ACCESSORIES servo brake; electrically-heated rear window.

Simca 1301 Special Berline

See Simca 1301 Berline, except for:

PRICE EX WORKS: 11,995 francs.

ENGINE compression ratio: 9-9.3; max power (DIN): 70 hp at 5,200 rpm; max torque (DIN): 72 lb ft, 10 kg m at 4,000 rpm; specific power: 54.3 hp/l; carburation: 1 Weber 28-36 DCB twin barrel carburettor.

TRANSMISSION axle ratio: 4.222 or 4.444.

PERFORMANCE max speeds: 27 mph, 43 km/h in 1st gear; 45 mph, 72 km/h in 2nd gear; 70 mph, 112 km/h in 3rd gear; 91 mph, 147 km/h in 4th gear; power-weight ratio: 31.5 lb/hp, 14.3 kg/hp.

BRAKES servo.

OPTIONAL ACCESSORIES Borg-Warner automatic gearbox.

Simca 1301 Special Break

See Simca 1301 Special Berline, except for:

PRICE EX WORKS: 12,745 francs.

TRANSMISSION tyres: 175 x 13.

PERFORMANCE power-weight ratio: 32.2 lb/hp, 14.6 kg/hp.

DIMENSIONS AND WEIGHT rear track: 51.97 in, 1,320 mm; overall length: 169.88 in, 4,315 mm; ground clearance: 4.92 in, 125 mm; dry weight: 2,481 lb, 1,025 kg; distribution of weight: 49% front axle, 51% rear axle.

BODY estate car/station wagon; doors: 4 + 1.

CHRYSLER FRANCE Simca 1200 S Coupé

CHRYSLER FRANCE 1301 Special Berline

CHRYSLER FRANCE Chrysler 180

Simca 1501 GL Berline

(Export model).

See Simca 1301 Berline, except for:

PRICE IN GB: £ 863.

ENGINE bore and stroke: 2.96 x 3.27 in, 75.2 x 83 mm; engine capacity: 90 cu in, 1,475 cu cm; compression ratio: 9.3; max power (DIN): 81 hp at 5,200 rpm; max torque (DIN): 88 lb ft, 12.2 kg m at 4,000 rpm; max engine rpm: 5,700; specific power: 54.9 hp/l; carburation: 1 Weber DCB 3 downdraught twin barrel carburettor; cooling system: electric thermostatic fan.

TRANSMISSION gear lever: central; axle ratio: 3.818; tyres: 165 x 13.

PERFORMANCE max speeds: 27 mph, 44 km/h in 1st gear; 47 mph, 75 km/h in 2nd gear; 72 mph, 116 km/h in 3rd gear; 100 mph, 161 km/h in 4th gear; power-weight ratio: 27.8 lb/hp, 12.6 kg/hp; max gradient in 1st gear: 38%; speed in direct drive at 1,000 rpm: 17.6 mph, 28.3 km/h; fuel consumption: 31.4 m/imp gal, 26.1 m/US gal, 9 l x 100 km.

BRAKES servo (standard).

ELECTRICAL EQUIPMENT headlamps: 4.

DIMENSIONS AND WEIGHT dry weight: 2,249 lb, 1,020 kg.

PRACTICAL INSTRUCTIONS tappet clearances (hot): inlet 0.012 in, 0.30 mm, exhaust 0.016 in, 0.40 mm; valve timing: inlet opens 22° before tdc and closes 60° after bdc, exhaust opens 56° before bdc and closes 24° after tdc.

OPTIONAL ACCESSORIES Borg-Warner automatic gearbox, hydraulic torque convertor and planetary gears with 3 ratios (I 2.390, II 1.450, III 1, rev 2.090), max ratio of convertor at stall 2, possible manual selection, max speeds (I) 42 mph, 67 km/h, (II) 69 mph, 111 km/h, (III) 100 mph, 161 km/h; electrically-heated rear window.

Simca 1501 GL Break

See Simca 1501 GL Berline, except for:

PRICE EX WORKS: 13,645 francs.

TRANSMISSION tyres: 175 x 13.

PERFORMANCE power-weight ratio: 29.8 lb/hp, 13.5 kg/hp; carrying capacity: 992 lb, 450 kg.

DIMENSIONS AND WEIGHT overall length: 169.88 in, 4,315 mm; dry weight: 2,403 lb, 1,090 kg.

BODY estate car/station wagon; doors: 4 + 1.

OPTIONAL ACCESSORIES only automatic gearbox.

Simca 1501 Special Berline

(Export model).

See Simca 1501 GL Berline, except for:

PRICE: —

Simca 1501 Special Break

See Simca 1501 GL Break, except for:

PRICE IN GB: £ 1,008.
PRICE EX WORKS: 14,895 francs.

Chrysler 160

PRICE EX WORKS: 13,760 francs.

ENGINE front, 4 stroke; cylinders: 4, in line; bore and stroke: 3.28 x 2.95 in, 83.4 x 75 mm; engine capacity: 100 cu in, 1,639 cu cm; compression ratio: 9.1; max power (DIN): 79 hp at 5,600 rpm; max torque (DIN): 90 lb ft, 12.4 kg m at 3,200 rpm; max engine rpm: 5,700; specific power: 48.2 hp/l; cylinder block: cast iron; cylinder head: light alloy; crankshaft bearings: 5; valves: 2 per cylinder, overhead, rockers; camshafts: 1, overhead; lubrication: gear pump, full flow filter; lubricating system capacity: 7.9 imp pt, 9.5 US pt, 4.5 l; carburation: 1 Weber 34 ICR 8 downdraught carburettor; fuel feed: mechanical pump; cooling system: water; cooling system capacity: 16.7 imp pt, 20.1 US pt, 9.5 l.

CHRYSLER 160

TRANSMISSION driving wheels: rear; clutch: single dry plate; gearbox: mechanical; gears: 4 + reverse; synchromesh gears: I, II, III, IV; gearbox ratios: I 3.546, II 2.141, III 1.383, IV 1, rev 3.300; gear lever: central; final drive: hypoid bevel; axle ratio: 3.909; width of rims: 4.5''; tyres: 165 x 13.

PERFORMANCE max speeds: 27 mph, 44 km/h in 1st gear; 45 mph, 73 km/h in 2nd gear; 70 mph, 113 km/h in 3rd gear; 98 mph, 157 km/h in 4th gear; power-weight ratio: 29.8 lb/hp, 13.5 kg/hp; carrying capacity: 882 lb, 400 kg; speed in direct drive at 1,000 rpm: 17.1 mph, 27.5 km/h; fuel consumption: 28.2 m/imp gal, 23.5 m/US gal, 10 l x 100 km.

CHASSIS integral; front suspension: independent, by Mc-Pherson, coil springs/telescopic damper struts, lower wishbones, anti-roll bar; rear suspension: rigid axle, lower longitudinal trailing arms, upper torque arms, transverse linkage bar, coil springs, anti-roll bar, telescopic dampers.

STEERING rack-and-pinion; turns of steering wheel lock to lock: 4.

BRAKES front disc, rear drum, servo; lining area: front 25.4 sq in, 164 sq cm, rear 62.9 sq in, 406 sq cm, total 88.3 sq in, 570 sq cm.

ELECTRICAL EQUIPMENT voltage: 12 V; battery: 40 Ah; generator type: alternator, 360 W; ignition distributor: Ducellier; headlamps: 2.

DIMENSIONS AND WEIGHT wheel base: 105 in, 2,667 mm; front track: 55.12 in, 1,400 mm; rear track: 55 in, 1,397 mm; overall length: 175.47 in, 4,457 mm; overall width: 68.03 in, 1,728 mm; overall height: 56.30 in, 1,430 mm; ground clearance: 4.72 in, 120 mm; dry weight: 2,359 lb, 1,070 kg; distribution of weight: 53.8% front axle, 46.2% rear axle; turning circle (between walls): 36.1 ft, 11 m; fuel tank capacity: 14.3 imp gal, 17.2 US gal, 65 l.

BODY saloon/sedan; doors: 4; seats: 5, front seats: separate.

PRACTICAL INSTRUCTIONS fuel: 98-100 oct petrol; engine sump oil: 7 imp pt, 8.5 US pt, 4 l, SAE 10W-50, change every 3,100 miles, 5,000 km; gearbox oil: 2.6 imp pt, 3.2 US pt, 1.5 l, SAE 90 EP, change every 12,400 miles, 20,000 km; final drive oil: 2.5 imp pt, 3 US pt, 1.4 l, SAE 90 EP, change every 12,400 miles, 20,000 km; greasing: none; sparking plug type: 225°; tappet clearances: inlet 0.010 in, 0.25 mm, exhaust 0.014 in, 0.35 mm; normal tyre pressure: front 24 psi, 1.7 atm, rear 27 psi, 1.9 atm.

OPTIONAL ACCESSORIES automatic gearbox, hydraulic torque convertor and planetary gears with 3 ratios (I 2.450, II 1.451, III 1, rev 2.200); electrically-heated rear window.

Chrysler 160 GT

See Chrysler 160, except for:

PRICE EX WORKS: 14,690 francs.

ENGINE bore and stroke: 3.45 x 2.95 in, 87.7 x 75 mm; engine capacity: 110.6 cu in, 1,812 cu cm; max power (DIN): 97 hp at 5,600 rpm; max torque (DIN): 107 lb ft, 14.8 kg m at 3,200 rpm; max engine rpm: 5,800; specific power: 53.5 hp/l; lubricating system capacity: 8.3 imp pt, 9.9 US pt, 4.7 l; carburation: 1 Weber 38 ADS downdraught twin barrel carburettor; cooling system capacity: 17.6 imp pt, 21.1 US pt, 10 l.

TRANSMISSION axle ratio: 3.727.

PERFORMANCE max speeds: 29 mph, 47 km/h in 1st gear; 49 mph, 79 km/h in 2nd gear; 78 mph, 125 km/h in 3rd gear; 106 mph, 170 km/h in 4th gear; power-weight ratio: 24.7 lb/hp, 11.2 kg/hp; carrying capacity: 948 lb, 430 kg; speed in direct drive at 1,000 rpm: 18 mph, 28.9 km/h; fuel consumption: 25.7 m/imp gal, 21.4 m/US gal, 11 l x 100 km.

BRAKES disc; lining area: front 23.6 sq in, 152 sq cm, rear 16.7 sq in, 108 sq cm, total 40.3 sq in, 260 sq cm.

DIMENSIONS AND WEIGHT overall length: 178.23 in, 4,527 mm; dry weight: 2,403 lb, 1,090 kg; turning circle (between walls): 37.7 ft, 11.5 m.

Chrysler 180

See Chrysler 160 GT, except for:

PRICE EX WORKS: 15,590 francs.

CITROËN 2 CV 4

CITROËN Dyane

CITROËN Mehari 2 + 2

CITROËN   FRANCE

2 CV 4

PRICE EX WORKS: 6,640 francs.

ENGINE front, 4 stroke; cylinders: 2, horizontally opposed; bore and stroke: 2.70 x 2.32 in, 68.5 x 59 mm; engine capacity: 26.5 cu in, 435 cu cm; compression ratio: 8.5; max power (SAE): 26 hp at 6,750 rpm; max torque (SAE): 22 lb ft, 3.1 kg m at 4,000 rpm; max engine rpm: 6,750; specific power: 59.8 hp/l; cylinder block: cast iron, dry liners, light alloy sump; cylinder head: light alloy, hemispherical combustion chambers; crankshaft bearings: 2; valves: 2 per cylinder, overhead, Vee-slanted at 70°, push-rods and rockers; camshafts: 1, central, lower; lubrication: rotary pump, filter in sump, oil cooler; lubricating system capacity: 3.5 imp pt, 4.2 US pt, 2 l; carburation: 1 Solex 34 PICS 4 downdraught carburettor; fuel feed: mechanical pump; cooling system: air cooled.

TRANSMISSION driving wheels: front (double homokinetic joints); clutch: single dry plate; gearbox: mechanical; gears: 4 + reverse; synchromesh gears: I, II, III, IV; gearbox ratios: I 6.964, II 3.555, III 2.134, IV 1.474, rev 6.964; gear lever: on facia; final drive: spiral bevel; axle ratio: 4.125; tyres: 125 x 380.

PERFORMANCE max speeds: 16 mph, 26 km/h in 1st gear; 32 mph, 51 km/h in 2nd gear; 53 mph, 85 km/h in 3rd gear; 63 mph, 102 km/h in 4th gear; power-weight ratio: 47.4 lb/hp, 21.5 kg/hp; carrying capacity: 706 lb, 320 kg; speed in top at 1,000 rpm: 11.3 mph, 18.2 km/h; fuel consumption: 51.4 m/imp gal, 42.8 m/US gal, 5.5 l x 100 km.

CHASSIS platform; front suspension: independent, swinging leading arms, 2 friction dampers, 2 inertia-type patter dampers; rear suspension: independent, swinging longitudinal trailing arms linked to front suspension by longitudinal coil springs, 2 inertia-type patter dampers, 2 telescopic dampers.

STEERING rack-and-pinion; turns of steering wheel lock to lock: 2.25.

BRAKES drum; lining area: front 29.1 sq in, 188 sq cm, rear 30.7 sq in, 198 sq cm, total 59.8 sq in, 386 sq cm.

ELECTRICAL EQUIPMENT voltage: 12 V; battery: 32 Ah; generator type: alternator, 390 W; headlamps: 2, height adjustable from driving seat.

DIMENSIONS AND WEIGHT wheel base: 94.49 in, 2,400 mm; front track: 49.61 in, 1,260 mm; rear track: 49.61 in, 1,260 mm; overall length: 150.79 in, 3,830 mm; overall width: 58.27 in, 1,480 mm; overall height: 62.99 in, 1,600 mm; ground clearance: 5.91 in, 150 mm; dry weight: 1,235 lb, 560 kg; turning circle (between walls): 35.1 ft, 10.7 m; fuel tank capacity: 4.4 imp gal, 5.3 US gal, 20 l.

BODY saloon/sedan; doors: 4; seats: 4; front seats: bench; details: back seat folding down to luggage table, fully opening canvas sunshine roof.

PRACTICAL INSTRUCTIONS fuel: 86 oct petrol; engine sump oil: 3.5 imp pt, 4.2 US pt, 2 l, SAE 10W-30, change every 3,100 miles, 5,000 km; gearbox and final drive oil: 1.8 imp pt, 2.1 US pt, 1 l, SAE 80, change every 12,400 miles, 20,000 km; greasing: every 1,900 miles, 3,000 km, 4 points; normal tyre pressure: front 18 psi, 1.3 atm, rear 26 psi, 1.8 atm.

OPTIONAL ACCESSORIES centrifugal clutch, separate front seats.

2 CV 6

See 2 CV 4, except for:

PRICE EX WORKS: 7,180 francs.

ENGINE bore and stroke: 2.91 x 2.76 in, 74 x 70 mm; engine capacity: 36.7 cu in, 602 cu cm; max power (SAE): 33 hp at 7,000 rpm; max torque (SAE): 31 lb ft, 4.3 kg m at 3,500-4,000 rpm; max engine rpm: 7,000; specific power: 54.8 hp/l; lubricating system capacity: 4.4 imp pt, 5.3 US pt, 2.5 l; carburation: 1 Solex 34 PICS 4 o 34 PCIS 4 downdraught carburettor.

TRANSMISSION gearbox ratios: I 5.203, II 2.657, III 1.786, IV 1.316, rev 5.203.

PERFORMANCE max speeds: 19 mph, 30 km/h in 1st gear; 40 mph, 65 km/h in 2nd gear; 59 mph, 95 km/h in 3rd gear; 68 mph, 110 km/h in 4th gear; power-weight ratio: 37.5 lb/hp, 17 kg/hp; fuel consumption: 50.4 m/imp gal, 42 m/US gal, 5.6 l x 100 km.

Dyane

PRICE IN GB: £ 436.
PRICE EX WORKS: 6,832 francs.

ENGINE front, 4 stroke; cylinders: 2, horizontally opposed;

CITROËN 2 CV 4

CITROËN Dyane

CITROËN Mehari 2 + 2

bore and stroke: 2.70 x 2.32 in, 68.5 x 59 mm; engine capacity: 26.2 cu in, 435 cu cm; compression ratio: 8.5; max power (SAE): 26 hp at 6,750 rpm; max torque (SAE): 22 lb ft, 3.1 kg m at 4,000 rpm; max engine rpm: 6,750; specific power: 59.8 hp/l; cylinder block: cast iron, dry liners, light alloy sump; cylinder head: light alloy, hemispherical combustion chambers; crankshaft bearings: 2; valves: 2 per cylinder, overhead, Vee-slanted at 70°, pushrods and rockers; camshafts: 1, central, lower; lubrication: rotary pump, filter in sump, oil cooler; lubricating system capacity: 4.4 imp pt, 5.3 US pt, 2.5 l; carburation: 1 Solex 34 PICS 4 downdraught carburettor; fuel feed: mechanical pump; cooling system: air cooled.

TRANSMISSION driving wheels: front (double universal joints); clutch: single dry plate; gearbox: mechanical; gears: 4 + reverse; synchromesh gears: I, II, III, IV; gearbox ratios: I 6.964, II 3.555, III 2.134, IV 1.474, rev 6.964; gear lever: on facia; final drive: spiral bevel; axle ratio: 4.125; tyres: 125 x 380.

PERFORMANCE max speeds: 16 mph, 26 km/h in 1st gear; 32 mph, 51 km/h in 2nd gear; 53 mph, 85 km/h in 3rd gear; 65 mph, 104 km/h in 4th gear; power-weight ratio: 50.1 lb/hp, 22.9 kg/hp; carrying capacity: 706 lb, 320 kg; speed in top at 1,000 rpm: 11.3 mph, 18.2 km/h; fuel consumption: 51.4 m/imp gal, 42.8 m/US gal, 5.5 l x 100 km.

CHASSIS platform; front suspension: independent, swinging leading arms, 2 friction dampers, 2 inertia-type patter dampers; rear suspension: independent, swinging longitudinal trailing arms linked to front suspension by longitudinal coil springs, 2 inertia-type patter dampers, 2 telescopic dampers.

STEERING rack-and-pinion; turns of steering wheel lock to lock: 2.25.

BRAKES drum; lining area: front 29.1 sq in, 188 sq cm, rear 30.7 sq in, 198 sq cm, total 59.8 sq in, 386 sq cm.

ELECTRICAL EQUIPMENT voltage: 12 V; battery: 32 Ah; generator type: alternator, 390 W; headlamps: 2.

DIMENSIONS AND WEIGHT wheel base: 94.49 in, 2,400 mm; front track: 49.61 in, 1,260 mm; rear track: 49.61 in, 1,260 mm; overall length: 148.82 in, 3,780 mm; overall width: 59.06 in, 1,500 mm; overall height: 60.63 in, 1,540 mm; ground clearance: 6.30 in, 160 mm; dry weight: 1,312 lb, 595 kg; turning circle (between walls): 35.1 ft, 10.7 m; fuel tank capacity: 4.4 imp gal, 5.3 US gal, 20 l.

BODY saloon/sedan; doors: 4 + 1; seats: 4; front seats: bench; details: fully opening canvas sunshine roof.

PRACTICAL INSTRUCTIONS fuel: 80-85 oct petrol; engine sump oil: 4.4 imp pt, 5.3 US pt, 2.5 l, SAE 10W-30, change every 3,100 miles, 5,000 km; gearbox and final drive oil: 1.8 imp pt, 2.1 US pt, 1 l, SAE 80, change every 12,400 miles, 20,000 km; greasing: every 1,900 miles, 3,000 km, 4 points; normal tyre pressure: front 18 psi, 1.3 atm, rear 26 psi, 1.8 atm.

OPTIONAL ACCESSORIES centrifugal clutch; back seat folding down to luggage table; commercial version.

Dyane 6

See Dyane, except for:

PRICE IN GB: £ 477.
PRICE EX WORKS: 7,980 francs.

ENGINE bore and stroke: 2.91 x 2.76 in, 74 x 70 mm; engine capacity: 36.7 cu in, 602 cu cm; compression ratio: 9; max power (SAE): 35 hp at 5,750 rpm; max torque (SAE): 34 lb ft, 4.7 kg m at 4,750 rpm; max engine rpm: 6,000; specific power: 58.1 hp/l; carburation: 1 Solex 26-35 CSIC or 26-35 SCIC downdraught twin barrel carburettor.

TRANSMISSION gearbox ratios: I 5.747, II 2.935, III 1.923, IV 1.350, rev 5.747; axle ratio: 3.875.

PERFORMANCE max speeds: 19 mph, 30 km/h in 1st gear; 36 mph, 58 km/h in 2nd gear; 55 mph, 89 km/h in 3rd gear; 73 mph, 118 km/h in 4th gear; power-weight ratio: 37.7 lb/hp, 17.1 kg/hp; speed in top at 1,000 rpm: 13.1 mph, 21.1 km/h; fuel consumption: 47.1 m/imp gal, 39.2 m/US gal, 6 l x 100 km.

BRAKES lining area: total 84.8 sq in, 547 sq cm.

DIMENSIONS AND WEIGHT dry weight: 1,323 lb, 600 kg; fuel tank capacity: 5.5 imp gal, 6.6 US gal, 25 l.

Mehari 2 + 2

See Dyane 6, except for:

PRICE IN USA: $ 1,795.
PRICE EX WORKS: 8,692 francs.

TRANSMISSION gearbox ratios: I 6.060, II 3.125, III 1.920, IV 1.420, rev 6.060; axle ratio: 3.875; tyres: 135 x 380.

MEHARI 2 + 2

PERFORMANCE max speed: 62 mph, 100 km/h; power-weight ratio: 35.1 lb/hp, 15.9 kg/hp; carrying capacity: 882 lb, 400 kg; fuel consumption: 51.4 m/imp gal, 42.8 m/US gal, 5.5 l x 100 km.

BRAKES lining area: total 84.8 sq in, 547 sq cm.

DIMENSIONS AND WEIGHT overall length: 138.98 in, 3,530 mm; overall width: 60.24 in, 1,530 mm; dry weight: 1,158 lb, 525 kg.

BODY open, in plastic material; doors: none; seats: 2 + 2; front seats: separate.

OPTIONAL ACCESSORIES only centrifugal clutch.

Ami 8 Berline Confort

PRICE IN GB: £ 508.
PRICE EX WORKS: 8,940 francs.

ENGINE front, 4 stroke; cylinders: 2, horizontally opposed; bore and stroke: 2.91 x 2.76 in, 74 x 70 mm; engine capacity: 36.7 cu in, 602 cu cm; compression ratio: 9; max power (SAE): 35 hp at 5,750 rpm; max torque (SAE): 34 lb ft, 4.7 kg m at 4,750 rpm; max engine rpm: 6,000; specific power: 58.1 hp/l; cylinder block: cast iron, dry liners, light alloy sump; cylinder head: light alloy, hemispherical combustion chambers; crankshaft bearings: 2; valves: 2 per cylinder, overhead, Vee-slanted at 70°; camshafts: 1, central; lubrication: gear pump, filter in sump, oil cooler; lubricating system capacity: 3.9 imp pt, 4.7 US pt, 2.2 l; carburation: 1 Solex 26-35 CSIC or 26-35 SCIC downdraught carburettor; fuel feed: mechanical pump; cooling system: air cooled.

TRANSMISSION driving wheels: front (double universal joints); clutch: single dry plate; gearbox: mechanical; gears: 4 + reverse; synchromesh gears: I, II, III, IV; gearbox ratios: I 5.760, II 2.940, III 1.920, IV 1.350, rev 5.760; gear lever: on facia; final drive: spiral bevel; axle ratio: 3.875; tyres: 125 x 380.

PERFORMANCE max speeds: 19 mph, 30 km/h in 1st gear; 36 mph, 58 km/h in 2nd gear; 55 mph, 89 km/h in 3rd gear; 76 mph, 123 km/h in 4th gear; power-weight ratio: 44.1 lb/hp, 20 kg/hp; carrying capacity: 706 lb, 320 kg; speed in top at 1,000 rpm: 13.1 mph, 21.1 km/h; fuel consumption: 44.1 m/imp gal, 36.8 m/US gal, 6.4 l x 100 km.

CHASSIS platform; front suspension: independent, swinging leading arms, 2 telescopic dampers, 2 inertia-type patter dampers, anti-roll bar; rear suspension: independent, swinging longitudinal trailing arms linked to front suspension by longitudinal coil springs, 2 telescopic dampers, 2 inertia-type patter dampers.

STEERING rack-and-pinion; turns of steering wheel lock to lock: 2.25.

BRAKES front disc, rear drum.

ELECTRICAL EQUIPMENT voltage: 12 V; battery: 30 Ah; generator type: alternator, 390 W; headlamps: 2.

DIMENSIONS AND WEIGHT wheel base: 94.49 in, 2,400 mm; front track: 49.61 in, 1,260 mm; rear track: 48.03 in, 1,220 mm; overall length: 157.09 in, 3,990 mm; overall width: 59.84 in, 1,520 mm; overall height: 58.46 in, 1,485 mm; ground clearance: 6.30 in, 160 mm; dry weight: 1,544 lb, 700 kg; turning circle (between walls): 37.4 ft, 11.4 m; fuel tank capacity: 7 imp gal, 8.4 US gal, 32 l.

BODY saloon/sedan; doors: 4; seats: 4-5; front seats: bench.

PRACTICAL INSTRUCTIONS fuel: 80-85 oct petrol; engine sump oil: 3.9 imp pt, 4.7 US pt, 2.2 l, SAE 10W-30, change every 3,100 miles, 5,000 km; gearbox and final drive oil: 1.8 imp pt, 2.1 US pt, 1 l, SAE 80, change every 12,400 miles, 20,000 km; greasing: every 1,900 miles, 3,000 km, 4 points; normal tyre pressure: front 18 psi, 1.3 atm, rear 21 psi, 1.5 atm.

OPTIONAL ACCESSORIES centrifugal clutch; separate front seats, reclining backrests.

Ami 8 Berline Club

See Ami 8 Berline Confort, except for:

PRICE IN GB: £ 574.
PRICE EX WORKS: 9,420 francs.

BODY front seats: separate, reclining backrests (standard); details: luxury interior.

CITROËN Ami 8 Berline Confort

CITROËN GS Confort

CITROËN DSpecial Berline

Ami 8 Break Confort

See Ami 8 Berline Confort, except for:

PRICE IN GB: £ 585.
PRICE EX WORKS: 9,420 francs.

TRANSMISSION tyres: 135 x 380.

PERFORMANCE carrying capacity: 882 lb, 400 kg.

CHASSIS reinforced suspension.

BODY estate car/station wagon; doors: 4 + 1.

Ami 8 Commerciale

See Ami 8 Break Confort, except for:

PRICE EX WORKS: 9,420 francs.

GS Confort

PRICE EX WORKS: 11,380 francs.

ENGINE front, 4 stroke; cylinders: 4, horizontally opposed; bore and stroke: 2.91 x 2.32 in, 74 x 59 mm; engine capacity: 61.9 cu in, 1,015 cu cm; compression ratio: 9; max power (SAE): 61 hp at 6,750 rpm; max torque (SAE): 54 lb ft, 7.5 kg m at 3,500 rpm; max engine rpm: 6,750; specific power: 60.1 hp/l; cylinder block: light alloy; cylinder head: cast iron liners with light alloy fins, hemispherical combustion chambers; crankshaft bearings: 3; valves: 2 per cylinder, overhead; camshafts: 1 per cylinder block, overhead; lubrication: gear pump, full flow filter, oil cooler; lubricating system capacity: 7 imp pt, 8.5 US pt, 4 l; carburation: 1 Solex 28 CICM downdraught twin barrel carburettor; fuel feed: mechanical pump; cooling system: air cooled.

TRANSMISSION driving wheels: front; clutch: single dry plate (diaphragm); gearbox: mechanical; gears: 4 + reverse; synchromesh gears: I, II, III, IV; gearbox ratios: I 3.818, II 2.375, III 1.524, IV 1.120, rev 4.182; gear lever: central; final drive: spiral bevel; axle ratio: 4.375; width of rims: 4.5''; tyres: 145 x 15.

PERFORMANCE max speeds: 28 mph, 45 km/h in 1st gear; 45 mph, 73 km/h in 2nd gear; 71 mph, 114 km/h in 3rd gear; 91 mph, 147 km/h in 4th gear; power-weight ratio: 31.7 lb/hp, 14.4 kg/hp; carrying capacity: 882 lb, 400 kg; acceleration: standing 1/4 mile 20.4 sec; speed in top at 1,000 rpm: 14.2 mph, 22.9 km/h; fuel consumption: 37.7 m/imp gal, 31.4 m/US gal, 7.5 l x 100 km.

CHASSIS integral; front suspension: independent, wishbones, hydropneumatic suspension, anti-roll bar, automatic levelling control; rear suspension: independent, swinging trailing arms, hydropneumatic suspension, anti-roll bar, automatic levelling control.

STEERING rack-and-pinion; turns of steering wheel lock to lock: 3.75.

BRAKES disc, dual circuit (front diameter 10.63 in, 270 mm, rear diameter 6.93 in, 176 mm); lining area: total 23.6 sq in, 152 sq cm.

ELECTRICAL EQUIPMENT voltage: 12 V; battery: 30 Ah; generator type: alternator, 390 W; ignition distributor: Sev; headlamps: 2.

DIMENSIONS AND WEIGHT wheel base: 100.39 in, 2,550 mm; front track: 54.25 in, 1,378 mm; rear track: 52.28 in, 1,328 mm; overall length: 162.20 in, 4,120 mm; overall width: 63.31 in, 1,608 mm; constant height: 53.11 in, 1,349 mm; ground clearance: 6.06 in, 154 mm; dry weight: 1,940 lb, 880 kg; distribution of weight: 62.5% front axle, 37.5% rear axle; turning circle between walls: 33.5 ft, 10.2 m; fuel tank capacity: 9.5 imp gal, 11.4 US gal, 43 l.

BODY saloon/sedan; doors: 4; seats: 5; front seats: separate.

PRACTICAL INSTRUCTIONS fuel: 98 oct petrol; engine sump oil: 7 imp pt, 8.5 US pt, 4 l, SAE 10W-30, change every 3,100 miles, 5,000 km; gearbox and final drive oil: 2.6 imp pt, 3.2 US pt, 1.5 l, SAE 90, change every 12,400 miles, 20,000 km; hydropneumatic suspension oil: 5.8 imp pt, 7 US pt, 3.3 l; greasing: none; normal tyre pressure: front 26 psi, 1.8 atm, rear 27 psi, 1.9 atm.

OPTIONAL ACCESSORIES Ferodo semi-automatic gearbox with 3 ratios; boosted heating for temperatures below —20°C, —4°F; electrically-heated rear window.

GS Club

See GS Confort, except for:

PRICE EX WORKS: 12,200 francs.

ELECTRICAL EQUIPMENT generator type: alternator, 490 W; headlamps: iodine.

BODY luxury equipment.

CITROËN Ami 8

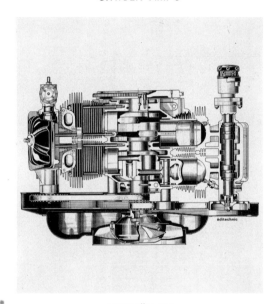

CITROËN GS

CITROËN DSpecial Berline

DSpecial Berline

PRICE IN GB: £ 1,126.
PRICE EX WORKS: 14,800 francs.

ENGINE front, 4 stroke; cylinders: 4, vertical, in line; bore and stroke: 3.39 x 3.37 in, 86 x 85.5 mm; engine capacity: 121.1 cu in, 1,985 cu cm; compression ratio: 8; max power (SAE): 91 hp at 5,750 rpm; max torque (SAE): 101 lb ft, 14 kg m at 3,000 rpm; max engine rpm: 5,750; specific power: 45.8 hp/l; cylinder block: cast iron, wet liners; cylinder head: light alloy, hemispherical combustion chambers; crankshaft bearings: 5; valves: 2 per cylinder, overhead, Vee-slanted at 60°, push-rods and rockers; camshafts: 1, side; lubrication: gear pump, filter in sump and full flow; lubricating system capacity: 7.9 imp pt, 9.5 US pt, 4.5 l; carburation: 1 Solex 34 PBIC 3 downdraught carburettor; fuel feed: mechanical pump; cooling system: water; cooling system capacity: 18.3 imp pt, 22 US pt, 10.4 l.

TRANSMISSION driving wheels: front; clutch: single dry plate, hydraulically controlled; gearbox: mechanical; gears: 4 + reverse; synchromesh gears: I, II, III, IV; gearbox ratios: I 3.251, II 1.833, III 1.207, IV 0.852, rev 3.155; gear lever: steering column; final drive: spiral bevel; axle ratio: 4.857; width of rims: 5''; tyres: 180 x 380 front, 155 x 380 rear.

PERFORMANCE max speeds: 28 mph, 45 km/h in 1st gear; 50 mph, 80 km/h in 2nd gear; 78 mph, 125 km/h in 3rd gear; 99 mph, 160 km/h in 4th gear; power-weight ratio: 30.4 lb/hp, 13.8 kg/hp; carrying capacity: 1,058 lb, 480 kg; speed in top at 1,000 rpm: 20.2 mph, 32.5 km/h; fuel consumption: 25.7 m/imp gal, 21.4 m/US gal, 11 l x 100 km.

CHASSIS platform, lateral box members; front suspension: independent, wishbones, hydropneumatic suspension, anti-roll bar, automatic levelling control; rear suspension: independent, trailing radius arms, hydropneumatic suspension, anti-roll bar, automatic levelling control.

STEERING rack-and-pinion; turns of steering wheel lock to lock: 3.

BRAKES front disc (diameter 11.61 in, 295 mm), rear drum, dual circuit, rear compensator, servo; area rubbed by linings: front 222.5 sq in, 1,435 sq cm, rear 86.5 sq in, 558 sq cm, total 309 sq in, 1,993 sq cm.

ELECTRICAL EQUIPMENT voltage: 12 V; battery: 40 Ah; generator type: alternator, 520 W; ignition distributor: Sev or Ducellier; headlamps: 4.

DIMENSIONS AND WEIGHT wheel base: 123.03 in, 3,125 mm; front track: 59.06 in, 1,500 mm; rear track: 51.18 in, 1,300 mm; overall length: 191.73 in, 4,870 mm; overall width: 70.87 in, 1,800 mm; overall height: 57.87 in, 1,470 mm; ground clearance: 2.56 5.31 9.84 in, 65 135 250 mm; dry weight: 2,778 lb, 1,260 kg; distribution of weight: 65.1% front axle, 34.9% rear axle; turning circle (between walls): 36.1 ft, 11 m; fuel tank capacity: 14.3 imp gal, 17.2 US gal, 65 l.

BODY saloon/sedan; doors: 4; seats: 5-6; front seats: separate; details: plastic roof.

PRACTICAL INSTRUCTIONS fuel: 90-95 oct petrol; engine sump oil: 7.9 imp pt, 9.5 US pt, 4.5 l, SAE 10W-30, change every 2,500 miles, 4,000 km; gearbox and final drive oil: 3.5 imp pt, 4.2 US pt, 2 l, SAE 90, change every 12,400 miles, 20,000 km; hydraulic suspension oil: 9.2 imp pt, 11 US pt, 5.2 l; greasing: every 2,500 miles, 4,000 km, 8 points; normal tyre pressure: front 28 psi, 2 atm, rear 28 psi, 2 atm.

OPTIONAL ACCESSORIES power-assisted steering, 4 headlamps automatically adjustable in height while running with 2 iodine long-distance lights automatically directed on bends by steering; iodine long-distance lights; headlamps automatically adjustable in height while running; boosted heating for temperatures below —15°C, 5°F; electrically-heated rear window.

DSuper Berline

See DSpecial Berline, except for:

PRICE IN GB: £ 1,241.
PRICE EX WORKS: 16,240 francs.

ENGINE compression ratio: 8.7; max power (SAE): 103 hp at 6,000 rpm; max torque (SAE): 108 lb ft, 14.9 kg m at 4,000 rpm; max engine rpm: 6,000; specific power: 51.9 hp/l; carburation: 1 Weber 28/36 DLE 2 or DLEA 2 downdraught twin barrel carburettor; cooling system capacity: 18.7 imp pt, 22.4 US pt, 10.6 l.

PERFORMANCE max speeds: 29 mph, 47 km/h in 1st gear; 52 mph, 83 km/h in 2nd gear; 81 mph, 130 km/h in 3rd gear; 106 mph, 170 km/h in 4th gear; power-weight ratio: 27.1 lb/hp, 12.3 kg/hp; fuel consumption: 24.8 m/imp gal, 20.6 m/US gal, 11.4 l x 100 km.

DIMENSIONS AND WEIGHT dry weight: 2,789 lb, 1,265 kg.

OPTIONAL ACCESSORIES 5-speed gearbox.

DS 20 Berline

See DSuper Berline, except for:

PRICE IN GB: £ 1,436.
PRICE EX WORKS: 19,200 francs.

TRANSMISSION clutch: automatically hydraulically controlled; gearbox: servo-assisted; axle ratio: 4.375.

PERFORMANCE power-weight ratio: 27.6 lb/hp, 12.5 kg/hp.

STEERING servo (standard).

DIMENSIONS AND WEIGHT dry weight: 2,844 lb, 1,290 kg.

DS 20 Pallas

See DS 20 Berline, except for:

PRICE EX WORKS: 21,340 francs.

ELECTRICAL EQUIPMENT headlamps: 4, iodine, automatically adjustable in height while running with 2 long-distance lights automatically directed on bends by steering (standard).

BODY details: electrically-heated rear window (standard).

DS 20 Prestige

See DS 20 Pallas, except for:

PRICE EX WORKS: 23,600 francs.

Familiale Luxe 20

See DSuper Berline, except for:

PRICE IN GB: £ 1,446.
PRICE EX WORKS: 19,820 francs.

TRANSMISSION tyres: 180 x 380 (front and rear).

PERFORMANCE max speed: 99 mph, 160 km/h; power-weight ratio: 29.5 lb/hp, 13.4 kg/hp; carrying capacity: 1,433 lb, 650 kg.

DIMENSIONS AND WEIGHT front track: 59.68 in, 1,516 mm; rear track: 51.81 in, 1,316 mm; overall length: 196.46 in, 4,990 mm; overall width: 70.47 in, 1,790 mm; overall height: 60.24 in, 1,530 mm; ground clearance: 3.54 5.71 11.02 in, 90 145 280 mm; dry weight: 3,043 lb, 1,380 kg; distribution of weight: 60.6% front axle, 39.4% rear axle.

BODY estate car/station wagon; doors: 4 + 1; seats: 8; front seats: bench.

OPTIONAL ACCESSORIES servo-assisted gearbox; electrically-heated rear window not available.

Familiale Confort 20

See Familiale Luxe 20, except for:

PRICE EX WORKS: 20,220 francs.

Break Luxe 20

See Familiale Luxe 20, except for:

PRICE EX WORKS: 19,400 francs.

Break Confort 20

See Familiale Luxe 20, except for:

PRICE EX WORKS: 20,440 francs.

Commerciale 20

See Familiale Luxe 20, except for:

PRICE EX WORKS: 19,180 francs.

DS 21 Berline

PRICE IN GB: £ 1,585.
PRICE IN USA: $ 4,066.

ENGINE front, 4 stroke; cylinders: 4, vertical, in line; bore and stroke: 3.54 x 3.37 in, 90 x 85.5 mm; engine

CITROËN DS 21 Pallas

CITROËN DS 21 (injection engine)

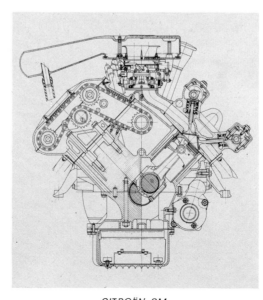

CITROËN SM

capacity: 132.7 cu in, 2,175 cu cm; compression ratio: 8.7; max power (SAE): 115 hp at 5,750 rpm; max torque (SAE): 126 lb ft, 17.4 kg m at 4,000 rpm; max engine rpm: 5,750; specific power: 52.9 hp/l; cylinder block: cast iron; cylinder head: light alloy, hemispherical combustion chambers; crankshaft bearings: 5; valves: 2 per cylinder, overhead, Vee-slanted at 60°, push-rods and rockers; camshafts: 1, side; lubrication: gear pump, filter in sump and full flow; lubricating system capacity: 8.8 imp pt, 10.6 US pt, 5 l; carburation: 1 Weber 28/36 DLE or 28/36 DLEA downdraught twin barrel carburettor; fuel feed: mechanical pump; cooling system: water; cooling system capacity: 19 imp pt, 22.8 US pt, 10.8 l.

TRANSMISSION driving wheels: front; clutch: single dry plate, automatically hydraulically controlled; gearbox: mechanical, servo-assisted; gears: 4 + reverse; synchromesh gears: I, II, III, IV; gearbox ratios: I 3.251, II 1.834, III 1.207, IV 0.852, rev 3.155; gear lever: steering column; final drive: spiral bevel; axle ratio: 4.375; width of rims: 5''; tyres: 180 x 380 front, 155 x 380 rear.

PERFORMANCE max speed: 112 mph, 180 km/h; power-weight ratio: 24.9 lb/hp, 11.3 kg/hp; carrying capacity: 1,058 lb, 480 kg; acceleration: standing ¼ mile 19 sec; speed in top at 1,000 rpm: 20.7 mph, 33.3 km/h; fuel consumption: 23.9 m/imp gal, 19.9 m/US gal, 11.8 l x 100 km.

CHASSIS platform, lateral box members; front suspension: independent, wishbones, hydropneumatic suspension, anti-roll bar, automatic levelling control; rear suspension: independent, trailing radius arms, hydropneumatic suspension, anti-roll bar, automatic levelling control.

STEERING rack-and-pinion, servo; turns of steering wheel lock to lock: 3.

BRAKES front disc (diameter 11.61 in, 295 mm), rear drum, dual circuit, rear compensator, servo; area rubbed by linings: front 222.5 sq in, 1,435 sq cm, rear 86.5 sq in, 558 sq cm, total 309 sq in, 1,993 sq cm.

ELECTRICAL EQUIPMENT voltage: 12 V; battery: 40 Ah; generator type: alternator, 520 W; ignition distributor: Sev or Ducellier; headlamps: 4.

DIMENSIONS AND WEIGHT wheel base: 123.03 in, 3,125 mm; front track: 59.68 in, 1,516 mm; rear track: 51.81 in, 1,316 mm; overall length: 191.73 in, 4,870 mm; overall width: 70.87 in, 1,800 mm; overall height: 57.87 in, 1,470 mm; ground clearance: 3.54 5.71 11.02 in, 90 145 280 mm; dry weight: 2,867 lb, 1,300 kg; distribution of weight: 60% front axle, 40% rear axle; turning circle (between walls): 36.1 ft, 11 m; fuel tank capacity: 14.3 imp gal, 17.1 US gal, 65 l.

BODY saloon/sedan; doors: 4; seats: 5-6; front seats: separate; details: warning light for worn brakes, plastic roof.

PRACTICAL INSTRUCTIONS fuel: 98 oct petrol; engine sump oil: 7.9 imp pt, 9.5 US pt, 4.5 l, SAE 10W-30, change every 3,100 miles, 5,000 km; gearbox and final drive oil: 3.5 imp pt, 4.2 US pt, 2 l, SAE 90, change every 12,400 miles, 20,000 km; hydraulic suspension oil: 9.2 imp pt, 11 US pt, 5.2 l; greasing: every 3,100 miles, 5,000 km, 6 points; tappet clearances: inlet 0.008 in, 0.20 mm, exhaust 0.010 in, 0.25 mm; normal tyre pressure: front 28 psi, 2 atm, rear 28 psi, 2 atm.

VARIATIONS

ENGINE (injection) 9 compression ratio, max power (SAE) 139 hp at 5,250 rpm, max torque (SAE) 145 lb ft, 20 kg m at 2,500 rpm, 63.9 hp/l specific power, oil cooler, Bosch electronically-controlled injection system.
TRANSMISSION 185 x 380 tyres.
PERFORMANCE max speed 118 mph, 190 km/h, power-weight ratio 20.5 lb/hp, 9.3 kg/hp.

OPTIONAL ACCESSORIES 5-speed mechanical gearbox; 4 headlamps automatically adjustable in height while running with 2 iodine long distance lights automatically directed on bends by steering; iodine long-distance lights; boosted heating for temperatures below —15°C, 5°F; electrically-heated rear window.

DS 21 Pallas

See DS 21 Berline, except for:

PRICE IN GB: £ 1,812.
PRICE IN USA: $ 4,329.

PERFORMANCE power-weight ratio: 25.1 lb/hp, 11.4 kg/hp.

ELECTRICAL EQUIPMENT headlamps: 4, iodine, automatically adjustable in height while running with 2 long-distance lights automatically directed on bends by steering (standard).

DIMENSIONS AND WEIGHT dry weight: 2,889 lb, 1,310 kg.

CITROËN DS 21 Pallas

CITROËN Break Luxe 21

CITROËN SM

DS 21 Prestige

See DS 21 Pallas, except for:

PRICE EX WORKS: 25,280.

DS 21 Cabriolet

See DS 21 Pallas, except for:

PRICE EX WORKS: 37,000 francs.

DIMENSIONS AND WEIGHT overall length: 192.91 in, 4,900 mm; overall height: 55.91 in, 1,420 mm; dry weight: 2,900 lb, 1,315 kg.

BODY convertible; doors: 2; seats: 4-5.

OPTIONAL ACCESSORIES only mechanical gearbox.

Familiale Luxe 21

See DS 21 Berline, except for:

PRICE IN GB: £ 1,598.
PRICE IN USA: $ 3,934.

TRANSMISSION gearbox: mechanical; tyres: 180 x 380 (front and rear).

PERFORMANCE max speed: 106 mph, 170 km/h; power-weight ratio: 26.9 lb/hp, 12.2 kg/hp; carrying capacity: 1,433 lb, 650 kg.

DIMENSIONS AND WEIGHT overall length: 196.46 in, 4,990 mm; overall width: 70.47 in, 1,790 mm; overall height: 60.24 in, 1,530 mm; dry weight: 3,087 lb, 1,400 kg; distribution of weight: 60.7% front axle, 39.3% rear axle.

BODY estate car/station wagon; doors: 4 + 1; seats: 8; front seats: bench.

OPTIONAL ACCESSORIES servo-assisted gearbox; power-assisted steering; electrically-heated rear window not available.

Familiale Confort 21

See Familiale Luxe 21, except for:

PRICE IN USA: $ 4,175.
PRICE EX WORKS: 21,420 francs.

Break Luxe 21

See Familiale Luxe 21, except for:

PRICE EX WORKS: 20,600 francs.

Break Confort 21

See Familiale Luxe 21, except for:

PRICE EX WORKS: 21,640 francs.

Commerciale 21

See Familiale Luxe 21, except for:

PRICE EX WORKS: 20,380 francs.

SM

PRICE EX WORKS: 46,000 francs.

ENGINE front, 4 stroke; cylinders: 6, Vee-slanted at 90°; bore and stroke: 3.43 x 2.95 in, 87 x 75 mm; engine capacity: 162.9 cu in, 2,670 cu cm; compression ratio: 9; max power (SAE): 180 hp at 6,250 rpm; max torque (SAE): 172 lb ft, 23.8 kg m at 4,000 rpm; max engine rpm: 6,500; specific power: 67.4 hp/l; cylinder block: light alloy, wet liners; cylinder head: light alloy; crankshaft bearings: 4; valves: 2 per cylinder, overhead, Vee-slanted; camshafts: 2 per cylinder block; lubrication: gear pump, full flow filter, oil cooler; lubricating system capacity: 12.3 imp pt, 14.8 US pt, 7 l; carburation: 3 Weber 42 DCNF downdraught carburettors; fuel feed: electric pump; cooling system: water, 2 electric thermostatic fans; cooling system capacity: 22.9 imp pt, 27.5 US pt, 13 l.

SM

TRANSMISSION driving wheels: front; clutch: single dry plate (diaphragm), hydraulically controlled; gearbox: mechanical; gears: 5 + reverse; synchromesh gears: I, II, III, IV, V; gearbox ratios: I 2.920, II 1.940, III 1.320, IV 0.970, V 0.760, rev 3.150; gear lever: central; final drive: spiral bevel; axle ratio: 4.375; width of rims: 6''; tyres: 195/70 x 15.

PERFORMANCE max speeds: 38 mph, 61 km/h in 1st gear; 57 mph, 92 km/h in 2nd gear; 84 mph, 135 km/h in 3rd gear; 115 mph, 185 km/h in 4th gear; 137 mph, 220 km/h in 5th gear; power-weight ratio: 17.6 lb/hp, 8 kg/hp; carrying capacity: 860 lb, 390 kg; acceleration: standing ¼ mile 16.2 sec; speed in top at 1,000 rpm: 22.6 mph, 36.3 km/h; fuel consumption: 22.6 m/imp gal, 18.8 m/US gal, 12.5 l x 100 km.

CHASSIS platform, lateral box members; front suspension: independent, wishbones, hydropneumatic suspension, anti-roll bar, automatic levelling control; rear suspension: independent, swinging longitudinal trailing arms, hydropneumatic suspension, anti-roll bar, automatic levelling control.

STEERING rack-and-pinion, adjustable steering wheel, variable ratio servo; turns of steering wheel lock to lock: 2.

BRAKES disc (front diameter 11.81 in, 300 mm, rear 10.08 in, 256 mm), dual circuit, compensator, servo; lining area: total 47.8 sq in, 308 sq cm.

ELECTRICAL EQUIPMENT voltage: 12 V; battery: 70 Ah; generator type: alternator, 780 W; ignition distributor: Sev or Ducellier; headlamps: 6, iodine, automatically adjustable in height while running, with long-distance lights automatically directed on bends by steering.

DIMENSIONS AND WEIGHT wheel base: 116.14 in, 2,950 mm; front track: 60.08 in, 1,526 mm; rear track: 52.20 in, 1,326 mm; overall length: 192.64 in, 4,893 mm; overall width: 72.28 in, 1,836 mm; overall height: 52.13 in, 1,324 mm; ground clearance: 6.10 in, 155 mm; dry weight: 3,197 lb, 1,450 kg; distribution of weight: 62% front axle, 38% rear axle; turning circle between walls: 34.4 ft, 10.5 m; fuel tank capacity: 19.8 imp gal, 23.8 US gal, 90 l.

BODY coupé; doors: 2; seats: 4; front seats: separate, adjustable backrests; details: electrically-controlled windows, electrically-heated rear window.

PRACTICAL INSTRUCTIONS fuel: 98-100 oct petrol; engine sump oil: 12.3 imp pt, 14.8 US pt, 7 l, SAE 10W-30, change every 3,100 miles, 5,000 km; gearbox and final drive oil: 3.9 imp pt, 4.7 US pt, 2.2 l, SAE 90, change every 12,400 miles, 20,000 km; hydraulic tank oil: 9.5 imp pt, 11.4 US pt, 5.4 l; tappet clearances: inlet 0.012-0.014 in, 0.30-0.35 mm, exhaust 0.020-0.022 in, 0.50-0.55 mm; normal tyre pressure: front 31 psi, 2.2 atm, rear 28 psi, 2 atm.

OPTIONAL ACCESSORIES air conditioning system.

MATRA SPORTS FRANCE

530 LX

PRICE EX WORKS: 21,500 francs.

ENGINE rear, 4 stroke; cylinders: 4, Vee-slanted at 60°; bore and stroke: 3.54 x 2.63 in, 90 x 66.8 mm; engine capacity: 103.7 cu in, 1,699 cu cm; compression ratio: 9; max power (DIN): 75 hp at 5,000 rpm; max torque (DIN): 98 lb ft, 13.5 kg m at 2,800 rpm; max engine rpm: 5,500; specific power: 44.1 hp/l; cylinder block: cast iron; cylinder head: cast iron; crankshaft bearings: 3; valves: 2 per cylinder, overhead, in line, push-rods and rockers; camshafts: 1, side; lubrication: gear pump, full flow filter; lubricating system capacity: 7.9 imp pt, 9.5 US pt, 4.5 l; carburation: 1 Solex 32 TDID downdraught twin barrel carburettor; fuel feed: mechanical pump; cooling system: water, electric automatic fan; cooling system capacity: 17.6 imp pt, 21.1 US pt, 10 l.

TRANSMISSION driving wheels: rear; clutch: single dry plate; gearbox: mechanical; gears: 4 + reverse; synchromesh gears: I, II, III, IV; gearbox ratios: I 3.400, II 1.990, III 1.370, IV 1, rev 3.650; gear lever: central; final drive: hypoid bevel; axle ratio: 3.500; width of rims: 4.5''; tyres: 145 x 14 front, 165 x 14 rear.

PERFORMANCE max speeds: 32 mph, 51 km/h in 1st gear; 55 mph, 88 km/h in 2nd gear; 80 mph, 129 km/h in 3rd gear; 109 mph, 175 km/h in 4th gear; power-weight ratio: 27.1 lb/hp, 12.3 kg/hp; carrying capacity: 617 lb, 280 kg; speed in direct drive at 1,000 rpm: 19.8 mph, 31.9 km/h; fuel consumption: 31.4 m/imp gal, 26.1 m/US gal, 9 l x 100 km.

CHASSIS platform; front suspension: independent, wishbones, lower trailing arms, coil springs, anti-roll bar, teles-

MATRA SPORTS 530 LX

PEUGEOT 204 Berline Grand Luxe

PEUGEOT 304 Berline

copic dampers; rear suspension: independent, longitudinal trailing arms, coil springs, anti-roll bar, telescopic dampers.

STEERING rack-and-pinion; turns of steering wheel lock to lock: 2.80.

BRAKES disc (diameter 8.31 in, 211 mm); lining area: front 18.6 sq in, 120 sq cm, rear 18.6 sq in, 120 sq cm, total 37.2 sq in, 240 sq cm.

ELECTRICAL EQUIPMENT voltage: 12 V; battery: 40 Ah; generator type: alternator, 420 W; ignition distributor: Bosch; headlamps: 2, retractable, iodine.

DIMENSIONS AND WEIGHT wheel base: 100.79 in, 2,560 mm; front track: 52.76 in, 1,340 mm; rear track: 53.15 in, 1,350 mm; overall length: 165.24 in, 4,197 mm; overall width: 63.78 in, 1,620 mm; overall height: 47.24 in, 1,200 mm; ground clearance: 5.51 in, 140 mm; dry weight: 2,029 lb, 920 kg; distribution of weight: 51.5% front axle, 48.5% rear axle; turning circle (between walls): 32.8 ft, 10 m; fuel tank capacity: 9.9 imp gal, 11.9 US gal, 45 l.

BODY coupé in plastic material; doors: 2; seats: 2 + 2; front seats: separate, reclining backrests; details: detachable roof.

PRACTICAL INSTRUCTIONS fuel: 98-100 oct petrol; engine sump oil: 7.9 imp pt, 9.5 US pt, 4.5 l, SAE 10W-30, change every 3,100 miles, 5,000 km; gearbox and final drive oil: 5.6 imp pt, 6.8 US pt, 3.2 l, SAE 90 EP, change every 12,400 miles, 20,000 km; greasing: every 12,400 miles, 20,000 km, 2 points; tappet clearances: inlet 0.014 in, 0.35 mm, exhaust 0.016 in, 0.40 mm; valve timing: inlet opens 20° before tdc and closes 55° after bdc, exhaust opens 62° before bdc and closes 14° after tdc; normal tyre pressure: front 24 psi, 1.7 atm, rear 27 psi, 1.9 atm.

OPTIONAL ACCESSORIES light alloy wheels; fixed top version.

MATRA SPORTS 530 LX

PEUGEOT   FRANCE

204 Berline Luxe

PRICE EX WORKS: 10,080 francs.

ENGINE front, transverse, 4 stroke; cylinders: 4, slanted 20° to front, in line; bore and stroke: 2.95 x 2.52 in, 75 x 64 mm; engine capacity: 69 cu in, 1,130 cu cm; compression ratio: 8.8; max power (SAE): 60 hp at 5,900 rpm; max torque (SAE): 66 lb ft, 9.1 kg m at 3,500 rpm; max engine rpm: 5,900; specific power: 53.1 hp/l; cylinder block: light alloy, wet liners; cylinder head: light alloy, polispherical combustion chambers; crankshaft bearings: 5; valves: 2 per cylinder, overhead, Vee-slanted, rockers; camshafts: 1, overhead; lubrication: gear pump, full flow filter; lubricating system capacity: 7 imp pt, 8.5 US pt, 4 l; carburation: 1 Solex 34 PBISA-3 downdraught single barrel carburettor; fuel feed: mechanical pump; cooling system: water; cooling system capacity: 10.2 imp pt, 12.3 US pt, 5.8 l.

TRANSMISSION driving wheels: front; clutch: single dry plate (diaphragm), hydraulically controlled; gearbox: mechanical; gears: 4 + reverse; synchromesh gears: I, II, III, IV; gearbox ratios: I 3.731, II 2.268, III 1.486, IV 1.009, rev 4.032; gear lever: steering column; final drive: helical spur gears; axle ratio: 4.060; width of rims: 4''; tyres: 135 x 14.

PERFORMANCE max speeds: 25 mph, 40 km/h in 1st gear; 41 mph, 66 km/h in 2nd gear; 63 mph, 101 km/h in 3rd gear; 87 mph, 140 km/h in 4th gear; power-weight ratio: 30.6 lb/hp, 13.9 kg/hp; carrying capacity: 882 lb, 400 kg; max gradient in 1st gear: 24.5%; acceleration: standing ¼ mile 20.7 sec; speed in top at 1,000 rpm: 15.8 mph, 25.4 km/h; fuel consumption: 30.7 m/imp gal, 25.6 m/US gal, 9.2 l x 100 km.

CHASSIS integral; front suspension: independent, by McPherson, coil springs/telescopic dampers, lower wishbones; rear suspension: independent, swinging longitudinal trailing arms, coil springs/telescopic dampers.

STEERING rack-and-pinion; turns of steering wheel lock to lock: 3.75.

BRAKES front disc (diameter 10.08 in, 256 mm), rear drum, rear compensator; area rubbed by linings: front 192.2 sq in, 1,240 sq cm, rear 89.1 sq in, 575 sq cm, total 281.3 sq in, 1,815 sq cm.

ELECTRICAL EQUIPMENT voltage: 12 V; battery: 40 Ah; generator type: alternator, 350 W; ignition distributor: Sev or Ducellier; headlamps: 2.

DIMENSIONS AND WEIGHT wheel base: 102.7 in, 2,595 mm; front track: 51.97 in, 1,320 mm; rear track: 49.61 in, 1,260 mm; overall length: 157.09 in, 3,990 mm; overall

PEUGEOT 204 Berline Grand Luxe

PEUGEOT 304 Berline

width: 41.42 in, 1,560 mm; overall height: 55.12 in, 1,400 mm; ground clearance: 5.51 in, 140 mm; dry weight: 1,841 lb, 835 kg; distribution of weight: 58.5% front axle, 41.5% rear axle; turning circle (between walls): 34.4 ft, 10.5 m; fuel tank capacity: 9.2 imp gal, 11.1 US gal, 42 l.

BODY saloon/sedan; doors: 4; seats: 4-5; front seats: separate, reclining backrests.

PRACTICAL INSTRUCTIONS fuel: 95 oct petrol; engine sump, gearbox and final drive oil: 7 imp pt, 8.5 US pt, 4 l, SAE 20W-40, change every 3,100 miles, 5,000 km; greasing: every 3,100 miles, 5,000 km, 5 points; tappet clearances: inlet 0.004 in, 0.10 mm, exhaust 0.010 in, 0.25 mm; valve timing: inlet opens 1°20' before tdc and closes 32° after bdc, exhaust opens 33° before bdc and closes 2°30' after tdc; normal tyre pressure: front 24 psi, 1.7 atm, rear 27 psi, 1.9 atm.

204 Berline Grand Luxe

See 204 Berline Luxe, except for:

PRICE IN GB: £ 837.
PRICE EX WORKS: 11,250 francs.

ENGINE cooling system: electromagnetically operated fan.

CHASSIS front and rear suspensions: anti-roll bar.

BRAKES servo, rear compensator.

OPTIONAL ACCESSORIES sunshine roof.

204 Break Grand Luxe

See 204 Berline Luxe, except for:

PRICE IN GB: £ 878.
PRICE EX WORKS: 11,740 francs.

ENGINE cooling system: electromagnetically operated fan.

TRANSMISSION width of rims: 4.5''; tyres: 145 x 14.

PERFORMANCE power-weight ratio: 31.3 lb/hp, 14.2 kg/hp; carrying capacity: 937 lb, 425 kg; speed in top at 1,000 rpm: 16.3 mph, 26.2 km/h; fuel consumption: 37.7 m/imp gal, 31.4 m/US gal, 7.5 l x 100 km.

BRAKES servo, rear compensator.

DIMENSIONS AND WEIGHT overall length: 156.30 in, 3,970 mm; dry weight: 1,885 lb, 855 kg.

BODY estate car/station wagon; doors: 4 + 1.

PRACTICAL INSTRUCTIONS normal tyre pressure: front 21 psi, 1.5 atm, rear 36 psi, 2.5 atm.

204 Break Grand Luxe Diesel

See 204 Break Grand Luxe, except for:

PRICE EX WORKS: 13,740 francs.

ENGINE Diesel; bore and stroke: 2.95 x 2.80 in, 75 x 71 mm; engine capacity: 76.6 cu in, 1,255 cu cm; compression ratio: 22.3; max power (SAE): 45 hp at 5,000 rpm; max torque (SAE): 53 lb ft, 7.3 kg m at 3,000 rpm; max engine rpm: 5,450; specific power: 35.9 hp/l; cylinder head: heating plugs; carburation: Bosch injection pump; cooling system: electromagnetically operated fan.

PERFORMANCE max speeds: 24 mph, 39 km/h in 1st gear; 40 mph, 64 km/h in 2nd gear; 61 mph, 98 km/h in 3rd gear; 76 mph, 122 km/h in 4th gear; power-weight ratio: 43.4 lb/hp, 19.7 kg/hp; fuel consumption: 42.2 m/imp gal, 35.1 m/US gal, 6.7 l x 100 km.

BRAKES servo, rear compensator.

ELECTRICAL EQUIPMENT battery: 65 Ah; generator type: alternator, 300 W.

DIMENSIONS AND WEIGHT dry weight: 1,962 lb, 890 kg.

304 Berline

PRICE IN GB: £ 913.
PRICE EX WORKS: 12,180 francs.

ENGINE front, transverse, 4 stroke; cylinders: 4, slanted 20° to front, in line; bore and stroke: 2.99 x 2.80 in, 76 x 71 mm; engine capacity: 78.6 cu in, 1,288 cu cm; compression ratio: 8.8; max power (SAE): 70 hp at 6,100 rpm;

304 BERLINE

max torque (SAE): 74 lb ft, 10.2 kg m at 3,750 rpm; max engine rpm: 6,100; specific power: 54.3 hp/l; cylinder block: light alloy, wet liners; cylinder head: light alloy, polispherical combustion chambers; crankshaft bearings: 5; valves: 2 per cylinder, overhead, Vee-slanted, rockers; camshafts: 1, overhead; lubrication: rotary pump, cartridge on by-pass; lubricating system capacity: 7 imp pt, 8.5 US pt, 4 l; carburation: 1 Solex 34 PBISA-3 downdraught single barrel carburettor; fuel feed: mechanical pump; cooling system: water, electric automatic fan; cooling system capacity: 10.2 imp pt, 12.3 US pt, 5.8 l.

TRANSMISSION driving wheels: front; clutch: single dry plate (diaphragm), hydraulically controlled; gearbox: mechanical; gears: 4 + reverse; synchromesh gears: I, II, III, IV; gearbox ratios: I 3.650, II 2.217, III 1.451, IV 0.986, rev 3.953; gear lever: steering column; final drive: helical spur gears; axle ratio: 4.060; width of rims: 4.5''; tyres: 145 x 14.

PERFORMANCE max speeds: 27 mph, 44 km/h in 1st gear; 45 mph, 73 km/h in 2nd gear; 69 mph, 111 km/h in 3rd gear; 93 mph, 150 km/h in 4th gear; power-weight ratio: 27.3 lb/hp, 12.4 kg/hp; carrying capacity: 882 lb, 400 kg; acceleration: standing ¼ mile 19.5 sec; speed in top at 1,000 rpm: 16.7 mph, 26.9 km/h; fuel consumption: 28 m/imp gal, 23.3 m/US gal, 10.1 l x 100 km.

CHASSIS integral; front suspension: independent, by McPherson, coil springs/telescopic dampers, lower wishbones, anti-roll bar; rear suspension: independent, swinging longitudinal trailing arms, anti-roll bar, coil springs/telescopic dampers.

STEERING rack-and-pinion; turns of steering wheel lock to lock: 3.75.

BRAKES front disc (diameter 10.08 in, 256 mm), rear drum, rear compensator, servo; area rubbed by linings: front 192.2 sq in, 1,240 sq cm, rear 89.1 sq in, 575 sq cm, total 281.3 sq in, 1,815 sq cm.

ELECTRICAL EQUIPMENT voltage: 12 V; battery: 40 Ah; generator type: alternator, 350 W; ignition distributor: Ducellier; headlamps: 2.

DIMENSIONS AND WEIGHT wheel base: 101.97 in, 2,590 mm; front track: 51.97 in, 1,320 mm; rear track: 49.61 in, 1,260 mm; overall length: 162.99 in, 4,140 mm; overall width: 61.81 in, 1,570 mm; overall height: 55.51 in, 1,410 mm; ground clearance: 5.51 in, 140 mm; dry weight: 1,918 lb, 870 kg; turning circle (between walls): 34.4 ft, 10.5 m; fuel tank capacity: 9.2 imp gal, 11.1 US gal, 42 l.

BODY saloon/sedan; doors: 4; seats: 4-5; front seats: separate, reclining backrests.

PRACTICAL INSTRUCTIONS fuel: 95 oct petrol; engine sump, gearbox and final drive oil: 7 imp pt, 8.5 US pt, 4 l, SAE 20W-40, change every 3,100 miles, 5,000 km; greasing: every 3,100 miles, 5,000 km, 5 points; normal tyre pressure: front 24 psi, 1.7 atm, rear 27 psi, 1.9 atm.

OPTIONAL ACCESSORIES sunshine roof.

304 Coupé

See 304 Berline, except for:

PRICE EX WORKS: 14,150 francs.

TRANSMISSION max speed: 94 mph, 152 km/h; power-weight ratio: 27.6 lb/hp, 12.5 kg/hp; carrying capacity: 706 lb, 320 kg; acceleration: standing ¼ mile 19.3 sec; fuel consumption: 28.2 m/imp gal, 23.5 m/US gal, 10 l x 100 km.

ELECTRICAL EQUIPMENT generator type: alternator, 500 W.

DIMENSIONS AND WEIGHT wheel base: 90.75 in, 2,305 mm; overall length: 147.24 in, 3,740 mm; overall width: 61.81 in, 1,570 mm; overall height: 51.18 in, 1,300 mm; dry weight: 1,929 lb, 875 kg; turning circle (between walls): 30.8 ft, 9.4 m.

BODY coupé; doors: 2; seats: 2 + 2.

304 Cabriolet

See 304 Coupé, except for:

PRICE EX WORKS: 13,550 francs.

PERFORMANCE power-weight ratio: 26.2 lb/hp, 11.9 kg/hp; acceleration: standing ¼ mile 19.2 sec; fuel consumption: 28.8 m/imp gal, 24 m/US gal, 9.8 l x 100 km.

PEUGEOT 304 Coupé

PEUGEOT 304 Break Super-Luxe

PEUGEOT 404 Berline Grand Tourisme

DIMENSIONS AND WEIGHT overall height: 51.97 in, 1,320 mm; dry weight: 1,841 lb, 835 kg.

BODY convertible; seats: 2.

OPTIONAL ACCESSORIES hardtop.

304 Break Super-Luxe

See 304 Berline, except for:

PRICE EX WORKS: 12,900 francs.

PERFORMANCE power-weight ratio: 28.4 lb/hp, 12.9 kg/hp.

DIMENSIONS AND WEIGHT overall length: 157.09 in, 3,990 mm; overall height: 56.30 in, 1,430 mm; dry weight: 1,996 lb, 905 kg.

BODY estate car/station wagon; doors: 4 + 1.

404 Berline Grand Tourisme

PRICE IN GB: £ 1,013.
PRICE EX WORKS: 12,720 francs.

ENGINE front, 4 stroke; cylinders: 4, slanted at 45°, in line; bore and stroke: 3.31 x 2.87 in, 84 x 73 mm; engine capacity: 98.7 cu in, 1,618 cu cm; compression ratio: 7.6; max power (SAE): 76 hp at 5,600 rpm; max torque (SAE): 98 lb ft, 13.5 kg m at 2,500 rpm; max engine rpm: 5,600; specific power: 47 hp/l; cylinder block: cast iron, wet liners; cylinder head: light alloy, hemispherical combustion chambers; crankshaft bearings: 5; valves: 2 per cylinder, overhead, Vee-slanted, push-rods and rockers; camshafts: 1, side; lubrication: gear pump, metal gauze filter; lubricating system capacity: 7 imp pt, 8.5 US pt, 4 l; carburation: 1 Solex 34 PBICA-9 downdraught carburettor; fuel feed: electric pump; cooling system: water, electric automatic fan; cooling system capacity: 13.7 imp pt, 16.5 US pt, 7.8 l.

TRANSMISSION driving wheels: rear; clutch: single dry plate (diaphragm), hydraulically controlled; gearbox: mechanical; gears: 4 + reverse; synchromesh gears: I, II, III, IV; gearbox ratios: I 3.660, II 2.160, III 1.540, IV 1, rev 3.740; gear lever: steering column; final drive: worm and wheel; axle ratio: 4.200; width of rims: 4.5''; tyres: 165 x 380.

PERFORMANCE max speeds: 25 mph, 40 km/h in 1st gear; 44 mph, 71 km/h in 2nd gear; 68 mph, 110 km/h in 3rd gear; 92 mph, 148 km/h in 4th gear; power-weight ratio: 29.5 lb/hp, 13.4 kg/hp; carrying capacity: 1,058 lb, 480 kg; max gradient in 1st gear: 29%; speed in direct drive at 1,000 rpm: 17.7 mph, 28.5 km/h; fuel consumption: 26.2 m/imp gal, 21.8 m/US gal, 10.8 l x 100 km.

CHASSIS integral; front suspension: independent, by McPherson, coil springs/telescopic damper struts, lower wishbones, anti-roll bar; rear suspension: rigid axle, coil springs, transverse linkage bar, anti-roll bar, telescopic dampers.

STEERING rack-and-pinion; turns of steering wheel lock to lock: 3.75.

BRAKES front disc (diameter 11.30 in, 287 mm), rear drum, rear compensator, servo; area rubbed by linings: front 207.1 sq in, 1,336 sq cm, rear 111.6 sq in, 720 sq cm, total 318.7 sq in, 2,056 sq cm.

ELECTRICAL EQUIPMENT voltage: 12 V; battery: 40 Ah; generator type: alternator, 350 W; ignition distributor: Sev or Ducellier; headlamps: 2.

DIMENSIONS AND WEIGHT wheel base: 104.33 in, 2,650 mm; front track: 52.95 in, 1,345 mm; rear track: 50.39 in, 1,280 mm; overall length: 175.20 in, 4,450 mm; overall width: 63.98 in, 1,625 mm; overall height: 57.09 in, 1,450 mm; ground clearance: 5.90 in, 150 mm; dry weight: 2,249 lb, 1,020 kg; distribution of weight: 53.9% front axle, 46.1% rear axle; turning circle (between walls): 35.8 ft, 10.9 m; fuel tank capacity: 12.1 imp gal, 14.5 US gal, 55 l.

BODY saloon/sedan; doors: 4; seats: 5-6; front seats: separate.

PRACTICAL INSTRUCTIONS fuel: 86 oct petrol; engine sump oil: 7 imp pt, 8.5 US pt, 4 l, SAE 20W-40, change every 3,100 miles, 5,000 km; gearbox oil: 2.1 imp pt, 2.5 US pt, 1.2 l, SAE 20W-40, change every 6,200 miles, 10,000 km; final drive oil: 3 imp pt, 3.6 US pt, 1.7 l, GP 90, change every 18,600 miles, 30,000 km; greasing: every 3,100 miles, 5,000 km, 10 points; sparking plug type: 200°; tappet clearances: inlet 0.004 in, 0.10 mm; exhaust 0.010 in, 0.25 mm; valve timing: inlet opens 0° before tdc and closes 30°30' after bdc, exhaust opens 35° before bdc and closes 4°30' after bdc; normal tyre pressure: front 20 psi, 1.4 atm, rear 23 psi, 1.6 atm.

OPTIONAL ACCESSORIES ZF automatic gearbox, hydraulic torque convertor and planetary gears with 3 ratios (I 2.557, II 1.519, III 1, rev 2), max ratio of convertor at stall 2.3; sunshine roof.

PEUGEOT 304 Coupé

PEUGEOT 304 Break Super-Luxe

PEUGEOT 404 Berline Grand Tourisme

404 Berline Diesel

See 404 Berline Grand Tourisme, except for:

PRICE EX WORKS: 14,770 francs.

ENGINE Diesel; bore and stroke: 3.46 x 3.15 in, 88 x 80 mm; engine capacity: 118.9 cu in, 1,948 cu cm; compression ratio: 21.5; max power (SAE): 68 hp at 4,500 rpm; max torque (SAE): 87 lb ft, 12.1 kg m at 2,250 rpm; max engine rpm: 4,800; specific power: 34.9 hp/l; carburation: Bosch injection pump.

PERFORMANCE max speeds: 21 mph, 34 km/h in 1st gear; 38 mph, 61 km/h in 2nd gear; 58 mph, 94 km/h in 3rd gear; 82 mph, 132 km/h in 4th gear; power-weight ratio: 35.7 lb/hp, 16.2 kg/hp; fuel consumption: 36.2 m/imp gal, 30.2 m/US gal, 7.8 l x 100 km.

BRAKES drum, 2 front leading shoes; area rubbed by linings: total 288.8 sq in, 1,863 sq cm.

ELECTRICAL EQUIPMENT battery: 65 Ah; generator type: alternator, 500 W.

DIMENSIONS AND WEIGHT dry weight: 2,426 lb, 1,100 kg.

OPTIONAL ACCESSORIES automatic gearbox not available.

404 Familiale Grand Luxe

See 404 Berline Grand Tourisme, except for:

PRICE IN GB: £ 1,146.
PRICE EX WORKS: 13,830 francs.

TRANSMISSION axle ratio: 4.630.

PERFORMANCE max speeds: 24 mph, 38 km/h in 1st gear; 42 mph, 67 km/h in 2nd gear; 65 mph, 104 km/h in 3rd gear; 90 mph, 145 km/h in 4th gear; power-weight ratio: 32.2 lb/hp, 14.6 kg/hp; carrying capacity: 1,411 lb, 640 kg; max gradient in 1st gear: 21%; acceleration: standing ¼ mile 21.6 sec, 0-50 mph (0-80 km/h) 12.3 sec; speed in direct drive at 1,000 rpm: 16.1 mph, 25.9 km/h; fuel consumption: 25.7 m/imp gal, 21.4 m/US gal, 11 l x 100 km.

CHASSIS rear suspension: 4 coil springs.

BRAKES drum, 2 front leading shoes, servo; area rubbed by linings: front 177.1 sq in, 1,142 sq cm, rear 136.1 sq in, 878 sq cm, total 313.2 sq in, 2,020 sq cm.

DIMENSIONS AND WEIGHT wheel base: 111.81 in, 2,840 mm; rear track: 51.18 in, 1,300 mm; overall length: 180.39 in, 4,582 mm; overall height: 58.82 in, 1,494 mm; dry weight: 2,580 lb, 1,170 kg; distribution of weight: 49.7% front axle, 50.3% rear axle; turning circle (between walls): 34.4 ft, 10.5 m.

BODY estate car/station wagon; doors: 4 + 1; seats: 7-8.

PRACTICAL INSTRUCTIONS normal tyre pressure: front 20 psi, 1.4 atm, rear 31 psi, 2.2 atm.

VARIATIONS

ENGINE Diesel, engine capacity 118.9 cu in, 1,948 cu cm, 21.5 compression ratio, max power (SAE) 68 hp at 4,500 rpm, max torque (SAE) 88 lb ft, 12.1 kg m at 2,250 rpm, max engine rpm 4,800, 42 hp/l specific power, Bosch injection pump.
TRANSMISSION 4.200 axle ratio.
PERFORMANCE max speed 81 mph, 130 km/h, power-weight ratio 38.8 lb/hp, 17.6 kg/hp, fuel consumption 36.2 m/imp gal, 30.2 m/US gal, 7.8 l x 100 km.
BRAKES no servo.
ELECTRICAL EQUIPMENT 65 Ah battery, 500 W alternator.
DIMENSIONS AND WEIGHT dry weight 2,646 lb, 1,200 kg.

OPTIONAL ACCESSORIES 185 x 380 tyres.

404 Break Super-Luxe

See 404 Familiale Grand Luxe, except for:

PRICE EX WORKS: 14,630 francs.

TRANSMISSION tyres: 185 x 380.

PERFORMANCE power-weight ratio: 31.8 lb/hp, 14.4 kg/hp.

DIMENSIONS AND WEIGHT dry weight: 2,536 lb, 1,150 kg.

BODY seats: 5-6.

VARIATIONS

Diesel engine not available.

404 Commerciale Grand Luxe

See 404 Familiale Grand Luxe, except for:

PRICE IN GB: £ 1,139.
PRICE EX WORKS: 12,580 francs.

PERFORMANCE power-weight ratio: 30.2 lb/hp, 13.7 kg/hp.

BRAKES no servo.

DIMENSIONS AND WEIGHT dry weight: 2,426 lb, 1,100 kg.

BODY seats: 5-6.

VARIATIONS

ENGINE Diesel, engine capacity 118.9 cu in, 1,948 cu cm, 21 compression ratio, max power (SAE) 63 hp at 4,000 rpm, 32.3 hp/l specific power, Bosch injection pump.
TRANSMISSION 4.200 axle ratio.
PERFORMANCE max speed 71 mph, 115 km/h, power-weight ratio 38.6 lb/hp, 17.5 kg/hp, fuel consumption 37.7 m/imp gal, 31.4 m/US gal, 7.5 l x 100 km.

504 Berline

PRICE IN GB: £ 1,219.
PRICE IN USA: $ 3,195.

ENGINE front, 4 stroke; cylinders: 4, slanted at 45°, in line; bore and stroke: 3.46 x 3.19 in, 88 x 81 mm; engine capacity: 120.3 cu in, 1,971 cu cm; compression ratio: 8.3; max power (SAE): 98 hp at 5,600 rpm; max torque (SAE): 125 lb ft, 17.2 kg m at 3,000 rpm; max engine rpm: 5,500; specific power: 49.7 hp/l; cylinder block: cast iron, wet liners; cylinder head: light alloy, hemispherical combustion chambers; crankshaft bearings: 5; valves: 2 per cylinder, overhead, Vee-slanted, push-rods and rockers; camshafts: 1, side; lubrication: gear pump, metal gauze filter; lubricating system capacity: 7 imp pt, 8.5 US pt, 4 l; carburation: 1 Solex 32-35 SEIEA downdraught twin barrel carburettor; fuel feed: mechanical pump; cooling system: water, electric automatic fan; cooling system capacity: 13.7 imp pt, 16.5 US pt, 7.8 l.

TRANSMISSION driving wheels: rear; clutch: single dry plate (diaphragm), hydraulically controlled; gearbox: mechanical; gears: 4 + reverse; synchromesh gears: I, II, III, IV; gearbox ratios: I 3.633, II 2.170, III 1.408, IV 1, rev 3.745; gear lever: steering column; final drive: hypoid bevel; axle ratio: 3.888; width of rims: 5''; tyres: 175 x 14.

PERFORMANCE max speeds: 27 mph, 44 km/h in 1st gear; 47 mph, 75 km/h in 2nd gear; 71 mph, 115 km/h in 3rd gear; 101 mph, 162 km/h in 4th gear; power-weight ratio: 25.6 lb/hp, 11.6 kg/hp; carrying capacity: 882 lb, 400 kg; acceleration: standing ¼ mile 18.3 sec; speed in direct drive at 1,000 rpm: 18.5 mph, 29.7 km/h; fuel consumption: 23.7 m/imp gal, 19.8 m/US gal, 11.9 l x 100 km.

CHASSIS integral; front suspension: independent, by McPherson, coil springs/telescopic dampers struts, lower wishbones, anti-roll bar; rear suspension: independent, oblique semi-trailing arms, coil springs/telescopic dampers, anti-roll bar.

STEERING rack-and-pinion; turns of steering wheel lock to lock: 4.50.

BRAKES disc (diameter 10.67 in, 271 mm), rear compensator, servo; area rubbed by linings: front 236.9 sq in, 1,528 sq cm, rear 201.6 sq cm, 1,300 sq cm, total 438.5 sq in, 2,828 sq cm.

ELECTRICAL EQUIPMENT voltage: 12 V; battery: 55 Ah; generator type: alternator, 500 W; ignition distributor: Ducellier; headlamps: 2, iodine.

DIMENSIONS AND WEIGHT wheel base: 107.87 in, 2,740 mm; front track: 55.91 in, 1,420 mm; rear track: 53.54 in, 1,360 mm; overall length: 176.77 in, 4,490 mm; overall width: 66.54 in, 1,690 mm; overall height: 57.48 in, 1,460 mm; ground clearance: 5.55 in, 141 mm; dry weight: 2,525 lb, 1,145 kg; turning circle (between walls): 35.8 ft, 10.9 m; fuel tank capacity: 12.3 imp gal, 14.8 US gal, 56 l.

BODY saloon/sedan; doors: 4; seats: 5; front seats: separate, reclining backrests; details: built-in adjustable headrests.

PRACTICAL INSTRUCTIONS fuel: 95 oct petrol; engine sump oil: 7 imp pt, 8.5 US pt, 4 l, SAE 20W-40, change every 3,100 miles, 5,000 km; gearbox oil: 1.9 imp pt, 2.3 US pt, 1.1 l, SAE 20W-40, change every 6,200 miles, 10,000 km; final drive oil: 2.1 imp pt, 2.5 US pt, 1.2 l, GP 90, change every 6,200 miles, 10,000 km; greasing: every 3,100 miles, 5,000 km, 6 points; tappet clearances: inlet 0.004 in, 0.10 mm, exhaust 0.010 in, 0.25 mm; valve timing: inlet opens 1°30' before tdc and closes 36° after bdc, exhaust opens 35°30' before bdc and closes 9° after tdc; normal tyre pressure: front 21 psi, 1.5 atm, rear 24 psi, 1.7 atm.

PEUGEOT 504 Berline

PEUGEOT 504 Coupé

RENAULT 4 Export

VARIATIONS

ENGINE (injection) max power (SAE) 110 hp at 5,600 rpm, max torque (SAE) 131 lb ft, 18.1 kg m at 3,000 rpm, 55.8 hp/l specific power, 4-cylinder injection pump in inlet pipes (Kugelfischer system).

PERFORMANCE max speeds (I) 29 mph, 46 km/h, (II) 48 mph, 78 km/h, (III) 75 mph, 121 km/h, (IV) 107 mph, 173 km/h, power-weight ratio 22.9 lb/hp, 10.4 kg/hp, acceleration standing ¼ mile 17.8 sec, speed in direct drive at 1,000 rpm 19 mph, 30.6 km/h, fuel consumption 28.2 m/imp gal, 23.5 m/US gal, 10 l x 100 km.

OPTIONAL ACCESSORIES ZF automatic gearbox, hydraulic torque convertor and planetary gears with 3 ratios (I 2.557, II 1.519, III 1, rev 2), max ratio of convertor at stall 2.3; central gear lever; sunshine roof.

504 Berline Diesel

See 504 Berline, except for:

PRICE EX WORKS: 17,750 francs.

ENGINE Diesel; bore and stroke: 3.58 x 3.27 in, 90 x 83 mm; engine capacity: 128.9 cu in, 2,112 cu cm; compression ratio: 22.2; max power (DIN): 65 hp at 4,500 rpm; max torque (DIN): 91 lb ft, 12.6 kg m at 2,000 rpm; specific power: 30.8 hp/l; cylinder block: heating plugs; carburation: Bosch injection pump.

PERFORMANCE max speeds: 23 mph, 37 km/h in 1st gear; 39 mph, 62 km/h in 2nd gear; 59 mph, 95 km/h in 3rd gear; 83 mph, 134 km/h in 4th gear; power-weight ratio: 38.8 lb/hp, 17.6 kg/hp; fuel consumption: 35.3 m/imp gal, 29.4 m/US gal, 8 l x 100 km.

504 Coupé

See 504 Berline, except for:

PRICE EX WORKS: 25,880 francs.

ENGINE max power (SAE): 110 hp at 5,600 rpm; max torque (SAE): 131 lb ft, 18.1 kg m at 3,000 rpm; max engine rpm: 5,600; specific power: 55.8 hp/l; carburation: 4-cylinder injection pump in inlet pipes (Kugelfischer system).

TRANSMISSION only with mechanical gearbox; gear lever: central; axle ratio: 3.777.

PERFORMANCE max speeds: 30 mph, 48 km/h in 1st gear; 50 mph, 80 km/h in 2nd gear; 77 mph, 124 km/h in 3rd gear; 111 mph, 179 km/h in 4th gear; power-weight ratio: 23.4 lb/hp, 10.6 kg/hp; carrying capacity: 706 lb, 320 kg; acceleration: standing ¼ mile 17.5 sec; speed in direct drive at 1,000 rpm: 19.3 mph, 31.1 km/h; fuel consumption: 27.7 m/imp gal, 23.1 m/US gal, 10.2 l x 100 km.

ELECTRICAL EQUIPMENT headlamps: 4, iodine.

DIMENSIONS AND WEIGHT wheel base: 100.39 in, 2,550 mm; rear track: 55.51 in, 1,410 mm; overall length: 171.65 in, 4,360 mm; overall width: 66.93 in, 1,700 mm; overall height: 53.15 in, 1,350 mm; ground clearance: 6.30 in, 160 mm; dry weight: 2,569 lb, 1,165 kg; distribution of weight: 52.5% front axle, 47.5% rear axle; turning circle (between walls): 33.8 ft, 10.3 m.

BODY coupé; doors: 2; seats: 4.

OPTIONAL ACCESSORIES sunshine roof not available.

504 Cabriolet

See 504 Coupé, except for:

PRICE EX WORKS: 24,730 francs.

DIMENSIONS AND WEIGHT overall height: 53.54 in, 1,360 mm.

BODY convertible.

RENAULT   FRANCE

4

PRICE IN GB: £ 457 (with 845 cu cm engine).
PRICE EX WORKS: 7,128 francs.

ENGINE front, 4 stroke; cylinders: 4, vertical, in line; bore and stroke: 2.15 x 3.15 in, 54.5 x 80 mm; engine capacity:

PEUGEOT 504 Berline

PEUGEOT 504 Coupé and Cabriolet

RENAULT 4

45.6 cu in, 747 cu cm; compression ratio: 8.5; max power (SAE): 30 hp at 4,700 rpm; max torque (SAE): 37 lb ft, 5.1 kg m at 2,600 rpm; max engine rpm: 4,800; specific power: 40.2 hp/l; cylinder block: cast iron, wet liners; cylinder head: light alloy; crankshaft bearings: 3; valves: 2 per cylinder, overhead, in line, push-rods and rockers; camshafts: 1, side; lubrication: gear pump, filter in sump; lubricating system capacity: 4.4 imp pt, 5.3 US pt, 2.5 l; carburation: 1 Solex 26 DIS 5 or Zenith 28 IF downdraught single barrel carburettor; fuel feed: mechanical pump; cooling system: liquid, sealed circuit; cooling system capacity: 8.4 imp pt, 10.1 US pt, 4.8 l.

TRANSMISSION driving wheels: front; clutch: single dry plate (diaphragm); gearbox: mechanical; gears: 4 + reverse; synchromesh gears: I, II, III, IV; gearbox ratios: I 3.800, II 2.059, III 1.364, IV 1.036, rev 3.800; gear lever: on facia; final drive: spiral bevel; axle ratio: 4.125; width of rims: 4''; tyres: 135 x 330.

PERFORMANCE max speeds: 19 mph, 30 km/h in 1st gear; 35 mph, 56 km/h in 2nd gear; 53 mph, 85 km/h in 3rd gear; 68 mph, 110 km/h in 4th gear; power-weight ratio: 46.5 lb/hp, 21.1 kg/hp; carrying capacity: 728 lb, 330 kg; acceleration: standing ¼ mile 27.1 sec, 0-50 mph (0-80 km/h) 34.2 sec; speed in top at 1,000 rpm: 14.5 mph, 23.3 km/h; fuel consumption: 47.1 m/imp gal, 39.2 m/US gal, 6 l x 100 km.

CHASSIS platform; front suspension: independent, wishbones, longitudinal torsion bars, anti-roll bar, telescopic dampers; rear suspension: independent, swinging longitudinal trailing arms, transverse torsion bars, telescopic dampers.

STEERING rack-and-pinion; turns of steering wheel lock to lock: 3.25.

BRAKES drum; lining area: front 68.2 sq in, 440 sq cm, rear 38.9 sq in, 251 sq cm, total 107.1 sq in, 691 sq cm.

ELECTRICAL EQUIPMENT voltage: 12 V; battery: 30 Ah; generator type: dynamo, 22 A; ignition distributor: Lucas; headlamps: 2.

DIMENSIONS AND WEIGHT wheel base: 96.42 in, 2,449 mm (right), 94.53 in, 2,401 mm (left); front track: 50.35 in, 1,279 mm; rear track: 48.98 in, 1,244 mm; overall length: 144.41 in, 3,668 mm; overall width: 58.46 in, 1,485 mm; overall height: 61.02 in, 1,550 mm; ground clearance: 7.87 in, 200 mm; dry weight: 1,400 lb, 635 kg; distribution of weight: 57.8% front axle, 42.2% rear axle; turning circle (between walls): 31.8 ft, 9.7 m; fuel tank capacity: 5.7 imp gal, 6.9 US gal, 26 l.

BODY estate car/station wagon; doors: 4 + 1; seats: 4; front seats: bench.

PRACTICAL INSTRUCTIONS fuel: 98-100 oct petrol; engine sump oil: 4.4 imp pt, 5.3 US pt, 2.5 l, SAE 10W-40, change every 3,100 miles, 5,000 km; gearbox and final drive oil: 1.9 imp pt, 2.3 US pt, 1.1 l, SAE 80; greasing: none; tappet clearances: inlet 0.006-0.007 in, 0.15-0.18 mm, exhaust 0.007-0.009 in, 0.18-0.22 mm; valve timing: inlet opens 6° before tdc and closes 30° after bdc, exhaust opens 45° before bdc and closes 7° after tdc; normal tyre pressure: front 18 psi, 1.3 atm, rear 21 psi, 1.5 atm.

VARIATIONS

ENGINE (only for export), engine capacity 51.6 cu in, 845 cu cm, bore and stroke 2.28 x 3.15 in, 58 x 80 mm, 8 compression ratio, max torque (SAE) 43 lb ft, 5.9 kg m at 2,300 rpm, 35.5 hp/l specific power.

4 Export

See 4, except for:

PRICE IN GB: £ 495 (with 845 cu cm engine).
PRICE EX WORKS: 7,990 francs.

PERFORMANCE power-weight ratio: 47.8 lb/hp, 21.7 kg/hp.

DIMENSIONS AND WEIGHT dry weight: 1,433 lb, 650 kg.

OPTIONAL ACCESSORIES sunshine roof; separate front seats; reclining backrests.

6 (850)

PRICE IN GB: £ 572.
PRICE EX WORKS: 8,990 francs.

ENGINE front, 4 stroke; cylinders: 4, vertical, in line; bore and stroke: 2.28 x 3.15 in, 58 x 80 mm; engine capacity: 51.6 cu in, 845 cu cm; compression ratio: 8; max power (SAE): 38 hp at 5,000 rpm; max torque (SAE): 42 lb ft, 5.8 kg m at 3,000 rpm; max engine rpm: 5,200; specific power: 45 hp/l; cylinder block: cast iron, wet liners; cylinder head: light alloy; crankshaft bearings: 3; valves: 2 per cylinder, overhead, in line, push-rods and rockers; camshafts: 1, side; lubrication: gear pump, filter in sump; lubricating system capacity: 4.4 imp pt, 5.3 US pt, 2.5 l; carburation: 1 Solex

6 (850)

32 PDIS 3 downdraught carburettor; fuel feed: mechanical pump; cooling system: liquid, sealed circuit; cooling system capacity: 9 imp pt, 10.8 US pt, 5.1 l.

TRANSMISSION driving wheels: front; clutch: single dry plate (diaphragm); gearbox: mechanical; gears: 4 + reverse; synchromesh gears: I, II, III, IV; gearbox ratios: I 3.800, II 2.059, III 1.364, IV 1.036, rev 3.800; gear lever: on facia; final drive: spiral bevel; axle ratio: 4.125; width of rims: 4''; tyres: 135 x 330.

PERFORMANCE max speeds: 21 mph, 33 km/h in 1st gear; 38 mph, 61 km/h in 2nd gear; 57 mph, 92 km/h in 3rd gear; 75 mph, 120 km/h in 4th gear; power-weight ratio: 43.4 lb/hp, 19.7 kg/hp; carrying capacity: 882 lb, 400 kg; max gradient in 1st gear: 28%; speed in top at 1,000 rpm: 14.5 mph, 23.3 km/h; fuel consumption: 44.8 m/imp gal, 37.3 m/US gal, 6.3 l x 100 km.

CHASSIS platform; front suspension: independent, wishbones, longitudinal torsion bars, anti-roll bar, telescopic dampers; rear suspension: independent, swinging longitudinal trailing arms, transverse torsion bars, telescopic dampers.

STEERING rack-and-pinion; turns of steering wheel lock to lock: 3.25.

BRAKES drum, rear compensator; lining area: front 89 sq in, 574 sq cm, rear 38.9 sq in, 251 sq cm, total 127.9 sq in, 825 sq cm.

ELECTRICAL EQUIPMENT voltage: 12 V; battery: 30 Ah; generator type: dynamo, 22 A; ignition distributor: Lucas; headlamps: 2.

DIMENSIONS AND WEIGHT wheel base: 94.53 in, 2,401 mm; front track: 50.35 in, 1,279 mm; rear track: 48.98 in, 1,244 mm; overall length: 151.61 in, 3,851 mm; overall width: 60.47 in, 1,536 mm; overall height: 58.07 in, 1,475 mm; ground clearance: 4.92 in, 125 mm; dry weight: 1,654 lb, 750 kg; distribution of weight: 56% front axle, 44% rear axle; turning circle (between walls): 32.5 ft, 9.9 m; fuel tank capacity: 8.8 imp gal, 10.6 US gal, 40 l.

BODY saloon/sedan; doors: 4 + 1; seats: 4-5; front seats: separate.

PRACTICAL INSTRUCTIONS fuel: 90 oct petrol; engine sump oil: 4.4 imp pt, 5.3 US pt, 2.5 l, change every 3,100 miles, 5,000 km; gearbox and final drive oil: 1.9 imp pt, 2.3 US pt, 1.1 l; greasing: none; tappet clearances: inlet 0.006-0.007 in, 0.15-0.18 mm, exhaust 0.007-0.009 in, 0.18-0.22 mm; valve timing: inlet opens 10° before tdc and closes 42° after bdc, exhaust opens 46° before bdc and closes 10° after tdc; normal tyre pressure: front 18 psi, 1.3 atm, rear 21 psi, 1.5 atm.

OPTIONAL ACCESSORIES reclining backrests; back seat folding down to luggage table.

6 L (1100)

See 6 (850), except for:

PRICE EX WORKS: 9,990 francs.

ENGINE bore and stroke: 2.76 x 2.83 in, 70 x 72 mm; engine capacity: 67.6 cu in, 1,108 cu cm; compression ratio: 8.3; max power (SAE): 48 hp at 5,300 rpm; max torque (SAE): 58 lb ft, 8 kg m at 3,000 rpm; max engine rpm: 5,500; specific power: 43.3 hp/l; crankshaft bearings: 5; lubrication: full flow filter; lubricating system capacity: 5.3 imp pt, 6.3 US pt, 3 l; carburation: 1 Solex 32 EISA downdraught carburettor; cooling system capacity: 11.1 imp pt, 13.3 US pt, 6.3 l.

TRANSMISSION gearbox ratios: I 3.667, II 2.053, III 1.360, IV 1.034, rev 3.077; axle ratio: 3.875; tyres: 135 x 330 or 145 x 330.

PERFORMANCE max speeds: 22 mph, 35 km/h in 1st gear; 42 mph, 68 km/h in 2nd gear; 60 mph, 97 km/h in 3rd gear; 82 mph, 132 km/h in 4th gear; power-weight ratio: 37.7 lb/hp, 17.1 kg/hp; carrying capacity: 750 lb, 340 kg; speed in top at 1,000 rpm: 15.3 mph, 24.7 km/h; fuel consumption: 41.5 m/imp gal, 34.6 m/US gal, 6.8 l x 100 km.

CHASSIS rear suspension: anti-roll bar.

BRAKES front disc, rear drum; area rubbed by linings: front 157.2 sq in, 1,014 sq cm, rear 52.7 sq in, 340 sq cm, total 209.9 sq in, 1,354 sq cm.

DIMENSIONS AND WEIGHT wheel base: 94.53 in, 2,401 mm (left), 96.42 in, 2,449 mm (right); front track: 50.63 in, 1,286 mm; rear track: 49.13 in, 1,248 mm; overall length: 151.93 in, 3,859 mm; dry weight: 1,808 lb, 820 kg; distribution of weight: 56.1% front axle, 43.9% rear axle; turning circle (between walls): 34.4 ft, 10.5 m.

RENAULT 6 TL (1100)

RENAULT 8 S

RENAULT 12 TL Berline

PRACTICAL INSTRUCTIONS engine sump oil: 5.3 imp pt, 6.3 US pt, 3 l; gearbox and final drive oil: 3.2 imp pt, 3.8 US pt, 1.8 l; normal tyre pressure: front 21 psi, 1.5 atm, rear 26 psi, 1.8 atm.

6 TL (1100)

See 6 L (1100), except for:

PRICE IN GB: £ 626.
PRICE EX WORKS: —

BODY front seats: separate, reclining backrests.

8 Major

PRICE IN GB: £ 556.
PRICE EX WORKS: 8,920 francs.

ENGINE rear, 4 stroke; cylinders: 4, vertical, in line; bore and stroke: 2.76 x 2.83 in, 70 x 72 mm; engine capacity: 67.6 cu in, 1,108 cu cm; compression ratio: 8.5; max power (SAE): 46 hp at 4,600 rpm; max torque (SAE): 57 lb ft, 7.9 kg m at 3,000 rpm; max engine rpm: 5,300; specific power: 41.5 hp/l; cylinder block: cast iron, wet liners; cylinder head: light alloy; crankshaft bearings: 5; valves: 2 per cylinder, overhead, in line, slanted, push-rods and rockers; camshafts: 1, side; lubrication: gear pump, filter in sump; lubricating system capacity: 4.4 imp pt, 5.3 US pt, 2.5 l; carburation: 1 Solex 32 DITA 3 downdraught carburettor; fuel feed: mechanical pump; cooling system: liquid, sealed circuit; cooling system capacity: 12.5 imp pt, 15 US pt, 7.1 l.

TRANSMISSION driving wheels: rear; clutch: single dry plate (diaphragm); gearbox: mechanical; gears: 4 + reverse; synchromesh gears: I, II, III, IV; gearbox ratios: I 3.610, II 2.260, III 1.480, IV 1.032, rev 3.080; gear lever: central; final drive: hypoid bevel; axle ratio: 4.125; width of rims: 4''; tyres: 135/145 x 380.

PERFORMANCE max speeds: 26 mph, 42 km/h in 1st gear; 42 mph, 68 km/h in 2nd gear; 64 mph, 103 km/h in 3rd gear; 83 mph, 133 km/h in 4th gear; power-weight ratio: 36.6 lb/hp, 16.6 kg/hp; carrying capacity: 882 lb, 400 kg; speed in top at 1,000 rpm: 16.3 mph, 26.3 km/h; fuel consumption: 41.5 m/imp gal, 34.6 m/US gal, 6.8 l x 100 km.

CHASSIS integral; front suspension: independent, wishbones, coil springs, anti-roll bar, telescopic dampers; rear suspension: independent, swinging semi-axles, swinging longitudinal trailing arms articulated at centre, coil springs, telescopic dampers.

STEERING rack-and-pinion; turns of steering wheel lock to lock: 3.60.

BRAKES disc (diameter 10.28 in, 261 mm), rear compensator; area rubbed by linings: total 342.9 sq in, 2,212 sq cm.

ELECTRICAL EQUIPMENT voltage: 12 V; battery: 40 Ah; generator type: dynamo, 22 A; headlamps: 2.

DIMENSIONS AND WEIGHT wheel base: 89.37 in, 2,270 mm; front track: 49.45 in, 1,256 mm; rear track: 48.27 in, 1,226 mm; overall length: 157.28 in, 3,995 mm; overall width: 58.66 in, 1,490 mm; overall height: 55.31 in, 1,405 mm; ground clearance: 4.72 in, 120 mm; dry weight: 1,687 lb, 765 kg; distribution of weight: 36.4% front axle, 63.6% rear axle; turning circle (between walls): 33.5 ft, 10.2 m; fuel tank capacity: 8.4 imp gal, 10 US gal, 38 l.

BODY saloon/sedan; doors: 4; seats: 4-5; front seats: separate.

PRACTICAL INSTRUCTIONS fuel: 86 oct petrol; engine sump oil: 4.4 imp pt, 5.3 US pt, 2.5 l, SAE 10W-40, change every 3,100 miles, 5,000 km; gearbox and final drive oil: 3.3 imp pt, 4 US pt, 1.9 l, SAE 80 EP, change every 6,200 miles, 10,000 km; greasing: every 12,400 miles, 20,000 km, 1 point; tappet clearances: inlet 0.004-0.006 in, 0.10-0.14 mm, exhaust 0.007-0.009 in, 0.18-0.22 mm; valve timing: inlet opens 10° before tdc and closes 34° after bdc, exhaust opens 46° before bdc and closes 10° after tdc; normal tyre pressure: front 14 psi, 1 atm, rear 26 psi, 1.8 atm.

OPTIONAL ACCESSORIES reclining backrests.

8 Automatic

See 8 Major, except for:

PRICE EX WORKS: —

ENGINE max power (SAE): 47 hp at 4,600 rpm; specific power: 42.4 hp/l.

TRANSMISSION clutch: Jaeger electromagnetic automatic; gearbox: automatic with 3 ratios + reverse, possible manual selection; gearbox ratios: I 3.540, II 1.810, III 1.034, rev 3.600; push button control: on facia; final drive: spiral bevel.

PERFORMANCE max speeds: 25 mph, 41 km/h in 1st gear; 49 mph, 79 km/h in 2nd gear; 82 mph, 132 km/h in 3rd gear; power-weight ratio: 36.4 lb/hp, 16.5 kg/hp.

DIMENSIONS AND WEIGHT dry weight: 1,709 lb, 775 kg.

8 S

See 8 Major, except for:

PRICE IN GB: £ 615.
PRICE EX WORKS: 9,840 francs.

ENGINE compression ratio: 9.5; max power (SAE): 60 hp at 5,500 rpm; max torque (SAE): 59 lb ft, 8.2 kg m at 3,000 rpm; max engine rpm: 6,000; specific power: 54.2 hp/l; carburation: 1 Weber 32 DIR downdraught twin barrel carburettor

TRANSMISSION width of rims: 4.5''; tyres: 135 x 380.

PERFORMANCE max speeds: 27 mph, 43 km/h in 1st gear; 43 mph, 69 km/h in 2nd gear; 65 mph, 105 km/h in 3rd gear; 90 mph, 145 km/h in 4th gear; power-weight ratio: 28.2 lb/hp, 12.8 kg/hp; speed in top at 1,000 rpm: 15.7 mph, 25.2 km/h; fuel consumption: 35.3 m/imp gal, 29.4 m/US gal, 8 l x 100 km.

DIMENSIONS AND WEIGHT dry weight: 1,698 lb, 770 kg.

PRACTICAL INSTRUCTIONS valve timing: inlet opens 22° before tdc and closes 62° after bdc, exhaust opens 60° before tdc and closes 20° after tdc; normal tyre pressure: front 16 psi, 1.1 atm, rear 31 psi, 2.2 atm.

10

PRICE IN GB: £ 610.
PRICE IN USA: $ 1,725.

ENGINE rear, 4 stroke; cylinders: 4, vertical, in line; bore and stroke: 2.87 x 3.03 in, 73 x 77 mm; engine capacity: 78.7 cu in, 1,289 cu cm; compression ratio: 8; max power (SAE): 52 hp at 4,800 rpm; max torque (SAE): 70 lb ft, 9.7 kg m at 2,500 rpm; max engine rpm: 5,300; specific power: 40.3 hp/l; cylinder block: cast iron, wet liners; cylinder head: light alloy; crankshaft bearings: 5; valves: 2 per cylinder, overhead, in line; camshafts: 1, side; lubrication: gear pump, filter in sump; lubricating system capacity: 5.3 imp pt, 6.3 US pt, 3 l; carburation: 1 Solex 32 DITA 3 downdraught carburettor; fuel feed: mechanical pump; cooling system: liquid, sealed circuit; cooling system capacity: 12.5 imp pt, 15 US pt, 7.1 l.

TRANSMISSION driving wheels: rear; clutch: single dry plate (diaphragm); gearbox: mechanical; gears: 4 + reverse; synchromesh gears: I, II, III, IV; gearbox ratios: I 3.610, II 2.250, III 1.480, IV 1.032, rev 3.080; gear lever: central; final drive: hypoid bevel; axle ratio: 4.125; width of rims: 4''; tyres: 145/135 x 380.

PERFORMANCE max speeds: 26 mph, 42 km/h in 1st gear; 42 mph, 68 km/h in 2nd gear; 64 mph, 103 km/h in 3rd gear; 84 mph, 135 km/h in 4th gear; power-weight ratio: 33.5 lb/hp, 15.2 kg/hp; carrying capacity: 882 lb, 400 kg; speed in top at 1,000 rpm: 16.3 mph, 26.3 km/h; fuel consumption: 37.7 m/imp gal, 31.4 m/US gal, 7.5 l x 100 km.

CHASSIS integral; front suspension: independent, wishbones, coil springs, anti-roll bar, telescopic dampers; rear suspension: independent, swinging semi-axles, swinging longitudinal trailing arms articulated at centre, coil springs, telescopic dampers.

STEERING rack-and-pinion; turns of steering wheel lock to lock: 3.60.

BRAKES disc (diameter 10.28 in, 261 mm), rear compensator; area rubbed by linings: total 342.9 sq in, 2,212 sq cm.

ELECTRICAL EQUIPMENT voltage: 12 V; battery: 40 Ah; generator type: dynamo, 22 A; headlamps: 2.

DIMENSIONS AND WEIGHT wheel base: 89.37 in, 2,270 mm; front track: 49.45 in, 1,256 mm; rear track: 48.27 in, 1,226 mm; overall length: 165.24 in, 4,197 mm; overall width: 60.08 in, 1,526 mm; overall height: 55.31 in, 1,405 mm; ground clearance: 4.72 in, 120 mm; dry weight: 1,742 lb, 790 kg; distribution of weight: 37.4% front axle, 62.6% rear axle; turning circle (between walls): 36.1 ft, 11 m; fuel tank capacity: 8.4 imp gal, 10 US gal, 38 l.

BODY saloon/sedan; doors: 4; seats: 4-5; front seats: separate.

RENAULT 6 TL (1100)

RENAULT 10

RENAULT 12 TL Berline

10

PRACTICAL INSTRUCTIONS fuel: 92 oct petrol; engine sump oil: 5.3 imp pt, 6.3 US pt, 3 l, SAE 10W-40, change every 3,100 miles, 5,000 km; gearbox and final drive oil: 3.3 imp pt, 4 US pt, 1.9 l, SAE 80 EP, change every 12,400 miles, 20,000 km; greasing: every 12,400 miles, 20,000 km, 1 point; tappet clearances: inlet 0.004-0.006 in, 0.10-0.14 mm, exhaust 0.007-0.009 in, 0.18-0.22 mm; valve timing: inlet opens 10° before tdc and closes 34° after bdc, exhaust opens 46° before bdc and closes 10° after tdc; normal tyre pressure: front 14 psi, 1 atm, rear 28 psi, 2 atm.

OPTIONAL ACCESSORIES reclining backrests.

10 Automatic

See 10, except for:

PRICE IN GB: £ 686.
PRICE EX WORKS: 10,660 francs.

ENGINE bore and stroke: 2.76 x 2.83 in, 70 x 72 mm; engine capacity: 67.6 cu in, 1,108 cu cm; compression ratio: 8.5; max power (SAE): 47 hp at 4,600 rpm; max torque (SAE): 57 lb ft, 7.9 kg m at 3,000 rpm; specific power: 42.4 hp/l.

TRANSMISSION clutch: Jaeger electromagnetic automatic; gearbox: automatic with 3 ratios + reverse, possible manual selection; gearbox ratios: I 3.540, II 1.810, III 1.034, rev 3.600; push button control: on facia; final drive: spiral bevel.

PERFORMANCE max speeds: 25 mph, 41 km/h in 1st gear; 49 mph, 79 km/h in 2nd gear; 82 mph, 132 km/h in 3rd gear; power-weight ratio: 36.8 lb/hp, 16.7 kg/hp; fuel consumption: 41.5 m/imp gal, 34.6 m/US gal, 6.8 l x 100 km.

DIMENSIONS AND WEIGHT dry weight: 1,731 lb, 785 kg.

12 L Berline

PRICE IN GB: £ 683.
PRICE EX WORKS: 10,780 francs.

ENGINE front, 4 stroke; cylinders: 4, vertical, in line; bore and stroke: 2.87 x 3.03 in, 73 x 77 mm; engine capacity: 78.7 cu in, 1,289 cu cm; compression ratio: 8.5; max power (SAE): 60 hp at 5,250 rpm; max torque (SAE): 70 lb ft, 9.7 kg m at 3,000 rpm; max engine rpm: 6,000; specific power: 46.5 hp/l; cylinder block: cast iron; cylinder head: light alloy; crankshaft bearings: 5; valves: 2 per cylinder, overhead, push-rods and rockers; camshafts: 1, side; lubrication: gear pump, filter in sump; lubricating system capacity: 5.3 imp pt, 6.3 US pt, 3 l; carburation: 1 Solex 32 EISA downdraught carburettor; fuel feed: mechanical pump; cooling system: liquid, sealed circuit; cooling system capacity: 8.8 imp pt, 10.6 US pt, 5 l.

TRANSMISSION driving wheels: front; clutch: single dry plate (diaphragm); gearbox: mechanical; gears: 4 + reverse; synchromesh gears: I, II, III, IV; gearbox ratios: I 3.615, II 2.263, III 1.480, IV 1.032, rev 3.076; gear lever: central; final drive: hypoid bevel; axle ratio: 3.777; width of rims: 4.5''; tyres: 145 x 330.

PERFORMANCE max speeds: 27 mph, 43 km/h in 1st gear; 43 mph, 70 km/h in 2nd gear; 67 mph, 108 km/h in 3rd gear; 89 mph, 143 km/h in 4th gear; power-weight ratio: 33.1 lb/hp, 15 kg/hp; carrying capacity: 882 lb, 400 kg; max gradient in 1st gear: 32%; speed in top at 1,000 rpm: 16.8 mph, 27.1 km/h; fuel consumption: 33.2 m/imp gal, 27.7 m/US gal, 8.5 l x 100 km.

CHASSIS integral; front suspension: independent, wishbones, anti-roll bar, coil springs/telescopic dampers; rear suspension: rigid axle, trailing arms, A-bracket, anti-roll bar, coil springs/telescopic dampers.

STEERING rack-and-pinion; turns of steering wheel lock to lock: 3.50.

BRAKES front disc, rear drum, rear compensator; area rubbed by linings: front 160 sq in, 1,032 sq cm, rear 70.1 sq in, 452 sq cm, total 230.1 sq in, 1,484 sq cm.

ELECTRICAL EQUIPMENT voltage: 12 V; battery: 40 Ah; generator type: dynamo, 264 W; headlamps: 2.

DIMENSIONS AND WEIGHT wheel base: 96.10 in, 2,441 mm; front track: 51.65 in, 1,312 mm; rear track: 51.65 in, 1,312 mm; overall length: 170.87 in, 4,340 mm; overall width: 64.41 in, 1,636 mm; overall height: 56.46 in, 1,434 mm; ground clearance: 5.51 in, 140 mm; dry weight: 1,985 lb, 900 kg; distribution of weight: 58.5% front axle, 41.5% rear axle; turning circle (between walls): 35.1 ft, 10.7 m; fuel tank capacity: 11 imp gal, 13.2 US gal, 50 l.

RENAULT 12 Break

RENAULT 12 Gordini

RENAULT 16 TS

BODY saloon/sedan; doors: 4; seats: 4-5; front seats: bench.

PRACTICAL INSTRUCTIONS fuel: 92 oct petrol; engine sump oil: 5.3 imp pt, 6.3 US pt, 3 l, SAE 10W-40, change every 3,100 miles, 5,000 km; gearbox and final drive oil: 8 imp pt, 3.4 US pt, 1.6 l, SAE 80 EP, change every 6,200 miles, 10,000 km; greasing: none; tappet clearances: inlet 0.004-0.006 in, 0.10-0.14 mm; exhaust 0.007-0.009 in, 0.18-0.22 mm; valve timing: inlet opens 20° before tdc and closes 60° after bdc, exhaust opens 60° before bdc and closes 20° after tdc; normal tyre pressure: front 21 psi, 1.5 atm, rear 24 psi, 1.7 atm.

OPTIONAL ACCESSORIES separate front seats.

12 TL Berline

See 12 L Berline, except for:

PRICE IN GB: £ 725.
PRICE EX WORKS: 11,580 francs.

BODY front seats: separate, reclining backrests (standard).

OPTIONAL ACCESSORIES electrically-heated rear window.

12 Break

See 12 L Berline, except for:

PRICE EX WORKS: 11,990 francs.

TRANSMISSION tyres: 155 x 330.

PERFORMANCE power-weight ratio: 34.8 lb/hp, 15.8 kg/hp; carrying capacity: 937 lb, 425 kg.

DIMENSIONS AND WEIGHT overall length: 173.39 in, 4,404 mm; overall height: 57.28 in, 1,455 mm; dry weight: 2,095 lb, 950 kg; distribution of weight: 54.7% front axle, 45.3% rear axle.

BODY estate car/station wagon; doors: 4 + 1.

12 Gordini

See 12 L Berline, except for:

PRICE EX WORKS: 16,500 francs.

ENGINE bore and stroke: 3.03 x 3.31 in, 77 x 84 mm; engine capacity: 95.5 cu in, 1,565 cu cm; compression ratio: 10.2; max power (SAE): 125 hp at 6,250 rpm; max torque (SAE): 109 lb ft, 15 kg m at 5,500 rpm; max engine rpm: 6,500; specific power: 80 hp/l; cylinder block: light alloy, wet liners; lubrication: rotary pump, full flow filter, oil cooler; lubricating system capacity: 7.6 imp pt, 9.1 US pt, 4.3 l; carburation: 2 Weber 45 DCOE horizontal twin barrel carburettors; cooling system capacity: 9.9 imp pt, 11.8 US pt, 5.6 l.

TRANSMISSION gears: 5 + reverse; synchromesh gears: I, II, III, IV, V; gearbox ratios: I 3.615, II 2.333, III 1.609, IV 1.214, V 0.968, rev 3.083; width of rims: 5.5''; tyres: 155 x 330.

PERFORMANCE max speeds: 32 mph, 51 km/h in 1st gear; 49 mph, 79 km/h in 2nd gear; 71 mph, 115 km/h in 3rd gear; 94 mph, 152 km/h in 4th gear; 115 mph, 185 km/h in 5th gear; power-weight ratio: 17.2 lb/hp, 7.8 kg/hp; speed in top at 1,000 rpm: 18.1 mph, 29.1 km/h; fuel consumption: 28.2 m/imp gal, 23.5 m/US gal, 10 l x 100 km.

STEERING turns of steering wheel lock to lock: 2.60.

BRAKES disc, front with internal radial fins; area rubbed by linings: front 157.2 sq in, 1,014 sq cm, rear 157.2 sq in, 1,014 sq cm; total 314.4 sq in, 2,028 sq cm.

ELECTRICAL EQUIPMENT battery: 45 Ah; generator type: alternator, 360/480 W; headlamps: 4, lights iodine.

DIMENSIONS AND WEIGHT front track: 52.76 in, 1,340 mm; rear track: 52.56 in, 1,335 mm; overall length: 169.29 in, 4,300 mm; dry weight: 2,161 lb, 980 kg; distribution of weight: 58.2% front axle, 41.8% rear axle; fuel tank capacity: 19.6 imp gal, 23.5 US gal, 89 l.

PRACTICAL INSTRUCTIONS fuel: 98-100 oct petrol; engine sump oil: 7.6 imp pt, 9.1 US pt, 4.3 l; gearbox and final drive oil: 3.5 imp pt, 4.2 US pt, 2 l; tappet clearances: inlet 0.010 in, 0.25 mm, exhaust 0.014 in, 0.35 mm; valve timing: inlet opens 40° before tdc and closes 72° after bdc, exhaust opens 72° before bdc and closes 40° after tdc; normal tyre pressure: front 26 psi, 1.8 atm, rear 26 psi, 1.8 atm.

RENAULT 12 Break

RENAULT 12 Gordini

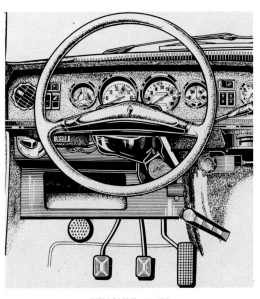

RENAULT 16 TS

16 L

PRICE IN GB: £ 786.
PRICE EX WORKS: 12,600 francs.

ENGINE front, 4 stroke; cylinders: 4, vertical, in line; bore and stroke: 3.03 x 3.31 in, 77 x 84 mm; engine capacity: 95.5 cu in, 1,565 cu cm; compression ratio: 8.6; max power (SAE): 71 hp at 5,000 rpm; max torque (SAE): 84 lb ft, 11.6 kg m at 3,000 rpm; max engine rpm: 5,500; specific power: 45.4 hp/l; cylinder block: light alloy, wet liners; cylinder head: light alloy; crankshaft bearings: 5; valves: 2 per cylinder, overhead, in line, slanted at 20°, push-rods and rockers; camshafts: 1, side; lubrication: eccentric pump, filter in sump; lubricating system capacity: 7 imp pt, 8.5 US pt, 4 l; carburation: 1 Weber 32 DIR downdraught carburettor; fuel feed: mechanical pump; cooling system: liquid, sealed circuit, electric thermostatic fan; cooling system capacity: 10.2 imp pt, 12.3 US pt, 5.8 l.

TRANSMISSION driving wheels: front; clutch: single dry plate (diaphragm); gearbox: mechanical; gears: 4 + reverse; synchromesh gears: I, II, III, IV; gearbox ratios: I 3.610, II 2.260, III 1.480, IV 1.032, rev 3.080; gear lever: steering column; final drive: hypoid bevel; axle ratio: 3.777; width of rims: 4.5''; tyres: 145 x 355.

PERFORMANCE max speeds: 27 mph, 43 km/h in 1st gear; 43 mph, 70 km/h in 2nd gear; 67 mph, 108 km/h in 3rd gear; 93 mph, 150 km/h in 4th gear; power-weight ratio: 31.3 lb/hp, 14.2 kg/hp; carrying capacity: 1,058 lb, 480 kg; max gradient in 1st gear: 32%; acceleration: 0-50 mph (0-80 km/h) 10.7 sec; speed in top at 1,000 rpm: 17.2 mph, 27.7 km/h; fuel consumption: 28.2 m/imp gal, 23.5 m/US gal, 10 l 100 km.

CHASSIS integral; front suspension: independent, wishbones, longitudinal torsion bars, anti-roll bar, telescopic dampers; rear suspension: independent, swinging longitudinal trailing arms, transverse torsion bars, anti-roll bar, telescopic dampers.

STEERING rack-and-pinion; turns of steering wheel lock to lock: 4.

BRAKES front disc (diameter 10 in, 254 mm), rear drum, rear compensator, servo; area rubbed by linings: front 192.6 sq in, 1,242 sq cm, rear 89 sq in, 574 sq cm, total 281.6 sq in, 1,816 sq cm.

ELECTRICAL EQUIPMENT voltage: 12 V; battery: 40 Ah; generator type: alternator, 30/40 A; headlamps: 2.

DIMENSIONS AND WEIGHT wheel base: 104.33 in, 2,650 mm (right), 106.97 in, 2,717 mm (left); front track: 52.83 in, 1,342 mm; rear track: 50.87 in, 1,292 mm; overall length: 166.81 in, 4,237 mm; overall width: 64.88 in, 1,648 mm; overall height: 55.12 in, 1,400 mm; ground clearance: 4.53 in, 115 mm; dry weight: 2,227 lb, 1,010 kg; distribution of weight: 56.2% front axle, 43.8% rear axle; turning circle (between walls): 34.8 ft, 10.6 m; fuel tank capacity: 11 imp gal, 13.2 US gal, 50 l.

BODY saloon/sedan; doors: 4 + 1; seats: 5-6; front seats: separate; details: rear door, back seat folding down to luggage table.

PRACTICAL INSTRUCTIONS engine sump oil: 7 imp pt, 8.5 US pt, 4 l, SAE 10W-40, change every 3,100 miles, 5,000 km; gearbox and final drive oil: 2.8 imp pt, 3.4 US pt, 1.6 l, SAE 80 EP, change every 6,200 miles, 10,000 km; greasing: none; tappet clearances: inlet 0.008 in, 0.20 mm, exhaust 0.010 in, 0.25 mm; valve timing: inlet opens 10° before tdc and closes 42° after bdc, exhaust opens 46° before bdc and closes 10° after tdc; normal tyre pressure: front 23 psi, 1.6 atm, rear 28 psi, 2 atm.

OPTIONAL ACCESSORIES automatic (electronic) gearbox, hydraulic torque convertor and planetary gears with 3 ratios (I 2.396, II 1.484, III 1.027, rev 2.054), max ratio of convertor at stall 2.3, possible manual selection, steering column selector lever; sunshine roof.

16 TL

See 16 L, except for:

PRICE IN GB: £ 839.
PRICE IN USA: $ 2,395.

BODY front seats: reclining backrests.

16 L Commerciale

See 16 L, except for:

PRICE EX WORKS: 12,800 francs.

TRANSMISSION tyres: 155 x 355.

OPTIONAL ACCESSORIES reclining backrests.

16 TS

See 16 L, except for:

PRICE IN GB: £ 978.
PRICE EX WORKS: 15,200 francs.

ENGINE max power (SAE): 90 hp at 5,750 rpm; max torque (SAE): 93 lb ft, 12.9 kg m at 3,500 rpm; max engine rpm: 6,000; specific power: 57.5 hp/l; carburation: 1 Weber 32 DAR downdraught twin barrel carburettor; cooling system capacity: 12 imp pt, 14.4 US pt, 6.8 l.

TRANSMISSION tyres: 155 x 355.

PERFORMANCE max speeds: 30 mph, 49 km/h in 1st gear; 49 mph, 79 km/h in 2nd gear; 75 mph, 120 km/h in 3rd gear; 99 mph, 160 km/h in 4th gear; power-weight ratio: 25.3 lb/hp, 11.7 kg/hp; speed in top at 1,000 rpm: 17.8 mph, 28.6 km/h.

DIMENSIONS AND WEIGHT dry weight: 2,337 lb, 1,060 kg.

BODY front seats: separate, reclining backrests; details: electrically-heated rear window.

16 TS Commerciale

See 16 TS, except for:

PRICE EX WORKS: 15,340 francs.

TRABANT   GERMANY (D.R.)

601 Limousine

PRICE: —

ENGINE front, 2 stroke; cylinders: 2, transverse, in line; bore and stroke: 2.83 x 2.87 in, 72 x 73 mm; engine capacity: 36.2 cu in, 594 cu cm; compression ratio: 7.6; max power (SAE): 30 hp at 4,200 rpm; max torque (SAE): 46 lb ft, 6.3 kg m at 3,000 rpm; max engine rpm: 4,500; specific power: 50.5 hp/l; cylinder block: light alloy; cylinder head: light alloy; crankshaft bearings: 3; valves: 1 per cylinder, rotary; lubrication: mixture 1:33.3; carburation: 1 BVF type 28 HB 2-7 horizontal single barrel carburettor; fuel feed: gravity; cooling system: air cooled.

TRANSMISSION driving wheels: front; clutch: single dry plate; gearbox: mechanical; gears: 4 + reverse; synchromesh gears: I, II, III, IV; gearbox ratios: I 4.080, II 2.320, III 1.520, IV 1.030, rev 3.830; gear lever: steering column; final drive: conic bevel; axle ratio: 4.330; width of rims: 4''; tyres: 5.20 x 13.

PERFORMANCE max speeds: 16 mph, 25 km/h in 1st gear; 28 mph, 45 km/h in 2nd gear; 43 mph, 70 km/h in 3rd gear; 62 mph, 100 km/h in 4th gear; power-weight ratio: 45.2 lb/hp, 20.5 kg/hp; carrying capacity: 849 lb, 385 kg; max gradient in 1st gear: 37%; acceleration: 0-50 mph (0-80 km/h) 22.5 sec; speed in top at 1,000 rpm: 14.6 mph, 23.5 km/h; fuel consumption: 40.4 m/imp gal, 33.6 m/US gal, 7 l x 100 km.

CHASSIS integral; front suspension: independent, wishbones, transverse leafspring upper arms, telescopic dampers; rear suspension: independent, swinging semi-axles, transverse semi-elliptic leafspring, telescopic dampers.

STEERING rack-and-pinion; turns of steering wheel lock to lock: 2.60.

BRAKES drum; lining area: front 38.9 sq in, 251 sq cm, rear 34.1 sq in, 220 sq cm, total 73 sq in, 471 sq cm.

ELECTRICAL EQUIPMENT voltage: 6 V; battery: 56 Ah; generator type: dynamo, 220 W; ignition distributor: IKA; headlamps: 2.

DIMENSIONS AND WEIGHT wheel base: 79.53 in, 2,020 mm; front track: 47.48 in, 1,206 mm; rear track: 49.41 in, 1,255 mm; overall length: 139.96 in, 3,555 mm; overall width: 59.21 in, 1,504 mm; overall height: 56.57 in, 1,437 mm; ground clearance: 6.10 in, 155 mm; dry weight: 1,356 lb, 615 kg; distribution of weight: 45% front axle, 55% rear axle; turning circle (between walls): 32.8 ft, 10 m; fuel tank capacity: 5.3 imp gal, 6.3 US gal, 24 l.

BODY saloon/sedan; doors: 2; seats: 4; front seats: separate.

PRACTICAL INSTRUCTIONS fuel: mixture 1:33.3, 88 oct petrol, SAE 10W-30, oil in separate tank; gearbox and final

TRABANT 601

WARTBURG 1000-353

AUDI 60 Variant

drive oil: 2.6 imp pt, 3.2 US pt, 1.5 l, SAE 20W-30, change every 9,300 miles, 15,000 km; greasing: every 3,100 mile 5,000 km, 9 points; sparking plug type: 260°; valve timin inlet opens 45° before tdc and closes 45° after bdc, exhau opens 72°5' before bdc and closes 72°5' after tdc; norm tyre pressure: front 23 psi, 1.6 atm, rear 23 psi, 1.6 atr

OPTIONAL ACCESSORIES Hycomat automatic clutch.

601 Universal

See 601 Limousine, except for

PRICE: —

PERFORMANCE max speed: 61 mph, 98 km/h; power-weigh ratio: 47.6 lb/hp, 21.6 kg/hp.

DIMENSIONS AND WEIGHT overall length: 140.16 in, 3,5 mm; dry weight: 1,433 lb, 650 kg; distribution of weigh 44% front axle, 56% rear axle.

BODY estate car/station wagon; doors: 2 + 1.

WARTBURG   GERMANY (D.R.

1000-353

PRICE IN GB: £ 572.

ENGINE front, 2 stroke; cylinders: 3, vertical, in line; bo and stroke: 2.89 x 3.07 in, 73.5 x 78 mm; engine capacit 60.5 cu in, 992 cu cm; compression ratio: 7.5; max pow (SAE): 55 hp at 4,250 rpm; max torque (DIN): 80 lb ft, kg m at 3,000 rpm; max engine rpm: 5,000; specific powe 55.4 hp/l; cylinder block: cast iron; cylinder head: lig alloy; crankshaft bearings: 4; lubrication: mixture 1 : 3 carburation: 1 BVF 40 F 1-11 single barrel carburettor; fu feed: mechanical pump; cooling system: liquid, seale circuit; cooling system capacity: 14.4 imp pt, 17.3 US p 8.2 l.

TRANSMISSION driving wheels: front; clutch: single d plate; gearbox: mechanical; gears: 4 + reverse; synchro mesh gears: I, II, III, IV; gearbox ratios: I 3.769, II 2.16 III 1.347, IV 0.906, rev 3.385; gear lever: steering colum final drive: spiral bevel; axle ratio: 4.222; width of rim 4.5''; tyres: 6.00 x 13.

PERFORMANCE max speeds: 20 mph, 32 km/h in 1st gea 35 mph, 57 km/h in 2nd gear; 56 mph, 90 km/h in 3rd gea 81 mph, 130 km/h in 4th gear; power-weight ratio: 34 lb/hp, 15.6 kg/hp; carrying capacity: 882 lb, 400 kg; ma gradient in 1st gear: 39%; acceleration: standing ¼ mil 22.6 sec, 0-50 mph (0-80 km/h) 14 sec; speed in top 1,000 rpm: 18 mph, 29 km/h; fuel consumption: 30.4 m/im gal, 25.3 m/US gal, 9.3 l x 100 km.

CHASSIS box-type ladder frame; front suspension: ind pendent, wishbones, coil springs, rubber elements, tele copic dampers; rear suspension: independent, semi-trailin arms, coil springs, rubber elements, anti-roll bar, telescop dampers.

STEERING rack-and-pinion; turns of steering wheel lock lock: 3.50.

BRAKES drum, rear compensator; lining area: front 65 sq in, 425 sq cm, rear 61.2 sq in, 395 sq cm, total 127.1 s in, 820 sq cm.

ELECTRICAL EQUIPMENT voltage: 12 V; battery: 42 A generator type: dynamo, 220 W; ignition distributor: Fe headlamps: 2.

DIMENSIONS AND WEIGHT wheel base: 96.46 in, 2,450 mm front track: 49.61 in, 1,260 mm; rear track: 51.18 in, 1,30 mm; overall length: 166.14 in, 4,220 mm; overall width 64.65 in, 1,642 mm; overall height: 58.86 in, 1,495 mm ground clearance: 6.10 in, 155 mm; dry weight: 1,890 lb 857 kg; distribution of weight: 57% front axle, 43% rea axle; turning circle (between walls): 33.5 ft, 10.2 m; fue tank capacity: 9.7 imp gal, 11.6 US gal, 44 l.

BODY saloon/sedan; doors: 4; seats: 5; front seats: sepa rate, reclining backrests.

PRACTICAL INSTRUCTIONS fuel: mixture 1:33, SAE 20-40 oil in separate tank; gearbox and final drive oil: 4.2 im pt, 3.8 US pt, 1.8 l, SAE 90 EP, change every 15,500 mile 25,000 km; greasing: every 31,100 miles, 50,000 km, 2 point sparking plug type: 240°; opening timing: inlet opens 62°17 before tdc and closes 62°17' after bdc, exhaust opens 78°

TRABANT 601 Limousine

WARTBURG 1000-353

AUDI 60 Variant

before bdc and closes 78°2' after tdc; normal tyre pressure: front 23 psi, 1.6 atm, rear 24 psi, 1.7 atm.

OPTIONAL ACCESSORIES sunshine roof; luxury version.

1000-353 Tourist

See 1000-353, except for:

PRICE IN GB: £ 611.

PERFORMANCE max speed: 78 mph, 125 km/h; power-weight ratio: 36.8 lb/hp, 16.7 kg/hp; carrying capacity: 992 lb, 450 kg.

DIMENSIONS AND WEIGHT overall length: 172.44 in, 4,380 mm; dry weight: 2,139 lb, 917 kg.

BODY estate car/station wagon; doors: 4 + 1.

PRACTICAL INSTRUCTIONS normal tyre pressure: front 24 psi, 1.7 atm, rear 36 psi, 2.5 atm.

AUDI GERMANY (F.R.)

2-door 60 Limousine

PRICE EX WORKS: 7,990 marks.

ENGINE front, 4 stroke; cylinders: 4, in line; bore and stroke: 3.15 x 2.93 in, 80 x 74.4 mm; engine capacity: 91.3 cu in, 1,496 cu cm; compression ratio: 9.1; max power (DIN): 55 hp at 4,750 rpm; max torque (DIN): 83 lb ft, 11.5 kg m at 2,600 rpm; max engine rpm: 5,500; specific power: 36.8 hp/l; cylinder block: cast iron; cylinder head: light alloy; crankshaft bearings: 5; valves: 2 per cylinder, overhead, push-rods and rockers; camshafts: 1, side; lubrication: gear pump, full flow filter; lubricating system capacity: 7 imp pt, 8.5 US pt, 4 l; carburation: 1 Solex 35 PDSIT-5 downdraught carburettor; fuel feed: mechanical pump; cooling system: water; cooling system capacity: 13.2 imp pt, 15.9 US pt, 7.5 l.

TRANSMISSION driving wheels: front; clutch: single dry plate; gearbox: mechanical; gears: 4 + reverse; synchromesh gears: I, II, III, IV; gearbox ratios: I 3.400, II 1.944, III 1.360, IV 0.966, rev 3.100; gear lever: steering column; final drive: spiral bevel; axle ratio: 4.111; width of rims: 4.5''; tyres: 6.15 x 13.

PERFORMANCE max speeds: 24 mph, 39 km/h in 1st gear; 42 mph, 68 km/h in 2nd gear; 65 mph, 104 km/h in 3rd gear; 86 mph, 138 km/h in 4th gear; power-weight ratio: 38.4 lb/hp, 17.4 kg/hp; carrying capacity: 882 lb, 400 kg; max gradient in 1st gear: 42%; acceleration: 0-50 mph (0-80 km/h) 11.2 sec; speed in top at 1,000 rpm: 16.2 mph, 26 km/h; fuel consumption: 32.5 m/imp gal, 27 m/US gal, 8.7 l x 100 km.

CHASSIS integral; front suspension: independent, wishbones, lower leading arms, longitudinal torsion bars, anti-roll bar, telescopic dampers; rear suspension: rigid axle, swinging longitudinal trailing arms, transverse linkage bar, transverse torsion bars, telescopic dampers.

STEERING rack-and-pinion; turns of steering wheel lock to lock: 4.

BRAKES front disc (diameter 11.02 in, 280 mm), rear drum; lining area: front 16.3 sq in, 105 sq cm, rear 45.3 sq in, 292 sq cm, total 61.6 sq in, 397 sq cm.

ELECTRICAL EQUIPMENT voltage: 12 V; battery: 45 Ah; generator type: alternator, 490 W; ignition distributor: Bosch; headlamps: 2.

DIMENSIONS AND WEIGHT wheel base: 98.03 in, 2,490 mm; front track: 52.83 in, 1,342 mm; rear track: 52.20 in, 1,326 mm; overall length: 172.44 in, 4,380 mm; overall width: 63.98 in, 1,625 mm; overall height: 57.13 in, 1,451 mm; ground clearance: 6.42 in, 163 mm; dry weight: 2,117 lb, 960 kg; distribution of weight: 61.4% front axle, 38.6% rear axle; turning circle (between walls): 35.8 ft, 10.9 m; fuel tank capacity: 12.8 imp gal, 15.3 US gal, 58 l.

BODY saloon/sedan; doors: 2; seats: 5; front seats: separate.

PRACTICAL INSTRUCTIONS fuel: 88 oct petrol; engine sump oil: 7 imp pt, 8.5 US pt, 4 l, SAE 10W-30, change every 6,200 miles, 10,000 km; gearbox and final drive oil: 3.5 imp pt, 4.2 US pt, 2 l, SAE 80, change every 18,600 miles, 30,000 km; greasing: none; sparking plug type: 225°; tappet clearances: inlet 0.004 in, 0.10 mm, exhaust 0.010 in, 0.25 mm; valve timing: inlet opens 6° before tdc and closes 38° after bdc, exhaust opens 41° before bdc and closes 5° after tdc; normal tyre pressure: front 24 psi, 1.7 atm, rear 24 psi, 1.7 atm.

2-DOOR 60 LIMOUSINE

VARIATIONS

ENGINE (only for export) max power (DIN) 65 hp at 5,000 rpm, max torque (DIN) 83 lb ft, 11.5 kg m at 3,000 rpm, 43.4 hp/l specific power.

PERFORMANCE max speed 89 mph, 144 km/h, power-weight ratio 32.6 lb/hp, 14.8 kg/hp, acceleration 0-50 mph (0-80 km/h) 10 sec.

OPTIONAL ACCESSORIES central gear lever; 6.45 x 13 tyres; dual circuit brakes, servo; reclining backrests; sunshine roof; electrically-heated rear window.

4-door 60 Limousine

See 2-door 60 Limousine, except for:

PRICE EX WORKS: 8,290 marks.

PERFORMANCE power-weight ratio: 39.5 lb/hp, 17.9 kg/hp.

DIMENSIONS AND WEIGHT dry weight: 2,172 lb, 985 kg.

2-door 60 L Limousine

See 2-door 60 Limousine, except for:

PRICE EX WORKS: 8,290 marks.

TRANSMISSION tyres: 6.45 x 13 (standard).

BRAKES dual circuit (standard).

4-door 60 L Limousine

See 4-door 60 Limousine, except for:

PRICE EX WORKS: 8,590 marks.

TRANSMISSION tyres: 6.45 x 13 (standard).

BRAKES dual circuit (standard).

60 Variant

See 2-door 60 Limousine, except for:

PRICE EX WORKS: 8,590 marks.

TRANSMISSION tyres: 6.45 x 13 (standard).

PERFORMANCE power-weight ratio: 41.7 lb/hp, 18.9 kg/hp; carrying capacity: 1,103 lb, 500 kg.

DIMENSIONS AND WEIGHT overall height: 57.32 in, 1,456 mm; dry weight: 2,293 lb, 1,040 kg.

BODY estate car/station wagon; doors: 2 + 1.

OPTIONAL ACCESSORIES sunshine roof not available.

2-door 75 L Limousine

See 2-door 60 Limousine, except for:

PRICE EX WORKS: 8,690 marks.

ENGINE bore and stroke: 3.15 x 3.32 in, 80 x 84.4 mm; engine capacity: 103.5 cu in, 1,696 cu cm; max power (SAE): 85 hp at 5,000 rpm; max torque (SAE): 94 lb ft, 13 kg m at 3,000 rpm; specific power: 50.1 hp/l.

TRANSMISSION axle ratio: 3.888; tyres: 6.45/165 x 13 (standard).

PERFORMANCE max speeds: 27 mph, 44 km/h in 1st gear; 48 mph, 78 km/h in 2nd gear; 71 mph, 115 km/h in 3rd gear; 93 mph, 150 km/h in 4th gear; power-weight ratio: 25.4 lb/hp, 11.5 kg/hp; max gradient in 1st gear: 48%; acceleration: 0-50 mph (0-80 km/h) 9.1 sec, speed in top at 1,000 rpm: 17.8 mph, 28.6 km/h.

BRAKES dual circuit.

ELECTRICAL EQUIPMENT battery: 55 Ah.

DIMENSIONS AND WEIGHT front track: 52.52 in, 1,334 mm; dry weight: 2,161 lb, 980 kg.

AUDI 4-door Super 90 Limousine

AUDI 4-door 100 Limousine

AUDI 2-door 100 LS Limousine

4-door 75 L Limousine

See 2-door 75 L Limousine, except for:

PRICE EX WORKS: 8,990 marks.

PERFORMANCE power-weight ratio: 27.1 lb/hp, 12.1 kg/hp.

DIMENSIONS AND WEIGHT dry weight: 2,260 lb, 1,025 kg.

75 Variant

See 2-door 75 L Limousine, except for:

PRICE IN GB: £ 1,107.
PRICE EX WORKS: 8,890 marks.

PERFORMANCE power-weight ratio: 26.9 lb/hp, 12.2 kg/hp; carrying capacity: 1,103 lb, 500 kg.

DIMENSIONS AND WEIGHT overall height: 57.32 in, 1,456 mm; dry weight: 2,293 lb, 1,040 kg.

BODY estate car/station wagon; doors: 2 + 1.

OPTIONAL ACCESSORIES sunshine roof not available.

2-door Super 90 Limousine

See 2-door 60 Limousine, except for:

PRICE IN GB: £ 1,047.
PRICE IN USA: $ 2,995.

ENGINE bore and stroke: 3.21 x 3.32 in, 81.5 x 84.4 mm; engine capacity: 107.4 cu in, 1,760 cu cm; compression ratio: 10.6; max power (DIN): 90 hp at 5,200 rpm; max torque: 109 lb ft, 15 kg m at 3,000 rpm; max engine rpm: 5,700; specific power: 51.1 hp/l; carburation: 1 Solex 32 DIDTA downdraught twin barrel carburettor.

TRANSMISSION gearbox ratios: IV 0.933; axle ratio: 3.888; tyres: 6.45/165 x 13 (standard).

PERFORMANCE max speeds: 30 mph, 48 km/h in 1st gear; 53 mph, 85 km/h in 2nd gear; 75 mph, 120 km/h in 3rd gear; 101 mph, 163 km/h in 4th gear; power-weight ratio: 26 lb/hp, 11.8 kg/hp; max gradient in 1st gear: 50%; acceleration: 0-50 mph (0-80 km/h) 8.5 sec; speed in top at 1,000 rpm: 18.6 mph, 30 km/h; fuel consumption: 31.7 m/imp gal, 26.4 m/US gal, 8.9 l x 100 km.

BRAKES dual circuit.

DIMENSIONS AND WEIGHT front track: 52.56 in, 1,335 mm; dry weight: 2,348 lb, 1,065 kg.

4-door Super 90 Limousine

See 2-door Super 90 Limousine, except for:

PRICE IN GB: £ 1,082.
PRICE IN USA: $ 3,095.

2-door 100 Limousine

PRICE EX WORKS: 10,190 marks.

ENGINE front, 4 stroke; cylinders: 4, in line; bore and stroke: 3.21 x 3.32 in, 81.5 x 84.4 mm; engine capacity: 107.4 cu in, 1,760 cu cm; compression ratio: 9.1; max power (DIN): 80 hp at 5,000 rpm; max torque (DIN): 100 lb ft, 13.8 kg m at 3,000 rpm; max engine rpm: 5,800; specific power: 45.4 hp/l; cylinder block: cast iron; cylinder head: light alloy; crankshaft bearings: 5; valves: 2 per cylinder, overhead, push-rods and rockers; camshafts: 1, side; lubrication: gear pump, full flow filter; lubricating system capacity: 7 imp pt, 8.5 US pt, 4 l; carburation: 1 Solex 35 PDSIT-5 downdraught carburettor; fuel feed: mechanical pump; cooling system: water; cooling system capacity: 13.2 imp pt, 15.9 US pt, 7.5 l.

TRANSMISSION driving wheels: front; clutch: single dry plate; gearbox: mechanical; gears: 4 + reverse; synchromesh gears: I, II, III, IV; gearbox ratios: I 3.400, II 1.944, III 1.360, IV 0.966, rev 3.100; gear lever: steering column; final drive: spiral bevel; axle ratio: 3.888; width of rims: 4.5''; tyres: 165 x 14.

PERFORMANCE max speeds: 27 mph, 44 km/h in 1st gear; 48 mph, 78 km/h in 2nd gear; 69 mph, 111 km/h in 3rd gear;

AUDI 60 and Super 90

AUDI 100 Limousine

*AUDI 100, 100 S, 100 LS Limousine
(rear suspension)*

97 mph, 156 km/h in 4th gear; power-weight ratio: 27.8 lb/hp, 12.6 kg/hp; carrying capacity: 1,058 lb, 480 kg; acceleration: 0-50 mph (0-80 km/h) 8.9 sec; speed in top at 1,000 rpm: 16.8 mph, 27 km/h; fuel consumption: 31.7 m/imp gal, 26.4 m/US gal, 8.9 l x 100 km.

CHASSIS integral; front suspension: independent, wishbones, anti-roll bar, coil springs/telescopic dampers; rear suspension: rigid axle, swinging longitudinal trailing arms, transverse linkage bar, transverse torsion bars, anti-roll bar in axle tube, telescopic dampers.

STEERING rack-and-pinion; turns of steering wheel lock to lock: 3.88.

BRAKES front disc (diameter 11.02 in, 280 mm), rear drum, dual circuit; lining area: front 16.3 sq in, 105 sq cm, rear 45.3 sq in, 292 sq cm, total 61.6 sq in, 397 sq cm.

ELECTRICAL EQUIPMENT voltage: 12 V; battery: 45 Ah; generator type: alternator, 490 W; ignition distributor: Bosch; headlamps: 2.

DIMENSIONS AND WEIGHT wheel base: 105.31 in, 2,675 mm; front track: 55.91 in, 1,420 mm; rear track: 56.10 in, 1,425 mm; overall length: 180.71 in, 4,590 mm; overall width: 68.07 in, 1,729 mm; overall height: 55.94 in, 1,421 mm; ground clearance: 6.38 in, 162 mm; dry weight: 2,216 lb, 1,005 kg; distribution of weight: 50% front axle, 50% rear axle; turning circle (between walls): 36.7 ft, 11.2 m; fuel tank capacity: 12.8 imp gal, 15.3 US gal, 58 l.

BODY saloon/sedan; doors: 2; seats: 5-6; front seats: separate.

PRACTICAL INSTRUCTIONS fuel: 98-100 oct petrol; engine sump oil: 7 imp pt, 8.5 US pt, 4 l, SAE 10W-30, change every 3,100 miles, 5,000 km; gearbox and final drive oil: 3.5 imp pt, 4.2 US pt, 2 l, SAE 80, change every 18,600 miles, 30,000 km; greasing: none; tappet clearances: inlet 0.004 in, 0.10 mm, exhaust 0.014 in, 0.35 mm; valve timing: inlet opens 8° before tdc and closes 40° after bdc, exhaust opens 43° before bdc and closes 7° after tdc; normal tyre pressure: front 26 psi, 1.8 atm, rear 26 psi, 1.8 atm.

OPTIONAL ACCESSORIES central gear lever; servo brake; sunshine roof; reclining backrests; electrically-heated rear window.

4-door 100 Limousine

See 2-door 100 Limousine, except for:

PERFORMANCE power-weight ratio: 28.9 lb/hp, 13.1 kg/hp.

DIMENSIONS AND WEIGHT dry weight: 2,315 lb, 1,050 kg.

2-door 100 S Limousine

See 2-door 100 Limousine, except for:

PRICE EX WORKS: 10,590 marks.

ENGINE compression ratio: 10.2; max power (DIN): 90 hp at 5,500 rpm; max torque (DIN): 105 lb ft, 14.5 kg m at 3,000 rpm; max engine rpm: 6,000; specific power: 51.1 hp/l.

PERFORMANCE max speeds: 30 mph, 48 km/h in 1st gear; 53 mph, 85 km/h in 2nd gear; 75 mph, 120 km/h in 3rd gear; 103 mph, 165 km/h in 4th gear; power-weight ratio: 24.7 lb/hp, 11.2 kg/hp; acceleration: 0-50 mph (0-80 km/h) 8.5 sec; speed in top at 1,000 rpm: 17.4 mph, 28 km/h.

BRAKES servo (standard).

BODY front seats: separate, reclining backrests (standard).

4-door 100 S Limousine

See 2-door 100 S Limousine, except for:

PERFORMANCE power-weight ratio: 25.8 lb/hp, 11.7 kg/hp.

DIMENSIONS AND WEIGHT dry weight: 2,315 lb, 1,050 kg.

2-door 100 LS Limousine

See 2-door 100 Limousine, except for:

PRICE IN GB: £ 1,192.
PRICE IN USA: $ 3,695.

ENGINE compression ratio: 10.2; max power (DIN): 100 hp at 5,500 rpm; max torque (DIN): 111 lb ft, 15.3 kg m at

2-DOOR 100 LS LIMOUSINE

3,200 rpm; max engine rpm: 6,000; specific power: 56.8 hp/l; carburation: 1 Solex 32 TDIT downdraught twin barrel carburettor.

PERFORMANCE max speeds: 31 mph, 50 km/h in 1st gear; 54 mph, 87 km/h in 2nd gear; 81 mph, 130 km/h in 3rd gear; 106 mph, 170 km/h in 4th gear; power-weight ratio: 22 lb/hp, 10 kg/hp; max gradient in 1st gear: 53%; acceleration: 0-50 mph (0-80 km/h) 8 sec; speed in top at 1,000 rpm: 17.7 mph, 28.5 km/h.

BRAKES servo (standard).

BODY front seats: separate, reclining backrests (standard).

4-door 100 LS Limousine

See 2-door 100 LS Limousine, except for:

PRICE IN GB £ 1,220.
PRICE IN USA: $ 3,795.

PERFORMANCE power-weight ratio: 23.1 lb/hp, 10.5 kg/hp.

DIMENSIONS AND WEIGHT dry weight: 2,315 lb, 1,050 kg.

2-door 100 LS Automatic Limousine

See 2-door 100 LS Limousine, except for:

PRICE IN GB £ 1,342.
PRICE EX WORKS: 12,090 marks.

TRANSMISSION gearbox: automatic, hydraulic torque convertor and planetary gears with 3 ratios + reverse, max ratio of convertor at stall 2.5, possible manual selection; gearbox ratios: I 2.650, II 1.590, III 1, rev 1.800; axle ratio: 3.727.

PERFORMANCE max speeds: 40 mph, 65 km/h in 1st gear; 71 mph, 115 km/h in 2nd gear; 104 mph, 167 km/h in 3rd gear; max gradient in 1st gear: 55%; fuel consumption: 28 m/imp gal, 23.3 m/US gal, 10.1 l x 100 km.

4-door 100 LS Automatic Limousine

See 2-door 100 LS Automatic Limousine, except for:

PRICE IN GB £ 1,370.

PERFORMANCE power-weight ratio: 23.1 lb/hp, 10.5 kg/hp.

DIMENSIONS AND WEIGHT dry weight: 2,315 lb, 1,050 kg.

100 Coupé S

See 2-door 100 Limousine, except for:

PRICE EX WORKS: 14,400 marks.

ENGINE bore and stroke: 3.31 x 3.32 in, 84 x 84.4 mm; engine capacity: 114.2 cu in, 1,871 cu cm; compression ratio: 10.2; max power (DIN): 115 hp at 5,500 rpm; max torque (DIN): 118 lb ft, 16.3 kg m at 4,000 rpm; max engine rpm: 6,000; specific power: 61.5 hp/l; carburation: 2 Solex 32 TDID downdraught twin barrel carburettors.

TRANSMISSION gearbox ratios: I 3.400, II 1.944, III 1.360, IV 0.966, rev 3.100; gear lever: central; axle ratio: 3.700; width of rims: 5''; tyres: 185/70 HR x 14.

PERFORMANCE max speeds: 34 mph, 55 km/h in 1st gear; 60 mph, 96 km/h in 2nd gear; 85 mph, 137 km/h in 3rd gear; 115 mph, 185 km/h in 4th gear; power-weight ratio: 19.2 lb/hp, 8.7 kg/hp; carrying capacity: 772 lb, 350 kg; speed in top at 1,000 rpm: 19.3 mph, 31 km/h.

BRAKES servo.

ELECTRICAL EQUIPMENT headlamps: 4.

DIMENSIONS AND WEIGHT wheel base: 100.79 in, 2,560 mm; front track: 56.69 in, 1,440 mm; rear track: 56.69 in, 1,440 mm; overall length: 173.15 in, 4,398 mm; overall width: 68.90 in, 1,750 mm; overall height: 52.20 in, 1,326 mm (with max load); turning circle (between walls): 33.1 ft, 10.1 m.

BODY coupé; seats: 4; front seats: separate, reclining backrests.

OPTIONAL ACCESSORIES sunshine roof.

AUDI 100 Coupé S

BMW 1600 Cabriolet

BMW 2002 TI

BMW   GERMANY (F.R.)

1600 Limousine

PRICE IN GB: £ 1,184.
PRICE IN USA: $ 2,899.

ENGINE front, 4 stroke; cylinders: 4, slanted at 30°; bore and stroke: 3.31 x 2.80 in, 84 x 71 mm; engine capacity: 96 cu in, 1,573 cu cm; compression ratio: 8.6; max power (DIN): 85 hp at 5,700 rpm; max torque (DIN): 91 lb ft, 12.6 kg m at 3,000 rpm; max engine rpm: 6,200; specific power: 54 hp/l; cylinder block: cast iron; cylinder head: light alloy hemispherical combustion chambers; crankshaft bearings: 5; valves: 2 per cylinder, overhead, Vee-slanted at 52°, rockers; camshafts: 1, overhead; lubrication: gear pump, full flow filter; lubricating system capacity: 7.4 imp pt, 8.9 US pt, 4.2 l; carburation: 1 Solex 38 PDSI downdraught carburettor; fuel feed: mechanical pump; cooling system: water; cooling system capacity: 12.3 imp pt, 14.8 US pt, 7 l.

TRANSMISSION driving wheels: rear; clutch: single dry plate; gearbox: mechanical; gears: 4 + reverse; synchromesh gears: I, II, III, IV; gearbox ratios: I 3.835, II 2.053, III 1.345, IV 1, rev 4.180; gear lever: central; final drive hypoid bevel; axle ratio: 4.110; width of rims: 4.5''; tyres 165 x 13.

PERFORMANCE max speeds: 25 mph, 41 km/h in 1st gear; 48 mph, 77 km/h in 2nd gear; 73 mph, 118 km/h in 3rd gear; 99 mph, 160 km/h in 4th gear; power-weight ratio: 24 lb/hp, 10.9 kg/hp; carrying capacity: 860 lb, 390 kg; max gradient in 1st gear: 65%; acceleration: standing ¼ mile 18.8 sec, 0-50 mph (0-80 km/h) 9 sec; speed in direct drive at 1,000 rpm: 16.5 mph, 26.5 km/h; fuel consumption: 28.5 m/imp gal, 23.8 m/US gal, 9.9 l x 100 km.

CHASSIS integral; front suspension: independent, by Mc Pherson, coil springs/telescopic damper struts, lower wishbones, lower trailing links; rear suspension: independent oblique semi-trailing arms, auxiliary rubber springs, coil springs, telescopic dampers.

STEERING ZF, worm and roller; turns of steering wheel lock to lock: 3.50

BRAKES front disc (diameter 9.45 in, 240 mm), rear drum, dual circuit, rear compensator, servo; lining area: front 16.3 sq in, 105 sq cm, rear 45.6 sq in, 294 sq cm, total 61.9 sq in, 399 sq cm.

ELECTRICAL EQUIPMENT voltage: 12 V; battery: 44 Ah; generator type: alternator, 500 W; ignition distributor: Bosch; headlamps: 2.

DIMENSIONS AND WEIGHT wheel base: 98.43 in, 2,500 mm; front track: 52.36 in, 1,330 mm; rear track: 52.36 in, 1,330 mm; overall length: 166.54 in, 4,230 mm; overall width: 62.60 in, 1,590 mm; overall height: 55.51 in, 1,410 mm; ground clearance: 6.30 in, 160 mm; dry weight: 2,051 lb, 930 kg; distribution of weight: 54.5% front axle, 45.5% rear axle; turning circle (between walls): 34.1 ft, 10.4 m; fuel tank capacity: 10.1 imp gal, 12.1 US gal, 46 l.

BODY saloon/sedan; doors: 2; seats: 5; front seats: separate.

PRACTICAL INSTRUCTIONS fuel: 98-100 oct petrol; engine sump oil: 7.4 imp pt, 8.9 US pt, 4.2 l, SAE 20W-50, change every 3,700 miles, 6,000 km; gearbox oil: 1.8 imp pt, 2.1 US pt, 1 l, SAE 80, change every 14,800 miles, 24,000 km; final drive oil: 1.6 imp pt, 1.9 US pt, 0.9 l, SAE 90, no change recommended; greasing: every 3,700 miles, 6,000 km, 4 points; sparking plug type: 200°; tappet clearances: inlet 0.006 in, 0.15 mm, exhaust 0.008 in, 0.20 mm; valve timing: inlet opens 4° before tdc and closes 52° after bdc, exhaust opens 52° before bdc and closes 4° after tdc; normal tyre pressure: front 26 psi, 1.8 atm, rear 26 psi, 1.8 atm.

OPTIONAL ACCESSORIES 4.100 axle ratio; 5-speed fully synchronized mechanical gearbox (I 3.368, II 2.160, III 1.579, IV 1.241, V 1, rev 4); limited slip final drive; anti-roll bar on front and rear suspensions; reclining backrests; sunshine roof; electrically-heated rear window; rev counter.

1600 Cabriolet

See 1600 Limousine, except for:

PRICE EX WORKS: 13,253 marks.

PERFORMANCE power-weight ratio: 24.9 lb/hp, 11.3 kg/hp; carrying capacity: 706 lb, 320 kg.

DIMENSIONS AND WEIGHT overall height: 53.54 in, 1,360 mm; dry weight: 2,117 lb, 960 kg.

BODY convertible; seats: 4; details: reclining backrests (standard).

OPTIONAL ACCESSORIES sunshine roof and electrically-heated rear window not available.

AUDI 100 Coupé S

BMW 1600 Limousine

BMW 2002 TI

2002

See 1600 Limousine, except for:

PRICE IN GB: £ 1,358.
PRICE IN USA: $ 3,159.

ENGINE bore and stroke: 3.50 x 3.15 in, 89 x 80 mm; engine capacity: 121.4 cu in, 1,990 cu cm; compression ratio: 8.5; max power (DIN): 100 hp at 5,500 rpm; max torque (DIN): 116 lb ft, 16 kg m at 3,000 rpm; specific power: 52.9 hp/l; carburation: 1 Solex 40 PDSI downdraught carburettor.

TRANSMISSION axle ratios: 3.640 or 4.100 or 4.110.

PERFORMANCE max speeds: 27 mph, 44 km/h in 1st gear; 51 mph, 82 km/h in 2nd gear; 78 mph, 125 km/h in 3rd gear; 106 mph, 170 km/h in 4th gear; power-weight ratio: 20.7 lb/hp, 9.4 kg/hp; acceleration: standing ¼ mile 17.6 sec, 0-50 mph (0-80 km/h) 7.3 sec; speed in direct drive at 1,000 rpm: 18.3 mph, 29.5 km/h; fuel consumption: 28.2 m/imp gal, 23.5 m/US gal, 10 l x 100 km.

CHASSIS front and rear suspensions: anti-roll bar (standard).

BRAKES lining area: front 19.5 sq in, 126 sq cm, rear 50.2 sq in, 324 sq cm, total 69.7 sq in, 450 sq cm.

DIMENSIONS AND WEIGHT dry weight: 2,073 lb, 940 kg.

BODY details: reclining backrests (standard).

2002 Automatic

See 2002, except for:

PRICE IN GB: £ 1,495.
PRICE IN USA: $ 3,475.

TRANSMISSION gearbox: ZF automatic, hydraulic torque convertor and planetary gears with 3 ratios + reverse, max ratio of convertor at stall 2.1, possible manual selection; gearbox ratios: I 2.560, II 1.520, III 1, rev 2; selector lever: central.

PERFORMANCE max speeds: 40 mph, 65 km/h in 1st gear; 68 mph, 110 km/h in 2nd gear; 103 mph, 165 km/h in 3rd gear.

2002 TI

See 2002, except for:

PRICE EX WORKS: 11,983 marks.

ENGINE compression ratio: 9.3; max power (DIN): 120 hp at 5,500 rpm; max torque (DIN): 123 lb ft, 17 kg m at 3,600 rpm; specific power: 60.3 hp/l; carburation: 2 Solex 40 PHH horizontal twin barrel carburettors.

TRANSMISSION width of rims: 5''.

PERFORMANCE max speed: 115 mph, 185 km/h; power-weight ratio: 17.2 lb/hp, 7.8 kg/hp; acceleration: standing ¼ mile 16.8 sec, 0-50 mph (0-80 km/h) 6.3 sec; speed in direct drive at 1,000 rpm: 18.3 mph, 29.5 km/h.

BRAKES lining area: front 29.5 sq in, 190 sq cm.

DIMENSIONS AND WEIGHT front track: 53.07 in, 1,348 mm; rear track: 53.07 in, 1,348 mm.

1800

PRICE IN GB: £ 1,375.
PRICE EX WORKS: 11,577 marks.

ENGINE front, 4 stroke; cylinders: 4, slanted at 30°; bore and stroke: 3.50 x 2.80 in, 89 x 71 mm; engine capacity: 107.8 cu in, 1,766 cu cm; compression ratio: 8.6; max power (DIN): 90 hp at 5,250 rpm; max torque (DIN): 106 lb ft, 14.6 kg m at 3,000 rpm; max engine rpm: 6,400; specific power: 51 hp/l; cylinder block: cast iron; cylinder head: light alloy, hemispherical combustion chambers; crankshaft bearings: 5; valves: 2 per cylinder, overhead, slanted at 52°, rockers; camshafts: 1, overhead; lubrication: gear pump, full flow filter; lubricating system capacity: 7.4 imp pt, 8.9 US pt, 4.2 l; carburation: 1 Solex 38 PDSI downdraught carburettor; fuel feed: mechanical pump; cooling system: water; cooling system capacity: 12.3 imp pt, 14.8 US pt, 7 l.

TRANSMISSION driving wheels: rear; clutch: single dry plate; gearbox: mechanical; gears: 4 + reverse; synchromesh gears: I, II, III, IV; gearbox ratios: I 3.835, II 2.053, III 1.345, IV 1, rev 4.180; gear lever: central; final drive: hypoid bevel; axle ratio: 4.100; width of rims: 5''; tyres: 165 x 14.

1800

PERFORMANCE max speeds: 27 mph, 44 km/h in 1st gear; 51 mph, 82 km/h in 2nd gear; 78 mph, 126 km/h in 3rd gear; 99 mph, 160 km/h in 4th gear; power-weight ratio: 26.9 lb/hp, 12.2 kg/hp; carrying capacity: 1,103 lb, 500 kg; acceleration: standing ¼ mile 19.3 sec, 0-50 mph (0-80 km/h) 8.4 sec; speed in direct drive at 1,000 rpm: 17 mph, 27.3 km/h; fuel consumption: 26.9 m/imp gal, 22.4 m/US gal, 10.5 l x 100 km.

CHASSIS integral; front suspension: independent, by McPherson, coil springs/telescopic damper struts, lower wishbones, lower trailing links; rear suspension: independent, oblique semi-trailing arms, auxiliary rubber springs, coil springs, telescopic dampers.

STEERING ZF, worm and roller; turns of steering wheel lock to lock: 3.50.

BRAKES front disc (diameter 10.71 in, 272 mm), rear drum, dual circuit, rear compensator, servo; lining area: front 29.5 sq in, 190 sq cm, rear 50.9 sq in, 328 sq cm, total 80.4 sq in, 518 sq cm.

ELECTRICAL EQUIPMENT voltage: 12 V; battery: 44 Ah; generator type: alternator, 500 W; ignition distributor: Bosch; headlamps: 2.

DIMENSIONS AND WEIGHT wheel base: 100.39 in, 2,550 mm; front track: 52.76 in, 1,340 mm; rear track: 54.17 in, 1,376 mm; overall length: 177.17 in, 4,500 mm; overall width: 67.32 in, 1,710 mm; overall height: 57.09 in, 1,450 mm; ground clearance: 5.51 in, 140 mm; dry weight: 2,426 lb, 1,100 kg; distribution of weight: 53% front axle, 47% rear axle; turning circle (between walls): 34.4 ft, 10.5 m; fuel tank capacity: 12.1 imp gal, 14.5 US gal, 55 l.

BODY saloon/sedan; doors: 4; seats: 5; front seats: separate, reclining backrests.

PRACTICAL INSTRUCTIONS fuel: 98 oct petrol; engine sump oil: 7.4 imp pt, 8.9 US pt, 4.2 l, SAE 10W-30, change every 3,700 miles, 6,000 km; gearbox oil: 1.8 imp pt, 2.1 US pt, 1 l, SAE 80, change every 14,800 miles, 24,000 km; final drive oil: 2.3 imp pt, 2.7 US pt, 1.3 l, SAE 90, no change recommended; greasing: every 3,700 miles, 6,000 km, 2 points; tappet clearances: inlet 0.006 in, 0.15 mm, exhaust 0.008 in, 0.20 mm; valve timing: inlet opens 4° before tdc and closes 52° after bdc, exhaust opens 52° before bdc and closes 4° after tdc; normal tyre pressure: front 26 psi, 1.8 atm, rear 26 psi, 1.8 atm.

OPTIONAL ACCESSORIES 4.110 axle ratio; anti-roll bar on front and rear suspensions; sunshine roof; electrically-heated rear window; rev counter.

1800 Automatic

See 1800, except for:

PRICE IN GB: £ 1,512.
PRICE EX WORKS: 12,798 marks.

TRANSMISSION gearbox: ZF automatic, hydraulic torque convertor and planetary gears with 3 ratios + reverse, max ratio of convertor at stall 2.1, possible manual selection; gearbox ratios: I 2.560, II 1.520, III 1, rev 2; selector lever: central.

PERFORMANCE max speeds: 37 mph, 60 km/h in 1st gear; 68 mph, 110 km/h in 2nd gear; 99 mph, 160 km/h in 3rd gear.

2000 Limousine

See 1800, except for:

PRICE IN GB: £ 1,528.
PRICE EX WORKS: 12,676 marks.

ENGINE bore and stroke: 3.50 x 3.15 in, 89 x 80 mm; engine capacity: 121.4 cu in, 1,990 cu cm; compression ratio: 8.5; max power (DIN): 100 hp at 5,500 rpm; max torque (DIN): 116 lb ft, 16 kg m at 3,000 rpm; specific power: 50.3 hp/l; carburation: 1 Solex 40 PDSI downdraught carburettor.

PERFORMANCE max speed: 104 mph, 168 km/h; power-weight ratio: 24.9 lb/hp, 11.3 kg/hp; carrying capacity: 926 lb, 420 kg; speed in direct drive at 1,000 rpm: 17 mph, 27.4 km/h; fuel consumption: 26.4 m/imp gal, 22 m/US gal, 10.7 l x 100 km.

DIMENSIONS AND WEIGHT rear track: 54.37 in, 1,386 mm; dry weight: 2,492 lb, 1,130 kg.

BMW 1800

BMW 2500 Limousine

BMW 2800 CS Coupé

2000 Automatic Limousine

See 2000 Limousine, except for:

PRICE IN GB: £ 1,665.
PRICE EX WORKS: 13,897 marks.

TRANSMISSION gearbox: ZF automatic, hydraulic torque convertor and planetary gears with 3 ratios + reverse, max ratio of convertor at stall 2.1, possible manual selection; gearbox ratios: I 2.560, II 1.520, III 1, rev 2; selector lever: central.

PERFORMANCE max speeds: 40 mph, 65 km/h in 1st gear; 70 mph, 112 km/h in 2nd gear; 104 mph, 168 km/h in 3rd gear.

2000 TII Limousine

See 2000 Limousine, except for:

PRICE EX WORKS: 14,286 marks.

ENGINE compression ratio: 10; max power (DIN): 230 hp at 5,500 rpm; max torque (DIN): 130 lb ft, 18 kg m at 4,000-4,700 rpm; specific power: 65.3 hp/l; carburation: 4-cylinder injection pump, injectors in inlet pipes (Kugelfischer system); fuel feed: electric pump.

TRANSMISSION axle ratio: 3.900; tyres: 175 x 14.

PERFORMANCE max speed: 115 mph, 185 km/h; power-weight ratio: 19.4 lb/hp, 8.8 kg/hp; acceleration: standing ¼ mile 16.8 sec, 0-50 mph (0-80 km/h) 6.6 sec.

CHASSIS front and rear suspension: anti-roll bar.

DIMENSIONS AND WEIGHT dry weight: 2,514 lb, 1,140 kg

BODY details: electrically-heated rear window.

OPTIONAL ACCESSORIES only sunshine roof.

2500 Limousine

PRICE IN GB: £ 2,294.
PRICE IN USA: $ 5,637.

ENGINE front, 4 stroke; cylinders: 6, in line; bore and stroke: 3.39 x 2.82 in, 86 x 71.6 mm; engine capacity: 152.2 cu in, 2,494 cu cm; compression ratio: 9; max power (DIN): 150 hp at 6,000 rpm; max torque (DIN): 156 lb ft, 21.5 kg m at 3,700 rpm; max engine rpm: 6,200; specific power: 60.1 hp/l; cylinder block: cast iron; cylinder head: light alloy, polispherical combustion chambers; crankshaft bearings: 7; valves: 2 per cylinder, overhead, Vee-slanted, rockers; camshafts: 1, overhead; lubrication: rotary pump, full flow filter; lubricating system capacity: 10 imp pt, 12 US pt, 5.7 l; carburation: 2 Zenith 35/40 INAT downdraught twin barrel carburettors; fuel feed: mechanical pump; cooling system: water; cooling system capacity: 21.1 imp pt, 25.4 US pt, 12 l.

TRANSMISSION driving wheels: rear; clutch: single dry plate, hydraulically controlled; gearbox: mechanical; gears: 4 + reverse; synchromesh gears: I, II, III, IV; gearbox ratios: I 3.850, II 2.080, III 1.375, IV 1, rev 4.130; gear lever: central; final drive: hypoid bevel; axle ratio: 3.640; width of rims: 6''; tyres: 175 x 14.

PERFORMANCE max speeds: 31 mph, 50 km/h in 1st gear; 56 mph, 90 km/h in 2nd gear; 86 mph, 138 km/h in 3rd gear; 118 mph, 190 km/h in 4th gear; power-weight ratio: 19.2 lb/hp, 8.7 kg/hp; carrying capacity: 1,433 lb, 650 kg; max gradient in 1st gear: 60%; acceleration: standing ¼ mile 7.1 sec, 0-50 mph (0-80 km/h) 7.2 sec; speed in direct drive at 1,000 rpm: 19.8 mph, 31.8 km/h; fuel consumption: 25.9 m/imp gal, 21.6 m/US gal, 10.9 l x 100 km.

CHASSIS integral; front suspension: independent, by McPherson, coil springs/telescopic damper struts, auxiliary rubber springs, lower wishbones; rear suspension: independent, semi-trailing arms, auxiliary rubber springs, coil springs, telescopic dampers.

STEERING worm and roller; turns of steering wheel lock to lock: 4.40.

BRAKES disc (diameter 10.71 in, 272 mm), dual circuit, rear compensator, servo; lining area: front 29.5 sq in, 190 sq cm, rear 11.9 sq in, 77 sq cm, total 41.4 sq in, 267 sq cm.

ELECTRICAL EQUIPMENT voltage: 12 V; battery: 55 Ah; generator type: alternator, 630 W; ignition distributor: Bosch; headlamps: 4, iodine.

DIMENSIONS AND WEIGHT wheel base: 105.98 in, 2,692 mm; front track: 56.93 in, 1,446 mm; rear track: 57.64 in, 1,464 mm; overall length: 185.04 in, 4,700 mm; overall width: 68.90 in, 1,750 mm; overall height: 57.09 in, 1,450 mm; ground clearance: 5.51 in, 140 mm; dry weight: 2,867 lb, 1,300 kg;

BMW 1800

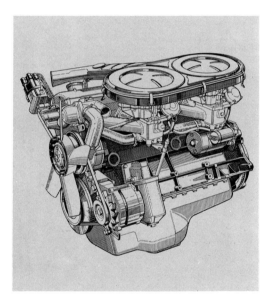
BMW 2500 Limousine

BMW 2800 CS Coupé

distribution of weight: 54% front axle, 46% rear axle; turning circle (between walls): 34.4 ft, 10.5 m; fuel tank capacity: 16.5 imp gal, 19.8 US gal, 75 l.

BODY saloon/sedan; doors: 4; seats: 5; front seats: separate, reclining backrests.

PRACTICAL INSTRUCTIONS fuel: 98 oct petrol; engine sump oil: 10 imp pt, 12 US pt, 5.7 l, SAE 20W-50; gearbox oil: 2.1 imp pt, 2.5 US pt, 1.2 l, SAE 80, change every 14,800 miles, 24,000 km; final drive oil: 2.6 imp pt, 3.2 US pt, 1.5 l, SAE 90, no change recommended; greasing: none; sparking plug type: 175°; tappet clearances: inlet 0.010 in, 0.25 mm, exhaust 0.012 in, 0.30 mm; valve timing: inlet opens 6° before tdc and closes 50° after bdc, exhaust opens 50° before bdc and closes 6° after tdc; normal tyre pressure: front 28 psi, 2 atm, rear 27 psi, 1.9 atm.

OPTIONAL ACCESSORIES limited slip final drive; DR 70 x 14 tyres; Nivomat (Boge system) units and anti-roll bar on rear suspension; sunshine roof; power-assisted steering; air-conditioning system; electrically-controlled windows; electrically-heated rear window.

2500 Automatic Limousine

See 2500 Limousine, except for:

PRICE IN GB: £ 2,446.
PRICE IN USA: $ 6,002.

TRANSMISSION gearbox: ZF automatic, hydraulic torque convertor and planetary gears with 3 ratios + reverse, max ratio of convertor at stall 2, possible manual selection; gearbox ratios: I 2.500, II 1.500, III 1, rev 2; selector lever: central.

PERFORMANCE max speeds: 50 mph, 80 km/h in 1st gear; 81 mph, 130 km/h in 2nd gear; 114 mph, 184 km/h in 3rd gear.

2800 Limousine

See 2500 Limousine, except for:

PRICE IN GB: £ 2,639.
PRICE IN USA: $ 6,663.

ENGINE bore and stroke: 3.39 x 3.15 in, 86 x 80 mm; engine capacity: 170.1 cu in, 2,788 cu cm; max power (DIN): 170 hp at 6,000 rpm; max torque (DIN): 174 lb ft, 24 kg m at 3,700 rpm; specific power: 61 hp/l.

TRANSMISSION final drive: limited slip (standard); axle ratio: 3.450; tyres: DR 70 x 14.

PERFORMANCE max speeds: 33 mph, 53 km/h in 1st gear; 59 mph, 95 km/h in 2nd gear; 91 mph, 146 km/h in 3rd gear; 124 mph, 200 km/h in 4th gear; power-weight ratio: 17.4 lb/hp, 7.9 kg/hp; acceleration: standing ¼ mile 16.6 sec; speed in direct drive at 1,000 rpm: 20.8 mph, 33.4 km/h.

CHASSIS rear suspension: Nivomat (Boge system) units, anti-roll bar (standard).

DIMENSIONS AND WEIGHT dry weight: 2,955 lb, 1,340 kg.

BODY details: electrically-heated rear window (standard).

2800 Automatic Limousine

See 2800 Limousine, except for:

PRICE IN GB: £ 2,791.
PRICE IN USA: $ 7,027.

TRANSMISSION gearbox: ZF automatic, hydraulic torque convertor and planetary gears with 3 ratios + reverse, max ratio of convertor at stall 2, possible manual selection; gearbox ratios: I 2.500, II 1.500, III 1, rev 2; selector lever: central.

PERFORMANCE max speeds: 52 mph, 83 km/h in 1st gear; 86 mph, 138 km/h in 2nd gear; 120 mph, 193 km/h in 3rd gear.

2800 CS Coupé

See 2800 Limousine, except for:

PRICE IN GB: £ 3,558.
PRICE IN USA: $ 7,973.

PERFORMANCE max speed: 127 mph, 205 km/h; power-weight ratio: 14.6 lb/hp, 6.6 kg/hp; carrying capacity: 805 lb,

2800 CS COUPÉ

365 kg; max gradient in 1st gear: 60%; acceleration: standing ¼ mile 16.3 sec, 0-50 mph (0-80 km/h) 6.4 sec; speed in direct drive at 1,000 rpm: 19.8 mph, 31.8 km/h; fuel consumption: 26.9 m/imp gal, 22.4 m/US gal, 10.5 l x 100 km.

CHASSIS anti-roll bar on front and rear suspensions.

STEERING servo.

BRAKES front disc, rear drum; lining area: front 29.5 sq in, 190 sq cm, rear 50.9 sq in, 328 sq cm, total 80.4 sq in, 518 sq cm.

DIMENSIONS AND WEIGHT wheel base: 103.35 in, 2,625 mm; rear track: 55.28 in, 1,404 mm; overall length: 183.46 in, 4,660 mm; overall width: 65.75 in, 1,670 mm; overall height: 53.94 in, 1,370 mm; dry weight: 2,811 lb, 1,275 kg; distribution of weight: 55% front axle, 45% rear axle.

BODY coupé; doors: 2; seats: 4.

2800 CS Automatic Coupé

See 2800 CS Coupé, except for:

PRICE IN GB: £ 3,710.
PRICE IN USA: $ 8,337.

TRANSMISSION gearbox: ZF automatic, hydraulic torque convertor and planetary gears with 3 ratios + reverse, max ratio of convertor at stall 2, possible manual selection; gearbox ratios: I 2.500, II 1.500, III 1, rev 2; selector lever: central.

PERFORMANCE max speed 123 mph, 198 km/h.

FORD
GERMANY (F.R.)

Escort Series, see FORD GREAT BRITAIN.

2-door Taunus Limousine

PRICE EX WORKS: 7,093 marks.

ENGINE front, 4 stroke; cylinders: 4, in line; bore and stroke: 3.11 x 2.60 in, 79 x 66 mm; engine capacity: 78.9 cu in, 1,293 cu cm; compression ratio: 8.2; max power (SAE): 63 hp at 5,700 rpm; max torque (SAE): 73 lb ft, 10.1 kg m at 3,000 rpm; max engine rpm: 6,000; specific power: 48.7 hp/l; cylinder block: cast iron; cylinder head: cast iron; crankshaft bearings: 5; valves: 2 per cylinder, overhead, rockers; camshafts: 1, overhead; lubrication: gear pump, full flow filter; lubricating system capacity: 6.2 imp pt, 7.4 US pt, 3.5 l; carburation: 1 Ford 71 HW/9510/AA downdraught carburettor; fuel feed: mechanical pump; cooling system: water; cooling system capacity: 11.4 imp pt, 13.7 US pt, 6.5 l.

TRANSMISSION driving wheels: rear; clutch: single dry plate; gearbox: mechanical; gears: 4 + reverse; gearbox ratios: I 3.660, II 2.180, III 1.430, IV 1, rev 4.240; gear lever: central; final drive: hypoid bevel; axle ratio: 4.110; width of rims: 4.5''; tyres: 5.60 x 13.

PERFORMANCE max speeds: 23 mph, 37 km/h in 1st gear; 39 mph, 62 km/h in 2nd gear; 58 mph, 94 km/h in 3rd gear; 84 mph, 135 km/h in 4th gear; power-weight ratio: 33.3 lb/hp, 15.1 kg/hp; carrying capacity: 882 lb, 400 kg; speed in direct drive at 1,000 rpm: 14 mph, 22.5 km/h; fuel consumption: 30.7 m/imp gal, 25.6 m/US gal, 9.2 l x 100 km.

CHASSIS integral, front subframe; front suspension: independent, wishbones, lower trailing links, coil springs/telescopic dampers; rear suspension: rigid axle, lower trailing arms, upper oblique trailing arms, coil springs, telescopic dampers.

STEERING rack-and-pinion.

BRAKES front disc, rear drum, dual circuit; lining area: front 23.4 sq in, 151 sq cm, rear 46 sq in, 297 sq cm, total 69.4 sq in, 448 sq cm.

ELECTRICAL EQUIPMENT voltage: 12 V; battery: 44 Ah; generator type: alternator, 28 A; ignition distributor: Bosch; headlamps: 2.

DIMENSIONS AND WEIGHT wheel base: 101.50 in, 2,578 mm; front track: 55.98 in, 1,422 mm; rear track: 55.98 in, 1,422 mm; overall length: 167.99 in, 4,267 mm; overall width: 66.97 in, 1,701 mm; overall height: 53.94 in, 1,370 mm; ground clearance: 3.94 in, 100 mm; dry weight: 2,095

FORD Taunus XL Limousine

FORD 5-door Taunus L Turnier

FORD Taunus GT Limousine

lb, 950 kg; turning circle (between walls): 31.5 ft, 9.6 m; fuel tank capacity: 11.9 imp gal, 14.3 US gal, 54 l.

BODY saloon/sedan; doors: 2; seats: 5; front seats: separate, reclining backrests.

PRACTICAL INSTRUCTIONS fuel: 97 oct petrol; engine sump oil: 6.2 imp pt, 7.4 US pt, 3.5 l, SAE 10W-40, change every 6,200 miles, 10,000 km; gearbox oil: 1.4 imp pt, 1.7 US pt, 0.8 l, SAE 80 EP, change every 12,400 miles, 20,000 km; final drive oil: 1.8 imp pt, 2.1 US pt, 1 l, SAE 90, change every 12,400 miles, 20,000 km; greasing: every 34,100 miles, 55,000 km, 2 points; normal tyre pressure: front 24 psi, 1.7 atm, rear 24 psi, 1.7 atm.

VARIATIONS

ENGINE (export) 9.2 compression ratio, max power (SAE) 67 hp at 5,700 rpm, max torque (SAE) 79 lb ft, 10.9 kg m at 3,000 rpm, 51.8 hp/l specific power, lubricating system capacity 7 imp pt, 8.5 US pt, 4 l, 1 Ford 71 HHW/9510/BA carburettor.
PERFORMANCE max speed 86 mph, 138 km/h, power-weight ratio 31.3 lb/hp, 14.2 kg/hp, fuel consumption 31.4 m/imp gal, 26.1 m/US gal, 9 l x 100 km.

ENGINE bore and stroke 3.45 x 2.60 in, 87.6 x 66 mm, engine capacity 97.1 cm in, 1,592 cu cm, 9.2 compression ratio, max power (SAE) 82 hp at 5,700 rpm, max torque (SAE) 96 lb ft, 13.2 kg m at 2,700 rpm, 51.5 hp/l specific power, 1 Ford 71 HW/9510/YA carburettor.
TRANSMISSION gearbox ratios I 3.650, II 1.970, III 1.370, IV 1, rev 3.660, 3.890 axle ratio (4.110 for Turnier), 6.45 x 13 tyres.
PERFORMANCE max speed 93 mph, 150 km/h, power-weight ratio 26 lb/hp, 11.8 kg/hp, fuel consumption 26.9 m/imp gal, 20.5 m/US gal, 10.5 l x 100 km.
BRAKES servo.
DIMENSIONS AND WEIGHT dry weight 2,128 lb, 965 kg.

OPTIONAL ACCESSORIES Borg-Warner 35 automatic gearbox with 55 Ah battery (only with 97.1 cu in, 1,592 cu cm engine), hydraulic torque convertor and planetary gears with 3 ratios (I 2.393, II 1.450, III 1, rev 2.094), max ratio of convertor at stall 1.91, possible manual selection; 4.440 axle ratio; 165 x 13 tyres; 175 x 13 tyres, 5.5'' wire rims; heavy-duty suspension; servo brake; sunshine roof; electrically-heated rear window.

4-door Taunus Limousine

See 2-door Taunus Limousine, except for:

PRICE EX WORKS: 7,393 marks.

PERFORMANCE power-weight ratio: 34.2 lb/hp, 15.5 kg/hp.

DIMENSIONS AND WEIGHT dry weight: 2,150 lb, 975 kg.

5-door Taunus Turnier

See 2-door Taunus Limousine, except for:

PRICE EX WORKS: 7,848 marks.

TRANSMISSION axle ratio: 4.440; tyres: 6.45 x 13.

PERFORMANCE power-weight ratio: 36.4 lb/hp, 16.5 kg/hp.

DIMENSIONS AND WEIGHT overall length: 172.01 in, 4,369 mm; overall height: 54.84 in, 1,393 mm; dry weight: 2,293 lb, 1,040 kg.

BODY estate car/station wagon; doors: 4 + 1.

2-door Taunus L Limousine

See 2-door Taunus Limousine, except for:

PRICE EX WORKS: 7,304 marks.

4-door Taunus L Limousine

See 4-door Taunus Limousine, except for:

PRICE EX WORKS: 7,592 marks.

Taunus L Coupé

See 4-door Taunus Limousine, except for:

PRICE EX WORKS: 7,703 marks.

PERFORMANCE power-weight ratio: 33.7 lb/hp, 15.3 kg/hp.

FORD 4-door Taunus XL Limousine

FORD 5-door Taunus L Turnier

FORD 2-door Taunus GT Limousine

DIMENSIONS AND WEIGHT overall width: 67.24 in, 1,708 mm; overall height: 52.80 in, 1,341 mm; dry weight: 2,128 lb, 965 kg.

BODY coupé.

5-door Taunus L Turnier

See 5-door Taunus Turnier, except for:

PRICE EX WORKS: 8,059 marks.

2-door Taunus XL Limousine

See 2-door Taunus Limousine, except for:

PRICE EX WORKS: 8,103 marks.

4-door Taunus XL Limousine

See 4-door Taunus Limousine, except for:

PRICE EX WORKS: 8,403 marks.

Taunus XL Coupé

See Taunus L Coupé, except for:

PRICE EX WORKS: 8,380 marks.

5-door Taunus XL Turnier

See 5-door Taunus Turnier, except for:

PRICE EX WORKS: 8,858 marks.

2-door Taunus GT Limousine

See 2-door Taunus Limousine, except for:

PRICE EX WORKS: 8,824 marks.

ENGINE bore and stroke: 3.45 x 2.60 in, 87.6 x 66 mm; engine capacity: 97.1 cu in, 1,592 cu cm; compression ratio: 9.2; max power (SAE): 100 hp at 6,000 rpm; max torque (SAE): 101 lb ft, 14 kg m at 4,000 rpm; max engine rpm: 6,200; specific power: 62.8 hp/l; lubricating system capacity: 7 imp pt, 8.5 US pt, 4 l; carburation: 1 Weber carburettor.

TRANSMISSION gearbox ratios: I 3.650, II 1.970, III 1.370, IV 1, rev 3.660; axle ratio: 3.890; width of rims: 5.5''; tyres: 175 x 13.

PERFORMANCE max speeds: 27 mph, 44 km/h in 1st gear; 51 mph, 82 km/h in 2nd gear; 73 mph, 118 km/h in 3rd gear; 101 mph, 162 km/h in 4th gear; power-weight ratio: 21.8 lb/hp, 9.9 kg/hp; speed in direct drive at 1,000 rpm: 16.8 mph, 27 km/h; fuel consumption: 27.4 m/imp gal, 22.8 m/US gal, 10.3 l x 100 km.

CHASSIS front suspension: anti-roll bar.

BRAKES servo (standard); lining area: rear 60.5 sq in, 390 sq cm.

ELECTRICAL EQUIPMENT generator type: alternator, 35 A.

DIMENSIONS AND WEIGHT dry weight: 2,194 lb, 995 kg.

VARIATIONS

ENGINE bore and stroke 3.31 x 2.37 in, 84 x 60.1 mm, engine capacity 121.9 cu in, 1,997 cu cm, max power (SAE) 103 hp at 5,300 rpm, max torque (SAE) 122 lb ft, 16.9 kg m at 3,000 rph, 51.6 hp/l specific power, 1 Solex twin barrel carburettor, cooling system capacity 13.7 imp pt, 16.5 US pt, 7.8 l.
TRANSMISSION 3.440 axle ratio.
PERFORMANCE max speed 102 mph, 163 km/h, power-weight ratio 22.5 lb/hp, 10.2 kg/hp, fuel consumption 26.2 m/imp gal, 21.8 m/US gal, 10.8 l x 100 km.
DIMENSIONS AND WEIGHT dry weight 2,326 lb, 1,055 kg.

OPTIONAL ACCESSORIES only Borg-Warner 35 automatic gearbox with 4.110 axle ratio, 3.700 axle ratio and 185/70 HR x 13 tyres with 5.5'' wide rims.

4-door Taunus GT Limousine

See 2-door Taunus GT Limousine, except for:

PRICE EX WORKS: 9,124 marks.

PERFORMANCE power-weight ratio: 22.5 lb/hp, 10.2 kg/hp.

DIMENSIONS AND WEIGHT dry weight: 2,249 lb, 1,020 kg.

Taunus GT Coupé

See 2-door Taunus GT Limousine, except for:

PRICE EX WORKS: 9,180 marks.

PERFORMANCE power-weight ratio: 22.3 lb/hp, 10.1 kg/hp.

DIMENSIONS AND WEIGHT overall width: 67.24 in, 1,708 mm; overall height: 52.80 in, 1,341 mm; dry weight: 2,227 lb, 1,010 kg.

BODY coupé.

2-door Taunus GXL Limousine

See 2-door Taunus GT Limousine, except for:

PRICE EX WORKS: 9,490 marks.

BODY details: electrically-heated rear window.

4-door Taunus GXL Limousine

See 4-door Taunus GT Limousine, except for:

PRICE EX WORKS: 9,790 marks.

BODY details: electrically-heated rear window.

Taunus GXL Coupé

See Taunus GT Coupé, except for:

PRICE EX WORKS: 9,846 marks.

BODY details: electrically-heated rear window.

2-door 17M Limousine

PRICE IN GB: £ 964.
PRICE EX WORKS: 8,658 marks.

ENGINE front, 4 stroke; cylinders: 4, Vee-slanted at 60°; bore and stroke: 3.54 x 2.32 in, 90 x 58.9 mm; engine capacity: 91.4 cu in, 1,498 cu cm; compression ratio: 8; max power (SAE): 75 hp at 5,000 rpm; max torque (SAE): 93 lb ft, 12.8 kg m at 3,000 rpm; max engine rpm: 5,000; specific power: 50.1 hp/l; cylinder block: cast iron; cylinder head: cast iron; crankshaft bearings: 3; valves: 2 per cylinder, overhead, push-rods and rockers; camshafts: 1, at centre of Vee; lubrication: rotary pump, full flow filter; lubricating system capacity: 6.2 imp pt, 7.4 US pt, 3.5 l; carburation: 1 FoMoCo C7JH-A downdraught carburettor; fuel feed: mechanical pump; cooling system: water, thermostatic fan; cooling system capacity: 11.3 imp pt, 13.5 US pt, 6.4 l.

TRANSMISSION driving wheels: rear; clutch: single dry plate; gearbox: mechanical; gears: 4 + reverse; synchromesh gears: I, II, III, IV; gearbox ratios: I 3.650, II 1.970, III 1.370, IV 1, rev 3.660; gear lever: steering column; final drive: hypoid bevel; axle ratio: 4.110; width of rims: 5''; tyres: 6.40 x 13.

PERFORMANCE max speeds: 24 mph, 38 km/h in 1st gear; 43 mph, 70 km/h in 2nd gear; 63 mph, 101 km/h in 3rd gear; 84 mph, 135 km/h in 4th gear; power-weight ratio: 30.9 lb/hp, 14 kg/hp; carrying capacity: 1,025 lb, 465 kg; speed in direct drive at 1,000 rpm: 17.3 mph, 27.8 km/h; fuel consumption: 29.7 m/imp gal, 24.8 m/US gal, 9.5 l x 100 km.

CHASSIS integral; front suspension: independent, by McPherson, coil springs/telescopic damper struts, lower wishbones, anti-roll bar; rear suspension: rigid axle, semi-elliptic leafsprings, telescopic dampers.

STEERING recirculating ball.

BRAKES front disc (diameter 9.45 in, 240 mm), rear drum, dual circuit, servo; lining area: front 16.3 sq in, 105 sq cm, rear 58.3 sq in, 376 sq cm, total 74.6 sq in, 481 sq cm.

FORD Taunus GT Coupé

FORD 4-door Taunus GXL Limousine

FORD 2-door 17M Limousine

ELECTRICAL EQUIPMENT voltage: 12 V; battery: 44 Ah; generator type: dynamo, 25 A; ignition distributor: Bosch; headlamps: 2.

DIMENSIONS AND WEIGHT wheel base: 106.50 in, 2,705 mm; front track: 56.97 in, 1,447 mm; rear track: 55.67 in, 1,414 mm; overall length: 185.87 in, 4,721 mm; overall width: 69.13 in, 1,756 mm; overall height: 58.19 in, 1,478 mm; ground clearance: 7.09 in, 180 mm; dry weight: 2,315 lb, 1,050 kg; turning circle (between walls): 35.4 ft, 10.8 m; fuel tank capacity: 12.1 imp gal, 14.5 US gal, 55 l.

BODY saloon/sedan; doors: 2; seats: 5; front seats: separate.

PRACTICAL INSTRUCTIONS fuel: 85-90 oct petrol; engine sump oil: 5.3 imp pt, 6.3 US pt, 3 l, SAE 20W-40, change every 6,200 miles, 10,000 km; gearbox oil: 2.3 imp pt, 2.7 US pt, 1.3 l, SAE 80, change every 12,400 miles, 20,000 km; final drive oil: 1.8 imp pt, 2.1 US pt, 1 l, SAE 90, change every 12,400 miles, 20,000 km; greasing: none; normal tyre pressure: front 20 psi, 1.4 atm, rear 23 psi, 1.6 atm.

VARIATIONS

ENGINE bore and stroke 3.54 x 2.63 in, 90 x 66.8 mm, engine capacity 103.7 cu in, 1,699 cu cm, max power (SAE) 83 hp at 5,000 rpm, max torque (SAE) 107 lb ft, 14.8 kg m at 2,400 rpm, 48.9 hp/l specific power.
TRANSMISSION 3.890 axle ratio (4.110 for Turnier).
PERFORMANCE max speeds (I) 25 mph, 40 km/h, (II) 47 mph, 75 km/h, (III) 66 mph, 107 km/h, (IV) 87 mph, 140 km/h, power-weight ratio 27.8 lb/hp, 12.6 kg/hp, speed in direct drive at 1,000 rpm 18.3 mph, 29.4 km/h, fuel consumption 31 m/imp gal, 25.8 m/US gal, 9.1 l x 100 km.

ENGINE bore and stroke 3.54 x 2.63 in, 90 x 66.8 mm, engine capacity 103.7 cu in, 1,699 cu cm, 9 compression ratio, max power (SAE) 90 hp at 5,200 rpm, max torque (SAE) 108 lb ft, 14.9 kg m at 2,500 rpm, 53 hp/l specific power, 1 Solex 32 TDID carburettor.
TRANSMISSION 3.890 axle ratio.
PERFORMANCE max speeds (I) 25 mph, 40 km/h, (II) 47 mph, 75 km/h, (III) 66 mph, 107 km/h, (IV) 93 mph, 150 km/h, power-weight ratio 25.8 lb/hp, 11.7 kg/hp, speed in direct drive at 1,000 rpm 18.3 mph, 29.4 km/h, fuel consumption 32.5 m/imp gal, 27 m/US gal, 8.7 l x 100 km.

ENGINE 6 Vee-slanted at 60° cylinders, bore and stroke 3.15 x 2.37 in, 80 x 60.1 mm, engine capacity 110.6 cu in, 1,812 cu cm, 9 compression ratio, max power (SAE) 98 hp at 5,500 rpm, max torque (SAE) 110 lb ft, 15.2 kg m at 3,000 rpm, 54.1 hp/l specific power, 4 crankshaft bearings, 1 Solex 32 DDIST twin barrel carburettor.
TRANSMISSION 3.890 axle ratio.
PERFORMANCE max speeds (I) 25 mph, 40 km/h, (II) 47 mph, 75 km/h, (III) 66 mph, 107 km/h, (IV) 95 mph, 153 km/h, power-weight ratio 24.7 lb/hp, 11.2 kg/hp, speed in direct drive at 1,000 rpm 18.3 mph, 29.4 km/h.
ELECTRICAL EQUIPMENT 25 A alternator (standard).
DIMENSIONS AND WEIGHT dry weight 2,414 lb, 1,095 kg.

ENGINE 6 Vee-slanted at 60° cylinders, bore and stroke 3.31 x 2.37 in, 84 x 60.1 mm, engine capacity 121.9 cu in, 1,998 cu cm, max power (SAE) 106 hp at 5,300 rpm, max torque (SAE) 121 lb ft, 16.7 kg m at 3,000 rpm, max engine rpm 5,300, 53 hp/l specific power, 4 crankshaft bearings, 1 Solex 32 DDIST twin barrel carburettor.
TRANSMISSION 3.700 axle ratio.
PERFORMANCE max speeds (I) 30 mph, 48 km/h, (II) 52 mph, 83 km/h, (III) 75 mph, 120 km/h, (IV) 96 mph, 155 km/h, power-weight ratio 22.7 lb/hp, 10.3 kg/hp, speed in direct drive at 1,000 rpm 19.3 mph, 31 km/h, fuel consumption 28 m/imp gal, 23.3 m/US gal, 10.1 l x 100 km.
ELECTRICAL EQUIPMENT 25 A alternator (standard).
DIMENSIONS AND WEIGHT dry weight 2,414 lb, 1,095 kg.

ENGINE 6 Vee-slanted at 60° cylinders, bore and stroke 3.31 x 2.37 in, 84 x 60.1 mm, engine capacity 121.9 cu in, 1,998 cu cm, 9 compression ratio, max power (SAE) 113 hp at 5,300 rpm, max torque (SAE) 125 lb ft, 17.3 kg m at 3,000 rpm, max engine rpm 5,300, 56.6 hp/l specific power, 4 crankshaft bearings, 1 Solex 32 DDIST twin barrel carburettor.
TRANSMISSION 3.700 axle ratio.
PERFORMANCE max speeds (I) 30 mph, 48 km/h, (II) 52 mph, 83 km/h, (III) 75 mph, 120 km/h, (IV) 99 mph, 160 km/h, power-weight ratio 21.4 lb/hp, 9.7 kg/hp, speed in direct drive at 1,000 rpm 19.3 mph, 31 km/h, fuel consumption 30.7 m/imp gal, 25.6 m/US gal, 9.2 l x 100 km.
ELECTRICAL EQUIPMENT 55 Ah battery, 35 A alternator (standard).
DIMENSIONS AND WEIGHT dry weight 2,414 lb, 1,095 kg.

ENGINE 6 Vee-slanted at 60° cylinders, bore and stroke 3.54 x 2.37 in, 90 x 60.1 mm, engine capacity 139.8 cu in, 2,293 cu cm, 9 compression ratio, max power (SAE) 126 hp at 5,600 rpm, max torque (SAE) 138 lb ft, 19.1 kg m at 3,500 rpm, max engine rpm 5,600, 46.2 hp/l specific power, 4 crankshaft bearings, 1 Solex 35 DDIST twin barrel carburettor.
TRANSMISSION 3.440 axle ratio.

FORD Taunus GT Coupé

FORD Taunus GXL Limousine

FORD 17M Limousine

PERFORMANCE max speeds (I) 32 mph, 51 km/h, (II) 58 mph, 94 km/h, (III) 85 mph, 136 km/h, (IV) 106 mph, 170 km/h, power-weight ratio 19.2 lb/hp, 8.7 kg/hp, speed in direct drive at 1,000 rpm 20.6 mph, 33.2 km/h, fuel consumption 28.5 m/imp gal, 23.8 m/US gal, 9.9 l x 100 km.
ELECTRICAL EQUIPMENT 55 Ah battery, 35 A alternator (standard).
DIMENSIONS AND WEIGHT dry weight 2,414 lb, 1,095 kg.

OPTIONAL ACCESSORIES central gear lever; 3-speed mechanical gearbox (I 3.290, II 1.610, III 1, rev 3.100); automatic gearbox with 55 Ah battery (except for models with 91.4 cu in, 1,498 cu cm and 103.7 cu in, 1,699 cu cm (83 hp) engines and RS models), hydraulic torque convertor and planetary gears with 3 ratios (I 2.460, II 1.460, III 1, rev 2.200), max ratio of convertor at stall 2.1, possible manual selection, 3.440 axle ratio (3.700 with 1.8-litre engine), 3.700 for Turnier (3.890 with 110.6 cu in, 1,812 cu cm engine); 175 x 14 tyres; power-assisted steering (only with V6 engines); alternator (only with V4 engines); bench front seats; sunshine roof; electrically-heated rear window (only with alternator).

4-door 17M Limousine

See 2-door 17M Limousine, except for:

PRICE EX WORKS: 9,013 marks.

PERFORMANCE power-weight ratio: 31.5 lb/hp, 14.3 kg/hp.

DIMENSIONS AND WEIGHT dry weight: 2,370 lb, 1,075 kg.

17M Hardtop

See 2-door 17M Limousine, except for:

PRICE EX WORKS: 9,413 marks.

ENGINE bore and stroke: 3.54 x 2.63 in, 90 x 66.8 mm; engine capacity: 103.7 cu in, 1,699 cu cm; compression ratio: 9; max power (SAE): 90 hp at 5,200 rpm; max torque (SAE): 108 lb ft, 14.9 kg m at 2,500 rpm; specific power: 53 hp/l; carburation: 1 Solex 32 TDID carburettor.

TRANSMISSION gear lever: central (standard); axle ratio: 3.890.

PERFORMANCE max speed: 93 mph, 150 km/h; power-weight ratio: 26.7 lb/hp, 12.1 kg/hp; fuel consumption: 32.5 m/imp gal, 27 m/US gal, 8.7 l x 100 km.

DIMENSIONS AND WEIGHT overall height: 57.64 in, 1,464 mm; dry weight: 2,392 lb, 1,085 kg.

BODY hardtop.

3-door 17M Turnier

See 2-door 17M Limousine, except for:

PRICE EX WORKS: 9,046 marks.

TRANSMISSION width of rims: 4.5''.

PERFORMANCE power-weight ratio: 32.4 lb/hp, 14.7 kg/hp.

DIMENSIONS AND WEIGHT front track: 56.57 in, 1,437 mm; rear track: 55.28 in, 1,404 mm; overall length: 183.98 in, 4,673 mm; overall height: 57.99 in, 1,473 mm; dry weight: 2,437 lb, 1,105 kg; fuel tank capacity: 9.9 imp gal, 11.9 US gal, 45 l.

BODY estate car/station wagon; doors: 2 + 1.

5-door 17M Turnier

See 3-door 17M Turnier, except for:

PRICE EX WORKS: 9,402 marks.

PERFORMANCE power-weight ratio: 33.3 lb/hp, 15.1 kg/hp.

DIMENSIONS AND WEIGHT dry weight: 2,492 lb, 1,130 kg.

2-door 17M RS Limousine

See 2-door 17M Limousine, except for:

PRICE EX WORKS: 10,329 marks.

ENGINE cylinders: 6, Vee-slanted at 60°; bore and stroke: 3.31 x 2.37 in, 84 x 60.1 mm; engine capacity: 121.9 cu in, 1,998 cu cm; compression ratio: 9; max power (SAE): 113

2-DOOR 17M RS LIMOUSINE

hp at 5,300 rpm; max torque (SAE): 125 lb ft, 17.3 kg m at 3,000 rpm; max engine rpm: 5,500; specific power: 56.6 hp/l; crankshaft bearings: 4; lubricating system capacity: 7.9 imp pt, 9.5 US pt, 4.5 l; carburation: 1 Solex 32 DDIST down-draught twin barrel carburettor; cooling system capacity: 13.7 imp pt, 16.5 US pt, 7.8 l.

TRANSMISSION gear lever: central; axle ratio: 3.700; tyres: 175 x 14.

PERFORMANCE max speeds: 30 mph, 48 km/h in 1st gear; 52 mph, 83 km/h in 2nd gear; 75 mph, 120 km/h in 3rd gear; 99 mph, 160 km/h in 4th gear; power-weight ratio: 20.5 lb/hp, 9.3 kg/hp; fuel consumption: 30.7 m/imp gal, 25.6 m/US gal, 9.2 l x 100 km.

BRAKES lining area: front 16.3 sq in, 105 sq cm, rear 50.5 sq in, 326 sq cm, total 66.8 sq in, 431 sq cm.

ELECTRICAL EQUIPMENT battery: 55 Ah; generator type: alternator, 35 A; headlamps: 4, 2 halogen.

DIMENSIONS AND WEIGHT front track: 57.13 in, 1,451 mm; rear track: 55.83 in, 1,418 mm.

BODY details: electrically-heated rear window (standard), 5'' wheels.

PRACTICAL INSTRUCTIONS fuel: 98-100 oct petrol; engine sump oil: 7 imp pt, 8.5 US pt, 4 l.

VARIATIONS

Only 139.8 cu in, 2,293 cu cm engine.

OPTIONAL ACCESSORIES only power-assisted steering and sunshine roof.

4-door 17M RS Limousine

See 2-door 17M RS Limousine, except for:

PRICE EX WORKS: 10,684 marks.

PERFORMANCE power-weight ratio: 20.9 lb/hp, 9.5 kg/hp.

DIMENSIONS AND WEIGHT dry weight: 2,370 lb, 1,075 kg.

17M RS Hardtop

See 2-door 17M RS Limousine, except for:

PRICE EX WORKS: 10,562 marks.

PERFORMANCE power-weight ratio: 21.2 lb/hp, 9.6 kg/hp.

DIMENSIONS AND WEIGHT overall height: 57.64 in, 1,464 mm; dry weight: 2,392 lb, 1,085 kg.

BODY hardtop.

Capri 1300

PRICE EX WORKS: 7,781 marks.

ENGINE front, 4 stroke; cylinders: 4, Vee-slanted at 60°; bore and stroke: 3.31 x 2.32 in, 84 x 58.9 mm; engine capacity: 79.6 cu in, 1,305 cu cm; compression ratio: 8.2; max power (SAE): 63 hp at 5,000 rpm; max torque (SAE): 78 lb ft, 10.8 kg m at 3,000 rpm; max engine rpm: 5,000; specific power: 48.3 hp/l; cylinder block: cast iron; cylinder head: cast iron; crankshaft bearings: 3; valves: 2 per cylinder, overhead, push-rods and rockers; camshafts: 1, at centre of Vee; lubrication: rotary pump, full flow filter; lubricating system capacity: 6.2 imp pt, 7.4 US pt, 3.5 l; carburation: 1 FoMoCo C8GH-A downdraught carburettor; fuel feed: mechanical pump; cooling system: water, thermostatic fan; cooling system capacity: 12 imp pt, 14.4 US pt, 6.8 l.

TRANSMISSION driving wheels: rear; clutch: single dry plate; gearbox: mechanical; gears: 4 + reverse; synchromesh gears: I, II, III, IV; gearbox ratios: I 3.424, II 1.968, III 1.368, IV 1, rev 3.780; gear lever: central; final drive: hypoid bevel; axle ratio: 4.110; width of rims: 4.5''; tyres: 6.00 x 13.

PERFORMANCE max speeds: 24 mph, 38 km/h in 1st gear; 42 mph, 67 km/h in 2nd gear; 60 mph, 96 km/h in 3rd gear; 83 mph, 133 km/h in 4th gear; power-weight ratio: 34.2 lb/hp, 15.5 kg/hp; carrying capacity: 706 lb, 320 kg; speed in direct drive at 1,000 rpm: 16.5 mph, 26.5 km/h; fuel consumption: 32.8 m/imp gal, 27.3 m/US gal, 8.6 l x 100 km.

FORD Capri 1300

FORD Capri XL

FORD Capri GT 2300

CHASSIS integral; front suspension: independent, by Mc Pherson, coil springs/telescopic damper struts, lower transverse arms, anti-roll bar; rear suspension: rigid axle, semi elliptic leafsprings, rubber springs, telescopic dampers.

STEERING rack-and-pinion.

BRAKES front disc (diameter 9.49 in, 241 mm), rear drum dual circuit; lining area: front 17.4 sq in, 112 sq cm, rear 34.3 sq in, 221 sq cm, total 51.7 sq in, 333 sq cm.

ELECTRICAL EQUIPMENT voltage: 12 V; battery: 38 Ah; generator type: dynamo, 25 A; ignition distributor: Bosch; head lamps: 2.

DIMENSIONS AND WEIGHT wheel base: 100.75 in, 2,559 mm; front track: 52.99 in, 1,346 mm; rear track: 51.97 in 1,320 mm; overall length: 167.79 in, 4,262 mm; overall width 64.80 in, 1,646 mm; overall height: 52.36 in, 1,330 mm ground clearance: 4.92 in, 125 mm; dry weight: 2,150 lb 975 kg; turning circle (between walls): 33.5 ft, 10.2 m; fuel tank capacity: 13.6 imp gal, 16.4 US gal, 62 l.

BODY coupé; doors: 2; seats: 4; front seats: separate.

PRACTICAL INSTRUCTIONS fuel: 90 oct petrol; engine sump oil: 5.3 imp pt, 6.3 US pt, 3 l, SAE 20W-40, change every 6,200 miles, 10,000 km; gearbox oil: 2.3 imp pt, 2.7 US pt 1.3 l, SAE 80, change every 12,400 miles, 20,000 km; final drive oil: 1.9 imp pt, 2.3 US pt, 1.1 l, SAE 90, change every 12,400 miles, 20,000 km; greasing: none; tappet clearances: inlet 0.014 in, 0.35 mm; exhaust 0.016 in, 0.40 mm; valve timing: inlet opens 23° before tdc and closes 84° after bdc, exhaust opens 65° before bdc and closes 42° after tdc; normal tyre pressure: front 24 psi, 1.7 atm, rear 27 psi 1.9 atm.

OPTIONAL ACCESSORIES automatic gearbox with 55 66 Ah battery (except for 1300 model, with 148 hp engine) hydraulic torque convertor and planetary gears with 3 ratios (I 2.393, II 1.450, III 1, rev 2.094), max ratio of convertor at stall 2.2, possible manual selection; 5'' wheels; 165 x 13 tyres; servo brake (only for 1300 and 1500 models); alternator; sunshine roof; X equipment; L equipment; XL equipment; XLR equipment only for GT models.

Capri 1500

See Capri 1300, except for:

PRICE EX WORKS: 8,125 marks.

ENGINE bore and stroke: 3.54 x 2.32 in, 90 x 58.9 mm; engine capacity: 91.4 cu in, 1,498 cu cm; compression ratio: 8; max power (SAE): 80 hp at 5,000 rpm; max torque (SAE): 93 lb ft, 12.8 kg m at 3,000 rpm; specific power: 53.4 hp/l.

TRANSMISSION axle ratio: 3.890.

PERFORMANCE max speeds: 25 mph, 41 km/h in 1st gear; 44 mph, 71 km/h in 2nd gear; 63 mph, 102 km/h in 3rd gear; 87 mph, 140 km/h in 4th gear; power-weight ratio: 26.9 lb/hp, 12.2 kg/hp; speed in direct drive at 1,000 rpm: 17.4 mph, 28 km/h; fuel consumption: 32.5 m/imp gal, 27 m/US gal, 8.7 l x 100 km.

ELECTRICAL EQUIPMENT battery: 44 Ah.

Capri GT 1700

See Capri 1300, except for:

PRICE EX WORKS: 8,902 marks.

ENGINE bore and stroke: 3.54 x 2.63 in, 90 x 66.8 mm; engine capacity: 103.7 cu in, 1,699 cu cm; compression ratio: 9; max power (SAE): 90 hp at 5,200 rpm; max torque (SAE): 108 lb ft, 14.9 kg m at 2,500 rpm; max engine rpm: 5,200; specific power: 53 hp/l; carburation: 1 Solex 32 TDID carburettor.

TRANSMISSION clutch: diaphragm; axle ratio: 3.700; tyres: 165 x 13 (standard).

PERFORMANCE max speeds: 28 mph, 45 km/h in 1st gear; 48 mph, 78 km/h in 2nd gear; 70 mph, 113 km/h in 3rd gear; 96 mph, 155 km/h in 4th gear; power-weight ratio: 23.9 lb/hp, 10.9 kg/hp; speed in direct drive at 1,000 rpm: 18.5 mph, 29.8 km/h; fuel consumption: 30.1 m/imp gal, 25 m/US gal, 9.4 l x 100 km.

BRAKES front disc (diameter 9.61 in, 244 mm), servo (standard); lining area: front 20.5 sq in, 132 sq cm, rear 45.6 sq in, 294 sq cm, total 66.1 sq in, 426 sq cm.

ELECTRICAL EQUIPMENT battery: 44 Ah.

DIMENSIONS AND WEIGHT dry weight: 2,161 lb, 980 kg.

FORD Capri 1500

FORD Capri GT 1700

FORD Capri GT 2300

Capri GT 2000

See Capri 1300, except for:

PRICE EX WORKS: 9,435 marks.

ENGINE cylinders: 6, Vee-slanted at 60°; bore and stroke: 3.31 x 2.37 in, 84 x 60.1 mm; engine capacity: 121.9 cu in, 1,998 cu cm; compression ratio: 9; max power (SAE): 113 hp at 5,300 rpm; max torque (SAE): 125 lb ft, 17.3 kg m at 3,000 rpm; max engine rpm: 5,300; specific power: 56.6 hp/l; crankshaft bearings: 4; lubricating system capacity: 7.9 imp pt, 9.5 US pt, 4.5 l; carburation: 1 Solex 32 DDIST down-draught twin barrel carburettor; cooling system capacity: 13.7 imp pt, 16.5 US pt, 7.8 l.

TRANSMISSION clutch: diaphragm; axle ratio: 3.440; width of rims: 5'' (standard); tyres: 165 x 13 (standard).

PERFORMANCE max speeds: 30 mph, 48 km/h in 1st gear; 52 mph, 83 km/h in 2nd gear; 75 mph, 120 km/h in 3rd gear; 103 mph, 165 km/h in 4th gear; power-weight ratio: 20.1 lb/hp, 9.1 kg/hp; speed in direct drive at 1,000 rpm: 19.4 mph, 31.2 km/h; fuel consumption: 28.5 m/imp gal, 23.8 m/US gal, 9.9 l x 100 km.

BRAKES front disc (diameter 9.61 in, 244 mm), servo (standard); lining area: front 20.5 sq in, 132 sq cm, rear 45.6 sq in, 294 sq cm, total 66.1 sq in, 426 sq cm.

ELECTRICAL EQUIPMENT battery: 44 Ah; headlamps: 2, halogen.

DIMENSIONS AND WEIGHT dry weight: 2,271 lb, 1,030 kg.

Capri GT 2300

See Capri 1300, except for:

PRICE EX WORKS: 9,979 marks.

ENGINE cylinders: 6, Vee-slanted at 60°; bore and stroke: 3.54 x 2.37 in, 90 x 60.1 mm; engine capacity: 139.9 cu in, 2,293 cu cm; compression ratio: 9; max power (SAE): 123 hp at 5,600 rpm; max torque (SAE): 138 lb ft, 19.1 kg m at 3,500 rpm; max engine rpm: 5,600; specific power: 54.9 hp/l; crankshaft bearings: 4; lubricating system capacity: 7.9 imp pt, 9.5 US pt, 4.5 l; carburation: 1 Solex 35 DDIST down-draught twin barrel carburettor; cooling system capacity: 13.7 imp pt, 16.5 US pt, 7.8 l.

TRANSMISSION clutch: diaphragm; axle ratio: 3.220; tyres: 165 x 13 (standard).

PERFORMANCE max speeds: 32 mph, 51 km/h in 1st gear; 56 mph, 90 km/h in 2nd gear; 81 mph, 130 km/h in 3rd gear; 111 mph, 178 km/h in 4th gear; power-weight ratio: 18.1 lb/hp, 8.2 kg/hp; speed in direct drive at 1,000 rpm: 19.9 mph, 32 km/h; fuel consumption: 28 m/imp gal, 23.3 m/US gal, 10.1 l x 100 km.

BRAKES front disc (diameter 9.61 in, 244 mm), servo (standard); lining area: front 20.5 sq in, 132 sq cm, rear 45.6 sq in, 294 sq cm, total 66.1 sq in, 426 sq cm.

ELECTRICAL EQUIPMENT battery: 55 Ah.

DIMENSIONS AND WEIGHT dry weight: 2,293 lb, 1,040 kg.

Capri GT 2600

See Capri GT 2300, except for:

PRICE EX WORKS: 10,501 marks.

ENGINE bore and stroke: 3.54 x 2.63 in, 90 x 66.8 mm; engine capacity: 155.5 cu in, 2,548 cu cm; compression ratio: 9; max power (SAE): 142 hp at 5,500 rpm; max torque (SAE): 163 lb ft, 22.5 kg m at 3,100 rpm; specific power: 55.7 hp/l.

PERFORMANCE max speed: 118 mph, 190 km/h; power-weight ratio: 16.1 lb/hp, 7.3 kg/hp; fuel consumption: 27.2 m/imp gal, 22.6 m/US gal, 10.4 l x 100 km.

2-door 20M Limousine

PRICE IN GB: £ 1,127.
PRICE EX WORKS: 10,112 marks.

ENGINE front, 4 stroke; cylinders: 6, Vee-slanted at 60°; bore and stroke: 3.31 x 2.37 in, 84 x 60.1 mm; engine capaci-ty: 121.9 cu in, 1,998 cu cm; compression ratio: 8; max power (SAE): 106 hp at 5,300 rpm; max torque (SAE): 121 lb ft, 16.7 kg m at 3,000 rpm; max engine rpm: 5,300; specific power: 53 hp/l; cylinder block: cast iron; cylinder head: cast iron; crankshaft bearings: 4; valves: 2 per cylin-

2-DOOR 20M LIMOUSINE

der, overhead, in line, push-rods and rockers; camshafts: 1, at centre of Vee; lubrication: rotary pump, full flow filter; lubricating system capacity: 7.9 imp pt, 9.5 US pt, 4.5 l; carburation: 1 Solex 32 DDIST downdraught twin barrel carburettor; fuel feed: mechanical pump; cooling system: water, thermostatic fan; cooling system capacity: 13.7 imp pt, 16.5 US pt, 7.8 l.

TRANSMISSION driving wheels: rear; clutch: single dry plate; gearbox: mechanical; gears: 4 + reverse; synchromesh gears: I, II, III, IV; gearbox ratios: I 3.650, II 1.970, III 1.370, IV 1, rev 3.660; gear lever: steering column; final drive: hypoid bevel; axle ratio: 3.700; width of rims: 5''; tyres· 6.40 x 13.

PERFORMANCE max speeds: 30 mph, 48 km/h in 1st gear; 52 mph, 83 km/h in 2nd gear; 75 mph, 120 km/h in 3rd gear; 96 mph, 155 km/h in 4th gear; power-weight ratio: 22.7 lb/hp, 10.3 kg/hp; carrying capacity: 1,047 lb, 475 kg; speed in direct drive at 1,000 rpm: 19.3 mph, 31 km/h; fuel consumption: 28 m/imp gal, 23.3 m/US gal, 10.1 l x 100 km.

CHASSIS integral; front suspension: independent, by McPherson, coil springs/telescopic damper struts, lower wishbones, anti-roll bar; rear suspension: rigid axle, semi-elliptic leafsprings, telescopic dampers.

STEERING recirculating ball.

BRAKES front disc (diameter 9.45 in, 240 mm), rear drum, dual circuit, servo; lining area: front 16.3 sq in, 105 sq cm, rear 50.5 sq in, 326 sq cm, total 66.8 sq in, 431 sq cm.

ELECTRICAL EQUIPMENT voltage: 12 V; battery: 44 Ah; generator type: alternator, 35 A; ignition distributor: Bosch; headlamps: 2.

DIMENSIONS AND WEIGHT wheel base: 106.50 in, 2,705 mm; front track: 56.97 in, 1,447 mm; rear track: 55.67 in, 1,414 mm; overall length: 185.87 in, 4,721 mm; overall width: 69.13 in, 1,756 mm; overall height: 58.19 in, 1,478 mm; ground clearance: 7.09 in, 180 mm; dry weight: 2,414 lb, 1,095 kg; turning circle (between walls): 35.4 ft, 10.8 m; fuel tank capacity: 12.1 imp gal, 14.5 US gal, 55 l.

BODY saloon/sedan; doors: 2; seats: 5; front seats: separate; details: electrically-heated rear window.

PRACTICAL INSTRUCTIONS fuel: 85-90 oct petrol; engine sump oil: 7 imp pt, 8.5 US pt, 4 l, SAE 20W-40, change every 6,200 miles, 10,000 km; gearbox oil: 2.3 imp pt, 2.7 US pt, 1.3 l, SAE 80, change every 12,400 miles, 20,000 km; final drive oil: 1.9 imp pt, 2.3 US pt, 1.1 l, SAE 90, change every 12,400 miles, 20,000 km; greasing: none; normal tyre pressure: front 21 psi, 1.5 atm, rear 27 psi, 1.9 atm.

VARIATIONS

ENGINE 9 compression ratio, max power (SAE) 113 hp at 5,300 rpm, max torque (SAE) 125 lb ft, 17.3 kg m at 3,000 rpm, 56.6 hp/l specific power.
PERFORMANCE max speed 99 mph, 160 km/h, power-weight ratio 21.4 lb/hp, 9.7 kg/hp, fuel consumption 30.7 m/imp gal, 25.6 m/US gal, 9.2 l x 100 km.
ELECTRICAL EQUIPMENT 55 Ah battery.

ENGINE bore and stroke 3.54 x 2.37 in, 90 x 60.1 mm, engine capacity 139.9 cu in, 2,293 cu cm, 9 compression ratio, max power (SAE) 126 hp at 5,600 rpm, max torque (SAE) 138 lb ft, 19.1 kg m at 3,500 rpm, 54.9 hp/l specific power, 1 Solex 35 DDIST twin barrel carburettor.
TRANSMISSION 3.440 axle ratio.
PERFORMANCE max speeds (I) 34 mph, 55 km/h, (II) 58 mph, 94 km/h, (III) 85 mph, 136 km/h, (IV) 106 mph, 170 km/h, power-weight ratio 19.2 lb/hp, 8.7 kg/hp, speed in direct drive at 1,000 rpm 20.6 mph, 33.2 km/h, fuel consumption 28.5 m/imp gal, 23.8 m/US gal, 9.9 l x 100 km.
ELECTRICAL EQUIPMENT 55 Ah battery.

ENGINE bore and stroke 3.54 x 2.63 in, 90 x 66.7 mm, engine capacity 155.5 cu in, 2,548 cu cm, 9 compression ratio, max power (SAE) 142 hp at 5,500 rpm, max torque (SAE) 163 lb ft, 22.5 kg m at 3,100 rpm, 55.7 hp/l specific power, 1 Solex 35 DDIST twin barrel carburettor.
TRANSMISSION 175 x 14 tyres.
PERFORMANCE max speed 112 mph, 180 km/h, power-weight ratio 17.2 lb/hp, 7.8 kg/hp, fuel consumption 26.2 m/imp gal, 21.8 m/US gal, 10.8 l x 100 km.
ELECTRICAL EQUIPMENT 55 Ah battery.
DIMENSIONS AND WEIGHT dry weight 2,459 lb, 1,115 kg.

OPTIONAL ACCESSORIES central gear lever; automatic gearbox with 55-66 Ah battery (except for RS models), hydraulic torque convertor and planetary gears with 3 ratios (I 2.460, II 1.460, III 1, rev 2.200), max ratio of convertor at stall 2.1, possible manual selection, 3.890 axle ratio (3.440 with 155.5 cu in, 2,548 cu cm engine); 175 x 14 tyres; power-assisted steering; sunshine roof.

FORD 2-door 20M Limousine

FORD 20M XL Hardtop

FORD 2-door 20M RS Limousine

4-door 20M Limousine

See 2-door 20M Limousine, except for:

PRICE EX WORKS: 10,467 marks.

PERFORMANCE power-weight ratio: 23.4 lb/hp, 10.6 kg/hp.

DIMENSIONS AND WEIGHT dry weight: 2,470 lb, 1,120 kg.

20M Hardtop

See 2-door 20M Limousine, except for:

PRICE EX WORKS: 10,501 marks.

TRANSMISSION gear lever: central (standard).

PERFORMANCE power-weight ratio: 23.6 lb/hp, 10.7 kg/hp.

DIMENSIONS AND WEIGHT overall height: 57.64 in, 1,464 mm; dry weight: 2,492 lb, 1,130 kg.

BODY hardtop.

3-door 20M Turnier

See 2-door 20M Limousine, except for:

PRICE EX WORKS: 10,501 marks.

TRANSMISSION width of rims: 4.5''.

PERFORMANCE power-weight ratio: 23.8 lb/hp, 10.8 kg/hp.

DIMENSIONS AND WEIGHT front track: 56.57 in, 1,437 mm; rear track: 55.28 in, 1,404 mm; overall length: 183.98 in, 4,673 mm; overall height: 57.99 in, 1,473 mm; dry weight: 2,525 lb, 1,145 kg; fuel tank capacity: 9.9 imp gal, 11.9 US gal, 45 l.

BODY estate car/station wagon; doors: 2 + 1.

VARIATIONS

ENGINE 155.5 cu in, 2,548 cu cm not available.

5-door 20M Turnier

See 3-door 20M Turnier, except for:

PRICE EX WORKS: 10,856 marks.

PERFORMANCE power-weight ratio: 24.2 lb/hp, 11 kg/hp.

DIMENSIONS AND WEIGHT dry weight: 2,580 lb, 1,170 kg.

BODY doors: 4 + 1.

2-door 20M XL Limousine

See 2-door 20M Limousine, except for:

PRICE EX WORKS: 10,933 marks.

TRANSMISSION gear lever: central (standard).

PERFORMANCE power-weight ratio: 22.9 lb/hp, 10.4 kg/hp.

DIMENSIONS AND WEIGHT dry weight: 2,437 lb, 1,105 kg.

4-door 20M XL Limousine

See 2-door 20M XL Limousine, except for:

PRICE EX WORKS: 11,289 marks.

PERFORMANCE power-weight ratio: 23.6 lb/hp, 10.7 kg/hp.

DIMENSIONS AND WEIGHT dry weight: 2,492 lb, 1,130 kg.

20M XL Hardtop

See 2-door 20M XL Limousine, except for:

PRICE EX WORKS: 11,167 marks.

PERFORMANCE power-weight ratio: 23.8 lb/hp, 10.8 kg/hp.

DIMENSIONS AND WEIGHT overall height: 57.64 in, 1,464 mm; dry weight: 2,514 lb, 1,140 kg.

BODY hardtop.

FORD 20M Limousine

FORD 20M Turnier

FORD 20M RS Limousine

2-door 20M RS Limousine

See 2-door 20M Limousine, except for:

PRICE EX WORKS: 11,605 marks.

ENGINE bore and stroke: 3.54 x 2.37 in, 90 x 60.1 mm; engine capacity: 139.9 cu in, 2,293 cu cm; compression ratio: 9; max power (SAE): 126 hp at 5,600 rpm; max torque (SAE): 138 lb ft, 19.1 kg m at 3,500 rpm; max engine rpm: 5,600; specific power: 54.9 hp/l; carburation: 1 Solex 35 DDIST twin barrel carburettor.

TRANSMISSION gear lever: central; axle ratio: 3.440; tyres: 175 x 14.

PERFORMANCE max speeds: 34 mph, 55 km/h in 1st gear; 59 mph, 95 km/h in 2nd gear; 85 mph, 137 km/h in 3rd gear; 106 mph, 170 km/h in 4th gear; power-weight ratio: 19.2 lb/hp, 8.7 kg/hp; fuel consumption: 28.5 m/imp gal, 23.8 m/US gal, 9.9 l x 100 km.

BRAKES lining area: front 24.2 sq in, 156 sq cm, rear 50.5 sq in, 326 sq cm, total 74.7 sq in, 482 sq cm.

ELECTRICAL EQUIPMENT battery: 55 Ah; headlamps: 4, 2 halogen.

BODY details: 5'' wheels.

PRACTICAL INSTRUCTIONS fuel: 98-100 oct petrol.

VARIATIONS

(Only 148 hp 139.9 cu in, 2,293 cu cm engine).

ENGINE max power (SAE) 148 hp at 5,700 rpm, 64.5 hp/l specific power.
TRANSMISSION 3.700 axle ratio.
PERFORMANCE max speed 112 mph, 180 km/h, power-weight ratio 16.3 lb/hp, 7.4 kg/hp, fuel consumption 27.4 m/imp gal, 22.8 m/US gal, 10.3 l x 100 km.

OPTIONAL ACCESSORIES only power-assisted steering and sunshine roof.

4-door 20M RS Limousine

See 2-door 20M RS Limousine, except for:

PRICE EX WORKS: 11,960 marks.

PERFORMANCE power-weight ratio: 19.6 lb/hp, 8.9 kg/hp.

DIMENSIONS AND WEIGHT dry weight: 2,470 lb, 1,120 kg.

20M RS Hardtop

See 2-door 20M RS Limousine, except for:

PRICE EX WORKS: 11,838 marks.

PERFORMANCE power-weight ratio: 19.8 lb/hp, 9 kg/hp.

DIMENSIONS AND WEIGHT overall height: 57.64 in, 1,464 mm; dry weight: 2,492 lb, 1,130 kg.

BODY hardtop.

4-door 26M Limousine

See 2-door 20M Limousine, except for:

PRICE EX WORKS: 14,774 marks.

ENGINE bore and stroke: 3.54 x 2.63 in, 90 x 66.8 mm; engine capacity: 155.5 cu in, 2,548 cu cm; compression ratio: 9; max power (SAE): 142 hp at 5,500 rpm; max torque (SAE): 163 lb ft, 22.5 kg m at 3,100 rpm; max engine rpm: 5,500; specific power: 55.7 hp/l; carburation: 1 Solex 35 DDIST twin barrel carburettor; cooling system capacity: 13.4 imp pt, 16.1 US pt, 7.6 l.

TRANSMISSION gearbox: automatic, hydraulic torque convertor and planetary gears with 3 ratios + reverse, max ratio of convertor at stall 2.1, possible manual selection; gearbox ratios: I 2.460, II 1.460, III 1, rev 2.200; selector lever: central; axle ratio: 3.440; tyres: 175 x 14.

PERFORMANCE max speed 109 mph, 175 km/h; power-weight ratio: 19 lb/hp, 8.6 kg/hp; fuel consumption: 23.9 m/imp gal, 19.9 m/US gal, 11.8 l x 100 km.

STEERING servo.

BRAKES front disc (diameter 10.67 in, 271 mm); lining area: front 24.2 sq in, 156 sq cm, rear 50.5 sq in, 326 sq cm, total 74.7 sq in, 482 sq cm.

4-DOOR 26M LIMOUSINE

ELECTRICAL EQUIPMENT battery: 66 Ah; headlamps: 4, halogen.

DIMENSIONS AND WEIGHT front track: 57.13 in, 1,451 mm; rear track: 55.83 in, 1,418 mm; dry weight: 2,690 lb, 1,220 kg.

BODY doors: 4; details: sunshine roof.

PRACTICAL INSTRUCTIONS fuel: 98-100 oct petrol.

VARIATIONS

None.

OPTIONAL ACCESSORIES only 4-speed mechanical gearbox (I 3.650, II 1.970, III 1.370, IV 1, rev 3.660) with 3.700 axle ratio and electrically-controlled sunshine roof.

26M Hardtop

See 4-door 26M Limousine, except for:

PERFORMANCE power-weight ratio: 19.2 lb/hp, 8.7 kg/hp.

DIMENSIONS AND WEIGHT overall height: 57.64 in, 1,464 mm; dry weight: 2,712 lb, 1,230 kg.

BODY hardtop; doors: 2.

MERCEDES-BENZ GERMANY (F.R.)

200

PRICE EX WORKS: 12,743 marks.

ENGINE front, 4 stroke; cylinders: 4, vertical, in line; bore and stroke: 3.43 x 3.29 in, 87 x 83.6 mm; engine capacity: 121.3 cu in, 1,988 cu cm; compression ratio: 9; max power (SAE): 105 hp at 5,000 rpm; max torque (SAE): 124 lb ft, 17.1 kg m at 3,000 rpm; max engine rpm: 6,000; specific power: 52.8 hp/l; cylinder block: cast iron; cylinder head: light alloy; crankshaft bearings: 5; valves: 2 per cylinder, overhead, in line, finger levers; camshafts: 1, overhead; lubrication: gear pump, oil-water heat exchanger, full flow filter; lubricating system capacity: 7.9 imp pt, 9.5 US pt, 4.5 l; carburation: 1 Stromberg 175 CDS horizontal carburettor; fuel feed: mechanical pump; cooling system: water; cooling system capacity: 18.8 imp pt, 22.6 US pt, 10.7 l.

TRANSMISSION driving wheels: rear; clutch: single dry plate, hydraulically controlled; gearbox: mechanical; gears: 4 + reverse; synchromesh gears: I, II, III, IV; gearbox ratios: I 3.900, II 2.300, III 1.410, IV 1, rev 3.660; gear lever: steering column; final drive: hypoid bevel; axle ratio: 3.920; tyres: 6.95 x 14 or 175 x 14.

PERFORMANCE max speeds: 28 mph, 45 km/h in 1st gear; 47 mph, 75 km/h in 2nd gear; 78 mph, 125 km/h in 3rd gear; 99 mph, 160 km/h in 4th gear; power-weight ratio: 28 lb/hp, 12.7 kg/hp; carrying capacity: 1,147 lb, 520 kg; max gradient in 1st gear: 45%; fuel consumption: 25.9 m/imp gal, 21.6 m/US gal, 10.9 l x 100 km.

CHASSIS integral, front auxiliary frame; front suspension: independent, wishbones, coil springs, auxiliary rubber springs, anti-roll bar, telescopic dampers; rear suspension: independent, oblique semi-trailing arms, coil springs, auxiliary rubber springs, anti-roll bar, telescopic dampers.

STEERING recirculating ball, damper; turns of steering wheel lock to lock: 4.60.

BRAKES disc (front diameter 10.75 in, 273 mm, rear 10.98 in, 279 mm), dual circuit, servo; lining area: front 23.6 sq in, 152 sq cm, rear 16.3 sq in, 105 sq cm, total 39.9 sq in, 257 sq cm.

ELECTRICAL EQUIPMENT voltage: 12 V; battery: 55 Ah; generator type: alternator, 490 W; ignition distributor: Bosch; headlamps: 2.

DIMENSIONS AND WEIGHT wheel base: 108.27 in, 2,750 mm; front track: 56.69 in, 1,440 mm; rear track: 56.85 in, 1,444 mm; overall length: 184.45 in, 4,685 mm; overall width: 69.68 in, 1,770 mm; overall height: 56.69 in, 1,440 mm; ground clearance: 6.85 in, 174 mm; dry weight: 2,492 lb, 1,330 kg; turning circle (between walls): 35.4 ft, 10.8 m; fuel tank capacity: 14.3 imp gal, 17.2 US gal, 65 l.

BODY saloon/sedan; doors: 4; seats: 5-6; front seats: separate, reclining backrests.

PRACTICAL INSTRUCTIONS fuel: 98 oct petrol; engine sump oil: 7.9 imp pt, 9.5 US pt, 4.5 l, SAE 20W-30, change every

FORD 26M Limousine

MERCEDES-BENZ 220 D

MERCEDES-BENZ 220

3,700 miles, 6,000 km; gearbox oil: 2.8 imp pt, 3.4 US pt, 1.6 l, ATF, change every 12,400 miles, 20,000 km; final drive oil: 1.9 imp pt, 2.3 US pt, 1.1 l, SAE 90, change every 12,400 miles, 20,000 km; greasing: none; normal tyre pressure: front 21 psi, 1.5 atm, rear 26 psi, 1.8 atm.

OPTIONAL ACCESSORIES central gear lever; DB automatic gearbox, hydraulic coupling and planetary gears with 4 ratios (I 3.980, II 2.390, III 1.460, IV 1, rev 5.470), possible manual selection; automatic levelling control on rear suspension; power-assisted steering; air-conditioning system; sunshine roof; electrically-heated rear window.

200 D

See 200, except for:

PRICE EX WORKS: 13,264 marks.

ENGINE Diesel; compression ratio: 21; max power (SAE): 60 hp at 4,200 rpm; max torque (SAE): 87 lb ft, 12 kg m at 2,400 rpm; max engine rpm: 4,350; specific power: 30.2 hp/l; cylinder head: cast iron; carburation: 4-cylinder Bosch injection pump; cooling system capacity: 18.8 imp pt, 22.6 US pt, 10.7 l.

PERFORMANCE max speeds: 21 mph, 33 km/h in 1st gear; 35 mph, 56 km/h in 2nd gear; 57 mph, 92 km/h in 3rd gear; 81 mph, 130 km/h in 4th gear; power-weight ratio: 50.1 lb/hp, 22.7 kg/hp; fuel consumption: 34.9 m/imp gal, 29 m/US gal, 8.1 l x 100 km.

ELECTRICAL EQUIPMENT battery: 66 Ah.

DIMENSIONS AND WEIGHT dry weight: 3,605 lb, 1,365 kg.

PRACTICAL INSTRUCTIONS fuel: Diesel oil.

220

See 200, except for:

PRICE IN GB: £ 1,971.
PRICE IN USA: $ 4,961.

ENGINE bore and stroke: 3.43 x 3.64 in, 87 x 92.4 mm; engine capacity: 134.1 cu in, 2,197 cu cm; max power (SAE): 116 hp at 5,000 rpm; max torque (SAE): 142 lb ft, 19.6 kg m at 3,000 rpm; specific power: 52.8 hp/l.

PERFORMANCE max speed: 104 mph, 168 km/h; power-weight ratio: 25.4 lb/hp, 11.5 kg/hp; fuel consumption: 25.4 m/imp gal, 21.2 m/Us gal, 11.1 l x 100 km.

220 D

See 200 D, except for:

PRICE IN GB: £ 2,124.
PRICE IN USA: $ 5,067.

ENGINE bore and stroke: 3.43 x 3.64 in, 87 x 92.4 mm; engine capacity: 134.1 cu in, 2,197 cu cm; max power (SAE): 65 hp at 4,200 rpm; max torque (SAE): 96 lb ft, 13.3 kg m at 2,400 rpm; specific power: 29.6 hp/l.

PERFORMANCE max speeds: 21 mph, 33 km/h in 1st gear; 35 mph, 56 km/h in 2nd gear; 57 mph, 92 km/h in 3rd gear; 84 mph, 135 km/h in 4th gear; power-weight ratio: 46.5 lb/hp, 21.1 kg/hp; max gradient in 1st gear: 39%.

ELECTRICAL EQUIPMENT battery: 88 Ah.

DIMENSIONS AND WEIGHT dry weight: 3,032 lb, 1,375 kg.

230

See 200, except for:

PRICE EX WORKS: 14,619 marks.

ENGINE cylinders: 6; bore and stroke: 3.22 x 2.87 in, 81.7 x 72.8 mm; engine capacity: 139.9 cu in, 2,292 cu cm; max power (SAE): 135 hp at 5,600 rpm; max torque (SAE): 145 lb ft, 20 kg m at 3,800 rpm; max engine rpm: 6,300; specific power: 58.9 hp/l; crankshaft bearings: 4; lubrication: oil cooler; lubricating system capacity: 9.7 imp pt, 11.6 US pt, 5.5 l; carburation: 2 Zenith 35-40 INAT downdraught twin barrel carburettors.

PERFORMANCE max speeds: 31 mph, 50 km/h in 1st gear; 52 mph, 84 km/h in 2nd gear; 88 mph, 142 km/h in 3rd gear; 109 mph, 175 km/h in 4th gear; power-weight ratio: 20.7 lb/hp, 9.4 kg/hp; fuel consumption: 24.1 m/imp gal, 20.1 m/US gal, 11.7 l x 100 km.

DIMENSIONS AND WEIGHT dry weight: 2,988 lb, 1,355 kg.

OPTIONAL ACCESSORIES 5-speed mechanical gearbox, 3.920 axle ratio.

FORD 4-door 26M Limousine

MERCEDES-BENZ 200

MERCEDES-BENZ 250 Limousine

250 Limousine

See 200, except for:

PRICE IN GB: £ 2,292.
PRICE IN USA: $ 5,539.

ENGINE cylinders: 6; bore and stroke: 3.23 x 3.10 in, 82 x 78.8 mm; engine capacity: 152.3 cu in, 2,496 cu cm; max power (SAE): 146 hp at 5,600 rpm; max torque (SAE): 162 lb ft, 22.3 kg m at 3,800 rpm; max engine rpm: 6,300; specific power: 58.5 hp/l; crankshaft bearings: 7; lubrication: oil cooler; lubricating system capacity: 9.7 imp pt, 11.6 US pt, 5.5 l; carburation: 2 Zenith 35-40 INAT downdraught twin barrel carburettors; cooling system capacity: 17.4 imp pt, 20.9 US pt, 9.9 l.

PERFORMANCE max speeds: 31 mph, 50 km/h in 1st gear; 52 mph, 84 km/h in 2nd gear; 88 mph, 142 km/h in 3rd gear; 112 mph, 180 km/h in 4th gear; power-weight ratio: 20.7 lb/hp, 9.4 kg/hp; fuel consumption: 24.1 m/imp gal, 20.1 m/US gal, 11.7 l x 100 km.

DIMENSIONS AND WEIGHT dry weight: 3,032 lb, 1,375 kg.

OPTIONAL ACCESSORIES 5-speed mechanical gearbox, 3.920 axle ratio.

250 C Coupé

See 250 Limousine, except for:

PRICE EX WORKS: 18,426 marks.

DIMENSIONS AND WEIGHT rear track: 56.69 in, 1,440 mm; overall width: 70.47 in, 1,790 mm; overall height: 54.92 in, 1,395 mm.

BODY coupé; doors: 2.

250 CE Coupé

See 250 C Coupé, except for:

PRICE IN GB: £ 2,793.
PRICE IN USA: $ 6,625.

ENGINE compression ratio: 9.5; max power (SAE): 170 hp at 5,600 rpm; max torque (SAE): 170 lb ft, 23.5 kg m at 4,650 rpm; max engine rpm: 6,500; specific power: 68.1 hp/l; carburation: Bosch electronically-controlled injection system; fuel feed: electric pump.

PERFORMANCE max speed: 118 mph, 190 km/h; power-weight ratio: 18.1 lb/hp, 8.2 kg/hp.

DIMENSIONS AND WEIGHT dry weight: 3,065 lb, 1,390 kg.

280 S Limousine

PRICE IN GB: £ 2,599.
PRICE IN USA: $ 6,588.

ENGINE front, 4 stroke; cylinders: 6, vertical, in line; bore and stroke: 3.41 x 3.10 in, 86.5 x 78.8 mm; engine capacity: 169.5 cu in, 2,778 cu cm; compression ratio: 9; max power (SAE): 157 hp at 5,400 rpm; max torque (SAE): 181 lb ft, 25 kg m at 3,800 rpm; max engine rpm: 6,500; specific power: 56.5 hp/l; cylinder block: cast iron; cylinder head: light alloy; crankshaft bearings: 7; valves: 2 per cylinder, overhead, in line, finger levers; camshafts: 1, overhead; lubrication: gear pump, oil-water heat exchanger, filter on by-pass, oil cooler; lubricating system capacity: 9.7 imp pt, 11.6 US pt, 5.5 l; carburation: 2 Zenith 35-40 INAT downdraught twin barrel carburettors; fuel feed: mechanical pump; cooling system: water, thermostatic fan; cooling system capacity: 18.7 imp pt, 22.4 US pt, 10.6 l.

TRANSMISSION driving wheels: rear; clutch: single dry plate, hydraulically controlled; gearbox: mechanical; gears: 4 + reverse; synchromesh gears: I, II, III, IV; gearbox ratios: I 3.960, II 2.340, III 1.430, IV 1, rev 3.720; gear lever: steering column; final drive: hypoid bevel; axle ratio: 3.690; width of rims: 6''; tyres: 7.35 x 14 or 185 x 14.

PERFORMANCE max speed: 115 mph, 185 km/h; power-weight ratio: 20.7 lb/hp, 9.4 kg/hp; carrying capacity: 1,103 lb, 500 kg; fuel consumption: 23 m/imp gal, 19.1 m/US gal, 12.3 l x 100 km.

CHASSIS integral, front auxiliary frame; front suspension: independent, wishbones, coil springs, auxiliary rubber springs, anti-roll bar, telescopic dampers; rear suspension: independent, single joint low pivot, swinging semi-

280 S LIMOUSINE

axles, trailing lower radius arms, coil springs, auxiliary rubber springs, hydropneumatic compensating spring with automatic levelling control, telescopic dampers.

STEERING recirculating ball, dampers; turns of steering wheel lock to lock: 4.

BRAKES disc, dual circuit, rear compensator, servo; lining area: front 23.6 sq in, 152 sq cm, rear 16.3 sq in, 105 sq cm, total 39.9 sq in, 257 sq cm.

ELECTRICAL EQUIPMENT voltage: 12 V; battery: 55 Ah; generator type: alternator, 490 W; ignition distributor: Bosch; headlamps: 2.

DIMENSIONS AND WEIGHT wheel base: 108.27 in, 2,750 mm; front track: 58.35 in, 1,482 mm; rear track: 58.46 in, 1,485 mm; overall length: 192.91 in, 4,900 mm; overall width: 71.26 in, 1,810 mm; overall height: 56.69 in, 1,440 mm; ground clearance: 6.61 in, 168 mm; dry weight: 3,263 lb, 1,480 kg; distribution of weight: 50.3% front axle, 49.7% rear axle; turning circle (between walls): 38.4 ft, 11.7 m; fuel tank capacity: 18 imp gal, 21.6 US gal, 82 l.

BODY saloon/sedan; doors: 4; seats: 5-6; front seats: separate, reclining backrests.

PRACTICAL INSTRUCTIONS fuel: 96 oct petrol; engine sump oil: 9.7 imp pt, 11.6 US pt, 5.5 l, SAE 20W-30, change every 3,700 miles, 6,000 km; gearbox oil: 3.2 imp pt, 3.8 US pt, 1.8 l, ATF, change every 12,400 miles, 20,000 km; final drive oil: 4.4 imp pt, 5.3 US pt, 2.5 l, SAE 90, change every 12,400 miles, 20,000 km; greasing: every 3,100 miles, 5,000 km, 20 points; normal tyre pressure: front 23 psi, 1.6 atm, rear 27 psi, 1.9 atm.

OPTIONAL ACCESSORIES central gear lever; 5-speed mechanical gearbox, 3.920 axle ratio; limited slip final drive; DB automatic gearbox, hydraulic coupling and planetary gears with 4 ratios (I 3.980, II 2.390, III 1.460, IV 1, rev 5.470), possible manual selection; power-assisted steering; air-conditioning system; sunshine roof; electrically-heated rear window.

280 SE Limousine

See 280 S Limousine, except for:

PRICE IN GB: £ 2,828.
PRICE IN USA: $ 6,866.

ENGINE compression ratio: 9.5; max power (SAE): 180 hp at 5,750 rpm; max torque (SAE): 193 lb ft, 26.7 kg m at 4,500 rpm; max engine rpm: 6,500; specific power: 64.8 hp/l; carburation: 6-cylinder Bosch intermittent injection pump in inlet pipes; fuel feed: electric pump.

PERFORMANCE max speeds: 32 mph, 52 km/h in 1st gear; 55 mph, 88 km/h in 2nd gear; 92 mph, 148 km/h in 3rd gear; 118 mph, 190 km/h in 4th gear; power-weight ratio: 18.3 lb/hp, 8.3 kg/hp; max gradient in 1st gear: 46%.

DIMENSIONS AND WEIGHT dry weight: 3,296 lb, 1,495 kg.

280 SEL Limousine

See 280 SE Limousine, except for:

PRICE IN USA: $ 7,657. (with power-assisted steering).
PRICE EX WORKS: 23,421 marks.

ENGINE cooling system capacity: 19 imp pt, 22.8 US pt, 10.8 l.

PERFORMANCE power-weight ratio: 18.7 lb/hp, 8.5 kg/hp.

DIMENSIONS AND WEIGHT wheel base: 112.20 in, 2,850 mm; overall length: 196.85 in, 5,000 mm; dry weight: 3,363 lb, 1,525 kg.

280 SE Coupé

See 280 SE Limousine, except for:

PRICE IN USA: $ 11,612.
(with power-assisted steering, air-conditioning system and radio).
PRICE EX WORKS: 29,137 marks.

TRANSMISSION gear lever: central (standard).

PERFORMANCE power-weight ratio: 18.5 lb/hp, 8.4 kg/hp; carrying capacity: 1,036 lb, 470 kg.

MERCEDES-BENZ 250 CE Coupé

MERCEDES-BENZ 280 SL Roadster

MERCEDES-BENZ 300 SEL 3.5 Limousine

DIMENSIONS AND WEIGHT overall length: 193.50 in, 4,915 mm; overall width: 72.64 in, 1,845 mm; overall height: 55.51 in, 1,410 mm; dry weight: 3,330 lb, 1,510 kg.

BODY coupé; doors: 2; seats: 5.

280 SE Cabriolet

See 280 SE Coupé, except for:

PRICE IN USA: $ 12,444.
(with power-assisted steering, air-conditioning system and radio).
PRICE EX WORKS: 31,302 marks.

PERFORMANCE power-weight ratio: 19.4 lb/hp, 8.8 kg/hp.

DIMENSIONS AND WEIGHT overall height: 55.91 in, 1,420 mm; dry weight: 3,506 lb, 1,590 kg.

BODY convertible.

OPTIONAL ACCESSORIES sunshine roof and electrically-heated rear window not available.

280 SL Roadster

PRICE IN GB: £ 3,419.
PRICE IN USA: $ 7,244.

ENGINE front, 4 stroke; cylinders: 6, slanted, in line; bore and stroke: 3.41 x 3.10 in, 86.5 x 78.8 mm; engine capacity: 169.5 cu in, 2,778 cu cm; compression ratio: 9.5; max power (SAE): 195 hp at 5,900 rpm; max torque (SAE): 196 lb ft, 27 kg m at 4,700 rpm; max engine rpm: 6,500; specific power: 70.2 hp/l; cylinder block: cast iron; cylinder head: light alloy; crankshaft bearings: 7; valves: 2 per cylinder, overhead, in line, rockers, finger levers; camshafts: 1; overhead; lubrication: gear pump, oil-water heat exchanger, full flow filter, oil cooler; lubricating system capacity: 9.7 imp pt, 11.6 US pt, 5.5 l; carburation: 6-cylinder Bosch intermittent injection pump in inlet pipes; fuel feed: electric pump; cooling system: water, thermostatic fan; cooling system capacity: 22 imp pt, 26.4 US pt, 12.5 l.

TRANSMISSION driving wheels: rear; clutch: single dry plate, hydraulically controlled; gearbox: mechanical; gears: 4 + reverse; synchromesh gears: I, II, III, IV; gearbox ratios: I 4.050, II 2.230, III 1.400, IV 1, rev 3.580; gear lever: central; final drive: hypoid bevel; axle ratio: 3.690; width of rims: 6''; tyres: 185 HR x 14.

PERFORMANCE max speeds: 31 mph, 50 km/h in 1st gear; 56 mph, 90 km/h in 2nd gear; 91 mph, 147 km/h in 3rd gear; 124 mph, 200 km/h in 4th gear; power-weight ratio: 15.4 lb/hp, 7 kg/hp; carrying capacity: 783 lb, 355 kg; max gradient in 1st gear: 44%; fuel consumption: 24.8 m/imp gal, 20.6 m/US gal, 11.4 l x 100 km.

CHASSIS integral, front auxiliary frame; front suspension: independent, wishbones, coil springs, anti-roll bar, telescopic dampers; rear suspension: independent, single joint low pivot, swinging semi-axles, trailing radius arms, coil springs, auxiliary rubber springs, hydropneumatic compensating spring with automatic levelling control, telescopic dampers.

STEERING recirculating ball, damper; turns of steering wheel lock to lock: 4.

BRAKES disc, dual circuit, rear compensator, servo; lining area: front 23.6 sq in, 152 sq cm, rear 16.3 sq in, 105 sq cm, total 39.9 sq in, 257 sq cm.

ELECTRICAL EQUIPMENT voltage: 12 V; battery: 55 Ah; generator type: alternator, 490 W; ignition distributor: Bosch; headlamps: 2.

DIMENSIONS AND WEIGHT wheel base: 94.49 in, 2,400 mm; front track: 58.43 in, 1,484 mm; rear track: 58.46 in, 1,485 mm; overall length: 168.70 in, 4,285 mm; overall width: 69.29 in, 1,760 mm; overall height: 51.38 in, 1,305 mm; ground clearance: 6.30 in, 160 mm; dry weight: 2,999 lb, 1,360 kg; distribution of weight: 53.3% front axle, 46.7% rear axle; turning circle (between walls): 33.8 ft, 10.3 m; fuel tank capacity: 18 imp gal, 21.6 US gal, 82 l.

BODY roadster; doors: 2; seats: 2-3; front seats: separate, reclining backrests.

PRACTICAL INSTRUCTIONS fuel: 96 oct petrol; engine sump oil: 9.7 imp pt, 11.6 US pt, 5.5 l, SAE 20W, change every 3,700 miles, 6,000 km; gearbox oil: 2.5 imp pt, 3 US pt, 1.4 l, SAE 90, change every 11,200 miles, 18,000 km; final drive oil: 4.4 imp pt, 5.3 US pt, 2.5 l, SAE 90, change every 11,200 miles, 18,000 km; greasing: every 1,900 miles, 3,000 km, 20 points; normal tyre pressure: front 26 psi, 1.8 atm, rear 31 psi, 2.2 atm.

MERCEDES-BENZ 250 CE Coupé

MERCEDES-BENZ 280 SL Roadster

MERCEDES-BENZ 300 SEL 3.5 Limousine

OPTIONAL ACCESSORIES 5-speed mechanical gearbox, 3.920 axle ratio; limited slip final drive; DB automatic gearbox, hydraulic coupling and planetary gears with 4 ratios (I 3.980, II 2.520, III 1.580., IV 1, rev 4.150), possible manual selection; power-assisted steering; air conditioning system; hardtop; electrically-heated rear window (only with hardtop).

300 SEL 3.5 Limousine

PRICE IN GB: £ 5,203.
PRICE EX WORKS: 31,024 marks.

ENGINE front, 4 stroke; cylinders: 8, Vee-slanted at 90°; bore and stroke: 3.62 x 2.59 in, 92 x 65.8 mm; engine capacity: 213.5 cu in, 3,499 cu cm; compression ratio: 9.5; max power (SAE): 230 hp at 6,050 rpm; max torque (SAE): 232 lb ft, 32 kg m at 4,200 rpm; max engine rpm: 6,500; specific power: 65.7 hp/l; cylinder block: cast iron; cylinder head: light alloy; crankshaft bearings: 5; valves: 2 per cylinder, overhead, finger levers; camshafts: 1 per cylinder block, overhead; lubrication: gear pump, full flow and by-pass filters, oil cooler; lubricating system capacity: 11.4 imp pt, 13.7 US pt, 6.5 l; carburation: Bosch electronically-controlled injection system; fuel feed: electric pump; cooling system: water, thermostatic fan; cooling system capacity: 23.2 imp pt, 27.9 US pt, 13.2 l.

TRANSMISSION driving wheels: rear; gearbox: DB automatic, hydraulic coupling and planetary gears with 4 ratios + reverse; gearbox ratios: I 3.980, II 2.390, III 1.460, IV 1, rev 5.470; selector lever: steering column; final drive: hypoid bevel; axle ratio: 3.690; width of rims: 6''; tyres: 185 x 14.

PERFORMANCE max speeds: 30 mph, 40 km/h in 1st gear; 55 mph, 88 km/h in 2nd gear; 92 mph, 148 km/h in 3rd gear; 127 mph, 205 km/h in 4th gear; power-weight ratio: 16.1 lb/hp, 7.3 kg/hp; carrying capacity: 1,103 lb, 500 kg; max gradient in 1st gear: 45%; fuel consumption: 20.9 m/imp gal, 17.4 m/US gal, 13.5 l x 100 km.

CHASSIS integral, front auxiliary frame; front suspension: independent, wishbones, air rubber springs, anti-roll bar, telescopic dampers; rear suspension: independent, single joint low pivot, swinging semi-axles, trailing lower radius arms, coil springs, auxiliary air rubber springs, anti-roll bar, telescopic dampers.

STEERING recirculating ball, damper, servo; turns of steering wheel lock to lock: 3.

BRAKES disc, dual circuit, rear compensator, servo; lining area: front 23.6 sq in, 152 sq cm, rear 16.3 sq in, 105 sq cm, total 39.9 sq in, 257 sq cm.

ELECTRICAL EQUIPMENT voltage: 12 V; battery: 66 Ah; generator type: alternator, 770 W; ignition distributor: Bosch (electronic); headlamps: 2.

DIMENSIONS AND WEIGHT wheel base: 112.20 in, 2,850 mm; front track: 58.35 in, 1,482 mm; rear track: 58.46 in, 1,485 mm; overall length: 196.85 in, 5,000 mm; overall width: 71.26 in, 1,810 mm; overall height: 55.51 in, 1,410 mm; ground clearance: 6.61 in, 168 mm; dry weight: 3,682 lb, 1,670 kg; distribution of weight: 52.4% front axle, 47.6% rear axle; turning circle (between walls): 39.7 ft, 12.1 m; fuel tank capacity: 18 imp gal, 21.6 US gal, 82 l.

BODY saloon/sedan; doors: 4; seats: 5-6; front seats: separate, reclining backrests; details: electrically-controlled windows.

PRACTICAL INSTRUCTIONS fuel: 96 oct petrol; engine sump oil: 11.4 imp pt, 13.7 US pt, 6.5 l, SAE 20W-40, change every 3,700 miles, 6,000 km; gearbox oil: 9.5 imp pt, 11.4 US pt, 5.4 l, ATF, change every 12,400 miles, 20,000 km; final drive oil: 4.4 imp pt, 5.3 US pt, 2.5 l, SAE 90, change every 12,400 miles, 20,000 km; normal tyre pressure: front 23 psi, 1.6 atm, rear 27 psi, 1.9 atm.

OPTIONAL ACCESSORIES 3.920 axle ratio; 4- or 5-speed mechanical gearbox; limited slip final drive; air-conditioning system; sunshine roof; electrically-heated rear window.

280 SE 3.5 Coupé

See 300 SEL 3.5 Limousine, except for:

PRICE IN GB: £ 5,187.
PRICE EX WORKS: 32,023 marks.

TRANSMISSION clutch: single dry plate, hydraulically controlled; gearbox: mechanical (standard); gears: 4 + reverse; synchromesh gears: I, II, III, IV; gearbox ratios: I 3.960, II 2.340, III 1.440, IV 1, rev 3.720; gear lever: steering column or central.

PERFORMANCE max speeds: 32 mph, 52 km/h in 1st gear; 55 mph, 88 km/h in 2nd gear; 92 mph, 148 km/h in 3rd gear; 130 mph, 210 km/h in 4th gear; power-weight ratio: 15 lb/hp, 6.8 kg/hp.

280 SE 3.5 COUPÉ

DIMENSIONS AND WEIGHT wheel base: 108.27 in, 2,750 mm; overall length: 193.11 in, 4,905 mm; overall width: 72.64 in, 1,845 mm; overall height: 55.51 in 1,410 mm; dry weight: 3,462 lb, 1,570 kg; distribution of weight: 52.5% front axle, 47.5% rear axle; turning circle (between walls): 38.7 ft, 11.8 m.

BODY coupé; doors: 2; seats: 5.

PRACTICAL INSTRUCTIONS gearbox oil: 3.2 imp pt, 3.8 US pt, 1.8 l.

OPTIONAL ACCESSORIES only DB automatic gearbox; limited slip final drive; air-conditioning system; sunshine roof; electrically-heated rear window.

280 SE 3.5 Cabriolet

See 300 SEL 3.5 Limousine, except for:

PRICE IN GB: £ 5,551.
PRICE EX WORKS: 35,631 marks.

PERFORMANCE power-weight ratio: 15.9 lb/hp, 7.2 kg/hp.

DIMENSIONS AND WEIGHT wheel base: 108.27 in, 2,750 mm; overall length: 193.11 in, 4,905 mm; overall width: 72.64 in, 1,845 mm; overall height: 55.91 in, 1,420 mm; dry weight: 3,638 lb, 1,650 kg; distribution of weight: 52.1% front axle, 47.9% rear axle; turning circle (between walls): 38.7 ft, 11.8 m.

BODY convertible; doors: 2; seats: 5.

OPTIONAL ACCESSORIES sunshine roof and electrically-heated rear window not available.

300 SEL 6.3 Limousine

PRICE IN GB: £ 6,214.
PRICE IN USA: $ 15,122.

ENGINE front, 4 stroke; cylinders: 8, Vee-slanted at 90°; bore and stroke: 4.06 x 3.74 in, 103 x 95 mm; engine capacity: 386.4 cu in, 6,332 cu cm; compression ratio: 9; max power (SAE): 300 hp at 4,100 rpm; max torque (SAE): 435 lb ft, 60 kg m at 3,000 rpm; max engine rpm: 5,250; specific power: 47.4 hp/l; cylinder block: cast iron; cylinder head: light alloy; crankshaft bearings: 5; valves: 2 per cylinder, overhead, finger levers; camshafts: 1 per cylinder block, overhead; lubrication: gear pump, full flow and by-pass filters, oil cooler; lubricating system capacity: 10.6 imp pt, 12.7 US pt, 6 l; carburation: 8-cylinder Bosch intermittent injection pump in inlet pipes; fuel feed: electric pump; cooling system: water, thermostatic fan; cooling system capacity: 31.7 imp pt, 38.1 US pt, 18 l.

TRANSMISSION driving wheels: rear; gearbox: DB automatic, hydraulic coupling and planetary gears with 4 ratios + reverse; gearbox ratios: I 3.980, II 2.460, III 1.580, IV 1, rev 4.150; selector lever: central; final drive: hypoid bevel, limited slip; axle ratio: 2.820; tyres: 195 x 14.

PERFORMANCE max speeds: 29 mph, 47 km/h in 1st gear; 56 mph, 90 km/h in 2nd gear; 87 mph, 140 km/h in 3rd gear; 137 mph, 220 km/h in 4th gear; power-weight ratio: 13 lb/hp, 5.9 kg/hp; carrying capacity: 1,103 lb, 500 kg; max gradient in 1st gear: 44%; fuel consumption: 18.2 m/imp gal, 15.2 m/US gal, 15.5 l x 100 km.

CHASSIS integral, front auxiliary frame; front suspension: independent, wishbones, air rubber springs, auxiliary air rubber springs, automatically and manually controlled levelling system, anti-roll bar, telescopic dampers; rear suspension: independent, single joint low pivot, swinging semi-axles, trailing lower radius arms, air rubber springs, auxiliary air rubber springs, automatically and manually controlled levelling system, anti-roll bar, telescopic dampers.

STEERING recirculating ball, damper, servo, adjustable height of steering wheel; turns of steering wheel lock to lock: 2.67.

BRAKES disc, dual circuit, rear compensator, servo; lining area: front 23.6 sq in, 152 sq cm, rear 16.3 sq in, 105 sq cm, total 39.9 sq in, 257 sq cm.

ELECTRICAL EQUIPMENT voltage: 12 V; battery: 88 Ah; generator type: alternator, 770 W; ignition distributor: Bosch; headlamps: 4, 2 iodine; fog lamps: 2.

DIMENSIONS AND WEIGHT wheel base: 112.80 in, 2,865 mm; front track: 58.66 in 1,490 mm; rear track: 58.46 in, 1,485 mm; overall length: 196.85 in, 5,000 mm; overall width: 71.26 in, 1,810 mm; overall height: 55.91 in, 1,420 mm; ground clearance: 6.77 in, 172 mm; dry weight: 3,925 lb, 1,780 kg; turning circle (between walls): 40.3 ft, 12.3 m; fuel tank capacity: 23.1 imp gal, 27.7 US gal, 105 l.

MERCEDES-BENZ 280 SE 3.5 Cabriolet

MERCEDES-BENZ 280 SE 3.5 Coupé

MERCEDES-BENZ 300 SEL 6.3 Limousine

BODY saloon/sedan; doors: 4; seats: 5-6; front seats: separate, reclining backrests; details: electrically-controlled windows.

PRACTICAL INSTRUCTIONS fuel: 96 oct petrol; engine sump oil: 10.6 imp pt, 12.7 US pt, 6 l, SAE 20W-20, change every 3,700 miles, 6,000 km; gearbox oil: 13.6 imp pt, 16.3 US pt, 7.7 l, ATF, change every 12,400 miles, 20,000 km; final drive oil: 4.4 imp pt, 5.3 US pt, 2.5 l, SAE 90, change every 12,400 miles, 20,000 km; greasing: none; sparking plug type: 215°; tappet clearances: inlet 0.004 in, 0.10 mm, exhaust 0.010 in, 0.25 mm; valve timing: inlet opens 2°30' before tdc and closes 52°30' after bdc, exhaust opens 37°30' before bdc and closes 18° after tdc; normal tyre pressure: front 28 psi, 2 atm, rear 33 psi, 2.3 atm.

OPTIONAL ACCESSORIES sunshine roof.

600 Limousine

PRICE IN GB: £ 7,654.
PRICE IN USA: $ 24,600.

ENGINE front, 4 stroke; cylinders: 8, Vee-slanted at 90°; bore and stroke: 4.06 x 3.74 in, 103 x 95 mm; engine capacity: 386.4 cu in, 6,332 cu cm; compression ratio: 9; max power (SAE): 300 hp at 4,100 rpm; max torque (SAE): 435 lb ft, 60 kg m at 3,000 rpm; max engine rpm: 4,800; specific power: 47.4 hp/l; cylinder block: cast iron; cylinder head: light alloy; crankshaft bearings: 5; valves: 2 per cylinder, overhead, finger levers; camshafts: 1 per cylinder block, overhead; lubrication: gear pump, full flow and by-pass filters; lubricating system capacity: 10.6 imp pt, 12.7 US pt, 6 l; carburation: 8-cylinder Bosch intermittent injection pump in inlet pipes; fuel feed: electric pump; cooling system: water, thermostatic fan; cooling system capacity: 40.5 imp pt, 48.6 US pt, 23 l.

TRANSMISSION driving wheels: rear; gearbox: DB automatic, hydraulic coupling and twin planetary gears with 4 ratios + reverse; gearbox ratios: I 3.980, II 2.460, III 1.580, IV 1, rev 4.150; selector lever: steering column; final drive: hypoid bevel, limited slip; axle ratio: 3.230; width of rims: 6.5''; tyres: 6.00 x 15.

PERFORMANCE max speeds: 31 mph, 50 km/h in 1st gear; 50 mph, 80 km/h in 2nd gear; 81 mph, 130 km/h in 3rd gear; 127 mph, 205 km/h in 4th gear; power-weight ratio: 18.1 lb/hp, 8.2 kg/hp; carrying capacity: 1,297 lb, 580 kg; max gradient in 1st gear: 45%; acceleration: 0-50 mph (0-80 km/h) 6.9 sec; speed in direct drive at 1,000 rpm: 26.4 mph, 42.5 km/h; fuel consumption: 15.9 m/imp gal, 13.2 m/US gal, 17.8 l x 100 km.

CHASSIS integral, front auxiliary frame; front suspension: independent, wishbones, air rubber springs, auxiliary air rubber springs, automatically and manually controlled levelling system, anti-roll bar, telescopic dampers adjustable while running; rear suspension: independent, single joint low pivot, swinging semi-axles, trailing lower radius arms, air rubber springs, auxiliary air rubber springs, automatically and manually controlled levelling system, anti-roll bar, telescopic dampers adjustable while running.

STEERING recirculating ball, damper, servo, adjustable height of steering wheel; turns of steering wheel lock to lock: 3.30.

BRAKES disc [front diameter (twin calipers) 11.46 in, 291 mm, rear 11.57 in, 294 mm], dual circuit, rear compensator, servo; lining area: front 31.6 sq in, 204 sq cm, rear 24.7 sq in, 159 sq cm, total 56.3 sq in, 363 sq cm.

ELECTRICAL EQUIPMENT voltage: 12 V; battery: 88 Ah; generator type: 2 alternators, 490 W; ignition distributor: Bosch; headlamps: 2.

DIMENSIONS AND WEIGHT wheel base: 125.98 in, 3,200 mm; front track: 62.48 in, 1,587 mm; rear track: 62.24 in, 1,581 mm; overall length: 218.11 in, 5,540 mm; overall width: 76.77 in, 1,950 mm; overall height: 58.46 in, 1,485 mm; ground clearance: 6.50 in, 165 mm; dry weight: 5,457 lb, 2,475 kg; distribution of weight: 50.6% front axle, 49.4% rear axle; turning circle (between walls): 41.7 ft, 12.7 m; fuel tank capacity: 24.6 imp gal, 29.6 US gal, 112 l.

BODY limousine; doors: 4; seats: 6; front seats: bench; details: windows, locks, glass partition and front and rear seats (shifting horizontally and vertically) hydraulically controlled.

PRACTICAL INSTRUCTIONS fuel: 96 oct petrol; engine sump oil: 10.6 imp pt, 12.7 US pt, 6 l, SAE 20W-20, change every 3,700 miles, 6,000 km; gearbox oil: 13.6 imp pt, 16.3 US pt, 7.7 l, ATF, change every 12,400 miles, 20,000 km; final drive oil: 5.6 imp pt, 6.8 US pt, 3.2 l, SAE 90, change every 12,400 miles, 20,000 km; greasing: none; sparking plug type: 215°; tappet clearances: inlet 0.004 in, 0.10 mm, exhaust 0.010 in, 0.25 mm; valve timing: inlet opens 2°30' before tdc and closes 52°30' after bdc, exhaust opens 37°30' before bdc and closes 18° after tdc; normal tyre pressure: front 28 psi, 2 atm, rear 33 psi, 2.3 atm.

OPTIONAL ACCESSORIES air-conditioning system; sunshine roof.

600 Pullman-Limousine

See 600 Limousine, except for:

PRICE IN GB: £ 8,538.
PRICE IN USA: $ 28,120.

PERFORMANCE power-weight ratio: 19.6 lb/hp, 8.9 kg/hp; carrying capacity: 1,544 lb, 700 kg; max gradient in 1st gear: 42.5%.

DIMENSIONS AND WEIGHT wheel base: 153.54 in, 3,900 mm; overall length: 245.67 in, 6,240 mm; overall height: 59.06 in, 1,500 mm; dry weight: 5,865 lb, 2,660 kg; distribution of weight: 51.5% front axle, 48.5% rear axle; turning circle (between walls): 49.2 ft, 15 m.

BODY doors: 4 or 6; seats: 7-8.

MERCEDES-BENZ 280 SE 3.5 Cabriolet

NSU   GERMANY (F.R.)

Prinz 4L

PRICE IN GB: £ 503.
PRICE EX WORKS: 4,990 marks.

ENGINE rear, transverse, 4 stroke; cylinders: 2, in line; bore and stroke: 2.99 x 2.60 in, 76 x 66 mm; engine capacity: 36.5 cu in, 598 cu cm; compression ratio: 7.5; max power (DIN): 30 hp at 5,500 rpm; max torque (DIN): 33 lb ft, 4.5 kg m at 3,250 rpm; max engine rpm: 6,500; specific power: 50.2 hp/l; cylinder block: cast iron; cylinder head: light alloy; crankshaft bearings: 2; valves: 2 per cylinder, overhead, Vee-slanted, rockers; camshafts: 1, overhead, driven by connecting rods; lubrication: gear pump, full flow filter; lubricating system capacity: 4.8 imp pt, 5.7 US pt, 2.7 l; carburation: 1 Solex 34 PCI downdraught carburettor; fuel feed: mechanical pump; cooling system: air cooled.

TRANSMISSION driving wheels: rear; clutch: single dry plate; gearbox: mechanical; engine-gearbox ratio: 2.08; gears: 4 + reverse; synchromesh gears: I, II, III, IV; gearbox ratios: I 4.140, II 2.210, III 1.410, IV 1, rev 5.380; gear lever: central; final drive: hypoid bevel; axle ratio: 2.310; width of rims: 4''; tyres: 5.65/135 x 12.

PERFORMANCE max speeds: 21 mph, 33 km/h in 1st gear; 38 mph, 61 km/h in 2nd gear; 60 mph, 96 km/h in 3rd gear; 75 mph, 120 km/h in 4th gear; power-weight ratio: 40.8 lb/hp, 18.5 kg/hp; carrying capacity: 981 lb, 445 kg; acceleration: standing 1/4 mile 23.6 sec, 0-50 mph (0-80 km/h) 15.8 sec; speed in direct drive at 1,000 rpm: 13 mph, 20.9 km/h; fuel consumption: 49.6 m/imp gal, 41.3 m/US gal, 5.7 l x 100 km.

CHASSIS integral; front suspension: independent, wishbones, coil springs, anti-roll bar, telescopic dampers; rear suspension: independent, swinging semi-axles, wide-based wishbones, coil springs, Prinzair auxiliary air rubber springs, telescopic dampers.

STEERING rack-and-pinion; turns of steering wheel lock to lock: 3.

BRAKES drum, 2 front leading shoes; lining area: total 58.5 sq in, 377 sq cm.

ELECTRICAL EQUIPMENT voltage: 12 V; battery: 32 Ah; generator type: dynamo, 130 W; ignition distributor: Bosch; headlamps: 2.

MERCEDES-BENZ 300 SEL 6.3 Limousine

DIMENSIONS AND WEIGHT wheel base: 80.31 in, 2,040 mm; front track: 48.70 in, 1,237 mm; rear track: 47.60 in, 1,209 mm; overall length: 135.43 in, 3,440 mm; overall width: 58.66 in, 1,490 mm; overall height: 53.54 in, 1,360 mm; ground clearance: 7.09 in, 180 mm; dry weight: 1,224 lb, 555 kg; distribution of weight: 44% front axle, 56% rear axle; turning circle (between walls): 28.9 ft, 8.8 m; fuel tank capacity: 8.1 imp gal, 9.8 US gal, 37 l.

BODY saloon/sedan; doors: 2; seats: 4; front seats: separate.

PRACTICAL INSTRUCTIONS fuel: 85-90 oct petrol; engine sump, gearbox and final drive oil: 4.2 imp pt, 5.1 US pt, 2.4 l, SAE 20 (winter) 30 (summer), change every 4,700 miles, 7,500 km; greasing: every 4,700 miles, 7,500 km, 2 points; sparking plug type: 225°; tappet clearances: inlet 0.004 in, 0.10 mm, exhaust 0.004 in, 0.10 mm; valve timing: inlet opens 48° before tdc and closes 72° after bdc, exhaust opens 78° before tdc and closes 42° after tdc; normal tyre pressure: front 20 psi, 1.4 atm, rear 24 psi, 1.7 atm.

OPTIONAL ACCESSORIES front disc brakes, diameter 8.94 in, 227 mm; sunshine roof.

MERCEDES-BENZ 600 Limousine

1000 C

PRICE IN GB: £ 595.
PRICE IN USA: $ 1,979.

ENGINE rear, transverse, 4 stroke; cylinders: 4, in line; bore and stroke: 2.72 x 2.62 in, 69 x 66.6 mm; engine capacity: 60.8 cu in, 996 cu cm; compression ratio: 7.5; max power (DIN): 40 hp at 5,500 rpm; max torque (DIN): 51 lb ft, 7 kg m at 2,500-3,500 rpm; max engine rpm: 5,800; specific power: 40.2 hp/l; cylinder block: light alloy; cylinder head: light alloy; crankshaft bearings: 5; valves: 2 per cylinder, overhead, Vee-slanted, rockers; camshafts: 1, overhead; lubrication: gear pump, full flow filter; lubricating system capacity: 6.2 imp pt, 7.4 US pt, 3.5 l; carburation: 1 Solex 34 PCI downdraught single barrel carburettor; fuel feed: mechanical pump; cooling system: air cooled.

TRANSMISSION driving wheels: rear; clutch: single dry plate; gearbox: mechanical; engine-gearbox ratio: 2.05; gears: 4 + reverse; synchromesh gears: I, II, III, IV; gearbox ratios: I 4.356, II 2.403, III 1.538, IV 1.100, rev 4.869; gear lever: central; final drive: cylindrical gears; axle ratio: 3.786; width of rims: 4.5''; tyres: 5.50 x 12.

PERFORMANCE max speeds: 22 mph, 36 km/h in 1st gear; 40 mph, 65 km/h in 2nd gear; 63 mph, 102 km/h in 3rd gear; 81 mph, 130 km/h in 4th gear; power-weight ratio: 36.4 lb/hp, 16.5 kg/hp; carrying capacity: 882 lb, 400 kg; acceleration: standing ¼ mile 20.7 sec, 0-50 mph (0-80 km/h) 12 sec; speed in top at 1,000 rpm: 15.5 mph, 25 km/h; fuel consumption: 36.7 m/imp gal, 30.5 m/US gal, 7.7 l x 100 km.

CHASSIS integral; front suspension: independent, wishbones, coil springs, anti-roll bar, telescopic dampers; rear suspension: independent, semi-trailing arms, coil springs, telescopic dampers.

STEERING rack-and-pinion; turns of steering wheel lock to lock: 3.50.

BRAKES drum; lining area: front 45.3 sq in, 292 sq cm, rear 28.5 sq in, 184 sq cm, total 73.8 sq in, 476 sq cm.

ELECTRICAL EQUIPMENT voltage: 12 V; battery: 32 Ah; generator type: dynamo, 350 W; ignition distributor: Bosch; headlamps: 2.

DIMENSIONS AND WEIGHT wheel base: 88.58 in, 2,250 mm; front track: 49.61 in, 1,260 mm; rear track: 49.13 in, 1,248 mm; overall length: 148.03 in, 3,760 mm; overall width: 58.66 in, 1,490 mm; overall height: 53.70 in, 1,364 mm; ground clearance: 7.68 in, 195 mm; dry weight: 1,455 lb, 660 kg; distribution of weight: 41.6% front axle, 58.4% rear axle; turning circle (between walls): 30.8 ft, 9.4 m; fuel tank capacity: 8.1 imp gal, 9.8 US gal, 37 l.

BODY saloon/sedan; doors: 2; seats: 5; front seats: separate.

PRACTICAL INSTRUCTIONS fuel: 85-90 oct petrol; engine sump oil: 6.2 imp pt, 7.4 US pt, 3.5 l, SAE 10W-30, change every 4,700 miles, 7,500 km; gearbox and final drive oil: 3.5 imp pt, 4.2 US pt, 2 l, SAE 80, change every 4,700 miles, 7,500 km; greasing: none; sparking plug type: 225°; tappet clearances: inlet 0.008 in, 0.20 mm, exhaust 0.008 in, 0.20 mm; normal tyre pressure: front 18 psi, 1.3 atm, rear 27 psi, 1.9 atm.

OPTIONAL ACCESSORIES front disc brakes, diameter 9.02 in, 229 mm; sunshine roof; 145 x 12 tyres.

TTS

See 1000 C, except for:

PRICE IN GB: £ 857.
PRICE EX WORKS: 8,500 marks.

ENGINE compression ratio: 10.5; max power (DIN): 70 hp at 6,150 rpm; max torque (DIN): 62 lb ft, 8.5 kg m at 5,500 rpm; specific power: 70.3 hp/l; lubrication: oil cooler; lubricating system capacity: 8.8 imp pt, 10.6 US pt, 5 l; carburation: 2 Solex 40 PHH downdraught twin barrel carburettors.

TRANSMISSION tyres: 135 x 13.

PERFORMANCE max speed: 99 mph, 160 km/h; power-weight ratio: 19.2 lb/hp, 8.7 kg/hp; acceleration: 0-50 mph (0-80 km/h) 7.6 sec; fuel consumption: 33.2 m/imp gal, 27.7 m/US gal, 8.5 l x 100 km.

CHASSIS front suspension: front wishbones with lower trailing links.

BRAKES front disc (diameter 9.02 in, 229 mm).

ELECTRICAL EQUIPMENT generator type: alternator, 490 W.

DIMENSIONS AND WEIGHT front track: 50.59 in, 1,285 mm;

NSU Prinz 4L

NSU 1000 C

NSU 1200 C

ear track: 50.16 in, 1,274 mm; overall length: 149.33 in, 793 mm; dry weight: 1,345 lb, 610 kg.

OPTIONAL ACCESSORIES 145 x 12 tyres.

1200

PRICE EX WORKS: 6,210 marks.

ENGINE rear, transverse, 4 stroke; cylinders: 4, in line; bore and stroke: 2.95 x 2.62 in, 75 x 66.6 mm; engine capacity: 71.8 cu in, 1,177 cu cm; compression ratio: 7.8; max power (DIN): 55 hp at 5,600 rpm; max torque (DIN): 62 lb ft, 8.5 kg m at 2,500-4,500 rpm; max engine rpm: 5,800; specific power: 46.7 hp/l; cylinder block: light alloy; cylinder head: light alloy; crankshaft bearings: 5; valves: 2 per cylinder, overhead, Vee-slanted, rockers; camshafts: 1, overhead; lubrication: gear pump, full flow filter; lubricating system capacity: 6.2 imp pt, 7.4 US pt, 3.5 l; carburation: 1 Solex 34 PCI downdraught single barrel carburettor; fuel feed: mechanical pump; cooling system: air cooled.

TRANSMISSION driving wheels: rear; clutch: single dry plate, hydraulically controlled; gearbox: mechanical; gears: 4 + reverse; synchromesh gears: I, II, III, IV; gearbox ratios: I 4.356, II 2.403, III 1.538, IV 1.100, rev 4.869; gear lever: central; final drive: cylindrical gears; axle ratio: 4.786; width of rims: 4.5''; tyres: 6.15/155 x 13.

PERFORMANCE max speeds: 23 mph, 37 km/h in 1st gear; 41 mph, 66 km/h in 2nd gear; 65 mph, 104 km/h in 3rd gear; 90 mph, 145 km/h in 4th gear; power-weight ratio: 17.6 lb/hp, 12.5 kg/hp; carrying capacity: 970 lb, 440 kg; max gradient in 1st gear: 63%; acceleration: 0-50 mph (0-80 km/h) 9.4 sec; speed in top at 1,000 rpm: 15.5 mph, 25 km/h; fuel consumption: 36.7 m/imp gal, 30.5 m/US gal, 7.7 l x 100 km.

CHASSIS integral; front suspension: independent, wishbones, lower trailing links, coil springs, anti-roll bar, telescopic dampers; rear suspension: independent, semi-trailing arms, coil springs, telescopic dampers.

STEERING rack-and-pinion; turns of steering wheel lock to lock: 3.20.

BRAKES drum; lining area: total 90.5 sq in, 584 sq cm.

ELECTRICAL EQUIPMENT voltage: 12 V; battery: 32 Ah; generator type: dynamo, 350 W; ignition distributor: Bosch; headlamps: 2.

DIMENSIONS AND WEIGHT wheel base: 96.06 in, 2,440 mm; front track: 50.39 in, 1,280 mm; rear track: 49.13 in, 1,248 mm; overall length: 157.48 in, 4,000 mm; overall width: 59.06 in, 1,500 mm; overall height: 54.72 in, 1,390 mm; ground clearance: 7.48 in, 190 mm; dry weight: 1,521 lb, 690 kg; distribution of weight: 45% front axle, 55% rear axle; turning circle (between walls): 32.5 ft, 9.9 m; fuel tank capacity: 9.7 imp gal, 11.6 US gal, 44 l.

BODY saloon/sedan; doors: 2; seats: 4-5; front seats: separate.

PRACTICAL INSTRUCTIONS fuel: 85-90 oct petrol; engine sump oil: 6.2 imp pt, 7.4 US pt, 3.5 l, SAE 10W-30, change every 4,700 miles, 7,500 km; gearbox and final drive oil: 3.5 imp pt, 4.2 US pt, 2 l, SAE 80; greasing: none; sparking plug type: 225°; tappet clearances: inlet 0.008 in, 0.20 mm, exhaust 0.008 in, 0.20 mm; valve timing: inlet opens 20° before tdc and closes 50° after bdc, exhaust opens 55° before bdc and closes 25° after tdc; normal tyre pressure: front 17 psi, 1.2 atm, rear 21 psi, 1.5 atm.

OPTIONAL ACCESSORIES front disc brakes, diameter 9.02 in, 229 mm; sunshine roof.

1200 C

See 1200, except for:

PRICE IN GB: £ 648.
PRICE IN USA: $ 2,252.

PERFORMANCE power-weight ratio: 28.4 lb/hp, 12.9 kg/hp; carrying capacity: 904 lb, 410 kg.

DIMENSIONS AND WEIGHT dry weight: 1,566 lb, 710 kg.

BODY details: special luxury interior.

1200 C Automatic

See 1200 C, except for:

PRICE IN GB: £ 723.
PRICE EX WORKS: 6,990 marks.

TRANSMISSION gearbox: semi-automatic with 3 ratios; gearbox ratios: I 2.995, II 1.679, III 1.095, rev 3.845.

NSU Prinz 4L

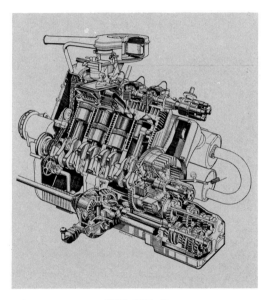

NSU 1000 C

NSU 1200 C Automatic

TT

See 1200, except for:

PRICE IN GB: £ 725.
PRICE IN USA: $ 2,352.

ENGINE compression ratio: 9.2; max power (DIN): 65 hp at 5,500 rpm; max torque (DIN): 65 lb ft, 9 kg m at 2,500-4,500 rpm; max engine rpm: 5,900; specific power: 55.2 hp/l; lubrication: oil cooler; lubricating system capacity: 7 imp pt, 8.5 US pt, 4 l; carburation: 2 Solex 34 PCI downdraught single barrel carburettors.

TRANSMISSION gearbox ratios: I 3.561, II 2.255, III 1.538, IV 1.100, rev 4.869; axle ratio: 3.533; tyres: 135 x 13.

PERFORMANCE max speeds: 31 mph, 50 km/h in 1st gear; 48 mph, 78 km/h in 2nd gear; 71 mph, 115 km/h in 3rd gear; 96 mph, 155 km/h in 4th gear; power-weight ratio: 20.7 lb/hp, 9.4 kg/hp; acceleration: 0-50 mph (0-80 km/h) 8.9 sec; speed in top at 1,000 rpm: 16.8 mph, 27 km/h; fuel consumption: 35.3 m/imp gal, 29.4 m/US gal, 8 l x 100 km.

BRAKES front disc (diameter 9.02 in, 229 mm).

ELECTRICAL EQUIPMENT generator type: alternator, 490 W.

DIMENSIONS AND WEIGHT wheel base: 88.58 in, 2,250 mm; front track: 49.45 in, 1,256 mm; rear track: 49.13 in, 1,248 mm; overall length: 149.33 in, 3,793 mm; overall width: 58.66 in, 1,490 mm; overall height: 53.70 in, 1,364 mm; dry weight: 1,345 lb, 610 kg; turning circle (between walls): 31.2 ft, 9.5 m.

OPTIONAL ACCESSORIES 145 x 12 tyres.

Ro 80

PRICE IN GB: £ 1,981.
PRICE EX WORKS: 16,500 marks.

ENGINE front, 4 stroke, Wankel type; 2 co-axial 3-lobe rotors; engine capacity: 30.3 x 2 cu in, 497 x 2 cu cm; compression ratio: 9; max power (DIN): 115 hp at 5,500 rpm; max torque (DIN): 121 lb ft, 16.7 kg m at 4,500 rpm; max engine rpm: 6,500; engine block: light alloy, dual ignition; rotors: light alloy; crankshaft bearings: 2; lubrication: gear pump, full flow filter, oil-water heat exchanger; lubricating system capacity: 12 imp pt, 14.4 US pt, 6.8 l; carburation: 2 Solex 18/32 HHD horizontal carburettors; fuel feed: mechanical pump; cooling system: engine block by water, rotors by oil; cooling system capacity: 15 imp pt, 18 US pt, 8.5 l.

TRANSMISSION driving wheels: front; clutch: single dry plate automatically operated by gear lever; gearbox: 3-speed semi-automatic, hydraulic torque convertor, max ratio of convertor at stall 2, possible manual selection; gearbox ratios: I 2.056, II 1.208, III 0.788, rev 2.105; gear lever: central; final drive: cylindrical gears; axle ratio: 4.857; width of rims: 5''; tyres: 175 x 14.

PERFORMANCE max speeds: 47 mph, 75 km/h in 1st gear; 80 mph, 129 km/h in 2nd gear; 112 mph, 180 km/h in 3rd gear; power-weight ratio: 24.5 lb/hp, 11.1 kg/hp; carrying capacity: 992 lb, 450 kg; acceleration: standing 1/4 mile 20.1 sec; speed in top at 1,000 rpm: 18.8 mph, 30.3 km/h; fuel consumption: 25.2 m/imp gal, 21 m/US gal, 11.2 l x 100 km.

CHASSIS integral; front suspension: independent, by McPherson, coil springs/telescopic damper struts, lower articulated wishbones, anti-roll bar; rear suspension: independent, semi-trailing arms, coil springs, telescopic dampers.

STEERING rack-and-pinion, ZF servo; turns of steering wheel lock to lock: 3.80.

BRAKES disc (front diameter 11.18 in, 284 mm, rear 10.71 in, 272 mm), servo; lining area: front 30.4 sq in, 196 sq cm, rear 12.9 sq in, 83 sq cm, total 43.3 sq in, 279 sq cm.

ELECTRICAL EQUIPMENT voltage: 12 V; battery: 66 Ah; generator type: alternator, 490 W; ignition distributors: 2, Bosch; headlamps: 4.

DIMENSIONS AND WEIGHT wheel base: 112.60 in, 2,860 mm; front track: 58.27 in, 1,480 mm; rear track: 56.46 in, 1,434 mm; overall length: 188.19 in, 4,780 mm; overall width: 69.29 in, 1,760 mm; overall height: 55.51 in, 1,410 mm; ground clearance: 4.49 in, 114 mm; dry weight: 2,822 lb, 1,280 kg; distribution of weight: 62% front axle, 38% rear axle; turning circle (between walls): 38.7 ft, 11.8 m; fuel tank capacity: 18 imp gal, 21.6 US gal, 82 l.

BODY saloon/sedan; doors: 4; seats: 5; front seats: separate.

PRACTICAL INSTRUCTIONS fuel: 100 oct petrol; engine sump oil: 12 imp pt, 14.4 US pt, 6.8 l, SAE 10W-30; gearbox and final drive oil: 3.5 imp pt, 4.2 US pt, 2 l, SAE 80, change every 12,400 miles, 20,000 km; normal tyre pressure: front 28 psi, 2 atm, rear 24 psi, 1.7 atm.

OPTIONAL ACCESSORIES light alloy wheels; sunshine roof.

OPEL GERMANY (F.R.)

2-door Kadett Limousine

PRICE IN GB: £ 643.
PRICE IN USA: $ 1,925.

ENGINE front, 4 stroke; cylinders: 4, in line; bore and stroke: 2.95 x 2.40 in, 75 x 61 mm; engine capacity: 65.8 cu in, 1,078 cu cm; compression ratio: 7.8; max power (DIN): 45 hp at 5,000 rpm; max torque (DIN): 55 lb ft, 7.6 kg m at 2,400-3,200 rpm; max engine rpm: 5,600; specific power: 41.7 hp/l; cylinder block: cast iron; cylinder head: cast iron; crankshaft bearings: 3; valves: 2 per cylinder, overhead, push-rods and rockers; camshafts: 1, side; lubrication: gear pump, full flow filter; lubricating system capacity: 4.8 imp pt, 5.7 US pt, 2.7 l; carburation: 1 Solex 35 PDSI-2 downdraught carburettor; fuel feed: mechanical pump; cooling system: liquid, sealed circuit; cooling system capacity: 8.4 imp pt, 10.1 US pt, 4.8 l.

TRANSMISSION driving wheels: rear; clutch: single dry plate (diaphragm); gearbox: mechanical; gear: 4 + reverse; synchromesh gears: I, II, III, IV; gearbox ratios: I 3.867, II 2.215, III 1.432, IV 1, rev 3.900; gear lever: central; final drive: hypoid bevel; axle ratio: 3.890; width of rims: 4''; tyres: 6.00 x 12.

PERFORMANCE max speeds: 24 mph, 38 km/h in 1st gear; 42 mph, 67 km/h in 2nd gear; 63 mph, 102 km/h in 3rd gear; 78 mph, 125 km/h in 4th gear; power-weight ratio: 36.4 lb/hp, 16.5 kg/hp; carrying capacity: 882 lb, 400 kg; max gradient in 1st gear: 39%; acceleration: 0-50 mph (0-80 km/h) 13.5 sec; speed in direct drive at 1,000 rpm: 16.3 mph, 26.2 km/h; fuel consumption: 36.2 m/imp gal, 30.2 m/US gal, 7.8 l x 100 km.

CHASSIS integral; front suspension: independent, wishbones, lower transverse semi-elliptic leafspring, telescopic dampers; rear suspension: rigid axle (torque tube), trailing radius arms, transverse linkage bar, coil springs, telescopic dampers.

STEERING rack-and-pinion; turns of steering wheel lock to lock: 2.80.

BRAKES drum, dual circuit; lining area: total 80 sq in, 516 sq cm.

ELECTRICAL EQUIPMENT voltage: 12 V; battery: 38 Ah; generator type: dynamo, 300 W; ignition distributor: Bosch; headlamps: 2.

DIMENSIONS AND WEIGHT wheel base: 95.12 in, 2,416 mm; front track: 49.21 in, 1,250 mm; rear track: 50.39 in, 1,280 mm; overall length: 161.61 in, 4,105 mm; overall width: 61.93 in, 1,573 mm; overall height: 55.12 in, 1,400 mm; ground clearance: 4.72 in, 20 mm; dry weight: 1,643 lb, 745 kg; turning circle (between walls): 34.8 ft, 10.6 m; fuel tank capacity: 8.8 imp gal, 10.6 US gal, 40 l.

BODY saloon/sedan; doors: 2; seats: 5; front seats: separate.

PRACTICAL INSTRUCTIONS fuel: 90 oct petrol; engine sump oil: 4.4 imp pt, 5.3 US pt, 2.5 l, SAE 20W-30, change every 3,100 miles, 5,000 km; gearbox oil: 1.2 imp pt, 1.5 US pt, 0.7 l, SAE 80, change every 18,600 miles, 30,000 km; final drive oil: 1.1 imp pt, 1.3 US pt, 0.6 l, SAE 90, change every 18,600 miles, 30,000 km; greasing: none; sparking plug type: 175°; tappet clearances: inlet 0.006 in, 0.15 mm, exhaust 0.010 in, 0.25 mm; valve timing: inlet opens 44° before tdc and closes 88° after bdc, exhaust opens 78° before bdc and closes 40° after tdc; normal tyre pressure: front 18 psi, 1.3 atm, rear 20 psi, 1.4 atm.

VARIATIONS

ENGINE 1.1-litre S, max power (DIN) 55 hp at 5,400 rpm, max torque (DIN) 60 lb ft, 8.3 kg m at 2,400-3,600 rpm, 9.2 compression ratio, 51 hp/l specific power.
TRANSMISSION 155 x 13 tyres.
PERFORMANCE max speed 84 mph, 135 km/h, power-weight ratio 29.8 lb/hp, 13.5 kg/hp, fuel consumption 36.7 m/imp gal, 30.5 m/US gal, 7.7 l x 100 km.
BRAKES front disc.
DIMENSIONS AND WEIGHT front track 49.29 in, 1,252 mm, rear track 50.24 in, 1,276 mm.

ENGINE 1.7-litre S, bore and stroke 3.46 x 2.75 in, 88 x 69.8 mm, engine capacity 103.6 cu in, 1,698 cu cm, max power (DIN) 75 hp at 5,200 rpm, max torque (DIN) 94 lb ft, 13 kg m at 2,500-2,900 rpm, max engine rpm 5,600, 8.8 compression ratio, 44.2 hp/l specific power, 5 crankshaft bearings, 1 overhead camshaft, 1 Solex 35 PDSI downdraught carburettor.
TRANSMISSION 4-speed mechanical gearbox (I 3.428, II 2.156, III 1.366, IV 1, rev 3.317), 3.670 axle ratio, 155 x 13 tyres.
PERFORMANCE max speeds (I) 28 mph, 45 km/h, (II) 44 mph, 71 km/h, (III) 70 mph, 112 km/h, (IV) 95 mph, 153 km/h, power-weight ratio 21.8 lb/hp, 9.9 kg/hp, fuel consumption 30.1 m/imp gal, 25 m/US gal, 9.4 l x 100 km.
BRAKES front disc, servo.

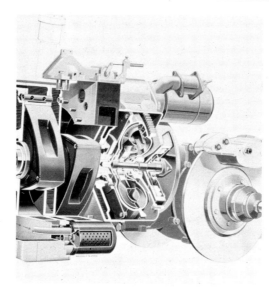

NSU Ro 80

OPEL Kadett Limousine

OPEL Kadett LS Rallye Coupé

DIMENSIONS AND WEIGHT front track 49.29 in, 1,252 mm, rear track 50.47 in, 1,282 mm.

OPTIONAL ACCESSORIES Opel automatic gearbox with ratios (I 2.400, II 1.480, III 1, rev 1.920) only with 1.1-litre S and 1.7-litre S engines; limited slip final drive; front disc brakes only with 155 x 13 tyres and servo brake; alternator; sunshine roof; electrically-heated rear window (only with alternator).

4-door Kadett Limousine

See 2-door Kadett Limousine, except for:

PRICE IN GB: £ 674.
PRICE EX WORKS: 6,466 marks.

PERFORMANCE power-weight ratio: 37.5 lb/hp, 17 kg/hp.

DIMENSIONS AND WEIGHT overall width: 63.54 in, 1,614 mm; dry weight: 1,687 lb, 765 kg.

2-door Kadett L Limousine

See 2-door Kadett Limousine, except for:

PRICE EX WORKS: 6,682 marks.

PERFORMANCE power-weight ratio: 36.8 lb/hp, 16.7 kg/hp.

DIMENSIONS AND WEIGHT overall length: 164.65 in, 4,182 mm; dry weight: 1,650 lb, 750 kg.

4-door Kadett L Limousine

See 2-door Kadett Limousine, except for:

PRICE EX WORKS: 7,015 marks.

PERFORMANCE power-weight ratio: 37.7 lb/hp, 17.1 kg/hp.

DIMENSIONS AND WEIGHT overall length: 164.65 in, 4,182 mm; overall width: 63.54 in, 1,614 mm; dry weight: 1,698 lb, 770 kg.

2-door Kadett LS Limousine

See 2-door Kadett Limousine, except for:

PRICE IN GB: £ 715.
PRICE EX WORKS: —

PERFORMANCE power-weight ratio: 37 lb/hp, 16.8 kg/hp.

DIMENSIONS AND WEIGHT overall length: 164.65 in, 4,182 mm; dry weight: 1,665 lb, 755 kg.

4-door Kadett LS Limousine

See 2-door Kadett Limousine, except for:

PRICE IN GB: £ 751.
PRICE EX WORKS: —

PERFORMANCE power-weight ratio: 37.9 lb/hp, 17.2 kg/hp.

DIMENSIONS AND WEIGHT overall length: 164.65 in, 4,182 mm; overall width: 63.54 in, 1,614 mm; dry weight: 1,709 lb, 775 kg.

Kadett Coupé

See 2-door Kadett Limousine, except for:

PRICE IN USA: $ 2,098.
PRICE EX WORKS: 7,110. marks.

PERFORMANCE max speed: 81 mph, 130 km/h; power-weight ratio: 37 lb/hp, 16.8 kg/hp.

DIMENSIONS AND WEIGHT overall length: 164.65 in, 4,182 mm; overall height: 55.31 in, 1,405 mm; dry weight: 1,665 lb, 755 kg.

BODY coupé; seats: 4.

VARIATIONS

ENGINE 1.1-litre SR, max power (DIN) 60 hp at 5,200 rpm, max torque (DIN) 62 lb ft, 8.5 kg m at 3,800-5,000 rpm, 9.2 compression ratio, 2 Solex 35 PDSI-2 downdraught carburettors.
TRANSMISSION 155 x 13 tyres.
PERFORMANCE max speed 90 mph, 145 km/h, power-weight ratio 28.2 lb/hp, 12.8 kg/hp, fuel consumption 35.8 m/imp gal, 29.8 m/US gal, 7.9 l x 100 km.

BRAKES front disc, servo.
DIMENSIONS AND WEIGHT front track 49.29 in, 1,252 mm; rear track 50.24 in, 1,276 mm.

Kadett LS Coupé

See Kadett Coupé, except for:

PRICE IN GB: £ 777.
PRICE IN USA: $ 2,197.

3-door Kadett Caravan

See 2-door Kadett Limousine, except for:

PRICE IN GB: £ 718.
PRICE IN USA: $ 2,218.

PERFORMANCE power-weight ratio: 41.7 lb/hp, 18.9 kg/hp.

DIMENSIONS AND WEIGHT overall length: 161.42 in, 4,100 mm; overall height: 54.92 in, 1,395 mm; dry weight: 1,874 lb, 850 kg.

BODY estate car/station wagon; doors: 2 + 1.

3-door Kadett L Caravan

See 2-door Kadett Limousine, except for:

PRICE IN GB: £ 760.
PRICE EX WORKS: 7,148. marks.

PERFORMANCE power-weight ratio: 41.9 lb/hp, 19 kg/hp.

DIMENSIONS AND WEIGHT overall length: 164.45 in, 4,177 mm; overall height: 54.92 in, 1,395 mm; dry weight: 1,885 lb, 855 kg.

BODY estate car/station wagon; doors: 2 + 1.

Kadett Rallye Coupé

PRICE IN USA: $ 2,446.
PRICE EX WORKS: 8,388 marks.

ENGINE front, 4 stroke; cylinders: 4, in line; bore and stroke: 2.95 x 2.40 in, 75 x 61 mm; engine capacity: 65.8 cu in, 1,078 cu cm; compression ratio: 9.2; max power (DIN): 60 hp at 5,200 rpm; max torque (DIN): 62 lb ft, 8.5 kg m at 3,800-5,000 rpm; max engine rpm: 5,400; specific power: 55.7 hp/l; cylinder block: cast iron; cylinder head: cast iron; crankshaft bearings: 3; valves: 2 per cylinder, overhead, push-rods and rockers; camshafts: 1, side; lubrication: gear pump, full flow filter; lubricating system capacity: 4.8 imp pt, 5.7 US pt, 2.7 l; carburation: 2 Solex 35 PDSI-2 down-draught carburettors; fuel feed: mechanical pump; cooling system: liquid, sealed circuit; cooling system capacity: 8.4 imp pt, 10.1 US pt, 4.8 l.

TRANSMISSION driving wheels: rear; clutch: single dry plate (diaphragm); gearbox: mechanical; gears: 4 + reverse; synchromesh gears: I, II, III, IV; gearbox ratios: I 3.867, II 2.215, III 1.432, IV 1, rev 3.900; gear lever: central; final drive: hypoid bevel; axle ratio: 4.110; width of rims: 5''; tyres: 155 x 13.

PERFORMANCE max speeds: 27 mph, 43 km/h in 1st gear; 47 mph, 75 km/h in 2nd gear; 72 mph, 116 km/h in 3rd gear; 92 mph, 148 km/h in 4th gear; power-weight ratio: 28.7 lb/hp, 13 kg/hp; carrying capacity: 706 lb, 320 kg; acceleration: 0-50 mph (0-80 km/h) 10.5 sec; speed in direct drive at 1,000 rpm: 17.1 mph, 27.6 km/h; fuel consumption: 35.8 m/imp gal, 29.8 m/US gal, 7.9 l x 100 km.

CHASSIS integral; front suspension: independent, wishbones, lower transverse semi-elliptic leafspring, telescopic dampers; rear suspension: rigid axle (torque tube), trailing radius arms, coil springs, anti-roll bar, telescopic dampers.

STEERING recirculating ball; turns of steering wheel lock to lock: 3.

BRAKES front disc, rear drum, dual circuit, servo; lining area: total 45.3 sq in, 292 sq cm.

ELECTRICAL EQUIPMENT voltage: 12 V; battery: 38 Ah; generator type: alternator; ignition distributor: Bosch; headlamps: 4.

DIMENSIONS AND WEIGHT wheel base: 95.12 in, 2,416 mm; front track: 49.29 in, 1,252 mm; rear track 50.24 in, 1,276 mm; overall length: 164.65 in, 4,182 mm; overall width: 61.93 in, 1,573 mm; overall height: 55.31 in, 1,405 mm; ground clearance: 4.45 in, 113 mm; dry weight: 1,720 lb, 780 kg; turning circle (between walls): 34.8 ft, 10.6 m; fuel tank capacity: 8.8 imp gal, 10.6 US gal, 40 l.

BODY coupé; doors: 2; seats: 4; front seats: separate.

NSU Ro 80

OPEL 4-door Kadett L Limousine

OPEL Kadett LS Rallye Coupé

KADETT RALLYE COUPÉ

PRACTICAL INSTRUCTIONS fuel: 98 oct petrol; engine sump oil: 4.4 imp pt, 5.3 US pt, 2.5 l, SAE 20W-30, change every 3,100 miles, 5,000 km; gearbox oil: 1.2 imp pt, 1.5 US pt, 0.7 l, SAE 80, change every 18,600 miles, 30,000 km; final drive oil: 1.1 imp pt, 1.3 US pt, 0.6 l, SAE 90, change every 18,600 miles, 30,000 km; greasing: none; tappet clearances: inlet 0.006 in, 0.15 mm, exhaust 0.010 in, 0.25 mm; valve timing: inlet opens 46° before tdc and closes 90° after bdc, exhaust opens 70° before bdc and closes 30° after tdc; normal tyre pressure: front 18 psi, 1.3 atm, rear 24 psi, 1.7 atm.

VARIATIONS

ENGINE 1.9-litre S, bore and stroke 3.66 x 2.71 in, 93 x 68.9 mm, engine capacity 115.8 cu in, 1,897 cu cm, max power (DIN) 90 hp at 5,100 rpm, max torque (DIN) 108 lb ft, 14.9 kg m at 2,500-3,100 rpm, 9 compression ratio, 47.4 hp/l specific power, 5 crankshaft bearings, 1 overhead camshaft, 1 Solex 32 DIDTA-4 downdraught carburettor.
TRANSMISSION 4-speed mechanical gearbox (I 3.428, II 2.156, III 1.366, IV 1, rev 3.317), 3.670 axle ratio.
PERFORMANCE max speeds (I) 30 mph, 49 km/h, (II) 48 mph, 78 km/h, (III) 76 mph, 123 km/h, (IV) 104 mph, 168 km/h, power-weight ratio 19.2 lb/hp, 8.7 kg/hp, fuel consumption 27.2 m/imp gal, 22.6 m/US gal, 10.4 l x 100 km.
ELECTRICAL EQUIPMENT 44 Ah battery.
DIMENSIONS AND WEIGHT rear track 50.47 in, 1,282 mm.

OPTIONAL ACCESSORIES limited slip final drive; electrically-heated rear window.

Kadett LS Rallye Coupé

See Kadett Rallye Coupé, except for:

PRICE IN GB: £ 913.
PRICE EX WORKS: —

PERFORMANCE max speed: 89 mph, 143 km/h (102 mph, 164 km/h with 1.9-litre S engine).

2-door Ascona 16 Limousine

PRICE EX WORKS: 7,365 marks.

ENGINE front, 4 stroke; cylinders: 4, in line; bore and stroke: 3.35 x 2.75 in, 85 x 69.8 mm; engine capacity: 96.7 cu in, 1,584 cu cm; compression ratio: 8.2; max power (DIN): 68 hp at 5,200 rpm; max torque (DIN): 80 lb ft, 11 kg m at 3,400 rpm; max engine rpm: 5,500; specific power: 42.9 hp/l; cylinder block: cast iron; cylinder head: cast iron; crankshaft bearings: 5; valves: 2 per cylinder, overhead, in line, rockers; camshafts: 1, overhead; lubrication: gear pump, full flow filter; lubricating system capacity: 5.3 imp pt, 6.3 US pt, 3 l; carburation: 1 Solex 35 PDSI downdraught carburettor; fuel feed: mechanical pump; cooling system: liquid, sealed circuit; cooling system capacity: 11.4 imp pt, 13.7 US pt, 6.5 l.

TRANSMISSION driving wheels: rear; clutch: single dry plate (diaphragm); gearbox: mechanical; gears: 4 + reverse; gearbox ratios: I 3.428, II 2.156, III 1.366, IV 1, rev 3.317; gear lever: central; final drive: hypoid bevel; axle ratio: 3.670; width of rims: 5''; tyres: 155 x 13.

PERFORMANCE max speeds: 26 mph, 42 km/h in 1st gear; 42 mph, 67 km/h in 2nd gear; 66 mph, 106 km/h in 3rd gear; 90 mph, 145 km/h in 4th gear; power-weight ratio: 30.4 lb/hp, 13.8 kg/hp; carrying capacity: 882 lb, 400 kg; speed in direct drive at 1,000 rpm: 16.2 mph, 26 km/h; fuel consumption: 28.2 m/imp gal, 23.5 m/US gal, 10 l x 100 km.

CHASSIS integral; front suspension: independent, wishbones, coil springs, anti-roll bar, telescopic dampers; rear suspension: rigid axle (torque tube), trailing radius arms, transverse linkage bar, coil springs, anti-roll bar, telescopic dampers.

STEERING rack-and-pinion; turns of steering wheel lock to lock: 3.

BRAKES front disc, rear drum, dual circuit, servo; lining area: total 79.1 sq in, 510 sq cm.

ELECTRICAL EQUIPMENT voltage: 12 V; battery: 44 Ah; generator type: alternator, 28 A; ignition distributor: Bosch; headlamps: 2.

DIMENSIONS AND WEIGHT wheel base: 95.67 in, 2,430 mm; front track: 52.40 in, 1,331 mm; rear track: 51.97 in, 1,320 mm; overall length: 162.36 in, 4,124 mm; overall width: 64.02 in, 1,626 mm; overall height: 54.53 in, 1,385 mm; ground clearance: 4.72 in, 120 mm; dry weight: 2,073 lb, 940 kg; turning circle (between walls): 31.8 ft, 9.7 m; fuel tank capacity: 10.6 imp gal, 12.7 US gal, 48 l.

BODY saloon/sedan; doors: 2; seats: 5; front seats: separate, adjustable backrests.

OPEL 4-door Ascona 16 L Limousine

OPEL Ascona 16 Voyage

OPEL Manta SR

PRACTICAL INSTRUCTIONS fuel: 90 oct petrol; engine sump oil: 5.3 imp pt, 6.3 US pt, 3 l, SAE 20W-30, change every 3,100 miles, 5,000 km; gearbox oil: 1.9 imp pt, 2.3 US pt, 1.1 l, SAE 80, change every 18,600 miles, 30,000 km; final drive oil: 1.9 imp pt, 2.3 US pt, 1.1 l, SAE 90, change every 18,600 miles, 30,000 km; greasing: none; tappet clearances (hot): inlet 0.012 in, 0.30 mm; exhaust 0.012 in, 0.30 mm; valve timing: inlet opens 44° before tdc and closes 86° after bdc, exhaust opens 84° before bdc and closes 46° after tdc; normal tyre pressure: front 23 psi, 1.6 atm, rear 26 psi, 1.8 atm.

VARIATIONS

ENGINE 9.5 compression ratio, max power (DIN) 80 hp at 5,200 rpm, max torque (DIN) 87 lb ft, 12 kg m at 3,800 rpm, 50.5 hp/l specific power, 1 Solex 32 DIDTA-4 carburettor.
TRANSMISSION 165 x 13 tyres.
PERFORMANCE max speed 96 mph, 155 km/h, power-weight ratio 25.8 lb/hp, 11.7 kg/hp, fuel consumption 29.7 m/imp gal, 24.8 m/US gal, 9.5 l x 100 km.
PRACTICAL INSTRUCTIONS 98 oct petrol.

OPTIONAL ACCESSORIES Opel automatic gearbox with 3 ratios (I 2.400, II 1.480, III 1, rev 1.920); 165 x 13 or 185/70 SR x 13 tyres, 5.5'' wide rims; sunshine roof; electrically-heated rear window; limited slip final drive (only for Manta models).

4-door Ascona 16 Limousine

See 2-door Ascona 16 Limousine, except for:

PRICE EX WORKS: 7,764 marks.

PERFORMANCE power-weight ratio: 31.1 lb/hp, 14.1 kg/hp.

DIMENSIONS AND WEIGHT dry weight: 2,117 lb, 960 kg.

2-door Ascona 16 L Limousine

See 2-door Ascona 16 Limousine, except for:

PRICE EX WORKS: 7,964 marks.

PERFORMANCE power-weight ratio: 30.6 lb/hp, 13.9 kg/hp.

DIMENSIONS AND WEIGHT dry weight: 2,084 lb, 945 kg.

4-door Ascona 16 L Limousine

See 4-door Ascona 16 Limousine, except for:

PRICE EX WORKS: 8,364 marks.

PERFORMANCE power-weight ratio: 31.3 lb/hp, 14.2 kg/hp.

DIMENSIONS AND WEIGHT dry weight: 2,128 lb, 965 kg.

Ascona 16 Voyage

See 2-door Ascona 16 Limousine, except for:

PRICE EX WORKS: 8,580 marks.

TRANSMISSION tyres: 165 x 13.

PERFORMANCE power-weight ratio: 32.2 lb/hp, 14.6 kg/hp; carrying capacity: 1,125 lb, 510 kg.

DIMENSIONS AND WEIGHT overall length: 164.57 in, 4,180 mm; overall width: 64.25 in, 1,632 mm; overall height: 55.12 in, 1,400 mm; dry weight: 2,194 lb, 995 kg.

BODY estate car/station wagon; door: 2 + 1.

Manta

See 2-door Ascona 16 Limousine, except for:

PRICE EX WORKS: 8,269 marks.

TRANSMISSION tyres: 165 x 13.

PERFORMANCE max speed: 96 mph, 154 km/h (102 mph, 164 km/h with 80 hp engine); power-weight ratio: 30.9 lb/hp, 14 kg/hp; fuel consumption: 31.4 m/imp gal, 26.1 m/US gal, 9 l x 100 km.

DIMENSIONS AND WEIGHT overall length: 168.98 in, 4,292 mm; overall height: 53.35 mm, 1,355 mm; dry weight: 2,095 lb, 950 kg.

BODY coupé.

OPEL Ascona 16 L Limousine

OPEL Ascona 16 Voyage

OPEL Manta (independent front suspension)

Manta L

See Manta, except for:

PRICE IN GB: £ 1,015.
PRICE EX WORKS: 8,719 marks.

PERFORMANCE power-weight ratio: 31.1 lb/hp, 14.1 kg/hp.

DIMENSIONS AND WEIGHT overall length: 170.98 in, 4,343 mm; overall width: 64.25 in, 1,632 mm; dry weight: 2,117 lb, 960 kg.

VARIATIONS

ENGINE bore and stroke 3.66 x 2.75 in, 93 x 69.8 mm, engine capacity 115.8 cu in, 1,897 cu cm, 9 compression ratio, max power (DIN) 90 hp at 5,100 rpm, max torque (DIN) 108 lb ft, 14.9 kg m at 2,500-3,100 rpm, 47.4 hp/l specific power, 1 Solex 32 DIDTA-4 carburettor, cooling system capacity 10.2 imp pt, 12.3 US pt, 5.8 l.
TRANSMISSION 3.440 axle ratio.
PERFORMANCE max speed 106 mph, 170 km/h, power-weight ratio 23.6 lb/hp, 10.7 kg/hp, fuel consumption 33.2 m/imp gal, 27.7 m/US gal, 8.5 l x 100 km.
PRACTICAL INSTRUCTIONS 98 oct petrol.

Manta SR

See Manta L, except for:

PRICE IN GB: £ 1,128.
PRICE EX WORKS: 9,718 marks.

ENGINE compression ratio: 9.5; max power (DIN): 80 hp at 5,200 rpm; max torque (DIN): 87 lb ft, 12 kg m at 3,800 rpm; specific power: 50.5 hp/l; carburation: 1 Solex 32 DIDTA-4 carburettor.

TRANSMISSION axle ratio: 3.890; width of rims: 5.5''; tyres: 185/70 SR x 13.

PERFORMANCE max speed: 102 mph, 164 km/h; power-weight ratio: 26.7 lb/hp, 12.1 kg/hp; fuel consumption: 31.7 m/imp gal, 26.4 m/US gal, 8.9 l x 100 km.

ELECTRICAL EQUIPMENT generator type: alternator, 35 A.

DIMENSIONS AND WEIGHT dry weight: 2,139 lb, 970 kg.

PRACTICAL INSTRUCTIONS fuel: 98 oct petrol.

VARIATIONS

3.670 axle ratio with 115.8 cu in, 1,897 cu cm and 90 hp engine.

2-door Rekord Limousine

PRICE IN GB: £ 995.
PRICE EX WORKS: 8,097 marks.

ENGINE front, 4 stroke; cylinders: 4, in line; bore and stroke: 3.35 x 2.75 in, 82.5 x 69.8 mm; engine capacity: 91 cu in, 1,492 cu cm; compression ratio: 8.2; max power (DIN): 60 hp at 5,400 rpm; max torque (DIN): 76 lb ft, 10.5 kg m at 2,000-3,000 rpm; max engine rpm: 5,600; specific power: 40.2 hp/l; cylinder block: cast iron; cylinder head: cast iron; crankshaft bearings: 5; valves: 2 per cylinder, overhead, in line, rockers; camshafts: 1, overhead; lubrication: gear pump, full flow filter; lubricating system capacity: 5.8 imp pt, 7 US pt, 3.3 l; carburation: 1 Solex 35 PDSI downdraught carburettor; fuel feed: mechanical pump; cooling system: anti-freeze liquid; cooling system capacity: 11.3 imp pt, 13.5 US pt, 6.4 l.

TRANSMISSION driving wheels: rear; clutch: single dry plate (diaphragm); gearbox: mechanical; gears: 4 + reverse; synchromesh gears: I, II, III, IV; gearbox ratios: I 3.428, II 2.156, III 1.366, IV 1, rev 3.317; gear lever: steering column; final drive: hypoid bevel; axle ratio: 4.220; width of rims: 5''; tyres: 6.40 x 13.

PERFORMANCE max speeds: 25 mph, 40 km/h in 1st gear; 40 mph, 65 km/h in 2nd gear; 62 mph, 100 km/h in 3rd gear; 87 mph, 140 km/h in 4th gear; power-weight ratio: 37.7 lb/hp, 17.1 kg/hp; carrying capacity: 882 lb, 400 kg; speed in direct drive at 1,000 rpm: 16.7 mph, 26.9 km/h; fuel consumption: 28.2 m/imp gal, 23.5 m/US gal, 10 l x 100 km.

CHASSIS integral; front suspension: independent, wishbones, coil springs, anti-roll bar, telescopic dampers; rear suspension: rigid axle, trailing lower radius arms, upper torque arms, transverse linkage bar, coil springs, telescopic dampers.

STEERING recirculating ball; turns of steering wheel lock to lock: 3.

BRAKES front disc (diameter 9.37 in, 238 mm), rear drum, dual circuit, servo.

ELECTRICAL EQUIPMENT voltage: 12 V; battery: 44 Ah; generator type: alternator, 490 W; ignition distributor: Bosch; headlamps: 2.

2-DOOR REKORD LIMOUSINE

DIMENSIONS AND WEIGHT wheel base: 105.04 in, 2,668 mm; front track: 55.51 in, 1,410 mm; rear track: 55.51 in, 1,410 mm; overall length: 179.13 in, 4,550 mm; overall width: 69.05 in, 1,754 mm; overall height: 57.32 in, 1,456 mm; ground clearance: 6.02 in, 153 mm; dry weight: 2,260 lb, 1,025 kg; turning circle (between walls): 38.4 ft, 11.7 m; fuel tank capacity: 12.1 imp gal, 14.5 US gal, 55 l.

BODY saloon/sedan; doors: 2; seats: 5; front seats: separate, reclining backrests.

PRACTICAL INSTRUCTIONS fuel: 90 oct petrol; engine sump oil: 5.3 imp pt, 6.3 US pt, 3 l, SAE 20W-30, change every 3,100 miles, 5,000 km; gearbox oil: 1.4 imp pt, 1.7 US pt, 0.8 l, SAE 80, change every 18,600 miles, 30,000 km; final drive oil: 2.1 imp pt, 2.5 US pt, 1.2 l, SAE 90, change every 18,600 miles, 30,000 km; greasing: none; sparking plug type: 175°; tappet clearances: inlet 0.012 in, 0.30 mm, exhaust 0.012 in, 0.30 mm; valve timing: inlet opens 34° before tdc and closes 76° after bdc, exhaust opens 70° before bdc and closes 28° after tdc; normal tyre pressure: front 20 psi, 1.4 atm, rear 21 psi, 1.5 atm.

VARIATIONS

ENGINE 1.7-litre (no extra charge), bore and stroke 3.46 x 2.75 in, 88 x 69.8 mm, engine capacity 103.6 cu in, 1,698 cu cm, max power (DIN) 66 hp at 5,300 rpm, max torque (DIN) 87 lb ft, 12 kg m at 2,000-3,100 rpm, 38.9 hp/l specific power. **TRANSMISSION** 3.890 axle ratio. **PERFORMANCE** max speed 89 mph, 143 km/h, power-weight ratio 34.2 lb/hp, 15.5 kg/hp, fuel consumption 29.1 m/imp gal, 24.2 m/US gal, 9.7 l x 100 km.

ENGINE 1.7-litre S, bore and stroke 3.46 x 2.75 in, 88 x 69.8 mm, engine capacity 103.6 cu in, 1,698 cu cm, max power (DIN) 75 hp at 5,200 rpm, max torque (DIN) 94 lb ft, 13 kg m at 2,500-2,900 rpm, 8.8 compression ratio, 44.2 hp/l specific power, 1 Solex 35 PDSIT-6 downdraught carburettor. **TRANSMISSION** 3.890 axle ratio. **PERFORMANCE** max speeds (I) 28 mph, 45 km/h, (II) 44 mph, 71 km/h, (III) 70 mph, 112 km/h, (IV) 95 mph, 153 km/h, power-weight ratio 30.2 lb/hp, 13.7 kg/hp, fuel consumption 28.8 m/imp gal, 24 m/US gal, 9.8 l x 100 km.

ENGINE 1.9-litre S, bore and stroke 3.66 x 2.75 in, 93 x 69.8 mm, engine capacity 115.7 cu in, 1,896 cu cm, max power (DIN) 90 hp at 5,100 rpm, max torque (DIN) 108 lb ft, 14.9 kg m at 2,500-3,100 rpm, 9 compression ratio, 47.4 hp/l specific power, 1 Solex 32 DIDTA-4 carburettor. **TRANSMISSION** 3.890 axle ratio. **PERFORMANCE** max speeds (I) 29 mph, 47 km/h, (II) 46 mph, 74 km/h, (III) 73 mph, 117 km/h, (IV) 99 mph, 160 km/h, power-weight ratio 25.1 lb/hp, 11.4 kg/hp, fuel consumption 27.7 m/imp gal, 23.1 m/US gal, 10.2 l x 100 km.

OPTIONAL ACCESSORIES central gear lever; Opel automatic gearbox with 3 ratios (I 2.400, II 1.480, III 1, rev 1.920), only with 1.7-litre S and 1.9-litre S engines; limited slip final drive; sunshine roof; electrically-heated rear window.

4-door Rekord Limousine

See 2-door Rekord Limousine, except for:

PRICE IN GB: £ 1,032.
PRICE EX WORKS: 8,414 marks.

PERFORMANCE power-weight ratio: 38.6 lb/hp, 17.5 kg/hp.

DIMENSIONS AND WEIGHT overall width: 69.21 in, 1,758 mm; overall height: 57.20 in, 1,453 mm; dry weight: 2,315 lb, 1,050 kg.

3-door Rekord Caravan

See 2-door Rekord Limousine, except for:

PRICE IN GB: £ 1,055.
PRICE EX WORKS: 8,486 marks.

PERFORMANCE max speed: 83 mph, 133 km/h; power-weight ratio: 42.8 lb/hp, 19.4 kg/hp.

DIMENSIONS AND WEIGHT overall height: 57.48 in, 1,460 mm; dry weight: 2,569 lb, 1,165 kg.

BODY estate car/station wagon; doors: 2 + 1.

5-door Rekord Caravan

See 2-door Rekord Limousine, except for:

PRICE EX WORKS: 8,886 marks.

PERFORMANCE max speed: 83 mph, 133 km/h; power-weight ratio: 43.7 lb/hp, 19.8 kg/hp.

OPEL Rekord (central gear lever)

OPEL 3-door Rekord Caravan

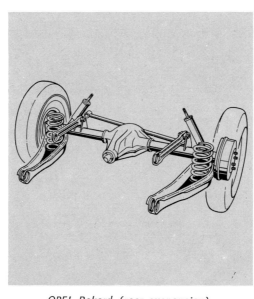

OPEL Rekord (rear suspension)

DIMENSIONS AND WEIGHT overall height: 57.36 in, 1,457 mm; dry weight: 2,624 lb, 1,190 kg.

BODY estate car/station wagon; doors: 4 + 1.

2-door Rekord L Limousine

See 2-door Rekord Limousine, except for:

PRICE EX WORKS: 8,408 marks.

ENGINE bore and stroke: 3.46 x 2.75 in, 88 x 68.9 mm; engine capacity: 103.6 cu in, 1,698 cu cm; max power (DIN): 66 hp at 5,300 rpm; max torque (DIN): 87 lb ft, 12 kg m at 2,000-3,100 rpm; specific power: 38.9 hp/l.

TRANSMISSION axle ratio: 3.890.

PERFORMANCE max speed: 89 mph, 143 km/h; power-weight ratio: 34.8 lb/hp, 15.8 kg/hp; fuel consumption: 29.1 m/imp gal, 24.2 m/US gal, 9.7 l x 100 km.

DIMENSIONS AND WEIGHT overall length: 180.08 in, 4,574 mm; dry weight: 2,304 lb, 1,045 kg.

VARIATIONS

1.7-litre engine not available.

4-door Rekord L Limousine

See 2-door Rekord L Limousine, except for:

PRICE IN GB: £ 1,076.
PRICE EX WORKS: 8,797 marks.

PERFORMANCE power-weight ratio: 35.7 lb/hp, 16.2 kg/hp.

DIMENSIONS AND WEIGHT overall width: 69.21 in, 1,758 mm; dry weight: 2,359 lb, 1,070 kg.

Rekord Coupé

See 2-door Rekord Limousine, except for:

PRICE IN GB: £ 1,177.
PRICE EX WORKS: 9,402 marks.

ENGINE bore and stroke: 3.46 x 2.75 in, 88 x 69.8 mm; engine capacity: 103.6 cu in, 1,698 cu cm; compression ratio: 8.8; max power (DIN): 75 hp at 5,200 rpm; max torque (DIN): 94 lb ft, 13 kg m at 2,500-2,900 rpm; specific power: 44.2 hp/l; carburation: 1 Solex 35 PDSIT-6 downdraught carburettor.

TRANSMISSION axle ratio: 3.890.

PERFORMANCE max speed: 98 mph, 158 km/h; power-weight ratio: 32 lb/hp, 14.5 kg/hp; fuel consumption: 29.7 m/imp gal, 24.8 m/US gal, 9.5 l x 100 km.

DIMENSIONS AND WEIGHT overall length: 187.16 in, 4,574 mm; overall height: 56.14 in, 1,426 mm; dry weight: 2,392 lb, 1,085 kg.

BODY coupé; seats: 4.

VARIATIONS

1.7-litre and 1.7-litre S engines not available; with 1.9-litre S engine, max speed 103 mph, 165 km/h.

Rekord L Caravan

See 2-door Rekord L Limousine, except for:

PRICE IN GB: £ 1,161.
PRICE EX WORKS: 9,346 marks.

PERFORMANCE power-weight ratio: 40.3 lb/hp, 18.3 kg/hp; fuel consumption: 25.2 m/imp gal, 21 m/US gal, 11.2 l x 100 km.

DIMENSIONS AND WEIGHT overall width: 69.21 in, 1,758 mm; overall height: 57.36 in, 1,457 mm; dry weight: 2,668 lb, 1,210 kg.

BODY estate car/station wagon; doors: 4 + 1.

Rekord Sprint Coupé

PRICE IN GB: £ 1,319.
PRICE EX WORKS: 11,104 marks.

ENGINE front, 4 stroke; cylinders: 4, in line; bore and stroke: 3.66 x 2.75 in, 93 x 69.8 mm; engine capacity: 115.8 cu in, 1,897 cu cm; compression ratio: 9.5; max power

(DIN): 106 hp at 5,600 rpm; max torque (DIN): 116 lb ft, 16 kg m at 3,500-3,800 rpm; max engine rpm: 6,000; specific power: 55.9 hp/l; cylinder block: cast iron; cylinder head: cast iron; crankshaft bearings: 5; valves: 2 per cylinder, overhead, in line, rockers; camshafts: 1, overhead; lubrication: gear pump, full flow filter; lubricating system capacity: 5.8 imp pt, 7 US pt, 3.3 l; carburation: 2 Weber 40 DFO carburettors; fuel feed: mechanical pump; cooling system: water; cooling system capacity: 10.7 imp pt, 12.9 US pt, 6.1 l.

TRANSMISSION driving wheels: rear; clutch: single dry plate (diaphragm); gearbox: mechanical; gears: 4 + reverse; synchromesh gears: I, II, III, IV; gearbox ratios: I 3.428, II 2.156, III 1.366, IV 1, rev 3.317; gear lever: central; final drive: hypoid bevel; axle ratio: 3.670; width of rims: 5''; tyres: 165 x 14.

PERFORMANCE max speeds: 34 mph, 55 km/h in 1st gear; 50 mph, 80 km/h in 2nd gear; 75 mph, 120 km/h in 3rd gear; 106 mph, 171 km/h in 4th gear; power-weight ratio: 23.6 lb/hp, 10.7 kg/hp; carrying capacity: 882 lb, 400 kg; speed in direct drive at 1,000 rpm: 17.1 mph, 27.5 km/h; fuel consumption: 28.2 m/imp gal, 23.5 m/US gal, 10 l x 100 km.

CHASSIS integral; front suspension: independent, wishbones, coil springs, anti-roll bar, telescopic dampers; rear suspension: rigid axle, trailing lower radius arms, upper torque arms, transverse linkage bar, coil springs, telescopic dampers.

STEERING recirculating ball; turns of steering wheel lock to lock: 3.

BRAKES front disc (diameter 9.37 in, 238 mm), rear drum, dual circuit, servo.

ELECTRICAL EQUIPMENT voltage: 12 V; battery: 44 Ah; generator type: alternator, 490 W; ignition distributor: Bosch; headlamps: 4, 2 halogen.

DIMENSIONS AND WEIGHT wheel base: 105.04 in, 2,668 mm; front track: 55.51 in, 1,410 mm; rear track: 55.51 in, 1,410 mm; overall length: 180.08 in, 4,574 mm; overall width: 69.05 in, 1,754 mm; overall height: 55.91 in, 1,420 mm; ground clearance: 6.02 in, 153 mm; dry weight: 2,503 lb, 1,135 kg; turning circle (between walls): 38.4 ft, 11.7 m; fuel tank capacity: 12.1 imp gal, 14.5 US gal 55 l.

BODY coupé; doors: 2; seats: 4; front seats: separate, reclining backrests.

PRACTICAL INSTRUCTIONS fuel: 98 oct petrol; engine sump oil: 5.3 imp pt, 6.3 US pt, 3 l, SAE 20W-30, change every 3,100 miles, 5,000 km; gearbox oil: 1.4 imp pt, 1.7 US pt, 0.8 l, SAE 80, change every 18,600 miles, 30,000 km; final drive oil: 2.1 imp pt, 2.5 US pt, 1.2 l, SAE 90, change every 18,600 miles, 30,000 km; greasing: none; tappet clearances: inlet 0.012 in, 0.30 mm, exhaust 0.012 in, 0.30 mm; valve timing: inlet opens 44° before tdc and closes 86° after bdc, exhaust opens 84° before bdc and closes 46° after tdc; normal tyre pressure: front 23 psi, 1.6 atm, rear 24 psi, 1.7 atm.

OPTIONAL ACCESSORIES limited slip final drive; sunshine roof; electrically-heated rear window.

OPEL 2-door Rekord Limousine

OPEL Rekord L Caravan

OPEL Rekord Sprint Coupé

GT 1100 Coupé

PRICE EX WORKS: 11,100 marks.

ENGINE front, 4 stroke; cylinders: 4, in line; bore and stroke: 2.95 x 2.40 in, 75 x 61 mm; engine capacity: 65.8 cu in, 1,078 cu cm; compression ratio: 9.2; max power (DIN): 60 hp at 5,000 rpm; max torque (DIN): 62 lb ft, 8.5 kg m at 3,800-5,000 rpm; max engine rpm: 6,000; specific power: 55.7 hp/l; cylinder block: cast iron; cylinder head: cast iron; crankshaft bearings: 3; valves: 2 per cylinder, overhead, in line, push-rods and rockers; camshafts: 1, side; lubrication: gear pump, full flow filter; lubricating system capacity: 4.8 imp pt, 5.7 US pt, 2.7 l; carburation: 2 Solex 35 PDSI-2 downdraught carburettors; fuel feed: mechanical pump; cooling system: liquid, sealed circuit; cooling system capacity: 8.3 imp pt, 9.9 US pt, 4.7 l.

TRANSMISSION driving wheels: rear; clutch: single dry plate (diaphragm); gearbox: mechanical; gears: 4 + reverse; synchromesh gears: I, II, III, IV; gearbox ratios: I 3.867, II 2.215, III 1.432, IV 1, rev 3.900; gear lever: central; final drive: hypoid bevel; axle ratio: 3.890; width of rims: 5''; tyres: 155 x 13.

PERFORMANCE max speeds: 25 mph, 40 km/h in 1st gear; 43 mph, 70 km/h in 2nd gear; 68 mph, 110 km/h in 3rd gear; 96 mph, 155 km/h in 4th gear; power-weight ratio: 31.1 lb/hp, 14.1 kg/hp; carrying capacity: 463 lb, 210 kg; max gradient in 1st gear: 41%; acceleration: 0-50 mph (0-80 km/h) 11 sec; speed in direct drive at 1,000 rpm: 16.8 mph, 27 km/h; fuel consumption: 37.7 m/imp gal, 31.4 m/US gal, 7.5 l x 100 km.

CHASSIS integral; front suspension: indipendent, wishbones, transverse leafspring lower arms, coil springs, telescopic dampers; rear suspension: rigid axle (torque tube), twin

GT 1100 COUPÉ

swinging longitudinal trailing arms, transverse linkage bar, coil springs, telescopic dampers.

STEERING rack-and-pinion; turns of steering wheel lock to lock: 3.

BRAKES front disc, rear drum, dual circuit, servo; lining area: total 49.1 sq in, 317 sq cm.

ELECTRICAL EQUIPMENT voltage: 12 V; battery: 38 Ah; generator type: alternator, 300 W; ignition distributor: Bosch; headlamps: 2, retractable; fog lamps: 2.

DIMENSIONS AND WEIGHT wheel base: 95.71 in, 2,431 mm; front track: 49.37 in, 1,254 mm; rear track: 50.31 in, 1,278 mm; overall length: 161.93 in, 4,113 mm; overall width: 62.20 in, 1,580 mm; overall height: 48.23 in, 1,225 mm; ground clearance: 5.08 in, 129 mm; dry weight: 1,863 lb, 845 kg; turning circle (between walls): 35.4 ft, 10.8 m; fuel tank capacity: 12.1 imp gal, 14.5 US gal, 55 l.

BODY coupé; doors: 2; seats: 2.

PRACTICAL INSTRUCTIONS fuel: 98 oct petrol; engine sump oil: 5.3 imp pt, 6.3 US pt, 3 l, SAE 20W-30, change every 3,100 miles, 5,000 km; gearbox oil: 1.9 imp pt, 2.3 US pt, 1.1 l, SAE 80, change every 18,600 miles, 30,000 km; final drive oil: 1.9 imp pt, 2.3 US pt, 1.1 l, SAE 90, change every 18,600 miles, 30,000 km; greasing: none; tappet clearances: inlet 0.006 in, 0.15 mm; exhaust 0.010 in, 0.25 mm; valve timing: inlet opens 46° before tdc and closes 90° after bdc, exhaust opens 70° before bdc and closes 30° after tdc; normal tyre pressure: front 26 psi, 1.8 atm, rear 26 psi, 1.8 atm.

OPTIONAL ACCESSORIES 4.110 axle ratio; limited slip final drive; 165 x 13 tyres; Opel automatic gearbox with 3 ratios (I 2.400, II 1.480, III 1, rev 1.920); anti-roll bar on front and rear suspensions; 44 Ah battery; electrically-heated rear window.

GT 1900 Coupé

See GT 1100 Coupé, except for:

PRICE IN GB: £ 1,574.
PRICE IN USA: $ 3,440.

ENGINE bore and stroke: 3.66 x 2.75 in, 93 x 69.8 mm; engine capacity: 115.8 cu in, 1,897 cu cm; compression ratio: 9.5; max power (DIN): 90 hp at 5,100 rpm; max torque (DIN): 108 lb ft, 14.9 kg m at 2,500-3,100 rpm; specific power: 47.4 hp/l; cylinder head: light alloy; crankshaft bearings: 5; valves: 2 per cylinder, overhead, in line, rockers; camshafts: 1, overhead; carburation: 1 Solex 32 TDID-2 downdraught twin barrel carburettor; cooling system capacity: 10.6 imp pt, 12.7 US pt, 6 l.

TRANSMISSION gearbox ratios: I 3.428, II 2.156, III 1.366, IV 1, rev 3.317; axle ratio: 3.440; tyres: 15 x 13 (standard).

PERFORMANCE max speeds: 34 mph, 54 km/h in 1st gear; 53 mph, 86 km/h in 2nd gear; 85 mph, 136 km/h in 3rd gear; 115 mph, 185 km/h in 4th gear; power-weight ratio: 22.9 lb/hp, 10.4 kg/hp; max gradient in 1st gear: 55%; acceleration: 0-50 mph (0-80 km/h) 7.5 sec; fuel consumption: 33.2 m/imp gal, 27.7 m/US gal, 8.5 l x 100 km.

BRAKES lining area: total 79.1 sq in, 510 sq cm.

ELECTRICAL EQUIPMENT battery: 44 Ah (standard); generator type: alternator, 380 W.

DIMENSIONS AND WEIGHT rear track: 50.55 in, 1,284 mm; dry weight: 2,073 lb, 940 kg.

PRACTICAL INSTRUCTIONS tappet clearances: inlet 0.012 in, 0.30 mm, exhaust 0.012 in, 0.30 mm; valve timing: inlet opens 44° before tdc and closes 86° after bdc, exhaust opens 84° before bdc and closes 46° after tdc.

OPTIONAL ACCESSORIES 4.110 axle ratio not available.

2-door Commodore Limousine

PRICE EX WORKS: 11,572 marks.

ENGINE front, 4 stroke; cylinders: 6, in line; bore and stroke: 3.43 x 2.75 in, 87 x 69.8 mm; engine capacity: 151.9 cu in, 2,490 cu cm; compression ratio: 9.5; max power (DIN): 120 hp at 5,500 rpm; max torque (DIN): 128 lb ft, 17.7 kg m at 4,200 rpm; max engine rpm: 6,000; specific power: 48.2 hp/l; cylinder block: cast iron; cylinder head: cast iron; crankshaft bearings: 7; valves: 2 per cylinder, overhead, in line, hydraulic tappets; camshafts: 1, overhead; lubrication: gear pump, full flow filter; lubricating system capacity: 7.9 imp pt, 9.5 US pt, 4.5 l; carburation: 1 Zenith 35/40 INAT downdraught twin barrel carburettor;

OPEL GT 1900 Coupé

OPEL 4-door Commodore GS Limousine

OPEL Commodore GS/E Coupé

fuel feed: mechanical pump; cooling system: anti-freeze liquid; cooling system capacity: 15.8 imp pt, 19 US pt, 9 l.

TRANSMISSION driving wheels: rear; clutch: single dry plate (diaphragm); gearbox: mechanical; gears: 4 + reverse; synchromesh gears: I, II, III, IV; gearbox ratios: I 3.428, II 2.156, III 1.366, IV 1, rev 3.317; gear lever: central; final drive: hypoid bevel; axle ratio: 3.560; width of rims: 5''; tyres: 165 x 14.

PERFORMANCE max speeds: 33 mph, 53 km/h in 1st gear; 53 mph, 85 km/h in 2nd gear; 83 mph, 134 km/h in 3rd gear; 110 mph, 177 km/h in 4th gear; power-weight ratio: 20.9 lb/hp, 9.5 kg/hp; carrying capacity: 1,014 lb, 460 kg; speed in direct drive at 1,000 rpm: 19.6 mph, 31.5 km/h; fuel consumption: 25.7 m/imp gal, 21.4 m/US gal, 11 l x 100 km.

CHASSIS integral; front suspension: independent, wishbones, coil springs, anti-roll bar, telescopic dampers; rear suspension: rigid axle, twin trailing radius arms, upper torque arms, transverse linkage bar, coil springs, anti-roll bar, telescopic dampers.

STEERING recirculating ball; turns of steering wheel lock to lock: 3.

BRAKES front disc (diameter 10.67 in, 271 mm), rear drum, dual circuit, servo; lining area: total 87.4 sq in, 564 sq cm.

ELECTRICAL EQUIPMENT voltage: 12 V; battery: 44 Ah; generator type: alternator, 490 W; ignition distributor: Bosch; headlamps: 2.

DIMENSIONS AND WEIGHT wheel base: 105.04 in, 2,668 mm; front track: 55.51 in, 1,410 mm; rear track: 55.51 in, 1,410 mm; overall length: 180.08 in, 4,574 mm; overall width: 69.05 in, 1,754 mm; overall height: 56.50 in, 1,435 mm; ground clearance: 6.02 in, 153 mm; dry weight: 2,525 lb, 1,145 kg; turning circle (between walls): 37.7 ft, 11.5 m; fuel tank capacity: 15.4 imp gal, 18.5 US gal, 70 l.

BODY saloon/sedan; doors: 2; seats: 5; front seats: separate, reclining backrests.

PRACTICAL INSTRUCTIONS fuel: 98 oct petrol; engine sump oil: 7.4 imp pt, 8.9 US pt, 4.2 l, SAE 20W-30, change every 3,100 miles, 5,000 km; gearbox oil: 1.4 imp pt, 1.7 US pt, 0.8 l, SAE 80, change every 18,600 miles, 30,000 km; final drive oil: 2.1 imp pt, 2.5 US pt, 1.2 l, SAE 90, change every 18,600 miles, 30,000 km; sparking plug type: 200°; valve timing: inlet opens 40° before tdc and closes 88° after bdc, exhaust opens 80° before bdc and closes 48° after tdc; normal tyre pressure: front 28 psi, 2 atm, rear 31 psi, 2.2 atm.

OPTIONAL ACCESSORIES Opel automatic gearbox with 3 ratios (I 2.400, II 1.480, III 1, rev 1.920); limited slip final drive; power-assisted steering; sunshine roof; electrically-heated rear window.

4-door Commodore Limousine

See 2-door Commodore Limousine, except for:

PRICE IN GB: £ 1,320.
PRICE EX WORKS: 11,905 marks.

PERFORMANCE power-weight ratio: 21.4 lb/hp, 9.7 kg/hp.

DIMENSIONS AND WEIGHT overall width: 69.21 in, 1,758 mm; dry weight: 2,580 lb, 1,170 kg.

Commodore Coupé

See 2-door Commodore Limousine, except for:

PRICE IN GB: £ 1,375.
PRICE EX WORKS: 12,160 marks.

PERFORMANCE max speed: 113 mph, 182 km/h; power-weight ratio: 21.8 lb/hp, 9.9 kg/hp; fuel consumption: 25 m/imp gal, 20.8 m/US gal, 11.3 l x 100 km.

DIMENSIONS AND WEIGHT dry weight: 2,613 lb, 1,185 kg.

BODY coupé; seats: 4.

2-door Commodore GS Limousine

See 2-door Commodore Limousine, except for:

PRICE EX WORKS: 12,813 marks.

ENGINE max power (DIN): 130 hp at 5,300 rpm; max torque (DIN): 138 lb ft, 19 kg m at 4,000-4,500 rpm; specific power: 52.2 hp/l; carburation: 2 Zenith 35/40 INAT downdraught twin barrel carburettors.

PERFORMANCE max speed 113 mph, 182 km/h; power-weight ratio: 19.8 lb/hp, 9 kg/hp; fuel consumption: 25 m/imp gal, 20.8 m/US gal, 11.3 l x 100 km.

OPEL GT 1900 Coupé

OPEL Commodore GS and GS/E

OPEL Commodore GS/E

ELECTRICAL EQUIPMENT headlamps: 4, 2 halogen.

DIMENSIONS AND WEIGHT dry weight: 2,591 lb, 1,175 kg.

VARIATIONS

ENGINE 2.8-litre, max power (DIN) 145 hp at 5,200 rpm.

4-door Commodore GS Limousine

See 2-door Commodore GS Limousine, except for:

PRICE IN GB: £ 1,514.
PRICE EX WORKS: 13,146 marks.

PERFORMANCE power-weight ratio: 20.3 lb/hp, 9.2 kg/hp.

DIMENSIONS AND WEIGHT overall width: 69.21 in, 1,758 mm; dry weight: 2,646 lb, 1,200 kg.

Commodore GS Coupé

See 2-door Commodore GS Limousine, except for:

PRICE IN GB: £ 1,569.
PRICE EX WORKS: 13,401 marks.

PERFORMANCE max speed: 116 mph, 187 km/h; power-weight ratio: 20.7 lb/hp, 9.4 kg/hp; fuel consumption: 25.7 m/imp gal, 21.4 m/US gal, 11 l x 100 km.

DIMENSIONS AND WEIGHT dry weight: 2,690 lb, 1,220 kg.

BODY coupé; seats: 4.

2-door Commodore GS/E Limousine

See 2-door Commodore Limousine, except for:

PRICE EX WORKS: 14,005 marks.

ENGINE max power (DIN): 150 hp at 5,800 rpm; max torque (DIN): 145 lb ft, 20 kg m at 4,500 rpm; specific power: 60.2 hp/l; carburation: Bosch electronically-controlled injection system.

PERFORMANCE max speed: 119 mph, 192 km/h; power-weight ratio: 17.4 lb/hp, 7.9 kg/hp; fuel consumption: 26.4 m/imp gal, 22 m/US gal, 10.7 l x 100 km.

DIMENSIONS AND WEIGHT dry weight: 2,613 lb, 1,185 kg.

4-door Commodore GS/E Limousine

See 2-door Commodore GS/E Limousine, except for:

PRICE EX WORKS: 14,338 marks.

PERFORMANCE power-weight ratio: 17.9 lb/hp, 8.1 kg/hp.

DIMENSIONS AND WEIGHT overall width: 69.21 in, 1,758 mm; dry weight: 2,668 lb, 1,210 kg.

Commodore GS/E Coupé

See 2-door Commodore GS/E Limousine, except for:

PRICE EX WORKS: 14,593 marks.

PERFORMANCE max speed: 122 mph, 197 km/h; power-weight ratio: 18.1 lb/hp, 8.2 kg/hp; fuel consumption: 26.9 m/imp gal, 22.4 m/US gal, 10.5 l x 100 km.

DIMENSIONS AND WEIGHT dry weight: 2,712 lb, 1,230 kg.

BODY coupé; seats: 4.

Admiral

PRICE EX WORKS: 15,429 marks.

ENGINE front, 4 stroke; cylinders: 6, in line; bore and stroke: 3.62 x 2.75 in, 92 x 69.8 mm; engine capacity: 169.9 cu in, 2,784 cu cm; compression ratio: 9.5; max power (DIN): 132 hp at 5,200 rpm; max torque (DIN): 152 lb ft, 21 kg m at 3,000-4,000 rpm; max engine rpm: 5,800; specific power: 47.4 hp/l; cylinder block: cast iron; cylinder head: cast iron; crankshaft bearings: 4; valves: 2 per cylinder, overhead, in line, hydraulic tappets; camshafts: 1, overhead; lubrication: gear pump, full flow filter; lubricating system capacity: 7.9 imp pt, 9.5 US pt, 4.5 l; carburation: 1 Zenith 35/40 INAT downdraught twin barrel carburettor; fuel feed: mechanical pump; cooling system: liquid, sealed circuit; cooling system capacity: 15 imp pt, 18 US pt, 8.5 l.

TRANSMISSION driving wheels: rear; clutch: single dry

ADMIRAL

plate, hydraulically controlled; gearbox: mechanical; gears: 4 + reverse; synchromesh gears: I, II, III, IV; gearbox ratios: I 3.428, II 2.156, III 1.366, IV 1, rev 3.317; gear lever: steering column; final drive: hypoid bevel; axle ratio: 3.890; width of rims: 6''; tyres: 7.00 x 14.

PERFORMANCE max speeds: 32 mph, 51 km/h in 1st gear; 50 mph, 81 km/h in 2nd gear; 80 mph, 129 km/h in 3rd gear; 109 mph, 175 km/h in 4th gear; power-weight ratio: 24.7 lb/hp, 11.2 kg/hp; carrying capacity: 1,103 lb, 500 kg; speed in direct drive at 1,000 rpm: 18.8 mph, 30.3 km/h; fuel consumption: 21.1 m/imp gal, 17.6 m/US gal, 13.4 l x 100 km.

CHASSIS integral; front suspension: independent, wishbones, coil springs, anti-roll bar, telescopic dampers; rear suspension: de Dion rigid axle, twin swinging longitudinal trailing arms, wide Vee transverse linkage radius arms, coil springs, anti-roll bar, telescopic dampers.

STEERING recirculating ball; turns of steering wheel lock to lock: 4.

BRAKES front disc, rear drum, dual circuit, servo; lining area: total 94.4 sq in, 609 sq cm.

ELECTRICAL EQUIPMENT voltage: 12 V; battery: 44 Ah; generator type: alternator, 490 W; ignition distributor: Bosch; headlamps: 2.

DIMENSIONS AND WEIGHT wheel base: 112.01 in, 2,845 mm; front track: 59.45 in, 1,510 mm; rear track: 59.25 in, 1,505 mm; overall length: 193.19 in, 4,907 mm; overall width: 72.91 in, 1,852 mm; overall height: 56.69 in, 1,440 mm; ground clearance: 5.91 in, 150 mm; dry weight: 3,252 lb, 1,475 kg; turning circle (between walls): 35.4 ft, 10.8 m; fuel tank capacity: 17.6 imp gal, 21.1 US gal, 80 l.

BODY saloon/sedan; doors: 4; seats: 5-6; front seats: separate, reclining backrests.

PRACTICAL INSTRUCTIONS fuel: 98 oct petrol; engine sump oil: 7.4 imp pt, 8.9 US pt, 4.2 l, SAE 20W-30, change every 3,100 miles, 5,000 km; gearbox oil: 1.9 imp pt, 2.3 US pt, 1.1 l, SAE 80, change every 18,600 miles, 30,000 km; final drive oil: 2.5 imp pt, 3 US pt, 1.4 l, SAE 90, change every 18,600 miles, 30,000 km; greasing: none; valve timing: inlet opens 40° before tdc and closes 88° after bdc, exhaust opens 80° before bdc and closes 48° after tdc; normal tyre pressure: front 23 psi, 1.6 atm, rear 26 psi, 1.8 atm.

OPTIONAL ACCESSORIES central gear lever; Opel automatic gearbox with 3 ratios (I 2.400, II 1.480, III 1, rev 1.920), 3.670 axle ratio; limited slip final drive; power-assisted steering; 55 Ah battery; electrically-controlled windows; electrically-heated rear window; sunshine roof.

Admiral 2800 S

See Admiral, except for:

PRICE EX WORKS: 15,856 marks.

ENGINE max power (DIN): 145 hp at 5,200 rpm; max torque (DIN): 164 lb ft, 22.7 kg m at 3,600-3,800 rpm; specific power: 52.1 hp/l; carburation: 2 Zenith 35/40 INAT down-draught twin barrel carburettors.

TRANSMISSION axle ratio: 3.670.

PERFORMANCE max speed: 113 mph, 182 km/h; power-weight ratio: 22.7 lb/hp, 10.3 kg/hp; fuel consumption: 20.9 m/imp gal, 17.4 m/US gal, 13.5 l x 100 km.

DIMENSIONS AND WEIGHT dry weight: 3,296 lb, 1,495 kg.

Admiral 2800 E

See Admiral, except for:

PRICE EX WORKS: 18,026 marks.

ENGINE max power (DIN): 165 hp at 5,600 rpm; max torque (DIN): 169 lb ft, 23.3 kg m at 4,100-4,600 rpm; max engine rpm: 6,000; specific power: 59.3 hp/l; carburation: Bosch electronically-controlled injection system; fuel feed: electric pump.

TRANSMISSION axle ratio: 3.670; tyres: 195 x 14.

PERFORMANCE max speed: 118 mph, 190 km/h; power-weight ratio: 20.3 lb/hp, 9.2 kg/hp; fuel consumption: 21.7 m/imp gal, 18.1 m/US gal, 13 l x 100 km.

BRAKES disc, rear compensator; lining area: total 40.9 sq in, 264 sq cm.

DIMENSIONS AND WEIGHT dry weight: 3,330 lb, 1,510 kg.

PRACTICAL INSTRUCTIONS valve timing: inlet opens 40° before tdc and closes 94° after bdc, exhaust opens 84° before bdc and closes 54° after tdc.

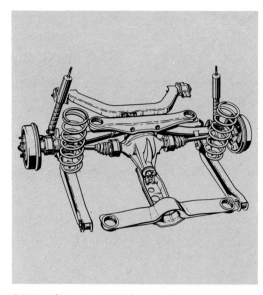

OPEL Admiral and Diplomat (rear suspension)

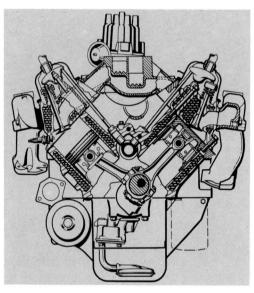

OPEL Diplomat V8

PORSCHE 911 E Targa

Diplomat E

See Admiral 2800 E, except for:

PRICE EX WORKS: 20,352 marks.

PERFORMANCE power-weight ratio: 20.5 lb/hp, 9.3 kg/hp.

STEERING servo (standard).

DIMENSIONS AND WEIGHT overall length: 193.70 in, 4,920 mm; dry weight: 3,374 lb, 1,530 kg.

BODY details: electrically-heated rear window (standard).

Diplomat V8

See Diplomat E, except for:

PRICE EX WORKS: 23,016 marks.

ENGINE cylinders: 8, Vee-slanted at 90°; bore and stroke: 4 x 3.25 in, 101.6 x 82.6 mm; engine capacity: 326.7 cu in, 5,354 cu cm; compression ratio: 10.5; max power (DIN): 230 hp at 4,700 rpm; max torque (DIN): 315 lb ft, 43.5 kg m at 3,000-3,200 rpm; max engine rpm: 5,000; specific power: 43 hp/l; crankshaft bearings: 5; valves: 2 per cylinder, overhead, in line, push-rods and rockers, hydraulic tappets; camshafts: 1, at centre of Vee; lubricating system capacity: 9.5 imp pt, 11.4 US pt, 5.4 l; carburation: 1 4-barrel carburettor; cooling system capacity: 24.1 imp pt, 29 US pt, 13.7 l.

TRANSMISSION gearbox: Turbo-Hydramatic automatic, hydraulic torque convertor and planetary gears with 3 ratios + reverse, max ratio of convertor at stall 2.1, possible manual selection; gearbox ratios: I 2.480, II 1.480, III 1, rev 2.080; axle ratio: 2.730; tyres: 195 x 14.

PERFORMANCE max speed: 127 mph, 205 km/h; power-weight ratio: 16.1 lb/hp, 7.3 kg/hp; fuel consumption: 20.5 m/imp gal, 17 m/US gal, 13.8 l x 100 km.

ELECTRICAL EQUIPMENT battery: 55 Ah (standard).

DIMENSIONS AND WEIGHT dry weight: 3,726 lb, 1,690 kg.

PRACTICAL INSTRUCTIONS engine sump oil: 7.9 imp pt, 9.5 US pt, 4.5 l; gearbox oil: 12.3 imp pt, 14.8 US pt, 7 l; final drive oil: 2.6 imp pt, 3.2 US pt, 1.5 l; valve timing: inlet opens 38° before tdc and closes 92° after bdc, exhaust opens 88° before bdc and closes 52° after tdc.

OPTIONAL ACCESSORIES Opel automatic gearbox not available; power-assisted steering and electrically-heated rear window standard.

PORSCHE   GERMANY (F.R.)

911 T Coupé

PRICE IN GB: £ 2,810.
PRICE IN USA: $ 6,430.

ENGINE rear, 4 stroke; cylinders: 6, horizontally opposed; bore and stroke: 3.31 x 2.60 in, 84 x 66 mm; engine capacity: 133.9 cu in, 2,195 cu cm; compression ratio: 8.6; max power (DIN): 125 hp at 5,800 rpm; max torque (DIN): 130 lb ft, 18 kg m at 4,200 rpm; max engine rpm: 6,500; specific power: 56.9 hp/l; cylinder block: cast iron liners with light alloy fins; cylinder head: light alloy; crankshaft bearings: 8; valves: 2 per cylinder, overhead, Vee-slanted, rockers; camshafts: 1, per cylinder block, overhead; lubrication: gear pump, filter on by-pass, dry sump, oil cooler; lubricating system capacity: 15.8 imp pt, 19 US pt, 9 l; carburation: 2 Zenith 40 TIN 3-barrel carburettors; fuel feed: electric pump; cooling system: air cooled.

TRANSMISSION driving wheels: rear; clutch: single dry plate; gearbox: mechanical; gears: 4 + reverse; synchromesh gears: I, II, III, IV; gearbox ratios: I 3.091, II 1.632, III 1.040, IV 0.759, rev 3.127; gear lever: central; final drive: spiral bevel; axle ratio: 4.430; width of rims: 5.5''; tyres: 165 x 15.

PERFORMANCE max speeds: 35 mph, 56 km/h in 1st gear; 66 mph, 106 km/h in 2nd gear; 103 mph, 166 km/h in 3rd gear; 127 mph, 205 km/h in 4th gear; power-weight ratio: 17.9 lb/hp, 8.1 kg/hp; carrying capacity: 706 lb, 320 kg; max gradient in 1st gear: 69%; speed in top at 1,000 rpm: 21.7 mph, 35 km/h; fuel consumption: 31.4 m/imp gal, 26.1 m/US gal, 9 l x 100 km.

CHASSIS integral; front suspension: independent, by McPherson, coil springs/telescopic damper struts, longitudinal torsion bars, lower wishbones; rear suspension: independent, trailing radius arms, transverse guide by oblique rods, transverse torsion bar, telescopic dampers.

STEERING ZF rack-and-pinion; turns of steering wheel lock to lock: 3.10.

OPEL Admiral

OPEL Diplomat V8

PORSCHE 911 E Targa

BRAKES disc (front diameter 11.10 in, 282 mm, rear 11.42 in, 290 mm), internal radial fins, dual circuit; lining area: front 16.3 sq in, 105 sq cm, rear 16.3 sq in, 105 sq cm, total 32.6 sq in, 210 sq cm.

ELECTRICAL EQUIPMENT voltage: 12 V; battery: 36 x 2 Ah; generator type: alternator, 770 W; ignition distributor: Bosch; headlamps: 2, iodine.

DIMENSIONS AND WEIGHT wheel base: 89.29 in, 2,268 mm; front track: 54.09 in, 1,374 mm; rear track: 53.35 in, 1,355 mm; overall length: 163.90 in, 4,163 mm; overall width: 63.39 in, 1,610 mm; overall height: 51.97 in, 1,320 mm; ground clearance: 5.12 in, 130 mm; dry weight: 2,238 lb, 1,015 kg; distribution of weight: 50% front axle, 50% rear axle; turning circle (between walls): 34.1 ft, 10.4 m; fuel tank capacity: 13.6 imp gal, 16.4 US gal, 62 l.

BODY coupé; doors: 2; seats: 2 + 2; front seats: separate, adjustable backrests; details: electrically-heated rear window.

PRACTICAL INSTRUCTIONS fuel: 98-100 oct petrol; engine sump oil: 15.8 imp pt, 19 US pt, 9 l, SAE 20W-30, change every 6,200 miles, 10,000 km; gearbox and final drive oil: 4.4 imp pt, 5.3 US pt, 2.5 l, SAE 90, change every 6,200 miles, 10,000 km; greasing: none; sparking plug type: 240°; tappet clearances: inlet 0.004 in, 0.10 mm, exhaust 0.004 in, 0.10 mm; valve timing: inlet opens 15° before tdc and closes 29° after bdc, exhaust opens 41° before bdc and closes 5° after tdc; normal tyre pressure: front 26 psi, 1.8 atm, rear 28 psi, 2 atm.

OPTIONAL ACCESSORIES 5-speed mechanical gearbox (I 3.091, II 1.778, III 1.218, IV 0.926, V 0.759), max speeds (I) 31 mph, 50 km/h, (II) 50 mph, 80 km/h, (III) 79 mph, 127 mph, 105 km/h, (IV) 105 mph, 169 km/h, (V) 128 mph, 206 km/h (standard for Great Britain); Sportomatic semiautomatic gearbox with 4 ratios (I 2.400, II 1.630, III 1.220, IV 0.930, rev 2.520; I 2.400, II 1.550, III 1.125, IV 0.858, rev 2.380 for 911 E), single dry plate clutch automatically operated by gear lever, hydraulic torque convertor, max ratio of convertor at stall 2, 3.857 axle ratio; light alloy wheels, 5.5'' or 6'' wide rims, 185 x 14 or 185/70 x 15 tyres; independent heating; air-conditioning system; electrically-controlled sunshine roof; electrically-controlled windows.

911 T Targa

See 911 T Coupé, except for:

PRICE IN GB: £ 3,120.
PRICE IN USA: $ 7,105.

BODY convertible; details: roll bar, detachable roof.

911 E Coupé

See 911 T Coupé, except for:

PRICE IN GB: £ 3,510.
PRICE IN USA: $ 7,895.

ENGINE compression ratio: 9.1; max power (DIN): 155 hp at 6,200 rpm; max torque (DIN): 141 lb ft, 19.5 kg m at 4,500 rpm; max engine rpm: 6,700; specific power: 70.6 hp/l; carburation: 6-cylinder Bosch intermittent injection pump in inlet pipes.

TRANSMISSION gears: 5 + reverse; gearbox ratios: I 3.091, II 1.778, III 1.218, IV 0.926, V 0.759, rev 3.127; width of rims: 6''; tyres: 185/70 x 15 (standard).

PERFORMANCE max speeds: 36 mph, 58 km/h in 1st gear; 63 mph, 102 km/h in 2nd gear; 92 mph, 148 km/h in 3rd gear; 121 mph, 195 km/h in 4th gear; 137 mph, 220 km/h in 5th gear; power-weight ratio: 14.3 lb/hp, 6.5 kg/hp; max gradient in 1st gear: 75%; fuel consumption: 25.7 m/imp gal, 21.4 m/US gal, 11 l x 100 km.

CHASSIS front suspension: hydropneumatic suspension, automatic levelling control.

BRAKES lining area: front 23.6 sq in, 152 sq cm, rear 16.3 sq in, 105 sq cm, total 39.9 sq in, 257 sq cm.

BODY details: 6'' light alloy wheels (standard).

PRACTICAL INSTRUCTIONS sparking plug type: 265°; valve timing: inlet opens 20° before tdc and closes 34° after bdc, exhaust opens 40° before bdc and closes 6° after tdc.

911 E Targa

See 911 E Coupé, except for:

PRICE IN GB: £ 3,820.
PRICE IN USA: $ 8,570.

BODY convertible; details: roll bar, detachable roof.

911 S Coupé

See 911 T Coupé, except for:

PRICE IN GB: £ 3,990.
PRICE IN USA: $ 8,675.

ENGINE compression ratio: 9.8; max power (DIN): 180 hp at 6,500 rpm; max torque (DIN): 147 lb ft, 20.3 kg m at 5,200 rpm; max engine rpm: 7,200; specific power: 82 hp/l; carburation: 6-cylinder Bosch intermittent injection pump in inlet pipes.

TRANSMISSION gears: 5 + reverse; gearbox ratios: I 3.091, II 1.778, III 1.218, IV 0.926, V 0.759, rev 3.127; width of rims: 6''; tyres: 185/70 x 15 (standard).

PERFORMANCE max speeds: 39 mph, 62 km/h in 1st gear; 68 mph, 109 km/h in 2nd gear; 98 mph, 158 km/h in 3rd gear; 129 mph, 208 km/h in 4th gear; 143 mph, 230 km/h in 5th gear; power-weight ratio: 12.6 lb/hp, 5.7 kg/hp; max gradient in 1st gear: 80%; fuel consumption: 23.5 m/imp gal, 19.6 m/US gal, 12 l x 100 km.

CHASSIS front and rear suspension: anti-roll bar.

BRAKES lining area: front 23.6 sq in, 152 sq cm, rear 16.3 in, 105 sq cm, total 39.9 sq in, 257 sq cm.

DIMENSIONS AND WEIGHT front track: 54.09 in, 1,374 mm; rear track: 53.35 in, 1,355 mm.

BODY details: 6'' light alloy wheels (standard).

PRACTICAL INSTRUCTIONS sparking plug type: 265°; valve timing: inlet opens 38° before tdc and closes 50° after bdc, exhaust opens 40° before bdc and closes 20° after tdc.

VARIATIONS

(Competition version)

PERFORMANCE power-weight ratio: 11.5 lb/hp, 5.2 kg/hp.
ELECTRICAL EQUIPMENT 45 Ah battery.
DIMENSIONS AND WEIGHT dry weight 2,051 lb, 930 kg, fuel tank capacity 24.2 imp gal, 29 US gal, 110 l.

OPTIONAL ACCESSORIES Sportomatic semi-automatic gearbox not available.

911 S Targa

See 911 S Coupé, except for:

PRICE IN GB: £ 4,300.
PRICE IN USA: $ 9,350.

BODY convertible; details: roll bar, detachable roof.

VOLKSWAGEN   GERMANY (F.R.)

1200 Standard

PRICE IN GB: £ 534.
PRICE IN USA: $ 1,839 (De Luxe Version).

ENGINE rear, 4 stroke; cylinders: 4, horizontally opposed; bore and stroke: 3.03 x 2.52 in, 77 x 64 mm; engine capacity: 72.7 cu in, 1,192 cu cm; compression ratio: 7; max power (DIN): 34 hp at 3,600 rpm; max torque (DIN): 61 lb ft, 8.4 kg m at 2,000 rpm; max engine rpm: 4,500; specific power: 28.5 hp/l; cylinder block: cast iron liners with light alloy fins; cylinder head: light alloy; crankshaft bearings: 4; valves: 2 per cylinder, overhead, push-rods and rockers; camshafts: 1, central, lower; lubrication: gear pump, filter in sump, oil cooler; lubricating system capacity: 4.4 imp pt, 5.3 US pt, 2.5 l; carburation: 1 Solex 28 PICT-2 downdraught single barrel carburettor; fuel feed: mechanical pump; cooling system: air cooled.

TRANSMISSION driving wheels: rear; clutch: single dry plate; gearbox: mechanical; gears: 4 + reverse; synchromesh gears: I, II, III, IV; gearbox ratios: I 3.800, II 2.060, III 1.320, IV 0.890, rev 3.880; gear lever: central; final drive: spiral bevel; axle ratio: 4.375; width of rims: 4''; tyres: 5.60 x 15.

PERFORMANCE max speeds: 19 mph, 31 km/h in 1st gear; 35 mph, 57 km/h in 2nd gear; 58 mph, 94 km/h in 3rd gear; 71 mph, 115 km/h in 4th gear; power-weight ratio: 49.8 lb/hp, 22.6 kg/hp; carrying capacity: 838 lb, 380 kg; max gradient in 1st gear: 41%; acceleration: standing 1/4 mile 23 sec, 0-50 mph (0-80 km/h) 18 sec; speed in top at 1,000 rpm: 18.3 mph, 29.5 km/h; fuel consumption: 37.7 m/imp gal, 31.4 m/US gal, 7.5 l x 100 km.

CHASSIS backbone platform; front suspension: independent, twin swinging longitudinal trailing arms, transverse laminated torsion bars, anti-roll bar, telescopic dampers; rear suspension: independent, swinging semi-axles, swinging longitudinal trailing arms, transverse torsion bars, telescopic dampers.

PORSCHE 911 S Coupé

VOLKSWAGEN 1302 Limousine

VOLKSWAGEN 1302 LS Cabriolet

STEERING worm and roller; turns of steering wheel lock to lock: 2.60.

BRAKES drum, dual circuit; lining area: front 55.8 sq in, 360 sq cm, rear 40.3 sq in, 260 sq cm, total 96.1 sq in, 620 sq cm.

ELECTRICAL EQUIPMENT voltage: 6 V; battery: 66 Ah; generator type: dynamo, 200 W; ignition distributor: Bosch; headlamps: 2.

DIMENSIONS AND WEIGHT wheel base: 94.49 in, 2,400 mm; front track: 51.57 in, 1,310 mm; rear track: 53.15 in, 1,350 mm; overall length: 160.24 in, 4,070 mm; overall width: 61.02 in, 1,550 mm; overall height: 59.06 in, 1,500 mm; ground clearance: 5.91 in, 150 mm; dry weight: 1,698 lb, 770 kg; distribution of weight: 43% front axle, 57% rear axle; turning circle (between walls): 36.1 ft, 11 m; fuel tank capacity: 8.8 imp gal, 10.6 US gal, 40 l.

BODY saloon/sedan; doors: 2; seats: 5; front seats: separate, adjustable backrests.

PRACTICAL INSTRUCTIONS fuel: 85 oct petrol; engine sump oil: 4.4 imp pt, 5.3 US pt, 2.5 l, SAE 10W-20 (winter) 20W-30 (summer), change every 3,100 miles, 5,000 km; gearbox and final drive oil: 5.3 imp pt, 6.3 US pt, 3 l, SAE 90, change every 31,000 miles, 50,000 km; greasing: every 6,200 miles, 10,000 km, 4 points; sparking plug type: 145°; tappet clearances: inlet 0.004 in, 0.10 mm, exhaust 0.004 in, 0.10 mm; valve timing: inlet opens 6° before tdc and closes 35°5' after bdc, exhaust opens 42°5' before bdc and closes 3° after tdc; normal tyre pressure: front 16 psi, 1.1 atm, rear 24 psi, 1.7 atm.

OPTIONAL ACCESSORIES sunshine roof; 12 V voltage; independent heating; front disc brakes only for export.

1200 (1.3-litre)

See 1200 Standard, except for:

PRICE EX WORKS: 4,795 marks.

ENGINE bore and stroke: 3.03 x 2.72 in, 77 x 69 mm; engine capacity: 78.4 cu in, 1,285 cu cm; compression ratio: 7.5; max power (DIN): 44 hp at 4,100 rpm; max torque (DIN): 64 lb ft, 8.8 kg m at 3,000 rpm; max engine rpm: 5,000; specific power: 34.2 hp/l.

PERFORMANCE max speeds: 24 mph, 39 km/h in 1st gear; 45 mph, 72 km/h in 2nd gear; 65 mph, 104 km/h in 3rd gear; 78 mph, 125 km/h in 4th gear; power-weight ratio: 41 lb/hp, 18.6 kg/hp; max gradient in 1st gear: 44%; acceleration: 0-50 mph (0-80 km/h) 14 sec; fuel consumption: 33.2 m/imp gal, 27.7 m/US gal, 8.5 l x 100 km.

ELECTRICAL EQUIPMENT voltage: 12 V; battery: 36 Ah; generator type: dynamo, 280 W.

DIMENSIONS AND WEIGHT dry weight: 1,808 lb, 820 kg.

PRACTICAL INSTRUCTIONS valve timing: inlet opens 7°30' before tdc and closes 37° after bdc, exhaust opens 44°30' before bdc and closes 4° after tdc.

OPTIONAL ACCESSORIES semi-automatic gearbox with 3 ratios (I 2.060, II 1.260, III 0.890, rev 3.070), single dry plate clutch automatically operated by gear lever, hydraulic torque convertor, max ratio of convertor at stall 2.1, independent rear suspension with semi-trailing arms, transverse linkage bar by oblique swinging trailing arms, transverse compensating torsion bar and telescopic dampers, max speed 75 mph, 120 km/h.

1300 (1.2-litre)

See 1200 Standard, except for:

PRICE EX WORKS: 5,395 marks.

CHASSIS rear suspension: transverse compensating torsion bar.

ELECTRICAL EQUIPMENT voltage: 12 V; battery: 36 Ah; generator type: dynamo, 280 W.

DIMENSIONS AND WEIGHT overall length: 158.66 in, 4,030 mm.

OPTIONAL ACCESSORIES headrests on front seats; L equipment.

1300

See 1200 (1.3-litre), except for:

PRICE EX WORKS: 5,495 marks.

CHASSIS rear suspension: transverse compensating torsion bar.

DIMENSIONS AND WEIGHT overall length: 158.66 in, 4,030 mm.

OPTIONAL ACCESSORIES headrests on front seats; front disc brakes; L equipment.

PORSCHE 911 S Coupé

VOLKSWAGEN 1302
(independent front suspension)

VOLKSWAGEN 1302 LS Cabriolet

1302 Limousine

PRICE IN GB: £ 611.
PRICE EX WORKS: 5,745 marks.

ENGINE rear, 4 stroke; cylinders: 4, horizontally opposed; bore and stroke: 3.03 x 2.72 in, 77 x 69 mm; engine capacity: 78.4 cu in, 1,285 cu cm; compression ratio: 7.5; max power (DIN): 44 hp at 4,100 rpm; max torque (DIN): 64 lb ft, 8.8 kg m at 3,000 rpm; max engine rpm: 4,600; specific power: 34.2 hp/l; cylinder block: cast iron liners with light alloy fins; cylinder head: light alloy; crankshaft bearings: 4; valves: 2 per cylinder, overhead, push-rods and rockers; camshafts: 1, central, lower; lubrication: gear pump, filter in sump, oil cooler; lubricating system capacity: 4.4 imp pt, 5.3 US pt, 2.5 l; carburation: 1 Solex 30 PITC-2 downdraught carburettor; fuel feed: mechanical pump; cooling system: air cooled.

TRANSMISSION driving wheels: rear; clutch: single dry plate; gearbox: mechanical; gears: 4 + reverse; gearbox ratios: I 3.800, II 2.060, III 1.260, IV 0.890, rev 3.610; final drive: spiral bevel; axle ratio: 4.375; width of rims: 4''; tyres: 5.60 x 15.

PERFORMANCE max speeds: 24 mph, 39 km/h in 1st gear; 45 mph, 72 km/h in 2nd gear; 65 mph, 104 km/h in 3rd gear; 78 mph, 125 km/h in 4th gear; power-weight ratio: 43.7 lb/hp, 19.8 kg/hp; carrying capacity: 882 lb, 400 kg; max gradient in 1st gear: 44%; acceleration: 0-50 mph (0-80 km/h) 14 sec; speed in top at 1,000 rpm: 16.8 mph, 27.1 km/h; fuel consumption: 33.2 m/imp gal, 27.7 m/US gal, 8.5 l x 100 km.

CHASSIS backbone platform; front suspension: independent, by McPherson, coil springs/telescopic damper struts, anti-roll bar, lower swinging trailing arms; rear suspension: independent, swinging semi-axles, swinging longitudinal trailing arms, transverse compensating torsion bar, telescopic dampers.

STEERING worm and roller, telescopic damper; turns of steering wheel lock to lock: 2.60.

BRAKES drum, dual circuit; lining area: front 55.8 sq in, 360 sq cm, rear 40.3 sq in, 260 sq cm, total 96.1 sq in, 620 sq cm.

ELECTRICAL EQUIPMENT voltage: 12 V, battery: 36 Ah; generator type: dynamo, 280 W; ignition distributor: Bosch; headlamps: 2.

DIMENSIONS AND WEIGHT wheel base: 95.28 in, 2,420 mm; front track: 54.29 in, 1,379 mm; rear track: 53.23 in, 1,352 mm; overall length: 160.63 in, 4,080 mm; overall width: 62.40 in, 1,585 mm; overall height: 59.06 in, 1,500 mm; ground clearance: 6.30 in, 160 mm; dry weight: 1,918 lb, 870 kg; turning circle (between walls): 31.5 ft, 9.6 m; fuel tank capacity: 9 imp gal, 10.8 US gal, 41 l.

BODY saloon/sedan; doors: 2; seats: 5; front seats: separate, adjustable backrests.

PRACTICAL INSTRUCTIONS fuel: 91 oct petrol; engine sump oil: 4.4 imp pt, 5.3 US pt, 2.5 l, SAE 20W-30, change every 3,100 miles, 5,000 km; gearbox and final drive oil: 5.3 imp pt, 6.3 US pt, 3 l, SAE 90, change every 31,000 miles, 50,000 km; greasing: every 6,200 miles, 10,000 km; tappet clearances: inlet 0.004 in, 0.10 mm, exhaust 0.004 in, 0.10 mm; normal tyre pressure: front 16 psi, 1.1 atm, rear 24 psi, 1.7 atm.

VARIATIONS

ENGINE bore and stroke 3.03 x 2.52 in, 77 x 64 mm, engine capacity 72.7 cu in, 1,192 cu cm, 7 compression ratio, max power (DIN) 34 hp at 3,600 rpm, max torque (DIN) 61 lb ft, 8.4 kg m at 2,000 rpm, 28.5 hp/l specific power, 1 Solex 28 PICT-2 downdraught carburettor.
PERFORMANCE max speed 71 mph, 115 km/h, power-weight ratio 56.5 lb/hp, 25.6 kg/hp, fuel consumption 37.7 m/imp gal, 31.4 m/US gal, 7.5 l x 100 km.

OPTIONAL ACCESSORIES semi-automatic gearbox with 3 ratios (I 2.060, II 1.260, III 0.890, rev 3.070), single dry plate clutch automatically operated by gear lever, hydraulic torque convertor, max ratio of convertor at stall 2.1; limited slip final drive; front disc brakes; sunshine roof; electrically-heated rear window; L equipment; independent heating.

1302 S Limousine

See 1302 Limousine, except for:

PRICE IN GB: £ 669.
PRICE EX WORKS: 5,945 marks.

ENGINE bore and stroke: 3.37 x 2.72 in, 85.5 x 69 mm; engine capacity: 96.7 cu in, 1,584 cu cm; max power (DIN): 50 hp at 4,000 rpm; max torque (DIN): 78 lb ft, 10.8 kg m at 2,800 rpm; specific power: 31.6 hp/l.

TRANSMISSION axle ratio: 4.125.

PERFORMANCE max speed: 81 mph, 130 km/h; power-weight ratio: 38.4 lb/hp, 17.4 kg/hp; max gradient in 1st gear: 47%; acceleration: 0-50 mph (0-80 km/h) 13 sec; fuel consumption: 31.4 m/imp gal, 26.1 m/US gal, 9 l x 100 km.

BRAKES front disc, rear drum; lining area: front 11.2 sq in, 72 sq cm, rear 55.5 sq in, 358 sq cm, total 66.7 sq in, 430 sq cm.

1302 LS Cabriolet

See 1302 S Limousine, except for:

PRICE IN USA: $ 2,249.
PRICE EX WORKS: 7,490 marks.

PERFORMANCE power-weight ratio: 39.7 lb/hp, 18 kg/hp; carrying capacity: 838 lb, 380 kg.

DIMENSIONS AND WEIGHT dry weight: 1,985 lb, 900 kg.

BODY convertible; seats: 4.

VARIATIONS

ENGINE (export) capacity 78.4 cu in, 1,285 cu cm, max power (DIN) 44 hp at 4,100 rpm, 34.2 hp/l specific power.
TRANSMISSION 4.375 axle ratio.
PERFORMANCE max speed 78 mph, 125 km/h.

OPTIONAL ACCESSORIES see 1302 Limousine, except for sunshine roof and L equipment.

1600 Karmann-Ghia Coupé

See 1302 S Limousine, except for:

PRICE IN USA: $ 2,399.
PRICE EX WORKS: 7,990 marks.

PERFORMANCE max speed: 86 mph, 138 km/h; carrying capacity: 728 lb, 330 kg.

CHASSIS front suspension: independent, twin swinging longitudinal trailing arms, transverse laminated torsion bars, anti-roll bar, telescopic dampers; rear suspension: independent, swinging semi-axles, swinging longitudinal trailing arms, transverse torsion bars, transverse compensating torsion bar, telescopic dampers.

DIMENSIONS AND WEIGHT wheel base: 94.49 in, 2,400 mm; front track: 51.97 in, 1,320 mm; rear track: 53.15 in, 1,350 mm; overall length: 162.99 in, 4,140 mm; overall width: 64.17 in, 1,630 mm; overall height: 51.97 in, 1,320 mm; turning circle (between walls): 37.1 ft, 11.3 m; fuel tank capacity: 8.8 imp gal, 10.6 US gal, 40 l.

BODY coupé; seats: 2 + 2.

OPTIONAL ACCESSORIES see 1302 Limousine, except for sunshine roof, L equipment and independent heating.

1600 Karmann-Ghia Cabriolet

See 1600 Karmann-Ghia Coupé, except for:
PRICE IN USA: $ 2,609.
PRICE EX WORKS: 8,790 marks.

BODY convertible.

181

See 1600 Karmann-Ghia Coupé, except for:

PRICE EX WORKS: 8,500 marks.

ENGINE compression ratio: 6.6; max power (DIN): 44 hp at 3,800 rpm; max torque (DIN): 72 lb ft, 10 kg m at 2,000 rpm; specific power: 36 hp/l.

TRANSMISSION transfer box; width of rims: 4.5''; tyres: 165 x 15.

PERFORMANCE max speeds: 15 mph, 24 km/h in 1st gear; 28 mph, 45 km/h in 2nd gear; 47 mph, 76 km/h in 3rd gear; 70 mph, 112 km/h in 4th gear; power-weight ratio: 45 lb/hp, 20.4 kg/hp; carrying capacity: 849 lb, 385 kg; max gradient in 1st gear: 55%; acceleration: 0-50 mph (0-80 km/h) 16 sec; speed in top at 1,000 rpm: 16.8 mph, 27 km/h; fuel consumption: 25 m/imp gal, 20.8 m/US gal, 11.3 l x 100 km.

CHASSIS reinforced; front suspension: reinforced swinging trailing arms, rubber cone springs, reinforced dampers.

BRAKES drum.

VOLKSWAGEN 1600 Karmann-Ghia Coupé

VOLKSWAGEN 181

VOLKSWAGEN 1600 L
(independent front suspension)

DIMENSIONS AND WEIGHT front track: 52.13 in, 1,324 mm; rear track: 55.75 in, 1,416 mm; overall length: 148.82 in, 3,780 mm; overall width: 64.57 in, 1,640 mm; overall height: 63.78 in, 1,620 mm; ground clearance: 8.07 in 205 mm; dry weight: 1,985 lb, 900 kg; turning circle (between walls): 36.7 ft, 11.2 m.

BODY open; doors: 4; details: independent heating (standard).

OPTIONAL ACCESSORIES see 1302 Limousine, except for sunshine roof, semi-automatic gearbox and L equipment.

1600 A (1.5-litre)

PRICE EX WORKS: 6,725 marks.

ENGINE rear, 4 stroke; cylinders: 4, horizontally opposed, bore and stroke: 3.27 x 2.72 in, 83 x 69 mm; engine capacity: 91.1 cu in, 1,493 cu cm; compression ratio: 7.5; max power (DIN): 45 hp at 3,800 rpm; max torque (DIN): 78 lb ft, 10.8 kg m at 2,000 rpm; max engine rpm: 4,200; specific power: 30.1 hp/l; cylinder block: cast iron liners with light alloy fins; cylinder head: light alloy; crankshaft bearings: 4; valves: 2 per cylinder, overhead, push-rods and rockers; camshafts: 1, central, lower; lubrication: gear pump, filter in sump, oil cooler; lubricating system capacity: 4.4 imp pt, 5.3 US pt, 2.5 l; carburation: 1 Solex 32 PHN 1 horizontal single barrel carburettor; fuel feed: mechanical pump; cooling system: air cooled.

TRANSMISSION driving wheels: rear; clutch: single dry plate; gearbox: mechanical; gears: 4 + reverse; synchromesh gears: I, II, III, IV; gearbox ratios: I 3.800, II 2.060, III 1.260, IV 0.890, rev 3.880; gear lever: central; final drive: spiral bevel; axle ratio: 4.125; width of rims: 4.5''; tyres: 6.00 x 15.

PERFORMANCE max speeds: 22 mph, 35 km/h in 1st gear; 40 mph, 65 km/h in 2nd gear; 66 mph, 107 km/h in 3rd gear; 78 mph, 125 km/h in 4th gear; power-weight ratio: 47.6 lb/hp, 21.6 kg/hp; carrying capacity: 882 lb, 400 kg; max gradient in 1st gear: 42.5%; acceleration: standing ¼ mile 21.4 sec, 0-50 mph (0-80 km/h) 15 sec; speed in top at 1,000 rpm: 19.6 mph, 31.5 km/h; fuel consumption: 33.6 m/imp gal, 28 m/US gal, 8.4 l x 100 km.

CHASSIS backbone platform, rear auxiliary frame; front suspension: independent, twin swinging longitudinal trailing arms, transverse torsion bars, anti-roll bar, telescopic dampers; rear suspension: independent, semi-trailing arms, transverse linkage by oblique swinging trailing arms, transverse torsion bars, telescopic dampers.

STEERING worm and roller, telescopic damper; turns of steering wheel lock to lock: 2.80.

BRAKES front disc (diameter 10.91 in, 277 mm), rear drum; dual circuit.

ELECTRICAL EQUIPMENT voltage: 12 V; battery: 36 Ah; generator type: dynamo, 420 W; ignition distributor: Bosch; headlamps: 2.

DIMENSIONS AND WEIGHT wheel base: 94.49 in, 2,400 mm; front track: 51.57 in, 1,310 mm; rear track: 53.15 in, 1,350 mm; overall length: 170.87 in, 4,340 mm; overall width: 63.39 in, 1,610 mm; overall height: 57.87 in, 1,470 mm; ground clearance: 5.91 in, 150 mm; dry weight: 2,150 lb, 975 kg; distribution of weight: 39.6% front axle, 60.4% rear axle; turning circle (between walls): 36.7 ft, 11.2 m; fuel tank capacity: 8.8 imp gal, 10.6 US gal, 40 l.

BODY saloon/sedan; doors: 2; seats: 5; front seats: separate, adjustable backrests.

PRACTICAL INSTRUCTIONS fuel: 85 oct petrol; engine sump oil: 4.4 imp pt, 5.3 US pt, 2.5 l, SAE 20W-30, change every 3,100 miles, 5,000 km; gearbox and final drive oil 5.3 imp pt, 6.3 US pt, 3 l, SAE 90; greasing: every 6,200 miles, 10,000 km, 4 points; sparking plug type: 145°; tappet clearances: inlet 0.004 in, 0.10 mm, exhaust 0.004 in 0.10 mm; valve timing: inlet opens 7°5' before tdc and closes 37° after bdc, exhaust opens 44°5' before bdc and closes 4° after tdc; normal tyre pressure: front 17 psi, 1.2 atm, rear 24 psi, 1.7 atm.

OPTIONAL ACCESSORIES sunshine roof; headrests on front seats; independent heating; electrically-heated rear window.

1600 A

See 1600 A (1.5-litre), except for:

PRICE EX WORKS: 6,845 marks.

ENGINE bore and stroke: 3.37 x 2.72 in, 85.5 x 69 mm; engine capacity: 96.7 cu in, 1,584 cu cm; compression ratio: 7.7; max power (DIN): 54 hp at 4,000 rpm; max torque (DIN): 81 lb ft, 11.2 kg m at 2,200 rpm; max engine rpm: 4,600; specific power: 34.1 hp/l; carburation: 2 Solex 32 PDSIT downdraught carburettors.

PERFORMANCE max speeds: 27 mph, 43 km/h in 1st gear; 39 mph, 62 km/h in 2nd gear; 63 mph, 102 km/h in 3rd gear; 84 mph, 135 km/h in 4th gear; power-weight ratio

VOLKSWAGEN 1600 Karmann-Ghia Coupé

VOLKSWAGEN 181

VOLKSWAGEN 1600 L

39.9 lb/hp, 18.1 kg/hp; max gradient in 1st gear: 44%; acceleration: 0-50 mph (0-80 km/h) 12.5 sec; fuel consumption: 31.7 m/imp gal, 26.4 m/US gal, 8.9 l x 100 km.

OPTIONAL ACCESSORIES electronically-controlled fuel injection system (constant pressure) with injectors in inlet pipes; automatic gearbox, hydraulic torque convertor and planetary gears with 3 ratios (I 2.650, II 1.590, III 1, rev 1.800), possible manual selection, max ratio of convertor at stall 2.5, central selector lever, hypoid bevel final drive, 3.670 axle ratio.

1600 (1.5-litre)

See 1600 A (1.5-litre), except for:
PRICE EX WORKS: 6,980 marks.

1600

See 1600 A, except for:
PRICE EX WORKS: 7,100 marks.

1600 L (1.5-litre)

See 1600 A (1.5-litre), except for:
PRICE EX WORKS: 7,380 marks.
DIMENSIONS AND WEIGHT overall length: 172.05 in, 4,370 mm; overall width: 64.57 in, 1,640 mm.

1600 L

See 1600 A, except for:
PRICE EX WORKS: 7,500 marks.
DIMENSIONS AND WEIGHT overall length: 172.05 in, 4,370 mm; overall width: 64.57 in, 1,640 mm.

1600 TA (1.5-litre)

See 1600 A (1.5-litre), except for:
PRICE EX WORKS: 6,725 marks.
PERFORMANCE power-weight ratio: 49.4 lb/hp, 22.4 kg/hp.
DIMENSIONS AND WEIGHT dry weight: 2,227 lb, 1,010 kg; distribution of weight: 40.8% front axle, 59.2% rear axle.
BODY coupé.

1600 TA

See 1600 A, except for:
PRICE IN GB: £ 748.
PRICE IN USA: $ 2,339.
PERFORMANCE power-weight ratio: 41.2 lb/hp, 18.7 kg/hp.
DIMENSIONS AND WEIGHT dry weight: 2,227 lb, 1,010 kg; distribution of weight: 40.8% front axle, 59.2% rear axle.
BODY coupé.

1600 T (1.5-litre)

See 1600 TA (1.5-litre), except for:
PRICE EX WORKS: 6,980 marks.

1600 T

See 1600 TA, except for:
PRICE EX WORKS: 7,100 marks.

1600 TL (1.5-litre)

See 1600 TA (1.5-litre), except for:
PRICE EX WORKS: 7,380 marks.
DIMENSIONS AND WEIGHT overall length: 172.05 in, 4,370 mm; overall width: 64.57 in, 1,640 mm.

1600 TL

See 1600 TA, except for:
PRICE EX WORKS: 7,500 marks.
DIMENSIONS AND WEIGHT overall length: 172.05 in, 4,370 mm; overall width: 64.57 in, 1,640 mm.

1600 Variant (1.5-litre)

See 1600 A (1.5-litre), except for:

PRICE EX WORKS: 7,180 marks.

PERFORMANCE power-weight ratio: 50.7 lb/hp, 23 kg/hp.

DIMENSIONS AND WEIGHT dry weight: 2,282 lb, 1,035 kg; distribution of weight: 35% front axle, 65% rear axle.

BODY estate car/station wagon; doors: 2 + 1.

1600 Variant

See 1600 A, except for:

PRICE IN GB: £ 849.
PRICE IN USA: $ 2,750.

PERFORMANCE power-weight ratio: 42.1 lb/hp, 19.1 kg/hp.

DIMENSIONS AND WEIGHT 2,282 lb, 1,035 kg; distribution of weight: 35% front axle, 65% rear axle.

BODY estate car/station wagon; doors: 2 + 1.

1600 Variant L (1.5-litre)

See 1600 Variant (1.5-litre), except for:

PRICE EX WORKS: 7,680 marks.

DIMENSIONS AND WEIGHT overall length: 172.05 in, 4,370 mm; overall width: 64.57 in, 1,640 mm.

1600 Variant L

See 1600 Variant, except for:

PRICE EX WORKS: 7,800 marks.

DIMENSIONS AND WEIGHT overall length: 172.05 in, 4,370 mm; overall width: 64.57 in, 1,640 mm.

K 70 (75 hp)

PRICE EX WORKS: 9,450 marks.

ENGINE front, 4 stroke; cylinders: 4, in line; bore and stroke: 3.23 x 2.99 in, 82 x 76 mm; engine capacity: 97.9 cu in, 1,605 cu cm; compression ratio: 8; max power (DIN): 75 hp at 5,200 rpm; max torque (DIN): 91 lb ft, 12.5 kg m at 3,500 rpm; max engine rpm: 5,500; specific power: 46.7 hp/l; cylinder block: cast iron; cylinder head: light alloy; crankshaft bearings: 5; valves: 2 per cylinder, overhead, rockers; camshafts: 1, overhead; lubrication: gear pump, full flow filter; lubricating system capacity: 7 imp pt, 8.5 US ut, 4 l; carburation: 1 Solex 40 DDH downdraught twin barrel carburettor; fuel feed: mechanical pump; cooling system: water; cooling system capacity: 13.4 imp pt, 16.1 US pt, 7.6 l.

TRANSMISSION driving wheels: front; clutch: single dry plate (diaphragm); gearbox: mechanical; gears: 4 + reverse; synchromesh gears: I, II, III, IV; gearbox ratios: I 3.106, II 1.826, III 1.214, IV 0.905, rev 3.185; gear lever: central; final drive: spiral bevel; axle ratio: 4.625; width of rims: 4.5''; tyres: 165 SR x 14.

PERFORMANCE max speeds: 25 mph, 40 km/h in 1st gear; 43 mph, 70 km/h in 2nd gear; 75 mph, 120 km/h in 3rd gear; 92 mph, 148 km/h in 4th gear; power-weight ratio: 30.9 lb/hp, 14 kg/hp; carrying capacity: 1,014 lb, 460 kg; max gradient in 1st gear: 49%; acceleration: 0-50 mph (0-80 km/h) 11 sec; speed in top at 1,000 rpm: 16.8 mph, 27 km/h; fuel consumption: 27.7 m/imp gal, 23.1 m/US gal, 10.2 l x 100 km.

CHASSIS integral; front suspension: independent, by McPherson, coil springs/telescopic damper struts, anti-roll bar, lower semi-trailing arms; rear suspension: independent, by McPherson, coil springs/telescopic damper struts, anti-roll bar, oblique wishbones.

STEERING rack-and-pinion.

BRAKES front disc, rear drum, dual circuit, rear compensator, servo; lining area: front 19.5 sq in, 126 sq cm, rear 54.6 sq in, 352 sq cm, total 74.1 sq in, 478 sq cm.

ELECTRICAL EQUIPMENT voltage: 12 V; battery: 44 Ah; generator type: alternator, 400 W; ignition distributor: Bosch; headlamps: 2.

DIMENSIONS AND WEIGHT wheel base: 105.91 in, 2,690 mm; front track: 54.72 in, 1,390 mm; rear track: 56.10 in, 1,425 mm; overall length: 174.02 in, 4,420 mm; overall width: 66.34 in, 1,685 mm; overall height: 57.09 in, 1,450 mm; ground clearance: 5.35 in, 136 mm; dry weight: 2,315 lb, 1,050 kg; turning circle (between walls): 35.4 ft, 10.8 m; fuel tank capacity: 11.4 imp gal, 13.7 US gal, 52 l.

VOLKSWAGEN K 70 L

VOLKSWAGEN 2-door 411 LE

VOLKSWAGEN 411 LE Variant

BODY saloon/sedan; doors: 4; seats: 5; front seats: separate.

PRACTICAL INSTRUCTIONS fuel: 90-91 oct petrol; engine sump oil: 7 imp pt, 8.5 US pt, 4 l, SAE 20W-30, change every 3,100 miles, 5,000 km; gearbox oil: 2.5 imp pt, 3 US pt, 1.4 l, SAE 90, change every 31,000 miles, 50,000 km; final drive oil: 0.7 imp pt, 0.8 US pt, 0.4 l, SAE 90, change every 31,000 miles, 50,000 km; greasing: none; normal tyre pressure: front 21 psi, 1.5 atm, rear 21 psi, 1.5 atm.

K 70 L (75 hp)

See K 70 (75 hp), except for:

PRICE EX WORKS: 9,790 marks.

BODY details: luxury equipment.

K 70 (90 hp)

See K 70 (75 hp), except for:

PRICE EX WORKS: 9,645 marks.

ENGINE compression ratio: 9.5; max power (DIN): 90 hp at 5,200 rpm; max torque (DIN): 99 lb ft, 13.7 kg m at 4,000 rpm; max engine rpm: 5,800; specific power: 56.1 hp/l.

PERFORMANCE max speeds: 27 mph, 43 km/h in 1st gear; 45 mph, 72 km/h in 2nd gear; 77 mph, 124 km/h in 3rd gear; 98 mph, 158 km/h in 4th gear; power-weight ratio: 25.6 lb/hp, 11.6 kg/hp; max gradient in 1st gear: 53.5%; acceleration: 0-50 mph (0-80 km/h) 8.9 sec; speed in top at 1,000 rpm: 17.8 mph, 28.7 km/h.

K 70 L (90 hp)

See K 70 (90 hp), except for:

PRICE EX WORKS: 9,985 marks.

BODY details: luxury equipment.

2-door 411 E

PRICE EX WORKS: 8,390 marks.

ENGINE rear, 4 stroke; cylinders: 4, horizontally opposed; bore and stroke: 3.54 x 2.60 in, 90 x 66 mm; engine capacity: 102.5 cu in, 1,679 cu cm; compression ratio: 8.6; max power (DIN): 80 hp at 4,900 rpm; max torque (DIN): 94 lb ft, 13 kg m at 2,600 rpm; max engine rpm: 5,000; specific power: 47.6 hp/l; cylinder block: cast iron liners with light alloy fins; cylinder head: light alloy; crankshaft bearings: 4; valves: 2 per cylinder, overhead, push-rods and rockers; camshafts: 1, central, lower; lubrication: gear pump, filter in sump, oil cooler; lubricating system capacity: 6.2 imp pt, 7.4 US pt, 3.5 l; carburation: Bosch electronically-controlled injection system; fuel feed: electric pump; cooling system: air cooled.

TRANSMISSION driving wheels: rear; clutch: single dry plate; gearbox: mechanical; gears: 4 + reverse, synchromesh gears: I, II, III, IV; gearbox ratios: I 3.813, II 2.113, III 1.403, IV 1, rev 4.305; gear lever: central; final drive: spiral bevel; axle ratio: 3.727; width of rims: 4.5''; tyres: 155 x 15.

PERFORMANCE max speeds: 24 mph, 39 km/h in 1st gear; 44 mph, 71 km/h in 2nd gear; 66 mph, 107 km/h in 3rd gear; 93 mph, 150 km/h in 4th gear; power-weight ratio: 28.4 lb/hp, 12.9 kg/hp; carrying capacity: 882 lb, 400 kg; max gradient in 1st gear: 47%; acceleration: 0-50 mph (0-80 km/h) 9.5 sec; speed in direct drive at 1,000 rpm: 20.3 mph, 32.6 km/h; fuel consumption: 27.2 m/imp gal, 22.6 m/US gal, 10.4 l x 100 km.

CHASSIS integral; front suspension: independent, by McPherson, coil springs/telescopic damper struts, lower wishbones, anti-roll bar; rear suspension: independent, semi-trailing arms, coil springs/telescopic damper struts.

STEERING recirculating ball; turns of steering wheel lock to lock: 3.50.

BRAKES front disc, rear drum, dual circuit, rear compensator; lining area: front 15.5 sq in, 100 sq cm, rear 69.8 sq in, 450 sq cm, total 85.3 sq in, 550 sq cm.

ELECTRICAL EQUIPMENT voltage: 12 V; battery: 45 Ah; generator type: alternator, 550 W; ignition distributor: Bosch; headlamps: 4, halogen.

DIMENSIONS AND WEIGHT wheel base: 98.43 in, 2,500 mm; front track: 54.33 in, 1,380 mm; rear track: 53.15 in, 1,350 mm; overall length: 179.13 in, 4,550 mm; overall width: 64.96 in, 1,650 mm; overall height: 58.66 in, 1,490 mm; ground clearance: 5.35 in, 136 mm; dry weight: 2,271 lb, 1,030 kg; distribution of weight: 45% front axle, 55% rear axle; turning circle (between walls): 37.4 ft, 11.4 m; fuel tank capacity: 11 imp gal, 13.2 US gal, 50 l.

BODY saloon/sedan; doors: 2; seats: 5; front seats: separate, reclining backrests; details: independent heating.

VOLKSWAGEN K 70 L (90 hp)

VOLKSWAGEN 411 E

VOLKSWAGEN 411 E (main control unit)

PRACTICAL INSTRUCTIONS fuel: 98 oct petrol; engine sump oil: 6.2 imp pt, 7.4 US pt, 3.5 l, SAE 10W-30, change every 3,100 miles, 5,000 km; gearbox and final drive oil: 4.4 imp pt, 5.3 US pt, 2.5 l, SAE 90, change every 31,100 miles, 50,000 km; greasing: none; sparking plug type: 175°; tappet clearances: inlet 0.004 in, 0.10 mm, exhaust 0.004 in, 0.10 mm; valve timing: inlet opens 12° before tdc and closes 42° after bdc, exhaust opens 43° before bdc and closes 4° after tdc; normal tyre pressure: front 20 psi, 1.4 atm, rear 26 psi, 1.8 atm.

OPTIONAL ACCESSORIES automatic gearbox, hydraulic torque convertor and planetary gears with 3 ratios (I 2.650, II 1.590, III 1, rev 1.800), max ratio of convertor at stall 2.5, possible manual selection, central selector lever, hypoid bevel final drive, 3.670 axle ratio (3.910 for Variant); sunshine roof; electrically-heated rear window; headrests on front seats.

4-door 411 E

See 2-door 411 E, except for:

PRICE EX WORKS: 8,735 marks.

2-door 411 LE

See 2-door 411 E, except for:

PRICE IN GB: £ 1,022.
PRICE EX WORKS: 8,810 marks.

4-door 411 LE

See 2-door 411 E, except for:

PRICE IN GB: £ 1,068.
PRICE EX WORKS: 9,155 marks.

411 E Variant

See 2-door 411 E, except for:

PRICE EX WORKS: 8,770 marks.

TRANSMISSION tyres: 165 x 15.

PERFORMANCE power-weight ratio: 30.2 lb/hp, 13.7 kg/hp; carrying capacity: 1,036 lb, 470 kg.

BRAKES no rear compensator.

DIMENSIONS AND WEIGHT overall length: 178.35 in, 4,530 mm; overall width: 64.57 in, 1,640 mm; dry weight: 2,414 lb, 1,095 kg.

BODY estate car/station wagon; doors: 2 + 1.

411 LE Variant

See 411 E Variant, except for:

PRICE IN GB: £ 1,094.
PRICE EX WORKS: 9,190 marks.

VOLKSWAGEN-PORSCHE
GERMANY (F.R.)

914

PRICE EX WORKS: 11,955 marks.

ENGINE rear, 4 stroke; cylinders: 4, horizontally opposed; bore and stroke: 3.54 x 2.60 in, 90 x 66 mm; engine capacity: 102.5 cu in, 1,679 cu cm; compression ratio: 8.6; max power (DIN): 80 hp at 4,900 rpm; max torque (DIN): 94 lb ft, 13 kg m at 2,600 rpm; max engine rpm: 5,000; specific power: 47.6 hp/l; cylinder block: light alloy, separate cylinders with Ferral chromium walls; cylinder head: light alloy; crankshaft bearings: 4; valves: 2 per cylinder, overhead, push-rods and rockers; camshafts: 1, central, lower; lubrication: gear pump, filter in sump; lubricating system capacity: 6.2 imp pt, 7.4 US pt, 3.5 l; carburation: Bosch electronically-controlled injection system; fuel feed: electric pump; cooling system: air cooled.

TRANSMISSION driving wheels: rear; clutch: single dry plate; gearbox: mechanical; gears: 5 + reverse, synchromesh gears: I, II, III, IV, V; gearbox ratios: I 3.091, II 1.889, III 1.261, IV 0.926, V 0.710, rev 3.127; gear lever: central; final drive: spiral bevel; axle ratio: 4.430; width of rims: 4.5''; tyres: 155 x 15.

PERFORMANCE max speeds: 25 mph, 41 km/h in 1st gear; 42 mph, 67 km/h in 2nd gear; 62 mph, 100 km/h in 3rd gear; 85 mph, 136 km/h in 4th gear; 111 mph, 178 km/h in 5th gear; power-weight ratio: 28.7 lb/hp, 13 kg/hp; carrying capacity: 353 lb, 160 kg; max gradient in 1st gear: 55%;

914

acceleration: 0-50 mph (0-80 km/h) 9 sec; speed in top at 1,000 rpm: 21.7 mph, 35 km/h; fuel consumption: 31.4 m/imp gal, 26.1 m/US gal, 9 l x 100 km.

CHASSIS integral; front suspension: independent, by McPherson, telescopic damper struts, longitudinal torsion bars, lower wishbones; rear suspension: independent, oblique semi-trailing arms, coil springs, auxiliary rubber elements, telescopic dampers.

STEERING ZF rack-and-pinion, damper; turns of steering wheel lock to lock: 3.

BRAKES disc (front diameter 11.06 in, 281 mm, rear 11.10 in, 282 mm), rear compensator; lining area: front 15.5 sq in, 100 sq cm, rear 12.4 sq in, 80 sq cm, total 27.9 sq in, 180 sq cm.

ELECTRICAL EQUIPMENT voltage: 12 V; battery: 45 Ah; generator type: alternator, 700 W; ignition distributor: Bosch; headlamps: 4, 2 retractable.

DIMENSIONS AND WEIGHT wheel base: 96.46 in, 2,450 mm; front track: 52.95 in, 1,345 mm; rear track: 54.72 in, 1,390 mm; overall length: 156.89 in, 3,985 mm; overall width: 64.96 in, 1,650 mm; overall height: 48.43 in, 1,230 mm; ground clearance: 4.72 in, 120 mm; dry weight: 2,018 lb, 915 kg; distribution of weight: 50% front axle, 50% rear axle; turning circle (between walls): 32.8 ft, 10 m; fuel tank capacity: 13.6 imp gal, 16.4 US gal, 62 l.

BODY roadster; doors: 2; seats: 2; details: roll bar, detachable roof.

PRACTICAL INSTRUCTIONS fuel: 98-100 oct petrol; engine sump oil: 6.2 imp pt, 7.4 US pt, 3.5 l, SAE 20W-30, change every 3,100 miles, 5,000 km; gearbox and final drive oil: 4.4 imp pt, 5.3 US pt, 2.5 l, SAE 90, change every 12,400 miles, 20,000 km; greasing: none; sparking plug type: 175°; tappet clearances: inlet 0.004 in, 0.10 mm, exhaust 0.004 in, 0.10 mm; valve timing: inlet opens 11°30' before tdc and closes 42° after bdc, exhaust opens 43° before bdc and closes 4° after tdc; normal tyre pressure: front 20 psi, 1.4 atm, rear 26 psi, 1.8 atm.

OPTIONAL ACCESSORIES Sportomatic semi-automatic gearbox (only for USA); 165 x 15 tyres.

914 S

See 914, except for:

PRICE IN GB: £ 1,730.
PRICE IN USA: $ 3,595.

914/6

See 914, except for:

PRICE IN GB: £ 2,660.
PRICE IN USA: $ 5,999.

ENGINE cylinders: 6, horizontally opposed; bore and stroke: 3.15 x 2.60 in, 80 x 66 mm; engine capacity: 121.5 cu in, 1,991 cu cm; max power (DIN): 110 hp at 5,800 rpm; max torque (DIN): 116 lb ft, 16 kg m at 4,200 rpm; max engine rpm: 6,500; specific power: 55.2 hp/l; cylinder block: cast iron liners with light alloy fins; crankshaft bearings: 8; valves: 2 per cylinder, Vee-slanted, rockers; camshafts: 1 per cylinder block, overhead; lubrication: dry sump; lubricating system capacity: 15.8 imp pt, 19 US pt, 9 l; carburation: 2 Zenith 40 TIN 3-barrel carburettors.

TRANSMISSION gearbox ratios: I 3.091, II 1.778, III 1.218, IV 0.926, V 0.759, rev 3.127; width of rims: 5.5''; tyres: 165 x 15 (standard).

PERFORMANCE max speeds: 31 mph, 50 km/h in 1st gear; 54 mph, 87 km/h in 2nd gear; 79 mph, 127 km/h in 3rd gear; 105 mph, 169 km/h in 4th gear; 128 mph, 206 km/h in 5th gear; power-weight ratio: 18.7 lb/hp, 8.5 kg/hp; max gradient in 1st gear: 68%; acceleration: 0-50 mph (0-80 km/h) 7 sec; fuel consumption: 31.4 m/imp gal, 26.1 m/US gal, 9 l x 100 km.

BRAKES disc (front diameter 11.10 in, 282 mm, rear 11.26 in, 286 mm), radial fins; lining area: front 16.3 sq in, 105 sq cm, rear 16.3 sq in, 105 sq cm, total 32.6 sq in, 210 sq cm.

ELECTRICAL EQUIPMENT generator type: alternator, 770 W; headlamps: 2, iodine.

DIMENSIONS AND WEIGHT front track: 53.58 in, 1,361 mm; rear track: 54.41 in, 1,382 mm; ground clearance: 5.04 in, 128 mm; dry weight: 2,073 lb, 940 kg.

PRACTICAL INSTRUCTIONS sparking plug type: 240°; valve timing: inlet opens 15° before tdc and closes 29° after bdc, exhaust opens 41° before bdc and closes 5° after tdc; normal tyre pressure: front 26 psi, 1.8 atm, rear 28 psi, 2 atm.

OPTIONAL ACCESSORIES 5.5'' light alloy wheels.

VOLKSWAGEN-PORSCHE 914/6

AC 428 Fastback

ASTON MARTIN DB6 Mk II (injection engine)

428 Convertible

PRICE IN GB: £ 5,800.

ENGINE front, 4 stroke; cylinders: 8, Vee-slanted at 90°; bore and stroke: 4.13 x 3.98 in, 104.9 x 101.1 mm; engine capacity: 428.1 cu in, 7,016 cu cm; compression ratio: 10.5; max power (SAE): 345 hp at 4,600 rpm; max torque (SAE): 462 lb ft, 63.8 kg m at 2,800 rpm; max engine rpm: 5,250; specific power: 49.2 hp/l; cylinder block: cast iron; cylinder head: cast iron; crankshaft bearings: 5; valves: 2 per cylinder, overhead, in line, push-rods and rockers, hydraulic tappets; camshafts: 1, at centre of Vee; lubrication: rotary pump, full flow filter, oil cooler; lubricating system capacity: 10 imp pt, 12 US pt, 5.7 l; carburation: 1 Ford downdraught 4-barrel carburettor; fuel feed: mechanical pump; cooling system: water; cooling system capacity: 17.1 imp pt, 20.5 US pt, 9.7 l.

TRANSMISSION driving wheels: rear; clutch: single dry plate; gearbox: mechanical; gears: 4 + reverse; synchromesh gears: I, II, III, IV; gearbox ratios: I 2.320, II 1.690, III 1.290, IV 1, rev 2.320; gear lever: central; final drive: hypoid bevel, limited slip; axle ratio: 2.880; width of rims: 6''; tyres: 205 x 15.

PERFORMANCE max speeds: 68 mph, 108 km/h in 1st gear; 93 mph, 150 km/h in 2nd gear; 121 mph, 195 km/h in 3rd gear; 150 mph, 241 km/h in 4th gear; power-weight ratio: 8.8 lb/hp, 4 kg/hp; carrying capacity: 353 lb, 160 kg; speed in direct drive at 1,000 rpm: 29.8 mph, 48 km/h; fuel consumption: 17 m/imp gal, 14.2 m/US gal, 16.6 l x 100 km.

CHASSIS tubular; front suspension: independent, wishbones, coil springs, telescopic dampers; rear suspension: independent, wishbones, trailing lower radius arms, coil springs, telescopic dampers.

STEERING rack-and-pinion; turns of steering wheel lock to lock: 3.30.

BRAKES disc (front diameter 11.73 in, 298 mm, rear 10.51 in, 267 mm), servo; area rubbed by linings: total 580 sq in, 3,741 sq cm.

ELECTRICAL EQUIPMENT voltage: 12 V; battery: 57 Ah; generator type: alternator; ignition distributor: Ford; headlamps: 2.

DIMENSIONS AND WEIGHT wheel base: 95.98 in, 2,438 mm; front track: 55 in, 1,397 mm; rear track: 55.98 in, 1,422 mm; overall length: 174.02 in, 4,420 mm; overall width: 67.01 in, 1,702 mm; overall height: 50.98 in, 1,295 mm; ground clearance: 7.99 in, 203 mm; dry weight: 3,025 lb, 1,372 kg; distribution of weight: 47.4% front axle, 52.6% rear axle; turning circle (between walls): 36.1 ft, 11 m; fuel tank capacity: 18.9 imp gal, 22.7 US gal, 86 l (2 separate interconnected tanks).

BODY convertible; doors: 2; seats: 2; front seats: separate, reclining backrests; details: electrically-controlled windows.

PRACTICAL INSTRUCTIONS fuel: 100 oct petrol; engine sump oil: 7.9 imp pt, 9.5 US pt, 4.5 l, SAE 10W-30, change every 4,000 miles, 6,400 km; gearbox oil: 4 imp pt, 4.9 US pt, 2.3 l, SAE 80; final drive oil: 2.5 imp pt, 3 US pt, 1.4 l, SAE 90; greasing: every 2,500 miles, 4,000 km, 9 points; valve timing: inlet opens 16° before tdc and closes 60° after bdc, exhaust opens 55° before bdc and closes 21° after tdc; normal tyre pressure: front 25 psi, 1.7 atm, rear 27 psi, 1.9 atm.

OPTIONAL ACCESSORIES light alloy wheels; automatic gearbox, hydraulic torque convertor and planetary gears with 3 ratios (I 2.460, II 1.460, III 1, rev 2.180), central selector lever, 3.070 axle ratio.

428 Fastback

See 428 Convertible, except for:

BODY coupé; seats: 2 + 2.

OPTIONAL ACCESSORIES electrically-heated rear window.

DB6 Mk II

PRICE IN GB: £ 4,212.

ENGINE front, 4 stroke; cylinders: 6, vertical, in line; bore and stroke: 3.78 x 3.62 in, 96 x 92 mm; engine capacity: 243.8 cu in, 3,995 cu cm; compression ratio: 8.9; max engine

VOLKSWAGEN-PORSCHE 914

AC 428 Convertible

ASTON MARTIN DB6 Mk II

rpm: 6,000; cylinder block: light alloy, wet liners; cylinder head: light alloy, hemispherical combustion chambers; crankshaft bearings: 7; valves: 2 per cylinder, overhead, slanted at 80°, thimble tappets; camshafts: 2, overhead; lubrication: rotary pump, full flow filter, oil cooler; lubricating system capacity: 28 imp pt, 33.6 US pt, 15.9 l; carburation: 3 SU type HD 8 horizontal carburettors; fuel feed: 2 electric pumps; cooling system: water, electric thermostatic fan; cooling system capacity: 28 imp pt, 33.6 US pt, 15.9 l.

TRANSMISSION driving wheels: rear; clutch: single dry plate (diaphragm), hydraulically controlled; gearbox: mechanical; gears: 5 + reverse; synchromesh gears: I, II, III, IV, V; gearbox ratios: I 2.970, II 1.760, III 1.230, IV 1, V 0.834, rev 3.310; gear lever: central; final drive: hypoid bevel; axle ratio: 3.730; width of rims: 6''; tyres: 8.15 x 15.

PERFORMANCE max speeds: 44 mph, 71 km/h in 1st gear; 74 mph, 119 km/h in 2nd gear; 106 mph, 170 km/h in 3rd gear; 131 mph, 211 km/h in 4th gear; 157 mph, 252 km/h in 5th gear; carrying capacity: 706 lb, 320 kg; speed in top at 1,000 rpm: 26.1 mph, 34.8 km/h; fuel consumption: 15 m/imp gal, 12.5 m/US gal, 18.8 l x 100 km.

CHASSIS box-type platform; front suspension: independent, wishbones, coil springs, anti-roll bar, telescopic dampers; rear suspension: rigid axle, parallel trailing links, transverse Watt linkage, coil springs, lever dampers adjustable while running.

STEERING rack-and-pinion, adjustable height and tilt of steering wheel, servo; turns of steering wheel lock to lock: 3.12.

BRAKES disc (front diameter 11.50 in, 292 mm, rear 10.80 in, 274 mm), dual circuit, each with vacuum servo; area rubbed by linings: front 241 sq in, 1,554 sq cm, rear 197 sq in, 1,270 sq cm, total 438 sq in, 2,824 sq cm.

ELECTRICAL EQUIPMENT voltage: 12 V; battery: 60 Ah; generator type: alternator, 45 A; ignition distributor: Lucas; headlamps: 2.

DIMENSIONS AND WEIGHT wheel base: 101.75 in, 2,584 mm; front track: 54 in, 1,371 mm; rear track: 54 in, 1,371 mm; overall length: 182 in, 4,623 mm; overall width: 66 in, 1,676 mm; overall height: 53.50 in, 1,359 mm; ground clearance: 6.25 in, 159 mm; dry weight: 3,300 lb, 1,496 kg; turning circle (between walls): 34 ft, 10.4 m; fuel tank capacity: 19 imp gal, 22.7 US gal, 86 l.

BODY coupé; doors: 2; seats: 4; front seats: separate, reclining backrests; details: electrically-controlled windows.

PRACTICAL INSTRUCTIONS fuel: 100 oct petrol; engine sump oil: 23 imp pt, 27.5 US pt, 13 l, SAE 10W-40 (summer), 10W-30 (winter), change every 2,500 miles, 4,000 km; gearbox oil: 3.5 imp pt, 4.2 US pt, 2 l, SAE 90, change every 10,000 miles, 16,100 km; final drive oil: 3 imp pt, 3.6 US pt, 1.7 l, SAE 90, change every 10,000 miles, 16,100 km; greasing: every 10,000 miles, 16,100 km, 8 points; normal tyre pressure: front 26 psi, 1.8 atm, rear 28 psi, 2 atm.

VARIATIONS

ENGINE (injection) 9.4 compression ratio.

ENGINE (Vantage) 9.4 compression ratio, 3 Weber 45 DCOE 9 horizontal twin barrel carburettors.
TRANSMISSION limited slip final drive (standard), 3.540 axle ratio.

OPTIONAL ACCESSORIES limited slip final drive.

DBS

PRICE IN GB: £ 4,755.
PRICE IN USA: $ 17,900 (with air-conditioning system).

ENGINE front, 4 stroke; cylinders: 6, vertical, in line; bore and stroke: 3.78 x 3.62 in, 96 x 62 mm; engine capacity: 243.8 cu in, 3,995 cu cm; compression ratio: 8.9; max engine rpm: 6,000; cylinder block: light alloy, wet liners; cylinder head: light alloy, hemispherical combustion chambers; crankshaft bearings: 7; valves: 2 per cylinder, overhead, slanted at 80°, thimble tappets; camshafts: 2, overhead; lubrication: rotary pump, full flow filter; lubricating system capacity: 28 imp pt, 33.6 US pt, 15.9 l; carburation: 3 SU type HD 8 horizontal carburettors; fuel feed: 2 electric pumps; cooling system: water, electric thermostatic fan; cooling system capacity: 28 imp pt, 33.6 US pt, 15.9 l.

TRANSMISSION driving wheels: rear; clutch: single dry plate (diaphragm), hydraulically controlled; gearbox: mechanical; gears: 5 + reverse; synchromesh gears: I, II, III, IV, V; gearbox ratios: I 2.970, II 1.760, III 1.230, IV 1, V 0.834, rev 3.310; gear lever: central; final drive: hypoid bevel; axle ratio: 3.730; width of rims: 6''; tyres: 8.15 x 15.

PERFORMANCE max speeds: 44 mph, 71 km/h in 1st gear; 74 mph, 119 km/h in 2nd gear; 106 mph, 170 km/h in 3rd gear; 131 mph, 211 km/h in 4th gear; 141 mph, 227 km/h in 5th gear; speed in top at 1,000 rpm: 26.1 mph, 42 km/h; fuel

DBS

consumption: 15.2 m/imp gal, 12.6 m/US gal, 18.6 l x 100 km.

CHASSIS box-type platform; front suspension: independent, wishbones, coil springs, anti-roll bar, telescopic dampers; rear suspension: de Dion rigid axle, parallel trailing arms, transverse Watt linkage, coil springs, lever dampers electrically adjustable while running.

STEERING rack-and-pinion, adjustable height and tilt of steering wheel, servo; turns of steering wheel lock to lock: 2.58.

BRAKES disc (front diameter 11.50 in, 292 mm, rear 10.80 in, 274 mm), dual circuit, each with vacuum servo; area rubbed by linings: front 241 sq in, 1,554 sq cm, rear 197 sq in, 1,270 sq cm, total 438 sq in, 2,824 sq cm.

ELECTRICAL EQUIPMENT voltage: 12 V; battery: 60 Ah; generator type: alternator, 45 A; ignition distributor: Lucas; headlamps: 4.

DIMENSIONS AND WEIGHT wheel base: 102.75 in, 2,610 mm; front track: 59 in, 1,499 mm; rear track: 59 in, 1,499 mm; overall length: 180.50 in, 4,585 mm; overall width: 72 in, 1,829 mm; overall height: 52.25 in, 1,327 mm; ground clearance: 5.50 in, 140 mm; dry weight: 3,499 lb, 1.587 kg; distribution of weight: 50% front axle, 50% rear axle; turning circle (between walls): 36 ft, 11 m; fuel tank capacity: 21 imp gal, 25.1 US gal, 95 l.

BODY coupé; doors: 2; seats: 4; front seats: separate, reclining backrests; details: adjustable two-positions clutch, brake and accelerator pedals, leather upholstery, electrically-heated rear window, electrically-controlled windows.

PRACTICAL INSTRUCTIONS fuel: 100 oct petrol.

OPTIONAL ACCESSORIES air-conditioning system.

DBS V8

See DBS, except for:

PRICE IN GB: £ 5,744.

ENGINE cylinders: 8, Vee-slanted at 90°; bore and stroke: 3.94 x 3.35 in, 100 x 85 mm; engine capacity: 325.8 cu in, 5,340 cu cm; compression ratio: 9; max engine rpm: 6,750; crankshaft bearings: 5; valves: slanted at 64°; camshafts: 2 per cylinder block, overhead; lubrication: 2 oil coolers; carburation: Bosch injection pump, injectors in inlet pipes; cooling system: water, viscous coupling fan drive.

TRANSMISSION gearbox ratios: I 2.900, II 1.780, III 1.220, IV 1, V 0.845, rev 2.630; final drive: limited slip; axle ratio: 3.540; width of rims: 7''; tyres: GR 70 VR x 15.

PERFORMANCE max speeds: 47 mph, 75 km/h in 1st gear; 76 mph, 122 km/h in 2nd gear; 111 mph, 178 km/h in 3rd gear; 136 mph, 219 km/h in 4th gear; 161 mph, 259 km/h in 5th gear; speed in top at 1,000 rpm: 26 mph, 41.8 km/h; fuel consumption: 13 m/imp gal, 10.8 m/US gal, 21.8 l x 100 km.

BRAKES rear compensator; area rubbed by linings: front 259 sq in, 1,670 sq cm, rear 209 sq in, 1,348 sq cm, total 468 sq in, 3,018 sq cm.

ELECTRICAL EQUIPMENT battery: 72 Ah; generator type: alternator, 60 A.

DIMENSIONS AND WEIGHT dry weight: 3,800 lb, 1,723 kg; turning circle (between walls): 38 ft, 11.6 m.

OPTIONAL ACCESSORIES Chrysler-Torqueflite automatic gearbox, hydraulic torque convertor and planetary gears with 3 ratios (I 2.450, II 1.450, III 1, rev 2.200), max ratio of convertor at stall 2.1, possible manual selection, 3.310 axle ratio.

AUSTIN   GREAT BRITAIN

1100 Mk II 2-door De Luxe Saloon

PRICE IN GB: £ 612.

ENGINE front, transverse, 4 stroke; cylinders: 4, vertical, in line; bore and stroke: 2.54 x 3.30 in, 64.5 x 83.7 mm; engine capacity: 67 cu in, 1,098 cu cm; compression ratio: 8.5; max power (DIN): 48 hp at 5,100 rpm; max torque (DIN): 60 lb ft, 8.3 kg m at 2,500 rpm; max engine rpm: 6,000; specific power: 43.7 hp/l; cylinder block: cast iron; cylinder head: cast iron; crankshaft bearings: 3; valves: 2 per cylinder overhead, in line, push-rods and rockers;

ASTON MARTIN DBS V8

AUSTIN 1100 Mk II 2-door De Luxe Saloon

AUSTIN 1300 G.T. Saloon

camshafts: 1, side; lubrication: eccentric pump, full flow filter; lubricating system capacity: 9 imp pt, 10.8 US pt, 5.1 l; carburation: 1 SU type HS 2 semi-downdraught carburettor; fuel feed: electric pump; cooling system: water; cooling system capacity: 6.7 imp pt, 8 US pt, 3.8 l.

TRANSMISSION driving wheels: front; clutch: single dry plate (diaphragm), hydraulically controlled; gearbox: mechanical, in unit with engine; gears: 4 + reverse; synchromesh gears: I, II, III, IV; gearbox ratios: I 3.628, II 2.172, III 1.412, IV 1, rev 3.628; gear lever: central; final drive: helical spur gears, in unit with engine; axle ratio: 4.133; width of rims: 4''; tyres: 5.20 x 12.

PERFORMANCE max speeds: 24 mph, 38 km/h in 1st gear; 41 mph, 66 km/h in 2nd gear; 62 mph, 100 km/h in 3rd gear; 79 mph, 127 km/h in 4th gear; power-weight ratio: 36.4 lb/hp, 16.5 kg/hp; carrying capacity: 882 lb, 400 kg; acceleration: standing ¼ mile 22 sec, 0-50 mph (0-80 km/h) 14.7 sec; speed in direct drive at 1,000 rpm: 14.7 mph, 23.6 km/h; fuel consumption: 34.4 m/imp gal, 28.7 m/US gal, 8.2 l x 100 km.

CHASSIS integral, front and rear auxiliary frames; front suspension: independent, wishbones, hydrolastic (liquid) rubber cone springs, hydraulic connecting pipes to rear wheels; rear suspension: independent, swinging longitudinal trailing arms, hydrolastic (liquid) rubber cone springs, hydraulic connecting pipes to front wheels, combined with transverse torsion bars, anti-roll bar.

STEERING rack-and-pinion; turns of steering wheel lock to lock: 3.12.

BRAKES front disc (diameter 8 in, 203 mm), rear drum, rear compensator; area rubbed by linings: front 143 sq in, 923 sq cm, rear 63 sq in, 407 sq cm, total 206 sq in, 1,330 sq cm.

ELECTRICAL EQUIPMENT voltage: 12 V; battery: 40 Ah; generator type: dynamo, 264 W; ignition distributor: Lucas; headlamps: 2.

DIMENSIONS AND WEIGHT wheel base: 93.50 in, 2,375 mm; front track: 51.50 in, 1,308 mm; rear track: 50.87 in, 1,292 mm; overall length: 146.73 in, 3,727 mm; overall width: 60.35 in, 1,533 mm; overall height: 52.99 in, 1,346 mm; ground clearance: 6.10 in, 155 mm; dry weight: 1,749 lb, 793 kg; distribution of weight: 62% front axle, 38% rear axle; turning circle (between walls): 36.1 ft, 11 m; fuel tank capacity: 7.9 imp gal, 9.5 US gal, 36 l.

BODY saloon/sedan; doors: 2; seats: 4-5; front seats: separate.

PRACTICAL INSTRUCTIONS fuel: 96 oct petrol; engine sump, gearbox and final drive oil: 7.9 imp pt, 9.5 US pt, 4.5 l, SAE 10W-30 (winter) 20W-50 (summer), change every 6,000 miles, 9,700 km; greasing: every 3,000 miles, 4,800 km, 4 points; sparking plug type: 225°; tappet clearances: inlet 0.012 in, 0.30 mm, exhaust 0.012 in, 0.30 mm; valve timing: inlet opens 5° before tdc and closes 45° after bdc, exhaust opens 51° before bdc and closes 21° after tdc; normal tyre pressure: front 28 psi, 2 atm, rear 24 psi, 1.7 atm.

VARIATIONS

ENGINE 7.5 compression ratio.

OPTIONAL ACCESSORIES AP automatic gearbox, hydraulic torque convertor with 2 conic bevel gears (twin concentric differential-like gear clusters) with 4 ratios (I 2.689, II 1.846, III 1.460, IV 1, rev 2.689), operated by 3 brake bands and 2 multi-disc clutches, max ratio of convertor at stall 2, possible manual selection, 3.760 axle ratio, with 8.9 compression ratio, 1 SU type HS 4 semi-downdraught carburettor, speed in direct drive at 1,000 rpm 18.8 mph, 30.2 km/h, area rubbed by brake linings front 148 sq in, 955 sq cm, rear 63 sq in, 407 sq cm, total 211 sq in, 1,362 sq cm; reclining backrests; electrically-heated rear window.

1100 Mk II 4-door Super De Luxe Saloon

See 1100 Mk II 2-door De Luxe Saloon, except for:

PRICE IN GB: £ 657.

PERFORMANCE power-weight ratio: 37.6 lb/hp, 17.1 kg/hp.

DIMENSIONS AND WEIGHT dry weight: 1,804 lb, 818 kg.

1300 2-door Super De Luxe Saloon

See 1100 Mk II 2-door De Luxe Saloon, except for:

PRICE IN GB: £ 653.

ENGINE bore and stroke: 2.78 x 3.20 in, 70.6 x 81.3 mm;

ASTON MARTIN DBS V8

AUSTIN 1300 Super De Luxe Saloon

AUSTIN 1300 G.T. Saloon

engine capacity: 77.8 cu in, 1,275 cu cm; compression ratio: 8.8; max power (DIN): 60 hp at 5,250 rpm; max torque (DIN): 69 lb ft, 9.5 kg m at 2,500 rpm; specific power: 47.1 hp/l; carburation: 1 SU type HS 4 semi-downdraught carburettor.

TRANSMISSION gearbox ratios: I 3.525, II 2.218, III 1.443, IV 1, rev 3.544; axle ratio: 3.647.

PERFORMANCE max speeds: 28 mph, 45 km/h in 1st gear; 45 mph, 72 km/h in 2nd gear; 69 mph, 111 km/h in 3rd gear; 87 mph, 140 km/h in 4th gear; power-weight ratio: 28.5 lb/hp, 12.9 kg/hp; acceleration: standing ¼ mile 20 sec, 0-50 mph (0-80 km/h) 11.4 sec; speed in direct drive at 1,000 rpm: 16.8 mph, 27 km/h; fuel consumption: 34 m/imp gal, 28.3 m/US gal, 8.3 l x 100 km.

BRAKES area rubbed by linings: front 148 sq in, 955 sq cm, rear 63 sq in, 407 sq cm, total 211 sq in, 1,362 sq cm.

DIMENSIONS AND WEIGHT dry weight: 1,711 lb, 776 kg.

PRACTICAL INSTRUCTIONS fuel: 98-100 oct petrol.

VARIATIONS

ENGINE 7.5 compression ratio not available.

1300 4-door Super De Luxe Saloon

See 1300 2-door Super De Luxe Saloon, except for:

PRICE IN GB: £ 678.

PERFORMANCE power-weight ratio: 29.4 lb/hp, 13.3 kg/hp.

DIMENSIONS AND WEIGHT dry weight: 1,766 lb, 801 kg.

1300 Countryman

See 1300 2-door Super De Luxe Saloon, except for:

PRICE IN GB: £ 733.

PERFORMANCE max speed: 85 mph, 136 km/h; power-weight ratio: 30.2 lb/hp, 13.7 kg/hp; acceleration: 0-50 mph (0-80 km/h) 11.6 sec.

DIMENSIONS AND WEIGHT dry weight: 1,815 lb, 823 kg.

BODY estate car/station wagon; doors: 2 + 1.

OPTIONAL ACCESSORIES electrically-heated rear window not available.

1300 G.T. Saloon

See 1300 2-door Super De Luxe Saloon, except for:

PRICE IN GB: £ 761.

ENGINE compression ratio: 9.7; max power (DIN): 70 hp at 6,000 rpm; max torque (DIN): 74 lb ft, 10.2 kg m at 3,250 rpm; max engine rpm: 6,000; specific power: 54.9 hp/l; carburation: 2 SU type HS 2 semi-downdraught carburettors.

TRANSMISSION gearbox ratios: I 3.300, II 2.070, III 1.350, IV 1, rev 3.350; width of rims: 4''.

PERFORMANCE max speeds: 32 mph, 51 km/h in 1st gear; 50 mph, 80 km/h in 2nd gear; 77 mph, 124 km/h in 3rd gear; 92 mph, 148 km/h in 4th gear; power-weight ratio: 24.4 lb/hp, 11.1 kg/hp; acceleration: standing ¼ mile 19.7 sec, 0-80 mph (0-80 km/h) 9.8 sec; speed in direct drive at 1,000 rpm: 16.7 mph, 26.8 km/h.

BRAKES front disc (diameter 8.39 in, 213 mm).

DIMENSIONS AND WEIGHT rear track: 50.88 in, 1,292 mm; overall length: 145.81 in, 3,703 mm; overall width: 60.38 in, 1,534 mm; overall height: 53.50 in, 1,359 mm; ground clearance: 5.50 in, 140 mm.

BODY front seats: reclining backrests.

OPTIONAL ACCESSORIES only electrically-heated rear window and servo brake.

Maxi 1500

PRICE IN GB: £ 808.

ENGINE front, transverse, 4 stroke; cylinders: 4, in line; bore and stroke: 3 x 3.20 in, 76.2 x 81.3 mm; engine capacity: 90.6 cu in, 1,485 cu cm; compression ratio: 9; max power (DIN): 74 hp at 5,500 rpm; max torque (DIN): 84

MAXI 1500

lb ft, 11.6 kg m at 3,500 rpm; max engine rpm: 6,000; specific power: 49.8 hp/l; cylinder block: cast iron; cylinder head: cast iron; crankshaft bearings: 5; valves: 2 per cylinder, overhead; camshafts: 1, overhead; lubrication: rotary pump, full flow filter; lubricating system capacity: 9.5 imp pt, 11.4 US pt, 5.4 l; carburation: 1 SU type HS 6 horizontal carburettor; fuel feed: mechanical pump; cooling system: water; cooling system capacity: 9.1 imp pt, 10.8 US pt, 5.1 l.

TRANSMISSION driving wheels: front; clutch: single dry plate (diaphragm), hydraulically controlled; gearbox: mechanical; gears: 5 + reverse; synchromesh gears: I, II, III, IV, V; gearbox ratios: I 3.202, II 2.004, III 1.372, IV 1, V 0.795, rev 3.467; gear lever: central; final drive: helical spur gears; axle ratio: 4.200; width of rims: 4.5''; tyres: 155 x 13.

PERFORMANCE max speeds: 30 mph, 48 km/h in 1st gear; 50 mph, 80 km/h in 2nd gear; 70 mph, 112 km/h in 3rd gear; 90 mph, 145 km/h in 4th gear; 87 mph, 140 km/h in 5th gear; power-weight ratio: 28.8 lb/hp, 13.1 kg/hp; carrying capacity: 882 lb, 400 kg; acceleration: standing ¼ mile 21 sec, 0-50 mph (0-80 km/h) 11 sec; speed in 4th gear at 1,000 rpm: 15.6 mph, 25.2 km/h; fuel consumption: 31.5 m/imp gal, 26.1 m/US gal, 9 l x 100 km.

CHASSIS integral; front suspension: independent, wishbones, hydrolastic (liquid) rubber cone springs, hydraulic connecting pipes to rear wheels; rear suspension: independent, swinging longitudinal trailing arms, hydrolastic (liquid) rubber cone springs, hydraulic connecting pipes to front wheels.

STEERING rack-and-pinion; turns of steering wheel lock to lock: 3.90.

BRAKES front disc (diameter 9.68 in, 246 mm), rear drum, servo; area rubbed by linings: front 182 sq in, 1,174 sq cm, rear 75.4 sq in, 486 sq cm, total 257.4 sq in, 1,660 sq cm.

ELECTRICAL EQUIPMENT voltage: 12 V; battery: 40 Ah; generator type: dynamo; ignition distributor: Lucas; headlamps: 2.

DIMENSIONS AND WEIGHT wheel base 104 in, 2,641 mm; front track: 53.80 in, 1,366 mm; rear track: 53.20 in, 1,351 mm; overall length: 158.33 in, 4,021 mm; overall width: 64.12 in, 1,629 mm; overall height: 55.28 in, 1,404 mm; ground clearance: 5.50 in, 140 mm; dry weight: 2,128 lb, 965 kg; distribution of weight: 62.3% front axle, 37.7% rear axle; turning circle (between walls): 30.5 ft, 9.3 m; fuel tank capacity: 10 imp gal, 11.9 US gal, 45 l.

BODY saloon/sedan; doors: 4 + 1; seats: 4-5; front seats: separate.

PRACTICAL INSTRUCTIONS fuel: 98-100 oct petrol; engine sump, gearbox and final drive oil: 9.5 imp pt, 11.4 US pt, 5.4 l, SAE 10W-30 (winter) 20W-50 (summer), change every 6,000 miles, 9,700 km; greasing: none; tappet clearances: inlet 0.016-0.018 in, 0.40-0.45 mm, exhaust 0.020-0.022 in, 0.50-0.55 mm; valve timing: inlet opens 9°4' before tdc and closes 50°56' after tdc, exhaust opens 48°56' before bdc and closes 11°4' after tdc; normal tyre pressure: front 26 psi, 1.8 atm, rear 24 psi, 1.7 atm.

OPTIONAL ACCESSORIES electrically-heated rear window.

Maxi 1750

See Maxi 1500, except for:

PRICE IN GB: £ 843.

ENGINE stroke: 3.77 in, 95.7 mm; engine capacity: 106.7 cu in, 1,748 cu cm; compression ratio: 8.7; max power (DIN): 84 hp at 5,000 rpm; max torque (DIN): 105 lb ft, 14.5 kg m at 3,000 rpm; specific power: 48.1 hp/l.

TRANSMISSION gearbox ratios: V 0.869; axle ratio: 3.888.

PERFORMANCE max speeds: 34 mph, 54 km/h in 1st gear; 56 mph, 90 km/h in 2nd gear; 78 mph, 125 km/h in 3rd gear; 92 mph, 148 km/h in 4th gear; 88 mph, 141 km/h in 5th gear; power-weight ratio: 25.4 lb/hp, 11.5 kg/hp; acceleration: standing ¼ mile 19.5 sec, 0-50 mph (0-80 km/h) 10 sec; speed in 4th gear at 1,000 rpm: 16.8 mph, 27 km/h; fuel consumption: 24.1 m/imp gal, 20.1 m/US gal, 11.7 l x 100 km.

DIMENSIONS AND WEIGHT dry weight: 2,128 lb, 965 kg; distribution of weight: 63% front axle, 37% rear axle.

PRACTICAL INSTRUCTIONS tappet clearances: inlet 0.012 in, 0.30 mm, exhaust 0.012 in, 0.30 mm; valve timing: inlet opens 9° before tdc and closes 51° after bdc, exhaust opens 49° before bdc and closes 11° after tdc.

OPTIONAL ACCESSORIES alternator.

AUSTIN Maxi 1750

AUSTIN 3-litre De Luxe Saloon

AUSTIN-HEALEY Sprite Mk IV

1800 Mk II De Luxe Saloon

PRICE IN GB: £ 891.

ENGINE front, transverse, 4 stroke; cylinders: 4, in line; bore and stroke: 3.16 x 3.50 in, 80.3 x 88.9 mm; engine capacity: 109.7 cu in, 1,798 cu cm; compression ratio: 9; max power (DIN): 86.5 hp at 5,400 rpm; max torque (DIN) 101 lb ft, 13.9 kg m at 3,000 rpm; max engine rpm: 5,600; specific power: 48.1 hp/l; cylinder block: cast iron; cylinder head: cast iron; crankshaft bearings: 5; valves: 2 per cylinder, overhead, push-rods and rockers; camshafts: 1 side; lubrication: eccentric pump, magnetic metal gauze filter in sump and full flow; lubricating system capacity: 12.5 imp pt, 15 US pt, 7.1 l; carburation: 1 SU type HS 6 semi-downdraught carburettor; fuel feed: mechanical pump; cooling system: water; cooling system capacity: 9.5 imp pt, 11.4 US pt, 5.4 l.

TRANSMISSION driving wheels: front; clutch: single dry plate (diaphragm), hydraulically controlled; gearbox: mechanical, in unit with engine; gears: 4 + reverse; synchromesh gears: I, II, III, IV; gearbox ratios: I 3.292, II 2.059, III 1.384, IV 1, rev 3.075; gear lever: central; final drive: spiral bevel; axle ratio: 3.882; width of rims: 4.5''; tyres: 165 x 14.

PERFORMANCE max speeds: 31 mph, 50 km/h in 1st gear; 49 mph, 79 km/h in 2nd gear; 74 mph, 119 km/h in 3rd gear; 91 mph, 146 km/h in 4th gear; power-weight ratio: 29.3 lb/hp, 13.3 kg/hp; carrying capacity: 882 lb, 400 kg; speed in direct drive at 1,000 rpm: 13.2 mph, 21.3 km/h; fuel consumption: 23.7 m/imp gal, 19.8 m/US gal, 11.9 l x 100 km.

CHASSIS integral; front suspension: independent, wishbones, lower trailing links, hydrolastic (liquid) rubber cone springs, hydraulic connecting pipes to rear wheels; rear suspension: independent, swinging longitudinal trailing arms, hydrolastic (liquid) rubber cone springs, hydraulic connecting pipes to front wheels, anti-roll bar.

STEERING rack-and-pinion; turns of steering wheel lock to lock: 3.80.

BRAKES front disc (diameter 9.29 in, 236 mm), rear drum, servo; area rubbed by linings: front 183 sq in, 1,181 sq cm, rear 99 sq in, 639 sq cm, total 282 sq in, 1,820 sq cm.

ELECTRICAL EQUIPMENT voltage: 12 V; battery: 50 Ah; generator type: dynamo, 22 A; ignition distributor: Lucas; headlamps: 4.

DIMENSIONS AND WEIGHT wheel base: 106.61 in, 2,708 mm; front track: 55.98 in, 1,422 mm; rear track: 55.51 in, 1,410 mm; overall length: 166.87 in, 4,239 mm; overall width: 66.26 in, 1,683 mm; overall height: 56.26 in, 1,429 mm; ground clearance: 6.61 in, 168 mm; dry weight: 2,536 lb, 1,150 kg; distribution of weight: 63% front axle, 37% rear axle; turning circle (between walls): 40.3 ft, 12.3 m; fuel tank capacity: 10.6 imp gal, 12.7 US gal, 48 l.

BODY saloon/sedan; doors: 4; seats: 4-5; front seats: separate.

PRACTICAL INSTRUCTIONS fuel: 96-98 oct petrol; engine sump, gearbox and final drive oil: 10.2 imp pt, 12.3 US pt, 5.8 l, SAE 10W-30 (winter) 20W-50 (summer), change every 6,000 miles, 9,700 km; tappet clearances: inlet 0.015 in, 0.38 mm, exhaust 0.015 in, 0.38 mm; valve timing: inlet opens 5° before tdc and closes 45° after bdc, exhaust opens 40° before bdc and closes 10° after tdc; normal tyre pressure: front 30 psi, 2.1 atm, rear 24 psi, 1.7 atm.

OPTIONAL ACCESSORIES Borg-Warner automatic gearbox, hydraulic torque convertor and planetary gears with 3 ratios (I 2.388, II 1.449, III 1, rev 2.388), max ratio of convertor at stall 2, 3.940 axle ratio, speed in direct drive at 1,000 rpm 17.8 mph, 28.7 km/h, max speeds (I) 42 mph, 68 km/h, (II) 69 mph, 111 km/h, (III) 100 mph, 161 km/h; power-assisted steering; reclining backrests; electrically-heated rear window.

1800 Mk II S De Luxe Saloon

See 1800 Mk II De Luxe Saloon, except for:

PRICE IN GB: £ 940.

ENGINE compression ratio: 9.5; max power (DIN): 95.5 hp at 5,700 rpm; max torque (DIN): 106 lb ft, 14.6 kg m at 3,000 rpm; max engine rpm: 6,000; specific power: 53.1 hp/l; carburation: 2 SU type H 6 semi-downdraught carburettors.

PERFORMANCE max speeds: 33 mph, 53 km/h in 1st gear; 53 mph, 85 km/h in 2nd gear; 79 mph, 127 km/h in 3rd gear; 100 mph, 161 km/h in 4th gear; power-weight ratio: 26.5 lb/hp, 12 kg/hp; fuel consumption: 22.9 m/imp gal, 19.1 m/US gal, 12.3 l x 100 km.

BRAKES front disc (twin calipers).

PRACTICAL INSTRUCTIONS fuel: 99 oct petrol; valve timing: inlet opens 16° before tdc and closes 56° after bdc, exhaust opens 51° before bdc and closes 21° after tdc.

AUSTIN Maxi 1750

AUSTIN 3-litre De Luxe Saloon

AUSTIN-HEALEY Sprite Mk IV

3-litre De Luxe Saloon

PRICE IN GB: £ 1,388.

ENGINE front, 4 stroke; cylinders: 6, in line; bore and stroke: 3.28 x 3.50 in, 83.4 x 88.9 mm; engine capacity: 177.7 cu in, 2,912 cu cm; compression ratio: 9; max power (DIN): 123.6 hp at 4,500 rpm; max torque (DIN): 161 lb ft, 22.2 kg m at 3,000 rpm; max engine rpm: 5,500; specific power: 42.4 hp/l; cylinder block: cast iron; cylinder head: cast iron; crankshaft bearings: 7; valves: 2 per cylinder, overhead, push-rods and rockers; camshafts: 1, side; lubrication: eccentric pump, full flow filter; lubricating system capacity: 12 imp pt, 14.4 US pt, 6.8 l; carburation: 2 SU type HS 6 horizontal carburettors; fuel feed: mechanical pump; cooling system: water; cooling system capacity: 21.5 imp pt, 25.8 US pt, 12.2 l.

TRANSMISSION driving wheels: rear; clutch: single dry plate (diaphragm), hydraulically controlled; gearbox: mechanical; gears: 4 + reverse; synchromesh gears: I, II, III, IV; gearbox ratios: I 2.980, II 2.058, III 1.307, IV 1, rev 2.680; gear lever: central; final drive: hypoid bevel; axle ratio: 3.545; width of rims: 5''; tyres: 185 x 14.

PERFORMANCE max speeds: 37 mph, 59 km/h in 1st gear; 54 mph, 87 km/h in 2nd gear; 85 mph, 136 km/h in 3rd gear; 100 mph, 161 km/h in 4th gear; power-weight ratio: 26.5 lb/hp, 12 kg/hp; carrying capacity: 1,058 lb, 480 kg; acceleration: standing ¼ mile 19.6 sec, 0-50 mph (0-80 km/h) 11.2 sec; speed in direct drive at 1,000 rpm: 20.1 mph, 32.4 km/h; fuel consumption: 21.7 m/imp gal, 18.1 m/US gal, 13 l x 100 km.

CHASSIS integral; front suspension: independent, wishbones, hydrolastic (liquid) rubber cone springs, hydraulic connecting pipes to rear wheels; rear suspension: independent, swinging trailing arms, hydrolastic (liquid) rubber cone springs, hydraulic connecting pipes to front wheels, automatic levelling control.

STEERING rack-and-pinion, servo; turns of steering wheel lock to lock: 3.94.

BRAKES front disc (diameter 10.39 in, 264 mm), rear drum, servo; area rubbed by linings: front 224 sq in, 1,445 sq cm, rear 127.2 sq in, 820 sq cm, total 351.2 sq in, 2,265 sq cm.

ELECTRICAL EQUIPMENT voltage: 12 V; battery: 67 Ah; generator type: alternator, 45 A; ignition distributor: Lucas; headlamps: 4.

DIMENSIONS AND WEIGHT wheel base: 115.51 in, 2,934 mm; front track: 56.26 in, 1,429 mm; rear track: 55.98 in, 1,422 mm; overall length: 185.75 in, 4,718 mm; overall width: 66.73 in, 1,695 mm; overall height: 56.73 in, 1,441 mm; ground clearance: 6.26 in, 159 mm; dry weight: 3,261 lb, 1,479 kg; distribution of weight: 55.8% front axle, 44.2% rear axle; turning circle (between walls): 40 ft, 12.2 m; fuel tank capacity: 14.5 imp gal, 17.4 US gal, 66 l.

BODY saloon/sedan; doors: 4; seats: 5-6; front seats: separate, reclining backrests.

PRACTICAL INSTRUCTIONS fuel: 97 oct petrol; engine sump oil: 11.1 imp pt, 13.3 US pt, 6.3 l, SAE 10W-30 (winter) 20W-50 (summer), change every 6,000 miles, 9,700 km; gearbox oil: 5.8 imp pt, 7 US pt, 3.3 l, SAE 20W-50; final drive oil: 2.5 imp pt, 3 US pt, 1.4 l, SAE 90, change every 6,000 miles, 9,700 km; greasing: none; tappet clearances: inlet 0.012 in, 0.30 mm, exhaust 0.012 in, 0.30 mm; valve timing: inlet opens 0° before tdc and closes 45° after bdc, exhaust opens 35° before bdc and closes 10° after tdc; normal tyre pressure: front 28 psi, 2 atm, rear 26 psi, 1.8 atm.

OPTIONAL ACCESSORIES overdrive on II, III and IV, 0.820 ratio; Borg-Warner 35 automatic gearbox, hydraulic torque convertor and planetary gears with 3 ratios (I 2.390, II 1.450, III 1, rev 2.090), max ratio of convertor at stall 1.9, possible manual selection, central selector lever, max speeds (I) 46 mph, 74 km/h, (II) 76 mph, 122 km/h, (III) 110 mph, 177 km/h; gearbox oil 7.9 imp pt, 9.5 US pt, 4.5 l; electrically-heated rear window.

AUSTIN-HEALEY　　　GREAT BRITAIN

Sprite Mk IV

PRICE IN GB: £ 692.
PRICE IN USA: $ 2,081.

ENGINE front, 4 stroke; cylinders: 4, vertical, in line; bore and stroke: 2.78 x 3.20 in, 70.6 x 81.3 mm; engine capacity: 77.8 cu in, 1,275 cu cm; compression ratio: 8.8; max power (SAE): 65 hp at 6,000 rpm; max torque (SAE): 72 lb ft, 9.9 kg m at 3,000 rpm; max engine rpm: 6,200; specific power: 51 hp/l; cylinder block: cast iron; cylinder head: cast iron; crankshaft bearings: 3; valves: 2 per cylinder, overhead, push-rods and rockers; camshafts: 1, side; lubrication: ec-

SPRITE Mk IV

centric pump, full flow filter; lubricating system capacity: 7 imp pt, 8.5 US pt, 4 l; carburation: 2 SU type HS 2 semi-downdraught carburettors; fuel feed: electric pump; cooling system: water; cooling system capacity: 10.6 imp pt, 12.7 US pt, 6 l.

TRANSMISSION driving wheels: rear; clutch: single dry plate (diaphragm), hydraulically controlled; gearbox: mechanical; gears: 4 + reverse; synchromesh gears: II, III, IV; gearbox ratios: I 3.200, II 1.916, III 1.357, IV 1, rev 4.120; gear lever: central; final drive: hypoid bevel; axle ratio: 4.220; tyres: 5.20 x 13.

PERFORMANCE max speeds: 30 mph, 48 km/h in 1st gear; 50 mph, 80 km/h in 2nd gear; 71 mph, 114 km/h in 3rd gear; 95 mph, 153 km/h in 4th gear; power-weight ratio: 23.2 lb/hp, 10.5 kg/hp; carrying capacity: 353 lb, 160 kg; acceleration: standing ¼ mile 19.1 sec, 0-50 mph (0-80 km/h) 9.2 sec; speed in direct drive at 1,000 rpm: 15.5 mph, 25 km/h; fuel consumption: 35.3 m/imp gal, 29.4 m/US gal, 8 l x 100 km.

CHASSIS integral; front suspension: independent, wishbones, coil springs, lever dampers as upper arms; rear suspension: rigid axle, semi-elliptic leafsprings, lever dampers.

STEERING rack-and-pinion; turns of steering wheel lock to lock: 2.30.

BRAKES front disc (diameter 8.25 in, 209 mm), rear drum; area rubbed by linings: front 135 sq in, 871 sq cm, rear 51.9 sq in, 355 sq cm, total 186.9 sq in, 1,226 sq cm.

ELECTRICAL EQUIPMENT voltage: 12 V; battery: 43 Ah; generator type: dynamo; ignition distributor: Lucas; headlamps: 2.

DIMENSIONS AND WEIGHT wheel base: 80 in, 2,032 mm; front track: 46.30 in, 1,176 mm; rear track: 44.75 in, 1,137 mm; overall length: 137.60 in, 3,495 mm; overall width: 54.90 in, 1,394 mm; overall height: 48.62 in, 1,235 mm; ground clearance: 5 in, 127 mm; dry weight: 1,510 lb, 685 kg; distribution of weight: 52.4% front axle, 47.6% rear axle; turning circle (between walls): 32 ft, 9.8 m; fuel tank capacity: 6 imp gal, 7.1 US gal, 27 l.

BODY convertible; doors: 2; seats: 2.

PRACTICAL INSTRUCTIONS fuel: 98 oct petrol; engine sump oil: 6.5 imp pt, 7.8 US pt, 3.7 l, SAE 10W-30 (winter) 20W-50 (summer), change every 6,000 miles, 9,700 km; gearbox oil: 2.3 imp pt, 2.7 US pt, 1.3 l, SAE 10W-30 (winter) 20W-50 (summer); final drive oil: 1.4 imp pt, 1.7 US pt, 0.8 l, SAE 90; greasing: every 3,000 miles, 4,800 km, 8 points; tappet clearances: inlet 0.012 in, 0.30 mm, exhaust 0.012 in, 0.30 mm; valve timing: inlet opens 5° before tdc and closes 45° after bdc, exhaust opens 51° before bdc and closes 21° after tdc; normal tyre pressure: front 18 psi, 1.3 atm, rear 20 psi, 1.4 atm.

OPTIONAL ACCESSORIES oil cooler; wire wheels; anti-roll bar on front suspension; hardtop.

BEDFORD Beagle

BEDFORD   GREAT BRITAIN

Beagle

PRICE IN GB: £ 556.

ENGINE front, 4 stroke; cylinders: 4, vertical, in line; bore and stroke: 3.06 x 2.40 in, 77.7 x 61 mm; engine capacity: 70.7 cu in, 1,159 cu cm; compression ratio: 7.3; max power (DIN): 41 hp at 5,000 rpm; max torque (DIN): 60 lb ft, 8.3 kg m at 2,000 rpm; max engine rpm: 5,800; specific power: 35.4 hp/l; cylinder block: cast iron; cylinder head: cast iron; crankshaft bearings: 3; valves: 2 per cylinder, overhead, push-rods and rockers; camshafts: 1, side; lubrication: gear pump, full flow filter; lubricating system capacity: 5.5 imp pt, 6.6 US pt, 3.1 l; carburation: 1 Solex PSEI-6 downdraught single barrel carburettor; fuel feed: mechanical pump; cooling system: water; cooling system capacity: 10.2 imp pt, 12.3 US pt, 5.8 l.

TRANSMISSION driving wheels: rear; clutch: single dry plate; gearbox: mechanical; gears: 4 + reverse; synchromesh gears: I, II, III, IV; gearbox ratios: I 3.765, II 2.213, III 1.404, IV 1, rev 3.707; gear lever: central; final drive: hypoid bevel; axle ratio: 4.125; width of rims: 4''; tyres: 5.50 x 12.

PERFORMANCE max speeds: 23 mph, 37 km/h in 1st gear; 39 mph, 62 km/h in 2nd gear; 62 mph, 100 km/h in 3rd gear; 73 mph, 117 km/h in 4th gear; power-weight ratio: 37.5 lb/hp, 17 kg/hp; carrying capacity: 882 lb, 400 kg; acceleration: standing ¼ mile 22.8 sec, 0-50 mph (0-80 km/h) 14.8

BENTLEY T Series H.J. Mulliner 2-door Saloon

BRISTOL 411

sec; speed in direct drive at 1,000 rpm: 15 mph, 24.1 km. h. fuel consumption: 26.2 m/imp gal, 21.8 m/US gal, 10.8 l x 100 km.

CHASSIS integral; front suspension: independent, wishbones, transverse lower leafspring, telescopic dampers; rear suspension: rigid torque-tube axle, semi-elliptic leafsprings, telescopic dampers.

STEERING rack-and-pinion; turns of steering wheel lock to lock: 3.14.

BRAKES drum, 2 front leading shoes; area rubbed by linings: front 63 sq in, 406 sq cm, rear 63 sq in, 406 sq cm, total 126 sq in, 812 sq cm.

ELECTRICAL EQUIPMENT voltage: 12 V; battery: 32 Ah; generator type: dynamo, 264 W; ignition distributor: Lucas; headlamps: 2.

DIMENSIONS AND WEIGHT wheel base: 91.50 in, 2,324 mm; front track: 47.40 in, 1,204 mm; rear track: 48.20 in, 1,224 mm; overall length: 150.20 in, 3,815 mm; overall width: 59.40 in, 1,509 mm; overall height: 59.50 in, 1,511 mm; ground clearance: 5 in, 127 mm; dry weight: 1,539 lb, 698 kg; distribution of weight: 51% front axle, 49% rear axle; turning circle (between walls): 32 ft, 9.8 m; fuel tank capacity: 7 imp gal, 8.4 US gal, 32 l.

BODY estate car/station wagon; doors: 2 + 1; seats: 5; front seats: separate.

PRACTICAL INSTRUCTIONS fuel: 85-90 oct petrol; engine sump oil: 3.7 imp pt, 4.4 US pt, 2.1 l, SAE 20W-20, change every 6,000 miles, 9,700 km or 6 months; gearbox oil: 0.9 imp pt, 1.1 US pt, 0.5 l, SAE 90, no change recommended; final drive oil: 1.2 imp pt, 1.5 US pt, 0.7 l, SAE 90, no change recommended; greasing: every 30,000 miles, 48,300 km or 6 months, 4 points; tappet clearances: inlet 0.006 in, 0.15 mm, exhaust 0.010 in, 0.25 mm; valve timing: inlet opens 39° before tdc and closes 93° after bdc, exhaust opens 65° before bdc and closes 45° after tdc; normal tyre pressure: front 21 psi, 1.5 atm, rear 27 psi, 1.9 atm.

OPTIONAL ACCESSORIES larger battery; alternator.

BEDFORD Beagle

BENTLEY   GREAT BRITAIN

T Series 4-door Saloon

PRICE IN GB: £ 7,005.
PRICE IN USA: $ 20,500.

ENGINE front, 4 stroke; cylinders: 8, Vee-slanted at 90°; bore and stroke: 4.10 x 3.90 in, 104.1 x 99 mm; engine capacity: 411.9 cu in, 6,745 cu cm; compression ratio: 9; cylinder block: light alloy, wet liners; cylinder head: light alloy; crankshaft bearings: 5; valves: 2 per cylinder, overhead, in line, slanted, push-rods and rockers, hydraulic tappets; camshafts: 1, at centre of Vee; lubrication: gear pump, full flow filter; lubricating system capacity: 14.4 imp pt, 17.3 US pt, 8.2 l; carburation: 2 SU type HD 8 horizontal carburettors; fuel feed: 2 electric pumps; cooling system: water; cooling system capacity: 28 imp pt, 33.6 US pt, 15.9 l.

TRANSMISSION driving wheels: rear; gearbox: automatic, hydraulic torque convertor and planetary gears with 3 ratios + reverse, max ratio of convertor at stall 2.04, possible manual selection; gearbox ratios: I 2.500, II 1.500, III 1, rev 2; selector lever: steering column; final drive: hypoid bevel; axle ratio: 3.080; tyres: 8.45 x 15.

PERFORMANCE max speeds: 40 mph, 64 km/h in 1st gear; 74 mph, 119 km/h in 2nd gear; 119 mph, 191 km/h in 3rd gear; carrying capacity: 1,058 lb, 480 kg; speed in direct drive at 1,000 rpm: 26.2 mph, 42.2 km/h; fuel consumption: 15 m/imp gal, 12.5 m/US gal, 18.8 l x 100 km.

CHASSIS integral, front and rear auxiliary frames; front suspension: independent, wishbones, coil springs, automatic levelling control, telescopic dampers; rear suspension: independent, semi-trailing arms, coil springs, automatic levelling control, telescopic dampers.

STEERING recirculating ball, progressive servo, right-hand drive; turns of steering wheel lock to lock: 3.50.

BRAKES disc [diameter (twin caliper) 11 in, 279 mm], 3 independent circuits, servo; area rubbed by linings: front 227 sq in, 1,464 sq cm, rear 287 sq in, 1,851 sq cm, total 514 sq in, 3,315 sq cm.

ELECTRICAL EQUIPMENT voltage: 12 V; battery: 64 Ah; generator type: dynamo, 35 A; ignition distributor: Lucas; headlamps: 4.

DIMENSIONS AND WEIGHT wheel base: 119.50 in, 3,035 mm; front track: 57.50 in, 1,460 mm; rear track: 57.50 in, 1,460 mm; overall length: 203.50 in, 5,169 mm; overall width: 71 in, 1,803 mm; overall height: 59.75 in, 1,518 mm;

BENTLEY T Series 4-door Saloon

BRISTOL 411

ground clearance: 6.50 in, 165 mm; dry weight: 4,556 lb, 2,067 kg; turning circle (between walls): 38 ft, 11.6 m; fuel tank capacity: 24 imp gal, 28.8 US gal, 109 l.

BODY saloon/sedan; doors: 4; seats: 5-6; front seats: separate, adjustable and reclining backrests; details: headrests, air-conditioning system, electrically-controlled windows.

PRACTICAL INSTRUCTIONS fuel: 98-100 oct petrol; engine sump oil: 14.1 imp pt, 16.9 US pt, 8 l, SAE 10W-30, change every 6,000 miles, 9,700 km; gearbox oil: 23.9 imp pt, 28.8 US pt, 13.6 l, change every 24,000 miles, 38,600 km; final drive oil: 4 imp pt, 4.9 US pt, 2.3 l, change every 24,000 miles, 38,600 km; crankshaft bearings: 5; power-assisted steering and automatic levelling control oil: change every 12,000 miles, 19,300 km; greasing: every 7,500 miles, 12,000 km; valve timing: inlet opens 26° before tdc and closes 52° after bdc, exhaust opens 68° before bdc and closes 10° after tdc; normal tyre pressure: front 23 psi, 1.6 atm, rear 25 psi, 1.8 atm.

VARIATIONS

ENGINE 8 compression ratio.

OPTIONAL ACCESSORIES alternator; iodine headlamps.

T Series H.J. Mulliner 2-door Saloon

See T Series 4-door Saloon, except for:

PRICE IN GB: £ 8,800.
PRICE IN USA: $ 29,000.

T Series H.J. Mulliner Drophead Coupé

See T Series 4-door Saloon, except for:

PRICE IN GB: £ 9,200.
PRICE IN USA: £ 31,400.

BODY convertible; doors: 2.

BRISTOL   GREAT BRITAIN

411

PRICE IN GB: £ 5,358.

ENGINE front, 4 stroke; cylinders: 8, Vee-slanted at 90°; bore and stroke: 4.25 x 3.37 in, 108 x 85.7 mm; engine capacity: 383 cu in, 6,277 cu cm; compression ratio: 10; max power (SAE): 335 hp at 5,200 rpm; max torque (SAE): 425 lb ft, 58.6 kg m at 3,400 rpm; max engine rpm: 5,500; specific power: 53 hp/l; cylinder block: cast iron; cylinder head: cast iron; crankshaft bearings: 5; valves: 2 per cylinder, overhead, push-rods and rockers, hydraulic tappets; camshafts: 1, at centre of Vee; lubrication: rotary pump, full flow filter; lubricating system capacity: 10.5 imp pt, 12.7 US pt, 6 l; carburation: 1 Carter downdraught 4-barrel carburettor; fuel feed: mechanical pump; cooling system: water; cooling system capacity: 29 imp pt, 34.9 US pt, 16.5 l.

TRANSMISSION driving wheels: rear; gearbox: Torqueflite automatic, hydraulic torque convertor and planetary gears with 3 ratios + reverse, max ratio of convertor at stall 2, possible manual selection; gearbox ratios: I 2.450, II 1.450, III 1, rev 2.200; selector lever: central; final drive: hypoid bevel; axle ratio: 3.070; width of rims: 5''; tyres: 205 x 15.

PERFORMANCE max speeds: 50 mph, 80 km/h in 1st gear; 90 mph, 145 km/h in 2nd gear; 140 mph, 225 km/h in 3rd gear; power-weight ratio: 11 lb/hp, 5 kg/hp; carrying capacity: 904 lb, 410 kg; acceleration: 0-50 (0-80 km/h) 6 sec; speed in direct drive at 1,000 rpm: 26.4 mph, 42.5 km/h; fuel consumption: 18 m/imp gal, 15 m/US gal, 15.7 l x 100 km.

CHASSIS box-type ladder frame; front suspension: independent, wishbones, coil springs, anti-roll bar, telescopic dampers; rear suspension: rigid axle, longitudinal torsion bars, trailing lower radius arms, upper torque arms, transverse Watt linkage, electrically-adjustable telescopic dampers.

STEERING recirculating ball; turns of steering wheel lock to lock: 3.

BRAKES disc (front diameter 10.91 in, 277 mm, rear 10.60 in, 269 mm), servo; area rubbed by linings: front 224 sq in, 1,445 sq cm, rear 196 sq in, 1,264 sq cm, total 420 sq in, 2,709 sq cm.

ELECTRICAL EQUIPMENT voltage: 12 V; battery: 71 Ah; generator type: alternator, 430 W; ignition distributor: Chrysler; headlamps: 4.

DIMENSIONS AND WEIGHT wheel base: 114 in, 2,896 mm;

411

front track: 54.50 in, 1,384 mm; rear track: 55.25 in, 1,403 mm; overall length: 193 in, 4,902 mm; overall width: 68 in, 1,727 mm; overall height: 57.50 in, 1,460 mm; ground clearance: 5 in, 127 mm; dry weight: 3,700 lb, 1,678 kg; distribution of weight: 53% front axle, 47% rear axle; turning circle (between walls): 40 ft, 12.2 m; fuel tank capacity: 18 imp gal, 21.6 US gal, 82 l.

BODY saloon/sedan; doors: 2; seats: 4; front seats: separate, reclining backrests.

PRACTICAL INSTRUCTIONS fuel: 100 oct petrol; engine sump oil: 9.5 imp pt, 11.4 US pt, 5.4 l, 20W-50, change every 4,000 miles, 6,400 km; gearbox oil: 13 imp pt, 15.6 US pt, 7.4 l, Dexron, change every 32,000 miles, 51,500 km; final drive oil: 3.5 imp pt, 4.2 US pt, 2 l, SAE 90 EP, change every 20,000 miles, 32,200 km; greasing: every 20,000 miles, 32,200 km, 4 points; valve timing: inlet opens 21° before tdc and closes 67° after bdc, exhaust opens 79° before bdc and closes 25° after tdc; normal tyre pressure: front 28 psi, 2 atm, rear 28 psi, 2 atm.

OPTIONAL ACCESSORIES air-conditioning system; electrically-controlled windows; automatic speed control.

DAIMLER GREAT BRITAIN

Sovereign 2.8-litre

PRICE IN GB: £ 1,958.

ENGINE front, 4 stroke; cylinders: 6, vertical, in line; bore and stroke: 3.27 x 3.39 in, 83 x 86 mm; engine capacity: 170 cu in, 2,791 cu cm; compression ratio: 9.1; max power (SAE): 180 hp at 6,000 rpm; max torque (SAE): 182 lb ft, 25.1 kg m at 3,750 rpm; max engine rpm: 6,800; specific power: 64.5 hp/l; cylinder block: cast iron, dry liners; cylinder head: light alloy, hemispherical combustion chambers; crankshaft bearings: 7; valves: 2 per cylinder, overhead, Vee-slanted at 70°, thimble tappets; camshafts: 2, overhead; lubrication: mechanical pump, full flow filter; lubricating system capacity: 14.5 imp pt, 16.7 US pt, 7.9 l; carburation: 2 SU type HD 8 horizontal carburettors; fuel feed: 2 electric pumps; cooling system: water, thermostatic fan; cooling system capacity: 30 imp pt, 35.9 US pt, 17 l.

TRANSMISSION driving wheels: rear; clutch: single dry plate (diaphragm), hydraulically controlled; gearbox: mechanical; gears: 4 + reverse and overdrive/top; synchromesh gears: I, II, III, IV; gearbox ratios: I 3.040, II 1.970, III 1.330, IV 1, overdrive 0.780, rev 3.374; gear lever: central; final drive: hypoid bevel; axle ratio: 4.550; width of rims: 6''; tyres: E 70 VR x 15.

PERFORMANCE max speeds: 33 mph, 53 km/h in 1st gear; 51 mph, 82 km/h in 2nd gear; 81 mph, 130 km/h in 3rd gear; 113 mph, 182 km/h in 4th gear; 116 mph, 186 km/h in overdrive; power-weight ratio: 18.7 lb/hp, 8.5 kg/hp; carrying capacity: 882 lb, 400 kg; acceleration: standing ¼ mile 17.9 sec, 0-50 mph (0-80 km/h) 8.5 sec; speed in overdrive/top at 1,000 rpm: 21.4 mph, 34.4 km/h; fuel consumption: 20.5 m/imp gal, 17 m/US gal, 13.8 l x 100 km.

CHASSIS integral, front and rear auxiliary frames; front suspension: independent, wishbones, coil springs, anti-roll bar, telescopic dampers; rear suspension: independent, wishbones, semi-axle as upper arm, trailing lower radius arms, 4 coil springs, 4 telescopic dampers.

STEERING rack-and-pinion, adjustable steering wheel, variable ratio servo; turns of steering wheel lock to lock: 3.50.

BRAKES disc (front diameter 11.80 in, 300 mm, rear 10.40 in, 264 mm), dual circuit, servo; area rubbed by linings: front 242.4 sq in, 1,563 sq cm, rear 193.2 sq in, 1,246 sq cm, total 435.6 sq in, 2,809 sq cm.

ELECTRICAL EQUIPMENT voltage: 12 V; battery 50 Ah; generator type: alternator, 45 A; ignition distributor: Lucas; headlamps: 4.

DIMENSIONS AND WEIGHT wheel base: 108.87 in, 2,765 mm; front track: 58 in, 1,473 mm; rear track: 58.33 in, 1,481 mm; overall length: 189.60 in, 4,816 mm; overall width: 69.75 in, 1,772 mm; overall height: 52.87 in, 1,343 mm; ground clearance: 6 in, 152 mm; dry weight: 3,389 lb, 1,537 kg; distribution of weight: 52% front axle, 48% rear axle; turning circle (between walls): 36 ft, 11 m; fuel tank capacity: 23 imp gal, 27.5 US gal, 104 l.

BODY saloon/sedan; doors: 4; seats: 5; front seats: separate, reclining backrests.

PRACTICAL INSTRUCTIONS fuel: 98 oct petrol; engine sump oil: 13.5 imp pt, 16.3 US pt, 7.7 l, SAE 10W-40 (winter) 20W-50 (summer), change every 3,000 miles, 4,800 km; gearbox oil: 2.5 imp pt, 3 US pt, 1.4 l, SAE 30, change every

DAIMLER Sovereign 2.8-litre

DAIMLER Limousine

FAIRTHORPE TX-GT

10,000 miles, 16,100 km; final drive oil: 2.7 imp pt, 3.4 US pt, 1.6 l, SAE 90, change every 10,000 miles, 16,100 km; greasing: none; tappet clearances: inlet 0.004 in, 0.10 mm, exhaust 0.006 in, 0.15 mm; valve timing: inlet opens 15° before tdc and closes 57° after bdc, exhaust opens 57° before bdc and closes 15° after tdc; normal tyre pressure: front 25 psi, 1.7 atm, rear 26 psi, 1.8 atm.

OPTIONAL ACCESSORIES Borg-Warner 35 automatic gearbox, hydraulic torque convertor and planetary gears with 3 ratios (I 2.401, II 1.450, III 1, rev 2.078), max ratio of convertor at stall 2, possible manual selection, 4.090 axle ratio, max speeds (I) 53 mph, 85 km/h, (II) 86 mph, 139 km/h, (III) 116 mph, 186 km/h; air-conditioning system; electrically-controlled windows.

Sovereign 4.2-litre

See Sovereign 2.8-litre, except for:

PRICE IN GB: £ 2,194.

ENGINE bore and stroke: 3.63 x 4.17 in, 92.1 x 106 mm; engine capacity: 258 cu in, 4,235 cu cm; compression ratio: 8; max power (SAE): 245 hp at 5,500 rpm; max torque (SAE): 283 lb ft, 39.1 kg m at 3,750 rpm; max engine rpm: 5,500; specific power: 62.6 hp/l.

TRANSMISSION axle ratio: 3.540.

PERFORMANCE max speeds: 37 mph, 60 km/h in 1st gear; 56 mph, 90 km/h in 2nd gear; 77 mph, 124 km/h in 3rd gear; 107 mph, 172 km/h in 4th gear; 124 mph, 200 km/h in overdrive; power-weight ratio: 14.1 lb/hp, 6.4 kg/hp; acceleration: standing ¼ mile 16.5 sec, 0-50 mph (0-80 km/h) 6.6 sec; speed in overdrive/top at 1,000 rpm: 27.5 mph, 44.2 km/h.

DIMENSIONS AND WEIGHT dry weight: 3,440 lb, 1,560 kg.

OPTIONAL ACCESSORIES Borg-Warner 35 automatic gearbox, hydraulic torque convertor and planetary gears with 3 ratios (I 2.401, II 1.450, III 1, rev 2.078), max ratio of convertor at stall 2, possible manual selection, 3.810 axle ratio, max speed 120 mph, 193 km/h.

Limousine

PRICE IN GB: £ 3,824.

ENGINE front, 4 stroke; cylinders: 6, vertical, in line; bore and stroke: 3.63 x 4.17 in, 92.1 x 106 mm; engine capacity: 258 cu in, 4,235 cu cm; compression ratio: 8; max power (SAE): 245 hp at 5,500 rpm; max torque (SAE): 282 lb ft, 38.9 kg m at 3,750 rpm; max engine rpm: 6,000; specific power: 57.9 hp/l; cylinder block: cast iron, dry liners; cylinder head: light alloy, hemispherical combustion chambers; crankshaft bearings: 7; valves: 2 per cylinder, overhead, Vee-slanted at 70°, thimble tappets; camshafts: 2, overhead; lubrication: mechanical pump, full flow filter; lubricating system capacity: 14.1 imp pt, 16.9 US pt, 8 l; carburation: 2 SU type HD 8 horizontal carburettors; fuel feed: 2 electric pumps; cooling system: water, thermostatic fan; cooling system capacity: 24.5 imp pt, 29.4 US pt, 13.9 l.

TRANSMISSION driving wheels: rear; gearbox: Borg-Warner automatic, hydraulic torque convertor and planetary gears with 3 ratios + reverse, max ratio of convertor at stall 2, possible manual selection; gearbox ratios: I 2.401, II 1.458, III 1, rev 2; selector lever: steering column; final drive: hypoid bevel; axle ratio: 3.540; tyres: 255 x 15.

PERFORMANCE max speeds: 48 mph, 78 km/h in 1st gear; 79 mph, 127 km/h in 2nd gear; 115 mph, 185 km/h in 3rd gear; power-weight ratio: 19.6 lb/hp, 8.9 kg/hp; carrying capacity: 1,235 lb, 560 kg; fuel consumption: 17.6 m/imp gal, 14.7 m/US gal, 16 l x 100 km.

CHASSIS integral, front and rear auxiliary frames; front suspension: independent, wishbones, lower trailing links, coil springs, anti-roll bar, telescopic dampers; rear suspension: independent, wishbones, semi-axle as upper arm, trailing lower radius arms, 4 coil springs, 4 telescopic dampers.

STEERING recirculating ball, adjustable steering wheel, variable ratio servo; turns of steering wheel lock to lock: 2.75.

BRAKES disc, dual circuit, servo.

ELECTRICAL EQUIPMENT voltage: 12 V; battery: 60 Ah; generator type: alternator, 45 A; ignition distributor: Lucas; headlamps: 4.

DIMENSIONS AND WEIGHT wheel base: 141 in, 3,582 mm; front track: 58 in, 1,473 mm; rear track: 58 in, 1,473 mm; overall length: 226 in, 5,741 mm; overall width: 77.50 in, 1,968 mm; overall height: 63.75 in, 1,619 mm; ground clearance: 7 in, 177 mm; dry weight: 4,787 lb, 2,172 kg; turning circle (between walls): 46 ft, 14 m; fuel tank capacity: 19.8 imp gal, 23.8 US gal, 90 l (2 separate tanks).

DAIMLER Sovereign 2.8-litre

DAIMLER Limousine

FAIRTHORPE TX-S

BODY limousine; doors: 4; seats: 7; front seats: separate; details: glass partition.

PRACTICAL INSTRUCTIONS fuel: 94 oct petrol; engine sump oil: 13 imp pt, 15.6 US pt, 7.4 l, multigrade, change every 3,600 miles, 5,800 km; tappet clearances: inlet 0.004 in, 0.10 mm, exhaust 0.006 in, 0.15 mm.

OPTIONAL ACCESSORIES air-conditioning system; electrically-controlled windows; electrically-controlled glass partition.

FAIRTHORPE   GREAT BRITAIN

Mark V EM

PRICE IN GB: £ 734.

ENGINE front, 4 stroke; cylinders: 4, in line; bore and stroke: 2.90 x 2.99 in, 73.7 x 76 mm; engine capacity: 79.1 cu in, 1,296 cu cm; compression ratio: 9.5; max power (SAE): 75 hp at 6,000 rpm; max torque (SAE): 75 lb ft, 10.3 kg m at 3,750 rpm; max engine rpm: 6,500; specific power: 57.9 hp/l; cylinder block: cast iron; cylinder head: cast iron; crankshaft bearings: 3; valves: 2 per cylinder, overhead, in line, push-rods and rockers; camshafts: 1, side; lubrication: gear pump, full flow filter; lubricating system capacity: 6 imp pt, 7.2 US pt, 3.4 l; carburation: 2 SU type HS 2 semi-downdraught carburettors; fuel feed: mechanical pump; cooling system: water; cooling system capacity: 7 imp pt, 8.5 US pt, 4 l.

TRANSMISSION driving wheels: rear; clutch: single dry plate (diaphragm), hydraulically controlled; gearbox: mechanical; gears: 4 + reverse; synchromesh gears: I, II, III, IV; gearbox ratios: I 3.753, II 2.159, III 1.306, IV 1, rev 3.753; gear lever: central; final drive: hypoid bevel; axle ratio: 3.890; width of rims: 4.5''; tyres: 155 x 13.

PERFORMANCE max speed: 104 mph, 168 km/h; power-weight ratio: 13.7 lb/hp, 6.2 kg/hp; carrying capacity: 397 lb, 180 kg; speed in direct drive at 1,000 rpm: 20.1 mph, 32.3 km/h; fuel consumption: 40 m/imp gal, 33.1 m/US gal, 7.1 l x 100 km.

CHASSIS double backbone, box section with outriggers; front suspension: independent, wishbones, coil springs, anti-roll bar, telescopic dampers; rear suspension: independent, wishbones, transverse leafspring as upper arms, lower trailing links, telescopic dampers.

STEERING rack-and-pinion; turns of steering wheel lock to lock: 3.50.

BRAKES front disc (diameter 9 in, 229 mm), rear drum; area rubbed by linings: front 197 sq in, 1,270 sq cm, rear 63 sq in, 406 sq cm, total 260 sq in, 1,676 sq cm.

ELECTRICAL EQUIPMENT voltage: 12 V; battery: 45 Ah; generator type: alternator, 16 A; ignition distributor: Lucas; headlamps: 2.

DIMENSIONS AND WEIGHT wheel base: 83 in, 2,108 mm; front track: 49.50 in, 1,257 mm; rear track: 49.50 in, 1,257 mm; overall length: 143 in, 3,632 mm; overall width: 58 in, 1,473 mm; overall height: 46 in, 1,168 mm; ground clearance: 5 in, 127 mm; dry weight: 1,030 lb, 467 kg; distribution of weight: 52% front axle, 48% rear axle; fuel tank capacity: 10.5 imp gal, 12.7 US gal, 48 l.

BODY sports in plastic material; doors: 2; seats: 2.

PRACTICAL INSTRUCTIONS fuel: 100 oct petrol; engine sump oil: 6 imp pt, 7.2 US pt, 3.4 l, SAE 20-30; gearbox oil: 1.5 imp pt, 1.7 US pt, 0.8 l, SAE 20-30; final drive oil: 1.2 imp pt, 1.5 US pt, 0.7 l, SAE 90 EP; greasing: every 6,000 miles, 9,700 km, 3 points; normal tyre pressure: front 18 psi, 1.3 atm, rear 18 psi, 1.3 atm.

OPTIONAL ACCESSORIES servo brake; electrically-heated rear window; supercharger.

TX-S

PRICE IN GB: £ 1,329.

ENGINE front, 4 stroke; cylinders: 6, in line; bore and stroke: 2.94 x 2.99 in, 74.7 x 76 mm; engine capacity: 121.9 cu in, 1,998 cu cm; compression ratio: 9.2; max power (DIN): 112 hp at 5,000 rpm; max torque (DIN): 117 lb ft, 16.1 kg m at 3,000 rpm; max engine rpm: 6,000; specific power: 56.1 hp/l; cylinder block: cast iron; cylinder head: cast iron; crankshaft bearings: 4; valves: 2 per cylinder, overhead, push-rods and rockers; camshafts: 1, side; lubrication: gear pump, full flow filter; lubricating system capacity: 9 imp pt, 10.8 US pt, 5.1 l; carburation: 2 Stromberg 150 CD horizontal carburettors; fuel feed: mechanical pump; cooling system: water; cooling system capacity: 6 imp pt, 7.2 US pt, 3.4 l.

TX-S

TRANSMISSION driving wheels: rear; clutch: single dry plate (diaphragm), hydraulically controlled; gearbox: mechanical; gears: 4 + reverse; synchromesh gears: I, II, III, IV; gearbox ratios: I 2.648, II 1.780, III 1.257, IV 1, rev 3.104; gear lever: central; final drive: hypoid bevel; axle ratio: 3.270; width of rims: 5.5''; tyres: 165 x 13.

PERFORMANCE max speeds: 42 mph, 67 km/h in 1st gear; 65 mph, 104 km/h in 2nd gear; 90 mph, 145 km/h in 3rd gear; 115 mph, 185 km/h in 4th gear; power-weight ratio: 14.3 lb/hp, 6.5 kg/hp; carrying capacity: 353 lb, 160 kg; speed in direct drive at 1,000 rpm: 20.1 mph, 32.3 km/h; fuel consumption: 28 m/imp gal, 23.3 m/US gal, 10.1 l x 100 km.

CHASSIS double backbone, box section with outriggers; front suspension: independent, wishbones, coil springs, anti-roll bar, telescopic dampers; rear suspension: independent, longitudinal trailing arms, transverse arms from top of articulated uprights to ends of longitudinal trailing arms (Torix-Bennet system), coil springs, telescopic dampers.

STEERING rack-and-pinion; turns of steering wheel lock to lock: 3.50.

BRAKES front disc (diameter 9 in, 229 mm), rear drum, dual circuit.

ELECTRICAL EQUIPMENT voltage: 12 V; battery: 52 Ah; generator type: alternator, 17 A; ignition distributor: Lucas; headlamps: 2.

DIMENSIONS AND WEIGHT wheel base: 83 in, 2,108 mm; front track: 49.50 in, 1,257 mm; rear track: 49.50 in, 1,257 mm; overall length: 144 in, 3,658 mm; overall width: 60 in, 1,524 mm; overall height: 44 in, 1,118 mm; ground clearance: 5 in, 127 mm; dry weight: 1,600 lb, 725 kg; distribution of weight: 52% front axle, 48% rear axle; turning circle (between walls): 25.3 ft, 7.7 m; fuel tank capacity: 10.7 imp gal, 12.7 US gal, 49 l.

BODY coupé in plastic material; doors: 2; seats: 2; details: electrically-heated rear window, rear window wiper.

PRACTICAL INSTRUCTIONS fuel: 98-100 oct petrol; engine sump oil: 6 imp pt, 7.2 US pt, 3.4 l, SAE 20W-30, change every 6,000 miles, 9,700 km; gearbox oil: 1.5 imp pt, 1.7 US pt, 0.8 l, SAE 20W-30, change every 3,700 miles, 6,000 km; final drive oil: 1.2 imp pt, 1.5 US pt, 0.7 l, SAE 90 EP, no change recommended; greasing: every 5,000 miles, 8,000 km, 3 points; tappet clearances: inlet 0.010 in, 0.25 mm, exhaust 0.010 in, 0.25 mm; valve timing: inlet opens 18° before tdc and closes 58° after bdc, exhaust opens 58° before bdc and closes 18° after tdc; normal tyre pressure: front 23 psi, 1.6 atm, rear 23 psi, 1.6 atm.

VARIATIONS

ENGINE light alloy cylinder head, 1 overhead camshaft.

OPTIONAL ACCESSORIES 3.900 or 4:110 axle ratio; servo brake; 4 halogen headlamps.

TX-SS

See TX-S, except for:

PRICE IN GB: £ 1,426.

ENGINE bore and stroke: 2.94 x 3.74 in, 74.7 x 95 mm; engine capacity: 152.5 cu in, 2,499 cu cm; max power (DIN): 142 hp at 6,000 rpm; max torque (DIN): 152 lb ft, 21 kg m at 3,000 rpm; max engine rpm: 6,500; specific power: 56.8 hp/l; carburation: Lucas injection pump, injectors in inlet pipes.

PERFORMANCE max speed: 130 mph, 209 km/h; power-weight ratio: 11.3 lb/hp, 5.1 kg/hp; speed in top at 1,000 rpm: 20.7 mph, 33.3 km/h; fuel consumption: 25 m/imp gal, 20.8 m/US gal, 11.3 l x 100 km.

BRAKES front disc (diameter 9.8 in, 250 mm).

PRACTICAL INSTRUCTIONS normal tyre pressure: front 25 psi, 1.7 atm, rear 25 psi, 1.7 atm.

TX-GT

See TX-S, except for:

PRICE IN GB: £ 1,284.

ENGINE max power (DIN): 104 hp at 5,300 rpm; specific power: 41.6 hp/l.

TRANSMISSION gears: 4 + reverse and overdrive (1.220 ratio).

FORD Escort 1300 Estate Car

FORD Escort GT 4-door Saloon

FORD Escort Mexico 1600 GT

PERFORMANCE max speed: 112 mph, 180 km/h; power-weight ratio: 16.1 lb/hp, 7.3 kg/hp.

DIMENSIONS AND WEIGHT overall height: 46.53 in, 1,182 mm; dry weight: 1,682 lb, 763 kg.

FORD   GREAT BRITAIN

Escort 1100 Standard 2-door Saloon

PRICE IN GB: £ 583.

ENGINE front, 4 stroke; cylinders: 4, vertical, in line; bore and stroke: 3.19 x 2.10 in, 81 x 53.3 mm; engine capacity: 67 cu in, 1,098 cu cm; compression ratio: 9; max power (SAE): 55 hp at 6,000 rpm; max torque (SAE): 60 lb ft, 8.3 kg m at 3,000 rpm; max engine rpm: 6,000; specific power: 50.1 hp/l; cylinder block: cast iron; cylinder head: cast iron; crankshaft bearings: 5; valves: 2 per cylinder, overhead, in line, push-rods and rockers; camshafts: 1, side; lubrication: rotary or vane-type pump, full flow filter; lubricating system capacity: 6.3 imp pt, 7.6 US pt, 3.6 l; carburation: 1 Autolite downdraught single barrel carburettor; fuel feed: mechanical pump; cooling system: water; cooling system capacity: 9 imp pt, 10.8 US pt, 5.1 l.

TRANSMISSION driving wheels: rear; clutch: single dry plate (diaphragm); gearbox: mechanical; gears: 4 + reverse; synchromesh gears: I, II, III, IV; gearbox ratios: I 3.656, II 2.185, III 1.425, IV 1, rev 4.235; gear lever: central; final drive: hypoid level; axle ratio: 3.900; width of rims: 3.5''; tyres: 5.50 x 12.

PERFORMANCE max speeds: 24 mph, 38 km/h in 1st gear; 41 mph, 66 km/h in 2nd gear; 62 mph, 100 km/h in 3rd gear; 82 mph, 132 km/h in 4th gear; power-weight ratio: 32.2 lb/hp, 14.6 kg/hp; carrying capacity: 882 lb, 400 kg; acceleration: standing ¼ mile 21.3 sec, 0-50 mph (0-80 km/h) 13.1 sec; speed in direct drive at 1,000 rpm: 15.8 mph, 25.4 km/h; fuel consumption: 33 m/imp gal, 27.7 m/US gal, 8.5 l x 100 km.

CHASSIS integral; front suspension: independent, by McPherson, coil springs/telescopic damper struts; rear suspension: rigid axle, semi-elliptic leafsprings, telescopic dampers.

STEERING rack-and-pinion; turns of steering wheel lock to lock: 3.50.

BRAKES drum; area rubbed by linings: front 75.4 sq in, 486 sq cm, rear 75.4 sq in, 486 sq cm, total 150.8 sq in, 972 sq cm.

ELECTRICAL EQUIPMENT voltage: 12 V; battery: 38 Ah; generator type: dynamo, 264 W; ignition distributor: Autolite; headlamps: 2.

DIMENSIONS AND WEIGHT wheel base: 94.50 in, 2,400 mm; front track: 49 in, 1,245 mm; rear track: 50 in, 1,270 mm; overall length: 156.60 in, 3,978 mm; overall width: 61.80 in, 1,570 mm; overall height: 53 in, 1,346 mm; ground clearance: 5 in, 127 mm; dry weight: 1,775 lb, 805 kg; distribution of weight: 54.3% front axle, 45.7% rear axle; turning circle (between walls): 29.5 ft, 9 m; fuel tank capacity: 9 imp gal, 10.8 US gal, 41 l.

BODY saloon/sedan; doors: 2; seats: 4-5; front seats: separate.

PRACTICAL INSTRUCTIONS fuel: 94 oct petrol; engine sump oil: 5.5 imp pt, 6.6 US pt, 3.1 l, SAE 10W-30, change every 5,000 miles, 8,000 km; gearbox oil: 1.6 imp pt, 1.9 US pt, 0.9 l, SAE 80, no change recommended; final drive oil: 2.6 imp pt, 3.2 US pt, 1.5 l, SAE 90, no change recommended; greasing: none; tappet clearances: inlet 0.010 in, 0.25 mm, exhaust 0.017 in, 0.43 mm; valve timing: inlet opens 17° before tdc and closes 51° after bdc, exhaust opens 51° before bdc and closes 17° after tdc; normal tyre pressure: front 24 psi, 1.7 atm, rear 24 psi, 1.7 atm.

VARIATIONS

(only for export for Escort 940 Standard 2- and 4-door Saloons and for Escort 940 2- and 4-door Saloons).

ENGINE bore and stroke 3.19 x 1.80 in, 81 x 45.6 mm, engine capacity 57.4 cu in, 940 cu cm, 9.5 compression ratio, max power (SAE) 44.5 hp at 5,600 rpm, max torque (SAE) 49 lb ft, 6.7 kg m at 3,200 rpm, 47.3 hp/l specific power.
TRANSMISSION 4.440 axle ratio, 6.00 x 12 tyres.
PERFORMANCE max speed 78 mph, 125 km/h, power-weight ratio 39.9 lb/hp, 18.1 kg/hp, acceleration 0-50 mph (0-80 km/h) 17.7 sec, fuel consumption 47.1 m/imp gal, 39.2 m/US gal, 6 l x 100 km.
ELECTRICAL EQUIPMENT 44 Ah battery.

OPTIONAL ACCESSORIES 3.770 axle ratio; 4.5'' wide rims with 6.00 x 12 tyres; 155 x 12 tyres; front disc brakes (dia-

FORD Escort 1300 (automatic)

FORD Escort GT 4-door Saloon

FORD Escort (front disc brake)

meter 8.60 in, 218 mm), servo brake, front area rubbed by linings 143.5 sq in, 925 sq cm; L equipment.

Escort 1100 Standard 4-door Saloon

See Escort 1100 Standard 2-door Saloon, except for:

PRICE IN GB: £ 608.

PERFORMANCE power-weight ratio: 33.1 lb/hp, 15 kg/hp.

DIMENSIONS AND WEIGHT dry weight: 1,820 lb, 825 kg.

Escort 1100 2-door Saloon

See Escort 1100 Standard 2-door Saloon, except for:

PRICE IN GB: £ 618.

OPTIONAL ACCESSORIES Borg-Warner 35 automatic gearbox only with engine capacity 79.2 cu in, 1,298 cu cm, max power (SAE) 65 hp at 5,700 rpm (see Escort 1300 L 2-door Saloon).

Escort 1100 4-door Saloon

See Escort 1100 Standard 2-door Saloon, except for:

PRICE IN GB: £ 643.

PERFORMANCE power-weight ratio: 33.1 lb/hp, 15 kg/hp.

DIMENSIONS AND WEIGHT dry weight: 1,820 lb, 825 kg.

OPTIONAL ACCESSORIES Borg-Warner 35 automatic gearbox only with engine capacity 79.2 cu in, 1,298 cu cm, max power (SAE) 57 hp at 5,000 rpm (see Escort 1300 Super 2-door Saloon).

Escort 1100 Estate Car

See Escort 1100 Standard 2-door Saloon, except for:

PRICE IN GB: £ 692.

TRANSMISSION axle ratio: 4.440.

PERFORMANCE power-weight ratio: 34.8 lb/hp, 15.8 kg/hp.

DIMENSIONS AND WEIGHT front track: 49.50 in, 1,257 mm; rear track: 50.50 in, 1,283 mm; overall length: 160.80 in, 4,084 mm; overall width: 61.60 in, 1,565 mm; overall height: 53.90 in, 1,369 mm; dry weight: 1,920 lb, 871 kg.

BODY estate car/station wagon; doors: 2 + 1.

OPTIONAL ACCESSORIES 4.125 axle ratio; L equipment.

Escort 1300 L 2-door Saloon

See Escort 1100 Standard 2-door Saloon, except for:

PRICE IN GB: £ 661.

ENGINE bore and stroke: 3.19 x 2.48 in, 81 x 63 mm; engine capacity: 79.2 cu in, 1,298 cu cm; max power (SAE): 65 hp at 5,700 rpm; max torque (SAE): 74 lb ft, 10.2 kg m at 2,500 rpm; max engine rpm: 5,700; specific power: 50.1 hp/l.

PERFORMANCE max speed: 90 mph, 145 km/h; power-weight ratio: 27.3 lb/hp, 12.4 kg/hp; acceleration: 0-50 mph (0-80 km/h) 16.5 sec; fuel consumption: 31 m/imp gal, 25.8 m/US gal, 9.1 l x 100 km.

BRAKES area rubbed by linings: front 88 sq in, 568 sq cm, rear 75.4 sq in, 486 sq cm, total 163.4 sq in, 1,054 sq cm.

VARIATIONS

ENGINE 8 compression ratio, max power (SAE) 57 hp at 5,000 rpm, max torque (SAE) 72 lb ft, 9.9 kg m at 2,500 rpm, 43.9 hp/l specific power.
PERFORMANCE power-weight ratio 28.8 lb/hp, 13.1 kg/hp.

OPTIONAL ACCESSORIES Borg-Warner 35 automatic gearbox, hydraulic torque convertor and planetary gears with 3 ratios (I 2.393, II 1:450, III 1, rev 2.090), max ratio of convertor at stall 2, possible manual selection, 4.125 axle ratio, 55 Ah battery, max speeds (I) 35 mph, 56 km/h, (II) 57 mph, 91 km/h, (III) 83 mph, 133 km/h, speed in direct drive at 1,000 rpm 14.9 mph, 23.9 km/h; XL equipment.

Escort 1300 L 4-door Saloon

See Escort 1300 L 2-door Saloon, except for:

PRICE IN GB: £ 686.

PERFORMANCE power-weight ratio: 28 lb/hp, 12.7 kg/hp.

DIMENSIONS AND WEIGHT dry weight: 1,820 lb, 825 kg.

Escort 1300 Estate Car

See Escort 1300 L 2-door Saloon, except for:

PRICE IN GB: £ 727.

TRANSMISSION axle ratio: 4.125 (3.770 on request); width of rims: 4.5''; tyres: 6.00 x 12.

PERFORMANCE power-weight ratio: 29.5 lb/hp, 13.4 kg/hp.

BRAKES front disc (diameter 8.60 in, 218 mm), rear drum, servo; area rubbed by linings: front 143.5 sq in, 925 sq cm, rear 75.4 sq in, 486 sq cm, total 218.9 sq in, 1,411 sq cm.

DIMENSIONS AND WEIGHT front track: 49.50 in, 1,257 mm; rear track: 50.50 in, 1,283 mm; overall length: 160.80 in, 4,084 mm; overall width: 61.60 in, 1,565 mm; overall height: 53.90 in, 1,369 mm; dry weight: 1,920 lb, 871 kg.

BODY estate car/station wagon; doors: 2 + 1.

OPTIONAL ACCESSORIES L equipment; XL equipment.

Escort GT 2-door Saloon

See Escort 1100 Standard 2-door Saloon, except for:

PRICE IN GB: £ 740.

ENGINE bore and stroke: 3.19 x 2.48 in, 81 x 63 mm; engine capacity: 79.2 cu in, 1,298 cu cm; compression ratio: 9.2; max power (SAE): 82 hp at 6,500 rpm; max torque (SAE): 75 lb ft, 10.4 kg m at 4,000 rpm; max engine rpm: 6,500; specific power: 63.2 hp/l; carburation: 1 Weber DIF 4 twin barrel carburettor.

TRANSMISSION gearbox ratios: I 3.337, II 1.995, III 1.418, IV 1, rev 3.868; axle ratio: 4.125; width of rims: 4.5''; tyres: 155 x 12.

PERFORMANCE max speeds: 29 mph, 47 km/h in 1st gear; 49 mph, 79 km/h in 2nd gear; 68 mph, 109 km/h in 3rd gear; 98 mph, 158 km/h in 4th gear; power-weight ratio: 21.8 lb/hp, 9.9 kg/hp; speed in direct drive at 1,000 rpm: 16.2 mph, 26 km/h; fuel consumption: 30 m/imp gal, 25 m/US gal, 9.4 l x 100 km.

BRAKES front disc (diameter 8.60 in, 218 mm), rear drum, dual circuit, servo; area rubbed by linings: front 143.5 sq in, 925 sq cm, rear 75.4 sq in, 486 sq cm, total 218.9 sq in, 1,411 sq cm.

DIMENSIONS AND WEIGHT wheel base: 94.80 in, 2,408 mm; dry weight: 1,795 lb, 814 kg.

OPTIONAL ACCESSORIES only centre console.

Escort GT 4-door Saloon

See Escort GT 2-door Saloon, except for:

PRICE IN GB: £ 765.

PERFORMANCE power-weight ratio: 22.5 lb/hp, 10.2 kg/hp.

DIMENSIONS AND WEIGHT dry weight: 1,840 lb, 834 kg.

Escort Twin Cam Saloon

PRICE IN GB: £ 1,042.

ENGINE front, 4 stroke; cylinders: 4, vertical, in line; bore and stroke: 3.25 x 2.87 in, 82.5 x 72.9 mm; engine capacity: 95.1 cu in, 1,558 cu cm; compression ratio: 9.5; max power (SAE): 115 hp at 6,000 rpm; max torque (SAE): 106 lb ft, 14.6 kg m at 4,500 rpm; max engine rpm: 6,600; specific power: 73.8 hp/l; cylinder block: cast iron; cylinder head: light alloy; crankshaft bearings: 5; valves: 2 per cylinder, overhead, Vee-slanted, thimble tappets; camshafts: 2, overhead; lubrication: rotary or vane-type pump, full flow filter; lubricating system capacity: 7.8 imp pt, 9.3 US pt, 4.4 l; carburation: 2 Weber 40 DCOE horizontal twin barrel carburettors; fuel feed: mechanical pump; cooling system: water; cooling system capacity: 11.6 imp pt, 14 US pt, 6.6 l.

FORD Escort RS 1600

FORD Cortina (independent front suspension)

FORD Cortina (rear suspension)

TRANSMISSION driving wheels: rear; clutch: single dry plate (diaphragm); gearbox: mechanical; gears: 4 + reverse; synchromesh gears: I, II, III, IV; gearbox ratios: I 2.972, II 2.210, III 1.397, IV 1, rev 3.324; gear lever: central; final drive: hypoid bevel; axle ratio: 3.777; width of rims: 5.5''; tyres: 165 x 13.

PERFORMANCE max speeds: 39 mph, 62 km/h in 1st gear; 58 mph, 93 km/h in 2nd gear; 84 mph, 135 km/h in 3rd gear; 115 mph, 185 km/h in 4th gear; power-weight ratio: 15 lb/hp, 6.8 kg/hp; acceleration: standing ¼ mile 17.2 sec, 0-50 mph (0-80 km/h) 7.2 sec; speed in direct drive at 1,000 rpm: 17.8 mph, 28.6 km/h; fuel consumption: 23.6 m/imp gal, 19.6 m/US gal, 12 l x 100 km.

CHASSIS integral; front suspension: independent, by McPherson, coil springs/telescopic damper struts, anti-roll bar; rear suspension: rigid axle, semi-elliptic leafsprings, trailing radius arms, telescopic dampers.

STEERING rack-and-pinion; turns of steering wheel lock to lock: 3.50.

BRAKES front disc (diameter 9.25 in, 235 mm), rear drum, dual circuit, servo; area rubbed by linings: front 190 sq in, 1,225 sq cm, rear 96 sq in, 619 sq cm, total 286 sq in, 1,844 sq cm.

ELECTRICAL EQUIPMENT voltage: 12 V; battery: 38 Ah; generator type: dynamo, 264 W; ignition distributor: Autolite; headlamps: 2.

DIMENSIONS AND WEIGHT wheel base: 94.50 in, 2,400 mm; front track: 49 in, 1,245 mm; rear track: 50 in, 1,270 mm; overall length: 160.80 in, 4,084 mm; overall width: 61.80 in, 1,570 mm; overall height: 53 in, 1,346 mm; ground clearance: 5.80 in, 147 mm; dry weight: 1,730 lb, 785 kg; distribution of weight: 51.6% front axle, 48.4% rear axle; turning circle (between walls): 29.7 ft, 9.1 m; fuel tank capacity: 9 imp gal, 10.8 US gal, 41 l.

BODY saloon/sedan; doors: 2; seats: 4; front seats: separate, bucket seats.

PRACTICAL INSTRUCTIONS fuel: 100 oct petrol; engine sump oil: 7.2 imp pt, 8.7 US pt, 4.1 l, SAE 10W-30, change every 2,500 miles, 4,000 km; gearbox oil: 1.7 imp pt, 2.1 US pt, 1 l, SAE 80, no change recommended; final drive oil: 2.6 imp pt, 3.2 US pt, 1.5 l, SAE 90, no change recommended; greasing: none; tappet clearances: inlet 0.005-0.006 in, 0.13-0.15 mm, exhaust 0.006-0.007 in, 0.15-0.18 mm; valve timing: inlet opens 26° before tdc and closes 66° after bdc, exhaust opens 66° before bdc and closes 26° after tdc; normal tyre pressure: front 24 psi, 1.7 atm, rear 24 psi, 1.7 atm.

OPTIONAL ACCESSORIES competition exhaust manifolds; limited slip final drive; 4.700 5.100 5.500 axle ratios; light alloy wheels, 6'' wide rims; heavy-duty front suspension; adjustable rear telescopic dampers; competition brakes.

Escort Mexico 1600 GT

See Escort Twin Cam Saloon, except for:

PRICE IN GB: £ 881.

ENGINE bore and stroke: 3.19 x 3.06 in, 81 x 77.6 mm; engine capacity: 97.5 cu in, 1,598 cu cm; compression ratio: 9; max power (SAE): 98 hp at 6,000 rpm; max torque (SAE): 102 lb ft, 14 kg m at 4,000 rpm; specific power: 61.3 hp/l; cylinder head: cast iron; valves: 2 per cylinder, overhead, in line, push-rods and rockers; camshafts: 1, side; carburation: 1 Weber 32 DFM downdraught twin barrel corburettor.

PERFORMANCE max speeds: 34 mph, 54 km/h in 1st gear; 45 mph, 73 km/h in 2nd gear; 71 mph, 115 km/h in 3rd gear; 100 mph, 161 km/h in 4th gear; power-weight ratio: 17.6 lb/hp, 8 kg/hp; speed in direct drive at 1,000 rpm: 15.2 mph, 24.4 km/h.

ELECTRICAL EQUIPMENT generator type: alternator, 28 A.

PRACTICAL INSTRUCTIONS tappet clearances: inlet 0.012 in, 0.30 mm, exhaust 0.022 in, 0.55 mm; valve timing: inlet opens 27° before tdc and closes 65° after bdc, exhaust opens 65° before bdc and closes 27° after tdc

Escort RS 1600

See Escort Twin Cam Saloon, except for:

PRICE IN GB: £ 1,108.

ENGINE bore and stroke: 3.19 x 3.06 in, 81 x 77.6 mm; engine capacity: 97.5 cu in, 1,598 cu cm; compression ratio: 10; max power (DIN): 120 hp at 6,500 rpm; max torque (DIN): 112 lb ft, 15.4 kg m at 4,000 rpm; specific power: 75.1 hp/l; valves: 4 per cylinder, overhead, Vee-slanted.

PERFORMANCE max speeds: 40 mph, 64 km/h in 1st gear;

FORD Escort RS 1600

FORD Cortina 1300 2-door Saloon

FORD Cortina 1600 XL Estate Car

60 mph, 96 km/h in 2nd gear; 85 mph, 136 km/h in 3rd gear; 113 mph, 182 km/h in 4th gear; power-weight ratio: 14.3 lb/hp, 6.5 kg/hp; acceleration: standing ¼ mile 16.7 sec, 0-50 mph (0-80 km/h) 6.8 sec; speed in direct drive at 1,000 rpm: 17.1 mph, 27.6 km/h; fuel consumption: 22 m/imp gal, 18.4 m/US gal, 12.8 l x 100 km.

ELECTRICAL EQUIPMENT generator type: alternator, 28 A; ignition distributor: Lucas.

PRACTICAL INSTRUCTIONS tappet clearances: inlet 0.005-0.007 in, 0.12-0.17 mm, exhaust 0.006-0.008 in, 0.15-0.20 mm; valve timing: inlet opens — before tdc and closes 107° after bdc, exhaust opens 112° before bdc and closes — after tdc; normal tyre pressure: front 28 psi, 2 atm, rear 28 psi, 2 atm.

Cortina 1300 2-door Saloon

PRICE IN GB: £ 700.

ENGINE front, 4 stroke; cylinders: 4, vertical, in line; bore and stroke: 3.19 x 2.48 in, 81.1 x 63.1 mm; engine capacity: 79.2 cu in, 1,298 cu cm; compression ratio: 9; max power (SAE): 65 hp at 5,700 rpm; max torque (SAE): 74 lb ft, 10.2 kg m at 3,000 rpm; max engine rpm: 6,000; specific power: 50.1 hp/l; cylinder block: cast iron; cylinder head: cast iron; crankshaft bearings: 5; valves: 2 per cylinder, overhead, push-rods and rockers; camshafts: 1, side; lubrication: rotary pump, full flow filter; lubricating system capacity: 6 imp pt, 7.2 US pt, 3.4 l; carburation: 1 Ford GPD downdraught single barrel carburettor; fuel feed: mechanical pump; cooling system: water; cooling system capacity: 10 imp pt, 12 US pt, 5.7 l.

TRANSMISSION driving wheels: rear; clutch: single dry plate (diaphragm); gearbox: mechanical; gears: 4 + reverse; synchromesh gears: I, II, III, IV; gearbox ratios: I 3.540, II 2.400, III 1.410, IV 1, rev 3.960; gear lever: central; final drive: hypoid bevel; axle ratio: 4.110; width of rims: 4.5''; tyres: 5.60 x 13.

PERFORMANCE max speeds: 27 mph, 44 km/h in 1st gear; 40 mph, 65 km/h in 2nd gear; 69 mph, 111 km/h in 3rd gear; 85 mph, 136 km/h in 4th gear; power-weight ratio: 32 lb/hp, 14.5 kg/hp; carrying capacity: 959 lb, 435 kg; speed in direct drive at 1,000 rpm: 16.2 mph, 26 km/h; fuel consumption: 35.9 m/imp gal, 29.8 m/US gal, 7.9 l x 100 km.

CHASSIS integral, front auxiliary frame; front suspension: independent, wishbones, coil spring/telescopic dampers; rear suspension: rigid axle, lower trailing arms, upper oblique torque arms, coil springs, telescopic dampers.

STEERING rack-and-pinion; turns of steering wheel lock to lock: 3.70.

BRAKES front disc (diameter 9.60 in, 244 mm), rear drum, dual circuit; area rubbed by linings: front 194.6 sq in, 1,255 sq cm, rear 75.3 sq in, 486 sq cm, total 269.9 sq in, 1,741 sq cm.

ELECTRICAL EQUIPMENT voltage: 12 V; battery: 38 Ah; generator type: dynamo, 22 A; ignition distributor: Ford; headlamps: 2.

DIMENSIONS AND WEIGHT wheel base: 101.50 in, 2,578 mm; front track: 56 in, 1,422 mm; rear track: 56 in, 1,422 mm; overall length: 168 in, 4,267 mm; overall width: 67.05 in, 1,703 mm; overall height: 52 in, 1,321 mm; ground clearance: 5 in, 127 mm; dry weight: 2,084 lb, 945 kg; distribution of weight: 53% front axle, 47% rear axle; turning circle (between walls): 33.5 ft, 10.2 m; fuel tank capacity: 12 imp gal, 14.3 US gal, 54 l.

BODY saloon/sedan; doors: 2; seats: 5; front seats: separate.

PRACTICAL INSTRUCTIONS fuel: 97 oct petrol; engine sump oil: 6 imp pt, 7.2 US pt, 3.4 l, SAE 10W-30, change every 6,000 miles, 9,700 km; gearbox oil: 1.6 imp pt, 1.9 US pt, 0.9 l, SAE 80 EP, no change recommended; final drive oil: 1.7 imp pt, 2.1 US pt, 1 l, SAE 90 EP, no change recommended; greasing: none; tappet clearances: inlet 0.004 in, 0.10 mm, exhaust 0.007 in, 0.17 mm; valve timing: inlet opens 17° before tdc and closes 51° after bdc, exhaust opens 51° before bdc and closes 17° after tdc; normal tyre pressure: front 27 psi, 1.9 atm, rear 34 psi, 2.4 atm.

OPTIONAL ACCESSORIES 5.5'' sport road wheels with 175 x 13 tyres; servo brake; alternator; reclining backrests; L equipment; XL equipment.

Cortina 1300 4-door Saloon

See Cortina 1300 2-door Saloon, except for:

PRICE IN GB: £ 725.

PERFORMANCE power-weight ratio: 32.8 lb/hp, 14.9 kg/hp.

DIMENSIONS AND WEIGHT dry weight: 2,139 lb, 970 kg.

Cortina 1300 Estate Car

See Cortina 1300 2-door Saloon, except for:

PRICE IN GB: £ 811.

PERFORMANCE power-weight ratio: 35.3 lb/hp, 16 kg/hp.

DIMENSIONS AND WEIGHT dry weight: 2,293 lb, 1,040 kg.

BODY estate car/station wagon; doors: 4 + 1.

Cortina 1600 2-door Saloon

See Cortina 1300 2-door Saloon, except for:

PRICE IN GB: £ 736.

ENGINE bore and stroke: 3.19 x 3.06 in, 81 x 77.6 mm; engine capacity: 97.5 cu in, 1,598 cu cm; compression ratio: 9; max power (SAE): 78 hp at 5,700 rpm; max torque (SAE): 94 lb ft, 13 kg m at 2,600 rpm; specific power: 48.8 hp/l.

TRANSMISSION axle ratio: 3.890.

PERFORMANCE max speeds: 29 mph, 47 km/h in 1st gear; 43 mph, 69 km/h in 2nd gear; 73 mph, 117 km/h in 3rd gear; 91 mph, 146 km/h in 4th gear; power-weight ratio: 27.1 lb/hp, 12.3 kg/hp; carrying capacity: 992 lb, 450 kg; speed in direct drive at 1,000 rpm: 17.1 mph, 27.5 km/h; fuel consumption: 32.1 m/imp gal, 26.7 US gal, 8.8 l x 100 km.

ELECTRICAL EQUIPMENT generator type: alternator (standard).

DIMENSIONS AND WEIGHT dry weight: 2,117 lb, 960 kg; distribution of weight: 54% front axle, 46% rear axle.

OPTIONAL ACCESSORIES 5.5'' sport road wheels with 175 x 13 tyres; servo brake; reclining backrests; L equipment; XL equipment; Borg-Warner 35/3 automatic gearbox, hydraulic torque convertor and planetary gears with 3 ratios (I 2.390, II 1.450, III 1, rev 2.094), max ratio of convertor at stall 2, possible manual selection.

Cortina 1600 4-door Saloon

See Cortina 1600 2-door Saloon, except for:

PRICE IN GB: £ 761.

PERFORMANCE power-weight ratio: 27.8 lb/hp, 12.6 kg/hp.

DIMENSIONS AND WEIGHT dry weight: 2,172 lb, 985 kg.

Cortina 1600 Estate Car

See Cortina 1600 2-door Saloon, except for:

PRICE IN GB: £ 847.

PERFORMANCE power-weight ratio: 29.8 lb/hp, 13.5 kg/hp.

DIMENSIONS AND WEIGHT dry weight: 2,326 lb, 1,055 kg.

BODY estate car/station wagon; doors: 4 + 1.

Cortina 1600 GT 2-door Saloon

See Cortina 1300 2-door Saloon, except for:

PRICE IN GB: £ 852.

ENGINE bore and stroke: 3.57 x 2.60 in, 87.6 x 66 mm; engine capacity: 97.2 cu in, 1.593 cu cm; compression ratio: 9.2; max power (SAE): 100 hp at 6,000 rpm; max torque (SAE): 101 lb ft, 13.9 kg m at 4,000 rpm; max engine rpm: 6,500; specific power: 62.8 hp/l; valves: 2 per cylinder, overhead, rockers; camshafts: 1, overhead; carburation: 1 Weber downdraught carburettor; cooling system capacity: 7.1 imp pt, 8.5 US pt, 4 l.

TRANSMISSION gearbox ratios: I 2.970, II 2.010, III 1.400, IV 1, rev 3.320; axle ratio: 3.890; width of rims: 5.5''; tyres: 175 x 13.

PERFORMANCE max speeds: 35 mph, 57 km/h in 1st gear; 52 mph, 84 km/h in 2nd gear; 75 mph, 121 km/h in 3rd gear; 101 mph, 162 km/h in 4th gear; power-weight ratio: 21.8 lb/hp, 9.9 kg/hp; speed in direct drive at 1,000 rpm: 17.6 mph, 28.3 km/h; fuel consumption: 30.3 m/imp gal, 25.3 m/US gal, 9.3 l x 100 km.

CHASSIS front suspension: anti-roll bar.

BRAKES servo; area rubbed by linings: rear 98.9 sq in, 638 sq cm.

FORD Cortina 1600 GT 2-door Saloon

FORD Cortina 2000 GXL 4-door Saloon

FORD Capri 1600

ELECTRICAL EQUIPMENT generator type: alternator; headlamps: 4, iodine.

DIMENSIONS AND WEIGHT dry weight: 2,194 lb, 995 kg; distribution of weight: 54% front axle, 46% rear axle.

PRACTICAL INSTRUCTIONS tappet clearances: inlet 0.008 in, 0.20 mm, exhaust 0.010 in, 0.25 mm; valve timing: inlet opens 18° before tdc and closes 70° after bdc, exhaust opens 64° before bdc and closes 24° after tdc.

OPTIONAL ACCESSORIES only Borg-Warner 35/3 automatic gearbox, hydraulic torque convertor and planetary gears with 3 ratios (I 2.390, II 1.450, III 1, rev 2.094), max ratio of convertor at stall 2, possible manual selection and 185 x 13 tyres.

Cortina 1600 GT 4-door Saloon

See Cortina 1600 GT 2-door Saloon, except for:

PRICE IN GB: £ 877.

PERFORMANCE power-weight ratio: 22.5 lb/hp, 10.2 kg/hp.

DIMENSIONS AND WEIGHT dry weight: 2,249 lb, 1,020 kg.

Cortina 1600 GXL 2-door Saloon

See Cortina 1600 GT 2-door Saloon, except for:

PRICE IN GB: £ 964.

BODY details: special interior and trimmed body.

Cortina 1600 GXL 4-door Saloon

See Cortina 1600 GT 4-door Saloon, except for:

PRICE IN GB: £ 989.

BODY details: special interior and trimmed body.

Cortina 2000 2-door Saloon

See Cortina 1300 2-door Saloon, except for:

PRICE IN GB: £ 787.

ENGINE bore and stroke: 3.89 x 3.03 in, 90.8 x 76.9 mm; engine capacity: 121.6 cu in, 1,993 cu cm; compression ratio: 9.2; max power (SAE): 112 hp at 6,000 rpm; max torque (SAE): 122 lb ft, 16.8 kg m at 3,500 rpm; max engine rpm: 6,500; specific power: 56.2 hp/l; valves: 2 per cylinder, rockers; camshafts: 1, overhead; carburation: 1 Weber downdraught carburettor; cooling system capacity: 7.1 imp pt, 8.5 US pt, 4 l.

TRANSMISSION gearbox ratios: I 3.650, II 1.970, III 1.370, IV 1; axle ratio: 3.440; width of rims: 5.5''; tyres: 175 x 13.

PERFORMANCE max speeds: 30 mph, 49 km/h in 1st gear; 57 mph, 91 km/h in 2nd gear; 81 mph, 131 km/h in 3rd gear; 103 mph, 165 km/h in 4th gear; power-weight ratio: 19.6 lb/hp, 8.9 kg/hp; carrying capacity: 992 lb, 450 kg; speed in direct drive at 1,000 rpm: 17.7 mph, 28.5 km/h; fuel consumption: 33 m/imp gal, 27.3 m/US gal, 8.6 l x 100 km.

CHASSIS front suspension: anti-roll bar.

ELECTRICAL EQUIPMENT generator type: alternator; headlamps: 4, iodine.

DIMENSIONS AND WEIGHT dry weight: 2,205 lb, 1,000 kg; distribution of weight: 54.5% front axle, 45.5% rear axle.

PRACTICAL INSTRUCTIONS tappet clearances: inlet 0.008 in, 0.20 mm, exhaust 0.010 in, 0.25 mm; valve timing: inlet opens 18° before tdc and closes 70° after bdc, exhaust opens 64° before bdc and closes 24° after tdc.

OPTIONAL ACCESSORIES only Borg-Warner 35/3 automatic gearbox, hydraulic torque convertor and planetary gears with 3 ratios (I 2.390, II 1.450, III 1, rev 2.094), max ratio of convertor at stall 2, possible manual selection; 185 x 13 tyres; L equipment; XL equipment.

Cortina 2000 4-door Saloon

See Cortina 2000 2-door Saloon, except for:

PRICE IN GB: £ 812.

PERFORMANCE power-weight ratio: 21.4 lb/hp, 9.7 kg/hp.

DIMENSIONS AND WEIGHT dry weight: 2,238 lb, 1,015 kg.

FORD Cortina 1600 GT Saloon

FORD Cortina 2000 GXL Saloon

FORD Capri

Cortina 2000 Estate Car

See Cortina 2000 2-door Saloon, except for:

PRICE IN GB: £ 898.

PERFORMANCE power-weight ratio: 21.4 lb/hp, 9.7 kg/hp.

DIMENSIONS AND WEIGHT dry weight: 2,392 lb, 1,085 kg.

BODY estate car/station wagon; doors: 4 + 1.

Cortina 2000 GT 2-door Saloon

See Cortina 2000 2-door Saloon, except for:

PRICE IN GB: £ 888.

BODY details: special interior and trimmed body.

OPTIONAL ACCESSORIES only Borg-Warner 35/3 automatic gearbox and 185 x 13 tyres.

Cortina 2000 GT 4-door Saloon

See Cortina 2000 GT 2-door Saloon, except for:

PRICE IN GB: £ 913.

PERFORMANCE power-weight ratio: 20.1 lb/hp, 9.1 kg/hp.

DIMENSIONS AND WEIGHT dry weight: 2,238 lb, 1,015 kg.

Cortina 2000 GXL 2-door Saloon

See Cortina 2000 2-door Saloon, except for:

PRICE IN GB: £ 1,000.

BODY details: special interior and trimmed body.

OPTIONAL ACCESSORIES only Borg-Warner 35/3 automatic gearbox and 185 x 13 tyres.

Cortina 2000 GXL 4-door Saloon

See Cortina 2000 GXL 2-door Saloon, except for:

PRICE IN GB: £ 1,025.

PERFORMANCE power-weight ratio: 20.1 lb/hp, 9.1 kg/hp.

DIMENSIONS AND WEIGHT dry weight: 2,238 lb, 1,015 kg.

Capri 1300

PRICE IN GB: £ 769.

ENGINE front, 4 stroke; cylinders: 4, vertical, in line; bore and stroke: 3.19 x 2.48 in, 81.1 x 63.1 mm; engine capacity: 79.2 cu in, 1,298 cu cm; compression ratio: 9; max power (SAE): 65 hp at 5,000 rpm; max torque (SAE): 75 lb ft, 10.3 kg m at 2,000 rpm; max engine rpm: 6,000; specific power: 50.1 hp/l; cylinder block: cast iron; cylinder head: cast iron; crankshaft bearings: 5; valves: 2 per cylinder, overhead, in line, push-rods and rockers; camshafts: 1, side; lubrication: rotary or vane-type pump, full flow filter; lubricating system capacity: 6.2 imp pt, 7.4 US pt, 3.5 l; carburation: 1 Ford GPD downdraught single barrel carburettor; fuel feed: mechanical pump; cooling system: water; cooling system capacity: 10 imp pt, 12 US pt, 5.7 l.

TRANSMISSION driving wheels: rear; clutch: single dry plate (diaphragm), hydraulically controlled; gearbox: mechanical; gears: 4 + reverse; synchromesh gears: I, II, III, IV; gearbox ratios: I 3.543, II 2.936, III 1.412, IV 1, rev 3.963; gear lever: central; final drive: hypoid bevel; axle ratio: 4.125; width of rims: 4.5''; tyres: 6.00 x 13.

PERFORMANCE max speeds: 27 mph, 44 km/h in 1st gear; 33 mph, 53 km/h in 2nd gear; 69 mph, 111 km/h in 3rd gear; 86 mph, 138 km/h in 4th gear; power-weight ratio: 30.2 lb/hp, 13.7 kg/hp; speed in direct drive at 1,000 rpm: 16.3 mph, 26.2 km/h; fuel consumption: 31 m/imp gal, 25.8 m/US gal, 9.1 l x 100 km.

CHASSIS integral; front suspension: independent, by McPherson, coil springs/telescopic damper struts, lower wishbones (trailing arms), anti-roll bar; rear suspension: rigid axle, semi-elliptic leafsprings, twin upper radius arms, telescopic dampers.

STEERING rack-and-pinion.

CAPRI 1300

BRAKES front disc (diameter 9.50 in, 241 mm), rear drum, dual circuit; area rubbed by linings: front 95.5 sq in, 616 sq cm, rear 75.6 sq in, 487 sq cm, total 171.1 sq in, 1,103 sq cm.

ELECTRICAL EQUIPMENT voltage: 12 V; battery: 38 Ah; generator type: dynamo, 22 A; ignition distributor: Autolite; headlamps: 2.

DIMENSIONS AND WEIGHT wheel base: 100.80 in, 2,560 mm; front track: 53 in, 1,346 mm; rear track: 52 in, 1,321 mm; overall length: 167.80 in, 4,262 mm; overall width: 64.80 in, 1,646 mm; overall height: 50.70 in, 1,465 mm; ground clearance: 4.50 in, 114 mm; dry weight: 1,960 lb, 889 kg; distribution of weight: 52.5% front axle, 47.5% rear axle; turning circle (between walls): 32 ft, 9.8 m; fuel tank capacity: 10.5 imp gal, 12.7 US gal, 48 l.

BODY coupé; doors: 2; seats: 2 + 2; front seats: separate.

PRACTICAL INSTRUCTIONS fuel: 97 oct petrol; engine sump oil: 5.4 imp pt, 6.3 US pt, 3 l, SAE 10W-30, change every 5,000 miles, 8,000 km; gearbox oil: 2 imp pt, 2.3 US pt, 1.1 l, SAE 80, no change recommended; final drive oil: 2 imp pt, 2.3 US pt, 1.1 l, SAE 90, no change recommended; greasing: none; tappet clearances: inlet 0.010 in, 0.25 mm, exhaust 0.017 in, 0.44 mm; valve timing: inlet opens 17° before tdc and closes 51° after bdc, exhaust opens 51° before bdc and closes 17° after tdc

VARIATIONS

ENGINE 8 compression ratio, max power (SAE) 62 hp at 5,000 rpm, max torque (SAE) 72 lb ft, 9.9 kg m at 2,500 rpm, 47.8 hp/l specific power.

OPTIONAL ACCESSORIES 5'' wide rims with 165 x 13 tyres; servo brake; 28 A alternator; reclining backrests; sunshine roof; sport road wheels; electrically-heated rear window and alternator; L equipment; XL equipment.

Capri 1300 GT

See Capri 1300, except for:

PRICE IN GB: £ 860.

ENGINE compression ratio: 9.2; max power (SAE): 82 hp at 6,000 rpm; max torque (SAE): 75 lb ft, 10.4 kg m at 4,300 rpm; max engine rpm: 6,200; specific power: 63.2 hp/l; carburation: 1 Weber downdraught twin barrel carburettor.

TRANSMISSION axle ratio: 3.900; tyres: 165 x 13.

PERFORMANCE max speeds: 30 mph, 48 km/h in 1st gear; 36 mph, 58 km/h in 2nd gear; 75 mph, 121 km/h in 3rd gear; 93 mph, 150 km/h in 4th gear; power-weight ratio: 24.2 lb/hp, 11 kg/hp; speed in direct drive: 17.2 mph, 27.7 km/h; fuel consumption: 29.4 m/imp gal, 24.5 m/US gal, 9.6 l x 100 km.

BRAKES front disc (diameter 9.60 in, 244 mm); area rubbed by linings: front 103 sq in, 664 sq cm, rear 98.8 sq in, 637 sq cm, total 201.8 sq in, 1,301 sq cm.

DIMENSIONS AND WEIGHT overall height: 50.20 in, 1,275 mm; dry weight: 1,995 lb, 905 kg.

VARIATIONS

None.

OPTIONAL ACCESSORIES L equipment; XL equipment; XLR equipment.

Capri 1600

See Capri 1300, except for:

PRICE IN GB: £ 823.

ENGINE bore and stroke: 3.19 x 3.05 in, 81 x 77.6 mm; engine capacity: 97.5 cu in, 1,598 cu cm; max power (SAE): 78 hp at 5,700 rpm; max torque (SAE): 94 lb ft, 13 kg m at 2,500 rpm; max engine rpm: 5,600; specific power: 46.9 hp/l.

TRANSMISSION axle ratio: 3.900.

PERFORMANCE max speed: 92 mph, 148 km/h; power-weight ratio: 25.6 lb/hp, 11.6 kg/hp; speed in direct drive at 1,000 rpm: 17.2 mph, 27.7 km/h; fuel consumption: 31.4 m/imp gal, 26.1 m/US gal, 9 l x 100 km.

BRAKES front disc (diameter 9.60 in, 244 mm); area rubbed

FORD Capri 1600 GT

FORD Capri 2000 GT

FORD Capri 3000 GT

by linings: front 108 sq in, 696 sq cm, rear 98.8 sq in 637 sq cm, total 206.8 sq in, 1,333 sq cm.

DIMENSIONS AND WEIGHT dry weight: 2,005 lb, 909 kg distribution of weight: 52.6% front axle, 47.4% rear axle

VARIATIONS

ENGINE 8 compression ratio, max power (SAE) 74 hp a 5,000 rpm, max torque (SAE) 93 lb ft, 12.8 kg m at 2,50 rpm, 46.3 hp/l specific power.

OPTIONAL ACCESSORIES 4.125 axle ratio; Borg-Warner 35/ automatic gearbox, hydraulic torque convertor and plane tary gears with 3 ratios (I 2.393, II 1.450, III 1, rev 2.094) max ratio of convertor at stall 2, possible manual selection central selector lever, max speeds (I) 38 mph, 61 km/h (II) 63 mph, 102 km/h, (III) 92 mph, 148 km/h; L equip ment; XL equipment.

Capri 1600 GT

See Capri 1300, except for:

PRICE IN GB: £ 901.

ENGINE bore and stroke: 3.19 x 3.05 in, 81 x 77.6 mm engine capacity: 97.5 cu in, 1,598 cu cm; max power (SAE) 98 hp at 6,000 rpm; max torque (SAE): 101 lb ft, 14 kg n at 3,600 rpm; max engine rpm: 5,600; specific power 58.2 hp/l; carburation: 1 Weber downdraught twin barre carburettor.

TRANSMISSION gearbox ratios: I 2.972, II 2.010, III 1.397 IV 1, rev 3.324; axle ratio: 3.770; tyres: 165 x 13.

PERFORMANCE max speeds: 34 mph, 54 km/h in 1st gear 50 mph, 80 km/h in 2nd gear; 71 mph, 114 km/h in 3rd gear; 99 mph, 160 km/h in 4th gear; power-weight ratio 20.5 lb/hp, 9.3 kg/hp; speed in direct drive at 1,000 rpm 17.9 mph, 28.8 km/h; fuel consumption: 28.8 m/imp gal 24 m/US gal, 9.8 l x 100 km.

BRAKES front disc (diameter 9.60 in, 244 mm); servo area rubbed by linings: front 108 sq in, 696 sq cm, rear 98.8 sq in, 637 sq cm, total 206.8 sq in, 1,333 sq cm

DIMENSIONS AND WEIGHT overall height: 50.20 in, 1,275 mm; dry weight: 2,010 lb, 911 kg; distribution of weight 52.6% front axle, 47.4% rear axle.

PRACTICAL INSTRUCTIONS tappet clearances: inlet 0.012 in, 0.30 mm, exhaust 0.022 in, 0.55 mm; valve timing: inlet opens 27° before tdc and closes 65° after bdc, exhaust opens 65° before bdc and closes 27° after tdc.

VARIATIONS

None.

OPTIONAL ACCESSORIES Borg-Warner 35/3 automatic gearbox, hydraulic torque convertor and planetary gears with 3 ratios (I 2.393, II 1.450, III 1, rev 2.094), max ratio of convertor at stall 2, possible manual selection, central selector lever, max speeds (I) 42 mph, 67 km/h, (II) 68 mph, 110 km/h, (III) 99 mph, 160 km/h; 55 57 66 Ah battery; 28 A alternator; reclining backrests; heavy-duty equipment; sunshine roof; sport road wheels; L equipment; XL equipment; XLR equipment.

Capri 2000 GT

See Capri 1300, except for:

PRICE IN GB: £ 935.

ENGINE cylinders: 4, Vee-slanted at 60°; bore and stroke: 3.69 x 2.85 in, 93.7 x 72.4 mm; engine capacity: 121.8 cu in, 1,996 cu cm; compression ratio: 8.9; max power (SAE): 113 hp at 5,700 rpm; max torque (SAE): 122 lb ft, 16.8 kg m at 4,000 rpm; specific power: 56.6 hp/l; crankshaft bearings: 3; camshafts: 1, at centre of Vee; lubricating system capacity: 8.1 imp pt, 9.7 US pt, 4.6 l; carburation: 1 Weber downdraught twin barrel carburettor; cooling system capacity: 13.2 imp pt, 15.9 US pt, 7.5 l.

TRANSMISSION gearbox ratios: I 2.972, II 2.010, III 1.397, IV 1, rev 3.324; axle ratio: 3.545; tyres: 165 x 13.

PERFORMANCE max speeds: 39 mph, 62 km/h in 1st gear; 57 mph, 91 km/h in 2nd gear; 81 mph, 131 km/h in 3rd gear; 106 mph, 171 km/h in 4th gear; power-weight ratio: 18.8 lb/hp, 8.5 kg/hp; speed in direct drive at 1,000 rpm: 19 mph, 30.6 km/h; fuel consumption: 23 m/imp gal, 19.1 m/US gal, 12.3 l x 100 km.

BRAKES front disc (diameter 9.60 in, 244 mm), servo; area rubbed by linings: front 108 sq in, 696 sq cm, rear 98.8 sq in, 637 sq cm, total 206.8 sq in, 1,333 sq cm.

DIMENSIONS AND WEIGHT overall height: 50.20 in, 1,275 mm; dry weight: 2,130 lb, 966 kg; distribution of weight: 55.1% front axle, 44.9% rear axle.

FORD Capri 1600 GT

FORD Capri 2000 GT

FORD Capri 3000 GT

PRACTICAL INSTRUCTIONS engine sump oil: 6.6 imp pt, 7.8 US pt, 3.7 l.

VARIATIONS

None.

OPTIONAL ACCESSORIES Borg-Warner 35/3 automatic gearbox, hydraulic torque convertor and planetary gears with 3 ratios (I 2.393, II 1.450, III 1, rev 2.094), max ratio of convertor at stall 2, possible manual selection, central selector lever, max speeds (I) 44 mph, 71 km/h, (II) 73 mph, 118 km/h, (III) 106 mph, 171 km/h; 5'' wide rims; 55 57 66 Ah battery; 28 A alternator; reclining backrests; sunshine roof; sport road wheels; L equipment; XL equipment; XLR equipment.

Capri 3000 GT

See Capri 1300, except for:

PRICE IN GB: £ 1,070.

ENGINE cylinders: 6, Vee-slanted at 60°; bore and stroke: 3.69 x 2.85 in, 93.7 x 72.4 mm; engine capacity: 182.7 cu in, 2,994 cu cm; compression ratio: 8.9; max power (SAE): 144 hp at 4,750 rpm; max torque (SAE): 192 lb ft, 26.5 kg m at 3,000 rpm; max engine rpm: 5,500; specific power: 48.1 hp/l; crankshaft bearings: 4; camshafts: 1, at centre of Vee; lubricating system capacity: 7.5 imp pt, 8.9 US pt, 4.2 l; carburation: 1 Weber downdraught twin barrel carburettor.

TRANSMISSION gearbox ratios: I 3.163, II 2.214, III 1.412, IV 1, rev 3.346; axle ratio: 3.220; width of rims: 5''; tyres: 185 x 13.

PERFORMANCE max speeds: 36 mph, 58 km/h in 1st gear; 51 mph, 82 km/h in 2nd gear; 81 mph, 131 km/h in 3rd gear; 104 mph, 167 km/h in 4th gear; power-weight ratio: 16.8 lb/hp, 7.6 kg/hp; speed in direct drive at 1,000 rpm: 20.7 mph, 33.3 km/h; fuel consumption: 23.4 m/imp gal, 19.4 m/US gal, 12.1 l x 100 km.

BRAKES front disc (diameter 9.60 in, 244 mm), servo; area rubbed by linings: front 108 sq in, 696 sq cm, rear 127.2 sq in, 820 sq cm, total 235.2 sq in, 1,516 sq cm.

ELECTRICAL EQUIPMENT battery: 55 Ah; generator type: alternator, 28 A.

DIMENSIONS AND WEIGHT overall height: 50.20 in, 1,275 mm; dry weight: 2,380 lb, 1,079 kg; distribution of weight: 56% front axle, 44% rear axle; turning circle (between walls): 34 ft, 10.4 m; fuel tank capacity: 13.5 imp gal, 16.1 US gal, 61 l.

PRACTICAL INSTRUCTIONS fuel: 94 oct petrol; engine sump oil: 6.7 imp pt, 8 US pt, 3.8 l; gearbox oil: 3.2 imp pt, 3.8 US pt, 1.8 l; final drive oil: 1.9 imp pt, 2.3 US pt, 1.1 l; tappet clearances: inlet 0.012 in, 0.30 mm, exhaust 0.012 in, 0.30 mm; valve timing: inlet opens 20° before tdc and closes 56° after bdc, exhaust opens 62° before bdc and closes 14° after tdc.

VARIATIONS

None.

OPTIONAL ACCESSORIES only Borg-Warner 35/3 automatic gearbox, hydraulic torque convertor and planetary gears with 3 ratios (I 2.393, II 1.450, III 1, rev 2.094), max ratio of convertor at stall 2, possible manual selection, central selector lever, max speeds (I) 48 mph, 77 km/h, (II) 79 mph, 127 km/h, (III) 114 mph, 183 km/h; 60 Ah battery; reclining backrests; sunshine roof; sport road wheels; electrically-heated rear window; L equipment; XL equipment; XLR equipment.

Capri 3000 E

See Capri 3000 GT, except for:

PRICE IN GB: £ 1,207.

PERFORMANCE power-weight ratio: 16.9 lb/hp, 7.7 kg/hp.

DIMENSIONS AND WEIGHT dry weight: 2,435 lb, 1,104 kg; distribution of weight: 55.7% front axle, 44.3% rear axle.

BODY front seats: reclining backrests (standard); details: special interior and trimmed body.

Zephyr Saloon

PRICE IN GB: £ 870.

ENGINE front, 4 stroke; cylinders: 4, Vee-slanted at 60°; bore and stroke: 3.69 x 2.85 in, 93.7 x 72.4 mm; engine

ZEPHIR SALOON

capacity: 121.8 cu in, 1,996 cu cm; compression ratio: 8.9; max power (SAE): 93 hp at 4,750 rpm; max torque (SAE): 123 lb ft, 17 kg m at 2,750 rpm; max engine rpm: 5,000; specific power: 46.6 hp/l; cylinder block: cast iron; cylinder head: cast iron; crankshaft bearings: 3; valves: 2 per cylinder, overhead, push-rods and rockers; camshafts: 1, at centre of Vee; lubrication: eccentric or vane-type pump, full flow filter; lubricating system capacity: 7.5 imp pt, 8.9 US pt, 4.2 l; carburation: 1 Ford downdraught carburettor; fuel feed: mechanical pump; cooling system: water; cooling system capacity: 15.4 imp pt, 18.4 US pt, 8.7 l.

TRANSMISSION driving wheels: rear; clutch: single dry plate (diaphragm); gearbox: mechanical; gears: 4 + reverse; synchromesh gears: I, II, III, IV; gearbox ratios: I 4.412, II 2.353, III 1.505, IV 1, rev 4.662; gear lever: steering column; final drive: hypoid bevel; axle ratio: 3.700; width of rims: 4.5''; tyres: 6.40 x 13.

PERFORMANCE max speeds: 22 mph, 35 km/h in 1st gear; 41 mph, 66 km/h in 2nd gear; 65 mph, 104 km/h in 3rd gear; 88 mph, 141 km/h in 4th gear; power-weight ratio: 29.5 lb/hp, 13.4 kg/hp; carrying capacity: 1,058 lb, 480 kg; speed in direct drive at 1,000 rpm: 19.4 mph, 31.3 km/h; fuel consumption: 27.7 m/imp gal, 23.1 m/US gal, 10.2 l x 100 km.

CHASSIS integral; front suspension: independent, by McPherson, coil springs/telescopic damper struts, lower wishbones, anti-roll bar; rear suspension: independent, semi-trailing arms, coil springs, telescopic dampers.

STEERING recirculating ball, adjustable steering wheel; turns of steering wheel lock to lock: 4.50.

BRAKES disc (diameter 9.60 in, 244 mm), dual circuit, servo; area rubbed by linings: front 189.5 sq in, 1,222 sq cm, rear 146.8 sq in, 947 sq cm, total 336.3 sq in, 2,169 sq cm.

ELECTRICAL EQUIPMENT voltage: 12 V; battery: 53 Ah; generator type: dynamo, 25 A; ignition distributor: Ford; headlamps: 2.

DIMENSIONS AND WEIGHT wheel base: 115 in, 2,921 mm; front track: 57 in, 1,448 mm; rear track: 58 in, 1,473 mm; overall length: 185 in, 4,699 mm; overall width: 71.30 in, 1,811 mm; overall height: 56.20 in, 1,427 mm; ground clearance: 6.40 in, 163 mm; dry weight: 2,756 lb, 1,250 kg; distribution of weight: 54.9% front axle, 45.1% rear axle; turning circle (between walls): 37.5 ft, 11.4 m; fuel tank capacity: 15 imp gal, 17.9 US gal, 68 l.

BODY saloon/sedan; doors: 4; seats: 6; front seats: separate.

PRACTICAL INSTRUCTIONS fuel: 94 oct petrol; engine sump oil: 6 imp pt, 7.2 US pt, 3.4 l, SAE 10W-30, change every 6,000 miles, 9,700 km; gearbox oil: 3.2 imp pt, 3.8 US pt, 1.8 l, SAE 80 EP, no change recommended; final drive oil: 3 imp pt, 3.6 US pt, 1.7 l, SAE 90, no change recommended; greasing: none; tappet clearances: inlet 0.012 in, 0.30 mm, exhaust 0.020 in, 0.51 mm; valve timing: inlet opens 20° before tdc and closes 56° after bdc, exhaust opens 62° before bdc and closes 14° after tdc; normal tyre pressure: front 24 psi, 1.7 atm, rear 27 psi, 1.9 atm.

VARIATIONS

ENGINE 8 compression ratio, max power (SAE) 88 hp at 4,750 rpm, max torque (SAE) 117 lb ft, 16.1 kg m at 2,750 rpm, 44.1 hp/l specific power.

OPTIONAL ACCESSORIES Borg-Warner 35/3 automatic gearbox, hydraulic torque convertor and planetary gears with 3 ratios (I 2.460, II 1.460, III 1, rev 2.200), max ratio of convertor at stall 2, possible manual selection, steering column selector lever, max speeds (I) 36 mph, 58 km/h, (II) 60 mph, 96 km/h, (III) 88 mph, 141 km/h; central gear lever; 5'' wide rims with 185 x 14 tyres; 6.70 x 13 tyres; 43 A alternator; reclining backrests; electrically-heated rear window.

Zephyr Estate Car

See Zephyr Saloon, except for:

PRICE IN GB: £ 1,239.

TRANSMISSION tyres: 6.70 x 13 (standard).

PERFORMANCE power-weight ratio: 31.7 lb/hp, 14.4 kg/hp.

DIMENSIONS AND WEIGHT dry weight: 2,952 lb, 1,339 kg.

BODY estate car/station wagon; doors: 4 + 1.

FORD Zephyr De Luxe Saloon

FORD Zodiac Saloon

FORD The Executive

Zephyr De Luxe Saloon

See Zephyr Saloon, except for:

PRICE IN GB: £ 941.

BODY details: special interior and trimmed body.

Zephyr De Luxe Estate Car

See Zephyr Estate Car, except for:

PRICE IN GB: £ 1,310.

BODY details: special interior and trimmed body.

Zephyr V6 Saloon

See Zephyr Saloon, except for:

PRICE IN GB: £ 936.

ENGINE cylinders: 6, Vee-slanted at 60°; bore and stroke: 3.69 x 2.38 in, 93.7 x 60.4 mm; engine capacity: 152.4 cu in, 2,498 cu cm; compression ratio: 9.1; max power (SAE): 118 hp at 4,750 rpm; max torque (SAE): 145 lb ft, 20 kg m at 3,000 rpm; max engine rpm: 5,200; specific power: 47.2 hp/l; crankshaft bearings: 4; lubricating system capacity: 9.5 imp pt, 11.4 US pt, 5.4 l; cooling system capacity: 20.8 imp pt, 17.2 US pt, 9.8 l.

TRANSMISSION gearbox ratios: I 3.163, II 2.214, III 1.412, IV 1, rev 3.346; tyres: 6.70 x 13 (standard).

PERFORMANCE max speeds: 33 mph, 53 km/h in 1st gear; 47 mph, 75 km/h in 2nd gear; 74 mph, 119 km/h in 3rd gear; 96 mph, 154 km/h in 4th gear; power-weight ratio: 24.3 lb/hp; carrying capacity: 882 lb, 400 kg; acceleration: 0-50 mph (0-80 km/h) 10.6 sec; speed in direct drive at 1,000 rpm: 19.3 mph, 31.1 km/h; fuel consumption: 23.7 m/imp gal, 19.8 m/US gal, 11.9 l x 100 km.

DIMENSIONS AND WEIGHT dry weight: 2,866 lb, 1,300 kg; turning circle (between walls): 39.5 ft, 12 m.

PRACTICAL INSTRUCTIONS engine sump oil: 7 imp pt, 8.5 US pt, 4 l.

VARIATIONS

ENGINE 8 compression ratio, max power (SAE) 114.5 hp at 4,750 rpm, max torque (SAE) 141 lb ft, 19.4 kg m at 3,000 rpm, 45.8 hp/l specific power.

OPTIONAL ACCESSORIES Laycock-de Normanville overdrive (0.820 ratio); power-assisted steering.

Zephyr V6 Estate Car

See Zephyr V6 Saloon, except for:

PRICE IN GB: £ 1,306.

PERFORMANCE power-weight ratio: 25.9 lb/hp, 11.7 kg/hp.

DIMENSIONS AND WEIGHT dry weight: 3,061 lb, 1,388 kg.

BODY estate car/station wagon; doors: 4 + 1.

Zephyr V6 De Luxe Saloon

See Zephyr V6 Saloon, except for:

PRICE IN GB: £ 1,007.

BODY details: special interior and trimmed body.

Zephyr V6 De Luxe Estate Car

See Zephyr V6 Estate Car, except for:

PRICE IN GB: £ 1,376.

BODY details: special interior and trimmed body.

Zodiac Saloon

PRICE IN GB: £ 1,238.

ENGINE front, 4 stroke; cylinders: 6, Vee-slanted at 60°; bore and stroke: 3.69 x 2.85 in, 93.7 x 72.4 mm; engine capacity: 182.7 cu in, 2,994 cu cm; compression ratio: 8.9; max power (SAE): 144 hp at 4,750 rpm; max torque (SAE): 192

FORD Zephyr De Luxe Saloon

FORD Zodiac Estate Car

FORD The Executive

lb ft, 26.5 kg m at 3,000 rpm; max engine rpm: 5,500; specific power: 48.1 hp/l; cylinder block: cast iron; cylinder head: cast iron; crankshaft bearings: 4; valves: 2 per cylinder, overhead, push-rods and rockers; camshafts: 1, at centre of Vee; lubrication: eccentric or vane-type pump, full flow filter; lubricating system capacity: 9.5 imp pt, 11.4 US pt, 5.4 l; carburation: 1 Weber DFA 2 downdraught twin barrel carburettor; fuel feed: mechanical pump; cooling system: water; cooling system capacity: 20.8 imp pt, 24.9 US pt, 11.8 l.

TRANSMISSION driving wheels: rear; clutch: single dry plate (diaphragm); gearbox: mechanical; gears: 4 + reverse; synchromesh gears: I, II, III, IV; gearbox ratios: I 3.163, II 2.214, III 1.412, IV 1, rev 3.346; gear lever: central; final drive: hypoid bevel; axle ratio: 3.700; width of rims: 5''; tyres: 185 x 14.

PERFORMANCE max speeds: 35 mph, 56 km/h in 1st gear; 50 mph, 80 km/h in 2nd gear; 78 mph, 125 km/h in 3rd gear; 103 mph, 165 km/h in 4th gear; power-weight ratio: 20.5 lb/hp, 9.3 kg/hp; carrying capacity: 1,058 lb, 480 kg; speed in direct drive at 1,000 rpm: 20.1 mph, 32.3 km/h; fuel consumption: 21.6 m/imp gal, 18 m/US gal, 13.1 l x 100 km.

CHASSIS integral; front suspension: independent, by McPherson, coil springs/telescopic damper struts, lower wishbones, anti-roll bar; rear suspension: independent, semi-trailing arms, coil springs, telescopic dampers.

STEERING recirculating ball, servo; turns of steering wheel lock to lock: 4.75.

BRAKES disc (front diameter 9.65 in, 245 mm, rear 9.90 in, 251 mm), dual circuit, servo; area rubbed by linings: front 189.5 sq in, 1,222 sq cm, rear 146.8 sq in, 947 sq cm, total 336.3 sq in, 2,169 sq cm.

ELECTRICAL EQUIPMENT voltage: 12 V; battery: 53 Ah; generator type: alternator, 43 A; ignition distributor: Ford; headlamps: 4.

DIMENSIONS AND WEIGHT wheel base: 115 in, 2,921 mm; front track: 57 in, 1,448 mm; rear track: 58 in, 1,473 mm; overall length: 185.80 in, 4,719 mm; overall width: 71.30 in, 1,811 mm; overall height: 56.60 in, 1,438 mm; ground clearance: 6.40 in, 163 mm; dry weight: 2,939 lb, 1,333 kg; distribution of weight: 56.8% front axle, 43.2% rear axle; turning circle (between walls): 36 ft, 11 m; fuel tank capacity: 15 imp gal, 18 US gal, 68 l.

BODY saloon/sedan; doors: 4; seats: 5; front seats: separate, reclining backrests.

PRACTICAL INSTRUCTIONS fuel: 96 oct petrol; engine sump oil: 7.9 imp pt, 9.5 US pt, 4.5 l, SAE 10W-30, change every 6,000 miles, 9,700 km; gearbox oil: 3.2 imp pt, 3.8 US pt, 1.8 l, SAE 80 EP, no change recommended; final drive oil: 3 imp pt, 3.6 US pt, 1.7 l, SAE 90, no change recommended; greasing: none; tappet clearances: inlet 0.012 in, 0.30 mm, exhaust 0.012 in, 0.30 mm; valve timing: inlet opens 20° before tdc and closes 56° after bdc, exhaust opens 62° before bdc and closes 14° after tdc; normal tyre pressure: front 24 psi, 1.7 atm, rear 24 psi, 1.7 atm.

VARIATIONS

ENGINE 8 compression ratio, max power (SAE) 137 hp at 4,750 rpm, max torque (SAE) 185 lb ft, 25.5 kg m at 2,750 rpm, 45.8 hp/l specific power.

OPTIONAL ACCESSORIES Laycock-de Normanville overdrive (0.988 ratio); Borg-Warner 35/3 automatic gearbox, hydraulic torque convertor and planetary gears with 3 ratios (I 2.460, II 1.460, III 1, rev 2.200), max ratio of convertor at stall 2, possible manual selection, central selector lever, max speeds (I) 42 mph, 67 km/h, (II) 70 mph, 112 km/h, (III) 103 mph, 165 km/h; steering column gear lever; bench front seats; sunshine roof.

Zodiac Estate Car

See Zodiac Saloon, except for:

PRICE IN GB: £ 1,607.

PERFORMANCE power-weight ratio: 21.8 lb/hp, 9.9 kg/hp.

DIMENSIONS AND WEIGHT dry weight: 3,135 lb, 1,422 kg.

BODY estate car/station wagon; doors: 4 + 1.

The Executive

See Zodiac Saloon, except for:

PRICE IN GB: £ 1,496.

TRANSMISSION gearbox: Borg-Warner 35/3 automatic, hydraulic torque convertor and planetary gears with 3 ratios +

THE EXECUTIVE

reverse, max ratio of convertor at stall 2, possible manual selection: gearbox ratios: I 2.460, II 1.460, III 1, rev 2.200; selector lever: central.

PERFORMANCE max speeds: 45 mph, 72 km/h in 1st gear; 76 mph, 122 km/h in 2nd gear; 103 mph, 165 km/h in 3rd gear; power-weight ratio: 21.5 lb/hp, 9.7 kg/hp.

DIMENSIONS AND WEIGHT dry weight: 3,100 lb, 1,406 kg.

OPTIONAL ACCESSORIES 4-speed fully synchronized mechanical gearbox with Laycock-de Normanville overdrive/top (0.988 ratio).

GILBERN   GREAT BRITAIN

Invader Saloon

PRICE IN GB: £ 1,649.

ENGINE front, 4 stroke; cylinders: 6, Vee-slanted at 60°; bore and stroke: 3.69 x 2.85 in, 93.7 x 72.4 mm; engine capacity: 182.7 cu in, 2,994 cu cm; compression ratio: 8.9; max power (DIN): 141 hp at 4,750 rpm; max torque (DIN): 181 lb ft, 25 kg m at 3,000 rpm; max engine rpm: 6,100; specific power: 47.1 hp/l; cylinder block: cast iron; cylinder head: cast iron; crankshaft bearings: 4; valves: 2 per cylinder, overhead, in line, push-rods and rockers; camshafts: 1, at centre of Vee; lubrication: rotary pump, full flow filter; lubricating system capacity: 9.9 imp pt, 11.8 US pt, 5.6 l; carburation: 1 Weber 40 DFA downdraught twin barrel carburettor; fuel feed: mechanical pump; cooling system: water, electric thermostatic fan; cooling system capacity: 16 imp pt, 19.2 US pt, 9.1 l.

TRANSMISSION driving wheels: rear; clutch: single dry plate (diaphragm); gearbox: mechanical; gears: 4 + reverse; synchromesh gears: I, II, III, IV; gearbox ratios: I 3.160, II 2.210, III 1.410, IV 1, rev 3.350; gear lever: central; final drive: hypoid bevel; axle ratio: 3.340; width of rims: 5.5''; tyres: 165 x 15.

PERFORMANCE max speeds: 41 mph, 66 km/h in 1st gear; 58 mph, 93 km/h in 2nd gear; 92 mph, 148 km/h in 3rd gear; 129 mph, 207 km/h in 4th gear; power-weight ratio: 17 lb/hp, 7.7 kg/hp; carrying capacity: 706 lb, 320 kg; speed in direct drive at 1,000 rpm: 21.1 mph, 33.9 km/h; fuel consumption: 25 m/imp gal, 20.8 m/US gal, 11.3 l x 100 km.

CHASSIS tubular; front suspension: independent, wishbones, coil springs, anti-roll bar, telescopic dampers; rear suspension: rigid axle, twin trailing radius arms, transverse Panhard linkage bar, coil springs/telescopic dampers unit.

STEERING rack-and-pinion; turns of steering wheel lock to lock: 2.87.

BRAKES front disc (diameter 11.25 in, 286 mm), rear drum, servo; area rubbed by linings: front 226 sq in, 1,458 sq cm, rear 127 sq in, 819 sq cm, total 353 sq in, 2,227 sq cm.

ELECTRICAL EQUIPMENT voltage: 12 V; battery: 53 Ah; generator type: alternator; headlamps: 2 halogen; fog lamps: 2.

DIMENSIONS AND WEIGHT wheel base: 92.75 in, 2,356 mm; front track: 54 in, 1,371 mm; rear track: 54 in, 1,371 mm; overall length: 159 in, 4,039 mm; overall width: 65 in, 1,651 mm; overall height: 52 in, 1,321 mm; ground clearance: 6 in, 152 mm; dry weight: 2,378 lb, 1,079 kg; turning circle (between walls): 31 ft, 9.4 m; fuel tank capacity: 14 imp gal, 16.6 US gal, 63 l.

BODY coupé in plastic material; doors: 2; seats: 2; details: electrically-controlled windows.

PRACTICAL INSTRUCTIONS fuel: 97 oct petrol; engine sump oil: 9.5 imp pt, 11.4 US pt, 5.4 l, SAE 10W-30, change every 5,000 miles, 8,000 km; gearbox oil: 3.2 imp pt, 3.8 US pt, 1.8 l, SAE 80; final drive oil: 1.5 imp pt, 1.9 US pt, 0.9 l, SAE 90 EP; greasing: every 3,000 miles, 4,800 km, 5 points; tappet clearances: inlet 0.010 in, 0.25 mm, exhaust 0.018 in, 0.46 mm; valve timing: inlet opens 20° before tdc and closes 56° after bdc, exhaust opens 62° before bdc and closes 14° after tdc; normal tyre pressure: front 21 psi, 1.5 atm, rear 24 psi, 1.7 atm.

OPTIONAL ACCESSORIES overdrive; automatic gearbox; sunshine roof.

Invader Estate Car

See Invader Saloon, except for:

PRICE IN GB: —

BODY estate car/station wagon in plastic material; doors: 2 + 1.

GILBERN Invader Saloon

GINETTA G15

GINETTA G21

GINETTA   GREAT BRITAIN

G15

PRICE IN GB: £ 849.

ENGINE rear, 4 stroke; cylinders: 4, in line; bore and stroke: 2.68 x 2.37 in, 68 x 60.3 mm; engine capacity: 53.4 cu in, 875 cu cm; compression ratio: 10; max power (DIN): 55 hp at 6,100 rpm; max torque (DIN): 52 lb ft, 7.2 kg m at 4,300 rpm; max engine rpm: 7,000; specific power: 62.9 hp/l; cylinder block: light alloy; cylinder head: light alloy; crankshaft bearings: 3; valves: 2 per cylinder, overhead, in line, thimble tappets; camshafts: 1, overhead; lubrication: eccentric pump, full flow filter; lubricating system capacity: 6.5 imp pt, 7.8 US pt, 3.7 l; carburation: 2 Stromberg 125 CDS horizontal carburettors; fuel feed: mechanical pump; cooling system: water; cooling system capacity: 12 imp pt, 14.4 US pt, 6.8 l.

TRANSMISSION driving wheels: rear; clutch: single dry plate (diaphragm), hydraulically controlled; gearbox: mechanical; gears: 4 + reverse; synchromesh gears: I, II, III, IV; gearbox ratios: I 4.317, II 1.833, III 1.174, IV 0.852, rev 2.846; gear lever: central; final drive: hypoid bevel; axle ratio: 4.875; width of rims: 4''; tyres: 5.20 x 13.

PERFORMANCE max speeds: 21 mph, 33 km/h in 1st gear; 56 mph, 90 km/h in 2nd gear; 88 mph, 141 km/h in 3rd gear; 101 mph, 162 km/h in 4th gear; power-weight ratio: 20.4 lb/hp, 9.3 kg/hp; carrying capacity: 380 lb, 172 kg; acceleration: standing ¼ mile 18.4 sec, 0-50 mph (0-80 km/h) 8.5 sec; speed in top at 1,000 rpm: 14.9 mph, 23.9 km/h; fuel consumption: 40 m/imp gal, 33.1 m/US gal, 7.1 l x 100 km.

CHASSIS tubular; front suspension: independent, wishbones, coil springs, telescopic dampers; rear suspension: independent, semi-trailing arms, coil springs, telescopic dampers.

STEERING rack-and-pinion; turns of steering wheel lock to lock: 2.75.

BRAKES front disc (diameter 9 in, 229 mm), rear drum.

ELECTRICAL EQUIPMENT voltage: 12 V; battery: 32 Ah; generator type: dynamo, 264 W; ignition distributor: Lucas; headlamps: 2.

DIMENSIONS AND WEIGHT wheel base: 82 in, 2,083 mm; front track: 49 in, 1,245 mm; rear track: 48.75 in, 1,238 mm; overall length: 144.50 in, 3,670 mm; overall width: 57 in, 1,448 mm; overall height: 44.50 in, 1,130 mm; ground clearance: 6 in, 152 mm; dry weight: 1,120 lb, 508 kg; distribution of weight: 45% front axle, 55% rear axle; turning circle (between walls): 33 ft, 10.1 m; fuel tank capacity: 5.9 imp gal, 7.1 US gal, 27 l.

BODY coupé in plastic material; doors: 2; seats: 2.

PRACTICAL INSTRUCTIONS fuel: 97 oct petrol; engine sump oil: 6.5 imp pt, 7.8 US pt, 3.7 l, SAE 20W-50, change every 5,000 miles, 8,000 km; gearbox and final drive oil: 3 imp pt, 3.6 US pt, 1.7 l, SAE 90 EP, change every 10,000 miles, 16,100 km; greasing: every 5,000 miles, 8,000 km, 2 points; tappet clearances: inlet 0.008 in, 0.20 mm, exhaust 0.008 in, 0.20 mm; normal tyre pressure: front 16 psi, 1.1 atm, rear 26 psi, 1.8 atm.

OPTIONAL ACCESSORIES light alloy wheels.

G21

PRICE IN GB: £ 1,845.

ENGINE front, 4 stroke; cylinders: 6, Vee-slanted at 60°; bore and stroke: 3.69 x 2.85 in, 93.7 x 72.4 mm; engine capacity: 182.7 cu in, 2,994 cu cm; compression ratio: 8.9; max power (SAE): 144 hp at 4,750 rpm; max torque (SAE): 192 lb ft, 26.5 kg m at 3,000 rpm; max engine rpm: 5,500; specific power: 48.1 hp/l; cylinder block: cast iron; cylinder head: cast iron; crankshaft bearings: 4; valves: 2 per cylinder, overhead, in line, push-rods and rockers; camshafts: 1, at centre of Vee; lubrication: eccentric or vane-type pump, full flow filter; lubricating system capacity: 10 imp pt, 12 US pt, 5.7 l; carburation: 1 Weber DFA 2 downdraught twin barrel carburettor; fuel feed: mechanical pump; cooling system: water; cooling system capacity: 12.5 imp pt, 15 US pt, 7.1 l.

TRANSMISSION driving wheels: rear; clutch: single dry plate; gearbox: mechanical; gears: 4 + reverse; synchromesh gears: I, II, III, IV; gearbox ratios: I 3.163, II 2.214, III 1.412, IV 1, rev 3.346; gear lever: central; final drive: hypoid bevel; axle ratio: 2.880; width of rims: 5.5''; tyres: 165 x 13.

PERFORMANCE max speeds: 45 mph, 72 km/h in 1st gear; 61 mph, 98 km/h in 2nd gear; 98 mph, 157 km/h in 3rd gear; 128 mph, 206 km/h in 4th gear; power-weight ratio: 29.3 lb/hp, 13.3 kg/hp; acceleration: standing ¼ mile 14.9 sec, 0-50 mph (0-80 km/h) 5.5 sec; speed in direct drive at 1,000 rpm: 23.4 mph, 37.6 km/h; fuel consumption: 26 m/imp gal, 21.6 m/US gal, 10.9 l x 100 km.

GILBERN Invader Saloon

GINETTA G15

GINETTA G21

CHASSIS tubular; front suspension: independent, wishbones, coil springs, anti-roll bar, telescopic dampers; rear suspension: independent, wishbones, twin trailing longitudinal radius arms, coil springs, telescopic dampers.

STEERING rack-and-pinion; turns of steering wheel lock to lock: 2.75.

BRAKES disc; area rubbed by linings: front 196.9 sq in, 1,270 sq cm, rear 193.2 sq in, 1,246 sq cm, total 390.1 sq in, 2,516 sq cm.

ELECTRICAL EQUIPMENT voltage: 12 V; battery: 57 Ah; generator type: alternator, 50 W; ignition distributor: Autolite; headlamps: 2.

DIMENSIONS AND WEIGHT wheel base: 91 in, 2,311 mm; front track: 50.75 in, 1,289 mm; rear track: 51 in, 1,295 mm; overall length: 156.50 in, 3,975 mm; overall width: 62.99 in, 1,600 mm; overall height: 45.98 in, 1,168 mm; ground clearance: 4.75 in, 121 mm; dry weight: 1,920 lb, 871 kg; distribution of weight: 49% front axle, 51% rear axle; turning circle (between walls): 35 ft, 10.7 m; fuel tank capacity: 10 imp gal, 11.9 US gal, 45 l.

BODY coupé in plastic material; doors: 2; seats: 2.

PRACTICAL INSTRUCTIONS fuel: 96 oct petrol; engine sump oil: 9.5 imp pt, 11.4 US pt, 5.4 l, SAE 20W-50, change every 10,000 miles, 16,100 km; gearbox oil: 3.2 imp pt, 3.8 US pt, 1.8 l, SAE 80 EP, change every 10,000 miles, 16,100 km; final drive oil: 2.8 imp pt, 3.4 US pt, 1.6 l, SAE 90 EP, change every 10,000 miles, 16,100 km; tappet clearances: inlet 0.012 in, 0.30 mm, exhaust 0.018 in, 0.45 mm; valve timing: inlet opens 20° before tdc and closes 56° after bdc, exhaust opens 62° before bdc and closes 14° after tdc; normal tyre pressure: front 22 psi, 1.6 atm, rear 24 psi, 1.7 atm.

OPTIONAL ACCESSORIES Laycock-de Normanville overdrive/top (0.820 ratio); automatic gearbox; reclining backrests; electrically-heated rear window; sunshine roof.

HILLMAN   GREAT BRITAIN

Imp

PRICE IN GB: £ 513.

ENGINE rear, 4 stroke; cylinders: 4, slanted at 45°, in line; bore and stroke: 2.68 x 2.38 in, 68 x 60.4 mm; engine capacity: 53.4 cu in, 875 cu cm; compression ratio: 10; max power (DIN): 37 hp at 4,800 rpm; max torque (DIN): 49 lb ft, 6.7 kg m at 2,600 rpm; max engine rpm: 5,600; specific power: 42.3 hp/l; cylinder block: light alloy, dry liners; cylinder head: light alloy; crankshaft bearings: 3; valves: 2 per cylinder, overhead, in line, thimble tappets; camshafts: 1, overhead; lubrication: eccentric pump, full flow filter; lubricating system capacity: 5.5 imp pt, 6.6 US pt, 3.1 l; carburation: 1 Solex 30 PIH-5 semi-downdraught single barrel carburettor; fuel feed: mechanical pump; cooling system: water; cooling system capacity: 10.9 imp pt, 13.1 US pt, 6.2 l.

TRANSMISSION driving wheels: rear; clutch: single dry plate (diaphragm), hydraulically controlled; gearbox: mechanical; gears: 4 + reverse; synchromesh gears: I, II, III, IV; gearbox ratios: I 3.417, II 1.833, III 1.174, IV 0.852, rev 2.846; gear lever: central; final drive: hypoid bevel; axle ratio: 4.857; width of rims: 4.5''; tyres: 5.50 x 12.

PERFORMANCE max speeds: 21 mph, 33 km/h in 1st gear; 39 mph, 62 km/h in 2nd gear; 61 mph, 98 km/h in 3rd gear; 80 mph, 129 km/h in 4th gear; power-weight ratio: 40 lb/hp, 18.1 kg/hp; carrying capacity: 706 lb, 320 kg; acceleration: 0-50 mph (0-80 km/h) 14.6 sec; speed in top at 1,000 rpm: 15.1 mph, 24.3 km/h; fuel consumption: 43.7 m/imp gal, 36.2 m/US gal, 6.5 l x 100 km.

CHASSIS integral; front suspension: independent, U-shaped swinging semi-axles, coil springs, telescopic dampers; rear suspension: independent, semi-trailing arms, coil springs, telescopic dampers.

STEERING rack-and-pinion; turns of steering wheel lock to lock: 2.63.

BRAKES drum, 2 front leading shoes; area rubbed by linings: total 150.8 sq in, 972 sq cm.

ELECTRICAL EQUIPMENT voltage: 12 V; battery: 32 Ah; generator type: dynamo, 297 W; ignition distributor: Lucas; headlamps: 2.

DIMENSIONS AND WEIGHT wheel base: 82 in, 2,083 mm; front track: 50.50 in, 1,283 mm; rear track: 48 in, 1,219 mm; overall length: 139 in, 3,531 mm; overall width: 60.25 in, 1,530 mm; overall height: 54.50 in, 1,384 mm; ground clearance: 6.50 in, 165 mm; dry weight: 1,480 lb, 671 kg; distribution of weight: 38% front axle, 62% rear axle; turning circle (between walls): 31.5 ft, 9.6 m; fuel tank capacity: 6 imp gal, 7.1 US gal, 27 l.

IMP

BODY saloon/sedan; doors: 2; seats: 4; front seats: separate.

PRACTICAL INSTRUCTIONS fuel: 97 oct petrol; engine sump oil: 5.5 imp pt, 6.6 US pt, 3.1 l, multigrade, change every 5,000 miles, 8,000 km; gearbox and final drive oil: 4.5 imp pt, 5.3 US pt, 2.5 l, SAE 80 EP, no change recommended; tappet clearances: inlet 0.005 in, 0.13 mm, exhaust 0.011 in, 0.28 mm; valve timing: inlet opens 36° before tdc and closes 76° after bdc, exhaust opens 43° before bdc and closes 3° after tdc; normal tyre pressure: front 18 psi, 1.3 atm, rear 30 psi, 2.1 atm.

Imp De Luxe

See Imp, except for:

PRICE IN GB: £ 554.

PERFORMANCE power-weight ratio: 40.2 lb/hp, 18.2 kg/hp.

DIMENSIONS AND WEIGHT dry weight: 1,486 lb, 674 kg.

Super Imp

See Imp, except for:

PRICE IN GB: £ 588.

PERFORMANCE power-weight ratio: 555 lb/hp, 18.6 kg/hp.

DIMENSIONS AND WEIGHT dry weight: 1,518 lb, 688 kg.

Avenger De Luxe

PRICE IN GB: £ 690.

ENGINE front, 4 stroke; cylinders: 4, in line; bore and stroke: 3.09 x 2.53 in, 78.4 x 64.2 mm; engine capacity: 76.2 cu in, 1,248 cu cm; compression ratio: 9.2; max power (DIN): 53 hp at 5,000 rpm; max torque (DIN): 66 lb ft, 9.1 kg m at 3,000 rpm; max engine rpm: 6,700; specific power: 42.5 hp/l; cylinder block: cast iron; cylinder head: cast iron; crankshaft bearings: 5; valves: 2 per cylinder, overhead, in line, push-rods and rockers; camshafts: 1, side; lubrication: rotary pump, full flow filter; lubricating system capacity: 7 imp pt, 8.5 US pt, 4 l; carburation: 1 Zenith-Stromberg 150 CDS carburettor; fuel feed: mechanical pump; cooling system: water; cooling system capacity: 12.9 imp pt, 15.6 US pt, 7.4 l.

TRANSMISSION driving wheels: rear; clutch: single dry plate (diaphragm); gearbox: mechanical; gears: 4 + reverse; synchromesh gears: I, II, III, IV; gearbox ratios: I 3.317, II 2.029, III 1.366, IV 1, rev 3.450; gear lever: central; final drive: hypoid bevel; axle ratio: 4.375; width of rims: 4.5''; tyres: 5.60 x 13.

PERFORMANCE max speeds: 25 mph, 40 km/h in 1st gear; 45 mph, 72 km/h in 2nd gear; 65 mph, 104 km/h in 3rd gear; 84 mph, 135 km/h in 4th gear; power-weight ratio: 34.1 lb/hp, 15.5 kg/hp; carrying capacity: 948 lb, 430 kg; acceleration: 0-50 mph (0-80 km/h) 11.1 sec; speed in direct drive at 1,000 rpm: 15.5 mph, 24.9 km/h; fuel consumption: 34 m/imp gal, 28.3 m/US gal, 8.3 l x 100 km.

CHASSIS integral; front suspension: independent, by McPherson, coil springs/telescopic damper struts, wishbones, anti-roll bar; rear suspension: rigid axle, swinging longitudinal trailing arms, upper oblique torque arms, coil springs, telescopic dampers.

STEERING rack-and-pinion; turns of steering wheel lock to lock: 3.66.

BRAKES front disc (diameter 9.50 in, 241 mm), rear drum; area rubbed by linings: front 164 sq in, 1,058 sq cm, rear 74 sq in, 477 sq cm, total 238 sq in, 1,535 sq cm.

ELECTRICAL EQUIPMENT voltage: 12 V; battery: 33 Ah; generator type: dynamo, 264 W; ignition distributor: Lucas; headlamps: 2.

DIMENSIONS AND WEIGHT wheel base: 98 in, 2,489 mm; front track: 51 in, 1,295 mm; rear track: 51.30 in, 1,303 mm; overall length: 161.40 in, 4,100 mm; overall width: 62.50 in, 1,587 mm; overall height: 56 in, 1,422 mm; ground clearance: 5.50 in, 140 mm; dry weight: 1,809 lb, 821 kg; distribution of weight: 55% front axle, 45% rear axle; turning circle (between walls): 34 ft, 10.4 m; fuel tank capacity: 9 imp gal, 10.8 US gal, 41 l.

BODY saloon/sedan; doors: 4; seats: 4-5; front seats: separate.

PRACTICAL INSTRUCTIONS fuel: 97 oct petrol; engine sump oil: 7 imp pt, 8.5 US pt, 4 l, SAE 20W-50, change every 5,000 miles, 8,000 km; gearbox oil: 3 imp pt, 3.6 US pt,

HILLMAN Super Imp

HILLMAN Avenger Super

HILLMAN Avenger GL

1.7 I, SAE 20W-50, no change recommended; final drive oil: 1.5 imp pt, 1.9 US pt, 0.9 I, SAE 90 EP, no change recommended; greasing: none; tappet clearances: inlet 0.008 in, 0.20 mm, exhaust 0.016 in, 0.40 mm; valve timing: inlet opens 38° before tdc and closes 66° after bdc, exhaust opens 72° before bdc and closes 20° after tdc; normal tyre pressure: front 22 psi, 1.5 atm, rear 24 psi, 1.7 atm.

VARIATIONS

ENGINE bore and stroke 3.39 x 2.53 in, 86 x 64.2 mm, engine capacity 91.4 cu in, 1,498 cu cm, max power (DIN) 63 hp at 5,000 rpm, max torque (DIN) 80 lb ft, 11 kg m at 3,000 rpm, 42.1 hp/l specific power.
TRANSMISSION 3.889 axle ratio.
PERFORMANCE max speeds (I) 30 mph, 48 km/h, (II) 50 mph, 80 km/h, (III) 75 mph, 120 km/h, (IV) 90 mph, 145 km/h, power-weight ratio 28.7 lb/hp, 13 kg/hp, acceleration 0-50 mph (0-80 km/h) 9.1 sec, fuel consumption 32 m/imp gal, 26.7 m/US gal, 8.8 I x 100 km.
ELECTRICAL EQUIPMENT 300 W dynamo.
PRACTICAL INSTRUCTIONS valve timing 35° 69° 69° 23°.

OPTIONAL ACCESSORIES servo brake.

Avenger Super

See Avenger De Luxe, except for:

PRICE IN GB: £ 719.

PERFORMANCE power-weight ratio: 34.2 lb/hp, 15.5 kg/hp.

DIMENSIONS AND WEIGHT dry weight: 1,812 lb, 822 kg.

Avenger GL

See Avenger De Luxe, except for:

PRICE IN GB: £ 806.

ENGINE bore and stroke: 3.39 x 2.53 in, 86 x 64.2 mm; engine capacity: 91.4 cu in, 1,498 cu cm; max power (DIN): 63 hp at 5,000 rpm; max torque (DIN): 80 lb ft, 11 kg m at 3,000 rpm; specific power: 42.1 hp/l.

TRANSMISSION axle ratio: 3.889.

PERFORMANCE max speeds: 30 mph, 48 km/h in 1st gear; 50 mph, 80 km/h in 2nd gear; 75 mph, 120 km/h in 3rd gear; 90 mph, 145 km/h in 4th gear; power-weight ratio: 29.1 lb/hp, 13.2 kg/hp; acceleration: 0-50 mph (0-80 km/h) 9.1 sec.

ELECTRICAL EQUIPMENT generator type: dynamo, 300 W; headlamps: 4.

DIMENSIONS AND WEIGHT dry weight: 1,831 lb, 831 kg.

PRACTICAL INSTRUCTIONS valve timing: inlet opens 35° before tdc and closes 69° after bdc, exhaust opens 69° before bdc and closes 23° after tdc.

VARIATIONS

None.

OPTIONAL ACCESSORIES Borg-Warner 35/3 automatic gearbox, hydraulic torque convertor and planetary gears with 3 ratios (I 2.390, II 1.450, III 1, rev 2.090), max ratio of convertor at stall 2, possible manual selection.

Avenger GT

See Avenger De Luxe, except for:

PRICE IN GB: £ 869.

ENGINE bore and stroke: 3.39 x 2.53 in, 86 x 64.2 mm; engine capacity: 91.4 cu in, 1,498 cu cm; max power (DIN): 75 hp at 5,400 rpm; max torque (DIN): 81 lb ft, 11.2 kg m at 3,750 rpm; specific power: 50.1 hp/l; carburation: 2 Zenith-Stromberg 150 CDS carburettors.

TRANSMISSION axle ratio: 3.890; width of rims: 5''; tyres: 155 x 13.

PERFORMANCE max speeds: 30 mph, 48 km/h in 1st gear; 50 mph, 80 km/h in 2nd gear; 75 mph, 120 km/h in 3rd gear; 98 mph, 157 km/h in 4th gear; power-weight ratio: 24.8 lb/hp, 11.2 kg/hp; acceleration: 0-50 mph (0-80 km/h) 8.9 sec; speed in direct drive at 1,000 rpm: 16.9 mph, 27.2 km/h; fuel consumption: 31 m/imp gal, 25.8 m/US gal, 9.1 I x 100 km.

BRAKES servo (standard).

HILLMAN Super Imp

HILLMAN Avenger GT

HILLMAN Avenger GL

ELECTRICAL EQUIPMENT generator type: alternator, 264 W; headlamps: 4.

DIMENSIONS AND WEIGHT front track: 50.80 in, 1,290 mm; rear track: 51.10 in, 1,298 mm; dry weight: 1,863 lb, 845 kg.

PRACTICAL INSTRUCTIONS tappet clearances: inlet 0.010 in, 0.25 mm, exhaust 0.016 in, 0.40 mm; valve timing: inlet opens 44° before tdc and closes 78° after bdc, exhaust opens 69° before bdc and closes 23° after tdc; normal tyre pressure: front 24 psi, 1.7 atm, rear 24 psi, 1.7 atm.

VARIATIONS

None.

OPTIONAL ACCESSORIES Borg-Warner 35/3 automatic gearbox, hydraulic torque convertor and planetary gears with 3 ratios (I 2.390, II 1.450, III 1, rev 2.090), max ratio of convertor at stall 2, possible manual selection, 3.889 axle ratio.

Hunter De Luxe Saloon

PRICE IN GB: £ 754.

ENGINE front, 4 stroke; cylinders: 4, in line; bore and stroke: 3.21 x 2.82 in, 81.5 x 71.6 mm; engine capacity: 91.3 cu in, 1,496 cu cm; compression ratio: 8.4; max power (DIN): 54 hp at 4,600 rpm; max torque (DIN): 73 lb ft, 10.1 kg m at 2,500 rpm; max engine rpm: 5,500; specific power: 36.1 hp/l; cylinder block: cast iron; cylinder head: cast iron; crankshaft bearings: 5; valves: 2 per cylinder, overhead, in line, push-rods and rockers; camshafts: 1, side; lubrication: eccentric pump, full flow filter; lubricating system capacity: 7.5 imp pt, 8.9 US pt, 4.2 I; carburation: 1 Zenith-Stromberg 150 CDS semi-downdraught carburettor; fuel feed: mechanical pump; cooling system: water; cooling system capacity: 12.6 imp pt, 15 US pt, 7.1 I.

TRANSMISSION driving wheels: rear; clutch: single dry plate (diaphragm), hydraulically controlled; gearbox: mechanical; gears: 4 + reverse; synchromesh gears: I, II, III, IV; gearbox ratios: I 3.352, II 2.139, III 1.391, IV 1, rev 3.568; gear lever: central; final drive: hypoid bevel; axle ratio: 3.890; width of rims: 4.5''; tyres: 5.60 x 13.

PERFORMANCE max speeds: 29 mph, 46 km/h in 1st gear; 45 mph, 72 km/h in 2nd gear; 69 mph, 111 km/h in 3rd gear; 83 mph, 133 km/h in 4th gear; power-weight ratio: 36.1 lb/hp, 16.4 kg/hp; carrying capacity: 882 lb, 400 kg; max gradient in 1st gear: 36.2%; acceleration: 0-50 mph (0-80 km/h) 12.5 sec; speed in direct drive at 1,000 rpm: 17.4 mph, 28 km/h; fuel consumption: 32 m/imp gal, 26.7 m/US gal, 8.8 I x 100 km.

CHASSIS integral; front suspension: independent, coil springs/telescopic damper struts, lower wishbones (trailing links), anti-roll bar; rear suspension: rigid axle, semi-elliptic leafsprings, telescopic dampers.

STEERING recirculating ball; turns of steering wheel lock to lock: 3.75.

BRAKES front disc (diameter 9.61 in, 244 mm), rear drum, servo; area rubbed by linings: front 179 sq in, 1,155 sq cm, rear 99 sq in, 639 sq cm, total 278 sq in, 1,794 sq cm.

ELECTRICAL EQUIPMENT voltage: 12 V; battery: 40 Ah; generator type: dynamo, 297 W; ignition distributor: Lucas; headlamps: 2.

DIMENSIONS AND WEIGHT wheel base: 98.50 in, 2,502 mm; front track: 52 in, 1,321 mm; rear track: 52 in, 1,321 mm; overall length: 168 in, 4,267 mm; overall width: 63.50 in, 1,613 mm; overall height: 56 in, 1,422 mm; ground clearance: 6.73 in, 171 mm; dry weight: 1,952 lb, 885 kg; distribution of weight: 55% front axle, 45% rear axle; turning circle (between walls): 36 ft, 11 m; fuel tank capacity: 10 imp gal, 11.9 US gal, 45. I.

BODY saloon/sedan; doors: 4; seats: 4-5; front seats: separate.

PRACTICAL INSTRUCTIONS fuel: 97 oct petrol; engine sump oil: 7 imp pt, 8.5 US pt, 4 I, SAE 20W-50, change every 5,000 miles, 8,000 km; gearbox oil: 3.5 imp pt, 4.2 US pt, 2 I, SAE 20W-50, no change recommended; final drive oil: 1.8 imp pt, 2.1 US pt, 1 I, SAE 90 EP, no change recommended; greasing: none; tappet clearance: inlet 0.012 in, 0.30 mm, exhaust 0.014 in, 0.36 mm; valve timing: inlet opens 37° beore tdc and closes 64° after bdc, exhaust opens 67° before bdc and closes 22° after tdc; normal tyre pressure: front 24 psi, 1.7 atm, rear 24 psi, 1.7 atm.

OPTIONAL ACCESSORIES Borg-Warner 35/3 automatic gearbox, hydraulic torque convertor and planetary gears with 3 ratios (I 2.393, II 1.450, III 1, rev 2.094), max ratio of convertor at stall 1.9, max speeds (I) 42 mph, 67 km/h, (II) 70 mph, 112 km/h, (III) 86 mph, 138 km/h, with stroke 3.25 in, 82.6 mm, engine capacity 105.3 cu in, 1,725 cu cm, max power (DIN) 61 hp at 4,700 rpm, max torque (DIN) 85 lb ft, 11.7 kg m at 2,600 rpm, max engine rpm 5,800.

Hunter De Luxe Estate Car

See Hunter De Luxe Saloon, except for:

PRICE IN GB: £ 855.

TRANSMISSION axle ratio: 4.222; tyres: 6.00 x 13.

PERFORMANCE max speeds: 26 mph, 42 km/h in 1st gear; 41 mph, 66 km/h in 2nd gear; 64 mph, 103 km/h in 3rd gear; 81 mph, 130 km/h in 4th gear; power-weight ratio: 38.8 lb/hp, 17.6 kg/hp; acceleration: 0-50 mph (0-80 km/h) 12.6 sec; speed in direct drive at 1,000 rpm: 16.4 mph, 26.4 km/h.

DIMENSIONS AND WEIGHT overall length: 171 in, 4,343 mm; dry weight: 2,096 lb, 951 kg; distribution of weight: 51% front axle, 49% rear axle.

BODY estate car/station wagon; doors: 4 + 1.

VARIATIONS

ENGINE 1.7-litre, max power (DIN) 61 hp at 4,700 rpm.

Hunter Super

PRICE IN GB: £ 812.

ENGINE front, 4 stroke; cylinders: 4, slanted at 10°, in line; bore and stroke: 3.21 x 3.25 in, 81.5 x 82.5 mm; engine capacity: 105.3 cu in, 1,725 cu cm; compression ratio: 8.4; max power (DIN): 61 hp at 4,700 rpm; max torque (DIN): 85 lb ft, 11.7 kg m at 2,600 rpm; max engine rpm: 6,100; specific power: 35.4 hp/l; cylinder block: cast iron; cylinder head: cast iron; crankshaft bearings: 5; valves: 2 per cylinder, overhead, in line, push-rods and rockers; camshafts: 1, side; lubrication: eccentric pump, full flow filter; lubricating system capacity: 7.5 imp pt, 8.9 US pt, 4.2 l; carburation: 1 Zenith-Stromberg 150 CDS single barrel carburettor; fuel feed: mechanical pump; cooling system: water; cooling system capacity: 12.6 imp pt, 15 US pt, 7.1 l.

TRANSMISSION driving wheels: rear; clutch: single dry plate (diaphragm), hydraulically controlled; gearbox: mechanical; gears: 4 + reverse; synchromesh gears: I, II, III, IV; gearbox ratios: I 3.354, II 2.140, III 1.392, IV 1, rev 3.568; gear lever: central; final drive: hypoid bevel; axle ratio: 3.890; width of rims: 4.5''; tyres: 5.60 x 13.

PERFORMANCE max speeds: 31 mph, 50 km/h in 1st gear; 48 mph, 77 km/h in 2nd gear; 75 mph, 120 km/h in 3rd gear; 89 mph, 143 km/h in 4th gear; power-weight ratio: 32.1 lb/hp, 14.6 kg/hp; carrying capacity: 882 lb, 400 kg; acceleration: 0-50 mph (0-80 km/h) 11 sec; speed in direct drive at 1,000 rpm: 17.4 mph, 28 km/h; fuel consumption: 34 m/imp gal, 28.3 m/US gal, 8.3 l x 100 km.

CHASSIS integral; front suspension: independent, coil springs/telescopic damper struts, lower wishbones (trailing links), anti-roll bar; rear suspension: rigid axle, semi-elliptic leafsprings, telescopic dampers.

STEERING recirculating ball; turns of steering wheel lock to lock: 3.75.

BRAKES front disc (diameter 9.61 in, 244 mm), rear drum, servo; area rubbed by linings: front 179 sq in, 1,155 sq cm, rear 99 sq in, 639 sq cm, total 278 sq in, 1,794 sq cm.

ELECTRICAL EQUIPMENT voltage: 12 V; battery: 40 Ah; generator type: dynamo, 297 W; ignition distributor: Lucas; headlamps: 2.

DIMENSIONS AND WEIGHT wheel base: 98.50 in, 2,502 mm; front track: 52 in, 1,321 mm; rear track: 52 in, 1,321 mm; overall length: 168 in, 4,267 mm; overall width: 63.50 in, 1,613 mm; overall height: 56 in, 1,422 mm; ground clearance: 6.73 in, 171 mm; dry weight: 1,961 lb, 889 kg; distribution of weight: 54% front axle, 46% rear axle; turning circle (between walls): 36 ft, 11 m; fuel tank capacity: 10 imp gal, 11.9 US gal, 45 l.

BODY saloon/sedan; doors: 4; seats: 4-5; front seats: separate.

PRACTICAL INSTRUCTIONS fuel: 97 oct petrol; engine sump oil: 7 imp pt, 8.5 US pt, 4 l, SAE 20W-50, change every 5,000 miles, 8,000 km; gearbox oil: 3.5 imp pt, 4.2 US pt, 2 l, SAE 20W-50, no change recommended; final drive oil: 1.8 imp pt, 2.1 US pt, 1 l, SAE 90 EP, no change recommended; greasing: none; tappet clearances: inlet 0.012 in, 0.30 mm, exhaust 0.014 in, 0.36 mm; valve timing: inlet opens 47° before tdc and closes 86° after bdc, exhaust opens 82° before bdc and closes 36° after tdc.

OPTIONAL ACCESSORIES overdrive; Borg-Warner 35/3 automatic gearbox, hydraulic torque convertor and planetary gears with 3 ratios (I 2.393, II 1.450, III 1, rev 2.049), max ratio of convertor at stall 1.94, central selector lever; electrically-heated rear window; reclining backrests.

HILLMAN Hunter Super

HILLMAN Hunter GT

HUMBER Sceptre

Hunter GL Saloon

PRICE IN GB: £ 880.

ENGINE front, 4 stroke; cylinders: 4, slanted at 10°, in line; bore and stroke: 3.21 x 3.25 in, 81.5 x 82.5 mm; engine capacity: 105.3 cu in, 1,725 cu cm; compression ratio: 9.2; max power (DIN): 67 hp at 4,800 rpm; max torque (DIN): 87 lb ft, 12 kg m at 2,800 rpm; max engine rpm: 6,100; specific power: 38.8 hp/l; cylinder block: cast iron; cylinder head: light alloy; crankshaft bearings: 5; valves 2 per cylinder, overhead, in line, push-rods and rockers; camshafts: 1, side; lubrication: eccentric pump, full flow filter; lubricating system capacity: 7.4 imp pt, 8.9 US pt, 4.2 l; carburation: 1 Zenith-Stromberg 150 CDS semi-downdraught single barrel carburettor; fuel feed: mechanical pump; cooling system: water; cooling system capacity: 12.6 imp pt, 15 US pt, 7.1 l.

TRANSMISSION driving wheels: rear; clutch: single dry plate (diaphragm), hydraulically controlled; gearbox: mechanical; gears: 4 + reverse; synchromesh gears: I, II, III, IV; gearbox ratios: I 3.354, II 2.140, III 1.392, IV 1, rev 3.568; gear lever: central; final drive: hypoid bevel; axle ratio: 3.700; width of rims: 4.5''; tyres: 5.60 x 13.

PERFORMANCE max speeds: 33 mph, 53 km/h in 1st gear; 52 mph, 84 km/h in 2nd gear; 80 mph, 129 km/h in 3rd gear; 90 mph, 145 km/h in 4th gear; power-weight ratio: 29.1 lb/hp, 13.2 kg/hp; carrying capacity: 882 lb, 400 kg; acceleration: 0-50 mph (0-80 km/h) 9.9 sec; speed in direct drive at 1,000 rpm: 18.3 mph, 29.5 km/h; fuel consumption: 34 m/imp gal, 28.3 m/US gal, 8.3 l x 100 km.

CHASSIS integral; front suspension: independent, coil springs/telescopic damper struts, lower wishbones (trailing links), anti-roll bar; rear suspension: rigid axle, semi-elliptic leafsprings, telescopic dampers.

STEERING recirculating ball; turns of steering wheel lock to lock: 3.75.

BRAKES front disc (diameter 9.61 in, 244 mm), rear drum, servo; area rubbed by linings: front 179 sq in, 1,154 sq cm, rear 99 sq in, 638 sq cm, total 278 sq in, 1,792 sq cm.

ELECTRICAL EQUIPMENT voltage: 12 V; battery: 40 Ah; generator type: alternator, 408 W; ignition distributor: Lucas; headlamps: 2.

DIMENSIONS AND WEIGHT wheel base: 98.50 in, 2,502 mm; front track: 52.01 in, 1,321 mm; rear track: 52.01 in, 1,321 mm; overall length: 168 in, 4,267 mm; overall width: 63.50 in, 1,613 mm; overall height: 56 in, 1,422 mm; ground clearance: 6.73 in, 171 mm; dry weight: 1,948 lb, 884 kg; distribution of weight: 54% front axle, 46% rear axle; turning circle (between walls): 36.8 ft, 11.2 m; fuel tank capacity: 10 imp gal, 11.9 US gal, 45 l.

BODY saloon/sedan; doors: 4; seats: 4-5; front seats: separate, reclining backrests.

PRACTICAL INSTRUCTIONS fuel: 97 oct petrol; engine sump oil: 7.5 imp pt, 8.9 US pt, 4.2 l, multigrade, change every 5,000 miles, 8,000 km; gearbox oil: 3.5 imp pt, 4.2 US pt, 2 l, multigrade, no change recommended; final drive oil: 1.7 imp pt, 2.1 US pt, 1 l, SAE 90 EP, no change recommended; greasing: none; tappet clearances: inlet 0.012 in, 0.30 mm, exhaust 0.014 in, 0.36 mm; valve timing: inlet opens 51° before tdc and closes 89° after bdc, exhaust opens 85° before bdc and closes 40° after tdc; normal tyre pressure: front 24 psi, 1.7 atm, rear 24 psi, 1.7 atm.

OPTIONAL ACCESSORIES Laycock overdrive on III and IV (0.803 ratio), 3.890 axle ratio; Borg-Warner 35/3 automatic gearbox, hydraulic torque convertor and planetary gears with 3 ratios (I 2.393, II 1.450, III 1, rev 2.094), max ratio of convertor at stall 1.9, steering column selector lever.

Hunter GL Estate Car

See Hunter GL Saloon, except for:

PRICE IN GB: £ 981.

TRANSMISSION axle ratio: 3.890; tyres: 6.00 x 13.

PERFORMANCE max speeds: 32 mph, 51 km/h in 1st gear; 50 mph, 80 km/h in 2nd gear; 76 mph, 122 km/h in 3rd gear; 90 mph, 145 km/h in 4th gear; power-weight ratio: 31.4 lb/hp, 14.2 kg/hp; acceleration: 0-50 mph (0-80 km/h) 11.2 sec; speed in direct drive at 1,000 rpm: 17.8 mph, 28.6 km/h.

DIMENSIONS AND WEIGHT overall length: 171 in, 4,343 mm; dry weight: 2,107 lb, 956 kg; distribution of weight: 50% front axle, 50% rear axle.

BODY estate car/station wagon; doors: 4 + 1.

Hunter GT

PRICE IN GB: £ 890.

ENGINE front, 4 stroke; cylinders: 4, slanted at 10°, in line; bore and stroke: 3.21 x 3.25 in, 81.5 x 82.5 mm; engine capacity: 105.3 cu in, 1,725 cu cm; compression ratio: 9.2; max power (DIN): 79 hp at 5,200 rpm; max torque (DIN): 91 lb ft, 12.5 kg m at 3,800 rpm; max engine rpm: 6,400; specific power: 45.8 hp/l; cylinder block: cast iron; cylinder head: light alloy; crankshaft bearings: 5; valves: 2 per cylinder, overhead, in line, push-rods and rockers; camshafts: 1, side; lubrication: eccentric pump, full flow filter; lubricating system capacity: 7.5 imp pt, 8.9 US pt, 4.2 l; carburation: 2 Zenith-Stromberg 150 CDS semi-downdraught carburettors; fuel feed: mechanical pump; cooling system: water; cooling system capacity: 13.7 imp pt, 16.5 US pt, 7.8 l.

TRANSMISSION driving wheels: rear; clutch: single dry plate (diaphragm), hydraulically controlled; gearbox: mechanical; gears: 4 + reverse; synchromesh gears: I, II, III, IV; gearbox ratios: I 3.353, II 2.141, III 1.392, IV 1, rev 3.568; gear lever: central; final drive: hypoid bevel; axle ratio: 3.700; width of rims: 5''; tyres: 165 x 13.

PERFORMANCE max speeds: 33 mph, 53 km/h in 1st gear; 51 mph, 82 km/h in 2nd gear; 79 mph, 127 km/h in 3rd gear; 100 mph, 161 km/h in 4th gear; power-weight ratio: 25.4 lb/hp, 11.5 kg/hp; carrying capacity: 871 lb, 395 kg; speed in direct drive at 1,000 rpm: 18.3 mph, 29.3 km/h; fuel consumption: 34 m/imp gal, 28.3 m/US gal, 8.3 l x 100 km.

CHASSIS integral; front suspension: independent, coil springs/telescopic damper struts, lower wishbones (trailing links), anti-roll bar; rear suspension: rigid axle, semi-elliptic leafsprings, telescopic dampers.

STEERING recirculating ball; turns of steering wheel lock to lock: 3.75.

BRAKES front disc (diameter 9.60 in, 244 mm), rear drum, servo; area rubbed by linings: front 175 sq in, 1,129 sq cm, rear 97 sq in, 626 sq cm, total 272 sq in, 1,755 sq cm.

ELECTRICAL EQUIPMENT voltage: 12 V; battery: 40 Ah; generator type: alternator, 408 W; ignition distributor: Lucas; headlamps: 2.

DIMENSIONS AND WEIGHT wheel base: 98.50 in, 2,502 mm; front track: 52.50 in, 1,334 mm; rear track: 52.50 in, 1,334 mm; overall length: 168 in, 4,267 mm; overall width: 63.50 in, 1,613 mm; overall height: 56 in, 1,422 mm; ground clearance: 6.50 in, 165 mm; dry weight: 2,011 lb, 912 kg; fuel tank capacity: 10 imp gal, 11.9 US gal, 45 l.

BODY saloon/sedan; doors: 4; seats: 4-5; front seats: separate.

PRACTICAL INSTRUCTIONS fuel: 96-98 oct petrol; engine sump oil: 7.5 imp pt, 8.9 US pt, 4.2 l, SAE 20W-50, change every 5,000 miles, 8,000 km; gearbox oil: 3.5 imp pt, 4.2 US pt, 2 l, SAE 20W-50, no change recommended; final drive oil: 1.7 imp pt, 2.1 US pt, 1 l, SAE 90 EP, no change recommended; greasing: none; tappet clearances: inlet 0.012 in, 0.30 mm, exhaust 0.014 in, 0.36 mm; valve timing: inlet opens 57° before tdc and closes 91° after bdc, exhaust opens 90° before bdc and closes 44° after tdc; normal tyre pressure: front 24 psi, 1.7 atm, rear 24 psi, 1.7 atm.

OPTIONAL ACCESSORIES Laycock overdrive on III and IV (0.803 ratio) with 3.890 axle ratio; reclining backrests; electrically-heated rear window.

HILLMAN Hunter Super

HILLMAN Hunter GT

HUMBER Sceptre

HUMBER   GREAT BRITAIN

Sceptre

PRICE IN GB: £ 1,075.

ENGINE front, 4 stroke; cylinders: 4, vertical, in line; bore and stroke: 3.21 x 3.25 in, 81.5 x 82.5 mm; engine capacity: 105.3 cu in, 1,725 cu cm; compression ratio: 9.2; max power (DIN): 79 hp at 5,200 rpm; max torque (DIN): 91 lb ft, 12.5 kg m at 3,800 rpm; max engine rpm: 6,400; specific power: 45.8 hp/l; cylinder block: cast iron; cylinder head: light alloy; crankshaft bearings: 5; valves: 2 per cylinder, overhead, in line, push-rods and rockers; camshafts: 1, side; lubrication: eccentric pump, full flow filter; lubricating system capacity: 7.5 imp pt, 8.9 US pt, 4.2 l; carburation: 2 Zenith-Stromberg 150 CDS semi-downdraught carburettors; fuel feed: mechanical pump; cooling system: water; cooling system capacity: 13.7 imp pt, 16.5 US pt, 7.8 l.

TRANSMISSION driving wheels: rear; clutch: single dry plate (diaphragm), hydraulically controlled; gearbox: mechanical; gears: 4 + reverse and overdrive on III and IV; synchromesh gears: I, II, III, IV; gearbox ratios: I 3.352, II 2.139, III 1.391, IV 1, overdrive/top 0.802, rev 3.568; gear lever: central; final drive: hypoid bevel; axle ratio: 3.890; width of rims: 4.5''; tyres: 6.00 x 13.

PERFORMANCE max speeds: 33 mph, 53 km/h in 1st gear; 51 mph, 82 km/h in 2nd gear; 79 mph, 127 km/h in 3rd

SCEPTRE

gear; 97 mph, 156 km/h in 4th gear; power-weight ratio: 27.8 lb/hp, 12.6 kg/hp; carrying capacity: 882 lb, 400 kg; acceleration: 0-50 mph (0-80 km/h) 9 sec; speed in top at 1,000 rpm: 17.8 mph, 28.7 km/h; fuel consumption: 29.7 m/imp gal, 24.8 m/US gal, 9.5 l x 100 km.

CHASSIS integral: front suspension: independent, coil springs/telescopic damper struts, lower wishbones (trailing links), anti-roll bar; rear suspension: rigid axle, semi-elliptic leafsprings, telescopic dampers.

STEERING recirculating ball, adjustable steering wheel; turns of steering wheel lock to lock: 3.75.

BRAKES front disc (diameter 9.60 in, 244 mm), rear drum, servo; area rubbed by linings: total 278 sq in, 1,793 sq cm.

ELECTRICAL EQUIPMENT voltage: 12 V; battery: 40 Ah; generator type: alternator, 35 A; ignition distributor: Lucas; headlamps: 4.

DIMENSIONS AND WEIGHT wheel base: 98.50 in, 2,502 mm; front track: 52 in, 1,321 mm; rear track: 52 in, 1,321 mm; overall length: 169.50 in, 4,305 mm; overall width: 64.75 in, 1,645 mm; overall height: 56 in, 1,422 mm; ground clearance: 6.75 in, 171 mm; dry weight: 2,187 lb, 992 kg; distribution of weight: 55% front axle, 45% rear axle; turning circle (between walls): 36 ft, 11 m; fuel tank capacity: 10 imp gal, 11.9 US gal, 45 l.

BODY saloon/sedan; doors: 4; seats: 5; front seats: separate, reclining backrests.

PRACTICAL INSTRUCTIONS fuel: 98 oct petrol; engine sump oil: 7.5 imp pt, 8.9 US pt, 4.2 l, SAE 20W-50, change every 5,000 miles, 8,000 km; gearbox oil: 4.5 imp pt, 5.3 US pt, 2.5 l, SAE 20W-50, no change recommended; final drive oil: 1.8 imp pt, 2.1 US pt, 1 l, SAE 80-90 EP, no change recommended; greasing: none; tappet clearances: inlet 0.012 in, 0.30 mm, exhaust 0.014 in, 0.36 mm; valve timing: inlet opens 57° before tdc and closes 91° after bdc, exhaust opens 90° before bdc and closes 44° after tdc; normal tyre pressure: front 25 psi, 1.8 atm, rear 25 psi, 1.8 atm.

OPTIONAL ACCESSORIES Borg-Warner 35/3 automatic gearbox, hydraulic torque convertor and planetary gears with 3 ratios (I 2.390, II 1.450, III 1, rev 2.090), max ratio of convertor at stall 1.9, central selector level, 3.700 axle ratio; 57 Ah battery.

JAGUAR   GREAT BRITAIN

XJ6 2.8-litre Standard Saloon

PRICE IN GB: £ 1,745.

ENGINE front, 4 stroke; cylinders: 6, vertical, in line; bore and stroke: 3.27 x 3.39 in, 83.1 x 86.1 mm; engine capacity: 170.2 cu in, 2,790 cu cm; compression ratio: 9; max power (SAE): 180 hp at 6,000 rpm; max torque (SAE): 182 lb ft, 25.1 kg m at 3,750 rpm; max engine rpm: 6,800; specific power: 64.5 hp/l; cylinder block: cast iron, dry liners; cylinder head: light alloy, hemispherical combustion chambers; crankshaft bearings: 7; valves: 2 per cylinder, overhead, Vee-slanted at 70°, thimble tappets; camshafts: 2, overhead; lubrication: mechanical pump, full flow filter; lubricating system capacity: 14.4 imp pt, 17.3 US pt, 8.2 l; carburation: 2 SU type HD 8 horizontal carburettors; fuel feed: electric pump; cooling system: water, thermostatic fan; cooling system capacity: 29.9 imp pt, 35.9 US pt, 17 l.

TRANSMISSION driving wheels: rear; clutch: single dry plate (diaphragm), hydraulically controlled; gearbox: mechanical; gears: 4 + reverse; synchromesh gears: I, II, III, IV; gearbox ratios: I 2.933, II 1.905, III 1.389, IV 1, rev 3.378; gear lever: central; final drive: hypoid bevel; axle ratio: 4.090; width of rims: 6''; tyres: E70 VR x 15.

PERFORMANCE max speeds: 41 mph, 66 km/h in 1st gear; 63 mph, 101 km/h in 2nd gear; 87 mph, 140 km/h in 3rd gear; 118 mph, 190 km/h in 4th gear; power-weight ratio: 18.7 lb/hp, 8.5 kg/hp; carrying capacity: 882 lb, 400 kg; acceleration: standing ¼ mile 17.7 sec, 0-50 mph (0-80 km/h) 8.5 sec; speed in direct drive at 1,000 rpm: 17.8 mph, 28.6 km/h; fuel consumption: 21.5 m/imp gal, 17.8 m/US gal, 13.2 l x 100 km.

CHASSIS integral, front and rear auxiliary frames; front suspension: independent, wishbones, lower trailing links, coil springs, anti-roll bar, telescopic dampers; rear suspension: independent, wishbones, semi-axles as upper arm, trailing lower radius arms, 4 coil springs, 4 telescopic dampers.

STEERING rack-and-pinion, adjustable steering wheel; turns of steering wheel lock to lock: 3.50.

JAGUAR XJ6 2.8-litre De Luxe Saloon

JAGUAR 420 G Limousine

JAGUAR 4.2-litre E Type Coupé

BRAKES disc (front diameter 11.80 in, 300 mm, rear 10.40 in, 264 mm), dual circuit, servo; area rubbed by linings: front 242.4 sq in, 1,563 sq cm, rear 189.6 sq in, 1,223 sq cm, total 432 sq in, 2,786 sq cm.

ELECTRICAL EQUIPMENT voltage: 12 V; battery: 51 Ah; generator type: alternator, 45 A; ignition distributor: Lucas; headlamps: 4.

DIMENSIONS AND WEIGHT wheel base: 108.87 in, 2,765 mm; front track: 58 in, 1,473 mm; rear track: 58.33 in, 1,481 mm; overall length: 189.60 in, 4,816 mm; overall width: 69.75 in, 1,772 mm; overall height: 52.87 in, 1,343 mm; ground clearance: 6 in, 152 mm; dry weight: 3,389 lb, 1,537 kg; distribution of weight: 52% front axle, 48% rear axle; turning circle (between walls): 37 ft, 11.3 m; fuel tank capacity: 23 imp gal, 27.5 US gal, 104 l.

BODY saloon/sedan; doors: 4; seats: 5; front seats: separate, reclining backrests.

PRACTICAL INSTRUCTIONS fuel: 98-100 oct petrol; engine sump oil: 13.5 imp pt, 16.1 US pt, 7.6 l, SAE 10W-40 (winter) 20W-50 (summer), change every 6,000 miles, 9,700 km; gearbox oil: 2.5 imp pt, 3 US pt, 1.4 l, SAE 30, change every 12,000 miles, 19,300 km; final drive oil: 2.7 imp pt, 3.2 US pt, 1.5 l, SAE 90, change every 12,000 miles, 19,300 km; greasing: none; tappet clearances: inlet 0.004 in, 0.10 mm, exhaust 0.006 in, 0.15 mm; valve timing: inlet opens 15° before tdc and closes 57° after bdc, exhaust opens 57° before bdc and closes 15° after tdc; normal tyre pressure: front 25 psi, 1.8 atm, rear 25 psi, 1.8 atm.

VARIATIONS

ENGINE 8 compression ratio.

OPTIONAL ACCESSORIES Laycock-de Normanville overdrive/top (0.779 ratio), 3.540 axle ratio; Borg-Warner automatic gearbox, hydraulic torque convertor and planetary gears with 3 ratios (I 2.389, II 1.450, III 1, rev 2.089), max ratio of convertor at stall 2, possible manual selection, max speeds (I) 51 mph, 82 km/h, (II) 83 mph, 133 km/h, (III) 118 mph, 190 km/h; power-assisted steering variable ratio; electrically-heated rear window.

XJ6 2.8-litre De Luxe Saloon

See XJ6 2.8-litre Standard Saloon, except for:

PRICE IN GB: £ 1,823.

STEERING variable ratio servo (standard).

BODY details: luxury interior.

OPTIONAL ACCESSORIES electrically-controlled windows; air-conditioning system.

XJ6 4.2-litre De Luxe Saloon

See XJ6 2.8-litre Standard Saloon, except for:

PRICE IN GB: £ 2,059.
PRICE IN USA: $ 6,585 (with automatic gearbox).

ENGINE bore and stroke: 3.63 x 4.17 in, 92.1 x 105.9 mm; engine capacity: 258.4 cu in, 4,235 cu cm; compression ratio: 8; max power (SAE): 265 hp at 5,400 rpm; max torque (SAE): 283 lb ft, 39 kg m at 4,000 rpm; max engine rpm: 6,000; specific power: 62.6 hp/l; carburation: 3 SU type HD 8 horizontal carburettors; cooling system capacity: 25.3 imp pt, 30.4 US pt, 14.4 l.

TRANSMISSION axle ratio: 3.310.

PERFORMANCE max speeds: 44 mph, 71 km/h in 1st gear; 67 mph, 108 km/h in 2nd gear; 92 mph, 148 km/h in 3rd gear; 124 mph, 200 km/h in 4th gear; power-weight ratio: 13.2 lb/hp, 6 kg/hp; acceleration: standing ¼ mile 16.5 sec, 0-50 mph (0-80 km/h) 6.6 sec; speed in direct drive at 1,000 rpm: 21.4 mph, 34.4 km/h; fuel consumption: 17.9 m/imp gal, 14.9 m/US gal, 15.8 l x 100 km.

STEERING variable ratio servo (standard).

ELECTRICAL EQUIPMENT battery: 60 Ah.

DIMENSIONS AND WEIGHT dry weight: 3,444 lb, 1,562 kg.

VARIATIONS

ENGINE 7 or 9 compression ratio.

OPTIONAL ACCESSORIES Borg-Warner automatic gearbox, hydraulic torque convertor and planetary gears with 3 ratios (I 2.401, II 1.458, III 1, rev 2), max ratio of convertor at stall 2, possible manual selection, max speeds (I) 53 mph, 85 km/h, (II) 88 mph, 141 km/h, (III) 124 mph, 200 km/h ;electrically-controlled windows; air-conditioning system.

JAGUAR XJ6 2.8-litre Saloon

JAGUAR XJ6 4.2-litre De Luxe Saloon

JAGUAR 4.2-litre E Type Convertible

420 G Saloon

PRICE IN GB: £ 2,090.

ENGINE front, 4 stroke; cylinders: 6, vertical, in line; bore and stroke: 3.63 x 4.17 in, 92.1 x 105.9 mm; engine capacity: 258.4 cu in, 4,235 cu cm; compression ratio: 8; max power (SAE): 265 hp at 5,400 rpm; max torque (SAE): 283 lb ft, 39 kg m at 4,000 rpm; max engine rpm: 5,500; specific power: 62.6 hp/l; cylinder block: cast iron, dry liners; cylinder head: light alloy, hemispherical combustion chambers; crankshaft bearings: 7; valves: 2 per cylinder, Vee-slanted at 70°, thimble tappets; camshafts: 2, overhead; lubrication: mechanical pump, full flow filter; lubricating system capacity: 14.4 imp pt, 17.3 US pt, 8.2 l; carburation: 3 SU type HD 8 horizontal carburettors; fuel feed: 2 electric pumps; cooling system: water; cooling system capacity: 25.3 imp pt, 30.4 US pt, 14.4 l.

TRANSMISSION driving wheels: rear; clutch: single dry plate (diaphragm), hydraulically controlled; gearbox: mechanical; gears: 4 + reverse; synchromesh gears: I, II, III, IV; gearbox ratios: I 3.040, II 1.972, III 1.328, IV 1, rev 3.489; gear lever: central; final drive: hypoid bevel; axle ratio: 3.540; width of rims: 6''; tyres: 205 x 14.

PERFORMANCE max speeds: 42 mph, 67 km/h in 1st gear; 65 mph, 104 km/h in 2nd gear; 97 mph, 156 km/h in 3rd gear; 120 mph, 193 km/h in 4th gear; power-weight ratio: 14.8 lb/hp, 6.7 kg/hp; carrying capacity: 1,058 lb, 480 kg; acceleration: standing ¼ mile 16.6 sec, 0-50 mph (0-80 km/h) 7 sec; speed in direct drive at 1,000 rpm: 21.4 mph, 34.4 km/h; fuel consumption: 17.1 m/imp gal, 14.3 m/US gal, 16.5 l x 100 km.

CHASSIS integral, front and rear auxiliary frames; front suspension: independent, wishbones, coil springs, anti-roll bar, telescopic dampers; rear suspension: independent, wishbones, semi-axles as upper arm, trailing lower radius arms, anti-roll bar, 4 coil springs, 4 telescopic dampers.

STEERING recirculating ball, adjustable steering wheel, variable ratio servo; turns of steering wheel lock to lock: 2.75.

BRAKES disc (front diameter 10.90 in, 277 mm, rear 10 in, 254 mm), dual circuit, servo.

ELECTRICAL EQUIPMENT voltage: 12 V; battery: 60 Ah; generator type: alternator, 45 A; ignition distributor: Lucas; headlamps: 4.

DIMENSIONS AND WEIGHT wheel base: 120 in, 3,048 mm; front track: 58 in, 1,473 mm; rear track: 58 in, 1,473 mm; overall length: 202 in, 5,131 mm; overall width: 76.30 in, 1,938 mm; overall height: 54.50 in, 1,384 mm; ground clearance: 6.50 in, 165 mm; dry weight: 3,947 lb, 1,790 kg; distribution of weight: 54% front axle, 46% rear axle; turning circle (between walls): 39 ft, 11.9 m; fuel tank capacity: 20 imp gal, 24 US gal, 91 l.

BODY saloon/sedan; doors: 4; seats: 6; front seats: separate, reclining backrests.

PRACTICAL INSTRUCTIONS fuel: 98 oct petrol; engine sump oil: 13.6 imp pt, 16.3 US pt, 7.7 l, SAE 20 (winter) 30 (summer), change every 3,000 miles, 4,800 km; gearbox oil: 2.6 imp pt, 3.2 US pt, 1.5 l, SAE 30; final drive oil: 2.8 imp pt, 3.4 US pt, 1.6 l, SAE 90; greasing: every 6,000 miles, 9,700 km, 6 points, every 2,500 miles, 4,000 km, 12 points; tappet clearances: inlet 0.004 in, 0.10 mm, exhaust 0.006 in, 0.15 mm; valve timing: inlet opens 15° before tdc and closes 57° after bdc, exhaust opens 57° before bdc and closes 15° after tdc; normal tyre pressure: front 30 psi, 2.1 atm, rear 28 psi, 2 atm.

VARIATIONS

ENGINE 7 or 9 compression ratio.

OPTIONAL ACCESSORIES Laycock-de Normanville overdrive/top (0.778 ratio), 3.770 axle ratio, max speed in overdrive/top 123 mph, 198 km/h; Borg-Warner 8 automatic gearbox, hydraulic torque convertor and planetary gears with 3 ratios (I 2.401, II 1.458, III 1, rev 2), max ratio of convertor at stall 2, max speeds (I) 53 mph, 85 km/h, (II) 88 mph, 141 km/h, (III) 120 mph, 193 km/h; air-conditioning system; electrically-controlled windows; electrically-heated rear window.

420 G Limousine

See 420 G Saloon, except for:

PRICE IN GB: £ 2,259.

BODY details: glass partition.

4.2-litre E Type Coupé

PRICE IN GB: £ 1,886.
PRICE IN USA: $ 5,725.

ENGINE front, 4 stroke; cylinders: 6, vertical, in line; bore

4.2-LITRE E TYPE COUPÉ

and stroke: 3.63 x 4.17 in, 92.1 x 106 mm; engine capacity: 258.4 cu in, 4,235 cu cm; compression ratio: 9; max power (SAE): 265 hp at 5,400 rpm; max torque (SAE): 283 lb ft, 39.1 kg m at 4,000 rpm; max engine rpm: 5,500; specific power: 62.6 hp/l; cylinder block: cast iron, dry liners; cylinder head: light alloy, hemispherical combustion chambers; crankshaft bearings: 7; valves: 2 per cylinder, overhead, Vee-slanted at 70°, thimble tappets; camshafts: 2, overhead; lubrication: mechanical pump, full flow filter; lubricating system capacity: 15.7 imp pt, 18.8 US pt, 8.9 l; carburation: 3 SU type HD 8 carburettors; fuel feed: electric pump; cooling system: water, automatic thermostatic fan; cooling system capacity: 22 imp pt, 26.4 US pt, 12.5 l.

TRANSMISSION driving wheels: rear; clutch: single dry plate (diaphragm), hydraulically controlled; gearbox: mechanical; gears: 4 + reverse, synchromesh gears: I, II, III, IV; gearbox ratios: I 2.935, II 1.906, III 1.391, IV 1, rev 3.452; gear lever: central; final drive: hypoid bevel, limited slip; axle ratio: 3.070; width of rims: 5''; tyres: 185 x 15.

PERFORMANCE max speeds: 58 mph, 93 km/h in 1st gear; 89 mph, 143 km/h in 2nd gear; 122 mph, 196 km/h in 3rd gear; 153 mph, 246 km/h in 4th gear; power-weight ratio: 10.6 lb/hp, 4.8 kg/hp; carrying capacity: 441 lb, 200 kg; acceleration: standing ¼ mile 15 sec, 0-50 mph (0-80 km/h) 5.3 sec; speed in direct drive at 1,000 rpm: 23.2 mph, 37.3 km/h; fuel consumption: 18.8 m/imp gal, 15.7 m/US gal, 15 l x 100 km.

CHASSIS integral, front tubular and rear auxiliary frames; front suspension: independent, wishbones, longitudinal torsion bars, anti-roll bar, telescopic dampers; rear suspension: independent, wishbones, semi-axle as upper arm, trailing lower radius arms, 4 coil springs, 4 telescopic dampers.

STEERING rack-and-pinion; turns of steering wheel lock to lock: 2.50.

BRAKES disc (front diameter 10.98 in, 279 mm, rear 10 in, 254 mm), dual circuit, servo.

ELECTRICAL EQUIPMENT voltage: 12 V; battery: 60 Ah; generator type: alternator, 45 A; ignition distributor: Lucas; headlamps: 2.

DIMENSIONS AND WEIGHT wheel base: 96 in, 2,439 mm; front track: 50 in, 1,270 mm; rear track: 50 in, 1,270 mm; overall length: 175.30 in, 4,453 mm; overall width: 65.25 in, 1,657 mm; overall height: 48 in, 1,219 mm; ground clearance: 5.50 in, 139 mm; dry weight: 2,790 lb, 1,265 kg; distribution of weight: 49.6% front axle, 50.4% rear axle; turning circle (between walls): 39.5 ft, 12 m; fuel tank capacity: 14 imp gal, 16.9 US gal, 64 l.

BODY coupé; doors: 2; seats: 2; front seats: separate.

PRACTICAL INSTRUCTIONS fuel: 95-100 oct petrol; engine sump oil: 15 imp pt, 18 US pt, 8.5 l, SAE 20 (winter) 30 (summer), change every 6,000 miles, 9,700 km; gearbox oil: 2.5 imp pt, 3 US pt, 1.4 l, SAE 30, change every 12,000 miles, 19,300 km; final drive oil: 2.8 imp pt, 3.4 US pt, 1.6 l, SAE 90, change every 10,000 miles, 16,100 km; greasing: every 2,500 miles, 4,000 km, 15 points, every 5,000 miles, 8,000 km, 6 points, every 12,000 miles, 19,300 km, 4 points; tappet clearances: inlet 0.004 in, 0.10 mm, exhaust 0.006 in, 0.15 mm; valve timing: inlet opens 15° before tdc and closes 57° after bdc, exhaust opens 57° before bdc and closes 15° after tdc; normal tyre pressure: front 30 psi, 2.1 atm, rear 36 psi, 2.5 atm.

VARIATIONS

ENGINE 8 compression ratio.

OPTIONAL ACCESSORIES 3.310 or 3.540 axle ratio; competition tyres 6.00 x 15 front, 6.50 x 15 rear; chrome-plated pressed steel wheels; rack-and-pinion steering with variable ratio servo.

4.2-litre E Type Convertible

See 4.2-litre E Type Coupé, except for:

PRICE IN GB: £ 1,799.
PRICE IN USA: $ 5,534.

PERFORMANCE power-weight ratio: 10.3 lb/hp, 4.7 kg/hp.

DIMENSIONS AND WEIGHT dry weight: 2,734 lb, 1,240 kg.

OPTIONAL ACCESSORIES hardtop.

4.2-litre E Type 2 + 2

See 4.2-litre E Type Coupé, except for:

PRICE IN GB: £ 2,073.
PRICE IN USA: $ 5,907.

PERFORMANCE power-weight ratio: 10.9 lb/hp, 4.9 kg/hp.

JENSEN Interceptor II

LOTUS Europa

LOTUS Elan + 2 'S'

STEERING turns of steering wheel lock to lock: 2.85.

DIMENSIONS AND WEIGHT wheel base: 105 in, 2,667 mm; overall length: 184.30 in, 4,681 mm; overall height: 48.20 in, 1,224 mm; dry weight: 2,902 lb, 1,316 kg; turning circle (between walls): 41 ft, 12.5 m.

BODY seats: 2 + 2.

OPTIONAL ACCESSORIES Borg-Warner automatic gearbox hydraulic torque convertor and planetary gears with 3 ratios (I 2.403, II 1.458, III 1, rev 2), max ratio of convertor at stall 2, 2.880 axle ratio, speed in direct drive at 1,000 rpm 26.9 mph, 43.3 km/h, max speeds (I) 56 mph, 90 km/h, (II) 87 mph, 140 km/h, (III) 136 mph, 219 km/h; chrome-plated pressed steel wheels; rack-and-pinion steering with variable ratio servo.

JENSEN   GREAT BRITAIN

Interceptor II

PRICE IN GB: £ 4,470.

ENGINE front, 4 stroke; cylinders: 8, Vee-slanted at 90°; bore and stroke: 4.25 x 3.38 in, 107.9 x 85.8 mm; engine capacity: 383 cu in, 6,276 cu cm; compression ratio: 10; max power (SAE): 330 hp at 5,000 rpm; max torque (SAE): 425 lb ft, 58.7 kg m at 2,800 rpm; max engine rpm: 5,200; specific power: 52.6 hp/l; cylinder block: cast iron; cylinder head: cast iron; crankshaft bearings: 5; valves: 2 per cylinder, overhead, in line, push-rods and rockers, hydraulic tappets; camshafts: 1, at centre of Vee; lubrication: rotary pump, full flow filter; lubricating system capacity: 6.5 imp pt, 7.8 US pt, 3.7 l; carburation: 1 Carter AVS4682SA down-draught 4-barrel carburettor; fuel feed: mechanical pump; cooling system: water, 2 electric thermostatic fans; cooling system capacity: 28.2 imp pt, 33.8 US pt, 16 l.

TRANSMISSION driving wheels: rear; gearbox: Torqueflite automatic, hydraulic torque convertor and planetary gears with 3 ratios + reverse, max ratio of convertor at stall 2, possible manual selection; gearbox ratios: I 2.448, II 1.444, III 1, rev 2.194; selector lever: central; final drive: hypoid bevel, limited slip; axle ratio: 2.880; tyres: ER70 x VR15.

PERFORMANCE max speeds: 56 mph, 90 km/h in 1st gear; 95 mph, 153 km/h in 2nd gear; 135 mph, 217 km/h in 3rd gear; power-weight ratio: 10.6 lb/hp, 4.8 kg/hp; carrying capacity: 706 lb, 320 kg; acceleration: 0-50 mph (0-80 km/h) 5 sec; speed in direct drive at 1,000 rpm: 26.5 mph, 42.6 km/h; fuel consumption: 17 m/imp gal, 14.2 m/US gal, 16.6 l x 100 km.

CHASSIS tubular; front suspension: independent, wishbones, coil springs, anti-roll bar, telescopic dampers; rear suspension: de Dion rigid axle, semi-elliptic leafsprings, telescopic dampers.

STEERING rack-and-pinion, adjustable steering wheel, servo; turns of steering wheel lock to lock: 3.40.

BRAKES disc (front diameter 11.38 in, 289 mm, rear diameter 10.75 in, 273 mm), dual circuit, servo; area rubbed by linings: total 524 sq in, 3,380 sq cm.

ELECTRICAL EQUIPMENT voltage: 12 V; battery: 67 Ah; generator type: alternator, 60 A; ignition distributor: Chrysler; headlamps: 4, halogen.

DIMENSIONS AND WEIGHT wheel base: 105 in, 2,667 mm; front track: 56.12 in, 1,425 mm; rear track: 56.90 in, 1,445 mm; overall length: 188 in, 4,775 mm; overall width: 69 in, 1,753 mm; overall height: 53 in, 1,346 mm; ground clearance 5.50 in, 140 mm; dry weight: 3,501 lb, 1,588 kg; turning circle (between walls): 38 ft, 11.6 m; fuel tank capacity: 20 imp gal, 24 US gal, 91 l.

BODY coupé; doors: 2; seats: 4; front seats: separate, reclining backrests; details: electrically-controlled windows.

PRACTICAL INSTRUCTIONS fuel: 100 oct petrol; engine sump oil: 6.5 imp pt, 7.8 US pt, 3.7 l, SAE 10W-30, change every 4,000 miles, 6,400 km; gearbox oil: 15.2 imp pt, 18.2 US pt, 8.6 l, Dexron automatic transmission fluid, change every 36,000 miles, 58,000 km; final drive oil: 3 imp pt, 3.6 US pt, 1.7 l, change every 12,000 miles, 19,300 km; greasing: every 4,000 miles, 6,400 km, 4 points.

OPTIONAL ACCESSORIES air-conditioning system.

FF II

See Interceptor II, except for:

PRICE IN GB: £ 5,900.

TRANSMISSION driving wheels: front without limited slip final drive, rear with limited slip final drive.

JENSEN Interceptor II

LOTUS Europa

LOTUS Elan + 2 'S'

PERFORMANCE power-weight ratio: 11.5 lb/hp, 5.2 kg/hp.

CHASSIS rear suspension: transverse linkage bar.

BRAKES Dunlop-Maxaret anti-skid device.

DIMENSIONS AND WEIGHT wheel base: 109 in, 2,796 mm; front track: 56.87 in, 1,444 mm; rear track: 56.87 in, 1,444 mm; overall length: 191 in, 4,851 mm; ground clearance: 5 in, 127 mm; dry weight: 3,808 lb, 1,727 kg; turning circle (between walls): 39 ft, 11.9 m.

LOTUS   GREAT BRITAIN

Europa

PRICE IN GB: £ 1,399.
PRICE IN USA: $ 4,295.

ENGINE rear, 4 stroke; cylinders: 4, in line; bore and stroke: 2.99 x 3.19 in, 76 x 81 mm; engine capacity: 89.7 cu in, 1,470 cu cm; compression ratio: 10.2; max power (DIN): 78 hp at 6,000 rpm; max torque (DIN): 74 lb ft, 10.2 kg m at 4,000 rpm; max engine rpm: 6,500; specific power: 53.1 hp/l; cylinder block: light alloy; cylinder head: light alloy; crankshaft bearings: 5; valves: 2 per cylinder, overhead, rockers; camshafts: 1, side; lubrication: eccentric pump, full flow filter; lubricating system capacity: 7.6 imp pt, 9.1 US pt, 4.3 l; carburation: 1 Solex 35 DIDSA-2 downdraught twin barrel carburettor; fuel feed: mechanical pump; cooling system: water; cooling system capacity: 18 imp pt, 21.6 US pt, 10.2 l.

TRANSMISSION driving wheels: rear; clutch: single dry plate; gearbox: mechanical; gears: 4 + reverse; synchromesh gears: I, II, III, IV; gearbox ratios: I 3.610, II 2.250, III 1.480, IV 1.030, rev 3.080; gear lever: central; final drive: hypoid bevel; axle ratio: 3.560; width of rims: 4.5''; tyres: 155 x 13.

PERFORMANCE max speeds: 33 mph, 53 km/h in 1st gear; 53 mph, 85 km/h in 2nd gear; 80 mph, 128 km/h in 3rd gear; 112 mph, 180 km/h in 4th gear; power-weight ratio: 17.2 lb/hp, 7.8 kg/hp; carrying capacity: 353 lb, 160 kg; acceleration: 0-50 mph (0-80 km/h) 7 sec; speed in top at 1,000 rpm: 17.9 mph, 28.8 km/h; fuel consumption: 40 m/imp gal, 33.1 m/US gal, 7.1 l x 100 km.

CHASSIS platform; front suspension: independent, wishbones, coil springs, telescopic dampers; rear suspension: independent, wishbones, trailing radius arms, telescopic dampers.

STEERING rack-and-pinion.

BRAKES front disc, rear drum; area rubbed by linings: front 197 sq in, 1,270 sq cm, rear 75.3 sq in, 486 sq cm, total 272.3 sq in, 1,756 sq cm.

ELECTRICAL EQUIPMENT voltage: 12 V; battery: 57 Ah; generator type: alternator, 420 W; ignition distributor: Ducellier; headlamps: 2.

DIMENSIONS AND WEIGHT wheel base: 91 in, 2,311 mm; front track: 53 in, 1,346 mm; rear track: 53.25 in, 1,352 mm; overall length: 157.25 in, 3,994 mm; overall width: 64.50 in, 1,638 mm; overall height: 42.50 in, 1,079 mm; ground clearance: 6.50 in, 165 mm; dry weight: 1,350 lb, 612 kg; turning circle (between walls): 44 ft, 13.4 m; fuel tank capacity: 7 imp gal, 8.4 US gal, 32 l.

BODY coupé in plastic material; doors: 2; seats: 2.

PRACTICAL INSTRUCTIONS fuel: 98-100 oct petrol; engine sump oil: 7.6 imp pt, 9.1 US pt, 4.3 l, SAE 10W-30, change every 3,000 miles, 4,800 km; gearbox and final drive oil: 3 imp pt, 3.6 US pt, 1.7 l, SAE 90, change every 6,000 miles, 9,700 km; greasing: every 3,000 miles, 4,800 km, 6 points; tappet clearances: inlet 0.008 in, 0.20 mm, exhaust 0.010 in, 0.25 mm; valve timing: inlet opens 35° before tdc and closes 65° after bdc, exhaust opens 65° before bdc and closes 35° after tdc; normal tyre pressure: front 18 psi, 1.3 atm, rear 29 psi, 2 atm.

OPTIONAL ACCESSORIES servo brake.

Elan S4 Drophead Coupé

PRICE IN GB: £ 1,498.
PRICE IN USA: $ 4,795.

ENGINE front, 4 stroke; cylinders: 4, vertical, in line; bore and stroke: 3.25 x 2.86 in, 82.5 x 72.7 mm; engine capacity: 95.1 cu in, 1,558 cu cm; compression ratio: 9.5; max power (DIN): 105 hp at 6,000 rpm; max torque (DIN): 108 lb ft, 14.9 kg m at 4,000 rpm; max engine rpm: 6,900; specific power: 67.4 hp/l; cylinder block: cast iron; cylinder head: light alloy; crankshaft bearings: 5; valves: 2 per cylinder, overhead, Vee-slanted, thimble tappets; camshafts:

ELAN S4 DROPHEAD COUPÉ

2, overhead; lubrication: rotary pump, full flow filter; lubricating system capacity: 7.2 imp pt, 8.7 US pt, 4.1 l; carburation: 2 Weber 40 DCOE 18 horizontal twin barrel carburettors; fuel feed: mechanical pump; cooling system: water; cooling system capacity: 13.9 imp pt, 16.7 US pt, 7.9 l.

TRANSMISSION driving wheels: rear; clutch: single dry plate; gearbox: mechanical; gears: 4 + reverse; synchromesh gears: I, II, III, IV; gearbox ratios: I 2.972, II 2.009, III 1.397, IV 1, rev 3.324; gear lever: central; final drive: hypoid bevel; axle ratio: 3.770; width of rims: 4.5''; tyres: 145 x 130.

PERFORMANCE max speeds: 41 mph, 66 km/h in 1st gear; 61 mph, 98 km/h in 2nd gear; 88 mph, 141 km/h in 3rd gear; 122 mph, 196 km/h in 4th gear; power-weight ratio: 14.2 lb/hp, 6.4 kg/hp; carrying capacity: 353 lb, 160 kg; acceleration: standing ¼ mile 15.7 sec, 0-50 mph (0-80 km/h) 6 sec; speed in direct drive at 1,000 rpm: 17.8 mph, 28.7 km/h; fuel consumption: 26.1 m/imp gal, 21.8 m/US gal, 10.8 l x 100 km.

CHASSIS backbone; front suspension: independent, wishbones, coil springs, anti-roll bar, telescopic dampers; rear suspension: independent, lower wishbones, coil springs/telescopic damper struts.

STEERING rack-and-pinion, adjustable steering wheel; turns of steering wheel lock to lock: 2.67.

BRAKES disc (front diameter 9.50 in, 241 mm, rear 10.50 in, 267 mm); area rubbed by linings: front 144 sq in, 929 sq cm, rear 160 sq in, 1,032 sq cm, total 304 sq in, 1,961 sq cm.

ELECTRICAL EQUIPMENT voltage: 12 V; battery: 57 Ah; generator type: dynamo, 18 A; ignition distributor: Lucas; headlamps: 2, retractable.

DIMENSIONS AND WEIGHT wheel base: 84 in, 2,134 mm; front track: 47.95 in, 1,218 mm; rear track: 48.45 in, 1,231 mm; overall length: 145 in, 3,683 mm; overall width: 56 in, 1,422 mm; overall height: 45.25 in, 1,149 mm; ground clearance: 6 in, 152 mm; dry weight: 1,495 lb, 678 kg; distribution of weight: 48% front axle, 52% rear axle; turning circle (between walls): 29.5 ft, 9 m; fuel tank capacity: 9.2 imp gal, 11.1 US gal, 42 l.

BODY convertible in plastic material; doors: 2; seats: 2.

PRACTICAL INSTRUCTIONS fuel: 98-100 oct petrol; engine sump oil: 6.5 imp pt, 7.8 US pt, 3.7 l, SAE 10W-30, change every 3,000 miles, 4,800 km; gearbox oil: 1.8 imp pt, 2.1 US pt, 1 l, SAE 80 EP, change every 6,000 miles, 9,700 km; final drive oil: 1.9 imp pt, 2.3 US pt, 1.1 l, SAE 90 EP, no change recommended; greasing: every 1,500 miles, 2,400 km, 3 points; tappet clearances: inlet 0.006 in, 0.15 mm, exhaust 0.010 in, 0.25 mm; valve timing: inlet opens 26° before tdc and closes 66° after bdc, exhaust opens 66° before bdc and closes 26° after tdc; normal tyre pressure: front 18 psi, 1.3 atm, rear 22 psi, 1.5 atm.

VARIATIONS

(Special Equipment Model)

ENGINE max power (DIN) 115 hp at 6,000 rpm, 73.8 hp/l specific power.

TRANSMISSION 4-speed mechanical gearbox (I 2.510, II 1.636, III 1.230, IV 1, rev 2.807), 3.550 axle ratio (3.770 on request), light alloy wheels and knock-on hubs.

PERFORMANCE max speeds (I) 52 mph, 83 km/h, (II) 80 mph, 123 km/h, (III) 106 mph, 170 km/h, (IV) 130 mph, 209 km/h, power-weight ratio 13 lb/hp, 5.9 kg/hp, speed in direct drive at 1,000 rpm 18.9 mph, 30.4 km/h.

CHASSIS tuned suspension.

BRAKES servo.

OPTIONAL ACCESSORIES 4-speed mechanical gearbox (I 2.510, II 1.636, III 1.230, IV 1, rev 2.807), max speeds (I) 49 mph, 79 km/h, (II) 75 mph, 120 km/h, (III) 100 mph, 161 km/h, (IV) 122 mph, 196 km/h; 3.550 axle ratio; light alloy wheels and knock-on hubs; servo brake.

Elan S4 Coupé

See Elan S4 Drophead Coupé, except for:

BODY coupé.

Elan "Sprint"

See Elan S4 Drophead Coupé, except for:

PRICE IN GB: —

ENGINE max power (DIN): 115 hp at 6,000 rpm; specific power: 73.8 hp/l.

TRANSMISSION axle ratio: 3.550 or 3.770 or 3.990.

PERFORMANCE max speed: 130 mph, 209 km/h; power-weight ratio: 13 lb/hp, 5.9 kg/hp.

LOTUS Seven S4

MARCOS 2-litre

MARCOS 3-litre (Volvo)

Elan + 2 'S'

See Elan S4 Drophead Coupé, except for:

PRICE IN GB: £ 2,002.
PRICE IN USA: $ 5,995.

ENGINE max power (DIN): 118 hp at 6,250 rpm; max torque (DIN): 112 lb ft, 15.5 kg m at 4,600 rpm; specific power: 75.7 hp/l; carburation: 2 Weber 40 DCOE 2 horizontal twin barrel carburettors.

TRANSMISSION tyres: 165 x 13.

PERFORMANCE max speed: 120 mph, 193 km/h; power-weight ratio: 17.1 lb/hp, 7.7 kg/hp; acceleration: standing ¼ mile 16.4 sec, 0-50 mph (0-80 km/h) 6.2 sec.

BRAKES disc (diameter 10 in, 254 mm), servo (standard); area rubbed by linings: front 159 sq in, 1,025 sq cm, rear 159 sq in 1,025 sq cm, total 318 sq in, 2,050 sq cm.

ELECTRICAL EQUIPMENT generator type: alternator.

DIMENSIONS AND WEIGHT wheel base: 96 in, 2,438 mm; front track: 54 in, 1,372 mm; rear track: 55 in, 1,397 mm; overall length: 169 in, 4,293 mm; overall width: 66 in, 1,676 mm; overall height: 47 in, 1,194 mm; dry weight: 2,020 lb, 916 kg; distribution of weight: 51% front axle, 49% rear axle; turning circle (between walls): 30 ft, 9.1 m.

BODY coupé; seats: 2 + 2; front seats: separate, reclining backrests.

PRACTICAL INSTRUCTIONS greasing: every 3,000 miles, 4,800 km, 2 points; tappet clearances: exhaust 0.007 in, 0.18 mm; valve timing: inlet opens 22° before tdc and closes 66° after bdc, exhaust opens 66° before bdc and closes 22° after tdc; normal tyre pressure: front 22 psi, 1.5 atm, rear 22 psi, 1.5 atm.

Seven S4

PRICE IN GB: £ 945.

ENGINE front, 4 stroke; cylinders: 4, vertical, in line; bore and stroke: 3.19 x 3.05 in, 81 x 77.6 mm; engine capacity: 97.5 cu in, 1,598 cu cm; compression ratio: 9; max power (DIN): 84 hp at 5,800 rpm; max torque (DIN): 96 lb ft, 13.2 kg m at 3,600 rpm; max engine rpm: 6,000; specific power: 52.6 hp/l; cylinder block: cast iron; cylinder head: cast iron; crankshaft bearings: 5; valves: 2 per cylinder, overhead, in line, push-rods and rockers; camshafts: 1, side; lubrication: rotary or vane-type pump, full flow filter; lubricating system capacity: 5.8 imp pt, 7 US pt, 3.3 l; carburation: 1 Weber downdraught carburettor; fuel feed: mechanical pump; cooling system: water; cooling system capacity: 10.9 imp pt, 13.1 US pt, 6.2 l.

TRANSMISSION driving wheels: rear; clutch: single dry plate (diaphragm), hydraulically controlled; gearbox: mechanical; gears: 4 + reverse; synchromesh gears: I, II, III, IV; gearbox ratios: I 2.972, II 2.010, III 1.397, IV 1, rev 3.324; gear lever: central; final drive: hypoid bevel; axle ratio: 3.770; width of rims: 5.5''; tyres: 165 x 13.

PERFORMANCE max speeds: 34 mph, 54 km/h in 1st gear; 50 mph, 80 km/h in 2nd gear; 71 mph, 114 km/h in 3rd gear; 99 mph, 160 km/h in 4th gear; power-weight ratio: 15.7 lb/hp, 7.1 kg/hp; carrying capacity: 397 lb, 180 kg; speed in direct drive at 1,000 rpm: 17.8 mph, 28.6 km/h; fuel consumption: 27 m/imp gal, 22.4 m/US gal, 10.5 l x 100 km.

CHASSIS tubular; front suspension: independent, double wishbones, anti-roll bar, coil springs/telescopic dampers units; rear suspension: rigid axle, double Watt linkage, coil springs/telescopic dampers units.

STEERING rack-and-pinion; turns of steering wheel lock to lock: 2.75.

BRAKES front disc (diameter 8.50 in, 216 mm), rear drum.

ELECTRICAL EQUIPMENT voltage: 12 V; battery: 35 Ah; generator type: dynamo, 22 A; headlamps: 2.

DIMENSIONS AND WEIGHT wheel base: 90 in, 1,286 mm; front track: 48.80 in, 1,239 mm; rear track: 51.50 in, 1,308 mm; overall length: 146.30 in, 3,716 mm; overall width: 60.50 in, 1,537 mm; overall height: 42.75 in, 1,086 mm; ground clearance: 6.50 in, 165 mm; dry weight: 1,310 lb, 594 kg; fuel tank capacity: 7.5 imp gal, 9 US gal, 34 l.

BODY roadster in plastic material; doors: none; seats: 2.

PRACTICAL INSTRUCTIONS fuel: 98-100 oct petrol; engine sump oil: 7.5 imp pt, 8.9 US pt, 4.2 l, SAE 10W-30, change every 3,000 miles, 4,800 km; gearbox oil: 2.4 imp pt, 2.7 US pt, 1.3 l, SAE 80 EP, change every 6,000 miles, 9,700 km; final drive oil: 2 imp pt, 2.3 US pt, 1.1 l, SAE 90 EP, change every 6,000 miles, 9,700 km; greasing: none; tappet

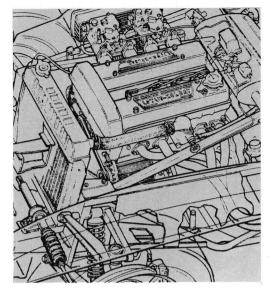

LOTUS Seven S4 (Lotus-Holbay Clubman engine)

MARCOS 2-litre (independent front suspension)

MARCOS 3-litre (Volvo) with automatic gearbox

clearances: inlet 0.012 in, 0.30 mm, exhaust 0.022 in, 0.55 mm; valve timing: inlet opens 27° before tdc and closes 65° after bdc, exhaust opens 65° before bdc and closes 27° after tdc; normal tyre pressure: front 16 psi, 1.1 atm, rear 22 psi, 1.6 atm.

VARIATIONS

ENGINE (Lotus Twin Cam) max power (DIN) 115 hp.

ENGINE (Lotus-Holbay Clubman) max power (DIN) 120 hp.

OPTIONAL ACCESSORIES light alloy wheels; roll bar; tonneau cover.

MARCOS   GREAT BRITAIN

2-litre

PRICE IN GB: £ 1,675.

ENGINE front, 4 stroke; cylinders: 4, Vee-slanted at 60°; bore and stroke: 3.69 x 2.85 in, 93.7 x 72.4 mm; engine capacity: 121.8 cu in, 1,996 cu cm; compression ratio: 8.9; max power (DIN): 85 hp at 5,500 rpm; max torque (DIN): 123 lb ft, 17 kg m at 2,750 rpm; max engine rpm: 5,800; specific power: 42.6 hp/l; cylinder block: cast iron; cylinder head: cast iron; crankshaft bearings: 3; valves: 2 per cylinder, overhead, in line, push-rods and rockers; camshafts: 1, at centre of Vee; lubrication: eccentric pump, full flow filter; lubricating system capacity: 7.8 imp pt, 9.3 US pt, 4.4 l; carburation: 1 Weber 32 DIF 4 downdraught carburettor; fuel feed: mechanical pump; cooling system: water; cooling system capacity: 12.5 imp pt, 15 US pt, 7.1 l.

TRANSMISSION driving wheels: rear; clutch: single dry plate; gearbox: mechanical; gears: 4 + reverse; synchromesh gears: I, II, III, IV; gearbox ratios: I 2.972, II 2.010, III 1.397, IV 1, rev 3.324; gear lever: central; final drive: hypoid bevel; axle ratio: 3.770; width of rims: 5.5''; tyres: 175 x 13.

PERFORMANCE max speeds: 35 mph, 56 km/h in 1st gear; 51 mph, 82 km/h in 2nd gear; 74 mph, 119 km/h in 3rd gear; 103 mph, 165 km/h in 4th gear; power-weight ratio: 22.3 lb/hp, 10.1 kg/hp; speed in direct drive at 1,000 rpm: 17.7 mph, 28.5 km/h; fuel consumption: 24 m/imp gal, 19.9 m/US gal, 11.8 l x 100 km.

CHASSIS multi-tubular space frame; front suspension: independent, wishbones, coil springs/telescopic dampers units; rear suspension: rigid axle, twin trailing radius arms, transverse linkage bar, coil springs/telescopic dampers units.

STEERING rack-and-pinion; turns of steering wheel lock to lock: 2.60.

BRAKES front disc, rear drum.

ELECTRICAL EQUIPMENT voltage: 12 V; battery: 40 Ah; generator type: dynamo; ignition distributor: Autolite; headlamps: 2.

DIMENSIONS AND WEIGHT wheel base: 89.50 in, 2.273 mm; front track: 48.75 in, 1,238 mm; rear track: 51 in, 1,295 mm; overall length: 160.25 in, 4,070 mm; overall width: 62.50 in, 1,587 mm; overall height: 42.50 in, 1,079 mm; ground clearance: 4 in, 102 mm; dry weight: 1,892 lb, 858 kg; distribution of weight: 53% front axle, 47% rear axle; turning circle (between walls): 31 ft, 9.1 m; fuel tank capacity: 12 imp gal, 14.3 US gal, 54 l.

BODY coupé in plastic material; doors: 2; seats: 2; front seats: separate, reclining backrests.

PRACTICAL INSTRUCTIONS fuel: 98 oct petrol; engine sump oil: 7.5 imp pt, 8.9 US pt, 4.2 l, SAE 20-30, change every 5,000 miles, 8,000 km; gearbox oil: 3.7 imp pt, 4.4 US pt, 2.1 l, SAE 80, change every 20,000 miles, 32,200 km; final drive oil: 2 imp pt, 2.3 US pt, 1.1 l, SAE 90 EP, change every 20,000 miles, 32,200 km; greasing: every 3,000 miles, 4,800 km, 3 points; tappet clearances: inlet 0.012 in, 0.30 mm, exhaust 0.020 in, 0.51 mm; valve timing: inlet opens 20° before tdc and closes 56° after bdc, exhaust opens 62° before bdc and closes 14° after tdc; normal tyre pressure: front 26 psi, 1.8 atm, rear 26 psi, 1.8 atm.

OPTIONAL ACCESSORIES sunshine roof; light alloy wheels.

3-litre

See 2-litre, except for:

PRICE IN GB: £ 1,895.

ENGINE cylinders: 6, Vee-slanted at 60°; engine capacity: 182.7 cu in, 2,994 cu cm; max power (DIN): 136 hp at 4,750

3-LITRE

rpm; max torque (DIN): 192 lb ft, 26.5 kg m at 3,000 rpm; lubricating system capacity: 9.8 imp pt, 11.6 US pt, 5.5 l; carburation: 1 Weber 32 DIF 1 downdraught carburettor; cooling system capacity: 14 imp pt, 16.7 US pt, 7.9 l.

TRANSMISSION gears: 4 + reverse and overdrive/top; gearbox ratios: I 3.163, II 2.214, III 1.412, IV 1, overdrive/top 0.820, rev 3.324; axle ratio: 3.580.

PERFORMANCE max speeds: 31 mph, 50 km/h in 1st gear; 44 mph, 71 km/h in 2nd gear; 68 mph, 109 km/h in 3rd gear; 107 mph, 172 km/h in 4th gear; 125 mph, 201 km/h in overdrive/top; power-weight ratio: 14.3 lb/hp, 6.5 kg/hp; acceleration: standing ¼ mile 15.8 sec, 0-50 mph (0-80 km/h) 5.7 sec; speed in overdrive/top at 1,000 rpm: 19.5 mph, 31.4 km/h; fuel consumption: 22.1 m/imp gal, 18.4 m/US gal, 12.8 l x 100 km.

DIMENSIONS AND WEIGHT dry weight: 1,949 lb, 884 kg; distribution of weight: 52% front axle, 48% rear axle.

BODY details: light alloy wheels (standard).

OPTIONAL ACCESSORIES only sunshine roof.

3-litre (Volvo)

See 2-litre, except for:

PRICE IN GB: £ 1,950.

ENGINE cylinders: 6, in line; bore and stroke: 3.50 x 3.15 in, 88.9 x 80 mm; engine capacity: 181.8 cu in, 2,980 cu cm; compression ratio: 9.3; max power (SAE): 145 hp at 5,500 rpm; max torque (SAE): 163 lb ft, 22.5 kg m at 3,000 rpm; max engine rpm: 6,000; specific power: 48.7 hp/l; crankshaft bearings: 7; valves: 2 per cylinder, overhead, push-rods and rockers; camshafts: 1, side; lubrication: gear pump, full flow filter; lubricating system capacity: 10.6 imp pt, 12.7 US pt, 6 l; carburation: 2 Zenith-Stromberg horizontal 175 CD2SE carburettors; cooling system capacity: 22.9 imp pt, 27.5 US pt, 13 l.

TRANSMISSION gearbox ratios: I 3.140, II 1.970, III 1.340, IV 1, rev. 3.200; axle ratio: 3.200.

PERFORMANCE max speeds: 38 mph, 61 km/h in 1st gear; 61 mph, 98 km/h in 2nd gear; 89 mph, 144 km/h in 3rd gear; 120 mph, 193 km/h in 4th gear; power-weight ratio: 13.2 lb/hp, 6 kg/hp; speed in direct drive at 1,000 rpm: 20 mph, 35.5 km/h; fuel consumption: 25 m/imp gal, 20.8 m/US gal, 11.3 l x 100 km.

ELECTRICAL EQUIPMENT battery: 38 Ah; generator type: alternator, 770 W; ignition distributor: Bosch.

DIMENSIONS AND WEIGHT fuel tank capacity: 11 imp gal, 13.2 US gal, 50 l.

OPTIONAL ACCESSORIES Borg-Warner 35 automatic gearbox, hydraulic torque convertor and planetary gears with 3 ratios (I 2.390, II 1.450, III 1, rev 2.094), max ratio of convertor at stall 2, possible manual selection, central selector lever; light alloy wheels; sunshine roof.

Mantis

PRICE IN GB: £ 2,438.

ENGINE front, 4 stroke; cylinder: 6, in line; bore and stroke: 2.94 x 3.74 in, 74.7 x 95 mm; engine capacity: 152.4 cu in, 2,498 cu cm; compression ratio: 9.5; max power (DIN): 150 hp at 5,500 rpm; max torque (DIN): 158 lb ft, 21.8 kg m at 3,000 rpm; max engine rpm: 6,000; specific power: 60.2 hp/l; cylinder block: cast iron; cylinder head: cast iron; crankshaft bearings: 5; valves: 2 per cylinder, overhead, in line, push-rods and rockers; camshafts: 1, side; lubrication: eccentric pump, full flow filter; lubricating system capacity: 9 imp pt, 10.8 US pt, 5.1 l; carburation: Lucas injection pump (constant pressure), injectors in inlet pipes; fuel feed: electric pump; cooling system: water; cooling system capacity: 11 imp pt, 13.3 US pt, 6.3 l.

TRANSMISSION driving wheels: rear; clutch: single dry plate (diaphragm), hydraulically controlled; gearbox: mechanical; gears: 4 + reverse and Laycock-de Normanville overdrive on II, III and IV; synchromesh gears: I, II, III IV; gearbox ratios: I 3.140, II 2.010, III 1.330, IV 1, overdrive 0.820, rev3 3.220; gear lever: central; final drive: hypoid bevel; axle ratio: 3.220; width of rims: 5.5''; tyres: 185 x 13.

PERFORMANCE max speeds: 42 mph, 68 km/h in 1st gear; 66 mph, 106 km/h in 2nd gear; 99 mph, 160 km/h in 3rd gear; 132 mph, 213 km/h in 4th gear; 123 mph, 198 km/h in overdrive; power-weight ratio: 15 lb/hp, 7 kg/hp; carrying capacity: 794 lb, 360 kg; speed in direct drive at 1,000

MARCOS Mantis

MG Midget Mk III

MG 1300 Mk II

rpm: 22.1 mph, 35.5 km/h; fuel consumption: 17.5 m/imp gal, 14.6 m/US gal, 16.1 l x 100 km.

CHASSIS multi-tubular space frame; front suspension: independent, wishbones, anti-roll bar, coil springs/telescopic dampers units; rear suspension: rigid axle, longitudinal radius arms, upper A-bracket, coil springs/telescopic damper units.

STEERING rack-and-pinion; turn of steering wheel lock to lock: 3.

BRAKES front disc, rear drum, dual circuit, servo.

ELECTRICAL EQUIPMENT voltage: 12 V; battery: 59 Ah; generator type: alternator; headlamps: 2.

DIMENSIONS AND WEIGHT wheel base: 102 in, 2,591 mm; front track: 57 in, 1,448 mm; rear track: 57 in, 1,448 mm; overall length: 186.75 in, 4,744 mm; overall width: 71 in, 1,804 mm; overall height: 46 in, 1,168 mm; ground clearance: 4.72 in, 120 mm; dry weight: 2,300 lb, 1,043 kg; turning circle (between walls): 34 ft, 10.4 m; fuel tank capacity: 17.5 imp gal, 21.1 US gal, 80 l.

BODY coupé; doors: 2; seats: 2 + 2; front seats: separate.

PRACTICAL INSTRUCTIONS fuel: 100 oct petrol; engine sump oil: 8 imp pt, 9.7 US pt, 4.6 l, SAE 20W-30, change every 6,000 miles, 9,700 km; gearbox oil: 2 imp pt, 2.5 US pt, 1.2 l, SAE 90, no change recommended; final drive oil: 2 imp pt, 2.5 US pt, 1.2 l, SAE 90, no change recommended; greasing: none; tappet clearances: inlet 0.010 in, 0.25 mm, exhaust 0.010 in, 0.25 mm; normal tyre pressure: front 22 psi, 1.5 atm, rear 24 psi, 1.7 atm.

Midget Mk III

PRICE IN GB: £ 692.
PRICE IN USA: $ 2,279.

ENGINE front, 4 stroke; cylinders: 4, vertical, in line; bore and stroke: 2.78 x 3.20 in, 70.6 x 81.3 mm; engine capacity 77.8 cu in, 1,275 cu cm; compression ratio: 8.8; max power (DIN): 65 hp at 6,000 rpm; max torque (DIN): 72 lb ft 9.9 kg m at 3,000 rpm; max engine rpm: 6,200; specific power: 51 hp/l; cylinder block: cast iron; cylinder head cast iron; crankshaft bearings: 3; valves: 2 per cylinder overhead, push-rods and rockers; camshafts: 1, side; lubrication: eccentric pump, full flow filter; lubricating system capacity: 7 imp pt, 8.5 US pt, 4 l; carburation: 2 SU type HS 2 semi-downdraught carburettors; fuel feed: electric pump; cooling system: water; cooling system capacity 10.6 imp pt, 12.7 US pt, 6 l.

TRANSMISSION driving wheels: rear; clutch: single dry plate (diaphragm), hydraulically controlled; gearbox: mechanical; gears: 4 + reverse; synchromesh gears: II, III IV; gearbox ratios: I 3.200, II 1.916, III 1.357, IV 1, rev 4.120; gear lever: central; final drive: hypoid bevel; axle ratio: 3.900; tyres: 5.20 x 13.

PERFORMANCE max speeds: 30 mph, 48 km/h in 1st gear; 50 mph, 80 km/h in 2nd gear; 71 mph, 114 km/h in 3rd gear; 95 mph, 153 km/h in 4th gear; power-weight ratio: 23.2 lb/hp, 10.5 kg/hp; carrying capacity: 353 lb, 160 kg; acceleration: standing ¼ mile 19.1 sec, 0-50 mph (0-80 km/h) 9.2 sec; speed in direct drive at 1,000 rpm: 15.5 mph, 24.9 km/h; fuel consumption: 35.3 m/imp gal, 29.4 m/US gal, 8 l x 100 km.

CHASSIS integral; front suspension: independent, wishbones, coil springs, lever dampers as upper arms; rear suspension: rigid axle, semi-elliptic leafsprings, lever dampers.

STEERING rack-and-pinion; turns of steering wheel lock to lock: 2.30.

BRAKES front disc (diameter 7 in, 178 mm), rear drum.

ELECTRICAL EQUIPMENT voltage: 12 V; battery: 43 Ah; generator type: dynamo, 22 A; ignition distributor: Lucas; headlamps: 2.

DIMENSIONS AND WEIGHT wheel base: 80 in, 2,032 mm; front track: 46.30 in, 1,176 mm; rear track: 44.75 in, 1,137 mm; overall length: 137.60 in, 3,495 mm; overall width: 54.90 in, 1,394 mm; overall height: 48.62 in, 1,235 mm; ground clearance: 5 in, 127 mm; dry weight: 1,510 lb, 685 kg; distribution of weight: 52.4% front axle, 47.6% rear axle; turning circle (between walls): 32 ft, 9.8 m; fuel tank capacity: 6 imp gal, 7.1 US gal, 27 l.

BODY convertible; doors: 2; seats: 2.

PRACTICAL INSTRUCTIONS fuel: 98 oct petrol; engine sump oil: 6.5 imp pt, 7.8 US pt, 3.7 l, SAE 10W-30 (winter)

20W-50 (summer), change every 6,000 miles, 9,700 km; gearbox oil: 2.3 imp pt, 2.7 US pt, 1.3 l, SAE 10W-30 (winter) 20W-50 (summer); final drive oil: 1.4 imp pt, 1.7 US pt, 0.8 l, SAE 90; greasing: every 3,000 miles, 4,800 km, 8 points; tappet clearances: inlet 0.012 in, 0.30 mm, exhaust 0.012 in, 0.30 mm; valve timing: inlet opens 5° before tdc and closes 45° after bdc, exhaust opens 51° before bdc and closes 21° after tdc; normal tyre pressure: front 18 psi, 1.3 atm, rear 20 psi, 1.4 atm.

VARIATIONS

ENGINE 8 compression ratio.

OPTIONAL ACCESSORIES oil cooler; wire wheels; anti-roll bar on front suspension; hardtop; tonneau cover.

1300 Mk II

PRICE IN GB: £ 740.

ENGINE front, transverse, 4 stroke; cylinders: 4, vertical, in line; bore and stroke: 2.78 x 3.20 in, 70.6 x 81.3 mm; engine capacity: 77.8 cu in, 1,275 cu cm; compression ratio: 9.7; max power (DIN): 70 hp at 6,000 rpm; max torque (DIN): 77 lb ft, 10.7 kg m at 3,000 rpm; max engine rpm: 6,000; specific power: 54.9 hp/l; cylinder block: cast iron; cylinder head: cast iron; crankshaft bearings: 3; valves: 2 per cylinder, overhead, in line, push-rods and rockers; camshafts: 1, side; lubrication: gear or vane-type pump, full flow filter; lubricating system capacity: 9 imp pt, 10.8 US pt, 5.1 l; carburation: 2 SU type HS 2 semi-downdraught carburettors; fuel feed: electric pump; cooling system: water; cooling system capacity: 6.9 imp pt, 8.2 US pt, 3.9 l.

TRANSMISSION driving wheels: front; clutch: single dry plate (diaphragm), hydraulically controlled; gearbox: mechanical; gears: 4 + reverse; synchromesh gears: I, II, III, IV; gearbox ratios: I 3.300, II 2.074, III 1.353, IV 1, rev 3.350; gear lever: central; final drive: helical spur gears; axle ratio: 3.650; width of rims: 4''; tyres: 145 x 12.

PERFORMANCE max speeds: 30 mph, 48 km/h in 1st gear; 49 mph, 79 km/h in 2nd gear; 74 mph, 119 km/h in 3rd gear; 97 mph, 156 km/h in 4th gear; power-weight ratio: 23.2 lb/hp, 10.5 kg/hp; carrying capacity: 882 lb, 400 kg; acceleration: standing ¼ mile 19.6 sec, 0-50 mph (0-80 km/h) 9.4 sec; speed in direct drive at 1,000 rpm: 16.8 mph, 27 km/h; fuel consumption: 32.5 m/imp gal, 27 m/US gal, 8.7 l x 100 km.

CHASSIS integral, front and rear auxiliary frames; front suspension: independent, wishbones, hydrolastic (liquid) rubber cone springs, hydraulic connecting pipes to rear wheels; rear suspension: independent, swinging longitudinal trailing arms, hydrolastic (liquid) rubber cone springs, hydraulic connecting pipes to front wheels, combined with transverse torsion bars, anti-roll bar.

STEERING rack-and-pinion; turns of steering wheel lock to lock: 3.12.

BRAKES front disc (diameter 8.40 in, 213 mm), rear drum; area rubbed by linings: front 143 sq in, 922 sq cm, rear 63 sq in, 406 sq cm, total 206 sq in, 1,328 sq cm.

ELECTRICAL EQUIPMENT voltage: 12 V; battery: 40 Ah; generator type: dynamo, 264 W; ignition distributor: Lucas; headlamps: 2.

DIMENSIONS AND WEIGHT wheel base: 93.50 in, 2,375 mm; front track: 51.50 in, 1,308 mm; rear track: 50.85 in, 1,292 mm; overall length: 146.75 in, 3,727 mm; overall width: 60.35 in, 1,533 mm; overall height: 53 in, 1,346 mm; ground clearance: 5.30 in, 135 mm; dry weight: 1,621 lb, 735 kg; distribution of weight: 61.4% front axle, 38.6% rear axle; turning circle (between walls): 37.5 ft, 11.4 m; fuel tank capacity: 8 imp gal, 9.5 US gal, 36 l.

BODY saloon/sedan; doors: 2; seats: 4-5; front seats: separate.

PRACTICAL INSTRUCTIONS fuel: 100 oct petrol; engine sump, gearbox and final drive oil: 8.4 imp pt, 10.1 US pt, 4.8 l, SAE 20W-50, change every 6,000 miles, 9,700 km; greasing: every 3,000 miles, 4,800 km, 4 points; sparking plug type: 225°; tappet clearances: inlet 0.012 in, 0.30 mm, exhaust 0.012 in, 0.30 mm; valve timing: inlet opens 5° before tdc and closes 45° after bdc, exhaust opens 51° before bdc and closes 21° after tdc; normal tyre pressure: front 28 psi, 2 atm, rear 24 psi, 1.7 atm.

OPTIONAL ACCESSORIES reclining backrests; electrically-heated rear window.

MGB GT

PRICE IN GB: £ 1,037.
PRICE IN USA: $ 3,260.

ENGINE front, 4 stroke; cylinders: 4, in line; bore and stroke: 3.16 x 3.50 in, 80.3 x 88.9 mm; engine capacity:

MARCOS Mantis

MG Midget Mk III

MG 1300 Mk II

MGB GT

109.7 cu in, 1,798 cu cm; compression ratio: 8.8; max power (DIN): 95 hp at 5,400 rpm; max torque (DIN): 110 lb ft, 15.2 kg m at 3,000 rpm; max engine rpm: 6,200; specific power: 52.8 hp/l; cylinder block: cast iron; cylinder head: cast iron; crankshaft bearings: 5; valves: 2 per cylinder, overhead, push-rods and rockers; camshafts: 1, side; lubrication: eccentric pump, full flow filter, oil cooler; lubricating system capacity: 8.3 imp pt, 9.9 US pt, 4.7 l; carburation: 2 SU type HS 4 semi-downdraught carburettors; fuel feed: electric pump; cooling system: water; cooling system capacity: 10 imp pt, 12 US pt, 5.7 l.

TRANSMISSION driving wheels: rear; clutch: single dry plate (diaphragm), hydraulically controlled; gearbox: mechanical; gears: 4 + reverse; synchromesh gears: II, III, IV; gearbox ratios: I 3.439, II 2.166, III 1.381, IV 1, rev 3.094; gear lever: central; final drive: hypoid bevel; axle ratio: 3.909; tyres: 5.60 x 14.

PERFORMANCE max speeds: 32 mph, 51 km/h in 1st gear; 51 mph, 82 km/h in 2nd gear; 81 mph, 130 km/h in 3rd gear; 106 mph, 170 km/h in 4th gear; power-weight ratio: 24.3 lb/hp, 11 kg/hp; carrying capacity: 529 lb, 240 kg; speed in direct drive at 1,000 rpm: 18 mph, 28.9 km/h; fuel consumption: 25.4 m/imp gal, 21.2 m/US gal, 11.1 l x 100 km.

CHASSIS integral; front suspension: independent, wishbones, coil springs, anti-roll bar, lever dampers as upper arms; rear suspension: rigid axle, semi-elliptic leafsprings, lever dampers.

STEERING rack-and-pinion; turns of steering wheel lock to lock: 2.90.

BRAKES front disc (diameter 10 in, 254 mm), rear drum; area rubbed by linings: front 203 sq in, 1,309 sq cm, rear 107 sq in, 690 sq cm, total 310 sq in, 1,999 sq cm.

ELECTRICAL EQUIPMENT voltage: 12 V; batteries: 2, 58 Ah; generator type: alternator, 43 A; ignition distributor: Lucas; headlamps: 2.

DIMENSIONS AND WEIGHT wheel base: 91 in, 2,311 mm; front track: 49 in, 1,245 mm; rear track: 49.25 in, 1,251 mm; overall length: 153.40 in, 3,896 mm; overall width: 59.90 in, 1,521 mm; overall height: 49.40 in, 1,255 mm; ground clearance: 5 in, 127 mm; dry weight: 2,311 lb, 1,048 kg; distribution of weight: 55% front axle, 45% rear axle; turning circle (between walls): 32 ft, 9.8 m; fuel tank capacity: 12 imp gal, 14.5 US gal, 55 l.

BODY coupé; doors: 2; seats: 2 + 2; front seats: separate.

PRACTICAL INSTRUCTIONS fuel: 98-100 oct petrol; engine sump oil: 7.7 imp pt, 9.3 US pt, 4.4 l, SAE 10W-30 (winter) 20W-50 (summer), change every 3,000 miles, 4,800 km; gearbox oil: 4.6 imp pt, 5.5 US pt, 2.6 l, SAE 20W-50; final drive oil: 2.3 imp pt, 2.7 US pt, 1.3 l, SAE 90; greasing: every 3,000 miles, 4,800 km, 8 points; tappet clearances: inlet 0.015 in, 0.38 mm, exhaust 0.015 in, 0.38 mm; valve timing: inlet opens 16° before tdc and closes 56° after bdc, exhaust opens 51° before bdc and closes 21° after tdc; normal tyre pressure: front 19 psi, 1.3 atm, rear 19 psi, 1.3 atm.

OPTIONAL ACCESSORIES Laycock-de Normanville overdrive on III and IV, 0.802 ratio; servo brake; wire wheels; electrically-heated rear window.

MGB Sports

See MGB GT, except for:

PRICE IN GB: £ 932.
PRICE IN USA: $ 2,875.

PERFORMANCE power-weight ratio: 20.8 lb/hp, 9.4 kg/hp; acceleration: standing ¼ mile 18.7 sec, 0-50 mph (0-80 km/h) 8.5 sec.

DIMENSIONS AND WEIGHT dry weight: 1,973 lb, 895 kg; distribution of weight: 54% front axle, 46% rear axle.

BODY sports; seats: 2.

OPTIONAL ACCESSORIES Borg-Warner 35 automatic gearbox, hydraulic torque convertor and planetary gears with 3 ratios (I 2.389, II 1.450, III 1, rev 2.090), max ratio of convertor at stall 2, possible manual selection, with 8 compression ratio engine, max power (DIN) 91 hp at 5,400 rpm, max torque (DIN) 105 lb ft, 14.5 kg m at 3,000 rpm, 50.6 hp/l specific power, max speeds (I) 47 mph, 75 km/h, (II) 77 mph, 124 km/h, (III) 100 mph, 161 km/h, power-weight ratio 21.7 lb/hp, 9.8 kg/hp; hardtop; tonneau cover; electrically-heated rear window not available.

MG MGB Sports

MINI (BRITISH LEYLAND) 850 Saloon

MINI (BRITISH LEYLAND) Clubman Saloon

MINI (BRITISH LEYLAND)
GREAT BRITAIN

850 Saloon

PRICE IN GB: £ 487.

ENGINE front, transverse, 4 stroke; cylinders: 4, vertical, in line; bore and stroke: 2.48 x 2.69 in, 63 x 68.4 mm; engine capacity: 51.7 cu in, 848 cu cm; compression ratio: 8.3; max power (DIN): 34 hp at 5,000 rpm; max torque (DIN): 44 lb ft, 6.1 kg m at 2,900 rpm; max engine rpm: 5,500; specific power: 40.1 hp/l; cylinder block: cast iron; cylinder head: cast iron; crankshaft bearings: 3; valves: 2 per cylinder, overhead, in line, push-rods and rockers; camshafts: 1, side; lubrication: eccentric pump, full flow filter; lubricating system capacity: 8.4 imp pt, 10.1 US pt, 4.8 l; carburation: 1 SU type HS 2 semi-downdraught carburettor; fuel feed: mechanical pump; cooling system: water; cooling system capacity: 6.2 imp pt, 7.4 US pt, 3.5 l.

TRANSMISSION driving wheels: front; clutch: single dry plate (diaphragm), hydraulically controlled; gearbox: mechanical, in unit with engine; gears: 4 + reverse; synchromesh gears: I, II, III, IV; gearbox ratios: I 3.628, II 2.172, III 1.412, IV 1, rev 3.628; gear lever: central; final drive: helical spur gears, in unit with engine and gearbox; axle ratio: 3.765; tyres: 5.20 x 10.

PERFORMANCE max speeds: 22 mph, 35 km/h in 1st gear; 37 mph, 59 km/h in 2nd gear; 58 mph, 93 km/h in 3rd gear; 73 mph, 117 km/h in 4th gear; power-weight ratio: 39.2 lb/hp, 17.8 kg/hp; carrying capacity: 706 lb, 320 kg; acceleration: standing ¼ mile 23.6 sec, 0-50 mph (0-80 km/h) 18.3 sec; speed in direct drive at 1,000 rpm: 14.8 mph, 23.8 km/h; fuel consumption: 42.8 m/imp gal, 35.6 m/US gal, 6.6 l x 100 km.

CHASSIS integral, front and rear auxiliary frames; front suspension: independent, wishbones, hydrolastic (liquid) rubber cone springs, hydraulic connecting pipes to rear wheels; rear suspension: independent, swinging longitudinal trailing arms, hydrolastic (liquid) rubber cone springs, hydraulic connecting pipes to front wheels, pitch control tension springs.

STEERING rack-and-pinion; turns of steering wheel lock to lock: 2.33.

BRAKES drum, 2 front leading shoes; area rubbed by linings: front 60.9 sq in, 393 sq cm, rear 54.9 sq in, 354 sq cm, total 115.8 sq in, 747 sq cm.

ELECTRICAL EQUIPMENT voltage: 12 V; battery: 36 Ah; generator type: dynamo, 22 A; ignition distributor: Lucas; headlamps: 2.

DIMENSIONS AND WEIGHT wheel base: 80.16 in, 2,036 mm; front track: 47.44 in, 1,205 mm; rear track: 45.87 in, 1,165 mm; overall length: 120.24 in, 3,054 mm; overall width: 55.51 in, 1,410 mm; overall height: 52.99 in, 1,346 mm; ground clearance: 6.14 in, 156 mm; dry weight: 1,398 lb, 634 kg; distribution of weight: 61% front axle, 39% rear axle; turning circle (between walls): 29.5 ft, 9 m; fuel tank capacity: 5.5 imp pt, 6.6 US gal, 25 l.

BODY saloon/sedan; doors: 2; seats: 4; front seats: separate.

PRACTICAL INSTRUCTIONS fuel: 94 oct petrol; engine sump, gearbox and final drive oil: 7.6 imp pt, 9.1 US pt, 4.3 l, SAE 20W-50, change every 6,000 miles, 9,700 km; greasing: every 3,000 miles, 4,800 km, 8 points; tappet clearances: inlet 0.012 in, 0.30 mm, exhaust 0.012 in, 0.30 mm; valve timing: inlet opens 5° before tdc and closes 45° after bdc, exhaust opens 40° before bdc and closes 10° after tdc; normal tyre pressure: front 24 psi, 1.7 atm, rear 21 psi, 1.5 atm.

VARIATIONS

ENGINE 8.8 compression ratio.

OPTIONAL ACCESSORIES AP automatic gearbox, hydraulic torque convertor with 2 conic bevel gears (twin concentric differential-like gear clusters) with 4 ratios (I 2.690, II 1.845, III 1.460, IV 1.269, rev 2.690), operated by 3 brake bands and 2 multi-disc clutches, max ratio of convertor at stall 2, possible manual selection, with 8.8 compression ratio; reclining backrests; electrically-heated rear window.

1000 Saloon

See 850 Saloon, except for:

PRICE IN GB: £ 552.

ENGINE bore and stroke: 2.54 x 3 in, 64.6 x 76.2 mm; engine capacity: 60.9 cu in, 998 cu cm; max power (DIN): 38 hp

MG MGB Sports

MINI (BRITISH LEYLAND) Cooper 'S' Saloon

MINI (BRITISH LEYLAND) Clubman Saloon

at 5,250 rpm; max torque (DIN): 52 lb ft, 7.2 kg m at 2,700 rpm; specific power: 38.1 hp/l.

TRANSMISSION gearbox ratios: I 3.525, II 1.845, III 1.460, IV 1, rev 2.690; axle ratio: 3.444.

PERFORMANCE max speeds: 26 mph, 42 km/h in 1st gear; 49 mph, 79 km/h in 2nd gear; 62 mph, 100 km/h in 3rd gear; 75 mph, 120 km/h in 4th gear; power-weight ratio: 36.8 lb/hp, 16.7 kg/hp; carrying capacity: 706 lb, 320 kg; acceleration: standing ¼ mile 22.5 sec, 0-50 mph (0-80 km/h) 13.7 sec; speed in direct drive at 1,000 rpm: 16.5 mph, 26.5 km/h.

OPTIONAL ACCESSORIES AP automatic gearbox with 8.9 compression ratio, max power (SAE) 41 hp at 4,850 rpm, max torque (SAE) 52 lb ft, 7.2 kg m at 2,750 rpm, 1 SU type HS 4 semi-downdraught carburettor, power-weight ratio 34 lb/hp, 15.4 kg/hp, fuel consumption 39.8 m/imp gal, 33.1 m/US gal, 7.1 l x 100 km.

Cooper 'S' Saloon

See 1000 Saloon, except for:

PRICE IN GB: £ 770.

ENGINE bore and stroke: 2.78 x 3.20 in, 70.7 x 81.4 mm; engine capacity: 77.8 cu in, 1,275 cu cm; compression ratio: 9.7; max power (DIN): 76 hp at 6,000 rpm; max torque (DIN): 79 lb ft, 10.9 kg m at 3,000 rpm; max engine rpm: 7,000; specific power: 59.6 hp/l; carburation: 2 SU type HS 2 semi-downdraught carburettors.

TRANSMISSION gearbox ratios: I 3.200, II 1.916, III 1.357, IV 1, rev 3.200; axle ratio: 3.440; width of rims: 3.5''; tyres: 145 x 10.

PERFORMANCE max speeds: 35 mph, 56 km/h in 1st gear; 59 mph, 95 km/h in 2nd gear; 83 mph, 133 km/h in 3rd gear; 98 mph, 157 km/h in 4th gear; power-weight ratio: 19.2 lb/hp, 8.7 kg/hp; carrying capacity: 750 lb, 340 kg; acceleration: standing ¼ mile 18.2 sec, 0-50 mph (0-80 km/h) 7.7 sec; speed in direct drive at 1,000 rpm: 16.1 mph, 25.9 km/h; fuel consumption: 29.4 m/imp gal, 24.5 m/US gal, 9.6 l x 100 km.

BRAKES front disc (diameter 7.48 in, 190 mm), rear drum, servo; area rubbed by linings: front 122 sq in, 787 sq cm, rear 55 sq in, 355 sq cm, total 177 sq in, 1,142 sq cm.

ELECTRICAL EQUIPMENT battery: 45 Ah.

DIMENSIONS AND WEIGHT front track: 47.53 in, 1,207 mm; rear track: 46.31 in, 1,176 mm; ground clearance: 6.12 in, 155 mm; dry weight: 1,458 lb, 661 kg; distribution of weight: 61.4% front axle, 38.6% rear axle; turning circle (between walls): 30 ft, 9.2 m; fuel tank capacity: 11 imp gal, 13.2 US gal, 50 l.

PRACTICAL INSTRUCTIONS fuel: 98-100 oct petrol; engine sump, gearbox and final drive oil: 8.4 imp pt, 10.1 US pt, 4.8 l, SAE 10W-30 (winter) 20W-50 (summer), change every 6,000 miles, 9,700 km; greasing: every 3,000 miles, 4,800 km, 8 points; tappet clearances: inlet 0.012 in, 0.30 mm, exhaust 0.012 in, 0.30 mm; valve timing: inlet opens 5° before tdc and closes 45° after bdc, exhaust opens 51° before bdc and closes 21° after tdc; normal tyre pressure: front 28 psi, 2 atm, rear 26 psi, 1.8 atm.

OPTIONAL ACCESSORIES 4-speed mechanical gearbox (I 2.570, II 1.780, III 1.240, IV 1, rev 2.570), max speeds (I) 44 mph, 71 km/h, (II) 63 mph, 101 km/h, (III) 91 mph, 146 km/h, (IV) 98 mph, 158 km/h; 4.133 3.938 3.765 axle ratios; 4.5'' wide rims; 5.00 x 10 tyres; reclining backrests; protective cap for oil sump; electrically-heated rear window.

Clubman Saloon

See 1000 Saloon, except for:

PRICE IN GB: £ 589.

TRANSMISSION gearbox ratios: I 3.525, II 2.218, III 1.433, IV 1, rev 3.544; axle ratio: 3.440.

PERFORMANCE max speeds: 25 mph, 40 km/h in 1st gear; 41 mph, 66 km/h in 2nd gear; 64 mph, 103 km/h in 3rd gear; 73 mph, 117 km/h in 4th gear; power-weight ratio: 37 lb/hp, 16.8 kg/hp; acceleration: 0-50 mph (0-80 km/h) 14.9 sec.

STEERING turns of steering wheel lock to lock: 2.72.

DIMENSIONS AND WEIGHT wheel base: 80.16 in, 2,036 mm; front track: 47.44 in, 1,205 mm; rear track: 45.88 in, 1,165 mm; overall length: 124.64 in, 3,166 mm; dry weight: 1,406 lb, 637 kg; turning circle (between walls): 30 ft, 9.2 m.

OPTIONAL ACCESSORIES AP automatic gearbox, hydraulic

CLUBMAN SALOON

torque convertor with 2 conic bevel gears (twin concentric differential-like gears clusters) with 4 ratios (I 2.690, II 1.845, III 1.460, IV 1.269, rev 2.690), operated by 3 brake bands and 2 multi-disc clutches, max ratio of convertor at stall 2, possible manual selection, with 8.9 compression ratio, max power (SAE) 41 hp at 4,850 rpm, max torque (SAE) 52 lb ft, 7.2 kg m at 2,750 rpm, 1 SU type HS 4 semi-downdraught carburettor, power-weight ratio 34.3 lb/hp, 15.6 kg/hp, fuel consumption 39.8 m/imp gal, 33.1 m/US gal, 7.1 l x 100 km; alternator (with 45 Ah battery).

Clubman Estate Car

See Clubman Saloon, except for:

PRICE IN GB: £ 634.

PERFORMANCE power-weight ratio: 38 lb/hp, 17.2 kg/hp; acceleration: 0-50 mph (0-80 km/h) 15.1 sec.

CHASSIS integral, front and rear auxiliary frames; front suspension: independent, wishbones, rubber cone springs, telescopic dampers; rear suspension: independent, swinging longitudinal trailing arms, rubber cone springs, telescopic dampers.

DIMENSIONS AND WEIGHT wheel base: 84.15 in, 2,138 mm; overall length: 133.92 in, 3,401 mm; overall height: 53.50 in, 1,359 mm; dry weight: 1,444 lb, 655 kg; fuel tank capacity: 6.7 imp gal, 7.9 US gal, 30 l.

BODY estate car/station wagon; doors: 2 + 1.

OPTIONAL ACCESSORIES electrically-heated rear window not available.

1275 G.T.

See 1000 Saloon, except for:

PRICE IN GB: £ 683.

ENGINE bore and stroke: 2.78 x 3.20 in, 70.7 x 81.4 mm; engine capacity: 77.8 cu in, 1,275 cu cm; compression ratio: 8.8; max power (DIN): 59 hp at 5,300 rpm; max torque (DIN): 65 lb ft, 9 kg m at 2,550 rpm; carburation: 1 SU type HS 4 semi-downdraught carburettor.

TRANSMISSION gearbox ratios: I 3.330, II 2.070, III 1.350, IV 1, rev 3.350; axle ratio: 3.650; width of rims: 4.5''.

PERFORMANCE max speeds: 33 mph, 53 km/h in 1st gear; 55 mph, 88 km/h in 2nd gear; 78 mph, 125 km/h in 3rd gear; 87 mph, 140 km/h in 4th gear; power-weight ratio: 25.8 lb/hp, 11.7 kg/hp; acceleration: 0-50 mph (0-80 km/h) 9.5 sec; speed in direct drive at 1,000 rpm: 15 mph, 24.1 km/h; fuel consumption: 40.4 m/imp gal, 33.6 m/US gal, 7 l x 100 km.

STEERING turns of steering wheel lock to lock: 2.72.

ELECTRICAL EQUIPMENT battery: 45 Ah.

DIMENSIONS AND WEIGHT wheel base: 80.16 in, 2,036 mm; front track: 48.53 in, 1,233 mm; rear track: 47.31 in, 1,202 mm; overall length: 124.64 in, 3,166 mm; dry weight: 1,520 lb, 690 kg; turning circle (between walls): 30.3 ft, 9.2 m; fuel tank capacity: 5.5 imp gal, 6.6 US gal, 25 l.

VARIATIONS

None.

MORGAN   GREAT BRITAIN

4/4 1600 2-seater

PRICE IN GB: £ 915.

ENGINE front, 4 stroke; cylinders: 4, vertical, in line; bore and stroke: 3.19 x 3.06 in, 81 x 77.7 mm; engine capacity: 97.6 cu in, 1,599 cu cm; compression ratio: 9.2; max power (DIN): 95 hp at 5,500 rpm; max torque (DIN): 103 lb ft, 14.2 kg m at 3,600 rpm; max engine rpm: 5,100; specific power: 59.4 hp/l; cylinder block: cast iron; cylinder head: cast iron; crankshaft bearings: 5; valves: 2 per cylinder, overhead, push-rods and rockers; camshafts: 1, side; lubrication: rotary pump, full flow filter; lubricating system capacity: 6 imp pt, 7.2 US pt, 3.4 l; carburation: 1 Weber 26/27 downdraught twin barrel carburettor; fuel feed: mechanical pump; cooling system: water; cooling system capacity: 12 imp pt, 14.4 US pt, 6.8 l.

MINI (BRITISH LEYLAND) 1275 G.T.

*MORGAN 4/4 1600
(independent front suspension)*

MORRIS Minor 1000 Saloon

TRANSMISSION driving wheels: rear; clutch: single dry plate, hydraulically controlled; gearbox: mechanical; gears: 4 + reverse; synchromesh gears: I, II, III, IV; gearbox ratios: I 2.976, II 2.024, III 1.390, IV 1, rev 3.317; gear lever: central; final drive: hypoid bevel; axle ratio: 4.100; tyres: 155 x 15.

PERFORMANCE max speeds: 37 mph, 59 km/h in 1st gear; 55 mph, 88 km/h in 2nd gear; 80 mph, 128 km/h in 3rd gear; 105 mph, 169 km/h in 4th gear; power-weight ratio: 15.2 lb/hp, 6.9 kg/hp; carrying capacity: 353 lb, 160 kg; speed in direct drive at 1,000 rpm: 18.5 mph, 29.7 km/h; fuel consumption: 35.3 m/imp gal, 29.4 m/US gal, 8 l x 100 km.

CHASSIS ladder frame, Z-section long members, tubular and box-type cross-members; front suspension: independent, vertical sliding pillars, coil springs, telescopic dampers; rear suspension: rigid axle, semi-elliptic leafsprings, lever dampers.

STEERING cam and peg; turns of steering wheel lock to lock: 2.25.

BRAKES front disc (diameter 11 in, 279 mm), rear drum; area rubbed by linings: total 325.1 sq in, 2,097 sq cm.

ELECTRICAL EQUIPMENT voltage: 12 V; battery: 38 Ah; generator type: alternator; headlamps: 2.

DIMENSIONS AND WEIGHT wheel base: 96 in, 2,438 mm; front track: 47 in, 1,194 mm; rear track: 49 in, 1,245 mm; overall length: 144 in, 3,658 mm; overall width: 56 in, 1,422 mm; overall height: 51 in, 1,295 mm; ground clearance: 7 in, 178 mm; dry weight: 1,455 lb, 660 kg; distribution of weight: 48% front axle, 52% rear axle; turning circle (between walls): 32 ft, 9.8 m; fuel tank capacity: 8.5 imp gal, 10.3 US gal, 39 l.

BODY roadster; doors: 2; seats: 2.

PRACTICAL INSTRUCTIONS fuel: 98 oct petrol; engine sump oil: 5.5 imp pt, 6.6 US pt, 3.1 l, SAE 10W-30, change every 6,000 miles, 9,700 km; gearbox oil: 1.8 imp pt, 2.1 US pt, 1 l, SAE 80; final drive oil: 1.9 imp pt, 2.3 US pt, 1.1 l, SAE 90; greasing: every 3,000 and 9,000 miles, 4,800 and 14,500 km, 10 points; normal tyre pressure: front 17 psi, 1.2 atm, rear 17 psi, 1.2 atm.

OPTIONAL ACCESSORIES wire wheels.

4/4 1600 4-seater

See 4/4 1600 2-seater, except for:

PRICE IN GB: £ 945.

PERFORMANCE power-weight ratio: 16.4 lb/hp, 7.5 kg/hp.

DIMENSIONS AND WEIGHT dry weight: 1,568 lb, 711 kg; fuel tank capacity: 10 imp gal, 12.1 US gal, 46 l.

BODY seats: 4.

Plus 8 2-seater

PRICE IN GB: £ 1,300.

ENGINE front, 4 stroke; cylinders: 8, Vee-slanted at 90°; bore and stroke: 3.50 x 2.80 in, 89 x 71 mm; engine capacity: 215.3 cu in, 3,528 cu cm; compression ratio: 10.5; max power (DIN): 184 hp at 5,200 rpm; max torque (DIN): 226 lb ft, 31.2 kg m at 3,000 rpm; max engine rpm: 6,050; specific power: 52.1 hp/l; cylinder block: light alloy; cylinder head: light alloy; crankshaft bearings: 5; valves: 2 per cylinder, overhead, in line, push-rods and rockers, hydraulic tappets; camshafts: 1, at centre of Vee; lubrication: gear pump, full flow filter; lubricating system capacity: 10.6 imp pt, 12.7 US pt, 6 l; carburation: 2 US type HS 6 semi-downdraught carburettors; fuel feed: mechanical pump; cooling system: water, electric thermostatic fan; cooling system capacity: 15 imp pt, 18 US pt, 8.5 l.

TRANSMISSION driving wheels: rear; clutch: single dry plate (diaphragm), hydraulically controlled; gearbox: mechanical; gears: 4 + reverse; synchromesh gears: II, III, IV; gearbox ratios: I 2.961, II 1.732, III 1.201, IV 1, rev 2.961; gear lever: central; final drive: hypoid bevel, limited slip; axle ratio: 3.580; width of rims: 5.5''; tyres: 185 x 15.

PERFORMANCE max speeds: 44 mph, 71 km/h in 1st gear; 76 mph, 122 km/h in 2nd gear; 109 mph, 175 km/h in 3rd gear; 130 mph, 209 km/h in 4th gear; power-weight ratio: 10.1 lb/hp, 4.6 kg/hp; carrying capacity: 353 lb, 160 kg; acceleration: standing ¼ mile 14.8 sec, 0-50 mph (0-80 km/h) 5.1 sec; speed in direct drive at 1,000 rpm: 21.8 mph, 35.1 km/h; fuel consumption: 23.5 m/imp gal, 19.6 m/US gal, 12 l x 100 km.

CHASSIS ladder frame, Z-section long members, tubular and box-type cross members; front suspension: independent, vertical sliding pillars, coil springs, telescopic dampers; rear suspension: rigid axle, semi-elliptic leafsprings, lever dampers.

STEERING cam and peg; turns of steering wheel lock to lock: 2.25.

BRAKES front disc (diameter 11 in, 279 mm), rear drum, servo; area rubbed by linings: total 325.1 sq in, 2,097 sq cm.

MORGAN 4/4 1600 2-seater

MORGAN Plus 8 2-seater

MORRIS Minor 1000 4-door Saloon

ELECTRICAL EQUIPMENT voltage: 12 V; battery: 58 Ah; generator type: alternator; ignition distributor: Lucas, headlamps: 4.

DIMENSIONS AND WEIGHT wheel base: 98 in, 2,489 mm; front track: 48 in, 1,219 mm; rear track: 50 in, 1,270 mm; overall length: 146 in, 3,708 mm; overall width: 57.50 in, 1,460 mm; overall height: 52 in, 1,321 mm; ground clearance: 7 in, 178 mm; dry weight: 1,876 lb, 851 kg; distribution of weight: 52% front axle, 48% rear axle; turning circle (between walls): 38 ft, 11.6 m; fuel tank capacity: 14.5 imp gal, 17.4 US gal, 66 l.

BODY roadster; doors: 2; seats: 2.

PRACTICAL INSTRUCTIONS fuel: 100 oct petrol; engine sump oil: 10 imp pt, 12 US pt, 5.7 l, SAE 20W-40, change every 5,000 miles, 8,000 km; gearbox oil: 2.5 imp pt, 3 US pt, 1.4 l, SAE 30, change every 2,000 miles, 3,200 km; final drive oil: 1.6 imp pt, 1.9 US pt, 0.9 l, SAE 90, change every 20,000 miles, 32,200 km; greasing: every 5,000 miles, 8,000 km, 6 points; valve timing: inlet opens 30° before tdc and closes 75° after bdc, exhaust opens 68° before bdc and closes 37° after tdc; normal tyre pressure: front 24 psi, 1.7 atm, rear 24 psi, 1.7 atm.

OPTIONAL ACCESSORIES dual exhaust system.

MORRIS GREAT BRITAIN

Minor 1000 2-door Saloon

PRICE IN GB: £ 566.

ENGINE front, 4 stroke; cylinders: 4, vertical, in line; bore and stroke: 2.54 x 3.30 in, 64.6 x 83.7 mm; engine capacity: 67 cu in, 1,098 cu cm; compression ratio: 8.5; max power (DIN): 48 hp at 5,100 rpm; max torque (DIN): 60 lb ft, 8.3 kg m at 2,500 rpm; max engine rpm: 5,800; specific power: 43.7 hp/l; cylinder block: cast iron; cylinder head: cast iron; crankshaft bearings: 3; valves: 2 per cylinder, overhead, in line, push-rods and rockers; camshafts: 1, side; lubrication: eccentric pump, full flow filter; lubricating system capacity: 6.2 imp pt, 7.4 US pt, 3.5 l; carburation: 1 SU type HS 2 semi-downdraught carburettor; fuel feed: electric pump; cooling system: water; cooling system capacity: 9.7 imp pt, 11.6 US pt, 5.5 l.

TRANSMISSION driving wheels: rear; clutch: single dry plate, hydraulically controlled; gearbox: mechanical; gears: 4 + reverse; synchromesh gears: II, III, IV; gearbox ratios: I 3.628, II 2.172, III 1.412, IV 1, rev 4.664; gear lever: central; final drive: hypoid bevel; axle ratio: 4.222; width of rims: 3.5''; tyres: 5.20 x 14.

PERFORMANCE max speeds: 26 mph, 42 km/h in 1st gear; 43 mph, 70 km/h in 2nd gear; 67 mph, 108 km/h in 3rd gear; 80 mph, 128 km/h in 4th gear; power-weight ratio: 33.9 lb/hp, 15.4 kg/hp; carrying capacity: 728 lb, 330 kg; acceleration: standing ¼ mile 22 sec, 0-50 mph (0-80 km/h) 15 sec; speed in direct drive at 1,000 rpm: 16.3 mph, 26.3 km/h; fuel consumption: 37.1 m/imp gal, 30.9 m/US gal, 7.6 l x 100 km.

CHASSIS integral; front suspension: independent, wishbones, longitudinal torsion bars, lever dampers; rear suspension: rigid axle, semi-elliptic leafsprings, lever dampers.

STEERING rack-and-pinion; turns of steering wheel lock to lock: 2.50.

BRAKES drum, 2 front leading shoes; area rubbed by linings: front 74 sq in, 477 sq cm, rear 53.7 sq in, 347 sq cm, total 127.7 sq in, 824 sq cm.

ELECTRICAL EQUIPMENT voltage: 12 V; battery: 40 Ah; generator type: dynamo, 22 A; ignition distributor: Lucas; headlamps: 2.

DIMENSIONS AND WEIGHT wheel base: 86 in, 2,184 mm; front track: 50.30 in, 1,278 mm; rear track: 50.30 in, 1,278 mm; overall length: 148 in, 3,759 mm; overall width: 61 in, 1,549 mm; overall height: 60 in, 1,524 mm; ground clearance: 6.75 in, 171 mm; dry weight: 1,625 lb, 737 kg; distribution of weight: 57% front axle, 43% rear axle; turning circle (between walls): 33 ft, 10.1 m; fuel tank capacity: 6.5 imp gal, 7.9 US gal, 30 l.

BODY saloon/sedan; doors: 2; seats: 4; front seats: separate.

PRACTICAL INSTRUCTIONS fuel: 95-98 oct petrol; engine sump oil: 5.5 imp pt, 6.6 US pt, 3.1 l, SAE 10W-30 (winter) 20W-50 (summer), change every 6,000 miles, 9,700 km; gearbox oil: 2.3 imp pt, 2.7 US pt, 1.3 l, SAE 20W-50; final drive oil: 1.8 imp pt, 2.1 US pt, 1 l, SAE 90; greasing: every 3,000 miles, 4,800 km, 10 points; tappet clearances: inlet 0.012 in, 0.30 mm, exhaust 0.012 in, 0.30 mm; valve timing: inlet opens 5° before tdc and closes 45° after bdc, exhaust opens 51° before bdc and closes 21° after tdc; normal tyre pressure: front 21 psi, 1.5 atm, rear 21 psi, 1.5 atm.

MINOR 1000 2-DOOR SALOON

VARIATIONS

ENGINE 7.5 compression ratio.

OPTIONAL ACCESSORIES reclining backrests.

Minor 1000 2-door De Luxe Saloon

See Minor 1000 2-door Saloon, except for:

PRICE IN GB: £ 588.

OPTIONAL ACCESSORIES reclining backrests standard.

Minor 1000 4-door Saloon

See Minor 1000 2-door Saloon, except for:

PRICE IN GB: £ 592.

PERFORMANCE power-weight ratio: 34.9 lb/hp, 15.8 kg/hp.

DIMENSIONS AND WEIGHT dry weight: 1,675 lb, 760 kg.

Minor 1000 4-door De Luxe Saloon

See Minor 1000 2-door Saloon, except for:

PRICE IN GB: £ 614.

PERFORMANCE power-weight ratio: 34.9 lb/hp, 15.8 kg/hp.

DIMENSIONS AND WEIGHT dry weight: 1,675 lb, 760 kg.

OPTIONAL ACCESSORIES reclining backrests standard.

Minor 1000 Traveller De Luxe

See Minor 1000 2-door Saloon, except for:

PRICE IN GB: £ 696.

PERFORMANCE power-weight ratio: 37.4 lb/hp, 17 kg/hp; fuel consumption: 37.6 m/imp gal, 31.4 m/US gal, 7.5 l x 100 km.

DIMENSIONS AND WEIGHT overall length: 149 in, 3,785 mm; overall height: 60.50 in, 1,587 mm; ground clearance: 6.70 in, 170 mm; dry weight: 1,795 lb, 814 kg.

BODY estate car/station wagon; doors: 2 + 1.

PRACTICAL INSTRUCTIONS normal tyre pressure: rear 24 psi, 1.7 atm.

1100 Mk II 2-door De Luxe Saloon

PRICE IN GB: £ 612.

ENGINE front, transverse, 4 stroke; cylinders: 4, vertical, in line; bore and stroke: 2.54 x 3.30 in, 64.6 x 83.7 mm; engine capacity: 67 cu in, 1,098 cu cm; compression ratio: 8.5; max power (DIN): 48 hp at 5,100 rpm; max torque (DIN): 60 lb ft, 8.3 kg m at 2,500 rpm; max engine rpm: 6,000; specific power: 43.7 hp/l; cylinder block: cast iron; cylinder head: cast iron; crankshaft bearings: 3; valves: 2 per cylinder, overhead, in line, push-rods and rockers; camshafts: 1, side; lubrication: eccentric pump, full flow filter; lubricating system capacity: 9 imp pt, 10.8 US pt, 5.1 l; carburation: 1 SU type HS 2 semi-downdraught carburettor; fuel feed: electric pump; cooling system: water; cooling system capacity: 6.7 imp pt, 8 US pt, 3.8 l.

TRANSMISSION driving wheels: front; clutch: single dry plate (diaphragm), hydraulically controlled; gearbox: mechanical, in unit with engine; gears: 4 + reverse; synchromesh gears: II, III, IV; gearbox ratios: I 3.628, II 2.172, III 1.412, IV 1, rev 3.628; gear lever: central; final drive: helical spur gears, in unit with engine; axle ratio: 4.133; width of rims: 4''; tyres: 5.50 x 12.

PERFORMANCE max speeds: 24 mph, 39 km/h in 1st gear; 41 mph, 66 km/h in 2nd gear; 62 mph, 100 km/h in 3rd gear; 79 mph, 127 km/h in 4th gear; power-weight ratio: 36.4 lb/hp, 16.5 kg/hp; carrying capacity: 882 lb, 400 kg; acceleration: standing ¼ mile 22 sec, 0-50 mph (0-80 km/h) 14.7 sec; speed in direct drive at 1,000 rpm: 14.7 mph, 23.6 km/h; fuel consumption: 34.4 m/imp gal, 28.7 m/US gal, 8.2 l x 100 km.

CHASSIS integral, front and rear auxiliary frames; front suspension: independent, wishbones, hydrolastic (liquid)

MORRIS 1300 2-door Super De Luxe Saloon

MORRIS 1300 G.T. Saloon

MORRIS Oxford Series VI Saloon

rubber cone springs, hydraulic connecting pipes to rear wheels; rear suspension: independent, swinging longitudinal trailing arms, hydrolastic (liquid) rubber cone springs, hydraulic connecting pipes to front wheels, combined with transverse torsion bars, anti-roll bar.

STEERING rack-and-pinion; turns of steering wheel lock to lock: 3.12.

BRAKES front disc (diameter 8.39 in, 213 mm), rear drum, rear compensator; area rubbed by linings: front 143 sq in, 923 sq cm, rear 63 sq in, 407 sq cm, total 206 sq in, 1,330 sq cm.

ELECTRICAL EQUIPMENT voltage: 12 V; battery: 40 Ah; generator type: dynamo, 264 W; ignition distributor: Lucas; headlamps: 2.

DIMENSIONS AND WEIGHT wheel base: 93.50 in, 2,375 mm; front track: 51.50 in, 1,308 mm; rear track: 50.87 in, 1,292 mm; overall length: 146.73 in, 3,727 mm; overall width: 60.35 in, 1,533 mm; overall height: 52.99 in, 1,346 mm; ground clearance: 6.10 in, 155 mm; dry weight: 1,749 lb, 793 kg; distribution of weight: 62% front axle, 38% rear axle; turning circle (between walls): 36.1 ft, 11 m; fuel tank capacity: 7.9 imp gal, 9.5 US gal, 36 l.

BODY saloon/sedan; doors: 2; seats: 4-5; front seats: separate.

PRACTICAL INSTRUCTIONS fuel: 96 oct petrol; engine sump, gearbox and final drive oil: 7.9 imp pt, 9.5 US pt, 4.5 l, SAE 10W-30 (winter) 20W-50 (summer), change every 6,000 miles, 9,700 km; greasing: every 3,000 miles, 4,800 km, 4 points; sparking plug type: 225°; tappet clearances: inlet 0.012 in, 0.30 mm, exhaust 0.012 in, 0.30 mm; valve timing: inlet opens 5° before tdc and closes 45° after bdc, exhaust opens 51° before bdc and closes 21° after tdc; normal tyre pressure: front 28 psi, 2 atm, rear 24 psi, 1.7 atm.

VARIATIONS
ENGINE 7.5 compression ratio.

OPTIONAL ACCESSORIES AP automatic gearbox, hydraulic torque convertor with 2 conic bevel gears (twin concentric differential-like gear clusters) with 4 ratios (I 2.689, II 1.846, III 1.460, IV 1, rev 2.689), operated by 3 brake bands and 2 multi-disc clutches, max ratio of convertor at stall 2, possible manual selection, 3.760 axle ratio, with 8.9 compression ratio, 1 SU type HS 4 semi-downdraught carburettor, speed in direct drive at 1,000 rpm 18.8 mph, 30.2 km/h, area rubbed by brake linings front 148 sq in, 955 sq cm, rear 63 sq in, 407 sq cm, total 211 sq in, 1,362 sq cm; reclining backrests; electrically-heated rear window.

1100 Mk II 4-door Super De Luxe Saloon

See 1100 Mk II 2-door De Luxe Saloon, except for:

PRICE IN GB: £ 657.

PERFORMANCE power-weight ratio: 37.6 lb/hp, 17.1 kg/hp.

DIMENSIONS AND WEIGHT dry weight: 1,804 lb, 818 kg.

1300 2-door Super De Luxe Saloon

See 1100 Mk II 2-door De Luxe Saloon, except for:

PRICE IN GB: £ 653.

ENGINE bore and stroke: 2.78 x 3.20 in, 70.6 x 81.3 mm; engine capacity: 77.8 cu in, 1,275 cu cm; compression ratio: 8.8; max power (DIN): 60 hp at 5,250 rpm; max torque (DIN): 69 lb ft, 9.5 kg m at 2,500 rpm; max engine rpm: 5,900; specific power: 47.1 hp/l; carburation: 1 SU type HS 4 semi-downdraught carburettor.

TRANSMISSION gearbox ratios: I 3.525, II 2.218, III 1.443, IV 1, rev 3.544; axle ratio: 3.647.

PERFORMANCE max speeds: 28 mph, 45 km/h in 1st gear; 45 mph, 73 km/h in 2nd gear; 69 mph, 111 km/h in 3rd gear; 87 mph, 140 km/h in 4th gear; power-weight ratio: 28.5 lb/hp, 12.9 kg/hp; acceleration: standing ¼ mile 20 sec, 0-50 mph (0-80 km/h) 11.4 sec; speed in direct drive at 1,000 rpm: 16.8 mph, 27 km/h; fuel consumption: 34 m/imp gal, 28.3 m/US gal, 8.3 l x 100 km.

BRAKES area rubbed by linings: front 148 sq in, 955 sq cm, rear 63 sq in, 407 sq cm, total 211 sq in, 1,362 sq cm.

DIMENSIONS AND WEIGHT dry weight: 1,711 lb, 776 kg.

PRACTICAL INSTRUCTIONS fuel: 98-100 oct petrol.

VARIATIONS
ENGINE 7.5 compression ratio not available.

MORRIS 1300 Super De Luxe Saloon

MORRIS 1300 G.T. Saloon

MORRIS Oxford Series VI Saloon

1300 4-door Super De Luxe Saloon

See 1300 2-door Super De Luxe Saloon, except for:

PRICE IN GB: £ 678.

PERFORMANCE power-weight ratio: 29.4 lb/hp, 13.3 kg/hp.

DIMENSIONS AND WEIGHT dry weight: 1,766 lb, 801 kg.

1300 Traveller

See 1300 2-door Super De Luxe Saloon, except for:

PRICE IN GB: £ 733.

PERFORMANCE power-weight ratio: 30.2 lb/hp, 13.7 kg/hp; acceleration: 0-50 mph (0-80 km/h) 11.6 sec.

DIMENSIONS AND WEIGHT dry weight: 1,815 lb, 823 kg.

BODY estate car/station wagon; doors: 2 + 1.

OPTIONAL ACCESSORIES electrically-heated rear window not available.

1300 G.T. Saloon

See 1300 4-door Super De Luxe Saloon, except for:

PRICE IN GB: £ 761.

ENGINE compression ratio: 9.7; max power (DIN): 70 hp at 6,000 rpm; max torque (DIN): 74 lb ft, 10.2 kg m at 3,250 rpm; max engine rpm: 6,000; specific power: 54.9 hp/l; carburation: 2 SU type HS 2 semi-downdraught carburettors.

TRANSMISSION gearbox ratios: I 3.300, II 2.090, III 1.350, IV 1, rev 3.350; axle ratio: 2.742; tyres: 145 x 12.

PERFORMANCE max speeds: 32 mph, 52 km/h in 1st gear; 50 mph, 80 km/h in 2nd gear; 77 mph, 124 km/h in 3rd gear; 92 mph, 148 km/h in 4th gear; power-weight ratio: 24.4 lb/hp, 11.1 kg/hp; acceleration: standing ¼ mile 19.7 sec, 0-50 mph (0-80 km/h) 9.8 sec; speed in direct drive at 1,000 rpm: 16.8 mph, 27 km/h.

BRAKES front disc (diameter 8.39 in, 213 mm).

DIMENSIONS AND WEIGHT front track: 51.50 in, 1,308 mm; rear track: 50.87 in, 1,292 mm; overall length: 145.81 in, 3,703 mm; overall width: 60.38 in, 1,534 mm; overall height: 53.50 in, 1,359 mm; ground clearance: 5.50 in, 139 mm.

BODY front seats: reclining backrests.

OPTIONAL ACCESSORIES only electrically-heated rear window and servo brake.

Oxford Series VI Saloon

PRICE IN GB: £ 738.

ENGINE front, 4 stroke; cylinders: 4, vertical, in line; bore and stroke: 3 x 3.50 in, 76.2 x 88.9 mm; engine capacity: 99 cu in, 1,622 cu cm; compression ratio: 8.3; max power (DIN): 61 hp at 4,500 rpm; max torque (DIN): 90 lb ft, 12.4 kg m at 2,100 rpm; max engine rpm: 5,400; specific power: 37.6 hp/l; cylinder block: cast iron; cylinder head: cast iron; crankshaft bearings: 3; valves: 2 per cylinder, overhead, in line, push-rods and rockers; camshafts: 1, side; lubrication: gear pump, full flow filter; lubricating system capacity: 8.8 imp pt, 10.6 US pt, 5 l; carburation: 1 SU type HS 2 semi-downdraught carburettor; fuel feed: electric pump; cooling system: water; cooling system capacity: 12.3 imp pt, 14.8 US pt, 7 l.

TRANSMISSION driving wheels: rear; clutch: single dry plate, hydraulically controlled; gearbox: mechanical; gears: 4 + reverse; synchromesh gears: II, III, IV; gearbox ratios: I 3.636, II 2.214, III 1.374, IV 1, rev 4.755; gear lever: central; final drive: hypoid bevel; axle ratio: 4.300; width of rims: 4''; tyres: 5.90 x 14.

PERFORMANCE max speeds: 25 mph, 40 km/h in 1st gear; 40 mph, 64 km/h in 2nd gear; 65 mph, 104 km/h in 3rd gear; 84 mph, 135 km/h in 4th gear; power-weight ratio: 39 lb/hp, 17.7 kg/hp; carrying capacity: 882 lb, 400 kg; acceleration: standing ¼ mile 21.5 sec, 0-50 mph (0-80 km/h) 14 sec; speed in direct drive at 1,000 rpm: 16.6 mph, 26.7 km/h; fuel consumption: 30 m/imp gal, 25 m/US gal, 9.4 l x 100 km.

CHASSIS integral; front suspension: independent, wishbones, coil springs, anti-roll bar, lever dampers as upper arms; rear suspension: rigid axle, semi-elliptic leafsprings, anti-roll bar, lever dampers.

STEERING cam and peg; turns of steering wheel lock to lock: 3.

OXFORD SERIES VI SALOON

BRAKES drum, 2 front leading shoes; area rubbed by linings: front 141 sq in, 910 sq cm, rear 99 sq in, 639 sq cm, total 240 sq in, 1,549 sq cm.

ELECTRICAL EQUIPMENT voltage: 12 V; battery: 57 Ah; generator type: dynamo, 22 A; ignition distributor: Lucas; headlamps: 2.

DIMENSIONS AND WEIGHT wheel base: 100.25 in, 2,546 mm; front track: 50.65 in, 1,286 mm; rear track: 51.35 in, 1,304 mm; overall length: 174.50 in, 4,432 mm; overall width: 63.50 in, 1,613 mm; overall height: 58.12 in, 1,476 mm; ground clearance: 6 in, 152 mm; dry weight: 2,374 lb, 1,077 kg; distribution of weight: 52.2% front axle, 47.8% rear axle; turning circle (between walls): 37 ft, 11.3 m; fuel tank capacity: 9.9 imp gal, 11.9 US gal, 45 l.

BODY saloon/sedan; doors: 4; seats: 4-5; front seats: separate.

PRACTICAL INSTRUCTIONS fuel: 95-98 oct petrol; engine sump oil: 7 imp pt, 8.5 US pt, 4 l, SAE 10W-30 (winter) 20W-50 (summer), change every 3,000 miles, 4,800 km; gearbox oil: 4.6 imp pt, 5.5 US pt, 2.6 l, SAE 20W-50; final drive oil: 2.3 imp pt, 2.7 US pt, 1.3 l, SAE 90; greasing: every 3,000 miles, 4,800 km, 7 points; tappet clearances: inlet 0.015 in, 0.38 mm, exhaust 0.015 in, 0.38 mm; valve timing: inlet opens 0° before tdc and closes 50° after bdc, exhaust opens 35° before bdc and closes 15° after tdc; normal tyre pressure: front 20 psi, 1.4 atm, rear 24 psi, 1.7 atm.

VARIATIONS

ENGINE 7.2 compression ratio.

ENGINE (Diesel) bore and stroke 2.87 x 3.50 in, 73 x 89 mm, engine capacity 90.9 cu in, 1,489 cu cm, 23 compression ratio, max power (DIN) 40 hp at 4,000 rpm, max torque (DIN) 64 lb ft, 8.8 kg m at 1,900 rpm, max engine rpm 4,700, 26.9 hp/l specific power, cooling system capacity 9.5 imp pt, 11.4 US pt, 5.4 l.
TRANSMISSION 4-speed mechanical gearbox (I 3.950, II 2.400, III 1.490, IV 1, rev 5.160), 4.550 axle ratio.
PERFORMANCE max speeds (I) 19 mph, 30 km/h, (II) 31 mph, 50 km/h, (III) 49 mph, 79 km/h, (IV) 68 mph, 109 km/h, power-weight ratio 62 lb/hp, 28.1 kg/hp, acceleration standing ¼ mile 25.9 sec, 0-50 mph (0-80 km/h) 23.8 sec, speed in direct drive at 1,000 rpm 15.7 mph, 25.2 km/h, fuel consumption 38.7 m/imp gal, 32.2 m/US gal, 7.3 l x 100 km.
ELECTRICAL EQUIPMENT 91 Ah battery.
DIMENSIONS AND WEIGHT dry weight 2,483 lb, 1,126 kg.

OPTIONAL ACCESSORIES Borg-Warner automatic gearbox, hydraulic torque convertor and planetary gears with 3 ratios (I 2.390, II 1.450, III 1, rev 2.090), max ratio of convertor at stall 2; steering column gear lever; 4.875 axle ratio only for export; heavy-duty rear suspension; reclining backrests; electrically-heated rear window.

Oxford Series VI De Luxe Saloon

See Oxford Series VI Saloon, except for:

PRICE IN GB: £ 769.

1800 Mk II De Luxe Saloon

PRICE IN GB: £ 891.

ENGINE front, transverse, 4 stroke; cylinders: 4, in line; bore and stroke: 3.16 x 3.50 in, 80.3 x 88.9 mm; engine capacity: 109.7 cu in, 1,798 cu cm; compression ratio: 9; max power (DIN): 86.5 hp at 5,400 rpm; max torque (DIN): 101 lb ft, 13.9 kg m at 3,000 rpm; max engine rpm: 5,600; specific power: 48.1 hp/l; cylinder block: cast iron; cylinder head: cast iron; crankshaft bearings: 5; valves: 2 per cylinder, overhead, push-rods and rockers; camshafts: 1, side; lubrication: eccentric pump, magnetic metal gauze filter in sump and full flow; lubricating system capacity: 12.5 imp pt, 15 US pt, 7.1 l; carburation: 1 SU type HS 6 carburettor; fuel feed: mechanical pump; cooling system: water; cooling system capacity: 9.5 imp pt, 11.4 US pt, 5.4 l.

TRANSMISSION driving wheels: front; clutch: single dry plate (diaphragm), hydraulically controlled; gearbox: mechanical, in unit with engine; gears: 4 + reverse; synchromesh gears: I, II, III, IV; gearbox ratios: I 3.292, II 2.059, III 1.384, IV 1, rev 3.075; gear lever: central; final drive: spiral bevel; axle ratio: 3.882; width of rims: 4.5''; tyres: 165 x 14.

PERFORMANCE max speeds: 31 mph, 50 km/h in 1st gear; 49 mph, 79 km/h in 2nd gear; 74 mph, 119 km/h in 3rd gear; 91 mph, 146 km/h in 4th gear; power-weight ratio: 29.3 lb/hp, 13.3 kg/hp; carrying capacity: 882 lb, 400 kg; speed in

MORRIS 1800 Mk II 'S' De Luxe Saloon

RELIANT Rebel 700 Saloon

RELIANT Scimitar GTE

direct drive at 1,000 rpm: 18.2 mph, 29.3 km/h; fuel consumption: 23.7 m/imp gal, 19.8 m/US gal, 11.9 l x 100 km.

CHASSIS integral; front suspension: independent, wishbones, lower trailing links, hydrolastic (liquid) rubber cone springs, hydraulic connecting pipes to rear wheels; rear suspension: independent, swinging longitudinal trailing arms, hydrolastic (liquid) rubber cone springs, hydraulic connecting pipes to front wheels, anti-roll bar.

STEERING rack-and-pinion; turns of steering wheel lock to lock: 3.80.

BRAKES front disc (diameter 9.29 in, 236 mm), rear drum, servo; area rubbed by linings: front 183 sq in, 1,181 sq cm, rear 99 sq in, 639 sq cm, total 282 sq in, 1,820 sq cm.

ELECTRICAL EQUIPMENT voltage: 12 V; battery: 50 Ah; generator type: dynamo, 22 A; ignition distributor: Lucas; headlamps: 2; fog lamps: 2.

DIMENSIONS AND WEIGHT wheel base: 106.61 in, 2,708 mm; front track: 55.98 in, 1,422 mm; rear track: 55.51 in, 1,410 mm; overall length: 166.87 in, 4,238 mm; overall width: 66.26 in, 1,683 mm; overall height: 56.26 in, 1,429 mm; ground clearance: 6.61 in, 168 mm; dry weight: 2,536 lb, 1,150 kg; distribution of weight: 63% front axle, 37% rear axle; turning circle (between walls): 40.3 ft, 12.3 m; fuel tank capacity: 10.6 imp gal, 12.7 US gal, 48 l.

BODY saloon/sedan; doors: 4; seats: 4-5; front seats: separate.

PRACTICAL INSTRUCTIONS fuel: 96-98 oct petrol; engine sump, gearbox and final drive oil: 10.2 imp pt, 12.3 US pt, 5.8 l, SAE 10W-30 (winter) 20W-50 (summer), change every 6,000 miles, 9,700 km; tappet clearances: inlet 0.015 in, 0.38 mm, exhaust 0.015 in, 0.38 mm; valve timing: inlet opens 5° before tdc and closes 45° after bdc, exhaust opens 40° before bdc and closes 10° after tdc; normal tyre pressure: front 30 psi, 2.1 atm, rear 24 psi, 1.7 atm.

OPTIONAL ACCESSORIES Borg-Warner automatic gearbox, hydraulic torque convertor and planetary gears with 3 ratios (I 2.388, II 1.449, III 1, rev 2.388), max ratio of convertor at stall 2, 3.940 axle ratio, max speeds (I) 42 mph, 68 km/h, (II) 69 mph, 111 km/h, (III) 100 mph, 161 km/h, speed in direct drive at 1,000 rpm 17.8 mph, 28.7 km/h; power-assisted steering; reclining backrests; electrically-heated rear window.

1800 Mk II 'S' De Luxe Saloon

See 1800 Mk II De Luxe Saloon, except for:

PRICE IN GB: £ 940.

ENGINE compression ratio: 9.5; max power (DIN): 95.5 hp at 5,700 rpm; max torque (DIN): 106 lb ft, 14.6 kg m at 3,000 rpm; max engine rpm: 6,000; specific power: 53.1 hp/l; carburation: 2 SU type H 6 semi-downdraught carburettors.

PERFORMANCE max speeds: 33 mph, 53 km/h in 1st gear; 53 mph, 85 km/h in 2nd gear; 79 mph, 127 km/h in 3rd gear; 100 mph, 161 km/h in 4th gear; power-weight ratio: 26.5 lb/hp, 12 kg/hp; fuel consumption: 22.9 m/imp gal, 19 m/US gal, 12.4 l x 100 km.

BRAKES front disc (twin calipers).

PRACTICAL INSTRUCTIONS fuel: 99 oct petrol; valve timing: inlet opens 16° before tdc and closes 56° after bdc, exhaust opens 51° before bdc and closes 21° after tdc.

RELIANT   GREAT BRITAIN

Rebel 700 Saloon

PRICE IN GB: £ 588.

ENGINE front, 4 stroke; cylinders: 4, vertical, in line; bore and stroke: 2.38 x 2.40 in, 60.4 x 61 mm; engine capacity: 42.7 cu in, 700 cu cm; compression ratio: 8.4; max power (DIN): 31 hp at 5,000 rpm; max torque (DIN): 38 lb ft, 5.2 kg m at 2,500 rpm; max engine rpm: 5,700; specific power: 44.3 hp/l; cylinder block: light alloy; cylinder head: light alloy; crankshaft bearings: 3; valves: 2 per cylinder, overhead, push-rods and rockers; camshafts: 1, side; lubrication: eccentric pump, full flow filter; lubricating system capacity: 4.9 imp pt, 5.9 US pt, 2.8 l; carburation: 1 Zenith 30 IZ downdraught carburettor; fuel feed: mechanical pump; cooling system: water; cooling system capacity: 7 imp pt, 8.5 US pt, 4 l.

TRANSMISSION driving wheels: rear; clutch: single dry plate; gearbox: mechanical; gears: 4 + reverse; synchromesh gears: I, II, III, IV; gearbox ratios: I 4.267, II 2.461, III 1.454, IV 1, rev 3.493; gear lever: central; final drive: spiral bevel; axle ratio: 4.375; width of rims: 3.5''; tyres: 5.50 x 12.

MORRIS 1800 Mk II De Luxe Saloon

RELIANT Rebel 700 Saloon

RELIANT Scimitar GTE

PERFORMANCE max speeds: 19 mph, 30 km/h in 1st gear; 33 mph, 53 km/h in 2nd gear; 56 mph, 90 km/h in 3rd gear; 68 mph, 109 km/h in 4th gear; power-weight ratio: 38.8 lb/hp, 17.6 kg/hp; carrying capacity: 706 lb, 320 kg; speed in direct drive at 1,000 rpm: 14.2 mph, 22.8 km/h; fuel consumption: 57.6 m/imp gal, 48 m/US gal, 4.9 l x 100 km.

CHASSIS box-type ladder frame; front suspension: independent, wishbones, coil springs, telescopic dampers; rear suspension: rigid axle, semi-elliptic leafsprings, telescopic dampers.

STEERING recirculating ball; turns of steering wheel lock to lock: 2.40.

BRAKES drum; area rubbed by linings: front 62.6 sq in, 404 sq cm, rear 55 sq in, 355 sq cm, total 117.6 sq in, 759 sq cm.

ELECTRICAL EQUIPMENT voltage: 12 V; battery: 20 Ah; generator type: dynamo; ignition distributor: Lucas; headlamps: 2.

DIMENSIONS AND WEIGHT wheel base: 89 in, 2,261 mm; front track: 48 in, 1,219 mm; rear track: 46.60 in, 1,184 mm; overall length: 137 in, 3,480 mm; overall width: 58 in, 1,473 mm; overall height: 56.50 in, 1,435 mm; ground clearance: 5.50 in, 140 mm; dry weight: 1,202 lb, 545 kg; turning circle (between walls): 27 ft, 8.2 m; fuel tank capacity: 6 imp gal, 7.1 US gal, 27 l.

BODY saloon/sedan; doors: 2; seats: 4; front seats: separate.

PRACTICAL INSTRUCTIONS fuel: 98 oct petrol; engine sump oil: 4.9 imp pt, 5.9 US pt, 2.8 l, SAE 20-30, change every 5,000 miles, 8,000 km; gearbox oil: 1.1 imp pt, 1.3 US pt, 0.6 l, SAE 20-30, change every 5,000 miles, 8,000 km; final drive oil: 1.9 imp pt, 2.3 US pt, 1.1 l, SAE 90 EP, change every 5,000 miles, 8,000 km; greasing: every 5,000 miles, 8,000 km, 5 points; tappet clearances: inlet 0.006 in, 0.15 mm, exhaust 0.006 in, 0.15 mm; normal tyre pressure: front 20 psi, 1.4 atm, rear 20 psi, 1.4 atm.

OPTIONAL ACCESSORIES 5.410 axle ratio.

Rebel 700 Estate Car

See Rebel 700 Saloon, except for:

PRICE IN GB: £ 642.

PERFORMANCE max speed: 66 mph, 106 km/h.

DIMENSIONS AND WEIGHT overall length: 145.75 in, 3,702 mm; overall height: 55.50 in, 1,410 mm.

BODY estate car/station wagon; doors: 2 + 1.

Scimitar GTE

PRICE IN GB: £ 1,641.

ENGINE front, 4 stroke; cylinders: 6, Vee-slanted at 60°; bore and stroke: 3.69 x 2.85 in, 93.7 x 72.4 mm; engine capacity: 182.7 cu in, 2,994 cu cm; compression ratio: 8.9; max power (SAE): 144 hp at 4,750 rpm; max torque (SAE): 192 lb ft, 26.5 kg m at 3,000 rpm; max engine rpm: 6,200; specific power: 48.1 hp/l; cylinder block: cast iron; cylinder head: cast iron; crankshaft bearings: 4; valves: 2 per cylinder, overhead, push-rods and rockers; camshafts: 1, at centre of Vee; lubrication: rotary pump, full flow filter; lubricating system capacity: 9.5 imp pt, 11.4 US pt, 5.4 l; carburation: 1 Weber downdraught twin barrel carburettor; fuel feed: mechanical pump; cooling system: water; cooling system capacity: 23 imp pt, 27.5 US pt, 13 l.

TRANSMISSION driving wheels: rear; clutch: single dry plate (diaphragm), hydraulically controlled; gearbox: mechanical; gears: 4 + reverse; synchromesh gears: I, II, III, IV; gearbox ratios: I 3.160, II 2.210, III 1.410, IV 1, rev 3.350; gear lever: central; final drive: hypoid bevel; axle ratio: 3.310; width of rims: 5.5''; tyres: 185 x 14.

PERFORMANCE max speeds: 40 mph, 64 km/h in 1st gear; 57 mph, 91 km/h in 2nd gear; 89 mph, 143 km/h in 3rd gear; 117 mph, 188 km/h in 4th gear; power-weight ratio: 15.5 lb/hp, 7 kg/hp; carrying capacity: 706 lb, 320 kg; acceleration: standing ¼ mile 17.5 sec, 0-50 mph (0-80 km/h) 7.7 sec; speed in direct drive at 1,000 rpm: 20.2 mph, 32.5 km/h; fuel consumption: 25 m/imp gal, 20.8 m/US gal, 11.3 l x 100 km.

CHASSIS box-type ladder frame; front suspension: independent, wishbones, anti-roll bar, coil springs/telescopic dampers units; rear suspension: rigid axle, twin trailing arms, transverse Watt linkage, coil springs/telescopic dampers units.

STEERING rack-and-pinion; turns of steering wheel lock to lock: 3.5.

SCIMITAR GTE

BRAKES front disc (diameter 10.60 in, 269 mm), rear drum, rear compensator, servo; area rubbed by linings: front 227 sq in, 1,464 sq cm, rear 99 sq in, 638 sq cm, total 326 sq in, 2,102 sq cm.

ELECTRICAL EQUIPMENT voltage: 12 V; battery: 55 Ah; generator type: alternator; ignition distributor: Lucas; headlamps: 4.

DIMENSIONS AND WEIGHT wheel base: 99.50 in, 2,527 mm; front track: 55 in, 1,397 mm; rear track: 53 in, 1,346 mm; overall length: 171 in, 4,343 mm; overall width: 64.50 in, 1,638 mm; overall height: 52 in, 1,321 mm; ground clearance: 5.50 in, 140 mm; dry weight: 2,226 lb, 1,010 kg; turning circle (between walls): 36 ft, 11 m; fuel tank capacity: 17.5 imp gal, 20.9 US gal, 79 l.

BODY coupé in plastic material; doors: 2; seats: 4; front seats: separate.

PRACTICAL INSTRUCTIONS fuel: 98 oct petrol; engine sump oil: 9 imp pt, 10.8 US pt, 5.1 l, SAE 10W-30, change every 5,000 miles, 8,000 km; gearbox oil: 3.2 imp pt, 3.8 US pt, 1.8 l, SAE 80, change every 5,000 miles, 8,000 km; final drive oil: 1.9 imp pt, 2.3 US pt, 1.1 l, SAE 90, change every 5,000 miles, 8,000 km; greasing: every 1,000 miles, 1,600 km, 5 points; tappet clearances: inlet 0.015 in, 0.38 mm, exhaust 0.022 in, 0.56 mm; valve timing: inlet opens 20° before tdc and closes 64° after bdc, exhaust opens 70° before bdc and closes 14° after tdc; normal tyre pressure: front 26 psi, 1.8 atm, rear 26 psi, 1.8 atm.

OPTIONAL ACCESSORIES Laycock-de Normanville overdrive on III and IV, 0.802 ratio; Borg-Warner 35 automatic gearbox, hydraulic torque convertor and planetary gears with 3 ratios (I 2.390, II 1.450, III 1, rev 2.090), max ratio of convertor at stall 2, possible manual selection, central selector lever, 3.070 axle ratio; light alloy wheels; electrically-heated rear window.

ROLLS-ROYCE   GREAT BRITAIN

Silver Shadow 4-door Saloon

PRICE IN GB: £ 7,100.
PRICE IN USA: $ 20,700.

ENGINE front, 4 stroke; cylinders: 8, Vee-slanted at 90°; bore and stroke: 4.10 x 3.90 in, 104.1 x 99.1 mm; engine capacity: 411.6 cu in, 6,745 cu cm; compression ratio: 9; cylinder block: light alloy, wet liners; cylinder head: light alloy; crankshaft bearings: 5; valves: 2 per cylinder, overhead, in line, slanted, push-rods and rockers, hydraulic tappets; camshafts: 1, at centre of Vee; lubrication: gear pump, full flow filter; lubricating system capacity: 14.4 imp pt, 17.3 US pt, 8.2 l; carburation: 2 SU type HD 8 horizontal carburettors; fuel feed: 2 electric pumps; cooling system: water; cooling system capacity: 28 imp pt, 33.6 US pt, 15.9 l.

TRANSMISSION driving wheels: rear; gearbox: automatic, hydraulic torque convertor and planetary gears with 3 ratios + reverse, possible manual selection; gearbox ratios: I 2.500, II 1.500, III 1, rev 2; max ratio of convertor at stall 2.04; selector lever: steering column; final drive: hypoid bevel; axle ratio: 3.080; tyres: 8.45 x 15.

PERFORMANCE max speeds: 40 mph, 64 km/h in 1st gear; 74 mph, 119 km/h in 2nd gear; 119 mph, 191 km/h in 3rd gear; carrying capacity: 1,058 lb, 480 kg; speed in direct drive at 1,000 rpm: 26.2 mph, 42.2 km/h; fuel consumption: 15 m/imp gal, 12.5 m/US gal, 18.8 l x 100 km.

CHASSIS integral, front and rear auxiliary frames; front suspension: independent, wishbones, coil springs, automatic levelling control, telescopic dampers; rear suspension: independent, semi-trailing arms, coil springs, automatic levelling control, telescopic dampers.

STEERING recirculating ball, progressive servo, right-hand drive; turns of steering wheel lock to lock: 3.50.

BRAKES disc [diameter (twin calipers) 11 in, 279 mm], 3 independent circuits, servo; area rubbed by linings: front 227 sq in, 1,464 sq cm, rear 287 sq in, 1,851 sq cm, total 514 sq in, 3,315 sq cm.

ELECTRICAL EQUIPMENT voltage: 12 V; battery: 64 Ah; generator type: dynamo, 35 A; ignition distributor: Lucas; headlamps: 4.

DIMENSIONS AND WEIGHT wheel base: 119.50 in, 3,035 mm; front track: 57.50 in, 1,460 mm; rear track: 57.50 in, 1,460 mm; overall length: 203.50 in, 5,169 mm; overall width: 72 in, 1,829 mm; overall height: 59.75 in, 1,518 mm; ground clearance: 6.50 in, 165 mm; dry weight: 4,556 lb,

ROLLS-ROYCE Silver Shadow 4-door Saloon

ROLLS-ROYCE Silver Shadow Long Wheelbase 4-door Saloon with division

ROLLS-ROYCE Phantom VI 7-passenger Limousine

2,067 kg; turning circle (between walls): 38 ft, 11.6 m; fuel tank capacity: 24 imp gal, 28.8 US gal, 109 l.

BODY saloon/sedan; doors: 4; seats: 5-6; front seats: separate, adjustable reclining backrests; details: headrests, air-conditioning system, electrically-controlled windows.

PRACTICAL INSTRUCTIONS fuel: 98-100 oct petrol; engine sump oil: 14.1 imp pt, 16.9 US pt, 8 l, SAE 10W-30, change every 6,000 miles, 9,700 km; gearbox oil: 23.9 imp pt, 28.8 US pt, 13.6 l, change every 24,000 miles, 38,600 km; final drive oil: 4 imp pt, 4.9 US pt, 2.3 l, change every 24,000 miles, 38,600 km; power-assisted steering and automatic levelling control oil: change every 12,000 miles, 19,300 km; greasing: every 7,500 miles, 12,000 km; valve timing: inlet opens 26° before tdc and closes 52° after bdc, exhaust opens 68° before bdc and closes 10° after tdc; normal tyre pressure: front 23 psi, 1.6 atm, rear 25 psi, 1.8 atm.

VARIATIONS

ENGINE 8 compression ratio.

OPTIONAL ACCESSORIES alternator; iodine headlamps.

Silver Shadow Long Wheelbase 4-door Saloon

See Silver Shadow 4-door Saloon, except for:

PRICE IN GB: £ 8,150.
PRICE IN USA: $ 24,500.

TRANSMISSION gearbox: automatic, hydraulic torque convertor and planetary gears with 3 ratios + reverse; gearbox ratios: I 2.050, II 1.050, III 1, rev 2.

PERFORMANCE max speeds: 59 mph, 95 km/h in 1st gear; 114 mph, 183 km/h in 2nd gear; 120 mph, 193 km/h in 3rd gear.

DIMENSIONS AND WEIGHT wheel base: 123.50 in, 3,137 mm; overall length: 207.50 in, 5,270 mm; turning circle (between walls): 39 ft, 11.9 m.

Silver Shadow Long Wheelbase 4-door Saloon with division

See Silver Shadow Long Wheelbase 4-door Saloon, except for:

PRICE IN GB: £ 8,690.
PRICE IN USA: $ 26,800.

BODY details: glass partition.

Silver Shadow H.J. Mulliner 2-door Saloon

See Silver Shadow 4-door Saloon, except for:

PRICE IN GB: £ 8,850.
PRICE IN USA: $ 29,200.

Silver Shadow H.J. Mulliner Drophead Coupé

See Silver Shadow 4-door Saloon, except for:

PRICE IN GB: £ 9,250.
PRICE IN USA: $ 31,600.

BODY convertible; doors: 2.

Phantom VI 7-passenger Limousine

PRICE IN GB: £ 10,050.

ENGINE front, 4 stroke; cylinders: 8, Vee-slanted at 90°; bore and stroke: 4.10 x 3.90 in, 104.1 x 99.1 mm; engine capacity: 411.6 cu in, 6,745 cu cm; compression ratio: 9; cylinder block: light alloy, wet liners; cylinder head: light alloy; crankshaft bearings: 5; valves: 2 per cylinder, overhead, in line, slanted, push-rods and rockers, hydraulic tappets; camshafts: 1, at centre of Vee; lubrication: gear pump, full flow filter; lubricating system capacity: 14.1 imp pt, 16.9 US pt, 8 l; carburation: 2 SU type HD 8 horizontal carburettors; fuel feed: 2 electric pumps; cooling system: water; cooling system capacity: 23.1 imp pt, 27.7 US pt, 13.1 l.

TRANSMISSION driving wheels: rear; gearbox: Rolls-Royce automatic, hydraulic coupling and planetary gears with 4

ROLLS-ROYCE Silver Shadow 4-door Saloon

*ROLLS-ROYCE
Silver Shadow Long Wheelbase 4-door Saloon*

*ROLLS-ROYCE
Phantom VI 7-passenger Limousine*

ratios + reverse, possible manual selection; gearbox ratios: I 3.310, II 2.620, III 1.440, IV 1, rev 4.290; selector lever: steering column; final drive: hypoid bevel; axle ratio: 3.890; tyres: 8.90 x 15.

PERFORMANCE max speeds: 18 mph, 29 km/h in 1st gear; 32 mph, 51 km/h in 2nd gear; 62 mph, 100 km/h in 3rd gear; 100 mph, 161 km/h in 4th gear; carrying capacity: 1,235 lb, 560 kg; acceleration: standing ¼ mile 19.4 sec, 0-50 mph (0-80 km/h) 9.7 sec; speed in direct drive at 1,000 rpm: 22.5 mph, 36.2 km/h; fuel consumption: 14 m/imp gal, 11.6 m/US gal, 20.2 l x 100 km.

CHASSIS box-type ladder frame; front suspension: independent, wishbones, coil springs, anti-roll bar, lever dampers; rear suspension: rigid axle, asymmetrical semi-elliptic leaf-springs, Z-type transverse linkage bar, electrically-adjustable lever dampers.

STEERING worm and roller, progressive servo (50%-80%); turns of steering wheel lock to lock: 4.25.

BRAKES drum, 2 independent hydraulic circuits, mechanical servo; area rubbed by linings: total 424 sq in, 2,735 sq cm.

ELECTRICAL EQUIPMENT voltage: 12 V; battery: 68 Ah; generator type: dynamo, 472 W; ignition distributor: AC Delco; headlamps: 4.

DIMENSIONS AND WEIGHT wheel base: 144 in, 3,658 mm; front track: 60.87 in, 1,546 mm; rear track: 64 in, 1,626 mm; overall length: 238 in, 6,045 mm; overall width: 79 in, 2,007 mm; overall height: 69 in, 1,753 mm; ground clearance: 7.25 in, 184 mm; dry weight: 5,713 lb, 2,591 kg; distribution of weight: 48% front axle, 52% rear axle; turning circle (between walls): 49.2 ft, 15 m; fuel tank capacity: 24 imp gal, 28.8 US gal, 109 l.

BODY limousine; doors: 4; seats: 7; front seats: separate; details: glass partition, air-conditioning system, electrically-controlled windows.

PRACTICAL INSTRUCTIONS fuel: 100 oct petrol; engine sump oil: 12 imp pt, 14.4 US pt, 6.8 l, SAE 10W-30, change every 6,000 miles, 9,700 km; gearbox oil: 20.1 imp pt, 24.1 US pt, 11.4 l, change every 24,000 miles, 38,600 km; final drive oil: 1.6 imp pt, 1.9 US pt, 0.9 l, SAE 90, change every 24,000 miles, 38,600 km; greasing: every 12,000 miles, 19,300 km, 21 points; valve timing: inlet opens 20° before tdc and closes 61° after bdc, exhaust opens 62° before bdc and closes 19° after tdc; normal tyre pressure: front 22 psi, 1.5 atm, rear 27 psi, 1.9 atm.

VARIATIONS

ENGINE 8 compression ratio.

ROVER   GREAT BRITAIN

2000 SC

PRICE IN GB: £ 1,281.

ENGINE front, 4 stroke; cylinders: 4, vertical, in line; bore and stroke: 3.37 x 3.37 in, 85.5 x 85.5 mm; engine capacity: 120.7 cu in, 1,978 cu cm; compression ratio: 9; max power (SAE): 99 hp at 5,000 rpm; max torque (SAE): 121 lb ft, 16.7 kg m at 3,600 rpm; max engine rpm: 6,000; specific power: 50 hp/l; cylinder block: cast iron; cylinder head: light alloy; crankshaft bearings: 5; valves: 2 per cylinder, overhead, thimble tappets; camshafts: 1, overhead; lubrication: rotary pump, full flow filter; lubricating system capacity: 9 imp pt, 10.8 US pt, 5.1 l; carburation: 1 SU type HS 6 horizontal carburettor; fuel feed: mechanical pump; cooling system: water; cooling system capacity: 14 imp pt, 16.9 US pt, 8 l.

TRANSMISSION driving wheels: rear; clutch: single dry plate (diaphragm), hydraulically controlled; gearbox: mechanical; gears: 4 + reverse; synchromesh gears: I, II, III, IV; gearbox ratios: I 3.624, II 2.133, III 1.390, IV 1, rev 3.429; gear lever: central; final drive: hypoid bevel; axle ratio: 3.540; width of rims: 5''; tyres: 165 SR x 14.

PERFORMANCE max speeds: 32 mph, 51 km/h in 1st gear; 54 mph, 87 km/h in 2nd gear; 82 mph, 132 km/h in 3rd gear; 100 mph, 161 km/h in 4th gear; power-weight ratio: 27.7 lb/hp, 12.6 kg/hp; carrying capacity: 882 lb, 400 kg; acceleration: standing ¼ mile 19.6 sec, 0-50 mph (0-80 km/h) 10.1 sec; speed in direct drive at 1,000 rpm: 19.1 mph, 30.7 km/h; fuel consumption: 26.2 m/imp gal, 21.8 m/US gal, 10.8 l x 100 km.

CHASSIS integral; front suspension: independent, upper leading arm, lower transverse arm, horizontal coil springs, anti-roll bar, telescopic dampers; rear suspension: de Dion rigid axle with variable track, fixed length semi-axle, transverse linkage bar from final drive, longitudinal Watt linkage, coil springs, telescopic dampers.

STEERING worm and roller, adjustable steering wheel; turns of steering wheel lock to lock: 3.75.

2000 SC

BRAKES disc (front diameter 10.30 in, 261 mm, rear 10.70 in, 272 mm), servo; area rubbed by linings: front 205 sq in, 1,322 sq cm, rear 152 sq in, 980 sq cm, total 357 sq in, 2,302 sq cm.

ELECTRICAL EQUIPMENT voltage: 12 V; battery: 60 Ah; generator type: alternator, 45 A; ignition distributor: Lucas; headlamps: 4.

DIMENSIONS AND WEIGHT wheel base: 103.37 in, 2,625 mm; front track: 53.37 in, 1,355 mm; rear track: 52.50 in, 1,333 mm; overall length: 179.31 in, 4,554 mm; overall width: 66 in, 1,676 mm; overall height: 55.25 in, 1,403 mm; ground clearance: 6 in, 152 mm; dry weight: 2,747 lb, 1,246 kg; distribution of weight: 53.7% front axle, 46.3% rear axle; turning circle (between walls): 31.5 ft, 9.6 m; fuel tank capacity: 12 imp gal, 14.5 US gal, 55 l.

BODY saloon/sedan; doors: 4; seats: 4-5; front seats: separate, reclining backrests.

PRACTICAL INSTRUCTIONS fuel: 100 oct petrol; engine sump oil: 9 imp pt, 10.8 US pt, 5.1 l, change every 5,000 miles, 8,000 km; gearbox oil: 1.7 imp pt, 2.1 US pt, 1 l, 90 EP, change every 20,000 miles, 32,000 km; final drive oil: 2.2 imp pt, 2.5 US pt, 1.2 l, 90 EP, change every 20,000 miles, 32,000 km; greasing: every 5,000 miles, 8,000 km, 1 point; tappet clearances: inlet 0.008-0.010 in, 0.20-0.25 mm, exhaust 0.013-0.015 in, 0.32-0.39 mm; valve timing: inlet opens 18° before tdc and closes 42° after bdc, exhaust opens 48° before bdc and closes 12° after tdc; normal tyre pressure: front 26 psi, 1.8 atm, rear 28 psi, 2 atm.

OPTIONAL ACCESSORIES electric immersion heater for cylinder block; headrests on front and rear seats; air-conditioning system; sunshine roof; electrically-heated rear window.

2000 Automatic

See 2000 SC, except for:

PRICE IN GB: £ 1,379.
PRICE IN USA: $ 4,198.

TRANSMISSION gearbox: Borg-Warner 35 automatic, hydraulic torque convertor and planetary gears with 3 ratios + reverse, max ratio of convertor at stall 2.1, possible manual selection; gearbox ratios: I 2.390, II 1.450, III 1, rev 2.090.

PERFORMANCE max speeds: 39 mph, 62 km/h in 1st gear; 68 mph, 109 km/h in 2nd gear; 100 mph, 161 km/h in 3rd gear; power-weight ratio: 28 lb/hp, 12.7 kg/hp; acceleration: standing ¼ mile 21.3 sec, 0-50 mph (0-80 km/h) 12.7 sec; fuel consumption: 24 m/imp gal, 20.1 m/US gal, 11.7 l x 100 km.

DIMENSIONS AND WEIGHT dry weight: 2,771 lb, 1,256 kg.

2000 TC

See 2000 SC, except for:

PRICE IN GB: £ 1,360.
PRICE IN USA: $ 4,198.

ENGINE compression ratio: 10; max power (SAE): 124 hp at 5,500 rpm; max torque (SAE): 132 lb ft, 18.2 kg m at 4,000 rpm; max engine rpm: 6,500; specific power: 62.6 hp/l; carburation: 2 SU type HS 8 horizontal carburettors.

PERFORMANCE max speeds: 39 mph, 62 km/h in 1st gear; 59 mph, 95 km/h in 2nd gear; 91 mph, 146 km/h in 3rd gear; 112 mph, 180 km/h in 4th gear; power-weight ratio: 22.6 lb/hp, 10.3 kg/hp; acceleration: standing ¼ mile 18.5 sec, 0-50 mph (0-80 km/h) 8.2 sec; speed in direct drive at 1,000 rpm: 19.1 mph, 30.7 km/h; fuel consumption: 25.6 m/imp gal, 21.4 m/US gal, 11 l x 100 km.

DIMENSIONS AND WEIGHT dry weight: 2,805 lb, 1,272 kg.

PRACTICAL INSTRUCTIONS valve timing: inlet opens 14° before tdc and closes 46° after bdc, exhaust opens 44° before bdc and closes 16° after tdc.

VARIATIONS

ENGINE (only for export), 9 compression ratio, max power (SAE) 117 hp at 5,500 rpm, max torque (SAE) 125 lb ft, 17.2 kg m at 3,750 rpm, 59.1 hp/l specific power.
PERFORMANCE max speed 110 mph, 177 km/h.
PRACTICAL INSTRUCTIONS 95 oct petrol.

OPTIONAL ACCESSORIES oil cooler; wire wheels.

3500

PRICE IN GB: £ 1,568.
PRICE IN USA: $ 5,398.

ENGINE front, 4 stroke; cylinders: 8, Vee-slanted at 90°; bore and stroke: 3.50 x 2.80 in, 88.9 x 71.1 mm; engine capa-

ROVER 2000 SC

ROVER 3500

ROVER 3.5-litre Saloon

city: 215.3 cu in, 3,528 cu cm; compression ratio: 10.5; max power (SAE): 184 hp at 5,200 rpm; max torque (SAE): 226 lb ft, 31.2 kg m at 3,000 rpm; max engine rpm: 5,200; specific power: 52.2 hp/l; cylinder block: light alloy, dry liners; cylinder head: light alloy; crankshaft bearings: 5; valves: 2 per cylinder, overhead, in line, push-rods and rockers, hydraulic tappets; camshafts: 1, at centre of Vee; lubrication: gear pump, full flow filter; lubricating system capacity: 9 imp pt, 10.8 US pt, 5.1 l; carburation: 2 SU type HS 6 semi-downdraught carburettors; fuel feed: mechanical pump; cooling system: water; cooling system capacity: 15.3 imp pt, 18.4 US pt, 8.7 l.

TRANSMISSION driving wheels: rear; gearbox: Borg-Warner 35 automatic, hydraulic torque convertor and planetary gears with 3 ratios + reverse, max ratio of convertor at stall 2.1 possible manual selection; gearbox ratios: I 2.390, II 1.450, III 1, rev 2.090; selector lever: central; final drive: hypoid bevel; axle ratio: 3.080; width of rims: 5.5''; tyres: 185 HR x 14.

PERFORMANCE max speeds: 51 mph, 82 km/h in 1st gear; 84 mph, 135 km/h in 2nd gear; 118 mph, 190 km/h in 3rd gear; power-weight ratio: 15 lb/hp, 6.8 kg/hp; carrying capacity: 882 lb, 400 kg; acceleration: standing ¼ mile 17.5 sec, 0-50 mph (0-80 km/h) 7 sec; speed in direct drive at 1,000 rpm: 23.5 mph, 37.8 km/h; fuel consumption: 21.6 m/imp gal, 13.1 l x 100 km.

CHASSIS integral; front suspension: independent, upper leading arm, lower transverse arm, horizontal coil springs, anti-roll bar, telescopic dampers; rear suspension: de Dion rigid axle with variable track, fixed length semi-axles, transverse linkage bar from final drive, longitudinal Watt linkage, coil springs, telescopic dampers.

STEERING recirculating ball, adjustable steering wheel, variable ratio servo; turns of steering wheel lock to lock: 4.50.

BRAKES disc (front diameter 10.82 in, 275 mm, rear 10.69 in, 271 mm), servo; area rubbed by linings: front 220 sq in, 1,419 sq cm, rear 152 sq in, 980 sq cm, total 372 sq in, 2,399 sq cm.

ELECTRICAL EQUIPMENT voltage: 12 V; battery 60 Ah; generator type: alternator, 45 A; ignition distributor: Lucas; headlamps: 4.

DIMENSIONS AND WEIGHT wheel base: 103.37 in, 2,625 mm; front track: 53.37 in, 1,355 mm; rear track: 51.75 in, 1,314 mm; overall length: 179.75 in, 4,566 mm; overall width: 66 in, 1,676 mm; overall height: 55.75 in, 1,416 mm; ground clearance: 6.13 in, 155 mm; dry weight: 2,765 lb, 1,254 kg; turning circle (between walls): 35.7 ft, 10.9 m; fuel tank capacity: 15 imp gal, 18 US gal, 68 l.

BODY saloon/sedan; doors: 4; seats: 4-5; front seats: separate, reclining backrests.

PRACTICAL INSTRUCTIONS fuel: 100 oct petrol; engine sump oil: 9 imp pt, 10.8 US pt, 5.1 l, SAE 20-30, change every 5,000 miles, 8,000 km; gearbox oil: 14 imp pt, 16.7 US pt, 7.9 l, ATF, no change recommended; final drive oil: 2.3 imp pt, 2.7 US pt, 1.3 l, SAE 90 EP, change every 20,000 miles, 32,000 km; greasing: every 5,000 miles, 8,000 km, 1 point; valve timing: inlet opens 30° before tdc and closes 75° after bdc, exhaust opens 68° before bdc and closes 37° after tdc; normal tyre pressure: front 28 psi, 2 atm, rear 30 psi, 2.1 atm.

OPTIONAL ACCESSORIES headrests on front and rear seats; sunshine roof; air-conditioning system.

3.5-litre Saloon

PRICE IN GB: £ 1,883.

ENGINE front, 4 stroke; cylinders: 8, Vee-slanted at 90°; bore and stroke: 3.50 x 2.80 in, 88.8 x 71 mm; engine capacity: 215.3 cu in, 3,528 cu cm; compression ratio: 10.5; max power (SAE): 184 hp at 5,200 rpm; max torque (SAE): 226 lb ft, 31.2 kg m at 3,000 rpm; max engine rpm: 5,500; specific power: 52.2 hp/l; cylinder block: light alloy, dry liners; cylinder head: light alloy; crankshaft bearings: 5; valves: 2 per cylinder, overhead, in line, push-rods and rockers, hydraulic tappets; camshafts: 1, at centre of Vee; lubrication: gear pump, full flow filter; lubricating system capacity: 9 imp pt, 10.8 US pt, 5.1 l; carburation: 2 SU type HS 6 semi-downdraught carburettors; fuel feed: mechanical pump; cooling system: water; cooling system capacity: 16 imp pt, 19.2 US pt, 9.1 l.

TRANSMISSION driving wheels: rear; gearbox: Borg-Warner 35 automatic, hydraulic torque convertor and planetary gears with 3 ratios + reverse, max ratio of convertor at stall 2.1, possible manual selection; gearbox ratios: I 2.390, II 1.450, III 1, rev 2.090; selector lever: central; final drive: hypoid bevel; axle ratio: 3.540; width of rims: 5''; tyres: 6.70 x 15.

PERFORMANCE max speeds: 46 mph, 74 km/h in 1st gear; 77 mph, 124 km/h in 2nd gear; 115 mph, 185 km/h in 3rd gear; power-weight ratio: 19 lb/hp, 8.6 kg/hp; carrying capacity: 882 lb, 400 kg; acceleration: standing ¼ mile 18.6 sec, 0-50 mph (0-80 km/h) 9 sec; speed in direct drive

ROVER 2000 SC

ROVER 3500

ROVER 3.5-litre Saloon

at 1,000 rpm: 21.5 mph, 34.6 km/h; fuel consumption: 18.2 m/imp gal, 15.2 m/US gal, 15.5 l x 100 km.

CHASSIS integral, front auxiliary frame; front suspension: independent, wishbones, lower trailing links, longitudinal laminated torsion bars, anti-roll bar, telescopic dampers; rear suspension: rigid axle, semi-elliptic leafsprings, telescopic dampers.

STEERING worm and peg, variable ratio servo; turns of steering wheel lock to lock: 2.50.

BRAKES front disc (diameter 10.75 in, 273 mm), rear drum, servo; area rubbed by linings: front 260 sq in, 1,677 sq cm, rear 154.8 sq in, 998 sq cm, total 414.8 sq in, 2,675 sq cm.

ELECTRICAL EQUIPMENT voltage: 12 V; battery: 58 Ah, generator type: alternator, 45 A; ignition distributor: Lucas; headlamps: 4.

DIMENSIONS AND WEIGHT wheel base: 110.50 in, 2,807 mm; front track: 56.20 in, 1,427 mm; rear track: 56.90 in, 1,445 mm; overall length: 187 in, 4,750 mm; overall width: 70.50 in, 1,791 mm; overall height: 61 in, 1,549 mm; ground clearance: 6.60 in, 167 mm; dry weight: 3,476 lb, 1,577 kg; distribution of weight: 51% front axle, 49% rear axle; turning circle (between walls): 40 ft, 12.2 m; fuel tank capacity: 14.1 imp gal, 16.9 US gal, 64 l.

BODY saloon/sedan; doors: 4; seats: 4-5; front seats: separate, reclining backrests.

PRACTICAL INSTRUCTIONS fuel: 100 oct petrol; engine sump oil: 9 imp pt, 10.8 US pt, 5.1 l, SAE 20-30, change every 5,000 miles, 8,000 km; gearbox oil: 14.1 imp pt, 16.9 US pt, 8 l, automatic transmission fluid; final drive oil: 3 imp pt, 3.6 US pt, 1.7 l, SAE 90 EP, change every 20,000 miles, 32,000 km; greasing: every 5,000 miles, 8,000 km, 1 point; valve timing: inlet opens 30° before tdc and closes 75° after bdc, exhaust opens 68° before bdc and closes 37° after tdc; normal tyre pressure: front 26 psi, 1.8 atm, rear 26 psi, 1.8 atm.

OPTIONAL ACCESSORIES bench rear seat; headrests on front and rear seats; sunshine roof; air-conditioning system.

3.5-litre Coupé

See 3.5-litre Saloon, except for:

PRICE IN GB: £ 1,964.

PERFORMANCE power-weight ratio: 18.7 lb/hp, 8.5 kg/hp.

DIMENSIONS AND WEIGHT overall height: 58 in, 1,473 mm; dry weight: 3,457 lb, 1,568 kg.

BODY coupé.

OPTIONAL ACCESSORIES bench rear seat not available.

Land Rover 88" Regular

PRICE IN GB: £ 889.
PRICE IN USA: $ 3,295.

ENGINE front, 4 stroke; cylinders: 4, vertical, in line; bore and stroke: 3.56 x 3.50 in, 90.5 x 88.9 mm; engine capacity: 139.5 cu in, 2,286 cu cm; compression ratio: 8; max power (SAE): 81 hp at 4,250 rpm; max torque (SAE): 127 lb ft, 17.5 kg m at 2,500 rpm; max engine rpm: 5,000; specific power: 35.4 hp/l; cylinder block: cast iron; cylinder head: cast iron; crankshaft bearings: 3; valves: 2 per cylinder, overhead, in line, roller tappets, push-rods and rockers; camshafts: 1, side; lubrication: gear pump, full flow filter; lubricating system capacity: 12.5 imp pt, 14.8 US pt, 7 l; carburation: 1 Zenith 36 IV downdraught single barrel carburettor; fuel feed: mechanical pump; cooling system: water; cooling system capacity: 14.2 imp pt, 16.9 US pt, 8 l.

TRANSMISSION driving wheels: front (automatically engaged with transfer box low ratio) and rear; clutch: single dry plate, hydraulically controlled; gearbox: mechanical; gears: 4 + reverse and 2-ratio transfer box; synchromesh gears: III, IV; gearbox ratios: I 3.600, II 2.220, III 1.500, IV 1, rev 3.020; transfer box ratios: I 1.148, II 2.350; gear lever and transfer lever: central; final drive: spiral bevel; axle ratio: 4.700; width of rims: 5''; tyres: 6.00 x 16.

PERFORMANCE max speeds: 21 mph, 33 km/h in 1st gear; 34 mph, 54 km/h in 2nd gear; 50 mph, 80 km/h in 3rd gear; 66 mph, 106 km/h in 4th gear; power-weight ratio: 35.9 lb/hp, 16.3 kg/hp; carrying capacity: 1,411 lb, 640 kg; acceleration: 0-50 mph (0-80 km/h) 16.3 sec; speed in direct drive at 1,000 rpm: 15 mph, 24.1 km/h; fuel consumption: 21.7 m/imp gal, 18.1 m/US gal, 13 l x 100 km.

CHASSIS box-type ladder frame; front suspension: rigid axle, semi-elliptic leafsprings, telescopic dampers; rear suspension: rigid axle, semi-elliptic leafsprings, telescopic dampers.

STEERING recirculating ball; turns of steering wheel lock to lock: 3.30.

LAND ROVER 88" REGULAR

BRAKES drum; area rubbed by linings: total 189 sq in, 1,219 sq cm.

ELECTRICAL EQUIPMENT voltage: 12 V; battery: 57 Ah; generator type: dynamo, 264 W; ignition distributor: Lucas; headlamps: 2.

DIMENSIONS AND WEIGHT wheel base: 88 in, 2,235 mm; front track: 51.50 in, 1,308 mm; rear track: 51.50 in, 1,308 mm; overall length: 142.35 in, 3,616 mm; overall width: 66 in, 1,676 mm; overall height: 77.85 in, 1,977 mm; ground clearance: 8 in, 203 mm; dry weight: 2,915 lb, 1,322 kg; distribution of weight: 52.5% front axle, 47.5% rear axle; turning circle (between walls): 38 ft, 11.6 m; fuel tank capacity: 10 imp gal, 12 US gal, 45 l.

BODY estate car/station wagon; doors: 2 + 1; seats: 7-8; front seats: separate.

PRACTICAL INSTRUCTIONS fuel: 82-90 oct petrol; engine sump oil: 12.5 imp pt, 14.8 US pt, 7 l, SAE 20W, change every 3,000 miles, 4,800 km; gearbox oil: 2.5 imp pt, 3 US pt, 1.4 l; transfer box oil: 4.4 imp pt, 5.3 US pt, 2.5 l, SAE 90 EP, change every 12,000 miles, 19,300 km; final drive oil: 3 imp pt, 3.6 US pt, 1.7 l, SAE 90 EP, change every 12,000 miles, 19,300 km; greasing: every 4,000 miles, 6,400 km, 1 point; tappet clearances: inlet 0.010 in, 0.25 mm, exhaust 0.010 in, 0.25 mm; valve timing: inlet opens 6° before tdc and closes 52° after bdc, exhaust opens 34° before bdc and closes 24° after tdc; normal tyre pressure: front 25 psi, 1.7 atm, rear 25 psi, 1.7 atm.

VARIATIONS

ENGINE Diesel, compression ratio 23, max power (SAE) 67 hp at 4,000 rpm, max torque (SAE) 105 lb ft, 14.5 kg m at 1,800 rpm, max engine rpm 4,500, 29.3 hp/l specific power, cast iron cylinder head with precombustion chambers.
PERFORMANCE power-weight ratio 43.4 lb/hp, 19.7 kg/hp.

OPTIONAL ACCESSORIES oil cooler; front and rear power take-off; 7/7.50 x 16 tyres; servo brake; alternator.

Land Rover 109" Estate Car

See Land Rover 88" Regular, except for:

PRICE IN GB: £ 1,019.

TRANSMISSION width of rims: 5.5"; tyres: 7.50 x 16.

PERFORMANCE power-weight ratio: 45.9 lb/hp, 20.8 kg/hp.

DIMENSIONS AND WEIGHT wheel base: 109 in, 2,769 mm; overall length: 175 in, 4,445 mm; overall height: 81.35 in, 2,066 mm; ground clearance: 8.25 in, 210 mm; dry weight: 3,712 lb, 1,684 kg; distribution of weight: 46.5% front axle, 53.5% rear axle; turning circle (between walls): 48 ft, 14.6 m; fuel tank capacity: 16 imp gal, 19.3 US gal, 73 l.

BODY seats: 10-12.

VARIATIONS

ENGINE Diesel (67 hp).

ENGINE 6 cylinders, bore and stroke 3.06 x 3.63 in, 77.8 x 92.1 mm, engine capacity 160.2 cu in, 2,625 cu cm, compression ratio 7.8, max power (SAE) 95 hp at 4,500 rpm, max torque (SAE) 134 lb ft, 18.5 kg m at 1,750 rpm; 36.2 hp/l specific power, 1 Zenith 175-CD2S carburettor.
PERFORMANCE max speed 72 mph, 116 km/h, power-weight ratio 39 lb/hp, 17.7 kg/hp.

Range Rover

PRICE IN GB: £ 1,529.

ENGINE front, 4 stroke; cylinder: 8, Vee-slanted at 90°; bore and stroke: 3.50 x 2.80 in, 88.9 x 71.1 mm; engine capacity: 215 cu in, 3,528 cu cm; compression ratio: 8.5; max power (SAE): 156 hp at 5,000 rpm; max torque (SAE): 205 lb ft, 28.3 kg m at 3,000 rpm; max engine rpm: 5,200; specific power: 44.2 hp/l; cylinder block: light alloy, dry liners; cylinder head: light alloy; crankshaft bearings: 5; valves: 2 per cylinder, overhead, in line, push-rods and rockers, hydraulic tappets; camshafts: 1, at centre of Vee; lubrication: gear pump, full flow filter; lubricating system capacity: 10 imp pt, 12 US pt, 5.7 l; carburation: 2 Zenith-Stromberg CD2 semi-downdraught carburettors; fuel feed: mechanical pump; cooling system: water; cooling system capacity: 20 imp pt, 23.9 US pt, 11.3 l.

TRANSMISSION driving wheels: front (automatically engaged with transfer box low ratio) and rear; clutch: single dry plate (diaphragm), hydraulically controlled; gearbox: me-

ROVER Land Rover 88" Regular

ROVER Range Rover

SUNBEAM Stiletto

hanical; gears: 4 + reverse and 2-ratio transfer box; synchromesh gears: I, II, III, IV; gearbox ratios: I 4.069, I 2.448, III 1.505, IV 1, rev 3.664; transfer box ratios: 1.174, II 3.321; gear lever and transfer lever: central; final drive: spiral bevel; axle ratio: 3.540; width of rims: 6''; tyres: 205 x 16.

PERFORMANCE max speeds: 24 mph, 39 km/h in 1st gear; 41 mph, 66 km/h in 2nd gear; 68 mph, 109 km/h in 3rd gear; 96 mph, 154 km/h in 4th gear; power-weight ratio: 24.2 lb/hp, 11 kg/hp; carrying capacity: 1,500 lb, 680 kg; acceleration: standing ¼ mile 19.3 sec, 0-50 mph (0-80 km/h) 11.1 sec; speed in direct drive at 1,000 rpm: 18.9 mph, 30.4 km/h; fuel consumption: 22 m/imp gal, 18.2 m/US gal, 12.9 l x 100 km.

CHASSIS box-type ladder frame; front suspension: rigid axle, longitudinal radius arms, transverse Panhard torsion bar, coil springs/telescopic dampers units; rear suspension: rigid axle, longitudinal radius arms, upper A bracket, Boge Hydromat self-energizing levelling device, coil springs, telescopic dampers.

STEERING Burman, recirculating ball, worm and nut; turns of steering wheel lock to lock: 3.75.

BRAKES disc (front diameter 11.75 in, 298 mm, rear 11.42 in, 290 mm); area rubbed by linings: front 261 sq in, 1,683 sq cm, rear 235 sq in, 1,516 sq cm, total 496 sq in, 3,199 sq cm.

ELECTRICAL EQUIPMENT voltage: 12 V; battery: 57 Ah; generator type: alternator, 408 W; ignition distributor: Lucas; headlamps: 2.

DIMENSIONS AND WEIGHT wheel base: 100 in, 2,450 mm; front track: 58.50 in, 1,486 mm; rear track: 58.50 in, 1,486 mm; overall length: 175.98 in, 4,470 mm; overall width: 70 in, 1,778 mm; overall height: 70 in, 1,778 mm; ground clearance: 7.50 in, 190 mm; dry weight: 3,800 lb, 1,724 kg; distribution of weight: 50% front axle, 50% rear axle; turning circle (between walls): 37 ft, 11.3 m; fuel tank capacity: 19 imp gal, 22.7 US gal, 86 l.

BODY estate car/station wagon; doors: 2 + 1; seats: 5; front seats: separate, reclining backrests.

PRACTICAL INSTRUCTIONS fuel: 91-93 oct petrol; engine sump oil: 10 imp pt, 12 US pt, 5.7 l, SAE 20W, change every 5,000 miles, 8,000 km; gearbox oil: 4.5 imp pt, 5.5 US pt, 2.6 l, SAE 80 EP, change every 20,000 miles, 32,000 km; transfer box oil: 5.5 imp pt, 6.6 US pt, 3.1 l, SAE 80 EP, change every 5,000 miles, 8,000 km; final drive oil: rear 2.7 imp pt, 3.2 US pt, 1.5 l, SAE 80 EP, change every 20,000 miles, 32,000 km, front 4.5 imp pt, 5.3 US pt, 2.5 l, SAE 80 EP, change every 5,000 miles, 8,000 km; greasing: every 5,000 miles, 8,000 km, 6 points; valve timing: inlet opens 30° before tdc and closes 75° after bdc, exhaust opens 68° before bdc and closes 37° after tdc; normal tyre pressure: front 25 psi, 1.7 atm, rear 25 psi, 1.7 atm.

ROVER Land Rover 88'' Regular

ROVER Range Rover

SUNBEAM   GREAT BRITAIN

Sport

PRICE IN GB: £ 666.

ENGINE rear, 4 stroke; cylinders: 4, slanted at 45°, in line; bore and stroke: 2.68 x 2.38 in, 68 x 60.4 mm; engine capacity: 53.4 cu in, 875 cu cm; compression ratio: 10; max power (DIN): 50 hp at 5,800 rpm; max torque (DIN): 49 lb ft, 6.7 kg m at 4,500 rpm; max engine rpm: 7,000; specific power: 57.1 hp/l; cylinder block: light alloy, dry liners; cylinder head: light alloy; crankshaft bearings: 3; valves: 2 per cylinder, overhead, in line, thimble tappets; camshafts: 1, overhead; lubrication: eccentric pump, full flow filter; lubricating system capacity: 6 imp pt, 7.2 US pt, 3.4 l; carburation: 2 Zenith-Stromberg 125 CD horizontal carburettors; fuel feed: mechanical pump; cooling system: water; cooling system capacity: 10.9 imp pt, 13.1 US pt, 6.2 l.

TRANSMISSION driving wheels: rear; clutch: single dry plate (diaphragm), hydraulically controlled; gearbox: mechanical; gears: 4 + reverse; synchromesh gears: I, II, III, IV; gearbox ratios: I 3.417, II 1.833, III 1.174, IV 0.852, rev 2.846; gear lever: central; final drive: hypoid bevel; axle ratio: 4.857; width of rims: 4.5''; tyres: 155 x 12.

PERFORMANCE max speeds: 26 mph, 42 km/h in 1st gear; 49 mph, 79 km/h in 2nd gear; 77 mph, 124 km/h in 3rd gear; 90 mph, 145 km/h in 4th gear; power-weight ratio: 31.9 lb/hp, 14.5 kg/hp; carrying capacity: 706 lb, 320 kg; acceleration: 0-50 mph (0-80 km/h) 12.4 sec; speed in top at 1,000 rpm: 15.1 mph, 24.3 km/h; fuel consumption: 40 m/imp gal, 33.1 m/US gal, 7.1 l x 100 km.

CHASSIS integral; front suspension: independent, U-shaped swinging semi-axles, coil springs, telescopic dampers; rear suspension: independent, semi-trailing arms, coil springs, telescopic dampers.

STEERING rack-and-pinion; turns of steering wheel lock to lock: 2.63.

BRAKES drum, 2 front leading shoes, servo; area rubbed by linings: total 151 sq in, 974 sq cm.

ELECTRICAL EQUIPMENT voltage: 12 V; battery: 32 Ah; generator type: dynamo, 297 W; ignition distributor: Lucas; headlamps: 4.

DIMENSIONS AND WEIGHT wheel base: 82 in, 2,083 mm; front track: 49.70 in, 1,262 mm; rear track: 48 in, 1,219 mm; overall length: 139 in, 3,531 mm; overall width: 60.25 in, 1,530 mm; overall height: 54.50 in, 1,384 mm; ground clearance: 6.50 in, 165 mm; dry weight: 1,596 lb, 724 kg; distribution of weight: 38% front axle, 62% rear axle; turning circle (between walls): 31.5 ft, 9.6 m; fuel tank capacity: 6 imp gal, 7.1 US gal, 27 l.

BODY saloon/sedan; doors: 2; seats: 4; front seats: separate, reclining backrests.

PRACTICAL INSTRUCTIONS fuel: 95-97 oct petrol; engine sump oil: 5.5 imp pt, 6.6 US pt, 3.1 l, SAE 20W-50, change every 5,000 miles, 8,000 km; gearbox and final drive oil: 4.6 imp pt, 5.5 US pt, 2.6 l, SAE 80 EP; greasing: every 5,000 miles, 8,000 km, 4 points; tappet clearances: inlet 0.007 in, 0.18 mm, exhaust 0.014 in, 0.36 mm; valve timing: inlet opens 67° before tdc and closes 93° after bdc, exhaust opens 63° before bdc and closes 13° after tdc; normal tyre pressure: front 18 psi, 1.3 atm, rear 30 psi, 2.1 atm.

Stiletto

See Sport, except for:

PRICE IN GB: £ 720.

ENGINE lubrication: oil cooler.

PERFORMANCE power-weight ratio: 31.3 lb/hp, 14.2 kg/hp; acceleration: 0-50 mph (0-80 km/h) 10.7 sec.

DIMENSIONS AND WEIGHT overall height: 52.50 in, 1,333 mm; dry weight: 1,566 lb, 710 kg; distribution of weight: 37% front axle, 63% rear axle.

BODY coupé.

Rapier

PRICE IN GB: £ 1,090.

ENGINE front, 4 stroke; cylinders: 4, slanted at 10°, in line; bore and stroke: 3.21 x 3.25 in, 81.5 x 82.5 mm; engine capacity: 105.3 cu in, 1,725 cu cm; compression ratio: 9.2; max power (DIN): 79 hp at 5,200 rpm; max torque (DIN): 91 lb ft, 12.5 kg m at 3,800 rpm; max engine rpm: 6,200; specific power: 45.8 hp/l; cylinder block: cast iron; cylinder head: light alloy; crankshaft bearings: 5; valves: 2 per cylinder, overhead, in line, push-rods and rockers; camshafts: 1, side; lubrication: eccentric pump, full flow filter; lubricating system capacity: 7.5 imp pt, 8.9 US pt, 4.2 l; carburation: 2 Zenith-Stromberg semi-downdraught carburettors; fuel feed: mechanical pump; cooling system: water; cooling system capacity: 13.7 imp pt, 16.5 US pt, 7.8 l.

TRANSMISSION driving wheels: rear; clutch: single dry plate (diaphragm), hydraulically controlled; gearbox: mechanical; gears: 4 + reverse and overdrive on III and IV; synchromesh gears: I, II, III, IV; gearbox ratios: I 3.123, II 1.993, III 1.296, IV 1, overdrive/top 0.803, rev 3.325; gear lever: central; final drive: hypoid bevel; axle ratio: 4.220; width of rims: 4.5''; tyres: 155 x 13.

PERFORMANCE max speeds: 31 mph, 50 km/h in 1st gear; 48 mph, 77 km/h in 2nd gear; 75 mph, 120 km/h in 3rd gear; 100 mph, 161 km/h in 4th gear; 103 mph, 165 km/h in overdrive/top; power-weight ratio: 27.1 lb/hp, 12.3 kg/hp; acceleration: 0-50 mph (0-80 km/h) 9 sec; speed in direct drive at 1,000 rpm: 15.6 mph, 25.1 km/h; fuel consumption: 30 m/imp gal, 25 m/US gal, 9.4 l x 100 km.

CHASSIS integral; front suspension: independent, coil springs/telescopic damper struts, lower wishbones (trailing links), anti-roll bar; rear suspension: rigid axle, semi-elliptic leafsprings, telescopic dampers.

STEERING recirculating ball, adjustable steering wheel; turns of steering wheel lock to lock: 3.75.

BRAKES front disc (diameter 9.60 in, 244 mm), rear drum, servo; area rubbed by linings: front 179 sq in, 1,154 sq cm, rear 99 sq in, 638 sq cm, total 278 sq in, 1,792 sq cm.

ELECTRICAL EQUIPMENT voltage: 12 V; battery: 40 Ah; generator type: alternator, 35 Ah; ignition distributor: Lucas; headlamps: 4.

DIMENSIONS AND WEIGHT wheel base: 98.50 in, 2,502 mm; front track: 52 in, 1,321 mm; rear track: 52 in, 1,321 mm; overall length: 174.50 in, 4,432 mm; overall

SUNBEAM Stiletto

RAPIER

width: 64.75 in, 1,645 mm; overall height: 55 in, 1,397 mm; ground clearance; 5 in, 127 mm; dry weight: 2,145 lb, 973 kg; distribution of weight: 53% front axle, 47% rear axle; turning circle (between walls): 36.8 ft, 11.2 m; fuel tank capacity: 15 imp gal, 17.9 US gal, 68 l.

BODY saloon/sedan (fastback); doors: 2; seats: 4-5; front seats: separate, reclining backrests.

PRACTICAL INSTRUCTIONS fuel: 97 oct petrol; engine sump oil: 7.5 imp pt, 8.9 US pt, 4.2 l, multigrade, change every 5,000 miles, 8,000 km; gearbox oil: 4.5 imp pt, 5.4 US pt, 2.6 l, multigrade; final drive oil: 1.7 imp pt, 1.9 US pt, 0.9 l, SAE 90 EP; greasing: none; valve timing: inlet opens 57° before tdc and closes 91° after bdc, exhaust opens 90° before bdc and closes 44° after tdc; normal tyre pressure: front 26 psi, 1.8 atm, rear 26 psi, 1.8 atm.

OPTIONAL ACCESSORIES Borg-Warner 45/3 automatic gearbox, hydraulic torque convertor and planetary gears with 3 ratios (I 2.393, II 1.450, III 1, rev 2.094), max ratio of convertor at stall 1.9, central selector lever, 3.700 axle ratio; electrically-heated rear window.

Rapier H120

See Rapier, except for:

PRICE IN GB: £ 1,268.

ENGINE compression ratio: 9.6; max power (DIN): 93 hp at 5,200 rpm; max torque (DIN): 106 lb ft, 14.6 kg m at 4,000 rpm; specific power: 53.9 hp/l; carburation: 2 Weber 40 DCOE horizontal twin barrel carburettors.

TRANSMISSION axle ratio: 3.890; width of rims: 5''; tyres: 165 x 13.

PERFORMANCE max speeds: 34 mph, 54 km/h in 1st gear; 54 mph, 87 km/h in 2nd gear; 83 mph, 133 km/h in 3rd gear; 107 mph, 172 km/h in 4th gear; 110 mph, 177 km/h in overdrive/top; power-weight ratio: 23.3 lb/hp, 10.6 kg/hp; acceleration: 0-50 mph (0-80 km/h) 8 sec; speed in direct drive at 1,000 rpm: 17.3 mph, 27.9 km/h; fuel consumption: 25.7 m/imp gal, 21.4 m/US gal, 11 l x 100 km.

DIMENSIONS AND WEIGHT dry weight: 2,170 lb, 984 kg.

Alpine

PRICE IN GB: £ 955.

ENGINE front, 4 stroke; cylinders: 4, in line; bore and stroke: 3.21 x 3.25 in, 81.5 x 82.5 mm; engine capacity: 105.3 cu in, 1,725 cu cm; compression ratio: 9.2; max power (DIN): 67 hp at 4,800 rpm; max torque (DIN): 87 lb ft, 12 kg m at 2,800 rpm; max engine rpm: 6,300; specific power: 38.8 hp/l; cylinder block: cast iron; cylinder head: light alloy; crankshaft bearings: 5; valves: 2 per cylinder, overhead, in line, push-rods and rockers; camshafts: 1, side; lubrication: eccentric pump, full flow filter; lubricating system capacity: 7.5 imp pt, 8.9 US pt, 4.2 l; carburation: 1 Zenith-Stromberg 150 CDS semi-downdraught carburettor: 1 feed: mechanical pump; cooling system: water; cooling system capacity: 12.6 imp pt, 15 US pt, 7.1 l.

TRANSMISSION driving wheels: rear; clutch: single dry plate (diaphragm), hydraulically controlled; gearbox: mechanical; gears: 4 + reverse; synchromesh gears: I, II, III, IV; gearbox ratios: I 3.353, II 2.141, III 1.392, IV 1, rev 3.569; gear lever: central; final drive: hypoid bevel; axle ratio: 3.889; width of rims: 4.5''; tyres: 6.00 x 13.

PERFORMANCE max speeds: 32 mph, 51 km/h in 1st gear; 51 mph, 82 km/h in 2nd gear; 78 mph, 125 km/h in 3rd gear; 92 mph, 148 km/h in 4th gear; power-weight ratio: 31.2 lb/hp, 14.1 kg/hp; carrying capacity: 882 lb, 400 kg; acceleration: 0-50 mph (0-80 km/h) 10.9 sec; speed in direct drive at 1,000 rpm: 17.8 mph, 28.6 km/h; fuel consumption: 34 m/imp gal, 28.3 m/US gal, 8.3 l x 100 km.

CHASSIS integral; front suspension: independent, coil springs/telescopic damper struts, lower wishbones (trailing links), anti-roll bar; rear suspension: rigid axle, semi-elliptic leafsprings, telescopic dampers.

STEERING recirculating ball; turns of steering wheel lock to lock: 3.75.

BRAKES front disc (diameter 9.60 in, 244 mm), rear drum, servo; area rubbed by linings: front 175 sq in, 1,129 sq cm, rear 97 sq in, 625 sq cm, total 272 sq in, 1,754 sq cm.

ELECTRICAL EQUIPMENT voltage: 12 V; battery: 40 Ah; generator type: alternator, 408 W; ignition distributor: Lucas; headlamps: 4.

DIMENSIONS AND WEIGHT wheel base: 98.50 in, 2,502 mm; front track: 52 in, 1,321 mm; rear track: 52 in, 1,321 mm;

SUNBEAM Rapier H120

SUNBEAM Alpine

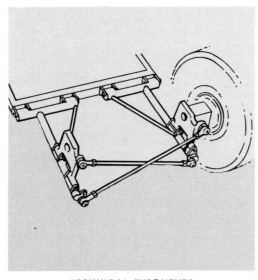

TECHNICAL EXPONENTS
(Torix-Bennet rear suspension)

overall length: 174.10 in, 4,422 mm; overall width: 64.75 in, 1,645 mm; overall height: 55 in, 1,397 mm; ground clearance: 5 in, 127 mm; dry weight: 2,091 lb, 948 kg; turning circle (between walls): 36 ft, 11 m; fuel tank capacity: 15 imp gal, 17.9 US gal, 68 l.

BODY coupé (fastback); doors: 2; seats: 4; front seats separate, high-backed seats.

PRACTICAL INSTRUCTIONS fuel: 96-98 oct petrol; engine sump oil: 7.5 imp pt, 8.9 US pt, 4.2 l, multigrade, change every 5,000 miles, 8,000 km; gearbox oil: 3.5 imp pt, 4.3 US pt, 2 l, multigrade, no change recommended; final drive oil: 1.7 imp pt, 1.9 US pt, 0.9 l, SAE 90 EP, no change recommended; greasing: none; tappet clearances: inlet 0.012 in, 0.31 mm, exhaust 0.014 in, 0.35 mm; valve timing: inlet opens 51° before tdc and closes 89° after bdc, exhaust opens 85° before bdc and closes 40° after tdc; normal tyre pressure: front 25 psi, 1.7 atm, rear 25 psi, 1.7 atm.

OPTIONAL ACCESSORIES Laycock overdrive on III and IV 0.803 ratio; Borg-Warner 35/3 automatic gearbox, hydraulic torque convertor and planetary gears with 3 ratios (I 2.393, II 1.450, III 1, rev 2.094), max ratio of convertor at stall 1.9, central selector lever, 3.890 axle ratio: low-backed seats with reclining backrests; electrically-heated rear window.

TX Tripper 1300

PRICE IN GB: £ 780.

ENGINE front, 4 stroke; cylinders: 4, in line; bore and stroke: 2.90 x 2.99 in, 73.7 x 76 mm; engine capacity: 79.1 cu in, 1,296 cu cm; compression ratio: 9.5; max power (DIN): 75 hp at 6,000 rpm; max torque (DIN): 75 lb ft, 10.3 kg m at 4,000 rpm; max engine rpm: 6,500; specific power: 57.9 hp/l; cylinder block: cast iron; cylinder head: cast iron; crankshaft bearings: 5; valves: 2 per cylinder, overhead, in line, push-rods and rockers; camshafts: 1 side; lubrication: gear pump, full flow filter; lubricating system capacity: 8 imp pt, 9.5 US pt, 4.5 l; carburation: 2 SU type HS2 semi-downdraught carburettors; fuel feed: mechanical pump; cooling system: water; cooling system capacity: 6 imp pt, 7.2 US pt, 3.4 l.

TRANSMISSION driving wheels: rear; clutch: single dry plate (diaphragm); gearbox: mechanical; gears: 4 + reverse; synchromesh gears: II, III, IV; gearbox ratios: I 3.750, II 2.160, III 1.390, IV 1, rev 3.750; gear lever: central; final drive: hypoid bevel; axle ratio: 3.890; width of rims: 5.5''; tyres: 155 x 13.

PERFORMANCE max speeds: 30 mph, 48 km/h in 1st gear; 52 mph, 83 km/h in 2nd gear; 81 mph, 130 km/h in 3rd gear; 108 mph, 174 km/h in 4th gear; power-weight ratio: 14.1 lb/hp, 6.4 kg/hp; carrying capacity: 784 lb, 356 kg; acceleration: standing ¼ mile 7.6 sec; speed in direct drive at 1,000 rpm: 17.3 mph, 27.8 km/h; fuel consumption: 40 m/imp gal, 33.1 m/US gal, 7.1 l x 100 km.

CHASSIS box-type double backbone with outriggers; front suspension: independent, wishbones, coil springs, telescopic dampers; rear suspension: independent, wishbones, transverse leafspring as upper arms, telescopic dampers.

STEERING rack-and-pinion; turns of steering wheel lock to lock: 3.50.

BRAKES front disc (diameter 9 in, 229 mm), rear drum; lining area: total 197 sq in, 1,271 sq cm.

ELECTRICAL EQUIPMENT voltage: 12 V; battery: 45 Ah; generator type: alternator, 15 W; ignition distributor: Lucas; headlamps: 2.

DIMENSIONS AND WEIGHT wheel base: 83.07 in, 2,110 mm; front track: 50.12 in, 1,273 mm; rear track: 49.61 in, 1,260 mm; overall length: 145.08 in, 3,685 mm; overall width: 57.05 in, 1,449 mm; overall height: 47.17 in, 1,198 mm; ground clearance: 6.50 in, 165 mm; dry weight: 1,067 lb, 484 kg; distribution of weight: 52% front axle, 48% rear axle; turning circle (between walls): 25.3 ft, 7.7 m; fuel tank capacity: 8.2 imp gal, 9.8 US gal, 37 l.

BODY open, in plastic material; doors: none; seats: 2; front seats: separate.

PRACTICAL INSTRUCTIONS fuel: 90 oct petrol; engine sump oil: 8 imp pt, 9.5 US pt, 4.5 l.

OPTIONAL ACCESSORIES 3.230, 4.110 axle ratios; 165 x 13 tyres.

TX Tripper 1600

See TX Tripper 1300, except for:

PRICE IN GB: £ 845.

ENGINE bore and stroke: 3.19 x 3.05 in, 81 x 77.6 mm; engine capacity: 97.6 cu in, 1,599 cu cm; max power (DIN):

93 hp at 5,400 rpm; max torque (DIN): 102 lb ft, 14.1 kg m at 3,600 rpm; max engine rpm: 6,000; specific power: 63.8 hp/l; carburation: 1 Weber 32 DFM downdraught twin barrel carburettor.

TRANSMISSION synchromesh gears: I, II, III, IV; gearbox ratios: I 2.970, II 2.010, III 1.400, IV 1, rev 3.320; axle ratio: 3.270.

PERFORMANCE max speed: 119 mph, 191 km/h; power-weight ratio: 11.5 lb/hp, 5.2 kg/hp; acceleration: standing ¼ mile 6.2 sec; speed in direct drive at 1,000 rpm: 21 mph, 33.8 km/h; fuel consumption: 38 m/imp gal, 31.8 m/US gal, 7.4 l x 100 km.

SUNBEAM Rapier

SUNBEAM Alpine

TECHNICAL EXPONENTS TX Tripper 1300

TRIUMPH   GREAT BRITAIN

Herald 13/60 Saloon

PRICE IN GB: £ 648.

ENGINE front, 4 stroke; cylinders: 4, vertical, in line; bore and stroke: 2.90 x 2.99 in, 73.7 x 76 mm; engine capacity: 79.1 cu in, 1,296 cu cm; compression ratio: 8.5; max power (SAE): 61 hp at 5,000 rpm; max torque (DIN): 72 lb ft, 9.9 kg m at 3,000 rpm; max engine rpm: 5,800; specific power: 47.1 hp/l; cylinder block: cast iron; cylinder head: cast iron; crankshaft bearings: 3; valves: 2 per cylinder, overhead, in line, push-rods and rockers; camshafts: 1, side; lubrication: rotary pump, full flow filter; lubricating system capacity: 7.9 imp pt, 9.5 US pt, 4.5 l; carburation: 1 Stromberg 1.50 CD semi-downdraught single barrel carburettor; fuel feed: mechanical pump; cooling system: water; cooling system capacity: 8.4 imp pt, 10.1 US pt, 4.8 l.

TRANSMISSION driving wheels: rear; clutch: single dry plate, hydraulically controlled; gearbox: mechanical; gears: 4 + reverse; synchromesh gears: II, III, IV; gearbox ratios: I 3.746, II 2.158, III 1.394, IV 1, rev 3.746; gear lever: central; final drive: hypoid bevel; axle ratio: 4.110; width of rims: 3.5''; tyres: 5.20 x 13.

PERFORMANCE max speeds: 24 mph, 38 km/h in 1st gear; 42 mph, 67 km/h in 2nd gear; 65 mph, 104 km/h in 3rd gear; 85 mph, 136 km/h in 4th gear; power-weight ratio: 29.5 lb/hp, 13.4 kg/hp; carrying capacity: 882 lb, 400 kg; acceleration: 0-50 mph (0-80 km/h) 12 sec; speed in direct drive at 1,000 rpm: 15.7 mph, 25.2 km/h; fuel consumption: 41.5 m/imp gal, 34.6 m/US gal, 6.8 l x 100 km.

CHASSIS double backbone, channel section with outriggers; front suspension: independent, wishbones, coil springs, anti-roll bar, telescopic dampers; rear suspension: independent, swinging semi-axles, transverse leafspring upper arms, swinging longitudinal trailing arms, telescopic dampers.

STEERING rack-and-pinion, adjustable steering wheel; turns of steering wheel lock to lock: 3.75.

BRAKES front disc (diameter 9 in, 229 mm), rear drum; area rubbed by linings: front 150 sq in, 968 sq cm, rear 55 sq in, 355 sq cm, total 205 sq in, 1,323 sq cm.

ELECTRICAL EQUIPMENT voltage: 12 V; battery: 40 Ah; generator type: dynamo, 264 W; headlamps: 2.

DIMENSIONS AND WEIGHT wheel base: 91.34 in, 2,320 mm; front track: 49.02 in, 1,245 mm; rear track: 48.03 in, 1,220 mm; overall length: 153.15 in, 3,890 mm; overall width: 60.04 in, 1,525 mm; overall height: 51.93 in, 1,319 mm; ground clearance: 6.69 in, 170 mm; dry weight: 1,797 lb, 815 kg; distribution of weight: 51.1% front axle, 48.5% rear axle; turning circle (between walls): 26 ft, 7.9 m; fuel tank capacity: 6.4 imp gal, 7.7 US gal, 29 l.

BODY saloon/sedan; doors: 2; seats: 4-5; front seats: separate.

PRACTICAL INSTRUCTIONS fuel: 95-100 oct petrol; engine sump oil: 7.6 imp pt, 9.1 US pt, 4.3 l, SAE 20, change every 6,000 miles, 9,700 km; gearbox oil: 1.4 imp pt, 1.7 US pt, 0.8 l, SAE 90; final drive oil: 1.1 imp pt, 1.3 US pt, 0.6 l, SAE 90; greasing: every 6,000 miles, 9,700 km, 2 points, every 12,000 miles, 19,300 km, 2 points; tappet clearances: inlet 0.010 in, 0.25 mm, exhaust 0.010 in, 0.25 mm; valve timing: inlet opens 18° before tdc and closes 58° after bdc, exhaust opens 58° before bdc and closes 18° after tdc; normal tyre pressure: front 18 psi, 1.3 atm, rear 24 psi, 1.7 atm.

OPTIONAL ACCESSORIES servo brake; sunshine roof.

Herald 13/60 Convertible

See Herald 13/60 Saloon, except for:

PRICE IN GB: £ 695.

PERFORMANCE power-weight ratio: 28.4 lb/hp, 12.9 kg/hp; acceleration: 0-50 mph (0-80 km/h) 11.5 sec.

HERALD 13/60 CONVERTIBLE

DIMENSIONS AND WEIGHT dry weight: 1,731 lb, 785 kg.

BODY convertible.

OPTIONAL ACCESSORIES tonneau cover.

.

Herald 13/60 Estate Car

See Herald 13/60 Saloon, except for:

PRICE IN GB: £ 717.

TRANSMISSION tyres: 5.60 x 13.

PERFORMANCE max speeds: 25 mph, 40 km/h in 1st gear; 44 mph, 71 km/h in 2nd gear; 68 mph, 109 km/h in 3rd gear; 83 mph, 133 km/h in 4th gear; power-weight ratio: 31.3 lb/hp, 14.2 kg/hp; acceleration: 0-50 mph (0-80 km/h) 12.8 sec; speed in direct drive at 1,000 rpm: 16.3 mph, 26.2 km/h.

DIMENSIONS AND WEIGHT dry weight: 1,907 lb, 865 kg; fuel tank capacity: 9 imp gal, 10.8 US gal, 41 l.

BODY estate car/station wagon; doors: 2 + 1.

OPTIONAL ACCESSORIES sunshine roof not available.

Toledo

PRICE IN GB: £ 679.

ENGINE front, 4 stroke; cylinders: 4, vertical, in line; bore and stroke: 2.90 x 2.99 in, 73.7 x 76 mm; engine capacity: 79.1 cu in, 1,296 cu cm; compression ratio: 8.5; max power (DIN): 58 hp at 5,300 rpm; max torque (DIN): 70 lb ft, 9.6 kg m at 3,000 rpm; max engine rpm: 5,300; specific power: 44.8 hp/l; cylinedr block: cast iron; cylinder head: cast iron; crankshaft bearings: 3; valves: 2 per cylinder, overhead, in line, push-rods and rockers; camshafts: 1, side; lubrication: rotary pump, full flow filter; lubricating system capacity: 7.2 imp pt, 8.7 US pt, 4.1 l; carburation: 1 SU HS4 semi-downdraught carburettor; fuel feed: mechanical pump; cooling system: water; cooling system capacity: 9.5 imp pt, 11.4 US pt, 5.4 l.

TRANSMISSION driving wheels: rear; clutch: single dry plate (diaphragm); gearbox: mechanical; gears: 4 + reverse; synchromesh gears: I, II, III, IV; gearbox ratios: I 3.504, II 2.158, III 1.394, IV 1, rev 3.988; gear lever: central; final drive: hypoid bevel; axle ratio: 4.110; width of rims: 4''; tyres: 5.20 x 13.

PERFORMANCE max speeds: 24 mph, 39 km/h in 1st gear; 39 mph, 63 km/h in 2nd gear; 60 mph, 97 km/h in 3rd gear; 85 mph, 137 km/h in 4th gear; power-weight ratio: 32 lb/hp, 14.5 kg/hp; carrying capacity: 838 lb, 380 kg; acceleration: 0-50 mph (0-80 km/h) 12.5 sec; speed in direct drive at 1,000 rpm: 15.9 mph, 25.6 km/h; fuel consumption: 38.7 m/imp gal, 32.2 m/US gal, 7.3 l x 100 km.

CHASSIS integral; front suspension: independent, wishbones, lower trailing links, coil springs, telescopic dampers; rear suspension: rigid axle, lower trailing arms, upper oblique torque arms, coil springs, telescopic dampers.

STEERING rack-and-pinion; turns of steering wheel lock to lock: 3.

BRAKES drum; area rubbed by linings: front 99.1 sq in, 639 sq cm, rear 75.5 sq in, 487 sq cm, total 174.6 sq in, 1,126 sq cm.

ELECTRICAL EQUIPMENT voltage: 12 V; battery: 40 Ah; generator type: alternator, 318 W; ignition distributor: Lucas; headlamps: 2.

DIMENSIONS AND WEIGHT wheel base: 96.85 in, 2,460 mm; front track: 53.07 in, 1,348 mm; rear track: 50 in, 1,270 mm; overall length: 156.30 in, 3,970 mm; overall width: 61.89 in, 1,572 mm; overall height: 54.02 in, 1,372 mm; ground clearance: 4.25 in, 108 mm; dry weight: 1,852 lb, 840 kg; distribution of weight: 48% front axle, 52% rear axle; turning circle (between walls): 24.6 ft, 7.5 m; fuel tank capacity: 10.6 imp gal, 12.7 US gal, 48 l.

BODY saloon/sedan; doors: 2; seats: 4; front seats: separate.

PRACTICAL INSTRUCTIONS fuel: 97 oct petrol; engine sump oil: 6.5 imp pt, 7.8 US pt, 3.7 l, SAE 20W-50, change every 6,000 miles, 9,700 km; gearbox oil: 1.4 imp pt, 1.7 US pt, 0.8 l, SAE 90, change every 6,000 miles, 9,700 km; final drive oil: 1.5 imp pt, 1.9 US pt, 0.9 l, SAE 90, change every 6,000 miles, 9,700 km; greasing: every 6,000 miles, 9,700 km, 3 points; tappet clearances: inlet 0.010 in, 0.25 mm, exhaust 0.010 in, 0.25 mm; valve timing: inlet opens 18° before tdc

TRIUMPH Herald 13/60 Saloon

TRIUMPH Toledo

TRIUMPH Spitfire Mk IV

and closes 58° after bdc, exhaust opens 58° before bdc and closes 18° after tdc; normal tyre pressure: front 25 psi, 1.7 atm, rear 30 psi, 2.1 atm.

1300

PRICE IN GB: £ 760.

ENGINE front, 4 stroke; cylinders: 4, vertical, in line; bore and stroke: 2.90 x 2.99 in, 73.7 x 76 mm; engine capacity: 79.1 cu in, 1,296 cu cm; compression ratio: 8.5; max power (DIN): 61 hp at 5,000 rpm; max torque (DIN): 73 lb ft, 10.1 kg m at 3,000 rpm; max engine rpm: 5,900; specific power: 47.1 hp/l; cylinder block: cast iron; cylinder head: light alloy; crankshaft bearings: 3; valves: 2 per cylinder, overhead, in line, push-rods and rockers; camshafts: 1, side; lubrication: rotary pump, full flow filter; lubricating system capacity: 6.5 imp pt, 7.8 US pt, 3.7 l; carburation: 1 Stromberg 1.50 CD horizontal single barrel carburettor; fuel feed: mechanical pump; cooling system: water; cooling system capacity: 6.3 imp pt, 7.6 US pt, 3.6 l.

TRANSMISSION driving wheels: front; clutch: single dry plate (diaphragm), hydraulically controlled; gearbox: mechanical; gears: 4 + reverse; synchromesh gears: I, II, III, IV; gearbox ratios: I 3.400, II 2.160, III 1.450, IV 1.060, rev 3.990; gear lever: central; final drive: hypoid bevel; axle ratio: 4.110; width of rims: 4''; tyres: 5.60 x 13.

PERFORMANCE max speeds: 27 mph, 43 km/h in 1st gear; 42 mph, 67 km/h in 2nd gear; 63 mph, 101 km/h in 3rd gear; 85 mph, 136 km/h in 4th gear; power-weight ratio: 31.3 lb/hp, 14.2 kg/hp; carrying capacity: 882 lb, 400 kg; acceleration: 0-50 mph (0-80 km/h) 13 sec; speed in top at 1,000 rpm: 15.4 mph, 24.8 km/h; fuel consumption: 38.7 m/imp gal, 32.2 m/US gal, 7.3 l x 100 km.

CHASSIS integral, front and rear auxiliary frames; front suspension: independent, wishbones, coil springs, telescopic dampers; rear suspension: independent, semi-trailing arms, coil springs, telescopic dampers.

STEERING rack-and-pinion, adjustable height and distance (of steering column); turns of steering wheel lock to lock: 3.25.

BRAKES front disc (diameter 8.74 in, 222 mm), rear drum: area rubbed by linings: front 145 sq in, 935 sq cm, rear 63 sq in, 407 sq cm, total 208 sq in, 1,342 sq cm.

ELECTRICAL EQUIPMENT voltage: 12 V; battery: 40 Ah; generator type: dynamo, 264 W; ignition distributor: Lucas; headlamps: 2.

DIMENSIONS AND WEIGHT wheel base: 96.61 in, 2,454 mm; front track: 52.99 in, 1,346 mm; rear track: 52.64 in, 1,337 mm; overall length: 151.06 in, 3,937 mm; overall width: 61.73 in, 1,568 mm; overall height: 52.24 in, 1,327 mm; ground clearance: 5.51 in, 140 mm; dry weight: 1,905 lb, 864 kg; turning circle (between walls): 31 ft, 9.4 m; fuel tank capacity: 11.7 imp gal, 14 US gal, 53 l.

BODY saloon/sedan; doors: 4; seats: 5; front seats: separate.

PRACTICAL INSTRUCTIONS fuel: 95 oct petrol; engine sump oil: 6.2 imp pt, 7.4 US pt, 3.5 l, SAE 20W, change every 6,000 miles, 9,700 km; gearbox oil: 2.5 imp pt, 3 US pt, 1.4 l, SAE 75; final drive oil: 1.2 imp pt, 1.5 US pt, 0.7 l, SAE 90; greasing: every 12,000 miles, 19,300 km, 2 points; tappet clearances: inlet 0.010 in, 0.25 mm, exhaust 0.010 in, 0.25 mm; valve timing: inlet opens 18° before tdc and closes 58° after bdc, exhaust opens 58° before bdc and closes 18° after tdc; normal tyre pressure: front 21 psi, 1.5 atm, rear 18 psi, 1.3 atm.

OPTIONAL ACCESSORIES servo brake.

1300 TC

See 1300, except for:

PRICE IN GB: £ 754.

ENGINE compression ratio: 9; max power (SAE): 75 hp at 6,000 rpm; max torque (SAE): 75 lb ft, 10.4 kg m at 4,000 rpm; max engine rpm: 6,000; specific power: 57.9 hp/l; carburation: 2 SU type HS 2 horizontal carburettors.

PERFORMANCE max speeds: 29 mph, 47 km/h in 1st gear; 45 mph, 72 km/h in 2nd gear; 67 mph, 108 km/h in 3rd gear; 92 mph, 148 km/h in 4th gear; power-weight ratio: 25.4 lb/hp, 11.5 kg/hp; acceleration: 0-50 mph (0-80 km/h) 11.5 sec; fuel consumption: 34 m/imp gal, 28.3 m/US gal, 8.3 l x 100 km.

BRAKES servo (standard).

PRACTICAL INSTRUCTIONS fuel: 100 oct petrol.

TRIUMPH Herald 13/60 Convertible

TRIUMPH Toledo

TRIUMPH Spitfire Mk IV

Spitfire Mk III

PRICE IN GB: £ 669.
PRICE IN USA: $ 2,295.

ENGINE front, 4 stroke; cylinders: 4, vertical, in line; bore and stroke: 2.90 x 2.99 in, 73.7 x 76 mm; engine capacity: 79.1 cu in, 1,296 cu cm; compression ratio: 9; max power (DIN): 76 hp at 6,000 rpm; max torque (DIN): 90 lb ft, 12.4 kg m at 4,000 rpm; max engine rpm: 6,700; specific power: 58.6 hp/l; cylinder block: cast iron; cylinder head: cast iron; crankshaft bearings: 3; valves: 2 per cylinder, overhead, in line, push-rods and rockers; camshafts: 1, side; lubrication: rotary pump, full flow filter; lubricating system capacity: 8.4 imp pt, 10.1 US pt, 4.8 l; carburation: 2 SU type HS 2 semi-downdraught carburettors; fuel feed: mechanical pump; cooling system: liquid, sealed circuit; cooling system capacity: 7.9 imp pt, 9.5 US pt, 4.5 l.

TRANSMISSION driving wheels: rear; clutch: single dry plate, hydraulically controlled; gearbox: mechanical; gears: 4 + reverse; synchromesh gears: II, III, IV; gearbox ratios: I 3.747, II 2.158, III 1.394, IV 1, rev 3.750; gear lever: central; final drive: hypoid bevel; axle ratio: 4.110; width of rims: 4.5''; tyres: 5.20 x 13.

PERFORMANCE max speeds: 28 mph, 45 km/h in 1st gear; 49 mph, 79 km/h in 2nd gear; 75 mph, 120 km/h in 3rd gear; 103 mph, 165 km/h in 4th gear; power-weight ratio: 17.8 lb/hp, 8.1 kg/hp; carrying capacity: 353 lb, 160 kg; acceleration: standing 1/4 mile 18.5 sec, 0-50 mph (0-80 km/h) 9 sec; speed in direct drive at 1,000 rpm: 15.7 mph, 25.2 km/h; fuel consumption: 33.2 m/imp gal, 27.7 m/US gal, 8.5 l x 100 km.

CHASSIS double backbone, channel section with outriggers; front suspension: independent, wishbones, coil springs, anti-roll bar, telescopic dampers; rear suspension: independent, swinging semi-axles, transverse leafspring upper arms, swinging longitudinal trailing arms, telescopic dampers.

STEERING rack-and-pinion; turns of steering wheel lock to lock: 3.75.

BRAKES front disc (diameter 9 in, 229 mm), rear drum; area rubbed by linings: front 197 sq in, 1,271 sq cm, rear 67 sq in, 432 sq cm, total 264 sq in, 1,703 sq cm.

ELECTRICAL EQUIPMENT voltage: 12 V; battery: 43 Ah; generator type: dynamo, 264 W; ignition distributor: Lucas; headlamps: 2.

DIMENSIONS AND WEIGHT wheel base: 82.99 in, 2,108 mm; front track: 49.02 in, 1,245 mm; rear track: 47.99 in, 1,219 mm; overall length: 107.64 in, 3,734 mm; overall width: 57.01 in, 1,448 mm; overall height: 47.48 in, 1,206 mm; ground clearance: 5 in, 127 mm; dry weight: 1,430 lb, 648 kg; distribution of weight: 56% front axle, 44% rear axle; turning circle (between walls): 24 ft, 7.3 m; fuel tank capacity: 8.6 imp gal, 10.3 US gal, 39 l.

BODY convertible; doors: 2; seats: 2.

PRACTICAL INSTRUCTIONS fuel: 100 oct petrol; engine sump oil: 7.9 imp pt, 9.5 US pt, 4.5 l, SAE 20, change every 6,000 miles, 9,700 km; gearbox oil: 1.4 imp pt, 1.7 US pt, 0.8 l, SAE 90; final drive oil: 1.1 imp pt, 1.3 US pt, 0.6 l, SAE 90; greasing: every 6,000 miles, 9,700 km, 2 points, every 12,000 miles, 19,300 km, 2 points; tappet clearances: inlet 0.010 in, 0.25 mm, exhaust 0.010 in, 0.25 mm; valve timing: inlet opens 18° before tdc and closes 58° after bdc, exhaust opens 58° before bdc and closes 18° after tdc; normal tyre pressure: front 18 psi, 1.3 atm, rear 24 psi, 1.7 atm.

OPTIONAL ACCESSORIES Laycock-de Normanville overdrive on III and IV (0.820 ratio), 3.750 axle ratio, max speed in overdrive/top 91 mph, 146 km/h; hardtop; tonneau cover.

Spitfire Mk IV

See Spitfire Mk III, except for:

PRICE IN GB: £ 735.

ENGINE max power (DIN): 63 hp at 6,000 rpm; max torque (DIN): 70 lb ft, 9.6 kg m at 3,500 rpm; max engine rpm: 6,500; specific power: 48.6 hp/l; lubricating system capacity: 8 imp pt, 9.5 US pt, 4.5 l; cooling system capacity: 9 imp pt, 10.8 US pt, 5.1 l.

TRANSMISSION synchromesh gears: I, II, III, IV; gearbox ratios: I 3.500, II 2.160, III 1.390, IV 1, rev 3.990; axle ratio: 3.890.

PERFORMANCE max speeds: 31 mph, 50 km/h in 1st gear; 50 mph, 80 km/h in 2nd gear; 78 mph, 126 km/h in 3rd gear; 97 mph, 156 km/h in 4th gear; power-weight ratio: 25.6 lb/hp, 11.6 kg/hp; acceleration: standing 1/4 mile 19.8

SPITFIRE MK IV

sec. 0-50 (0-80 km/h) 9 sec; speed in direct drive at 1,000 rpm: 16.7 mph, 26.8 km/h.

BRAKES area rubbed by linings: front 149.9 sq in, 967 sq cm, rear 55 sq in, 355 sq cm, total 204.9 sq in, 1,322 sq cm.

ELECTRICAL EQUIPMENT battery: 40 Ah; generator type: alternator, 318 W; ignition distributor: Delco.

DIMENSIONS AND WEIGHT dry weight: 1,618 lb, 734 kg; fuel tank capacity: 8.4 imp gal, 10 US gal, 38 l.

PRACTICAL INSTRUCTIONS fuel: 97 oct petrol; engine sump oil: 7 imp pt, 8.5 US pt, 4 l; gearbox oil: 1.5 imp pt, 1.9 US pt, 0.9 l; final drive oil: .1 imp pt, 1.3 US pt, 0.6 l; greasing: 3 points; valve timing: inlet opens 25° before tdc and closes 65° after bdc, exhaust opens 65° before bdc and closes 25° after tdc; normal tyre pressure: front 21 psi, 1.5 atm, rear 26 psi, 1.8 atm.

OPTIONAL ACCESSORIES 145SR x 13 tyres.

1500

PRICE IN GB: £ 851.

ENGINE front, 4 stroke; cylinders: 4, vertical, in line; bore and stroke: 2.90 x 3.44 in, 73.7 x 87.5 mm; engine capacity: 91.1 cu in, 1,493 cu cm; compression ratio: 8.5; max power (DIN): 65 hp at 5,000 rpm; max torque (DIN): 81 lb ft, 11.2 kg m at 2,700 rpm; max engine rpm: 5,500; specific power: 43.5 hp/l; cylinder block: cast iron; cylinder head: cast iron; crankshaft bearings: 3; valves: 2 per cylinder, overhead, in line, push-rods and rockers; camshafts: 1, side; lubrication: rotary pump, full flow filter; lubricating system capacity: 7.2 imp pt, 8.7 US pt, 4.1 l; carburation: 1 SU HS4 semi-downdraught carburettor; fuel feed: mechanical pump; cooling system: water; cooling system capacity: 8.2 imp pt, 9.7 US pt, 4.6 l.

TRANSMISSION driving wheels: front; clutch: single dry plate (diaphragm); gearbox: mechanical; gears: 4 + reverse; synchromesh gears: I, II, III, IV; gearbox ratios: I 3.020, II 1.918, III 1.289, IV 0.889, rev 3.600; gear lever: central; final drive: hypoid bevel; axle ratio: 4.550; width of rims: 4''; tyres: 5.60 x 13.

PERFORMANCE max speeds: 27 mph, 44 km/h in 1st gear; 42 mph, 68 km/h in 2nd gear; 62 mph, 100 km/h in 3rd gear; 87 mph, 140 km/h in 4th gear; power-weight ratio: 32.6 lb/hp, 14.8 kg/hp; acceleration: 0-50 mph (0-80 km/h) 12.5 sec; speed in top at 1,000 rpm: 16.7 mph, 26.8 km/h.

CHASSIS integral, front subframe; front suspension: independent, wishbones (lower leading arms), coil springs, tele-scopic dampers; rear suspension: rigid axle, lower trail-ing arms, upper oblique torque arms, coil springs, tele-scopic dampers.

STEERING rack-and-pinion, adjustable steering wheel; turns of steering wheel lock to lock: 3.

BRAKES front disc (diameter 8.74 in, 222 mm), rear drum, servo; area rubbed by linings: front 165.1 sq in, 1,065 sq cm, rear 75.5 sq in, 487 sq cm, total 240.6 sq in, 1,552 sq cm.

ELECTRICAL EQUIPMENT voltage: 12 V; battery: 40 Ah; generator type: alternator, 318 W; ignition distributor: Lu-cas; headlamps: 2.

DIMENSIONS AND WEIGHT wheel base: 96.85 in, 2,460 mm; front track: 53.54 in, 1,360 mm, rear track: 50.47 in, 1,282 mm; overall length: 161.81 in, 4,110 mm; overall width: 61.89 in, 1,572 mm; overall height: 54.02 in, 1,372 mm; dry weight: 2,128 lb, 965 kg; fuel tank capacity: 12.5 imp gal, 15 US gal, 57 l.

BODY saloon/sedan; doors: 4; seats: 4; front seats: sepa-rate.

PRACTICAL INSTRUCTIONS fuel: 95 oct petrol; engine sump oil: 6.2 imp pt, 7.4 US pt, 3.5 l; gearbox oil: 2.2 imp pt, 2.5 US pt, 1.2 l; final drive oil: 1.2 imp pt, 1.5 US pt, 0.7 l; valve timing: inlet opens 18° before tdc and closes 58° after bdc, exhaust opens 58° before bdc and closes 18° after tdc.

OPTIONAL ACCESSORIES anti-roll bar on rear suspension.

2-litre Mk II Vitesse Saloon

PRICE IN GB: £ 827.

ENGINE front, 4 stroke; cylinders: 6, vertical, in line; bore and stroke: 2.94 x 2.99 in, 74.7 x 76 mm; engine capacity: 121.9 cu in, 1,998 cu cm; compression ratio: 9.2;

TRIUMPH 1500
(independent front suspension)

TRIUMPH 2-litre Mk II Vitesse Saloon

TRIUMPH 2000 Mk II Saloon

max power (DIN): 104 hp at 5,300 rpm; max torque (DIN) 117 lb ft, 16.1 kg m at 3,000 rpm; max engine rpm: 6,400 specific power: 52 hp/l; cylinder block: cast iron; cylinder head: cast iron; crankshaft bearings: 4; valves: 2 per cylinder, overhead, push-rods and rockers; camshafts: 1 side; lubrication: rotary pump, full flow filter; lubricating system capacity: 9 imp pt, 10.8 US pt, 5.1 l; carburation 2 Stromberg 1.50 CD semi-downdraught carburettors; fuel feed: mechanical pump; cooling system: water; cooling system capacity: 11.1 imp pt, 13.3 US pt, 6.3 l.

TRANSMISSION driving wheels: rear; clutch: single dry plate (diaphragm), hydraulically controlled; gearbox: mech-anical; gears: 4 + reverse; synchromesh gears: I, II, III, IV; gearbox ratios: I 2.650, II 1.780, III 1.250, IV 1, rev 3.100; gear lever: central; final drive: hypoid bevel; axle ratio: 3.890; width of rims: 4.5''; tyres: 5.60 x 13.

PERFORMANCE max speeds: 41 mph, 66 km/h in 1st gear; 61 mph, 98 km/h in 2nd gear; 88 mph, 141 km/h in 3rd gear; 103 mph, 165 km/h in 4th gear; power-weight ratio: 20.3 lb/hp, 9.2 kg/hp; carrying capacity: 706 lb, 320 kg; acceleration: standing ¼ mile 18 sec, 0-50 mph (0-80 km/h) 8 sec; speed in direct drive at 1,000 rpm: 17.1 mph, 27.5 km/h; fuel consumption: 23.3 m/imp gal, 19.4 m/US gal, 12.1 l x 100 km.

CHASSIS double backbone, channel section with outriggers; front suspension: independent, wishbones, coil springs, anti-roll bar, telescopic dampers; rear suspension: inde-pendent, wishbones, transverse leafspring upper arms, swinging lower trailing arms, lever dampers.

STEERING rack-and-pinion, adjustable steering wheel; turns of steering wheel lock to lock: 4.37.

BRAKES front disc (diameter 9.69 in, 246 mm), rear drum; area rubbed by linings: front 197 sq in, 1,271 sq cm, rear 63 sq in, 407 sq cm, total 260 sq in, 1,678 sq cm.

ELECTRICAL EQUIPMENT voltage: 12 V; battery: 40 Ah; generator type: dynamo, 300 W; ignition distributor: Lucas; headlamps: 4.

DIMENSIONS AND WEIGHT wheel base: 91.54 in, 2,325 mm; front track: 49.02 in, 1,245 mm; rear track: 48.46 in, 1,231 mm; overall length: 152.95 in, 3,885 mm; overall width: 60.04 in, 1,525 mm; overall height: 53.74 in, 1,365 mm; ground clearance: 5.47 in, 139 mm; dry weight: 1,932 lb, 876 kg; turning circle (between walls): 25 ft, 7.6 m; fuel tank capacity: 8.8 imp gal, 10.6 US gal, 40 l.

BODY saloon/sedan; doors: 2; seats: 4; front seats: separate.

PRACTICAL INSTRUCTIONS fuel: 100 oct petrol; engine sump oil: 7.9 imp pt, 9.5 US pt, 4.5 l, SAE 20W-30, change every 6,000 miles, 9,700 km; gearbox oil: 1.6 imp pt, 1.9 US pt, 0.9 l, SAE 90, no change recommended; final drive oil: 1.1 imp pt, 1.3 US pt, 0.6 l, no change recom-mended; greasing: every 6,000 miles, 9,700 km, 2 points, every 12,000 miles, 19,300 km, 2 points; tappet clearances: inlet 0.010 in, 0.25 mm, exhaust 0.010 in, 0.25 mm; valve timing: inlet opens 18° before tdc and closes 58° after bdc, exhaust opens 58° before bdc and closes 18° after tdc; normal tyre pressure: front 23 psi, 1.6 atm, rear 26 psi, 1.8 atm.

OPTIONAL ACCESSORIES Laycock-de Normanville overdrive on III and IV, 0.800 ratio; servo brake.

2-litre Mk II Vitesse Convertible

See 2-litre Mk II Vitesse Saloon, except for:

PRICE IN GB: £ 865.

DIMENSIONS AND WEIGHT overall height: 55.24 in, 1,403 mm.

BODY convertible.

OPTIONAL ACCESSORIES tonneau cover.

2000 Mk II Saloon

PRICE IN GB: £ 1,185.

ENGINE front, 4 stroke; cylinders: 6, slanted at 8°, in line; bore and stroke: 2.94 x 2.99 in, 74.7 x 76 mm; engine capacity: 121.9 cu in, 1,998 cu cm; compression ratio: 9.2; max power (DIN): 90 hp at 5,000 rpm; max torque (DIN): 117 lb ft, 16.1 kg m at 2,900 rpm; max engine rpm: 6,000; specific power: 45 hp/l; cylinder block: cast iron; cylinder head: cast iron; crankshaft bearings: 4; valves: 2 per cylinder, overhead, push-rods and rockers; camshafts: 1, side; lubrication: eccentric pump, full flow filter; lubrica-ting system capacity: 9 imp pt, 10.8 US pt, 5.1 l; carbura-tion: 2 Stromberg 1.50 CD semi-downdraught carburettors;

TRIUMPH 1500

TRIUMPH 2-litre Mk II Vitesse Saloon

TRIUMPH 2000 Mk II Saloon

fuel feed: mechanical pump; cooling system: water; cooling system capacity: 13.6 imp pt, 16.3 US pt, 7.7 l.

TRANSMISSION driving wheels: rear; clutch: single dry plate (diaphragm), hydraulically controlled; gearbox: mechanical; gears: 4 + reverse; synchromesh gears: I, II, III, IV; gearbox ratios: I 3.281, II 2.100, III 1.386, IV 1, rev 3.369; gear lever: central; final drive: hypoid bevel; axle ratio: 4.100; width of rims: 5''; tyres: 6.50 x 13.

PERFORMANCE max speeds: 31 mph, 50 km/h in 1st gear; 49 mph, 79 km/h in 2nd gear; 74 mph, 119 km/h in 3rd gear; 100 mph, 161 km/h in 4th gear; power-weight ratio: 28.9 lb/hp, 13.1 kg/hp; carrying capacity: 882 lb, 400 kg; acceleration: standing $\frac{1}{4}$ mile 19.5 sec, 0-50 mph (0-80 km/h) 9.8 sec; speed in direct drive at 1,000 rpm: 17 mph, 27.3 km/h; fuel consumption: 23.9 m/imp gal, 19.9 m/US gal, 11.8 l x 100 km.

CHASSIS integral, rear auxiliary frame; front suspension: independent, by McPherson, coil springs/telescopic damper struts, lower wishbones (leading arms); rear suspension: independent, semi-trailing arms, coil springs, telescopic dampers.

STEERING rack-and-pinion, steering wheel adjustable in height; turns of steering wheel lock to lock: 4.

BRAKES front disc (diameter 9.75 in, 248 mm), rear drum, servo; area rubbed by linings: front 200 sq in, 1,290 sq cm, rear 99 sq in, 639 sq cm, total 299 sq in, 1,929 sq cm.

ELECTRICAL EQUIPMENT voltage: 12 V; battery: 56 Ah; generator type: alternator, 336 W; headlamps: 4.

DIMENSIONS AND WEIGHT wheel base: 106 in, 2,693 mm; front track: 52.50 in, 1,334 mm; rear track: 52.87 in, 1,343 mm; overall length: 182.31 in, 4,631 mm; overall width: 65 in, 1,651 mm; overall height: 56 in, 1,423 mm; ground clearance: 5.91 in, 150 mm; dry weight: 2,602 lb, 1,180 kg; distribution of weight: 54.6% front axle, 45.4% rear axle; turning circle (between walls): 34 ft, 10.4 m; fuel tank capacity: 14.1 imp gal, 16.9 US gal, 64 l.

BODY saloon/sedan; doors: 4; seats: 4-5; front seats: separate, reclining backrests.

PRACTICAL INSTRUCTIONS fuel: 98 oct petrol; engine sump oil: 7.9 imp pt, 9.5 US pt, 4.5 l, SAE 20W-30, change every 6,000 miles, 9,700 km; gearbox oil: 2.5 imp pt, 3 US pt, 1.4 l, SAE 90, no change recommended; final drive oil: 2 imp pt, 2.5 US pt, 1.2 l, SAE 90, no change recommended; greasing: none; sparking plug type: 225°; tappet clearances: inlet 0.010 in, 0.25 mm, exhaust 0.010 in, 0.25 mm; valve timing: inlet opens 18° before tdc and closes 58° after bdc, exhaust opens 58° before bdc and closes 18° after tdc; normal tyre pressure: front 26 psi, 1.8 atm, rear 26 psi, 1.8 atm.

OPTIONAL ACCESSORIES Laycock-de Normanville overdrive on III and IV, 0.820 ratio; Borg-Warner 35 automatic gearbox, hydraulic torque convertor and planetary gears with 3 ratios (I 2.390, II 1.450, III 1, rev 2.090), max ratio of convertor at stall 2, possible manual selection, 3.700 axle ratio, speed in top at 1,000 rpm 18.7 mph, 30.1 km/h, max speeds (I) 47 mph, 75 km/h, (II) 77 mph, 124 km/h, (III) 112 mph, 180 km/h; 185 SR x 13 tyres; power-assisted steering.

2000 Mk II Estate Car

See 2000 Mk II Saloon, except for:

PRICE IN GB: £ 1,400.

TRANSMISSION tyres: 175 x 13.

PERFORMANCE power-weight ratio: 30.4 lb/hp, 13.8 kg/hp; acceleration: 0-50 mph (0-80 km/h) 10.3 sec; speed in direct drive at 1,000 rpm: 16.7 mph, 26.9 km/h.

DIMENSIONS AND WEIGHT overall length: 177.25 in, 4,502 mm; dry weight: 2,734 lb, 1,240 kg.

BODY estate car/station wagon; doors: 4 + 1.

PRACTICAL INSTRUCTIONS normal tyre pressure: rear 28 psi, 2 atm.

2.5-litre P.I. MK II Saloon

See 2000 Mk II Saloon, except for:

PRICE IN GB: £ 1,360.

ENGINE bore and stroke: 2.94 x 3.74 in, 74.7 x 95 mm; engine capacity: 152.4 cu in, 2,498 cu cm; compression ratio: 9.5; max power (DIN): 132 hp at 5,450 rpm; max torque (DIN): 153 lb ft, 20.1 kg m at 2,000 rpm; max

2.5-LITRE P.I. MK II SALOON

engine rpm: 5,800; specific power: 52.8 hp/l; carburation: Lucas injection pump (constant pressure), injectors in inlet pipes; fuel feed: electric pump.

TRANSMISSION axle ratio: 3.450; tyres: 185 SR x 13 (standard).

PERFORMANCE max speeds: 35 mph, 56 km/h in 1st gear; 55 mph, 88 km/h in 2nd gear; 84 mph, 135 km/h in 3rd gear; 110 mph, 177 km/h in 4th gear; power-weight ratio: 17 lb/hp, 7.7 kg/hp; acceleration: standing ¼ mile 17.5 sec, 0-50 mph (0-80 km/h) 7.5 sec; speed in direct drive at 1,000 rpm: 20.2 mph, 32.5 km/h; fuel consumption: 22.9 m/imp gal, 19 m/US gal, 12.4 l x 100 km.

ELECTRICAL EQUIPMENT generator type: alternator, 408 W.

DIMENSIONS AND WEIGHT dry weight: 2,242 lb, 1,017 kg.

TRIUMPH 2.5-litre P.I. Mk II Saloon

2.5-litre P.I. Mk II Estate Car

See 2000 Mk II Saloon, except for:

PRICE IN GB: £ 1,575.

ENGINE bore and stroke: 2.94 x 3.74 in, 74.7 x 95 mm; engine capacity: 152.4 cu in, 2,498 cu cm; compression ratio: 9.5; max power (DIN): 132 hp at 5,450 rpm; max torque (DIN): 153 lb ft, 20.1 kg m at 2,000 rpm; max engine rpm: 5,800; specific power: 52.8 hp/l; carburation: Lucas injection pump (constant pressure), injectors in inlet pipes; fuel feed: electric pump.

TRANSMISSION axle ratio: 3.450; tyres: 185 SR x 13 (standard).

PERFORMANCE max speeds: 35 mph, 56 km/h in 1st gear; 55 mph, 88 km/h in 2nd gear; 84 mph, 135 km/h in 3rd gear; 110 mph, 177 km/h in 4th gear; power-weight ratio: 21.2 lb/hp, 9.6 kg/hp; speed in direct drive at 1,000 rpm: 20.2 mph, 32.5 km/h; fuel consumption: 22.9 m/imp gal, 19 m/US gal, 12.4 l x 100 km.

ELECTRICAL EQUIPMENT generator type: alternator, 408 W.

DIMENSIONS AND WEIGHT overall length: 177.25 in, 4,502 mm; dry weight: 2,811 lb, 1,275 kg.

BODY estate car/station wagon; doors: 4 + 1.

PRACTICAL INSTRUCTIONS normal tyre pressure: rear 28 psi, 2 atm.

TRIUMPH GT6 Mk II

GT6 Mk II

PRICE IN GB: £ 925.
PRICE IN USA: $ 2,995.

ENGINE front, 4 stroke; cylinders: 6, in line; bore and stroke: 2.94 x 2.99 in, 74.7 x 76 mm; engine capacity: 121.9 cu in, 1,998 cu cm; compression ratio: 9.2; max power (SAE): 104 hp at 5,300 rpm; max torque (SAE): 117 lb ft, 16.1 kg m at 3,000 rpm; max engine rpm: 6,000; specific power: 52 hp/l; cylinder block: cast iron; cylinder head: cast iron; crankshaft bearings: 4; valves: 2 per cylinder, overhead, push-rods and rockers; camshafts: 1, side; lubrication: eccentric pump, full flow filter; lubricating system capacity: 9 imp pt, 10.8 US pt, 5.1 l; carburation: 2 Stromberg 1.50 CD horizontal carburettors; fuel feed: mechanical pump; cooling system: water; cooling system capacity: 11.1 imp pt, 13.3 US pt, 6.3 l.

TRANSMISSION driving wheels: rear; clutch: single dry plate (diaphragm), hydraulically controlled; gearbox: mechanical; gears: 4 + reverse; synchromesh gears: I, II, III, IV; gearbox ratios: I 2.650, II 1.780, III 1.250, IV 1, rev 3.100; gear lever: central; final drive: hypoid bevel; axle ratio: 3.270; width of rims: 4.5''; tyres: 155 x 13.

PERFORMANCE max speeds: 45 mph, 72 km/h in 1st gear; 68 mph, 109 km/h in 2nd gear; 96 mph, 154 km/h in 3rd gear; 110 mph, 177 km/h in 4th gear; power-weight ratio: 17.4 lb/hp, 7.9 kg/hp; carrying capacity: 353 lb, 160 kg; acceleration: standing ¼ mile 17.5 sec, 0-50 mph (0-80 km/h) 7.5 sec; speed in direct drive at 1,000 rpm: 20.1 mph, 32.3 km/h; fuel consumption: 25.7 m/imp gal, 21.4 m/US gal, 11 l x 100 km.

CHASSIS double backbone, channel section with outriggers; front suspension: independent, wishbones, coil springs, anti-roll bar, telescopic dampers; rear suspension: independent, wishbones, transverse leafspring upper arms, swinging lower trailing arms, telescopic dampers.

STEERING rack-and-pinion, adjustable steering wheel; turns of steering wheel lock to lock: 4.25.

TRIUMPH TR6 P.I.

BRAKES front disc (diameter 9.69 in, 246 mm), rear drum; area rubbed by linings: front 197 sq in, 1,271 sq cm, rear 63 sq in, 407 sq cm, total 260 sq in, 1,678 sq cm.

ELECTRICAL EQUIPMENT voltage: 12 V; battery: 48 Ah; generator type: alternator, 324 W; ignition distributor: Lucas; headlamps: 2.

DIMENSIONS AND WEIGHT wheel base: 83.43 in, 2,119 mm; front track: 49.02 in, 1,245 mm; rear track: 49.02 in, 1,245 mm; overall length: 147.01 in, 3,734 mm; overall width: 57.01 in, 1,448 mm; overall height: 47.05 in, 1,195 mm; ground clearance: 4.02 in, 102 mm; dry weight: 1,819 lb, 825 kg; turning circle (between walls): 25 ft, 7.6 m; fuel tank capacity: 9.7 imp gal, 11.6 US gal, 44 l.

BODY coupé; doors: 2; seats: 2.

PRACTICAL INSTRUCTIONS fuel: 100 oct petrol; engine sump oil: 7.9 imp pt, 9.5 US pt, 4.5 l, SAE 20W-30, change every 6,000 miles, 9,700 km; gearbox oil: 1.6 imp pt, 1.9 US pt, 0.9 l, no change recommended; final drive oil: 1.1 imp pt, 1.3 US pt, 0.6 l, no change recommended; greasing: every 6,000 miles, 9,700 km, 2 points, every 12,000 miles, 19,300 km, 2 points; tappet clearances: inlet 0.010 in, 0.25 mm, exhaust 0.010 in, 0.25 mm; valve timing: inlet opens 18° before tdc and closes 58° after bdc, exhaust opens 58° before bdc and closes 18° after tdc; normal tyre pressure: front 23 psi, 1.6 atm, rear 24 psi, 1.7 atm.

OPTIONAL ACCESSORIES Laycock-de Normanville overdrive on II, III and IV (0.800 ratio), also with 3.890 axle ratio; wire wheels; servo brake.

GT6 Mk III

See GT6 Mk II, except for·

PRICE IN GB: £ 970.

ENGINE max power (DIN): 98 hp at 5,300 rpm; max torque (DIN): 108 lb ft, 14.9 kg m at 3,000 rpm; specific power: 49.1 hp/l; cooling system capacity: 12 imp pt, 14.4 US pt, 6.8 l.

PERFORMANCE max speeds: 46 mph, 74 km/h in 1st gear; 68 mph, 110 km/h in 2nd gear; 96 mph, 155 km/h in 3rd gear; 112 mph, 180 km/h in 4th gear; power-weight ratio: 19.8 lb/hp, 9 kg/hp; acceleration: standing ¼ mile 18.2 sec, 0-50 mph (0-80 km/h) 8 sec.

ELECTRICAL EQUIPMENT battery: 56 Ah; generator type: alternator, 336 W; ignition distributor: Delco.

DIMENSIONS AND WEIGHT wheel base: 83.07 in, 2,110 mm; overall length: 149.02 in, 3,785 mm; overall width: 58.58 in, 1,488 mm; overall height: 47.05 in, 1,195 mm; dry weight: 1,936 lb, 878 kg.

PRACTICAL INSTRUCTIONS engine sump oil: SAE 20W-50; valve timing: inlet opens 25° before tdc and closes 65° after tdc, exhaust opens 65° before bdc and closes 25° after tdc; normal tyre pressure: front 24 psi, 1.7 atm, rear 28 psi, 2 atm.

TR6 P.I.

PRICE IN GB: £ 1,111.
PRICE IN USA: $ 3,275.

ENGINE front, 4 stroke; cylinders: 6, in line; bore and stroke: 2.94 x 3.74 in, 74.7 x 95 mm; engine capacity: 152.4 cu in, 2,498 cu cm; compression ratio: 9.5; max power (DIN): 150 hp at 5,500 rpm; max torque (DIN): 158 lb ft, 21.8 kg m at 3,000 rpm; max engine rpm: 6,000; specific power: 60.2 hp/l; cylinder block: cast iron; cylinder head: cast iron; crankshaft bearings: 4; valves: 2 per cylinder, overhead, in line, push-rods and rockers; camshafts: 1, side; lubrication: eccentric pump, full flow filter; lubricating system capacity: 9 imp pt, 10.8 US pt, 5.1 l; carburation: Lucas injection pump (constant pressure), injectors in inlet pipes; fuel feed: electric pump; cooling system: water; cooling system capacity: 11 imp pt, 13.3 US pt, 6.3 l.

TRANSMISSION driving wheels: rear; clutch: single dry plate (diaphragm), hydraulically controlled; gearbox: mechanical; gears: 4 + reverse; synchromesh gears: I, II, III, IV; gearbox ratios: I 3.140, II 2.010, III 1.330, IV 1, rev 3.220; gear lever: central; final drive: hypoid bevel; axle ratio: 3.450; width of rims: 5.5''; tyres: 165 x 15.

PERFORMANCE max speeds: 37 mph, 59 km/h in 1st gear; 58 mph, 93 km/h in 2nd gear; 88 mph, 141 km/h in 3rd gear; 125 mph, 201 km/h in 4th gear; power-weight ratio: 14.6 lb/hp, 6.6 kg/hp; carrying capacity: 353 lb, 160 kg; acceleration: standing ¼ mile 16.5 sec, 0-50 mph, (0-80 km/h) 6.5 sec; speed in direct drive at 1,000 rpm: 21.2

TRIUMPH 2.5-litre P.I. Mk II Saloon

TRIUMPH GT6 Mk II

TRIUMPH TR6 P.I.

mph, 34.1 km/h; fuel consumption: 23 m/imp gal, 19.1 m/US gal, 12.3 l x 100 km.

CHASSIS box-type ladder frame, X cross members; front suspension: independent, wishbones, coil springs, anti-roll bar, telescopic dampers; rear suspension: independent, semi-trailing arms, coil springs, telescopic dampers.

STEERING rack-and-pinion; turns of steering wheel lock to lock: 3.25.

BRAKES front disc (diameter 10.85 in, 276 mm), rear drum, dual circuit, servo; area rubbed by linings: front 233 sq in, 1,503 sq cm, rear 99 sq in, 639 sq cm, total 332 sq in, 2,142 sq cm.

ELECTRICAL EQUIPMENT voltage: 12 V; battery: 57 Ah; generator type: alternator, 408 W; headlamps: 2.

DIMENSIONS AND WEIGHT wheel base: 88 in, 2,235 mm; front track: 50.25 in, 1,276 mm; rear track: 49.75 in, 1,264 mm; overall length: 155 in, 3,937 mm; overall width: 58 in, 1,473 mm; overall height: 50 in, 1,270 mm; ground clearance: 6 in, 152 mm; dry weight: 2,194 lb, 995 kg; turning circle (between walls): 33 ft, 10.1 m; fuel tank capacity: 11.2 imp gal, 13.5 US gal, 51 l.

BODY convertible; doors: 2; seats: 2.

PRACTICAL INSTRUCTIONS fuel: 100 oct petrol; engine sump oil: 8 imp pt, 9.7 US pt, 4.6 l, SAE 20W-30, change every 6,000 miles, 9,700 km; gearbox oil: 2 imp pt, 2.5 US pt, 1.2 l, SAE 90, no change recommended; final drive oil: 2.5 imp pt, 3 US pt, 1.4 l, SAE 90, no change recommended; greasing: none; tappet clearances: inlet 0.010 in, 0.25 mm, exhaust 0.010 in, 0.25 mm; normal tyre pressure: front 22 psi, 1.5 atm, rear 24 psi, 1.7 atm.

OPTIONAL ACCESSORIES Laycock-de Normanville overdrive on II, III and IV (0.820 ratio); wire wheels; hardtop; tonneau cover.

Stag

PRICE IN GB: £ 1,650.

ENGINE front, 4 stroke; cylinders: 8, Vee-slanted at 90°; bore and stroke: 3.39 x 2.54 in, 86 x 64.5 mm; engine capacity: 182.9 cu in, 2,997 cu cm; compression ratio: 8.8; max power (DIN): 145 hp at 5,500 rpm; max torque (DIN): 170 lb ft, 23.4 kg m at 3,500 rpm; max engine rpm: 6,500; specific power: 72.6 hp/l; cylinder block: cast iron; cylinder head: light alloy; crankshaft bearings: 5; valves: 2 per cylinder, overhead, in line, thimble tappets; camshafts: 2, overhead (1 per cylinder block); lubrication: rotary pump, full flow filter; lubricating system capacity: 9 imp pt, 10.8 US pt, 5.1 l; carburation: 2 Stromberg 175 CDS semi-down-draught carburettors; fuel feed: electric pump; cooling system: water, sealed circuit; cooling system capacity: 18.5 imp pt, 22.2 US pt, 10.5 l.

TRANSMISSION driving wheels: rear; clutch: single dry plate (diaphragm), hydraulically controlled; gearbox: mechanical; gears: 4 + reverse; synchromesh gears: I, II, III, IV; gearbox ratios: I 2.995, II 2.100, III 1.386, IV 1, rev 3.639; gear lever: central; final drive: hypoid bevel; axle ratio: 3.700; width of rims: 5''; tyres: 185 x 14.

PERFORMANCE max speeds: 36 mph, 58 km/h in 1st gear; 52 mph, 84 km/h in 2nd gear; 79 mph, 127 km/h in 3rd gear; 113 mph, 190 km/h in 4th gear; power-weight ratio: 18.3 lb/hp, 8.3 kg/hp; carrying capacity: 728 lb, 330 kg; acceleration: standing ¼ mile 18 sec, 0-50 mph (0-80 km/h) 7 sec; speed in direct drive at 1,000 rpm: 19.9 mph, 32 km/h; fuel consumption: 20.9 m/imp gal, 17.4 m/US gal, 13.5 l x 100 km.

CHASSIS integral; front suspension: independent, wishbones, lower leading arms, coil springs, anti-roll bar, telescopic dampers; rear suspension: independent, semi-trailing arms, coil springs, telescopic dampers.

STEERING rack-and-pinion, servo; turns of steering wheel lock to lock: 4.

BRAKES front disc, rear drum, servo; area rubbed by linings: front 220.2 sq in, 1,420 sq cm, rear 127 sq in, 819 sq cm, total 347.2 sq in, 2,239 sq cm.

ELECTRICAL EQUIPMENT voltage: 12 V; battery: 56 Ah; generator type: alternator, 540 W; ignition distributor: Lucas; headlamps: 4, iodine.

DIMENSIONS AND WEIGHT wheel base: 100 in, 2,540 mm; front track 52.36 in, 1,330 mm; rear track: 52.83 in, 1,342 mm; overall length: 174.01 in, 4,420 mm; overall width: 63.46 in, 1,612 mm; overall height: 49.53 in, 1,258 mm; ground clearance: 4.02 in, 102 mm; dry weight: 2,646 lb, 1,200 kg; distribution of weight: 47.4% front axle, 52.6% rear axle; turning circle (between walls): 34.1 ft, 10.4 m; fuel tank capacity: 13.9 imp gal, 16.6 US gal, 63 l.

BODY convertible; doors: 2; seats: 2 + 2; front seats separate.

STAG

PRACTICAL INSTRUCTIONS fuel: 97 oct petrol; engine sump oil: 7.9 imp pt, 9.5 US pt, 4.5 l, SAE 20W-40, change every 6,200 miles, 10,000 km; gearbox oil: 2.3 imp pt, 2.7 US pt, 1.3 l, SAE 90, no change recommended; final drive oil: 1.9 imp pt, 2.3 US pt, 1.1 l, SAE 90, no change recommended; greasing: none; tappet clearances: inlet 0.008 in, 0.20 mm, exhaust 0.018 in, 0.46 mm; valve timing: inlet opens 16° before tdc and closes 56° after bdc, exhaust opens 56° before bdc and closes 16° after tdc; normal tyre pressure: front 26 psi, 1.8 atm, rear 30 psi, 2.1 atm.

OPTIONAL ACCESSORIES Laycock-de Normanville overdrive on III and IV, 0.820 ratio; Borg-Warner 35 automatic gearbox, hydraulic torque convertor and planetary gears with 3 ratios (I 2.390, II 1.450, III 1, rev 2.090), max ratio of convertor at stall 2, possible manual selection; air-conditioning system; tonneau cover; hardtop.

TVR   GREAT BRITAIN

Vixen S2

PRICE IN GB: £ 1,242.

ENGINE front, 4 stroke; cylinders: 4, in line; bore and stroke: 3.19 x 3.05 in, 81 x 77.6 mm; engine capacity: 97.6 cu in, 1,599 cu cm; compression ratio: 9; max power (SAE): 98 hp at 5,500 rpm; max torque (SAE): 108 lb ft, 14.9 kg m at 3,600 rpm; max engine rpm: 6,000; specific power: 61.3 hp/l; cylinder block: cast iron; cylinder head: cast iron; crankshaft bearings: 5; valves: 2 per cylinder, overhead, in line, push-rods and rockers; camshafts: 1, side; lubrication: eccentric pump, full flow filter; lubricating system capacity: 5.8 imp pt, 7 US pt, 3.3 l; carburation: 1 Weber twin barrel carburettor; fuel feed: mechanical pump; cooling system: water; cooling system capacity: 12 imp pt, 14.4 US pt, 6.8 l.

TRANSMISSION driving wheels: rear; clutch: single dry plate (diaphragm), hydraulically controlled; gearbox: mechanical; gears 4 + reverse; synchromesh gears: I, II, III, IV; gearbox ratios: I 2.972, II 2.010, III 1.397, IV 1, rev 3.324; gear lever: central; final drive: hypoid bevel; axle ratio: 3.890; width of rims: 5.5''; tyres: 165 x 15.

PERFORMANCE max speeds: 42 mph, 67 km/h in 1st gear; 62 mph, 99 km/h in 2nd gear; 89 mph, 143 km/h in 3rd gear; 115 mph, 185 km/h in 4th gear; power-weight ratio: 17.2 lb/hp, 7.8 kg/hp; carrying capacity: 353 lb, 160 kg; acceleration: standing 1/4 mile 17 sec, 0-50 mph (0-80 km/h) 6.9 sec; speed in direct drive at 1,000 rpm: 18.8 mph, 30.2 km/h; fuel consumption: 30 m/imp gal, 25 m/US gal, 9.4 l x 100 km.

CHASSIS multi-tubular backbone; front suspension: independent, wishbones, coil springs, anti-roll bar, telescopic dampers; rear suspension: independent, wishbones, coil springs, 4 telescopic dampers.

STEERING rack-and-pinion; turns of steering wheel lock to lock: 3.50.

BRAKES front disc (diameter 10.85 in, 276 mm), rear drum, servo; area rubbed by linings: front 233 sq in, 1,503 sq cm, rear 99 sq in, 638 sq cm, total 332 sq in, 2,141 sq cm.

ELECTRICAL EQUIPMENT voltage: 12 V; battery: 58 Ah; generator type: dynamo, 264 W; ignition distributor: Lucas; headlamps: 2.

DIMENSIONS AND WEIGHT wheel base: 90 in, 2,286 mm; front track: 53 in, 1,346 mm; rear track: 54 in, 1,372 mm; overall length: 145 in, 3,683 mm; overall width: 64 in, 1,626 mm; overall height: 48 in, 1,219 mm; ground clearance: 5 in, 127 mm; dry weight: 1,680 lb, 762 kg; distribution of weight: 50% front axle, 50% rear axle; turning circle (between walls): 27 ft, 8.2 m; fuel tank capacity: 15 imp gal, 17.9 US gal, 68 l.

BODY coupé in plastic material; doors: 2; seats: 2.

PRACTICAL INSTRUCTIONS fuel: 98-100 oct petrol; engine sump oil: 5.5 imp pt, 6.6 US pt, 3.1 l, SAE 20W-50, change every 6,000 miles, 9,700 km; gearbox oil: 1.8 imp pt, 2.1 US pt, 1 l, SAE 90, change every 6,000 miles, 9,700 km; final drive oil: 2.5 imp pt, 3 US pt, 1.4 l, SAE 90; greasing: every 3,000 miles, 4,800 km, 11 points; tappet clearances: inlet 0.012 in, 0.30 mm, exhaust 0.022 in, 0.56 mm; valve timing: inlet opens 17° before tdc and closes 51° after bdc, exhaust opens 51° before bdc and closes 17° after tdc; normal tyre pressure: front 22 psi, 1.5 atm, rear 24 psi, 1.7 atm.

OPTIONAL ACCESSORIES light alloy wheels.

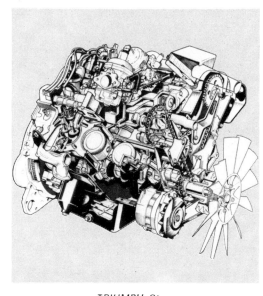

TRIUMPH Stag

TVR Vixen S2

VANDEN PLAS Princess 1300

Tuscan V6

See Vixen S2, except for:

PRICE IN GB: £ 1,558.

ENGINE cylinders: 6, Vee-slanted at 90°; bore and stroke: 3.69 x 2.85 in, 93.8 x 72.5 mm; engine capacity: 182.7 cu in, 2,994 cu cm; compression ratio: 8.9; max power (SAE): 147 hp at 4,750 rpm; max torque (SAE): 192 lb ft, 26.5 kg m at 3,000 rpm; specific power: 49 hp/l; crankshaft bearings: 4; camshafts: 1, at centre of Vee; lubricating system capacity: 10 imp pt, 12 US pt, 5.7 l; carburation: 1 Weber 40 DFA downdraught twin barrel carburettor; cooling system capacity: 26 imp pt, 31.3 US pt, 14.8 l.

TRANSMISSION gearbox ratios: I 3.163, II 2.214, III 1.412, IV 1, rev 3.310; axle ratio: 3.540.

PERFORMANCE max speeds: 35 mph, 56 km/h in 1st gear; 55 mph, 88 km/h in 2nd gear; 85 mph, 136 km/h in 3rd gear; 125 mph, 201 km/h in 4th gear; power-weight ratio: 13.6 lb/hp, 6.2 kg/hp; acceleration: standing 1/4 mile 16 sec, 0-50 mph (0-80 km/h) 5.5 sec; speed in direct drive at 1,000 rpm: 23.4 mph, 37.6 km/h; fuel consumption: 25 m/imp gal, 20.8 m/US gal, 11.3 l x 100 km.

ELECTRICAL EQUIPMENT battery: 57 Ah; generator type: dynamo, 300 W.

DIMENSIONS AND WEIGHT dry weight: 2,000 lb, 907 kg; turning circle (between walls): 27 ft, 8.2 m.

PRACTICAL INSTRUCTIONS engine sump oil: 8 imp pt, 9.5 US pt, 4.5 l; gearbox oil: 3.2 imp pt, 3.8 US pt, 1.8 l; final drive oil: 2.5 imp pt, 3 US pt, 1.4 l; greasing: 9 points; tappet clearances: exhaust 0.012 in, 0.30 mm; valve timing: inlet opens 20° before tdc and closes 56° after bdc, exhaust opens 62° before bdc and closes 14° after tdc; normal tyre pressure: front 24 psi, 1.7 atm, rear 26 psi, 1.8 atm.

OPTIONAL ACCESSORIES overdrive on III and IV, 0.820 ratio.

VANDEN PLAS   GREAT BRITAIN

Princess 1300

PRICE IN GB: £ 919.

ENGINE front, transverse, 4 stroke; cylinders: 4, vertical, in line; bore and stroke: 2.78 x 3.20 in, 70.6 x 81.3 mm; engine capacity: 77.8 cu in, 1,275 cu cm; compression ratio: 8.8; max power (DIN): 65 hp at 5,750 rpm; max torque (DIN): 70 lb ft, 9.7 kg m at 3,000 rpm; max engine rpm: 5,900; specific power: 51 hp/l; cylinder block: cast iron; cylinder head: cast iron; crankshaft bearings: 3; valves: 2 per cylinder, overhead, in line, push-rods and rockers; camshafts: 1, side; lubrication: gear or vane-type pump, full flow filter; lubricating system capacity: 9 imp pt, 10.8 US pt, 5.1 l; carburation: 2 SU type HS 2 semi-downdraught carburettors; fuel feed: electric pump; cooling system: water; cooling system capacity: 6.9 imp pt, 8.2 US pt, 3.9 l.

TRANSMISSION driving wheels: front; clutch: single dry plate (diaphragm), hydraulically controlled; gearbox: mechanical; gears: 4 + reverse; synchromesh gears: I, II, III, IV; gearbox ratios: I 3.628, II 2.172, III 1.412, IV 1, rev 3.628; gear lever: central; final drive: helical spur gears; axle ratio: 3.650; width of rims: 4''; tyres: 145 x 12.

PERFORMANCE max speeds: 27 mph, 43 km/h in 1st gear; 46 mph, 74 km/h in 2nd gear; 70 mph, 113 km/h in 3rd gear; 90 mph, 145 km/h in 4th gear; power-weight ratio: 30.2 lb/hp, 13.7 kg/hp; carrying capacity: 882 lb, 400 kg; acceleration: 0-50 mph (0-80 km/h) 11.4 sec; speed in direct drive at 1,000 rpm: 16.8 mph, 27 km/h; fuel consumption: 32.4 m/imp gal, 27 m/US gal, 8.7 l x 100 km.

CHASSIS integral, front and rear auxiliary frames; front suspension: independent, wishbones, hydrolastic (liquid) rubber cone springs, hydraulic connecting pipes to rear wheels; rear suspension: independent, swinging longitudinal trailing arms, hydrolastic (liquid) rubber cone springs, hydraulic connecting pipes to front wheels, combined with transverse torsion bars, anti-roll bar.

STEERING rack-and-pinion; turns of steering wheel lock to lock: 3.12.

BRAKES front disc (diameter 8 in, 203 mm), rear drum, rear compensator; area rubbed by linings: front 96 sq in, 619 sq cm, rear 63 sq in, 406 sq cm, total 159 sq in, 1,025 sq cm.

ELECTRICAL EQUIPMENT voltage: 12 V; battery: 40 Ah; generator type: dynamo, 264 W; ignition distributor: Lucas; headlamps: 4.

DIMENSIONS AND WEIGHT wheel base: 93.50 in, 2,375 mm;

TRIUMPH Stag

TVR Vixen S2

VANDEN PLAS Princess 1300

front track: 51.50 in, 1,308 mm; rear track: 50.85 in, 1,292 mm; overall length: 146.75 in, 3,727 mm; overall width: 60.35 in, 1,533 mm; overall height: 53 in, 1,346 mm; ground clearance: 5.30 in, 135 mm; dry weight: 1,962 lb, 890 kg; distribution of weight: 62% front axle, 38% rear axle; turning circle (between walls): 36 ft, 11 m; fuel tank capacity: 8 imp gal, 9.5 US gal, 36 l.

BODY saloon/sedan; doors: 4; seats: 4-5; front seats: separate.

PRACTICAL INSTRUCTIONS fuel: 98-100 oct petrol; engine sump, gearbox and final drive oil: 7.6 imp pt, 9.1 US pt, 4.3 l, SAE 10W-30, change every 6,000 miles, 9,700 km; greasing: every 3,000 miles, 4,800 km, 4 points; sparking plug type: 225°; tappet clearances: inlet 0.012 in, 0.30 mm, exhaust 0.012 in, 0.30 mm; valve timing: inlet opens 5° before tdc and closes 45° after bdc, exhaust opens 51° before bdc and closes 21° after tdc; normal tyre pressure: front 28 psi, 2 atm, rear 24 psi, 1.7 atm.

OPTIONAL ACCESSORIES AP automatic gearbox, hydraulic torque convertor with conic bevel gears (twin concentric differential-like gear clusters) with 4 ratios (I 2.612, II 1.807, III 1.446, IV 1, rev 2.612) operated by 3 brake bands and 2 multi-disc clutches, max ratio of convertor at stall 2, possible manual selection, with engine max power (DIN) 60 hp at 5,250 rpm, max torque (DIN) 69 lb ft, 9.5 kg m at 3,500 rpm, 47.1 hp/l specific power, 1 SU type HS 4 carburettor, 3.760 axle ratio, max speeds (I) 37 mph, 59 km/h, (II) 53 mph, 85 km/h, (III) 66 mph, 106 km/h, (IV) 87 mph, 140 km/h, power-weight ratio 32.7 lb/hp, 14.8 kg/hp, speed in direct drive at 1,000 rpm 16.3 mph, 26.2 km/h, fuel consumption 34 m/imp gal, 28.3 m/US gal, 8.3 l x 100 km; reclining backrests; sunshine roof; electrically-heated rear window.

VAUXHALL   GREAT BRITAIN

Viva

PRICE IN GB: £ 598.

ENGINE front, 4 stroke; cylinders: 4, vertical, in line; bore and stroke: 3.06 x 2.40 in, 77.7 x 61 mm; engine capacity: 70.7 cu in, 1,159 cu cm; compression ratio: 8.5; max power (SAE): 60 hp at 5,500 rpm; max torque (SAE): 68 lb ft, 9.4 kg m at 3,000 rpm; max engine rpm: 6,000; specific power: 51.8 hp/l; cylinder block: cast iron; cylinder head: cast iron; crankshaft bearings: 3; valves: 2 per cylinder, overhead, in line, push-rods and rockers; camshafts: 1, side; lubrication: gear pump, full flow filter; lubricating system capacity: 5.5 imp pt, 6.6 US pt, 3.1 l; carburation: 1 Zenith 30 IV downdraught single barrel carburettor; fuel feed: mechanical pump; cooling system: water; cooling system capacity: 10.2 imp pt, 12.3 US pt, 5.8 l.

TRANSMISSION driving wheels: rear; clutch: single dry plate (diaphragm); gearbox: mechanical; gears: 4 + reverse; synchromesh gears: I, II, III, IV; gearbox ratios: I 3.765, II 2.213, III 1.404, IV 1, rev 3.707; gear lever: central; final drive: hypoid bevel; axle ratio: 4.125; width of rims: 4''; tyres: 5.20 x 13.

PERFORMANCE max speeds: 25 mph, 41 km/h in 1st gear; 43 mph, 69 km/h in 2nd gear; 67 mph, 108 km/h in 3rd gear; 80 mph, 128 km/h in 4th gear; power-weight ratio: 28 lb/hp, 12.7 kg/hp; carrying capacity: 976 lb, 443 kg; acceleration: 0-50 mph (0-80 km/h) 13 sec; speed in direct drive at 1,000 rpm: 15.8 mph, 25.4 km/h; fuel consumption: 29 m/imp gal, 24.2 m/US gal, 9.7 l x 100 km.

CHASSIS integral; front suspension: independent, wishbones, coil springs, telescopic dampers; rear suspension: rigid axle, 2 trailing lower radius arms, 2 upper oblique radius arms, coil springs, telescopic dampers.

STEERING rack-and-pinion; turns of steering wheel lock to lock: 3.16.

BRAKES drum, 2 front leading shoes, dual circuit; area rubbed by linings: total 125.7 sq in, 811 sq cm.

ELECTRICAL EQUIPMENT voltage: 12 V; battery: 32 Ah; generator type: alternator, 336 W; ignition distributor: AC Delco; headlamps: 2.

DIMENSIONS AND WEIGHT wheel base: 97 in, 2,464 mm; front track: 51.40 in, 1,306 mm; rear track: 51.50 in, 1,308 mm; overall length: 162 in, 4,115 mm; overall width: 64.70 in, 1,643 mm; overall height: 53.10 in, 1,349 mm; ground clearance: 5.30 in, 135 mm; dry weight: 1,684 lb, 764 kg; distribution of weight: 53.2% front axle, 46.8% rear axle; turning circle (between walls): 34.1 ft, 10.4 m; fuel tank capacity: 8 imp gal, 9.5 US gal, 36 l.

BODY saloon/sedan; doors: 2; seats: 4-5; front seats: separate.

PRACTICAL INSTRUCTIONS fuel: 98 oct petrol; engine

VIVA

sump oil: 4.9 imp pt, 5.9 US pt, 2.8 l, SAE 20W-20, change every 6,000 miles, 9,700 km; gearbox oil: 0.9 imp pt, 1.1 US pt, 0.5 l, SAE 90, change every 6 months; final drive oil: 1.2 imp pt, 1.5 US pt, 0.7 l, SAE 90, no change recommended; greasing: every 6 months, 4 points; tappet clearances: inlet 0.006 in, 0.15 mm, exhaust 0.010 in, 0.25 mm; valve timing: inlet opens 39° before tdc and closes 93° after bdc, exhaust opens 65° before bdc and closes 45° after tdc; normal tyre pressure: front 22 psi, 1.5 atm, rear 22 psi, 1.5 atm.

Viva De Luxe 2-door Saloon

See Viva, except for:

PRICE IN GB: £ 650.

PERFORMANCE power-weight ratio: 28.7 lb/hp, 13 kg/hp.

DIMENSIONS AND WEIGHT dry weight: 1,720 lb, 780 kg.

VARIATIONS

ENGINE 9 compression ratio, max power (SAE) 73 hp at 5,700 rpm, max torque (SAE) 70 lb ft, 9.6 kg m at 4,000 rpm, max engine rpm 6,200, 63 hp/l specific power, 1 Zenith 150 CDS semi-downdraught single barrel carburettor, 4 crankshaft bearings.
TRANSMISSION 6.20 x 13 tyres.
PERFORMANCE max speeds (I) 25 mph, 40 km/h, (II) 43 mph, 69 km/h, (III) 68 mph, 109 km/h, (IV) 85 mph, 137 km/h, power-weight ratio 24.9 lb/hp, 11.3 kg/hp, carrying capacity 1,006 lb, 456 kg, acceleration 0-50 mph (0-80 km/h) 11 sec, speed in direct drive at 1,000 rpm 15.6 mph, 25.1 km/h.
BRAKES front disc, rear drum, dual circuit, servo, total area rubbed by linings 199 sq in, 1,289 sq cm.
DIMENSIONS AND WEIGHT overall height 53.10 in, 1,349 mm, dry weight 1,816 lb, 824 kg.
PRACTICAL INSTRUCTIONS tappet clearances inlet 0.008 in, 0.20 mm, exhaust 0.008 in, 0.20 mm, valve timing 39° 73° 71° 41°.

OPTIONAL ACCESSORIES G.M. automatic gearbox, hydraulic torque convertor and planetary gears with 3 ratios (I 2.390, II 1.450, III 1, rev 2.390), max ratio of convertor at stall 2 only with engine capacity 97.6 cu in, 1,599 cu cm, max power (SAE) 81 hp at 5,500 rpm (see below Viva SL 2-door Saloon), front disc brakes with servo and 6.20 x 13 tyres; 6.20 x 13 tyres; front disc brakes (diameter 8.39 in, 213 mm) with servo; heavy-duty alternator; electrically-heated rear window.

Viva De Luxe 4-door Saloon

See Viva De Luxe 2-door Saloon, except for:

PRICE IN GB: £ 675.

PERFORMANCE power-weight ratio: 29.3 lb/hp, 13.3 kg/hp.

DIMENSIONS AND WEIGHT dry weight: 1,760 lb, 798 kg.

Viva De Luxe Estate Car

See Viva De Luxe 2-door Saloon, except for:

PRICE IN GB: £ 725.

TRANSMISSION tyres: 6.20 x 13 (standard).

PERFORMANCE power-weight ratio: 30.1 lb/hp, 13.6 kg/hp.

DIMENSIONS AND WEIGHT dry weight: 1,810 lb, 821 kg.

BODY estate car/station wagon; doors: 2 + 1.

OPTIONAL ACCESSORIES heavy-duty suspension.

Viva SL 2-door Saloon

See Viva, except for:

PRICE IN GB: £ 736.

ENGINE compression ratio: 9; max power (SAE): 73 hp at 5,700 rpm; max torque (SAE): 70 lb ft, 9.6 kg m at 4,000 rpm; max engine rpm: 6,200; specific power: 63 hp/l; crankshaft bearings: 4; carburation: 1 Zenith 150 CDS semi-downdraught single barrel carburettor.

TRANSMISSION tyres: 6.20 x 13.

PERFORMANCE max speeds: 25 mph, 40 km/h in 1st gear; 43 mph, 69 km/h in 2nd gear; 68 mph, 109 km/h in 3rd gear; 85 mph, 137 km/h in 4th gear; power-weight ratio: 24.9 lb/hp, 11.3 kg/hp; carrying capacity: 1,006 lb, 456 kg; acceleration: 0-50 mph (0-80 km/h) 11 sec; speed in direct drive at 1,000 rpm: 15.6 mph, 25.1 km/h.

BRAKES front disc, rear drum, dual circuit, servo; area rubbed by linings: total 199 sq in, 1,289 sq cm.

VAUXHALL Viva SL 4-door Saloon

VAUXHALL Victor 2000 SL Saloon

VAUXHALL Victor 2000 SL Estate Car

DIMENSIONS AND WEIGHT overall height: 53.10 in, 1,349 mm; dry weight: 1,816 lb, 824 kg.

PRACTICAL INSTRUCTIONS tappets clearances: inlet 0.008 in, 0.20 mm, exhaust 0.008 in, 0.20 mm; valve timing: inlet opens 39° before tdc and closes 73° after bdc, exhaust opens 71° before bdc and closes 41° after tdc.

VARIATIONS

ENGINE bore and stroke 3.37 x 2.73 in, 85.7 x 69.2 mm, engine capacity 97.6 cu in, 1,599 cu cm, 8.5 compression ratio, max power (SAE) 81 hp at 5,500 rpm, max torque (SAE) 96 lb ft, 13.3 kg m at 2,700 rpm, max engine rpm 5,600, 50.6 hp/l specific power, 5 crankshaft bearings, valves with thimble tappets, 1 overhead camshaft, lubricating system capacity 8.5 imp pt, 10.1 US pt, 4.8 l, 1 Zenith 36 IV downdraught single barrel carburettor, cooling system capacity 13.5 imp pt, 16.1 US pt, 7.6 l.
TRANSMISSION 4-speed fully synchronized mechanical gearbox (I 2.786, II 1.981, III 1.413, IV 1, rev 3.064).
PERFORMANCE max speeds (I) 37 mph, 59 km/h, (II) 52 mph, 83 km/h, (III) 73 mph, 117 km/h, (IV) 91 mph, 146 km/h, power-weight ratio 24.8 lb/hp, 11.2 kg/hp, carrying capacity 917 lb, 416 kg, acceleration 0-50 mph (0-80 km/h) 10.5 sec.
DIMENSIONS AND WEIGHT dry weight 2,012 lb, 913 kg, distribution of weight 56.2% front axle, 43.8% rear axle, fuel tank capacity 12 imp gal, 14.5 US gal, 55 l.
PRACTICAL INSTRUCTIONS engine sump oil 8.5 imp pt, 10.1 US pt, 4.8 l, SAE 20W-20, change every 6,000 miles, 9,700 km, tappet clearances inlet 0.007 in, 0.19 mm, exhaust 0.015 in, 0.39 mm, valve timing 24° 56° 56° 24°.

OPTIONAL ACCESSORIES G.M. automatic gearbox, hydraulic torque convertor and planetary gears with 3 ratios (I 2.390, II 1.450, III 1, rev 2.390), max ratio of convertor at stall 2; heavy-duty alternator; electrically-heated rear window.

Viva SL 4-door Saloon

See Viva SL 2-door Saloon, except for:

PRICE IN GB: £ 761.

PERFORMANCE power-weight ratio: 25.4 lb/hp, 11.5 kg/hp.

DIMENSIONS AND WEIGHT dry weight: 1,856 lb, 815 kg.

Viva SL Estate Car

See Viva SL 2-door Saloon, except for:

PRICE IN GB: £ 806.

PERFORMANCE power-weight ratio: 26.2 lb/hp, 11.9 kg/hp.

DIMENSIONS AND WEIGHT dry weight: 1,910 lb, 866 kg.

BODY estate car/station wagon; doors: 2 + 1.

OPTIONAL ACCESSORIES heavy-duty suspension.

Victor Super Saloon

PRICE IN GB: £ 796.

ENGINE front, 4 stroke; cylinders: 4, slanted at 45°, in line; bore and stroke: 3.37 x 2.72 in, 85.7 x 69.2 mm; engine capacity: 97.6 cu in, 1,599 cu cm; compression ratio: 8.5; max power (SAE): 83 hp at 5,800 rpm; max torque (SAE): 90 lb ft, 12.4 kg m at 3,200 rpm; max engine rpm: 6,400; specific power: 51.9 hp/l; cylinder block: cast iron; cylinder head: cast iron, hemispherical combustion chambers; crankshaft bearings: 5; valves: 2 per cylinder, overhead, in line, thimble tappets; camshafts: 1, overhead, cogged belt; lubrication: gear pump, full flow filter; lubricating system capacity: 8.5 imp pt, 10.1 US pt, 4.8 l; carburation: 1 Zenith 36 IV downdraught single barrel carburettor; fuel feed: mechanical pump; cooling system: water; cooling system capacity 13.5 imp pt, 16.1 US pt, 7.6 l.

TRANSMISSION driving wheels: rear; clutch: single dry plate (diaphragm), hydraulically controlled; gearbox: mechanical; gears: 3 + reverse; synchromesh gears: I, II, III; gearbox ratios: I 3.200, II 1.671, III 1, rev 3.064; gear lever: steering column; final drive: hypoid bevel; axle ratio: 3.900; width of rims: 4.5''; tyres: 5.60 x 13.

PERFORMANCE max speeds: 33 mph, 53 km/h in 1st gear; 62 mph, 100 km/h in 2nd gear; 96 mph, 154 km/h in 3rd gear; power-weight ratio: 26.5 lb/hp, 12 kg/hp; carrying capacity: 882 lb, 400 kg; speed in direct drive at 1,000 rpm: 16.4 mph, 26.4 km/h; fuel consumption: 23.6 m/imp gal, 19.6 m/US gal, 12 l x 100 km.

CHASSIS integral; front suspension: independent, wishbones, lower trailing links, coil springs, anti-roll bar, telescopic dampers; rear suspension: rigid axle, lower trailing arms, upper torque arms, transverse linkage bar, coil springs, telescopic dampers.

STEERING rack-and-pinion; turns of steering wheel lock to lock: 4.40.

VAUXHALL Viva (rear suspension)

VAUXHALL Victor 2000 SL Saloon

VAUXHALL Victor 2000 SL

BRAKES drum.

ELECTRICAL EQUIPMENT voltage: 12 V; battery: 38 Ah; generator type: alternator, 336 W; ignition distributor: Lucas; headlamps: 4.

DIMENSIONS AND WEIGHT wheel base: 102 in, 2,591 mm; front track: 54 in, 1,372 mm; rear track: 54 in, 1,372 mm; overall length: 176.70 in, 4,488 mm; overall width: 66.90 in, 1,699 mm; overall height: 52.40 in, 1,331 mm; ground clearance: 5.20 in, 132 mm; dry weight: 2,199 lb, 997 kg; distribution of weight: 52.8% front axle, 47.2% rear axle; turning circle (between walls): 33.5 ft, 10.2 m; fuel tank capacity: 12 imp gal, 14.5 US gal, 55 l.

BODY saloon/sedan; doors: 4; seats: 4-5; front seats: separate.

PRACTICAL INSTRUCTIONS fuel: 98 oct petrol; engine sump oil: 7.5 imp pt, 8.9 US pt, 4.2 l, SAE 20W-20, change every 6 months; gearbox oil: 2.1 imp pt, 2.5 US pt, 1.2 l, SAE 80-90, no change recommended; final drive oil: 2.5 imp pt, 3 US pt, 1.4 l, SAE 90, no change recommended; greasing: every 30,000 miles, 48,300 km or 6 months, 4 points; normal tyre pressure: front 24 psi, 1.7 atm, rear 24 psi, 1.7 atm.

VARIATIONS

ENGINE 7 compression ratio, max power (SAE) 79 hp at 5,800 rpm, max torque (SAE) 88 lb ft, 12.2 kg m at 3,000 rpm, 49.4 hp/l specific power.
PERFORMANCE power-weight ratio 27.8 lb/hp, 12.6 kg/hp.

OPTIONAL ACCESSORIES 4-speed fully synchronized mechanical gearbox (I 3.300, II 2.145, III 1.413, IV 1, rev 3.064), central gear lever, max speeds (I) 29 mph, 47 km/h, (II) 45 mph, 72 km/h, (III) 70 mph, 112 km/h, (IV) 96 mph, 154 km/h; Laycock-de Normanville overdrive on III and IV, 0.778 ratio; G.M. automatic gearbox, hydraulic torque convertor and planetary gears with 3 ratios (I 2.390, II 1.450, III 1, rev 2.390), max ratio of convertor at stall 2 only with engine capacity 120.5 cu in, 1,975 cu cm, max power (SAE) 104 hp (see below Victor 2000 SL Saloon), front disc brakes with servo and 6.20 x 13 tyres, max speeds (I) 40 mph, 65 km/h, (II) 69 mph, 111 km/h, (III) 96 mph, 154 km/h; 6.90 x 13 or 165 x 13 tyres with 5'' wide rims; front disc brakes (diameter 10.03 in, 255 mm) with servo; 55 Ah battery; reclining backrests; electrically-heated rear window.

Victor Super Estate Car

See Victor Super Saloon, except for:

PRICE IN GB: £ 884.

TRANSMISSION width of rims: 5''; tyres: 6.90 x 13.

PERFORMANCE max speed: 94 mph, 151 km/h; power-weight ratio: 28.1 lb/hp, 12.7 kg/hp; speed in direct drive at 1,000 rpm: 14.7 mph, 23.6 km/h.

DIMENSIONS AND WEIGHT overall height: 51.70 in, 1,313 mm; dry weight: 2,336 lb, 1,060 kg.

BODY estate car/station wagon; doors: 4 + 1.

Victor 2000 SL Saloon

See Victor Super Saloon, except for:

PRICE IN GB: £ 881.

ENGINE bore and stroke: 3.75 x 2.73 in, 95.2 x 69.3 mm; engine capacity: 120.5 cu in, 1,975 cu cm; max power (SAE): 108 hp at 5,800 rpm; max torque (SAE): 122 lb ft, 16.8 kg m at 3,200 rpm; specific power: 54.7 hp/l; lubricating system capacity: 7 imp pt, 8.5 US pt, 4 l; carburation: 1 Zenith 175 CD downdraught single barrel carburettor.

TRANSMISSION gearbox ratios: I 2.879, II 1.671, III 1, rev 3.064; tyres: 6.20 x 13.

PERFORMANCE max speeds: 36 mph, 58 km/h in 1st gear; 63 mph, 101 km/h in 2nd gear; 98 mph, 157 km/h in 3rd gear; power-weight ratio: 20.8 lb/hp, 9.4 kg/hp; speed in direct drive at 1,000 rpm: 16.4 mph, 26.4 km/h; fuel consumption: 25 m/imp gal, 20.8 m/US gal, 11.3 l x 100 km.

BRAKES front disc (diameter 10.03 in, 255 mm), rear drum, servo; area rubbed by linings: front 188 sq in, 1,212 sq cm, rear 99 sq in, 638 sq cm, total 287 sq in, 1,850 sq cm.

ELECTRICAL EQUIPMENT generator type: alternator, 444 W.

DIMENSIONS AND WEIGHT front track: 54.60 in, 1,387 mm; overall height: 51.70 in, 1,313 mm; dry weight: 2,245 lb, 1,018 kg.

PRACTICAL INSTRUCTIONS tappet clearances: inlet 0.007-0.010 in, 0.18-0.25 mm, exhaust 0.010-0.013 in, 0.25-0.33 mm; valve timing: inlet opens 33°26' before tdc and closes 65°26' after bdc, exhaust opens 65°26' before bdc and closes 33°26' after tdc.

VICTOR 2000 SL SALOON

VARIATIONS

ENGINE 7.3 compression ratio, max power (SAE) 95 hp at 5,800 rpm, max torque (SAE) 113 lb ft, 15.6 kg m at 3,000 rpm, 48.1 hp/l specific power.
PERFORMANCE power-weight ratio 23.6 lb/hp, 10.7 kg/hp.

OPTIONAL ACCESSORIES 4-speed fully synchronized mechanical gearbox (I 2.773, II 1.942, III 1.355, IV 1, rev 3.050), central gear lever, max speeds (I) 37 mph, 59 km/h, (II) 54 mph, 87 km/h, (III) 77 mph, 124 km/h, (IV) 98 mph, 157 km/h; Laycock-de Normanville overdrive on III and IV, 0.778 ratio; G.M. automatic gearbox, hydraulic torque convertor and planetary gears with 3 ratios (I 2.390, II 1.450, III 1, rev 2.090), max ratio of convertor at stall 2, max speeds (I) 41 mph, 66 km/h, (II) 70 mph, 113 km/h, (III) 98 mph, 157 km/h.

Victor 2000 SL Estate Car

See Victor 2000 SL Saloon, except for:

PRICE IN GB: £ 975.

TRANSMISSION width of rims: 5''; tyres: 6.90 x 13.

PERFORMANCE max speed: 96 mph, 154 km/h; power-weight ratio: 22.5 lb/hp, 10 kg/hp; speed in direct drive at 1,000 rpm: 17.3 mph, 27.9 km/h.

DIMENSIONS AND WEIGHT dry weight: 2,435 lb, 1,105 kg.

BODY estate car/station wagon; doors: 4 + 1.

VX 4/90

PRICE IN GB: £ 1,019.

ENGINE front, 4 stroke; cylinders: 4, slanted at 45°, in line; bore and stroke: 3.75 x 2.73 in, 95.2 x 69.3 mm; engine capacity: 120.5 cu in, 1,975 cu cm; compression ratio: 8.5; max power (SAE) 112 hp at 5,400 rpm; max torque (SAE): 127 lb ft, 17.5 kg m at 3,400 rpm; max engine rpm: 6,200; specific power: 56.7 hp/l; cylinder block: cast iron; cylinder head: cast iron, hemispherical combustion chambers; crankshaft bearings: 5; valves: 2 per cylinder, overhead, in line, thimble tappets; camshafts: 1, overhead, cogged belt; lubrication: gear pump, full flow filter; lubricating system capacity: 8.2 imp pt, 9.7 US pt, 4.6 l; carburation: 2 Zenith-Stromberg 175-CD25 horizontal Venturi variable single barrel carburettors; fuel feed: mechanical pump; cooling system: water; cooling system capacity: 14 imp pt, 16.7 US pt, 7.9 l.

TRANSMISSION driving wheels: rear; clutch: single dry plate (diaphragm), hydraulically controlled; gearbox: mechanical; gears: 4 + reverse and overdrive/top; synchromesh gears: I, II, III, IV; gearbox ratios: I 3.300, II 2.145, III 1.413, IV 1, overdrive/top 0.778, rev 3.064; gear lever: central; final drive: hypoid bevel; axle ratio: 3.900; width of rims: 5''; tyres: 6.90 x 13.

PERFORMANCE max speeds: 31 mph, 50 km/h in 1st gear; 47 mph, 75 km/h in 2nd gear; 72 mph, 116 km/h in 3rd gear; 99 mph, 159 km/h in 4th gear; 101 mph, 162 km/h in overdrive/top; power-weight ratio: 20.4 lb/hp, 9.2 kg/hp; carrying capacity: 882 lb, 400 kg; speed in direct drive at 1,000 rpm: 16.4 mph, 26.4 km/h; fuel consumption: 26.6 m/imp gal, 22.2 m/US gal, 10.6 l x 100 km.

CHASSIS integral; front suspension: independent, wishbones, lower trailing links, coil springs, anti-roll bar, telescopic dampers; rear suspension: rigid axle, lower trailing arms, upper torque arms, transverse linkage bar, coil springs, telescopic dampers.

STEERING rack-and-pinion; turns of steering wheel lock to lock: 4.40.

BRAKES front disc (diameter 10.03 in, 255 mm), rear drum, servo; area rubbed by linings: front 188 sq in, 1,212 sq cm, rear 99 sq in, 638 sq cm, total 287 sq in, 1,850 sq cm.

ELECTRICAL EQUIPMENT voltage: 12 V; battery: 38 Ah; generator type: alternator, 444 W; ignition distributor: Lucas; headlamps: 4.

DIMENSIONS AND WEIGHT wheel base: 102 in, 2,591 mm; front track: 54.60 in, 1,387 mm; rear track: 54 in, 1,372 mm; overall length: 176.60 in, 4,486 mm; overall width: 66.90 in, 1,699 mm; overall height: 51.70 in, 1,313 mm; ground clearance: 6.69 in, 170 mm; dry weight: 2,287 lb, 1,037 kg; distribution of weight: 52.7% front axle, 47.3% rear axle; turning circle (between walls): 33.4 ft, 10.2 m; fuel tank capacity: 12 imp gal, 14.5 US gal, 55 l.

BODY saloon/sedan; doors: 4; seats: 4-5; front seats: separate, reclining backrests.

PRACTICAL INSTRUCTIONS fuel: 98 oct petrol; engine sump oil: 7.7 imp pt, 9.3 US pt, 4.4 l, SAE 20W-20, change every 6 months; gearbox oil: 2.1 imp pt, 2.3 US pt, 1.1 l, SAE 80-90, no change recommended; final drive oil: 2.5 imp pt, 3 US pt, 1.4 l, SAE 80-90, no change recommended; greasing: every 6 months, 4 points; tappet clearances: inlet 0.007-

VAUXHALL VX 4/90

VAUXHALL Ventora 2

VAUXHALL Viscount

0.010 in, 0.18-0.25 mm, exhaust 0.015-0.018 in, 0.38-0.46 mm; valve timing: inlet opens 33°26' before tdc and closes 65°26' after bdc, exhaust opens 65°26' before bdc and closes 33°26' after tdc; normal tyre pressure: front 24 psi, 1.7 atm, rear 24 psi, 1.7 atm.

OPTIONAL ACCESSORIES G.M. automatic gearbox, hydraulic torque convertor and planetary gears with 3 ratios (I 2.390, II 1.450, III 1, rev 2.390), max ratio of convertor at stall 2, possible manual selection; 175/70 HR x 13 tyres; electrically-heated rear window.

Ventora 2

PRICE IN GB: £ 1,113.

ENGINE front, 4 stroke; cylinders: 6, vertical, in line; bore and stroke: 3.62 x 3.25 in, 92 x 82.5 mm; engine capacity: 201 cu in, 3,294 cu cm; compression ratio: 8.5; max power (SAE): 140.2 hp at 4,800 rpm; max torque (SAE): 186 lb ft, 25.6 kg m at 2,400 rpm; max engine rpm: 5,300; specific power: 42.6 hp/l; cylinder block: cast iron; cylinder head: cast iron; crankshaft bearings: 4; valves: 2 per cylinder, overhead, in line, push-rods and rockers; camshafts: 1, side; lubrication: gear pump, full flow filter; lubricating system capacity: 9.5 imp pt, 11.4 US pt, 5.4 l; carburation: 1 Zenith WIAT 42 downdraught carburettor; fuel feed: mechanical pump; cooling system: water; cooling system capacity: 16.6 imp pt, 19.9 US pt, 9.4 l.

TRANSMISSION driving wheels: rear; clutch: single dry plate (diaphragm), hydraulically controlled; gearbox: mechanical; gears: 4 + reverse; synchromesh gears: I, II, III, IV; gearbox ratios: I 3.300, II 2.145, III 1.413, IV 1, rev 3.064; gear lever: central; final drive: hypoid bevel; axle ratio: 3.090; width of rims: 4.5''; tyres: 6.90 x 13.

PERFORMANCE max speeds: 35 mph, 56 km/h in 1st gear; 54 mph, 87 km/h in 2nd gear; 83 mph, 133 km/h in 3rd gear; 105 mph, 169 km/h in 4th gear; power-weight ratio: 17.7 lb/hp, 8 kg/hp; speed in direct drive at 1,000 rpm: 22 mph, 35.4 km/h; fuel consumption: 20 m/imp gal, 16.7 m/US gal, 14.1 l x 100 km.

CHASSIS integral; front suspension: independent, wishbones, lower trailing links, coil springs, anti-roll bar, telescopic dampers; rear suspension: rigid axle, trailing lower radius arms, upper torque arms, transverse linkage bar, coil springs, telescopic dampers.

STEERING rack-and-pinion; turns of steering wheel lock to lock: 4.40.

BRAKES front disc (diameter 10.12 in, 257 mm), rear drum, servo; area rubbed by linings: front 204 sq in, 1,316 sq cm, rear 98 sq in, 632 sq cm, total 302 sq in, 1,948 sq cm.

ELECTRICAL EQUIPMENT voltage: 12 V; battery: 55 Ah; generator type: alternator, 444 W; ignition distributor: Lucas; headlamps: 4.

DIMENSIONS AND WEIGHT wheel base: 102 in, 2,591 mm; front track: 54.60 in, 1,387 mm; rear track: 54 in, 1,372 mm; overall length: 176.70 in, 4,488 mm; overall width: 66.90 in, 1,699 mm; overall height: 51.70 in, 1,313 mm; ground clearance: 5.20 in, 132 mm; dry weight: 2,488 lb, 1,129 kg; distribution of weight: 56% front axle, 44% rear axle; turning circle (between walls): 33.4 ft, 10.2 m; fuel tank capacity: 12 imp gal, 14.5 US gal, 55 l.

BODY saloon/sedan; doors: 4; seats: 5; front seats: separate, reclining backrests; details: electrically-heated rear window.

PRACTICAL INSTRUCTIONS fuel: 98 oct petrol; engine sump oil: 9 imp pt, 10.8 US pt, 5.1 l, SAE 20W (winter) 20 (summer), change every 6 months; gearbox oil: 2.5 imp pt, 3 US pt, 1.4 l, SAE 90, no change recommended; final drive oil: 2.5 imp pt, 3 US pt, 1.4 l, SAE 90, no change recommended; greasing: every 6 months, 4 points; tappet clearances: inlet 0.013 in, 0.33 mm, exhaust 0.013 in, 0.33 mm; valve timing: inlet opens 39° before tdc and closes 84° after bdc, exhaust opens 81° before bdc and closes 42° after tdc; normal tyre pressure: front 24 psi, 1.7 atm, rear 24 psi, 1.7 atm.

OPTIONAL ACCESSORIES Laycock-de Normanville overdrive on III and IV (0.788 ratio) with 3.455 axle ratio and 175/70 HR x 13 tyres; G.M. automatic gearbox, hydraulic torque convertor and planetary gears with 3 ratios (I 2.390, II 1.450, III 1, rev 2.390), max ratio of convertor at stall 2, max speeds (I) 45 mph, 72 km/h, (II) 77 mph, 124 km/h, (III) 105 mph, 169 km/h, power-assisted steering, 3.36 turns of steering wheel lock to lock.

Victor 3300 SL Estate Car

See Ventora 2, except for:

PRICE IN GB: £ 1,085.

PERFORMANCE power-weight ratio: 18.4 lb/hp, 8.3 kg/hp; acceleration: standing ¼ mile 20.3 sec, 0-50 mph (0-80 km/h) 9.2 sec.

DIMENSIONS AND WEIGHT dry weight: 2,581 lb, 1,170 kg.

VAUXHALL VX 4/90

VAUXHALL Ventora 2

VAUXHALL Viscount

BODY estate car/station wagon; doors: 4 + 1; seats: 5-6.

OPTIONAL ACCESSORIES 175 HR x 13 tyres; with overdrive 175 HR x 13 tyres; heavy-duty rear suspension; reclining backrests.

Cresta

PRICE IN GB: £ 1,042.

ENGINE front, 4 stroke; cylinders: 6, vertical, in line; bore and stroke: 3.62 x 3.25 in, 92 x 82.5 mm; engine capacity: 201 cu in, 3,294 cu cm; compression ratio: 8.5; max power (SAE): 140.2 hp at 4,800 rpm; max torque (SAE): 186 lb ft, 25.6 kg m at 2,400 rpm; max engine rpm: 5,300; specific power: 42.6 hp/l; cylinder block: cast iron; cylinder head: cast iron; crankshaft bearings: 4; valves: 2 per cylinder, overhead, in line, push-rods and rockers; camshafts: 1, side; lubrication: gear pump, full flow filter; lubricating system capacity: 9.5 imp pt, 11.4 US pt, 5.4 l; carburation: 1 Zenith WIAT 42 downdraught carburettor; fuel feed: mechanical pump; cooling system: water; cooling system capacity: 16.5 imp pt, 19.9 US pt, 9.4 l.

TRANSMISSION driving wheels: rear; clutch: single dry plate (diaphragm); gearbox: mechanical; gears: 4 + reverse; synchromesh gears: I, II, III, IV; gearbox ratios: I 2.521, II 1.765, III 1.353, IV 1, rev 2.773; gear lever: central; final drive: hypoid bevel; axle ratio: 3.445; width of rims: 4.5''; tyres: 5.90 x 14.

PERFORMANCE max speeds: 44 mph, 71 km/h in 1st gear; 62 mph, 99 km/h in 2nd gear; 81 mph, 131 km/h in 3rd gear; 110 mph, 177 km/h in 4th gear; power-weight ratio: 19 lb/hp, 8.6 kg/hp; carrying capacity: 882 lb, 400 kg; acceleration: standing ¼ mile 20.3 sec, 0-50 mph (0-80 km/h) 9.2 sec; speed in direct drive at 1,000 rpm: 20.8 mph, 33.4 km/h; fuel consumption: 18.4 m/imp gal, 15.3 m/US gal, 15.4 l x 100 km.

CHASSIS integral; front suspension: independent, wishbones, coil springs, anti-roll bar, telescopic dampers; rear suspension: rigid axle, semi-elliptic leafsprings with secondary helper spring leaf, telescopic dampers.

STEERING recirculating ball.

BRAKES front disc (diameter 10.51 in, 267 mm), rear drum, servo; area rubbed by linings: total 302 sq in, 1,948 sq cm.

ELECTRICAL EQUIPMENT voltage: 12 V; battery: 55 Ah; generator type: alternator, 444 W; ignition distributor: Lucas; headlamps: 4.

DIMENSIONS AND WEIGHT wheel base: 107.50 in, 2,730 mm; front track: 55.20 in, 1,402 mm; rear track: 56.20 in, 1,427 mm; overall length: 187.10 in, 4,752 mm; overall width: 69.76 in, 1,772 mm; overall height: 56.60 in, 1,438 mm; ground clearance: 5 in, 127 mm; dry weight: 2,662 lb, 1,207 kg; distribution of weight: 53% front axle, 47% rear axle; turning circle (between walls): 36.5 ft, 11.1 m; fuel tank capacity: 15 imp gal, 18 US gal, 68 l.

BODY saloon/sedan; doors: 4; seats: 4-5; front seats: separate.

PRACTICAL INSTRUCTIONS fuel: 98 oct petrol; engine sump oil: 9 imp pt, 10.8 US pt, 5.1 l, SAE 20W (winter) 20 (summer), change every 6 months; gearbox oil: 2.5 imp pt, 3 US pt, 1.4 l, SAE 90, no change recommended; final drive oil: 3.9 imp pt, 4.7 US pt, 2.2 l, SAE 90, no change recommended; greasing: every 6 months, 12 points; tappet clearances (hot): inlet 0.013 in, 0.33 mm, exhaust 0.013 in, 0.33 mm; valve timing: inlet opens 39° before tdc and closes 84° after bdc, exhaust opens 81° before bdc and closes 42° after tdc; normal tyre pressure: front 24 psi, 1.7 atm, rear 27 psi, 1.9 atm.

OPTIONAL ACCESSORIES Laycock-de Normanville overdrive on II and III (0.778 ratio) with 3.700 axle ratio; G.M. automatic gearbox, hydraulic torque convertor and planetary gears with 3 ratios (I 2.390, II 1.450, III 1, rev 2.390), max ratio of convertor at stall 2, max speeds (I) 45 mph, 72 km/h, (II) 77 mph, 124 km/h, (III) 105 mph, 169 km/h; 7.00 x 14 tyres; power-assisted steering; reclining backrests; leather upholstery; electrically-heated rear window.

Cresta De Luxe

See Cresta, except for:

PRICE IN GB: £ 1,131.

PERFORMANCE power-weight ratio: 19.3 lb/hp, 8.7 kg/hp.

DIMENSIONS AND WEIGHT dry weight: 2,700 lb, 1,224 kg.

BODY front seats: reclining backrests (standard); details: leather upholstery (standard), electrically-heated rear window (standard).

OPTIONAL ACCESSORIES bench front seats.

Viscount

See Cresta, except for:

PRICE IN GB: £ 1,525.

TRANSMISSION gearbox: G.M. automatic (standard); tyres: 7.00 x 14 (standard).

PERFORMANCE max speed: 100 mph, 161 km/h; power-weight ratio: 21.4 lb/hp, 9.7 kg/hp; carrying capacity: 1,058 lb, 480 kg; fuel consumption: 15.6 m/imp gal, 13 m/US gal, 18.1 l x 100 km.

STEERING servo (standard); turns of steering wheel lock to lock: 4.25.

ELECTRICAL EQUIPMENT generator type: alternator, 420 W.

DIMENSIONS AND WEIGHT dry weight: 2,999 lb, 1,360 kg.

BODY front seats: reclining backrests (standard); details: leather upholstery (standard), electrically-heated rear window (standard).

OPTIONAL ACCESORIES 4-speed mechanical gearbox (I 2.251, II 1.765, III 1.353, IV 1, rev 2.773), central gear lever, max speeds (I) 42 mph, 67 km/h, (II) 60 mph, 96 km/h, (III) 79 mph, 127 km/h, (IV) 100 mph, 161 km/h.

WOLSELEY 1300 Mk II

WOLSELEY   GREAT BRITAIN

1300 Mk II

PRICE IN GB: £ 740.

ENGINE front, transverse, 4 stroke; cylinders: 4, vertical, in line; bore and stroke: 2.78 x 3.20 in, 70.6 x 81.3 mm; engine capacity: 77.8 cu in, 1,275 cu cm; compression ratio: 8.8; max power (DIN): 65 hp at 5,750 rpm; max torque (DIN): 70 lb ft, 9.7 kg m at 3,000 rpm; max engine rpm: 5,900; specific power: 51 hp/l; cylinder block: cast iron; cylinder head: cast iron; crankshaft bearings: 3; valves: 2 per cylinder, overhead, in line, push-rods and rockers; camshafts: 1, side; lubrication: gear or vane-type pump, full flow filter; lubricating system capacity: 9 imp pt, 10.8 US pt, 5.1 l; carburation: 2 SU type HS 2 semi-downdraught carburettors; fuel feed: electric pump; cooling system: water; cooling system capacity: 6.9 imp pt, 8.2 US pt, 3.9 l.

TRANSMISSION driving wheels: front; clutch: single dry plate (diaphragm), hydraulically controlled; gearbox: mechanical; gears: 4 + reverse; synchromesh gears: I, II, III, IV; gearbox ratios: I 3.628, II 2.172, III 1.412, IV 1, rev 3.628; gear lever: central; final drive: helical spur gears; axle ratio: 3.650; tyres: 5.50 x 12.

PERFORMANCE max speeds: 27 mph, 43 km/h in 1st gear; 46 mph, 74 km/h in 2nd gear; 70 mph, 112 km/h in 3rd gear; 90 mph, 145 km/h in 4th gear; power-weight ratio: 28.5 lb/hp, 13 kg/hp; carrying capacity: 882 lb, 400 kg; acceleration: 0-50 mph (0-80 km/h) 11.4 sec; speed in direct drive at 1,000 rpm: 16.8 mph, 27 km/h; fuel consumption: 33.6 m/imp gal, 28 m/US gal, 8.4 l x 100 km.

CHASSIS integral, front and rear auxiliary frames; front suspension: independent, wishbones, hydrolastic (liquid) rubber cone springs, hydraulic connecting pipes to rear wheels; rear suspension: independent, swinging longitudinal trailing arms, hydrolastic (liquid) rubber cone springs, hydraulic connecting pipes to front wheels, combined with transverse torsion bars, anti-roll bar.

STEERING rack-and-pinion; turns of steering wheel lock to lock: 3.12.

BRAKES front disc (diameter 8 in, 203 mm), rear drum; area rubbed by linings: front 96 sq in, 619 sq cm, rear 63 sq in, 406 sq cm, total 159 sq in, 1,025 sq cm.

ELECTRICAL EQUIPMENT voltage: 12 V; battery: 40 Ah; generator type: dynamo, 264 W; ignition distributor: Lucas; headlamps: 2.

DIMENSIONS AND WEIGHT wheel base: 93.50 in, 2,375 mm; front track: 51.50 in, 1,308 mm; rear track: 50.85 in, 1,292 mm; overall length: 146.75 in, 3,727 mm; overall width: 60.35 in, 1,533 mm; overall height: 53 in, 1,346 mm; ground clearance: 5.30 in, 135 mm; dry weight: 1,852 lb, 840 kg; distribution of weight: 62% front axle, 38% rear axle; turning circle (between walls): 36 ft, 11 m; fuel tank capacity: 8 imp gal, 9.5 US gal, 36 l.

BODY saloon/sedan; doors: 4; seats: 4-5; front seats: separate.

PRACTICAL INSTRUCTIONS fuel: 98-100 oct petrol; engine sump, gearbox and final drive oil: 7.6 imp pt, 9.1 US pt, 4.3 l, SAE 10W-30, change every 6,000 miles, 9,700 km;

WOLSELEY Sixteen-Sixty

WOLSELEY 18/85 Mk II

reasing: every 3,000 miles, 4,800 km, 4 points; sparking lug type: 225°; tappet clearances: inlet 0.012 in, 0.30 mm; exhaust 0.012 in, 0.30 mm; valve timing: inlet opens 5° before tdc and closes 45° after bdc, exhaust opens 51° before bdc and closes 21° after tdc; normal tyre pressure: front 28 psi, 2 atm, rear 24 psi, 1.7 atm.

OPTIONAL ACCESSORIES AP automatic gearbox, hydraulic torque convertor with 2 conic bevel gears (twin concentric differential-like gear clusters) with 4 ratios (I 2.612, II 1.807, III 1.446, IV 1, rev 2.612) operated by 3 brake bands and 2 multi-disc clutches, max ratio of convertor at stall 2, possible manual selection, with engine max power (DIN) 70 hp at 5,250 rpm, max torque (DIN) 69 lb ft, 9.5 kg m at 3,500 rpm, 47.1 hp/l specific power, 1 SU type HS 4 carburettor, 3.760 axle ratio, max speeds (I) 38 mph, 59 km/h, (II) 53 mph, 85 km/h, (III) 66 mph, 106 km/h, (IV) 87 mph, 140 km/h, power-weight ratio 30.9 lb/hp, 14 kg/hp, speed in direct drive at 1,000 rpm 16.3 mph, 26.2 km/h, fuel consumption 34 m/imp gal, 28.3 m/US gal, 8.3 l x 100 km; reclining backrests; electrically-heated rear window.

Sixteen-Sixty

PRICE IN GB: £ 827.

ENGINE front, 4 stroke; cylinders: 4, vertical, in line; bore and stroke: 3 x 3.50 in, 76.2 x 88.9 mm; engine capacity: 99 cu in, 1,662 cu cm; compression ratio: 8.3; max power (DIN): 61 hp at 4,500 rpm; max torque (DIN): 90 lb ft, 12.4 kg m at 2,100 rpm; max engine rpm: 5,400; specific power: 38 hp/l; cylinder block: cast iron; cylinder head: cast iron; crankshaft bearings: 3; valves: 2 per cylinder, overhead, in-line, push-rods and rockers; camshafts: 1, side; lubrication: gear pump, full flow filter; lubricating system capacity: 7.6 imp pt, 9.1 US pt, 4.3 l; carburation: 1 SU type HS 2 semi-downdraught carburettor; fuel feed: electric pump; cooling system: water; cooling system capacity: 12.3 imp pt, 14.8 US pt, 7 l.

TRANSMISSION driving wheels: rear; clutch: single dry plate, hydraulically controlled; gearbox: mechanical; gears: 4 + reverse; synchromesh gears: II, III, IV; gearbox ratios: I 3.636, II 2.214, III 1.374, IV 1, rev 4.755; gear lever: central; final drive: hypoid bevel; axle ratio: 4.300; tyres: 5.90 x 14.

PERFORMANCE max speeds: 25 mph, 40 km/h in 1st gear; 40 mph, 64 km/h in 2nd gear; 65 mph, 104 km/h in 3rd gear; 84 mph, 135 km/h in 4th gear; power-weight ratio: 40.5 lb/hp, 18.3 kg/hp; carrying capacity: 882 lb, 400 kg; acceleration: standing ¼ mile 21.5 sec, 0-50 mph (0-80 km/h) 14 sec; speed in direct drive at 1,000 rpm: 16.6 mph, 26.7 km/h; fuel consumption: 30.1 m/imp gal, 25 m/US gal, 9.4 l x 100 km.

CHASSIS integral; front suspension: independent, wishbones, coil springs, anti-roll bar, lever dampers as upper arms; rear suspension: rigid axle, semi-elliptic leafsprings, anti-roll bar, lever dampers.

STEERING cam and peg; turns of steering wheel lock to lock: 3.

BRAKES drum, 2 front leading shoes; area rubbed by linings: front 141 sq in, 909 sq cm, rear 99 sq in, 639 sq cm, total 240 sq in, 1,548 sq cm.

ELECTRICAL EQUIPMENT voltage: 12 V; battery: 43 Ah; generator type: dynamo, 22 A; ignition distributor: Lucas; headlamps: 2.

DIMENSIONS AND WEIGHT wheel base: 100.25 in, 2,546 mm; front track: 50.65 in, 1,286 mm; rear track: 51.35 in, 1,304 mm; overall length: 174.50 in, 4,432 mm; overall width: 63.50 in, 1,613 mm; overall height: 58.90 in, 1,496 mm; ground clearance: 6 in, 152 mm; dry weight: 2,471 lb, 1,121 kg; distribution of weight: 53% front axle, 47% rear axle; turning circle (between walls): 37 ft, 11.3 m; fuel tank capacity: 10 imp gal, 11.9 US gal, 45 l.

BODY saloon/sedan; doors: 4; seats: 4-5; front seats: separate.

PRACTICAL INSTRUCTIONS fuel: 95-98 oct petrol; engine sump oil: 6.7 imp pt, 8 US pt, 3.8 l, SAE 10W-40 (winter) 20W-50 (summer), change every 3,000 miles, 4,800 km; gearbox oil: 4.6 imp pt, 5.5 US pt, 2.6 l, SAE 20W-50; final drive oil: 2.3 imp pt, 2.7 US pt, 1.3 l, SAE 90; greasing: every 3,000 miles, 4,800 km, 7 points; tappet clearances: inlet 0.015 in, 0.38 mm, exhaust 0.015 in, 0.38 mm; valve timing: inlet opens 0° before tdc and closes 50° after bdc, exhaust opens 35° before bdc and closes 15° after tdc; normal tyre pressure: front 20 psi, 1.4 atm, rear 24 psi, 1.7 atm.

VARIATIONS

ENGINE 7.2 compression ratio.

OPTIONAL ACCESSORIES Borg-Warner automatic gearbox, hydraulic torque convertor and planetary gears with 3 ratios (I 2.390, II 1.450, III 1, rev 2.090), max ratio of convertor at stall 2, max speeds (I) 37 mph, 59 km/h, (II) 62 mph, 99 km/h, (III) 84 mph, 135 km/h; 4.875 axle ratio only for export; reclining backrests; electrically-heated rear window.

WOLSELEY 1300 Mk II

WOLSELEY Sixteen-Sixty

WOLSELEY 18/85 Mk II

18/85 Mk II

PRICE IN GB: £ 1,009.

ENGINE front, transverse, 4 stroke; cylinders: 4, in line; bore and stroke: 3.16 x 3.50 in, 80.3 x 88.9 mm; engine capacity: 109.7 cu in, 1,798 cu cm; compression ratio: 9; max power (DIN): 86.5 hp at 5,400 rpm; max torque (DIN): 101 lb ft, 13.9 kg m at 3,000 rpm; max engine rpm: 5,600; specific power: 48.1 hp/l; cylinder block: cast iron; cylinder head: cast iron; crankshaft bearings: 5; valves: 2 per cylinder, overhead, push-rods and rockers; camshafts: 1, side; lubrication: eccentric pump, magnetic metal gauze filter in sump and full flow; lubricating system capacity: 11.3 imp pt, 13.5 US pt, 6.4 l; carburation: 1 SU type HS 6 carburettor; fuel feed: electric pump; cooling system: water; cooling system capacity: 9.5 imp pt, 11 US pt, 5.4 l.

TRANSMISSION driving wheels: front; clutch: single dry plate (diaphragm), hydraulically controlled; gearbox: mechanical, in unit with engine; gears: 4 + reverse; synchromesh gears: I, II, III, IV; gearbox ratios: I 3.292, II 2.059, III 1.384, IV 1, rev 3.015; gear lever: central; final drive: spiral bevel; axle ratio: 3.882; width of rims: 4.5''; tyres: 165 x 14.

PERFORMANCE max speeds: 31 mph, 50 km/h in 1st gear; 49 mph, 79 km/h in 2nd gear; 73 mph, 117 km/h in 3rd gear; 90 mph, 145 km/h in 4th gear; power-weight ratio: 29.8 lb/hp, 13.5 kg/hp; carrying capacity: 882 lb, 400 kg; speed in direct drive at 1,000 rpm: 18.1 mph, 29.1 km/h; fuel consumption: 23.7 m/imp gal, 19.8 m/US gal, 11.9 l x 100 km.

CHASSIS integral; front suspension: independent, wishbones, lower trailing links, hydrolastic (liquid) rubber cone springs, hydraulic connecting pipes to rear wheels; rear suspension: independent, swinging longitudinal trailing arms, hydrolastic (liquid) rubber cone springs, hydraulic connecting pipes to front wheels, anti-roll bar.

STEERING rack-and-pinion, servo; turns of steering wheel lock to lock: 3.56.

BRAKES front disc (diameter 9.30 in, 236 mm), rear drum, rear compensator, servo; area rubbed by linings: front 183 sq in, 1,180 sq cm, rear 99 sq in, 639 sq cm, total 282 sq in, 1,819 sq cm.

ELECTRICAL EQUIPMENT voltage: 12 V; battery: 50 Ah; generator type: dynamo, 22 A; ignition distributor: Lucas; headlamps: 2.

DIMENSIONS AND WEIGHT wheel base: 106 in, 2,692 mm; front track: 56 in, 1,442 mm; rear track: 55.50 in, 1,410 mm; overall length: 166.60 in, 4,232 mm; overall width: 67 in, 1,702 mm; overall height: 56 in, 1,422 mm; ground clearance: 6.50 in, 165 mm; dry weight: 2,575 lb, 1,168 kg; turning circle (between walls): 38.5 ft, 11.7 m; fuel tank capacity: 10.8 imp gal, 12.9 US gal, 49 l.

BODY saloon/sedan; doors: 4; seats: 4-5; front seats: separate.

PRACTICAL INSTRUCTIONS fuel: 96-98 oct petrol; engine sump, gearbox and final drive oil: 10.6 imp pt, 12.7 US pt, 6 l, SAE 10W-30 (winter) 20W-50 (summer), change every 6,000 miles, 9,700 km; greasing: every 6,200 miles, 10,000 km, 1 point; tappet clearances: inlet 0.015 in, 0.38 mm, exhaust 0.015 in, 0.38 mm; valve timing: inlet opens 5° before tdc and closes 45° after bdc, exhaust opens 40° before bdc and closes 10° after tdc; normal tyre pressure: front 30 psi, 2.1 atm, rear 24 psi, 1.7 atm.

OPTIONAL ACCESSORIES Borg-Warner automatic gearbox, hydraulic torque convertor and planetary gears with 3 ratios (I 2.390, II 1.450, III 1, rev 2.030), max ratio of convertor at stall 2, 3.940 axle ratio, max speeds (I) 42 mph, 67 km/h, (II) 69 mph, 111 km/h, (III) 90 mph, 145 km/h, speed in direct drive at 1,000 rpm 17.8 mph, 28.7 km/h; reclining backrests; electrically-heated rear window.

18/85 Mk II S

See 18/85 Mk II, except for:

PRICE IN GB: £ 1,058.

ENGINE compression ratio: 9.5; max power (DIN): 95.5 hp at 5,700 rpm; max torque (DIN): 106 lb ft, 14.6 kg m at 3,000 rpm; max engine rpm: 6,000; specific power: 55.3 hp/l; carburation: 2 SU type H 6 semi-downdraught carburettors.

PERFORMANCE max speed: 33 mph, 53 km/h in 1st gear; 53 mph, 85 km/h in 2nd gear; 79 mph, 127 km/h in 3rd gear; 100 mph, 161 km/h in 4th gear; power-weight ratio: 26.9 lb/hp, 12.2 kg/hp; fuel consumption: 22.9 m/imp gal, 19 m/US gal, 12.4 l x 100 km.

BRAKES front disc (twin calipers), (diameter 9.70 in, 246 mm).

PRACTICAL INSTRUCTIONS fuel: 99 oct petrol; valve timing: inlet opens 16° before tdc and closes 56° after bdc, exhaust opens 51° before bdc and closes 21° after tdc.

DAF   HOLLAND

33 De Luxe Saloon

PRICE IN GB: £ 534.

ENGINE front, 4 stroke; cylinders: 2, horizontally opposed; bore and stroke: 3.37 x 2.56 in, 85.5 x 65 mm; engine capacity: 45.5 cu in, 746 cu cm; compression ratio: 7.5; max power (SAE): 32 hp at 4,200 rpm; max torque (SAE): 42 lb ft, 5.8 kg m at 2,700 rpm; max engine rpm: 4,500; specific power: 42.9 hp/l; cylinder block: light alloy; cylinder head: light alloy; crankshaft bearings: 2; valves: 2 per cylinder, overhead, push-rods and rockers; camshafts: 1, central, lower; lubrication: gear pump, full flow filter; lubricating system capacity: 3.5 imp pt, 4.2 US pt, 2 l; lubrication: 1 Solex 34 PICS-2 downdraught carburettor; fuel feed: mechanical pump; cooling system: air-cooled.

TRANSMISSION driving wheels: rear; clutch: automatic, 2-stage centrifugal; transmission: Daf-Variomatic automatic acting as limited slip final drive; gears: progressive, infinite number of ratios between 16.4 and 3.9; selector lever: central; axle ratio: 4.750; tyres: 135 x 13.

PERFORMANCE max speed: 70 mph, 112 km/h; power-weight ratio: 46 lb/hp, 20.9 kg/hp; carrying capacity: 706 lb, 320 kg; acceleration: 0-50 mph (0-80 km/h) 17 sec; fuel consumption: 42.1 m/imp gal, 35.1 m/US gal, 6.7 l x 100 km.

CHASSIS integral; front suspension: independent, transverse lower leafspring, vertical sliding pillars, co-axial telescopic dampers; rear suspension: independent, semi-trailing arms, coil springs, telescopic dampers.

STEERING rack-and-pinion; turns of steering wheel lock to lock: 2.90.

BRAKES drum; lining area: front 34 sq in, 219 sq cm, rear 34 sq in, 219 sq cm, total 68 sq in, 438 sq cm.

ELECTRICAL EQUIPMENT voltage: 6 V; battery: 66 Ah; generator type: dynamo, 300 W; ignition distributor: Bosch; headlamps: 2.

DIMENSIONS AND WEIGHT wheel base: 80.71 in, 2,050 mm; front track: 47.01 in, 1,194 mm; rear track: 47.01 in, 1,194 mm; overall length: 142.52 in, 3,620 mm; overall width: 56.69 in, 1,440 mm; overall height: 54.33 in, 1,380 mm; ground clearance: 7.48 in, 190 mm; dry weight: 1,477 lb, 670 kg; distribution of weight: 50% front axle, 50% rear axle; turning circle (between walls): 31.2 ft, 9.5 m; fuel tank capacity: 7 imp gal, 8.4 US gal, 32 l.

BODY saloon/sedan; doors: 2; seats: 4-5; front seats: separate.

PRACTICAL INSTRUCTIONS fuel: 88 oct petrol; engine sump oil: 3.5 imp pt, 4.2 US pt, 2 l, SAE 10W-30, change every 3,100 miles, 5,000 km; transmission oil: central conic bevels 0.9 imp pt, 1.1 US pt, 0.5 l, SAE 80-90, axle reduction gears and pulleys (one per wheel) 0.5 imp pt, 0.6 US pt, 0.3 l, SAE 80-90, Variomatic belt-pulley/drums sealed for life; greasing: none; sparking plug type: 200°; tappet clearances: inlet 0.004 in, 0.10 mm, exhaust 0.006 in, 0.15 mm; valve timing: inlet opens 13° before tdc and closes 27° after bdc, exhaust opens 27° before bdc and closes 13° after tdc; normal tyre pressure: front 20 psi, 1.4 atm, rear 24 psi, 1.7 atm.

OPTIONAL ACCESSORIES sunshine roof.

44 De Luxe Saloon

See 33 De Luxe Saloon, except for:

PRICE IN GB: £ 611.

ENGINE bore and stroke: 3.37 x 2.89 in, 85.5 x 73.5 mm; engine capacity: 51.5 cu in, 844 cu cm; max power (SAE): 40 hp at 4,500 rpm; max torque (SAE): 51 lb ft, 7.1 kg m at 2,400 rpm; max engine rpm: 5,200; specific power: 47.4 hp/l; carburation: 1 Solex 40 PICS downdraught carburettor.

TRANSMISSION gears: progressive, infinite number of ratios between 15.44 and 3.87; axle ratio: 3.640; tyres: 135 x 14.

PERFORMANCE max speed: 76 mph, 123 km/h; power-weight ratio: 40.8 lb/hp, 18.5 kg/hp; carrying capacity: 728 lb, 330 kg; acceleration: 0-50 mph (0-80 km/h) 15 sec; fuel consumption: 37.6 m/imp gal, 31.4 m/US gal, 7.5 l x 100 km.

STEERING turns of steering wheel lock to lock: 3.25.

BRAKES lining area: front 48.7 sq in, 314 sq cm, rear 48.7 sq in, 314 sq cm, total 97.4 sq in, 628 sq cm.

DIMENSIONS AND WEIGHT wheel base: 88.58 in, 2,250 mm; front track: 50.39 in, 1,280 mm; rear track: 49.21 in, 1,250 mm; overall length: 151.57 in, 3,850 mm; ground clearance: 6.69 in, 170 mm; dry weight: 1,632 lb, 740 kg; distribution of weight: 54% front axle, 46% rear axle; fuel tank capacity: 8.4 imp gal, 10 US gal, 38 l.

PRACTICAL INSTRUCTIONS normal tyre pressure: front 22 psi, 1.5 atm, rear 28 psi, 2 atm.

DAF 33 De Luxe Saloon

DAF 44 De Luxe Saloon

DAF Variomatic transmission

DAF 55

DAF 55 De Luxe Saloon

DAF 55 T Coupé

DAF 55 C Estate Car

44 C Estate Car

See 44 De Luxe Saloon, except for:

PRICE IN GB: £ 695.

PERFORMANCE power-weight ratio: 42.3 lb/hp, 19.2 kg/hp; carrying capacity: 772 lb, 350 kg.

DIMENSIONS AND WEIGHT dry weight: 1,698 lb, 770 kg; distribution of weight: 51% front axle, 49% rear axle.

BODY estate car/station wagon; doors: 2 + 1.

55 De Luxe Saloon

PRICE IN GB: £ 672.

ENGINE front, 4 stroke; cylinders: 4, vertical, in line; bore and stroke: 2.76 x 2.83 in, 70 x 72 mm; engine capacity: 67.6 cu in, 1,108 cu ˉcm; compression ratio: 8.5; max power (SAE): 50 hp at 5,000 rpm; max torque (SAE): 62 lb ft, 8.5 kg m at 3,000 rpm; max engine rpm: 5,500; specific power: 45.1 hp/l; cylinder block: cast iron; cylinder head: light alloy; crankshaft bearings: 5; valves: 2 per cylinder, overhead, in line, slanted, push-rods and rockers; camshafts: 1, side; lubrication: gear pump, full flow filter; lubricating system capacity: 4.4 imp pt, 5.3 US pt, 2.5 l; carburation: 1 Solex 32 EHSA horizontal carburettor; fuel feed: mechanical pump; cooling system: water; cooling system capacity: 8.4 imp pt, 10.1 US pt, 4.8 l.

TRANSMISSION driving wheels: rear; clutch: automatic, 2-stage centrifugal; transmission: Daf Variomatic automatic acting as limited slip final drive; gears: progressive, infinite number of ratios between 14.87 and 3.73; gear lever: central; axle ratio: 3.875; tyres: 135 x 14.

PERFORMANCE max speed: 85 mph, 136 km/h; power-weight ratio: 34.4 lb/hp, 15.6 kg/hp; carrying capacity: 728 lb, 330 kg; acceleration: 0-50 mph (0-80 km/h) 12 sec; fuel consumption: 34.4 m/imp gal, 28.7 m/US gal, 8.2 l x 100 km.

CHASSIS integral; front suspension: independent, longitudinal torsion bars, telescopic damper struts, lower wishbones (trailing links), anti-roll bar; rear suspension: independent, semi-trailing arms, coil springs, telescopic dampers.

STEERING rack-and-pinion; turns of steering wheel lock to lock: 3.25.

BRAKES front disc, rear drum; lining area: front 12.4 sq in, 80 sq cm, rear 48.7 sq in, 314 sq cm, total 61.1 sq in, 394 sq cm.

ELECTRICAL EQUIPMENT voltage: 12 V; battery: 36 Ah; generator type: dynamo, 265 W; ignition distributor: Ducellier; headlamps: 2.

DIMENSIONS AND WEIGHT wheel base: 88.58 in, 2,250 mm; front track: 50.39 in, 1,280 mm; rear track: 49.21 in, 1,250 mm; overall length: 152.76 in, 3,880 mm; overall width: 60.63 in, 1,540 mm; overall height: 54.33 in, 1,380 mm; ground clearance: 6.69 in, 170 mm; dry weight: 1,720 lb, 780 kg; distribution of weight: 55% front axle, 45% rear axle; turning circle (between walls): 31.2 ft, 9.5 m; fuel tank capacity: 8.4 imp gal, 10 US gal, 38 l.

BODY saloon/sedan; doors: 2; seats: 4-5; front seats: separate.

PRACTICAL INSTRUCTIONS fuel: 88 oct petrol; engine sump oil: 4.4 imp pt, 5.3 US pt, 2.5 l, SAE 10W-30, change every 3,100 miles, 5,000 km; transmission oil: central conic bevels 0.7 imp pt, 0.8 US pt, 0.4 l, SAE 80-90, axle reduction gears and pulleys (one per wheel) 0.5 imp pt, 0.6 US pt, 0.3 l, SAE 80-90, Variomatic belt-pulley drums sealed for life; greasing: none; tappet clearances: inlet 0.006 in, 0.15 mm, exhaust 0.008 in, 0.20 mm; valve timing: inlet opens 10° before tdc and closes 34° after bdc, exhaust opens 46° before bdc and closes 10° after tdc; normal tyre pressure: front 22 psi, 1.5 atm, rear 28 psi, 2 atm.

OPTIONAL ACCESSORIES sunshine roof.

55 T Coupé

See 55 De Luxe Saloon, except for:

PRICE IN GB: £ 764.

PERFORMANCE max speed 87 mph, 140 km/h; power-weight ratio: 35 lb/hp, 15.9 kg/hp; carrying capacity: 518 lb, 235 kg.

DIMENSIONS AND WEIGHT overall height: 51.57 in, 1,310 mm; dry weight: 1,753 lb, 795 kg; distribution of weight: 56% front axle, 44% rear axle.

BODY coupé; seats: 2 + 2.

55 C Estate Car

See 55 De Luxe Saloon, except for:

PRICE IN GB: £ 740.

PERFORMANCE power-weight ratio: 35.3 lb/hp, 16 kg/hp; carrying capacity: 794 lb, 360 kg.

DIMENSIONS AND WEIGHT dry weight: 1,764 lb, 800 kg.

BODY estate car/station wagon; doors: 2 + 1.

ABARTH   ITALY

Fiat Abarth 595

PRICE EX WORKS: 720,000 liras.

ENGINE rear, 4 stroke; cylinders: 2, vertical, in line; bore
and stroke: 2.89 x 2.76 in, 73.5 x 70 mm; engine capacity:
36.2 cu in, 593 cu cm; compression ratio: 9.2; max power
(DIN): 27 hp at 5,000 rpm; max torque (DIN): 31 lb ft,
4.3 kg m at 4,000 rpm; max engine rpm: 5,500; specific
power: 45.5 hp/l; cylinder block: cast iron; cylinder head:
light alloy; crankshaft bearings: 2; valves: 2 per cylinder,
overhead, push-rods and rockers; camshafts: 1, side; lubrication: gear pump, centrifugal filter; lubricating system
capacity: 5.3 imp pt, 6.3 US pt, 3 l; carburation: 1 Solex
C 28 IB 2 downdraught carburettor; fuel feed: mechanical
pump; cooling system: air cooled.

TRANSMISSION driving wheels: rear; clutch: single dry
plate; gearbox: mechanical; gears: 4 + reverse; silent claw
coupling gears: II, III, IV; gearbox ratios: I 3.273, II 2.067,
III 1.300, IV 0.875, rev 4.134; gear lever: central; final
drive: hypoid bevel; axle ratio: 5.125; width of rims: 3.5'';
tyres: 125 x 12 front, 135 x 12 rear.

PERFORMANCE max speeds: 19 mph, 31 km/h in 1st gear;
32 mph, 51 km/h in 2nd gear; 50 mph, 80 km/h in 3rd gear;
75 mph, 120 km/h in 4th gear; power-weight ratio: 46.5
lb/hp, 21.1 kg/hp; carrying capacity: 706 lb, 320 kg; speed
in top at 1,000 rpm: 13.1 mph, 21.1 km/h; fuel consumption:
47.1 m/imp gal, 39.2 m/US gal, 6 l x 100 km.

CHASSIS integral; front suspension: independent, wishbones, transverse leafspring lower arms, telescopic dampers;
rear suspension: independent, semi-trailing arms, coil
springs, telescopic dampers.

STEERING screw and sector; turns of steering wheel lock
to lock: 3.05.

BRAKES drum; area rubbed by linings: total 67 sq in,
432 sq cm.

ELECTRICAL EQUIPMENT voltage: 12 V; battery: 32 Ah;
generator type: dynamo, 230 W; ignition distributor: Marelli; headlamps: 2.

DIMENSIONS AND WEIGHT wheel base: 72.44 in, 1,840 mm;
front track: 44.13 in, 1,121 mm; rear track: 44.68 in, 1,135
mm; overall length: 116.93 in, 2,970 mm; overall width: 51.97
in, 1,320 mm; overall height: 52.16 in, 1,325 mm; ground
clearance: 4.92 in, 125 mm; dry weight: 1,257 lb, 570 kg;
distribution of weight: 42% front axle, 58% rear axle; turning circle (between walls): 28.2 ft, 8.6 m; fuel tank capacity:
4.6 imp gal, 5.5 US gal, 21 l.

BODY saloon/sedan; doors: 2; seats: 4; front seats: separate.

PRACTICAL INSTRUCTIONS fuel: 95 oct petrol; engine sump
oil: 5.3 imp pt, 6.3 US pt, 3 l, SAE 20W-40, change every
3,100 miles, 5,000 km; gearbox and final drive oil: 1.9 imp
pt, 2.3 US pt, 1.1 l, SAE 90, change every 18,600 miles,
30,000 km; greasing: every 1,600 miles, 2,500 km, 2 points;
tappet clearances: inlet 0.008 in, 0.20 mm, exhaust 0.008 in,
0.20 mm; valve timing: inlet opens 40° before tdc and
closes 80° after bdc, exhaust opens 80° before bdc and
closes 40° after tdc; normal tyre pressure: front 18 psi,
1.3 atm, rear 24 psi, 1.7 atm.

OPTIONAL ACCESSORIES Luxury, Competition and Luxury
Competition versions.

Fiat Abarth 595 SS

See Fiat Abarth 595, except for:

PRICE EX WORKS: 830,000 liras.

ENGINE compression ratio: 10; max power (DIN): 32 hp
at 5,000 rpm; max torque (DIN): 38 lb ft, 5.2 kg m at 3,800
rpm; specific power: 54 hp/l; carburation: 1 Solex 34 PBIC
downdraught carburettor.

PERFORMANCE max speeds: 20 mph, 32 km/h in 1st gear;
34 mph, 55 km/h in 2nd gear; 54 mph, 87 km/h in 3rd gear;
81 mph, 130 km/h in 4th gear; power-weight ratio: 39.2
lb/hp, 17.8 kg/hp; speed in top at 1,000 rpm: 13.5 mph,
21.7 km/h.

OPTIONAL ACCESSORIES Luxury, Competition and Luxury
Competition versions.

Fiat Abarth 695 SS

See Fiat Abarth 595, except for:

PRICE EX WORKS: 905,000 liras.

ENGINE bore and stroke: 2.99 x 2.99 in, 76 x 76 mm; engine
capacity: 42 cu in, 689 cu cm; compression ratio: 10; max

ABARTH Fiat Abarth 595 SS Competition

ABARTH Fiat Abarth 1000 Berlina Corsa Gr. 2

ABARTH Fiat Abarth Scorpione 1300 S

power (DIN): 38 hp at 5,350 rpm; max torque (DIN): 42 lb ft, 5.8 kg m at 4,000 rpm; max engine rpm: 6,400; specific power: 55.2 hp/l; carburation: 1 Solex 34 PBIC downdraught carburettor.

TRANSMISSION axle ratio: 4.720; width of rims: 4.5''.

PERFORMANCE max speeds: 22 mph, 35 km/h in 1st gear; 37 mph, 60 km/h in 2nd gear; 59 mph, 95 km/h in 3rd gear; 87 mph, 140 km/h in 4th gear; power-weight ratio: 33 lb/hp, 15 kg/hp; speed in top at 1,000 rpm: 15.5 mph, 25 km/h; fuel consumption: 43.5 m/imp gal, 36.2 m/US gal, 6.5 l x 100 km.

PRACTICAL INSTRUCTIONS normal tyre pressure: front 20 psi, 1.4 atm, rear 26 psi, 1.8 atm.

OPTIONAL ACCESSORIES Luxury, Competition and Luxury Competition versions.

Fiat Abarth 695 SS Assetto Corsa

See Fiat Abarth 695 SS, except for:

PRICE EX WORKS: 1,040,000 liras.

DIMENSIONS AND WEIGHT front track: 46.65 in, 1,185 mm; rear track: 47.20 in, 1,199 mm; overall width: 53.74 in, 1,365 mm.

OPTIONAL ACCESSORIES light alloy wheels; semi-axles with cardan joints; competition exhaust manifolds.

Fiat Abarth 850 TC Corsa Gr. 2

PRICE EX WORKS: 2,690,000 liras.

ENGINE rear, 4 stroke; cylinders: 4, vertical, in line; bore and stroke: 2.46 x 2.72 in, 62.5 x 69 mm; engine capacity: 51.7 cu in, 847 cu cm; compression ratio: 12.5; max power (DIN): 78 hp at 8,000 rpm; max torque (DIN): 54 lb ft, 7.5 kg m at 6,000 rpm; max engine rpm: 8,200; specific power: 92.1 hp/l; cylinder block: cast iron; cylinder head: light alloy; crankshaft bearings: 3; valves: 2 per cylinder, overhead, in line, slanted at 10°, push-rods and rockers; camshafts: 1, side; lubrication: gear pump, full flow filter (cartridge), oil cooler; lubricating system capacity: 10.6 imp pt, 12.7 US pt, 6 l; carburation: 1 Weber 36 DCD 7 downdraught twin barrel carburettor; fuel feed: electric pump; cooling system: water, front supplementary radiator, electric thermostatic fan; cooling system capacity: 14.1 imp pt, 16.9 US pt, 8 l.

TRANSMISSION driving wheels: rear; clutch: single dry plate; gearbox: mechanical; gears: 5 + reverse; synchromesh gears: I, II, III, IV, V; gearbox ratios: I 3.385, II 2.111, III 1.591, IV 1.240, V 1.037, rev 4.275; gear lever: central; final drive: hypoid bevel, limited slip; axle ratio: 4.555; width of rims: 5.5''; tyres: 4.50M x 13 front, 4.50L x 13 rear.

PERFORMANCE max speeds: 34 mph, 55 km/h in 1st gear; 55 mph, 89 km/h in 2nd gear; 73 mph, 118 km/h in 3rd gear; 94 mph, 151 km/h in 4th gear; 112 mph, 180 km/h in 5th gear; power-weight ratio: 16.5 lb/hp, 7.5 kg/hp; carrying capacity: 706 lb, 320 kg; speed in top at 1,000 rpm: 13.7 mph, 22.1 km/h; fuel consumption: 37.7 m/imp gal, 31.4 m/US gal, 7.5 l x 100 km.

CHASSIS integral; front suspension: independent, wishbones, transverse semi-elliptic leafspring lower arms, anti-roll bar, telescopic dampers; rear suspension: independent, semi-trailing arms, coil springs, anti-roll bar, telescopic dampers.

STEERING screw and sector; turns of steering wheel lock to lock: 2.12.

BRAKES front disc, rear drum; lining area: total 32.6 sq in, 210 sq cm.

ELECTRICAL EQUIPMENT voltage: 12 V; battery: 32 Ah; generator type: alternator, 460 W; ignition distributor: Marelli; headlamps: 2.

DIMENSIONS AND WEIGHT wheel base: 78.74 in, 2,000 mm; front track: 45.67 in, 1,160 mm; rear track: 45.67 in, 1,160 mm; overall length: 138.98 in, 3,530 mm; overall width: 54.72 in, 1,390 mm; overall height: 55.12 in, 1,400 mm; ground clearance: 5.51 in, 140 mm; dry weight: 1,286 lb, 583 kg; distribution of weight: 45% front axle, 55% rear axle; turning circle (between walls): 28.5 ft, 8.7 m; fuel tank capacity: 6.8 imp gal, 8.2 US gal, 31 l.

BODY saloon/sedan; doors: 2; seats: 4; front seats: separate.

PRACTICAL INSTRUCTIONS fuel: 98 oct petrol; engine sump oil: 10.6 imp pt, 12.7 US pt, 6 l, 20W-40, change every 1,200 miles, 2,000 km; gearbox and final drive oil: 2.6 imp pt, 3.2 US pt, 1.5 l, SAE 90, change every 1,200 miles, 2,000 km; greasing: every 1,600 miles, 2,500 km, 6 points; tappet

ABARTH Fiat Abarth 595 SS Luxury Competition

ABARTH Fiat Abarth 1000 Berlina Corsa Gr. 2

ABARTH Fiat Abarth Scorpione 1300 S

clearances: inlet 0.008 in, 0.20 mm, exhaust 0.010 in, 0.25 mm; valve timing: inlet opens 52° before tdc and closes 83° after bdc, exhaust opens 83° before bdc and closes 52° after tdc; normal tyre pressure: front 26 psi, 1.8 atm, rear 31 psi, 2.2 atm.

OPTIONAL ACCESSORIES 5.375 4.875 4.333 3.900 axle ratios.

Fiat Abarth 1000 Berlina Corsa Gr. 2

See Fiat Abarth 850 TC Corsa Gr. 2, except for:

PRICE EX WORKS: 3,710,000 liras.

ENGINE bore and stroke: 2.56 x 2.91 in, 65 x 74 mm; engine capacity: 59.9 cu in, 982 cu cm; max power (DIN): 112 hp at 8,200 rpm; max torque (DIN): 65 lb ft, 9 kg m at 5,500 rpm; specific power: 117 hp/l; lubricating system capacity: 12.3 imp pt, 14.8 US pt, 7 l; carburation: 2 Weber 40 DCOE horizontal twin barrel carburettors.

TRANSMISSION axle ratio: 4.333; width of rims: front 7'', rear 8''; tyres: 4.25/9.50 x 13.

PERFORMANCE max speed: 124 mph, 200 km/h; power-weight ratio: 11.2 lb/hp, 5.1 kg/hp; fuel consumption: 35.3 m/imp gal, 29.4 m/US gal, 8 l x 100 km.

CHASSIS front suspension: independent, wishbones, coil springs, anti-roll bar, telescopic dampers.

ELECTRICAL EQUIPMENT battery: 48 Ah.

DIMENSIONS AND WEIGHT front track: 47.83 in, 1,215 mm; rear track: 49.21 in, 1,250 mm; overall length: 55.91 in, 1,420 mm; overall height: 51.18 in, 1,300 mm; fuel tank capacity: 6.6 imp gal, 7.9 US gal, 30 l.

PRACTICAL INSTRUCTIONS engine sump oil: 7 imp pt, 8.5 US pt, 4 l; gearbox and final drive oil: 3.2 imp pt, 3.8 US pt, 1.8 l; greasing: 2 points; valve timing: inlet opens 30° before tdc and closes 70° after bdc, exhaust opens 70° before bdc and closes 30° after tdc.

Fiat Abarth Scorpione 1300 S

PRICE EX WORKS: 1,840,000 liras.

ENGINE rear, 4 stroke; cylinders: 4, vertical, in line; bore and stroke: 2.97 x 2.81 in, 75.5 x 71.5 mm; engine capacity: 87.1 cu in, 1,280 cu cm; compression ratio: 10.5; max power (DIN): 75 hp at 6,000 rpm; max torque (DIN): 80 lb ft, 11 kg m at 3,000 rpm; max engine rpm: 6,000; specific power: 58.6 hp/l; cylinder block: cast iron; cylinder head: light alloy; crankshaft bearings: 5; valves: 2 per cylinder, overhead, push-rods and rockers; camshafts: 1, side; lubrication: gear pump, full flow filter (cartridge); lubricating system capacity: 12.3 imp pt, 14.8 US pt, 7 l; carburation: 1 Weber 32 PHH horizontal twin barrel carburettor; fuel feed: mechanical pump; cooling system: water, front supplementary radiator, electric thermostatic fan; cooling system capacity: 12.3 imp pt, 14.8 US pt, 7 l.

TRANSMISSION driving wheels: rear; clutch: single dry plate; gearbox: mechanical; gears: 4 + reverse; synchromesh gears: I, II, III, IV; gearbox ratios: I 3.636, II 2.055, III 1.409, IV 0.966, rev 3.615; gear lever: central; final drive: hypoid bevel; axle ratio: 3.888; width of rims: 5''; tyres: 155 x 13.

PERFORMANCE max speeds: 28 mph, 45 km/h in 1st gear; 51 mph, 82 km/h in 2nd gear; 78 mph, 125 km/h in 3rd gear; 112 mph, 180 km/h in 4th gear; power-weight ratio: 19.6 lb/hp, 8.9 kg/hp; carrying capacity: 419 lb, 190 kg; speed in top at 1,000 rpm: 18.6 mph, 30 km/h; fuel consumption: 31.4 m/imp gal, 26.1 m/US gal, 9 l x 100 km.

CHASSIS integral; front suspension: independent, wishbones, transverse semi-elliptic leafspring lower arms, anti-roll bar, telescopic dampers; rear suspension: independent, semi-trailing arms, coil springs, anti-roll bar, telescopic dampers.

STEERING screw and sector; turns of steering wheel lock to lock: 3.75.

BRAKES front disc, rear drum; lining area: total 41.9 sq in, 270 sq cm.

ELECTRICAL EQUIPMENT voltage: 12 V; battery: 48 Ah; generator type: dynamo, 230 W; ignition distributor: Marelli; headlamps: 2, retractable.

DIMENSIONS AND WEIGHT wheel base: 80.51 in, 2,045 mm; front track: 49.41 in, 1,255 mm; rear track: 49.41 in, 1,255 mm; overall length: 142.13 in, 3,610 mm; overall width: 58.86 in, 1,495 mm; overall height: 42.13 in, 1,070 mm; ground clearance: 4.72 in, 120 mm; dry weight: 1,477 lb, 670 kg; turning circle (between walls): 31.5 ft, 9.6 m; fuel tank capacity: 6.6 imp gal, 7.9 US gal, 30 l.

BODY coupé; doors: 2; seats: 2.

FIAT ABARTH SCORPIONE 1300 S

PRACTICAL INSTRUCTIONS fuel: 98 oct petrol; engine sump oil: 7.9 imp pt, 9.5 US pt, 4.5 l, SAE 20W-40, change every 3,100 miles, 5,000 km; gearbox and final drive oil: 3.5 imp pt, 4.2 US pt, 2 l, SAE 90, change every 18,600 miles, 30,000 km; greasing: every 1,600 miles, 2,500 km, 2 points; tappet clearances: inlet 0.010 in, 0.25 mm, exhaust 0.012 in, 0.30 mm; valve timing: inlet opens 30° before tdc and closes 70° after bdc, exhaust opens 70° before bdc and closes 30° after tdc; normal tyre pressure: front 20 psi, 1.4 atm, rear 26 psi, 1.8 atm.

Fiat Abarth Scorpione 1300 SS

See Fiat Abarth Scorpione 1300 S, except for:

PRICE EX WORKS: 2,050,000 liras.

CHASSIS front suspension: independent, semi-trailing arms, coil springs, anti-roll bar, telescopic dampers.

BRAKES disc (front and rear).

ALFA ROMEO   ITALY

Giulia 1300

PRICE EX WORKS: 1,310,000 liras.

ENGINE front, 4 stroke; cylinders: 4, vertical, in line; bore and stroke: 2.91 x 2.95 in, 74 x 75 mm; engine capacity: 78.7 cu in, 1,290 cu cm; compression ratio: 9; max power (SAE): 89 hp at 6,000 rpm; max torque (SAE): 87 lb ft, 12 kg m at 4,500 rpm; max engine rpm: 6,000; specific power: 69 hp/l; cylinder block: light alloy, wet liners; cylinder head: light alloy, hemispherical combustion chambers; crankshaft bearings: 5; valves: 2 per cylinder, overhead, Vee-slanted, thimble tappets; camshafts: 2, overhead; lubrication: gear pump, full flow filter (cartridge); lubricating system capacity: 12.7 imp pt, 15.2 US pt, 7.2 l; carburation: 1 Solex 32 PAIA 7 downdraught twin barrel carburettor; fuel feed: mechanical pump; cooling system: water; cooling system capacity: 13.2 imp pt, 15.9 US pt, 7.5 l.

TRANSMISSION driving wheels: rear; clutch: single dry plate; gearbox: mechanical; gears: 4 + reverse; synchromesh gears: I, II, III, IV; gearbox ratios: I 3.300, II 1.990, III 1.350, IV 1, rev 3.010; gear lever: central; final drive: hypoid bevel; axle ratio: 4.555; width of rims: 4.5''; tyres: 155 x 15.

PERFORMANCE max speeds: 29 mph, 47 km/h in 1st gear; 48 mph, 78 km/h in 2nd gear; 72 mph, 116 km/h in 3rd gear; over 96 mph, 155 km/h in 4th gear; power-weight ratio: 24.7 lb/hp, 11.2 kg/hp; carrying capacity: 882 lb, 400 kg; acceleration: standing ¼ mile 20.2 sec; speed in direct drive at 1,000 rpm: 15.7 mph, 25.2 km/h; fuel consumption: 29.1 m/imp gal, 24.2 m/US gal, 9.7 l x 100 km.

CHASSIS integral; front suspension: independent, wishbones, coil springs, anti-roll bar, telescopic dampers; rear suspension: rigid axle, trailing lower radius arms, upper transverse Vee radius arm, coil springs, telescopic dampers.

STEERING recirculating ball or worm and roller; turns of steering wheel lock to lock: 3.70.

BRAKES disc (diameter 10.51 in, 267 mm); area rubbed by linings: front 184.5 sq in, 1,190 sq cm, rear 167.1 sq in, 1,078 sq cm, total 351.6 sq in, 2,268 sq cm.

ELECTRICAL EQUIPMENT voltage: 12 V; battery: 50 Ah; generator type: dynamo, 300 W; ignition distributor: Bosch or Marelli; headlamps: 2.

DIMENSIONS AND WEIGHT wheel base: 98.82 in, 2,510 mm; front track: 52.13 in, 1,324 mm; rear track: 50.16 in, 1,274 mm; overall length: 163.78 in, 4,160 mm; overall width: 61.42 in, 1,560 mm; overall height: 56.30 in, 1,430 mm; ground clearance: 4.72 in, 120 mm; dry weight: 2,205 lb, 1,000 kg; turning circle (between walls): 35.7 ft, 10.9 m; fuel tank capacity: 10.1 imp gal, 12.1 US gal, 46 l.

BODY saloon/sedan; doors: 4; seats: 5; front seats: bench.

PRACTICAL INSTRUCTIONS fuel: 98-100 oct petrol; engine sump oil: 11.8 imp pt, 14.2 US pt, 6.7 l, SAE 20W-40, change every 3,700 miles, 6,000 km; gearbox oil: 3.2 imp pt, 3.8 US pt, 1.8 l, SAE 90 EP, change every 11,200 miles, 18,000 km; final drive oil: 2.5 imp pt, 3 US pt, 1.4 l, SAE 90 EP, change every 11,200 miles, 18,000 km; greasing: every 7,400 miles, 12,000 km, 1 point; tappet clearances: inlet 0.019-0.020 in, 0.48-0.50 mm, exhaust 0.021-0.024 in, 0.53-0.55 mm; valve timing: inlet opens 24°40' before tdc and closes 72°40' after bdc, exhaust opens 66° before bdc

ALFA ROMEO Giulia 1300 Super

ALFA ROMEO GT 1300 Junior

ALFA ROMEO GT 1300 Junior Z

and closes 18° after tdc; normal tyre pressure: front 23 psi, 1.6 atm, rear 24 psi, 1.7 atm.

OPTIONAL ACCESSORIES separate front seats.

Giulia 1300 TI

See Giulia 1300, except for:

PRICE IN GB: £ 993.
PRICE EX WORKS: 1,515,000 liras.

ENGINE max power (SAE): 94 hp at 6,000 rpm; max torque (SAE): 88 lb ft, 12.1 kg m at 4,900 rpm; specific power: 72.9 hp/l.

TRANSMISSION clutch: single dry plate (diaphragm), hydraulically controlled; gears: 5 + reverse; synchromesh gears: I, II, III, IV, V; gearbox ratios: I 3.300, II 1.990, III 1.350, IV 1, V 0.790, rev 3.010; axle ratio: 5.125.

PERFORMANCE max speeds: 25 mph, 40 km/h in 1st gear; 41 mph, 66 km/h in 2nd gear; 60 mph, 97 km/h in 3rd gear; 81 mph, 131 km/h in 4th gear; over 99 mph, 160 km/h in 5th gear; power-weight ratio: 23.6 lb/hp, 10.7 kg/hp; acceleration: standing ¼ mile 19.6 sec; speed in top at 1,000 rpm: 17.6 mph, 28.3 km/h; fuel consumption: 28.8 m/imp gal, 24 m/US gal, 9.8 l x 100 km.

BRAKES rear compensator, servo.

ELECTRICAL EQUIPMENT ignition distributor: Bosch.

DIMENSIONS AND WEIGHT dry weight: 2,227 lb, 1,010 kg.

OPTIONAL ACCESSORIES 165 x 14 tyres with 5'' wheels; separate front seats.

Giulia 1300 Super

See Giulia 1300 TI, except for:

PRICE EX WORKS: 1,595,000 liras.

ENGINE max power (SAE): 103 hp at 6,000 rpm; max torque (SAE): 101 lb ft, 14 kg m at 3,200 rpm; specific power: 79.8 hp/l; carburation: 2 Weber (or Solex or Dell'Orto) 40 DCOE 28 horizontal twin barrel carburettors.

TRANSMISSION axle ratio: 4.770.

PERFORMANCE max speeds: 26 mph, 42 km/h in 1st gear; 44 mph, 71 km/h in 2nd gear; 65 mph, 104 km/h in 3rd gear; 88 mph, 141 km/h in 4th gear; over 103 mph, 165 km/h in 5th gear; power-weight ratio: 21.6 lb/hp, 9.8 kg/hp; speed in top at 1,000 rpm: 18.5 mph, 29.7 km/h; fuel consumption: 28.5 m/imp gal, 23.8 m/US gal, 9.9 l x 100 km.

BRAKES dual circuit.

ELECTRICAL EQUIPMENT generator type: alternator, 420 W.

PRACTICAL INSTRUCTIONS valve timing: inlet opens 36°50' before tdc and closes 60°50' after bdc, exhaust opens 54°10' before bdc and closes 30°10' after tdc.

GT 1300 Junior

See Giulia 1300 TI, except for:

PRICE IN GB: £ 1,414.
PRICE EX WORKS: 1,845,000 liras.

ENGINE max power (SAE): 103 hp at 6,000 rpm; max torque (SAE): 101 lb ft, 14 kg m at 3,200 rpm; specific power: 79.8 hp/l; carburation: 2 Weber (or Solex or Dell'Orto) 40 DCOE 28 horizontal twin barrel carburettors.

TRANSMISSION gearbox ratios: V 0.860; axle ratio: 4.555.

PERFORMANCE max speeds: 27 mph, 44 km/h in 1st gear; 46 mph, 74 km/h in 2nd gear; 67 mph, 108 km/h in 3rd gear; 91 mph, 146 km/h in 4th gear; over 106 mph, 170 km/h in 5th gear; power-weight ratio: 21.2 lb/hp, 9.6 kg/hp; carrying capacity: 772 lb, 350 kg; acceleration: standing ¼ mile 19.1 sec; speed in top at 1,000 rpm: 18.2 mph, 29.3 km/h.

CHASSIS rear suspension: anti-roll bar.

BRAKES dual circuit.

ELECTRICAL EQUIPMENT generator type: alternator, 420 W.

DIMENSIONS AND WEIGHT wheel base: 92.52 in, 2,350 mm; overall length: 160.63 in, 4,080 mm; overall width: 62.20 in, 1,580 mm; overall height: 51.77 in, 1,315 mm; dry weight: 2,183 lb, 990 kg; turning circle (between walls): 35.1 ft, 10.7 m.

BODY coupé; doors: 2; seats: 4; front seats: separate (standard).

ALFA ROMEO Giulia 1300 Super

ALFA ROMEO GT 1300 Junior

ALFA ROMEO GT 1300 Junior Z

PRACTICAL INSTRUCTIONS valve timing: inlet opens 36°50' before tdc and closes 60°50' after bdc, exhaust opens 54°10' before bdc and closes 30°10' after tdc; normal tyre pressure: front 24 psi, 1.7 atm, rear 26 psi, 1.8 atm.

OPTIONAL ACCESSORIES only 165 x 14 tyres with 5'' wheels.

GTA 1300 Junior

See GT 1300 Junior, except for:

PRICE EX WORKS: 2,385,000 liras.

ENGINE bore and stroke: 3.07 x 2.66 in, 78 x 67.5 mm; max power (SAE): 110 hp at 6,000 rpm; max torque (SAE): 96 lb ft, 13.3 kg m at 5,000 rpm; specific power: 85.3 hp/l; cylinder head: dual ignition; lubricating system capacity: 13 imp pt, 15.6 US pt, 7.4 l; fuel feed: 2 electric pumps; cooling system capacity: 12.3 imp pt, 14.8 US pt, 7 l.

TRANSMISSION clutch: single dry plate, mechanically controlled; gearbox ratios: I 2.540, II 1.700, III 1.260, IV 1, V 0.860, rev 3.010; width of rims: 5.5''; tyres: 165 HR x 14.

PERFORMANCE max speeds: 36 mph, 58 km/h in 1st gear; 54 mph, 87 km/h in 2nd gear; 73 mph, 117 km/h in 3rd gear; 91 mph, 147 km/h in 4th gear; 109 mph, 175 km/h in 5th gear; power-weight ratio: — lb/hp, — kg/hp; speed in top at 1,000 rpm: 17.8 mph, 28.7 km/h; fuel consumption: — m/imp gal, — m/US gal, — l x 100 km.

STEERING worm and roller.

ELECTRICAL EQUIPMENT battery: 24 Ah.

DIMENSIONS AND WEIGHT dry weight: — lb, — kg.

BODY seats: 2 + 2; details: light alloy trimmed body.

VARIATIONS

ENGINE (competition version tuned by Autodelta) max power (SAE) 160 hp at 7,800 rpm, 124 hp/l specific power, oil cooler.
TRANSMISSION gearbox ratios I 2.330 2.760 3.300, II 1.580 1.780 1.990, III 1.210 1.300 1.350, IV 1, V 0.880 0.820 0.790, rev 3.010, limited slip final drive, 5.860 5.375 5.125 4.780 4.100 3.910 3.728 axle ratios.
PERFORMANCE max speed 130 mph, 210 km/h.

OPTIONAL ACCESSORIES none.

Spider 1300 Junior

See GT 1300 Junior, except for:

PRICE IN GB: £ 1,338.
PRICE EX WORKS: 1,940,000 liras.

PERFORMANCE carrying capacity: 706 lb, 320 kg.

DIMENSIONS AND WEIGHT wheel base: 88.58 in, 2,250 mm; overall length: 162.20 in, 4,120 mm; overall width: 64.17 in, 1,630 mm; overall height: 50.79 in, 1,290 mm; turning circle (between walls): 34.4 ft, 10.5 m.

BODY convertible; seats: 2 + 2.

OPTIONAL ACCESSORIES 165 x 14 tyres with 5'' wheels and hardtop.

GT 1300 Junior Z

See GT 1300 Junior, except for:

PRICE EX WORKS: 2,335,000 liras.

TRANSMISSION width of rims: 5.5''; tyres: 165 x 14.

PERFORMANCE power-weight ratio: 20.7 lb/hp, 9.4 kg/hp; carrying capacity: 507 lb, 230 kg; acceleration: standing ¼ mile 18.9 sec; speed in top at 1,000 rpm: 18 mph, 29 km/h.

BRAKES no dual circuit.

ELECTRICAL EQUIPMENT generator type: dynamo, 300 W.

DIMENSIONS AND WEIGHT wheel base: 88.58 in, 2,250 mm; overall length: 153.54 in, 3,900 mm; overall width: 61.02 in, 1,550 mm; overall height: 50.39 in, 1,280 mm; dry weight: 2,139 lb, 970 kg; turning circle (between walls): 32.8 ft, 10 m; fuel tank capacity: 11 imp gal, 13.2 US gal, 50 l.

BODY seats: 2.

OPTIONAL ACCESSORIES none.

Giulia Super

PRICE IN GB: £ 1,223.
PRICE EX WORKS: 1,795,000 liras.

ENGINE front, 4 stroke; cylinders: 4, vertical, in line; bore and stroke: 3.07 x 3.23 in, 78 x 82 mm; engine capacity: 95.8 cu in, 1,570 cu cm; compression ratio: 9; max power (SAE): 116 hp at 5,500 rpm; max torque (SAE): 120 lb ft, 16.5 kg m at 2,900 rpm; max engine rpm: 5,500; specific power: 73.9 hp/l; cylinder block: light alloy, wet liners; cylinder head: light alloy, hemispherical combustion chambers; crankshaft bearings: 5; valves: 2 per cylinder, overhead, Vee-slanted, thimble tappets; camshafts: 2, overhead; lubrication: gear pump, full flow filter (cartridge); lubricating system capacity: 12.7 imp pt, 15.2 US pt, 7.2 l; carburation: 2 Weber (or Solex or Dell'Orto) 40 DCOE 33 horizontal twin barrel carburettors; fuel feed: mechanical pump; cooling system: water; cooling system capacity: 13.2 imp pt, 15.9 US pt, 7.5 l.

TRANSMISSION driving wheels: rear; clutch: single dry plate (diaphragm), hydraulically controlled; gearbox: mechanical; gears: 5 + reverse; synchromesh gears: I, II, III, IV, V; gearbox ratios: I 3.300, II 1.990, III 1.350, IV 1, V 0.790, rev 3.010; gear lever: central; final drive: hypoid bevel; axle ratio: 4.555; width of rims: 4.5''; tyres: 155 x 15.

PERFORMANCE max speeds: 26 mph, 42 km/h in 1st gear; 43 mph, 69 km/h in 2nd gear; 63 mph, 102 km/h in 3rd gear; 86 mph, 138 km/h in 4th gear; over 109 mph, 175 km/h in 5th gear; power-weight ratio: 19.8 lb/hp, 9 kg/hp; carrying capacity: 882 lb, 400 kg; acceleration: standing ¼ mile 18.4 sec; speed in top at 1,000 rpm: 19.8 mph, 31.8 km/h; fuel consumption: 27.2 m/imp gal, 22.6 m/US gal, 10.4 l x 100 km.

CHASSIS integral; front suspension: independent, wishbones, coil springs, telescopic dampers, anti-roll bar; rear suspension: rigid axle, trailing lower radius arms, upper transverse Vee radius arm, coil springs, telescopic dampers, anti-roll bar.

STEERING recirculating ball or worm and roller; turns of steering wheel lock to lock: 3.70.

BRAKES disc, dual circuit, rear compensator, servo; area rubbed by linings: front 184.5 sq in, 1,190 sq cm, rear 167.1 sq in, 1,078 sq cm, total 351.6 sq in, 2,268 sq cm.

ELECTRICAL EQUIPMENT voltage: 12 V; battery: 50 Ah; generator type: alternator, 420 W; ignition distributor: Bosch or Marelli; headlamps: 4.

DIMENSIONS AND WEIGHT wheel base: 98.82 in, 2,510 mm; front track: 52.13 in, 1,324 mm; rear track: 50.16 in, 1,274 mm; overall length: 163.78 in, 4,160 mm; overall width: 61.42 in, 1,560 mm; overall height: 56.30 in, 1,430 mm; ground clearance: 4.72 in, 120 mm; dry weight: 2,293 lb, 1,040 kg; turning circle (between walls): 35.8 ft, 10.9 m; fuel tank capacity: 10.1 imp gal, 12.1 US gal, 46 l.

BODY saloon/sedan; doors: 4; seats: 5; front seats: separate, reclining backrests.

PRACTICAL NSTRUCTIONS fuel: 98-100 oct petrol; engine sump oil: 11.8 imp pt, 14.2 US pt, 6.7 l, SAE 20W-40, change every 3,700 miles, 6,000 km; gearbox oil: 3.2 imp pt, 3.8 US pt, 1.8 l, SAE 90 EP, change every 11,200 miles, 18,000 km; final drive oil: 2.5 imp pt, 3 US pt, 1.4 l, SAE 90 EP, change every 11,200 miles, 18,000 km; greasing: every 7,400 miles, 12,000 km, 1 point; tappet clearances: inlet 0.019-0.020 in, 0.48-0.50 mm, exhaust 0.021-0.22 in, 0.53-0.55 mm; valve timing: inlet opens 36°50', before tdc and closes 60°30' after bdc, exhaust opens 54°10' before bdc and closes 29°50' after tdc; normal tyre pressure: front 23 psi, 1.6 atm, rear 24 psi, 1.7 atm.

OPTIONAL ACCESSORIES 165 x 14 tyres, 5'' wheels.

1750 Berlina

PRICE IN GB: £ 1,480.
PRICE IN USA: $ 3,595.

ENGINE front, 4 stroke; cylinders: 4, vertical, in line; bore and stroke: 3.15 x 3.48 in, 80 x 88.5 mm; engine capacity: 108.6 cu in, 1,779 cu cm; compression ratio: 9; max power (SAE): 132 hp at 5,500 rpm; max torque (SAE): 138 lb ft, 19 kg m at 3,000 rpm; max engine rpm: 5,500; specific power: 74.2 hp/l; cylinder block: light alloy, wet liners; cylinder head: light alloy, hemispherical combustion chambers; crankshaft bearings: 5; valves: 2 per cylinder, overhead, Vee-slanted at 80°, thimble tappets; camshafts: 2, overhead; lubrication: gear pump, full flow filter (cartridge); lubricating system capacity: 12.7 imp pt, 15.2 US pt, 7.2 l; carburation: 2 Weber 40 DCOE 32 horizontal twin barrel carburettors; fuel feed: mechanical pump; cooling system: liquid, sealed circuit; cooling system capacity: 17.1 imp pt, 20.5 US pt, 9.7 l.

TRANSMISSION driving wheels: rear; clutch: single dry plate (diaphragm), hydraulically controlled; gearbox: me-

ALFA ROMEO 1750 Berlina

ALFA ROMEO 1750 Spider Veloce

ALFA ROMEO Montreal

chanical; gears: 5 + reverse; synchromesh gears: I, II, III, IV, V; gearbox ratios: I 3.300, II 1.990, III 1.350, IV 1, V 0.790, rev 3.010; gear lever: central; final drive: hypoid bevel; axle ratio: 4.300; width of rims: 5.5''; tyres: 165 x 14.

PERFORMANCE max speeds: 28 mph, 45 km/h in 1st gear; 46 mph, 74 km/h in 2nd gear; 68 mph, 109 km/h in 3rd gear; 91 mph, 146 km/h in 4th gear; 112 mph, 180 km/h in 5th gear; power-weight ratio: 18.5 lb/hp, 8.4 kg/hp; carrying capacity: 882 lb, 400 kg; acceleration: standing ¼ mile 18.3 sec; speed in top at 1,000 rpm: 20.9 mph, 33.7 km/h; fuel consumption: 24.4 m/imp gal, 20.3 m/US gal, 11.6 l x 100 km.

CHASSIS integral; front suspension: independent, wishbones (lower trailing links), coil springs, anti-roll bar, telescopic dampers; rear suspension: rigid axle, trailing lower radius arms, upper transverse Vee radius arm, coil springs, anti-roll bar, telescopic dampers.

STEERING recirculating ball or worm and roller; turns of steering wheel lock to lock: 3.70.

BRAKES disc (front diameter 10.71 in, 272 mm, rear 10.51 in, 267 mm), dual circuit, rear compensator, servo; area rubbed by linings: front 229.8 sq in, 1,482 sq cm, rear 167.1 sq in, 1,078 sq cm, total 396.9 sq in, 2,560 sq cm.

ELECTRICAL EQUIPMENT voltage: 12 V; battery: 50 Ah; generator type: alternator, 420 W; headlamps: 4, iodine.

DIMENSIONS AND WEIGHT wheel base: 101.18 in, 2,570 mm; front track: 52.13 in, 1,324 mm; rear track: 50.16 in, 1,274 mm; overall length: 172.83 in, 4,390 mm; overall width: 61.61 in, 1,565 mm; overall height: 56.30 in, 1,430 mm; ground clearance: 4.72 in, 120 mm; dry weight: 2,448 lb, 1,110 kg; distribution of weight: 55.9% front axle, 44.1% rear axle; turning circle (between walls): 36.4 ft, 11.1 m; fuel tank capacity: 10.1 imp gal, 12.1 US gal, 46 l.

BODY saloon/sedan; doors: 4; seats: 5; front seats: separate, reclining backrests.

PRACTICAL INSTRUCTIONS fuel: 98-100 oct petrol; engine sump oil: 11.8 imp pt, 14.2 US pt, 6.7 l, SAE 20W-40, change every 3,700 miles, 6,000 km; gearbox oil: 3.2 imp pt, 3.8 US pt, 1.8 l, SAE 90 EP, change every 11,200 miles, 18,000 km; final drive oil: 2.5 imp pt, 3 US pt, 1.4 l, SAE 90 EP, change every 11,200 miles, 18,000 km; greasing: every 7,400 miles, 12,000 km, 1 point; tappet clearances: inlet 0.019-0.020 in, 0.48-0.50 mm, exhaust 0.021-0.024 in, 0.53-0.55 mm; valve timing: inlet opens 41°20' before tdc and closes 60°20' after bdc, exhaust opens 54°40' after bdc and closes 34°40' after tdc; normal tyre pressure: front 24 psi, 1.7 atm, rear 26 psi, 1.8 atm.

VARIATIONS

ENGINE with Spica injection pump (only for USA).

OPTIONAL ACCESSORIES electrically-heated rear window.

1750 GT Veloce

See 1750 Berlina, except for:

PRICE IN GB: £ 1,860.
PRICE IN USA: $ 4,546.

TRANSMISSION axle ratio: 4.100; tyres: 165 HR x 14.

PERFORMANCE max speeds: 29 mph, 47 km/h in 1st gear; 48 mph, 77 km/h in 2nd gear; 71 mph, 114 km/h in 3rd gear; 96 mph, 154 km/h in 4th gear; 118 mph, 190 km/h in 5th gear; power-weight ratio: 17.4 lb/hp, 7.9 kg/hp; carrying capacity: 706 lb, 320 kg; acceleration: standing ¼ mile 17.5 sec; speed in top at 1,000 rpm: 22 mph, 35.4 km/h; fuel consumption: 24.8 m/imp gal, 20.6 m/US gal, 11.4 l x 100 km.

DIMENSIONS AND WEIGHT wheel base: 92.52 in, 2,350 mm; overall length: 161.42 in, 4,100 mm; overall width: 62.20 in, 1,580 mm; overall height: 51.77 in, 1,315 mm; dry weight: 2,293 lb, 1,040 kg; distribution of weight: 55.3% front axle, 44.7% rear axle; turning circle (between walls): 34.4 ft, 10.5 m.

BODY coupé; doors: 2; seats: 4; details: electrically-heated rear window (standard).

1750 Spider Veloce

See 1750 GT Veloce, except for:

PRICE IN GB: £ 1,683.
PRICE IN USA: $ 4,298.

ELECTRICAL EQUIPMENT headlamps: 2.

DIMENSIONS AND WEIGHT wheel base: 88.58 in, 2,250 mm;

ALFA ROMEO 1750 Berlina

ALFA ROMEO 1750 Spider Veloce

ALFA ROMEO Montreal

overall length: 162.20 in, 4,120 mm; overall width: 64.17 in, 1,630 mm; overall height: 50.79 in, 1,290 mm; distribution of weight: 57.7% front axle, 42.3% rear axle.

BODY convertible; seats: 2 + 2.

OPTIONAL ACCESSORIES hardtop; headrests.

Montreal

PRICE EX WORKS: —

ENGINE front, 4 stroke; cylinders: 8, Vee-slanted at 90°; bore and stroke: 3.15 x 2.54 in, 80 x 64.5 mm; engine capacity: 158.2 cu in, 2,593 cu cm; compression ratio: 9; max power (SAE): 230 hp at 6,500 rpm; max torque (SAE): 199 lb ft, 27.5 kg m at 4,750 rpm; max engine rpm: 6,500; specific power: 88.7 hp/l; cylinder block: light alloy, wet liners; cylinder head: light alloy, hemispherical combustion chambers; crankshaft bearings: 5; valves: 2 per cylinder, overhead, Vee-slanted, thimble tappets; camshafts: 2 per cylinder block, overhead; lubrication: gear pump, separate oil tank, full flow filter, dry sump, oil cooler; lubricating system capacity: 21.3 imp pt, 25.6 US pt, 12.1 l; carburation: Spica injection pump, injectors in inlet pipes; fuel feed: 2 electric pumps; cooling system: liquid, sealed circuit, electric thermostatic fan; cooling system capacity: 11.1 imp pt, 13.3 US pt, 6.3 l.

TRANSMISSION driving wheels: rear; clutch: single dry plate (diaphragm), hydraulically controlled; gearbox: mechanical; gears: 5 + reverse; synchromesh gears: I, II, III, IV, V; gearbox ratios: I 2.990, II 1.760, III 1.300, IV 1, V 0.870, rev 3.640; gear lever: central; final drive: hypoid bevel, limited slip; axle ratio: 4.100; width of rims: 6.5''; tyres: 195/70 VR x 14.

PERFORMANCE max speeds: 38 mph, 61 km/h in 1st gear; 64 mph, 103 km/h in 2nd gear; 87 mph, 140 km/h in 3rd gear; 113 mph, 182 km/h in 4th gear; 137 mph, 220 km/h in 5th gear; power-weight ratio: 12.1 lb/hp, 5.5 kg/hp; carrying capacity: 706 lb, 320 kg; acceleration: standing ¼ mile 16 sec; speed in top at 1,000 rpm: 20 mph, 32.2 km/h; fuel consumption: not declared.

CHASSIS integral; front suspension: independent, wishbones, coil springs, telescopic dampers, anti-roll bar; rear suspension: rigid axle, trailing lower radius arms, upper transverse Vee radius arm, coil springs, telescopic dampers, anti-roll bar.

STEERING recirculating ball; turns of steering wheel lock to lock: 3.70.

BRAKES disc, internal radial fins, dual circuit, rear compensator, servo; area rubbed by linings: total 425.1 sq in, 2,742 sq cm.

ELECTRICAL EQUIPMENT voltage: 12 V; battery: 64 Ah; generator type: alternator, 720 W; headlamps: 4.

DIMENSIONS AND WEIGHT wheel base: 92.52 in, 2,350 mm; front track: 54.09 in, 1,374 mm; rear track: 52.76 in, 1,340 mm; overall length: 166.14 in, 4,220 mm; overall width: 65.83 in, 1,672 mm; overall height: 47.44 in, 1,205 mm; ground clearance: 4.72 in, 120 mm; dry weight: 2,800 lb, 1,270 kg; turning circle (between walls): 36.1 ft, 11 m; fuel tank capacity: 13.9 imp gal, 16.6 US gal, 63 l.

BODY coupé; doors: 2; seats: 2 + 2; front seats: separate, adjustable backrests; details: electrically-heated rear window.

PRACTICAL INSTRUCTIONS fuel: 98-100 oct petrol; engine sump oil: 17.4 imp pt, 20.9 US pt, 9.9 l, SAE 20W-30, change every 3,700 miles, 6,000 km; gearbox oil: 3.2 imp pt, 3.8 US pt, 1.8 l, T 30 HD, change every 11,200 miles, 18,000 km; final drive oil: 2.5 imp pt, 3 US pt, 1.4 l, 90 HD, change every 11,200 miles, 18,000 km; greasing: every 7,400 miles, 12,000 km, 1 point; tappet clearances: inlet 0.019-0.020 in, 0.48-0.50 mm, exhaust 0.021-0.022 in, 0.53-0.55 mm; normal tyre pressure: front 31 psi, 2.2 atm, rear 28 psi, 2 atm.

AUTOBIANCHI   **ITALY**

Bianchina Giardiniera

PRICE IN GB: £ 442.
PRICE EX WORKS: 660,000 liras.

ENGINE rear, 4 stroke; cylinders: 2, horizontal, in line; bore and stroke: 2.65 x 2.76 in, 67.4 x 70 mm; engine capacity: 30.4 cu in, 499 cu cm; compression ratio: 7.1; max power (DIN): 17.5 hp at 4,600 rpm; max torque (DIN): 22 lb ft, 3 kg m at 3,200 rpm; specific power: 35.1 hp/l; cylinder block: cast iron; cylinder head: light alloy; crankshaft bearings: 2; valves: 2 per cylinder, in line, push-rods and rockers; camshafts: 1, side; lubrication: gear pump, centrifugal filter; lubricating system capacity: 4.4 imp pt, 5.3 US pt,

BIANCHINA GIARDINIERA

2.5 l; carburation: 1 Weber 26 OC horizontal single barrel carburettor; fuel feed: mechanical pump; cooling system: air cooled.

TRANSMISSION driving wheels: rear; clutch: single dry plate; gearbox: mechanical; gears: 4 + reverse; silent claw coupling gears: II, III, IV; gearbox ratios: I 3.700, II 2.066, III 1.300, IV 0.875, rev 5.140; gear lever: central; final drive: hypoid bevel; axle ratio: 5.125; width of rims: 3.5''; tyres: 125 x 12.

PERFORMANCE max speeds: 14 mph, 23 km/h in 1st gear; 25 mph, 40 km/h in 2nd gear; 40 mph, 65 km/h in 3rd gear; over 59 mph, 95 km/h in 4th gear; power-weight ratio: 67.5 lb/hp, 30.6 kg/hp; carrying capacity: 706 lb, 320 kg; max gradient in 1st gear: 22%; acceleration: standing ¼ mile 30.8 sec, 0-50 mph (0-80 km/h) 40 sec; speed in top at 1,000 rpm: 12.9 mph, 20.7 km/h; fuel consumption: 54.3 m/imp gal, 45.2 m/US gal, 5.2 l x 100 km.

CHASSIS integral; front suspension: independent, wishbones, transverse leafspring lower arms, telescopic dampers; rear suspension: independent, oblique semi-trailing arms, coil springs, telescopic dampers.

STEERING screw and sector; turns of steering wheel lock to lock: 3.

BRAKES drum; lining area: front 33.5 sq in, 216 sq cm, rear 33.5 sq in, 216 sq cm, total 67 sq in, 432 sq cm

ELECTRICAL EQUIPMENT voltage: 12 V; battery: 32 Ah; generator type: dynamo, 230 W; ignition distributor: Marelli; headlamps: 2.

DIMENSIONS AND WEIGHT wheel base: 76.38 in, 1,940 mm; front track: 44.53 in, 1,131 mm; rear track: 44.53 in, 1,131 mm; overall length: 125.39 in, 3,185 mm; overall width: 51.97 in, 1,320 mm; overall height: 53.31 in, 1,354 mm; ground clearance: 5.31 in, 135 mm; dry weight: 1,180 lb, 535 kg; distribution of weight: 40% front axle, 60% rear axle; turning circle (between walls): 28.2 ft, 8.6 m; fuel tank capacity: 4.8 imp gal, 5.8 US gal, 22 l.

BODY estate car/station wagon; doors: 2 + 1; seats: 4; front seats: separate; details: sunshine roof.

PRACTICAL INSTRUCTIONS fuel: 80-85 oct petrol; engine sump oil: 4.4 imp pt, 5.3 US pt, 2.5 l, SAE 10W (winter) 40 (summer), change every 6,200 miles, 10,000 km; gearbox and final drive oil: 1.9 imp pt, 2.3 US pt, 1.1 l, W90/M, change every 18,600 miles, 30,000 km; greasing: every 1,600 miles, 2,500 km, 2 points; sparking plug type: 260°; tappet clearances: inlet 0.006 in, 0.15 mm, exhaust 0.006 in, 0.15 mm; valve timing: inlet opens 25° before tdc and closes 51° after bdc, exhaust opens 64° before bdc and closes 12° after tdc; normal tyre pressure: front 17 psi, 1.2 atm, rear 27 psi, 1.9 atm.

OPTIONAL ACCESSORIES reclining backrests.

A 112 Berlina

PRICE EX WORKS: 980,000 liras.

ENGINE front, transverse, 4 stroke; cylinders: 4, in line; bore and stroke: 2.56 x 2.68 in, 65 x 68 mm; engine capacity: 55.1 cu in, 903 cu cm; compression ratio: 9; max power (DIN): 44 hp at 5,600 rpm; max torque (DIN): 46 lb ft, 6.3 kg m at 3,800 rpm; specific power: 48.7 hp/l; cylinder block: cast iron; cylinder head: light alloy; crankshaft bearings: 3; valves: 2 per cylinder, overhead, push-rods and rockers; camshafts: 1, side; lubrication: gear pump, centrifugal filter; lubricating system capacity: 6.5 imp pt, 7.8 US pt, 3.7 l; carburation: 1 Weber 32 IBA downdraught carburettor; fuel feed: mechanical pump; cooling system: water, electric thermostatic fan; cooling system capacity: 8.8 imp pt, 10.6 US pt, 5 l.

TRANSMISSION driving wheels: front; clutch: single dry plate; gearbox: mechanical; gears: 4 + reverse; synchromesh gears: I, II, III, IV; gearbox ratios: I 3.636, II 2.055, III 1.409, IV 0.963, rev 3.615; gear lever: central; final drive: cylindrical gears; axle ratio: 4.692; width of rims: 4''; tyres: 135 x 13.

PERFORMANCE max speeds: 25 mph, 40 km/h in 1st gear; 43 mph, 70 km/h in 2nd gear; 62 mph, 100 km/h in 3rd gear; over 84 mph, 135 km/h in 4th gear; power-weight ratio: 32 lb/hp, 14.5 kg/hp; carrying capacity: 816 lb, 370 kg; max gradient in 1st gear: 32%; speed in top at 1,000 rpm: 13.8 mph, 22.2 km/h; fuel consumption: 40.9 m/imp gal, 34.1 m/US gal, 6.9 l x 100 km.

CHASSIS integral; front suspension: independent, by McPherson, coil springs/telescopic damper struts, lower wishbones (trailing links), anti-roll bar; rear suspension: independent, wishbones, transverse leafspring, lower arms, telescopic dampers.

AUTOBIANCHI A 112 Berlina

AUTOBIANCHI A 111 Berlina

DE TOMASO Deauville 4-door

STEERING rack-and-pinion; turns of steering wheel lock to lock: 3.40.

BRAKES front disc, rear drum; lining area: front 22.5 sq in, 145 sq cm, rear 33.5 sq in, 216 sq cm, total 56 sq in, 361 sq cm.

ELECTRICAL EQUIPMENT voltage: 12 V; battery: 34 Ah; generator type: dynamo, 230 W; ignition distributor: Marelli; headlamps: 2.

DIMENSIONS AND WEIGHT wheel base: 80.24 in, 2,038 mm; front track: 49.21 in, 1,250 mm; rear track: 48.19 in, 1,224 mm; overall length: 127.20 in, 3,231 mm; overall width: 58.27 in, 1,480 mm; overall height: 50.79 in, 1,290 mm; ground clearance: 5.59 in, 142 mm; dry weight: 1,411 lb, 640 kg; distribution of weight: 47% front axle, 53% rear axle; turning circle (between walls): 29.2 ft, 8.9 m; fuel tank capacity: 6.6 imp gal, 7.9 US gal, 30 l.

BODY saloon/sedan; doors: 2 + 1; seats: 4; front seats: separate, reclining backrests.

PRACTICAL INSTRUCTIONS fuel: 98 oct petrol; engine sump oil: 6.5 imp pt, 7.8 US pt, 3.7 l, SAE 10W-40, change every 6,200 miles, 10,000 km; gearbox and final drive oil: 4 imp pt, 4.9 US pt, 2.3 l, SAE 90, change every 18,600 miles, 30,000 km; greasing: none; tappet clearances: inlet 0.006 in, 0.15 mm, exhaust 0.008 in, 0.20 mm; valve timing: inlet opens 25° before tdc and closes 51° after bdc, exhaust opens 64° before bdc and closes 12° after tdc; normal tyre pressure: front 24 psi, 1.7 atm, rear 27 psi, 1.9 atm.

OPTIONAL ACCESSORIES rev counter.

A 111 Berlina

PRICE EX WORKS: 1,440,000 liras.

ENGINE front, transverse, 4 stroke; cylinders: 4, in line; bore and stroke: 3.15 x 2.81 in, 80 x 71.5 mm; engine capacity: 87.7 cu in, 1,438 cu cm; compression ratio: 9.3; max power (DIN): 70 hp at 5,400 rpm; max torque (DIN): 80 lb ft, 11 kg m at 3,000 rpm; specific power: 48.7 hp/l; cylinder block: cast iron; cylinder head: light alloy; crankshaft bearings: 5; valves: 2 per cylinder, overhead, in line, push-rods and rockers; camshafts: 1, side; lubrication: gear pump, filter on by-pass; lubricating system capacity: 6.5 imp pt, 7.8 US pt, 3.7 l; carburation: 1 Weber 32 DFB downdraught twin barrel carburettor; fuel feed: mechanical pump; cooling system: water, electric thermostatic fan; cooling system capacity: 12.3 imp pt, 14.8 US pt, 7 l.

TRANSMISSION driving wheels: front; clutch: single dry plate, hydraulically controlled; gearbox: mechanical; gears: 4 + reverse; synchromesh gears: I, II, III, IV; gearbox ratios: I 3.585, II 2.310, III 1.525, IV 1.042, rev 3.570; gear lever: central; final drive: cylindrical gears; axle ratio: 3.846; width of rims: 4.5''; tyres: 150 x 13.

PERFORMANCE max speeds: 28 mph, 45 km/h in 1st gear; 43 mph, 70 km/h in 2nd gear; 65 mph, 105 km/h in 3rd gear; 96 mph, 155 km/h in 4th gear; power-weight ratio: 28.4 lb/hp, 12.9 kg/hp; carrying capacity: 882 lb, 400 kg; max gradient in 1st gear: 38%; speed in top at 1,000 rpm: 16 mph, 25.8 km/h; fuel consumption: 33.2 m/imp gal, 27.7 m/US gal, 8.5 l x 100 km.

CHASSIS integral; front suspension: independent, wishbones, transverse leafspring upper arms, telescopic dampers; rear suspension: rigid axle, semi-elliptic leafsprings, telescopic dampers.

STEERING rack-and-pinion; turns of steering wheel lock to lock: 3.50.

BRAKES disc, dual circuit, rear compensator, servo; lining area: front 19.2 sq in, 124 sq cm, rear 19.2 sq in, 124 sq cm, total 38.4 sq in, 248 sq cm.

ELECTRICAL EQUIPMENT voltage: 12 V; battery: 45 Ah; generator type: alternator, 770 W; ignition distributor: Marelli; headlamps: 2.

DIMENSIONS AND WEIGHT wheel base: 93.03 in, 2,363 mm; front track: 53.54 in, 1,360 mm; rear track: 51.18 in, 1,300 mm; overall length: 155.91 in, 3,960 mm; overall width: 55.51 in, 1,610 mm; overall height: 56.30 in, 1,430 mm; ground clearance: 4.80 in, 122 mm; dry weight: 1,985 lb, 900 kg; distribution of weight: 60% front axle, 40% rear axle; turning circle (between walls): 34.1 ft, 10.4 m; fuel tank capacity: 8.6 imp gal, 10.3 US gal, 39 l.

BODY saloon/sedan; doors: 4; seats: 5; front seats: separate.

PRACTICAL INSTRUCTIONS fuel: 98 oct petrol; engine sump oil: 6.5 imp pt, 7.8 US pt, 3.7 l, SAE 10W-40, change every 6,200 miles, 10,000 km; gearbox and final drive oil: 3.5 imp pt, 4.2 US pt, 2 l, SAE 90 EP, change every 18,600 miles, 30,000 km; greasing: every 12,400 miles, 20,000 km, 2 points; tappet clearances: inlet 0.008 in, 0.20 mm, exhaust 0.008 in, 0.20 mm; valve timing: inlet opens 10° before tdc and closes 49° after bdc, exhaust opens 50° before bdc and closes 9° after tdc; normal tyre pressure: front 26 psi, 1.8 atm, rear 24 psi, 1.7 atm.

OPTIONAL ACCESSORIES electrically-heated rear window.

AUTOBIANCHI A 112 Berlina

DE TOMASO   ITALY

Deauville 4-door

PRICE EX WORKS: —

ENGINE front, 4 stroke; cylinders: 8, Vee-slanted at 90°; bore and stroke: 4 x 2.87 in, 101.6 x 72.9 mm; engine capacity: 228.6 cu in, 4,729 cu cm; compression ratio: 9.8; max power (DIN): 335 hp at 6,000 rpm; max torque (DIN): 351 lb ft, 48.5 kg m at 4,000 rpm; max engine rpm: 6,500; specific power: 70.8 hp/l; cylinder block: cast iron; cylinder head: cast iron; crankshaft bearings: 5; valves: 2 per cylinder, overhead, rockers; camshafts 2, overhead; lubrication: rotary pump, full flow filter; lubricating system capacity: 7.9 imp pt, 9.5 US pt, 4.5 l; carburation: 4 twin barrel carburettors; fuel feed: mechanical pump; cooling system: water; cooling system capacity: 35.2 imp pt, 42.3 US pt, 20 l.

TRANSMISSION driving wheels: rear; gearbox: Select Shift Cruise-o-Matic automatic, hydraulic torque convertor and planetary gears with 3 ratios + reverse, max ratio of convertor at stall 2.05, possible manual selection; gearbox ratios: I 2.460, II 1.460, III 1, rev 2.175; selector lever: central; final drive: hypoid bevel; axle ratio: not declared; width of rims: 7''; tyres: GR 70 VR x 15.

PERFORMANCE max speeds: 58 mph, 93 km/h in 1st gear; 98 mph, 157 km/h in 2nd gear; over 143 mph, 230 km/h in 3rd gear; carrying capacity: 882 lb, 400 kg; speed in direct drive at 1,000 rpm: 22 mph, 35.4 km/h; fuel consumption: 15.7 m/imp gal, 13.1 m/US gal, 18 l x 100 km.

CHASSIS integral; front suspension: independent, wishbones, coil springs, anti-roll bar, telescopic dampers; rear suspension: independent, wishbones, 4 coil springs, anti-roll bar, 4 telescopic dampers.

STEERING rack-and-pinion, servo.

BRAKES disc, internal radial fins, dual circuit, servo.

ELECTRICAL EQUIPMENT voltage: 12 V; battery: 60 Ah; generator type: alternator, 600 W; ignition distributor: Ford; headlamps: 4.

DIMENSIONS AND WEIGHT wheel base: 109.05 in, 2,770 mm; front track: 59.84 in, 1,520 mm; rear track: 59.84 in, 1,520 mm; overall length: 191.14 in, 4,855 mm; overall width: 73.82 in, 1,875 mm; overall height: 52.76 in, 1,340 mm; ground clearance: 4.72 in, 120 mm; dry weight: not declared; fuel tank capacity: not declared.

BODY saloon/sedan; doors: 4; seats: 5; front seats: separate, reclining backrests.

VARIATIONS

ENGINE bore and stroke 4 x 3.50 in, 101.6 x 88.9 mm, engine capacity 351.6 cu in, 5,762 cu cm, 10 compression ratio, max power (DIN) 370 hp at 6,000 rpm, max torque (DIN) 380 lb ft, 52.5 kg m at 4,000 rpm, 64.2 hp/l specific power.

AUTOBIANCHI A 111 Berlina

Mangusta

PRICE EX WORKS: 6,845,000 liras.

ENGINE rear, 4 stroke; cylinders: 8, Vee-slanted at 90°; bore and stroke: 4 x 3 in, 101.6 x 76.2 mm; engine capacity: 301.3 cu in, 4,937 cu cm; compression ratio: 9.5; max power (DIN): 305 hp at 6,200 rpm; max torque (DIN): 411 lb ft, 56.7 kg m at 3,500 rpm; max engine rpm: 6,500; specific power: 61.8 hp/l; cylinder block: cast iron; cylinder head: cast iron; crankshaft bearings: 5; valves: 2 per cylinder, overhead, slanted, push-rods and rockers; camshafts: 1, at centre of Vee; lubrication: rotary pump, full flow filter; lubricating system capacity: 7.9 imp pt, 9.5 US pt, 4.5 l; carburation: 1 Autolite 4-barrel carburettor; fuel feed: mechanical pump; cooling system: water; cooling system capacity: 35.2 imp pt, 42.3 US pt, 20 l.

TRANSMISSION driving wheels: rear; clutch: single dry plate; gearbox: mechanical; gears: 5 + reverse; synchromesh gears: I, II, III, IV, V, rev; gearbox ratios: I 2.420, II 1.470, III 1.090, IV 0.960, V 0.840, rev 3.750; gear lever: central; final drive: spiral bevel, limited slip; axle ratio: 4.220; width of rims: 7'' front, 8'' rear; tyres: 185 x 15 front, 225 x 15 rear.

PERFORMANCE max speeds: 54 mph, 87 km/h in 1st gear;

DE TOMASO Deauville 4-door

MANGUSTA

89 mph, 143 km/h in 2nd gear; 120 mph, 193 km/h in 3rd gear; 137 mph, 220 km/h in 4th gear; 155 mph, 250 km/h in 5th gear; power-weight ratio: 8.6 lb/hp, 3.9 kg/hp; carrying capacity: 353 lb, 160 kg; fuel consumption: 17.7 m/imp gal, 14.7 m/US gal, 16 l x 100 km.

CHASSIS backbone; front suspension: independent, wishbones, coil springs, anti-roll bar, telescopic dampers; rear suspension: independent, wishbones, coil springs, anti-roll bar, telescopic dampers.

STEERING rack-and-pinion; turns of steering wheel lock to lock: 3.50.

BRAKES disc, dual circuit, servo; lining area: front 11.3 sq in, 73 sq cm, rear 7.6 sq in, 49 sq cm, total 18.9 sq in, 122 sq cm.

ELECTRICAL EQUIPMENT voltage: 12 V; battery: 60 Ah; generator type: alternator, 600 W; ignition distributor: Ford; headlamps: 4.

DIMENSIONS AND WEIGHT wheel base: 98.43 in, 2,500 mm; front track: 54.92 in, 1,395 mm; rear track: 57.09 in, 1,450 mm; overall length: 168.31 in, 4,275 mm; overall width: 72.05 in, 1,830 mm; overall height: 43.31 in, 1,100 mm; ground clearance: 4.72 in, 120 mm; dry weight: 2,613 lb, 1,185 kg; distribution of weight: 44% front axle, 56% rear axle; fuel tank capacity: 20.9 imp gal, 25.1 US gal, 95 l.

BODY coupé; doors: 2; seats: 2; details: electrically-controlled windows, air-conditioning system.

PRACTICAL INSTRUCTIONS fuel: 98-100 oct petrol; engine sump oil: 7.9 imp pt, 9.5 US pt, 4.5 l, SAE 20W-40, change every 3,100 miles, 5,000 km; gearbox and final drive oil: 4.4 imp pt, 5.3 US pt, 2.5 l, change every 12,400 miles, 20,000 km; greasing: every 1,200 miles, 2,000 km, 4 points; normal tyre pressure: front 30 psi, 2.1 atm, rear 33 psi, 2.3 atm.

OPTIONAL ACCESSORIES electrically-heated rear window.

FERRARI ITALY

Dino 246 GT

PRICE EX WORKS: 5,500,000 liras.

ENGINE rear, transverse, 4 stroke; cylinders: 6, Vee-slanted at 65°; bore and stroke: 3.64 x 2.36 in, 92.5 x 60 mm; engine capacity: 147.5 cu in, 2,418 cu cm; compression ratio: 9; max power (DIN): 195 hp at 7,600 rpm; max torque (DIN): 167 lb ft, 23 kg m at 5,500 rpm; max engine rpm: 7,600; specific power: 80.6 hp/l; cylinder block: cast iron; cylinder head: light alloy, hemispherical combustion chambers; crankshaft bearings: 4; valves: 2 per cylinder, overhead, Vee-slanted, thimble tappets; camshafts: 2 per cylinder block, overhead; lubrication: gear pump, cartridge; lubricating system capacity: 11.4 imp pt, 13.7 US pt, 6.5 l; carburation: 3 Weber 40 DCNF-6 downdraught twin barrel carburettors; fuel feed: 2 electric pumps; cooling system: water, electric automatic fan; cooling system capacity: 21.1 imp pt, 25.4 US pt, 12 l.

TRANSMISSION driving wheels: rear; clutch: single dry plate; gearbox: mechanical; gears: 5 + reverse, synchromesh gears: I, II, III, IV, V; gearbox ratios: I 3.760, II 2.590, III 1.863, IV 1.376, V 1.046, rev 3.255; gear lever: central; final drive: spiral bevel, limited slip; axle ratio: 3.625; width of rims: 6.5''; tyres: 205 x 14.

PERFORMANCE max speeds: 40 mph, 65 km/h in 1st gear; 59 mph, 95 km/h in 2nd gear; 82 mph, 132 km/h in 3rd gear; 111 mph, 179 km/h in 4th gear; 146 mph, 235 km/h in 5th gear; power-weight ratio: 12.1 lb/hp, 5.5 kg/hp; carrying capacity: 353 lb, 160 kg; speed in top at 1,000 rpm: 19 mph, 30.5 km/h; fuel consumption: 21.7 m/imp gal, 18.1 m/US gal, 13 l x 100 km.

CHASSIS tubular; front suspension: independent, wishbones, anti-roll bar, coil springs/telescopic dampers; rear suspension: independent, wishbones, anti-roll bar, coil springs/telescopic dampers.

STEERING rack-and-pinion; turns of steering wheel lock to lock: 3.20.

BRAKES disc, dual circuit, compensator, servo; lining area: front 25.4 sq in, 164 sq cm, 16.1 sq in, 104 sq cm, total 41.5 sq in, 268 sq cm.

ELECTRICAL EQUIPMENT voltage: 12 V; battery: 60 Ah; generator type: alternator, 720 W; ignition distributor: Marelli; headlamps: 2, iodine.

DIMENSIONS AND WEIGHT wheel base: 88.19 in, 2,340 mm;

DE TOMASO Mangusta

FERRARI Dino 246 GT

FERRARI 365 GT 2 + 2

front track: 56.10 in, 1,425 mm; rear track: 56.30 in, 1,430 mm; overall length: 163.39 in, 4,150 mm; overall width: 66.93 in, 1,700 mm; overall height: 43.90 in, 1,115 mm; ground clearance: 4.72 in, 120 mm; dry weight: 2,381 lb, 1,080 kg; turning circle (between walls): 43.3 ft, 13.2 m; fuel tank capacity: 14.3 imp gal, 17.2 US gal, 65 l.

BODY coupé; doors: 2; seats: 2.

PRACTICAL INSTRUCTIONS fuel: 98-100 oct petrol; engine sump oil: 11.4 imp pt, 13.7 US pt, 6.5 l, SAE 20W-40, change every 6,200 miles, 10,000 km; gearbox and final drive oil: 7 imp pt, 8.5 US pt, 4 l, change every 6,200 miles, 10,000 km; greasing: every 3,100 miles, 5,000 km, 4 points; tappet clearances: inlet 0.020 in, 0.50 mm, exhaust 0.020 in, 0.50 mm; normal tyre pressure: front 27 psi, 1.9 atm, rear 31 psi, 2.2 atm.

365 GT 2 + 2

PRICE IN GB: £ 6,700.
PRICE IN USA: $ 21,700.

ENGINE front, 4 stroke; cylinders: 12, Vee-slanted at 60°; bore and stroke: 3.19 x 2.80 in, 81 x 71 mm; engine capacity: 267.9 cu in, 4,390 cu cm; compression ratio: 8.8; max power (DIN): 320 hp at 6,600 rpm; max torque (DIN): 268 lb ft, 37 kg m at 5,000 rpm; max engine rpm: 6,600; specific power: 72.9 hp/l; cylinder block: light alloy; cylinder head: light alloy, hemispherical combustion chambers; crankshaft bearings: 7; valves: 2 per cylinder, overhead, Vee-slanted at 54°, roller rockers; camshafts: 1 per cylinder block, overhead; lubrication: gear pump, cartridge; lubricating system capacity: 17.6 imp pt, 21.1 US pt, 10 l; carburation: 3 Weber 40 DFI downdraught twin barrel carburettors; fuel feed: mechanical and electric pump; cooling system: water, electric automatic fans; cooling system capacity: 24.6 imp pt, 29.6 US pt, 14 l.

TRANSMISSION driving wheels: rear; clutch: Borg & Beck single dry plate; gearbox: mechanical; gears: 5 + reverse; synchromesh gears: I, II, III, IV, V; gearbox ratios: I 2.536, II 1.700, III 1.256, IV 1, V 0.797, rev 3.218; gear lever: central; final drive: spiral bevel, limited slip; axle ratio: 4.250; width of rims: 7.5''; tyres: 215/70 x 15.

PERFORMANCE max speeds: 49 mph, 79 km/h in 1st gear; 73 mph, 118 km/h in 2nd gear; 99 mph, 159 km/h in 3rd gear; 124 mph, 200 km/h in 4th gear; 152 mph, 245 km/h in 5th gear; power-weight ratio: 10.6 lb/hp, 4.8 kg/hp; carrying capacity: 706 lb, 320 kg; speed in top at 1,000 rpm: 18.8 mph, 30.3 km/h; fuel consumption: 14.5 m/imp gal, 12.1 m/US gal, 19.5 l x 100 km.

CHASSIS tubular; front suspension: independent, wishbones, anti-roll bar, coil springs/telescopic dampers; rear suspension: independent, wishbones, automatic levelling control, anti-roll bar, coil springs/telescopic dampers.

STEERING recirculating ball, ZF servo; turns of steering wheel lock to lock: 3.20.

BRAKES disc (front diameter 12.36 in, 314 mm, rear 11.73 in, 298 mm), dual circuit, compensator, servo; lining area: front 37.2 sq in, 240 sq cm, rear 21.1 sq in, 136 sq cm, total 58.3 sq in, 376 sq cm.

ELECTRICAL EQUIPMENT voltage: 12 V; battery: 74 Ah; generator type: alternator, 660 W; ignition distributors: 2, Marelli; headlamps: 2, iodine.

DIMENSIONS AND WEIGHT wheel base: 104.33 in, 2,650 mm; front track: 56.61 in, 1,438 mm; rear track: 57.80 in, 1,468 mm; overall length: 196.06 in, 4,980 mm; overall width: 70.47 in, 1,790 mm; overall height: 52.95 in, 1,345 mm; ground clearance: 5.12 in, 130 mm; dry weight: 3,418 lb, 1,550 kg; turning circle (between walls): 44 ft, 13.4 m; fuel tank capacity: 22 imp gal, 26.4 US gal, 100 l.

BODY coupé; doors: 2; seats: 2 + 2; front seats: separate, reclining backrests; details: air-conditioning system and radio.

PRACTICAL INSTRUCTIONS fuel: 98-100 oct petrol; engine sump oil: 17.6 imp pt, 21.1 US pt, 10 l, SAE 20W-40, change every 6,200 miles, 10,000 km; gearbox oil: 8.8 imp pt, 10.6 US pt, 5 l, SAE 90 EP, change every 6,200 miles, 10,000 km; final drive oil: 4.4 imp pt, 5.3 US pt, 2.5 l, change every 6,200 miles, 10,000 km; greasing: every 3,100 miles, 5,000 km, 18 points; tappet clearances: inlet 0.006 in, 0.15 mm, exhaust 0.008 in, 0.20 mm; normal tyre pressure: front 27 psi, 1.9 atm, rear 33 psi, 2.3 atm.

365 GTB 4 Berlinetta

PRICE IN GB: £ 7,020.
PRICE IN USA: $ 20,500.

ENGINE front, 4 stroke; cylinders: 12, Vee-slanted at 60°; bore and stroke: 3.19 x 2.80 in, 81 x 71 mm; engine capacity: 267.9 cu in, 4,390 cu cm; compression ratio: 8.8; max power (DIN): 352 hp at 7,500 rpm; max torque (DIN): 319

DE TOMASO Mangusta

FERRARI Dino 246 GT

FERRARI 365 GT 2 + 2

lb ft, 44 kg m at 5,000 rpm; max engine rpm: 7,700; specific power: 80.2 hp/l; cylinder block: light alloy; cylinder head: light alloy, hemispherical combustion chambers; crankshaft bearings: 7; valves: 2 per cylinder, overhead, Vee-slanted at 46°, thimble tappets; camshafts: 2 per cylinder block, overhead; lubrication: gear pump, separate oil tank, cartridge, dry sump; lubricating system capacity: 26.4 imp pt, 31.7 US pt, 15 l; carburation: 6 Weber 40 DCN-20 downdraught twin barrel carburettors; fuel feed: 2 electric pumps; cooling system: water, electric automatic fans; cooling system capacity: 24.6 imp pt, 29.6 US pt, 14 l.

TRANSMISSION driving wheels: rear; clutch: Borg & Beck single dry plate; gearbox: mechanical, in unit with final drive, rear; gears: 5 + reverse; synchromesh gears: I, II, III, IV, V; gearbox ratios: I 3.075, II 2.120, III 1.572, IV 1.250, V 0.964, rev 2.675; gear lever: central; final drive: spiral bevel, limited slip; axle ratio: 3.300; width of rims: 7.5''; tyres: 215/70 x 15.

PERFORMANCE max speeds: 59 mph, 95 km/h in 1st gear; 86 mph, 139 km/h in 2nd gear; 116 mph, 187 km/h in 3rd gear; 146 mph, 235 km/h in 4th gear; 174 mph, 280 km/h in 5th gear; power-weight ratio: 7.5 lb/hp, 3.4 kg/hp; carrying capacity: 353 lb, 160 kg; speed in top at 1,000 rpm: 24.7 mph, 39.7 km/h; fuel consumption: 13.1 m/imp gal, 10.9 m/US gal, 21.5 l x 100 km.

CHASSIS tubular; front suspension: independent, wishbones, anti-roll bar, coil springs/telescopic dampers; rear suspension: independent, wishbones, coil springs/telescopic dampers.

STEERING ZF worm and roller; turns of steering wheel lock to lock: 3.50.

BRAKES disc, dual circuit, compensator, servo; lining area: front 28.8 sq in, 186 sq cm, rear 19.5 sq in, 126 sq cm, total 48.3 sq in, 312 sq cm.

ELECTRICAL EQUIPMENT voltage: 12 V; battery: 74 Ah; generator type: alternator, 660 W; ignition distributors: 2, Marelli; headlamps: 4, iodine.

DIMENSIONS AND WEIGHT wheel base: 94.49 in, 2,400 mm; front track: 56.69 in, 1,440 mm; rear track: 56.10 in, 1,425 mm; overall length: 174.21 in, 4,425 mm; overall width: 69.29 in, 1,760 mm; overall height: 49.80 in, 1,265 mm; ground clearance: 5.12 in, 130 mm; dry weight: 2,646 lb, 1,200 kg; turning circle (between walls): 44 ft, 13.4 m; fuel tank capacity: 22 imp gal, 26.4 US gal, 100 l.

BODY coupé; doors: 2; seats: 2.

PRACTICAL INSTRUCTIONS fuel: 98-100 oct petrol; engine sump oil: 26.4 imp pt, 31.7 US pt, 15 l, SAE 20W-40, change every 6,200 miles, 10,000 km; gearbox and final drive oil: 7.9 imp pt, 9.5 US pt, 4.5 l, change every 6,200 miles, 10,000 km; greasing: every 3,100 miles, 5,000 km, 8 points; tappet clearances: inlet 0.010 in, 0.25 mm, exhaust 0.010 in, 0.25 mm; normal tyre pressure: front 34 psi, 2.4 atm, rear 38 psi, 2.7 atm.

FIAT   ITALY

500 Berlina

PRICE IN GB: £ 380.
PRICE EX WORKS: 545,000 liras.

ENGINE rear, 4 stroke; cylinders: 2, vertical, in line; bore and stroke: 2.65 x 2.76 in, 67.4 x 70 mm; engine capacity: 30.4 cu in, 499 cu cm; compression ratio: 7.1; max power (DIN): 18 hp at 4,600 rpm; max torque (DIN): 22 lb ft, 3.1 kg m at 3,000 rpm; max engine rpm: 4,600; specific power: 36 hp/l; cylinder block: light alloy; cylinder head: light alloy; crankshaft bearings: 2; valves: 2 per cylinder, overhead, in line, push-rods and rockers; camshafts: 1, side; lubrication: gear pump, centrifugal filter; lubricating system capacity: 4.8 imp pt, 5.7 US pt, 2.7 l; carburation: 1 Weber 26 IMB downdraught carburettor; fuel feed: mechanical pump; cooling system: air cooled.

TRANSMISSION driving wheels: rear; clutch: single dry plate; gearbox: mechanical; gears: 4 + reverse; silent claw coupling gears: II, III, IV; gearbox ratios: I 3.700, II 2.067, III 1.300, IV 0.875, rev 5.144; gear lever: central; final drive: spiral bevel; axle ratio: 5.125; width of rims: 3.5''; tyres: 125 x 12.

PERFORMANCE max speeds: 14 mph, 23 km/h in 1st gear; 25 mph, 40 km/h in 2nd gear; 40 mph, 65 km/h in 3rd gear; 63 mph, 101 km/h in 4th gear; power-weight ratio: 63.7 lb/hp, 28.9 kg/hp; carrying capacity: 706 lb, 320 kg; max gradient in 1st gear: 26%; acceleration: standing ¼ mile 29.6 sec, 0-50 mph (0-80 km/h) 37 sec; speed in top at 1,000 rpm: 12.7 mph, 20.4 km/h; fuel consumption: 53.3 m/imp gal, 44.4 m/US gal, 5.3 l x 100 km.

CHASSIS integral; front suspension: independent, wishbones, transverse leafspring lower arms, telescopic dampers; rear

500 BERLINA

suspension: independent, oblique semi-trailing arms, coil springs, telescopic dampers.

STEERING screw and sector; turns of steering wheel lock to lock: 3.

BRAKES drum; lining area: front 33.5 sq in, 216 sq cm, rear 33.5 sq in, 216 sq cm, total 67 sq in, 432 sq cm.

ELECTRICAL EQUIPMENT voltage: 12 V; battery: 32 Ah; generator type: dynamo, 230 W; ignition distributor: Marelli; headlamps: 2.

DIMENSIONS AND WEIGHT wheel base: 72.44 in, 1,840 mm; front track: 44.13 in, 1,121 mm; rear track: 44.68 in, 1,135 mm; overall length: 116.93 in, 2,970 mm; overall width: 51.97 in, 1,320 mm; overall height: 52.17 in, 1,325 mm; ground clearance: 4.92 in, 125 mm; dry weight: 1,147 lb, 520 kg; distribution of weight: 43% front axle, 57% rear axle; turning circle (between walls): 29.8 ft, 9.1 m; fuel tank capacity: 4.8 imp gal, 5.8 US gal, 22 l.

BODY saloon/sedan; doors: 2; seats: 4; front seats: separate; details: canvas sunshine roof.

PRACTICAL INSTRUCTIONS fuel: 80-85 oct petrol; engine sump oil: 4.4 imp pt, 5.3 US pt, 2.5 l, SAE 20W (winter) 30 (summer); change every 6,200 miles, 10,000 km; gearbox and final drive oil: 1.9 imp pt, 2.3 US pt, 1.1 l, SAE 90 EP, change every 18,600 miles, 30,000 km; greasing: every 1,600 miles, 2,500 km, 2 points; sparking plug type: 225°; tappet clearances: inlet 0.006 in, 0.15 mm, exhaust 0.006 in, 0.15 mm; valve timing: inlet opens 25° before tdc and closes 51° after bdc, exhaust opens 64° before bdc and closes 12° after tdc; normal tyre pressure: front 18 psi, 1.3 atm, rear 27 psi, 1.9 atm.

OPTIONAL ACCESSORIES reclining backrests.

500 L Berlina

See 500 Berlina, except for:

PRICE IN GB: £ 411.
PRICE EX WORKS: 595,000 liras.

PERFORMANCE power-weight ratio: 64.8 lb/hp, 29.4 kg/hp.

DIMENSIONS AND WEIGHT overall length: 119.09 in, 3,025 mm; dry weight: 1,169 lb, 530 kg.

BODY front seats: reclining backrests (standard).

PRACTICAL INSTRUCTIONS normal tyre pressure: front 16 psi, 1.1 atm, rear 23 psi, 1.6 atm.

850 Berlina

PRICE EX WORKS: 820,000 liras.

ENGINE rear, 4 stroke; cylinders: 4, vertical, in line; bore and stroke: 2.56 x 2.50 in, 65 x 63.5 mm; engine capacity: 51.4 cu in, 843 cu cm; compression ratio: 8; max power (DIN): 34 hp at 4,800 rpm; max torque (DIN): 40 lb ft, 5.5 kg m at 3,200 rpm; max engine rpm: 5,000; specific power: 40.3 hp/l; cylinder block: cast iron; cylinder head: light alloy; crankshaft bearings: 3; valves: 2 per cylinder, overhead, in line, push-rods and rockers; camshafts: 1, side, in crankcase; lubrication: gear pump, centrifugal filter; lubricating system capacity: 6.5 imp pt, 7.8 US pt, 3.7 l; carburation: 1 Weber Holley 30 ICF downdraught carburettor; fuel feed: mechanical pump; cooling system: liquid, sealed circuit; cooling system capacity: 13.2 imp pt, 15.9 US pt, 7.5 l.

TRANSMISSION driving wheels: rear; clutch: single dry plate; gearbox: mechanical; gears: 4 + reverse; synchromesh gears: I, II, III, IV; gearbox ratios: I 3.636, II 2.055, III 1.409, IV 0.963, rev 3.615; gear lever: central; final drive: hypoid bevel; axle ratio: 4.625; width of rims: 4''; tyres: 5.50 x 12.

PERFORMANCE max speeds: 19 mph, 30 km/h in 1st gear; 34 mph, 55 km/h in 2nd gear; 53 mph, 85 km/h in 3rd gear; 75 mph, 120 km/h in 4th gear; power-weight ratio: 43.4 lb/hp, 19.7 kg/hp; carrying capacity: 882 lb, 400 kg; max gradient in 1st gear: 31%; acceleration: standing ¼ mile 23.5 sec, 0-50 mph (0-80 km/h) 20 sec; speed in top at 1,000 rpm: 13.5 mph, 21.7 km/h; fuel consumption: 47.1 m/imp gal, 39.2 m/US gal, 6 l x 100 km.

CHASSIS integral; front suspension: independent, wishbones, transverse leafspring lower arms, anti-roll bar, telescopic dampers; rear suspension: independent, semi-trailing arms, coil springs, anti-roll bar, telescopic dampers.

STEERING screw and sector; turns of steering wheel lock to lock: 3.75.

FIAT 500 L Berlina

FIAT 850 Sport Coupé

FIAT 850 Sport Spider

BRAKES drum; lining area: front 33.5 sq in, 216 sq cm, rear 33.5 sq in, 216 sq cm, total 67 sq in, 432 sq cm.

ELECTRICAL EQUIPMENT voltage: 12 V; battery: 34 Ah; generator type: dynamo, 230 W; ignition distributor: Marelli; headlamps: 2.

DIMENSIONS AND WEIGHT wheel base: 79.80 in, 2,027 mm; front track: 45.12 in, 1,146 mm; rear track: 47.99 in, 1,219 mm; overall length: 140.75 in, 3,575 mm; overall width: 56.1 in, 1,425 mm; overall height: 54.53 in, 1,385 mm; ground clearance: 4.72 in, 120 mm; dry weight: 1,477 lb, 670 kg; distribution of weight: 37.5% front axle, 62.5% rear axle; turning circle (between walls): 33.5 ft, 10.2 m; fuel tank capacity: 6.6 imp gal, 7.9 US gal, 30 l.

BODY saloon/sedan; doors: 2; seats: 5; front seats: separate.

PRACTICAL INSTRUCTIONS fuel: 80-85 oct petrol; engine sump oil: 5.6 imp pt, 6.8 US pt, 3.2 l, SAE 20W (winter) 30 (summer); change every 6,200 miles, 10,000 km; gearbox and final drive oil: 3.7 imp pt, 4.4 US pt, 2.1 l, SAE 90, change every 18,600 miles, 30,000 km; greasing: every 1,600 miles, 2,500 km, 1 point; sparking plug type: 240°; tappet clearances: inlet 0.006 in, 0.15 mm, exhaust 0.006 in, 0.15 mm; valve timing: inlet opens 16° before tdc and closes 56° after bdc, exhaust opens 56° before bdc and closes 16° after tdc; normal tyre pressure: front 16 psi, 1.1 atm, rear 26 psi, 1.8 atm.

OPTIONAL ACCESSORIES reclining backrests.

850 Super Berlina

See 850 Berlina, except for:

PRICE IN GB: £ 502.
PRICE IN USA: $ 1,504.

ENGINE compression ratio: 8.8; max power (DIN): 37 hp at 5,000 rpm; max torque (DIN): 41 lb ft, 5.6 kg m at 3,400 rpm; specific power: 43.9 hp/l; carburation: 1 Weber Holley 30 ICF carburettor.

PERFORMANCE max speed: 78 mph, 125 km/h; power-weight ratio: 39.9 lb/hp, 18.1 kg/hp; acceleration: standing ¼ mile 23 sec, 0-50 mph (0-80 km/h) 18.7 sec.

OPTIONAL ACCESSORIES 4-speed Idroconvert semi-automatic gearbox with hydraulic torque convertor, hydraulically controlled automatic clutch, central gear lever, 45 Ah battery, 350 W dynamo.

850 Special Berlina

See 850 Berlina, except for:

PRICE IN GB: £ 572.
PRICE EX WORKS: 870,000 liras.

ENGINE compression ratio: 9.3; max power (DIN): 47 hp at 6,400 rpm; max torque (DIN): 43 lb ft, 6 kg m at 3,600 rpm; max engine rpm: 6,400; specific power: 55.8 hp/l; carburation: 1 Weber 30 DIC twin barrel carburettor.

TRANSMISSION axle ratio: 5.125; width of rims: 4.5''; tyres: 145 x 13.

PERFORMANCE max speeds: 22 mph, 35 km/h in 1st gear; 37 mph, 60 km/h in 2nd gear; 56 mph, 90 km/h in 3rd gear; 84 mph, 135 km/h in 4th gear; power-weight ratio: 32.4 lb/hp, 14.7 kg/hp; max gradient in 1st gear: 35%; acceleration: standing ¼ mile 21.5 sec, 0-50 mph (0-80 km/h) 12.6 sec; speed in top at 1,000 rpm: 12.6 mph, 20.2 km/h; fuel consumption: 39.8 m/imp gal, 33.1 m/US gal, 7.1 l x 100 km.

BRAKES front disc (diameter 8.94 in, 227 mm), rear drum; lining area: front 19.2 sq in, 124 sq cm.

ELECTRICAL EQUIPMENT battery: 45 Ah.

DIMENSIONS AND WEIGHT front track: 45.20 in, 1,148 mm; rear track: 47.52 in, 1,207 mm; dry weight: 1,521 lb, 690 kg; distribution of weight: 36.1% front axle, 63.9% rear axle.

PRACTICAL INSTRUCTIONS fuel: 98 oct petrol; greasing: 2 points; sparking plug type: 260°; tappet clearances: exhaust 0.008 in, 0.20 mm; valve timing: inlet opens 25° before tdc and closes 51° after bdc, exhaust opens 64° before bdc and closes 12° after tdc.

OPTIONAL ACCESSORIES 4-speed Idroconvert semi-automatic gearbox with hydraulic torque convertor, hydraulically controlled automatic clutch, central gear lever, 350 W dynamo.

850 Sport Coupé

PRICE IN GB: £ 717.
PRICE IN USA $ 1,988.

ENGINE rear, 4 stroke; cylinders: 4, vertical, in line; bore and stroke: 2.56 x 2.68 in, 65 x 68 mm; engine capacity: 55.1 cu in, 903 cu cm; compression ratio: 9.5; max power (DIN): 52 hp at 6,500 rpm; max torque (DIN): 48 lb ft, 6.6 kg m at

4,000 rpm; max engine rpm: 6,600; specific power: 57.6 hp/l; cylinder block: cast iron; cylinder head: light alloy; crankshaft bearings: 3; valves: 2 per cylinder, overhead, in line, push-rods and rockers; camshafts: 1, side; lubrication: gear pump, centrifugal filter; lubricating system capacity: 7.6 imp pt, 9.1 US pt, 4.3 l; carburation: 1 Weber 30 DIC twin barrel carburettor; fuel feed: mechanical pump; cooling system: liquid, sealed circuit; cooling system capacity: 13.2 imp pt, 15.9 US pt, 7.5 l.

TRANSMISSION driving wheels: rear; clutch: single dry plate; gearbox: mechanical; gears: 4 + reverse; synchromesh gears: I, II, III, IV; gearbox ratios: I 3.636, II 2.055, III 1.409, IV 0.963, rev 3.615; gear lever: central; final drive: hypoid bevel; axle ratio: 4.875; width of rims: 5''; tyres: 150/155 x 13.

PERFORMANCE max speeds: 25 mph, 40 km/h in 1st gear; 43 mph, 70 km/h in 2nd gear; 65 mph, 105 km/h in 3rd gear; 90 mph, 145 km/h in 4th gear; power-weight ratio: 31.5 lb/hp, 14.3 kg/hp; carrying capacity: 706 lb, 320 kg; max gradient in 1st gear: 36%; acceleration: standing ¼ mile 20.3 sec, 0-50 mph (0-80 km/h) 12.3 sec; speed in top at 1,000 rpm: 13.7 mph, 22.1 km/h; fuel consumption: 39.2 m/imp gal, 32.7 m/US gal, 7.2 l x 100 km.

CHASSIS integral; front suspension: independent, wishbones, transverse leafspring lower arms, anti-roll bar, telescopic dampers; rear suspension: independent, semi-trailing arms, coil springs, anti-roll bar, telescopic dampers.

STEERING screw and sector; turns of steering wheel lock to lock: 3.75.

BRAKES front disc (diameter 8.90 in, 226 mm), rear drum; lining area: front 19.2 sq in, 124 sq cm, rear 34.1 sq in, 220 sq cm, total 53.3 sq in, 344 sq cm.

ELECTRICAL EQUIPMENT voltage: 12 V; battery: 48 Ah; generator type: alternator, 770 W; ignition distributor: Marelli; headlamps: 4.

DIMENSIONS AND WEIGHT wheel base: 77.80 in, 2,027 mm; front track: 46.06 in, 1,170 mm; rear track: 48.11 in, 1,222 mm; overall length: 143.78 in, 3,652 mm; overall width: 59.06 in, 1,500 mm; overall height: 51.18 in, 1,300 mm; ground clearance: 4.92 in, 125 mm; dry weight: 1,643 lb, 745 kg; distribution of weight: 36% front axle, 64% rear axle; turning circle (between walls): 33.5 ft, 10.2 m; fuel tank capacity: 6.6 imp gal, 7.9 US gal, 30 l.

BODY coupé; doors: 2; seats: 2 + 2; front seats: separate.

PRACTICAL INSTRUCTIONS fuel: 98 oct petrol; engine sump oil: 6.5 imp pt, 7.8 US pt, 3.7 l, SAE 20W (winter) 30 (summer), change every 6,200 miles, 10,000 km; gearbox and final drive oil: 3.7 imp pt, 4.4 US pt, 2.1 l, SAE 90 EP, change every 18,600 miles, 30,000 km; greasing: every 1,600 miles, 2,500 km, 2 points; sparking plug type: 260°; tappet clearances: inlet 0.006 in, 0.15 mm, exhaust 0.008 in, 0.20 mm; valve timing: inlet opens 25° before tdc and closes 51° after bdc, exhaust opens 64° before bdc and closes 12° after tdc; normal tyre pressure: front 16 psi, 1.1 atm, rear 26 psi, 1.8 atm.

OPTIONAL ACCESSORIES light alloy wheels.

850 Sport Spider

See 850 Sport Coupé, except for:

PRICE IN USA: $ 2,168.
PRICE EX WORKS: 1,200,000 liras.

ENGINE lubricating system capacity: 7.9 imp pt, 9.5 US pt, 4.5 l.

PERFORMANCE max speed: 95 mph, 153 km/h; power-weight ratio: 30.9 lb/hp, 14 kg/hp; carrying capacity: 441 lb, 200 kg; max gradient in 1st gear: 38%; acceleration: standing ¼ mile 19.8 sec, 0-50 (0-80 km/h) 11.8 sec.

DIMENSIONS AND WEIGHT overall length: 150.55 in, 3,824 mm; overall width: 58.98 in, 1,498 mm; overall height: 48.03 in, 1,220 mm; ground clearance: 5.12 in, 130 mm; dry weight: 1,621 lb, 735 kg; distribution of weight: 40% front axle, 60% rear axle.

BODY sports; seats: 2.

OPTIONAL ACCESSORIES hardtop.

850 Familiare

PRICE EX WORKS: 1,130,000 liras.

ENGINE rear, 4 stroke; cylinders: 4, vertical, in line; bore and stroke: 2.56 x 2.68 in, 65 x 68 mm; engine capacity: 55.1 cu in, 903 cu cm; compression ratio: 7.9; max power (DIN): 33 hp at 4,800 rpm; max torque (DIN): 41 lb ft, 5.6 kg m at 3,200 rpm; max engine rpm: 5,000; specific power: 36.5 hp/l; cylinder block: cast iron; cylinder head: light

FIAT 500 L Berlina

FIAT 850 Sport Coupé

FIAT 850 Sport Spider

850 FAMILIARE

alloy; crankshaft bearings: 3; valves: 2 per cylinder, over-head, in line, push-rods and rockers; camshafts: 1, side; lubrication: gear pump, centrifugal filter; lubricating system capacity: 6.5 imp pt, 7.8 US pt, 3.7 l; carburation: 1 Weber Holley 30 ICF downdraught carburettor; fuel feed: mechanical pump; cooling system: liquid, sealed circuit; cooling system capacity: 13.2 imp pt, 15.9 US pt, 7.5 l.

TRANSMISSION driving wheels: rear; clutch: single dry plate; gearbox: mechanical; gears: 4 + reverse; synchromesh gears: I, II, III, IV; gearbox ratios: I 3.636, II 2.055, III 1.409, IV 0.963, rev 3.615; gear lever: central; final drive: hypoid bevel; axle ratio: 5.571; width of rims: 4''; tyres: 5.60 x 12.

PERFORMANCE max speeds: 16 mph, 25 km/h in 1st gear; 28 mph, 45 km/h in 2nd gear; 43 mph, 70 km/h in 3rd gear; over 62 mph, 100 km/h in 4th gear; power-weight ratio: 60 lb/hp, 27.2 kg/hp; carrying capacity: 1,235 lb, 560 kg; max gradient in 1st gear: 24%; acceleration: standing ¼ mile 28.5 sec, 0-50 mph (0-80 km/h) 32 sec; speed in top at 1,000 rpm: 11.7 mph, 18.9 km/h; fuel consumption: 35.8 m/imp gal, 29.8 m/US gal, 7.9 l x 100 km.

CHASSIS integral; front suspension: independent, wishbones, coil springs, anti-roll bar, telescopic dampers; rear suspension: independent, semi-trailing arms, coil springs, telescopic dampers.

STEERING worm and roller; turns of steering wheel lock to lock: 3.

BRAKES drum; lining area: front 51.6 sq in, 333 sq cm, rear 51.6 sq in, 333 sq cm, total 103.2 sq in, 666 sq cm.

ELECTRICAL EQUIPMENT voltage: 12 V; battery: 45 Ah; generator type: dynamo, 360 W; ignition distributor: Marelli; headlamps: 4.

DIMENSIONS AND WEIGHT wheel base: 78.74 in, 2,000 mm; front track: 48.19 in, 1,224 mm; rear track: 50.87 in, 1,192 mm; overall length: 149.76 in, 3,804 mm; overall width: 58.59 in, 1,488 mm; overall height: 65.35 in, 1,660 mm; ground clearance: 5.31 in, 135 mm; dry weight: 1,985 lb, 900 kg; distribution of weight: 45% front axle, 55% rear axle; turning circle (between walls): 32.5 ft, 9.9 m; fuel tank capacity: 7 imp gal, 8.4 US gal, 32 l.

BODY estate car/station wagon; doors: 4 + 1; seats: 7; front seats: bench.

PRACTICAL INSTRUCTIONS fuel: 83 oct petrol; engine sump oil: 5.6 imp pt, 6.8 US pt, 3.2 l, SAE 20W (winter) 30 (summer), change every 6,200 miles, 10,000 km; gearbox and final drive oil: 3.7 imp pt, 4.4 US pt, 2.1 l, SAE 90, change every 18,600 miles, 30,000 km; greasing: every 1,600 miles, 2,500 km, 5 points; sparking plug type: 240°; tappet clearances: inlet 0.006 in, 0.15 mm, exhaust 0.006 in, 0.15 mm; valve timing: inlet opens 16° before tdc and closes 56° after bdc, exhaust opens 56° before bdc and closes 16° after tdc; normal tyre pressure: front 24 psi, 1.7 atm, rear 40 psi, 2.8 atm.

2-door 128 Berlina

PRICE IN GB: £ 636.
PRICE EX WORKS: 1,000,000 liras.

ENGINE front, transverse, 4 stroke; cylinders: 4, in line; bore and stroke: 3.15 x 2.19 in, 80 x 55.5 mm; engine capacity: 68.1 cu in, 1,116 cu cm; compression ratio: 8.8; max power (DIN): 55 hp at 6,000 rpm; max torque (DIN): 57 lb ft, 7.9 kg m at 3,000 rpm; max engine rpm: 6,600; specific power: 49.3 hp/l; cylinder block: cast iron; cylinder head: light alloy; crankshaft bearings: 5; valves: 2 per cylinder, overhead, thimble tappets; camshafts: 1, overhead; lubrication: gear pump, cartridge filter; lubricating system capacity: 7.2 imp pt, 8.7 US pt, 4.1 l; carburation: 1 Weber 32 ICEV or Solex C 32 DISA downdraught carburettor; fuel feed: mechanical pump; cooling system: water, electric thermostatic fan; cooling system capacity: 11.4 imp pt, 13.7 US pt, 6.5 l.

TRANSMISSION driving wheels: front; clutch: single dry plate; gearbox: mechanical; gears: 4 + reverse; synchromesh gears: I, II, III, IV; gearbox ratios: I 3.583, II 2.235, III 1.454, IV 1.037, rev 3.714; gear lever: central; final drive: cylindrical gears; axle ratio: 4.077; width of rims: 4.5''; tyres: 145 x 13.

PERFORMANCE max speeds: 28 mph, 45 km/h in 1st gear; 47 mph, 75 km/h in 2nd gear; 71 mph, 115 km/h in 3rd gear; 84 mph, 135 km/h in 4th gear; power-weight ratio: 31.5 lb/hp, 14.3 kg/hp; carrying capacity: 882 lb, 400 kg; max gradient in 1st gear: 30%; acceleration: standing ¼ mile 21 sec, 0-50 mph (0-80 km/h) 12.7 sec; speed in top at 1,000 rpm: 15.5 mph, 25 km/h; fuel consumption: 35.3 m/imp gal, 29.4 m/US gal, 8 l x 100 km.

CHASSIS integral; front suspension: independent, by McPherson, coil springs, telescopic damper struts, lower wish-

FIAT 850 Familiare

FIAT 2-door 128 Berlina

FIAT 124 Berlina

ones, anti-roll bar; rear suspension: independent, single wide based wishbone, transverse leafspring, telescopic dampers.

STEERING rack-and-pinion; turns of steering wheel lock to lock: 3.50.

BRAKES front disc (diameter 8.94 in, 227 mm), rear drum, dual circuit, rear compensator; lining area: front 19.2 sq in, 124 sq cm, rear 33.5 sq in, 216 sq cm, total 52.7 sq in, 340 sq cm.

ELECTRICAL EQUIPMENT voltage: 12 V; battery: 34 Ah; generator type: dynamo, 230 W; ignition distributor: Marelli; headlamps: 2.

DIMENSIONS AND WEIGHT wheel base: 96.38 in, 2,448 mm; front track: 51.50 in. 1,308 mm; rear track: 51.42 in, 1,306 mm; overall length: 151.81 in, 3,856 mm; overall width: 62.60 in, 1,590 mm; overall height: 55.91 in, 1,420 mm; ground clearance: 5.71 in, 145 mm; dry weight: 1,731 lb, 785 kg; distribution of weight: 61.5% front axle, 38.5% rear axle; turning circle (between walls): 35.8 ft, 10.9 m; fuel tank capacity: 8.4 imp gal, 10 US gal, 38 l.

BODY saloon/sedan; doors: 2; seats: 5; front seats: separate.

PRACTICAL INSTRUCTIONS fuel: 98 oct petrol; engine sump oil: 5.8 imp pt, 7 US pt, 3.3 l, SAE 20W (winter) 30 (summer), change every 6,200 miles, 10,000 km; gearbox and final drive oil: 5.5 imp pt, 6.6 US pt, 3.1 l, SAE 90, change every 18,600 miles, 30,000 km; greasing: none; sparking plug type: 240°; tappet clearances: inlet 0.012 in, 0.30 mm, exhaust 0.016 in, 0.40 mm; valve timing: inlet opens 12° before tdc and closes 52° after bdc, exhaust opens 52° before bdc and closes 12° after tdc; normal tyre pressure: front 26 psi, 1.8 atm, rear 24 psi, 1.7 atm.

OPTIONAL ACCESSORIES reclining backrests.

4-door 128 Berlina

See 2-door 128 Berlina, except for:

PRICE IN GB: £ 669.
PRICE EX WORKS: 1,060,000 liras.

PERFORMANCE power-weight ratio: 32.2 lb/hp, 14.6 kg/hp.

DIMENSIONS AND WEIGHT dry weight: 1,775 lb, 805 kg

128 Familiare

See 2-door 128 Berlina, except for:

PRICE IN GB: £ 721.
PRICE EX WORKS: 1,115,000 liras.

ENGINE lubricating system capacity: 8.8 imp pt, 10.6 US pt, 5 l.

TRANSMISSION axle ratio: 4.416.

PERFORMANCE max speeds: 25 mph, 40 km/h in 1st gear; 43 mph, 70 km/h in 2nd gear; 65 mph, 105 km/h in 3rd gear; 86 mph, 138 km/h in 4th gear; power-weight ratio: 33.1 lb/hp, 15 kg/hp; carrying capacity: 948 lb, 430 kg; speed in top at 1,000 rpm: 14 mph, 22.5 km/h.

DIMENSIONS AND WEIGHT rear track: 51.69 in, 1,313 mm; overall length: 52.09 in, 3,863 mm; dry weight: 1,819 lb, 825 kg; distribution of weight: 60% front axle, 40% rear axle.

BODY estate car/station wagon; doors: 2 + 1.

PRACTICAL INSTRUCTIONS normal tyre pressure: front 27 psi, 1.9 atm, rear 28 psi, 2 atm.

124 Berlina

PRICE IN GB: £ 718.
PRICE IN USA: $ 2,015.

ENGINE front, 4 stroke; cylinders: 4, in line; bore and stroke: 2.87 x 2.81 in, 73 x 71.5 mm; engine capacity: 73 cu in, 1,197 cu cm; compression ratio: 8.8; max power (DIN): 60 hp at 5,600 rpm; max torque (DIN): 64 lb ft, 8.9 kg m at 3,400 rpm; max engine rpm: 5,800; specific power: 50.1 hp/l; cylinder block: cast iron; cylinder head: light alloy; crankshaft bearings: 5; valves: 2 per cylinder, overhead, push-rods and rockers; camshafts: 1, side, in crankcase; lubrication: gear pump, full flow filter; lubricating system capacity: 7.7 imp pt, 9.3 US pt, 4.4 l; carburation: 1 Weber 32 DHS or Solex C 32 EIES downdraught twin barrel carburettor; fuel feed: mechanical pump; cooling system: water; cooling system capacity: 13.2 imp pt, 15.9 US pt, 7.5 l.

TRANSMISSION driving wheels: rear; clutch: single dry

FIAT 850 Familiare

FIAT 128 Berlina

FIAT 124 Berlina

plate; gearbox: mechanical; gears: 4 + reverse; synchromesh gears: I, II, III, IV; gearbox ratios: I 3.750, II 2.300, III 1.490, IV 1, rev 3.870; gear lever: central; final drive: hypoid bevel; axle ratio: 4.300; width of rims: 4.5''; tyres: 150/155 x 13.

PERFORMANCE max speeds: 22 mph, 35 km/h in 1st gear; 37 mph, 60 km/h in 2nd gear; 59 mph, 95 km/h in 3rd gear; over 87 mph, 140 km/h in 4th gear; power-weight ratio: 33 lb/hp, 15 kg/hp; carrying capacity: 882 lb, 400 kg; max gradient in 1st gear: 36%; acceleration: standing ¼ mile 20.8 sec, 0-50 mph (0-80 km/h) 12 sec; speed in direct drive at 1,000 rpm: 15 mph, 24.2 km/h; fuel consumption: 33.2 m/imp gal, 27.7 m/US gal, 8.5 l x 100 km.

CHASSIS integral; front suspension: independent, wishbones, coil springs, anti-roll bar, telescopic dampers; rear suspension: rigid axle, twin trailing radius arms, transverse linkage bar, coil springs, telescopic dampers.

STEERING worm and roller; turns of steering wheel lock to lock: 2.75.

BRAKES disc (diameter 8.94 in, 227 mm) dual circuit, rear compensator, servo; lining area: front 19.2 sq in, 124 sq cm, rear 19.2 sq in, 124 sq cm, total 38.4 sq in, 248 sq cm.

ELECTRICAL EQUIPMENT voltage: 12 V; battery: 45 Ah; generator type: alternator, 770 W; ignition distributor: Marelli; headlamps: 2.

DIMENSIONS AND WEIGHT wheel base: 95.28 in, 2,420 mm; front track: 52.36 in, 1,330 mm; rear track: 51.18 in, 1,300 mm; overall length: 159.13 in, 4,042 mm; overall width: 63.98 in, 1,625 mm; overall height: 55.91 in, 1,420 mm; ground clearance: 4.72 in, 120 mm; dry weight: 1,985 lb, 900 kg; distribution of weight: 53% front axle, 47% rear axle; turning circle (between walls): 37.4 ft, 11.4 m; fuel tank capacity: 8.6 imp gal, 10.3 US gal, 39 l.

BODY saloon/sedan; doors: 4; seats: 5; front seats: separate.

PRACTICAL INSTRUCTIONS fuel: 98 oct petrol; engine sump oil: 6.5 imp pt, 7.8 US pt, 3.7 l, SAE 20W (winter) 30 (summer), change every 6,200 miles, 10,000 km; gearbox oil: 2.3 imp pt, 2.7 US pt, 1.3 l, SAE 90 EP, change every 18,600 miles, 30,000 km; final drive oil: 1.2 imp pt, 1.5 US pt, 0.7 l, SAE 90 EP, change every 18.600 miles, 30,000 km; greasing: none; sparking plug type: 240°; tappet clearances: inlet 0.006 in, 0.15 mm, exhaust 0.006 in, 0.15 mm; valve timing: inlet opens 25° before tdc and closes 59° after bdc, exhaust opens 65° before bdc and closes 19° after tdc; normal tyre pressure: front 24 psi, 1.7 atm, rear 26 psi 1.8 atm.

OPTIONAL ACCESSORIES reclining backrests; electrically-heated rear window.

124 Familiare

See 124 Berlina, except for:

PRICE IN GB: £ 798.
PRICE IN USA: $ 2,273.

TRANSMISSION axle ratio: 4.444; tyres: 5.60 x 13 or 160 x 13.

PERFORMANCE max speed: 87 mph, 140 km/h; power-weight ratio: 34.2 lb/hp, 15.5 kg/hp; carrying capacity: 948 lb, 430 kg; max gradient in 1st gear: 35%; speed in direct drive at 1,000 rpm: 14.9 mph, 23.9 km/h; fuel consumption: 31.7 m/imp gal, 26.4 m/US gal, 8.9 l x 100 km.

DIMENSIONS AND WEIGHT overall length: 159.25 in, 4,045 mm; overall height: 56.69 in, 1,440 mm; dry weight: 2,051 lb, 930 kg; distribution of weight: 50% front axle, 50% rear axle; fuel tank capacity: 10.3 imp gal, 12.4 US gal, 47 l.

BODY estate car/station wagon; doors: 4 +1.

OPTIONAL ACCESSORIES electrically-heated rear window not available.

124 Special Berlina

See 124 Berlina, except for:

PRICE IN GB: £ 783.
PRICE EX WORKS: 1,340,000 liras.

ENGINE bore and stroke: 3.15 x 2.81 in, 80 x 71.5 mm; engine capacity: 87.7 cu in, 1,438 cu cm; compression ratio: 9; max power (DIN): 70 hp at 5,400 rpm; max torque (DIN): 81 lb ft, 11.2 kg m at 3,300 rpm; specific power: 48.7 hp/l; carburation: 1 Weber 32 DHS 3 or Solex C 32 EIES downdraught twin barrel carburettor.

TRANSMISSION gearbox ratios: I 3.797, II 2.175, III 1.410, IV 1, rev 3.652; axle ratio: 4.100.

124 SPECIAL BERLINA

PERFORMANCE max speeds: 25 mph, 40 km/h in 1st gear; 43 mph, 70 km/h in 2nd gear; 68 mph, 110 km/h in 3rd gear; over 93 mph, 150 km/h in 4th gear; power-weight ratio: 29.1 lb/hp, 13.2 kg/hp; max gradient in 1st gear: 40%; acceleration: standing ¼ mile 19.7 sec, 0-50 mph (0-80 km/h) 10.7 sec; speed in direct drive at 1,000 rpm: 15.7 mph, 25.3 km/h; fuel consumption: 32.1 m/imp gal, 26.7 m/US gal, 8.8 l x 100 km.

BRAKES servo.

ELECTRICAL EQUIMENT headlamps: 4.

DIMENSIONS AND WEIGHT overall length: 159.80 in, 4,059 mm; overall width: 63.43 in, 1,611 mm; dry weight: 2,040 lb, 925 kg.

PRACTICAL INSTRUCTIONS tappet clearances: inlet 0.008 in, 0.20 mm, exhaust 0.008 in, 0.20 mm; valve timing: inlet opens 19° before tdc and closes 48° after bdc, exhaust opens 59° before bdc and closes 8° after tdc.

OPTIONAL ACCESSORIES GM automatic gearbox, hydraulic torque convertor and planetary gears with 3 ratios (I 2.400, II 1.480, III 1, rev 1.920), possible manual selection, max speeds (I) 40 mph, 65 km/h, (II) 65 mph, 105 km/h, (III) 93 mph, 150 km/h; electrically-heated rear window.

124 Special T Berlina

See 124 Special Berlina, except for:

PRICE EX WORKS: 1,390,000 liras.

ENGINE compression ratio: 8.9; max power (DIN): 80 hp at 5,800 rpm; max torque (DIN): 80 lb ft, 11.2 kg m at 4,000 rpm; specific power: 55.6 hp/l; carburation: 1 Weber 32 DHS downdraught twin barrel carburettor.

PERFORMANCE max speeds: 28 mph, 45 km/h in 1st gear; 50 mph, 80 km/h in 2nd gear; 75 mph, 120 km/h in 3rd gear; 99 mph, 160 km/h in 4th gear; power-weight ratio: 26.2 lb/hp, 11.9 kg/hp; acceleration: standing ¼ mile 19 sec, 0-50 mph (0-80 km/h) 9.7 sec; fuel consumption: 30.4 m/imp gal, 25.3 m/US gal, 9.3 l x 100 km.

DIMENSIONS AND WEIGHT dry weight: 2,095 lb, 950 kg.

PRACTICAL INSTRUCTIONS tappet clearances: inlet 0.018 in, 0.45 mm, exhaust 0.020 in, 0.50 mm; valve timing: inlet opens 26° before tdc and closes 66° after bdc, exhaust opens 66° before bdc and closes 26° after tdc.

OPTIONAL ACCESSORIES GM automatic gearbox, hydraulic torque convertor and planetary gears with 3 ratios (I 2.400, II 1.480, III 1, rev 1.920), possible manual selection; electronic ignition; rev counter; electrically-heated rear window.

124 Sport Coupé

PRICE IN GB: £ 1,260 (with 5-speed mechanical gearbox).
PRICE IN USA: $ 2,999.

ENGINE front, 4 stroke; cylinders: 4, in line; bore and stroke: 3.15 x 2.81 in, 80 x 71.5 mm; engine capacity: 87.7 cu in, 1,438 cu cm; compression ratio: 8.9; max power (DIN): 90 hp at 6,500 rpm; max torque (DIN): 80 lb ft, 11 kg m at 3,600 rpm; max engine rpm: 6,600; specific power: 62.6 hp/l; cylinder block: cast iron; cylinder head: light alloy; crankshaft bearings: 5; valves: 2 per cylinder, overhead, Vee-slanted, thimble tappets; camshafts: 2, overhead, cogged belt; lubrication: gear pump, centrifugal filter, supplementary cartridge; lubricating system capacity: 8.3 imp pt, 9.9 US pt, 4.7 l; carburation: 1 Weber 34 DHS downdraught twin barrel carburettor; fuel feed: mechanical pump; cooling system: water, electric thermostatic fan; cooling system capacity: 13.2 imp pt, 15.9 US pt, 7.5 l.

TRANSMISSION driving wheels: rear; clutch: single dry plate; gearbox: mechanical; gears: 4 + reverse; synchromesh gears: I, II, III, IV; gearbox ratios: I 3.750, II 2.300, III 1.490, IV 1, rev 3.870; gear lever: central; final drive: hypoid bevel; axle ratio: 4.100; width of rims: 5''; tyres: 165 x 13.

PERFORMANCE max speeds: 28 mph, 45 km/h in 1st gear; 47 mph, 75 km/h in 2nd gear; 75 mph, 120 km/h in 3rd gear; 106 mph, 170 km/h in 4th gear; power-weight ratio: 24 lb/hp, 10.9 kg/hp; carrying capacity: 706 lb, 320 kg; max gradient in 1st gear: 38%; acceleration: standing ¼ mile 18.5 sec, 0-50 mph (0-80 km/h) 9.2 sec; speed in direct drive at 1,000 rpm: 16.2 mph, 26 km/h; fuel consumption: 26.6 m/imp gal, 22.2 m/US gal, 10.6 l x 100 km.

CHASSIS integral; front suspension: independent, wishbones, coil springs, anti-roll bar, telescopic dampers; rear suspension: rigid axle, twin trailing radius arms, transverse linkage bar, coil springs, telescopic dampers.

FIAT 124 Special T Berlina

FIAT 124 Sport Coupé 1600

FIAT 125 Special Berlina

STEERING worm and roller; turns of steering wheel lock to lock: 2.75.

BRAKES disc (diameter 8.94 in, 227 mm), dual circuit, rear compensator, servo; lining area: front 19.2 sq in, 124 sq cm, rear 19.2 sq in, 124 sq cm, total 38.4 sq in, 248 sq cm.

ELECTRICAL EQUIPMENT voltage: 12 V; battery: 45 Ah; generator type: alternator, 770 W; ignition distributor: Marelli; headlamps: 4.

DIMENSIONS AND WEIGHT wheel base: 95.28 in, 2,420 mm; front track: 52.99 in, 1,346 mm; rear track: 51.81 in, 1,316 mm; overall length: 162.32 in, 4,123 mm; overall width: 65.75 in, 1,670 mm; overall height: 52.76 in, 1,340 mm; ground clearance: 4.72 in, 120 mm; dry weight: 2,161 lb, 980 kg; distribution of weight: 55% front axle, 45% rear axle; turning circle (between walls): 38.4 ft, 11.7 m; fuel tank capacity: 9.9 imp gal, 11.9 US gal, 45 l.

BODY coupé; doors: 2; seats: 4; front seats: separate.

PRACTICAL INSTRUCTIONS fuel: 98 oct petrol; engine sump oil: 6.7 imp pt, 8 US pt, 3.8 l, SAE 20W (winter) 30 (summer), change every 6,200 miles, 10,000 km; gearbox oil: 2.3 imp pt, 2.7 US pt, 1.3 l, SAE 90 EP, change every 18,600 miles, 30,000 km; final drive oil: 2.3 imp pt, 2.7 US pt, 1.3 l, SAE 90 EP, change every 18,600 miles, 30,000 km; greasing: none; tappet clearances: inlet 0.018 in, 0.45 mm, exhaust 0.020 in, 0.50 mm; valve timing: inlet opens 26° before tdc and closes 66° after bdc, exhaust opens 66° before bdc and closes 26° after tdc; normal tyre pressure: front 23 psi, 1.6 atm, rear 26 psi, 1.8 atm.

OPTIONAL ACCESSORIES 5-speed mechanical gearbox (I 3.797, II 2.175, III 1.410, IV 1, V 0.912, rev 3.652), max speeds (I) 28 mph, 45 km/h, (II) 50 mph, 80 km/h, (III) 78 mph, 125 km/h, (IV) 106 mph, 170 km/h, (V) over 99 mph, 160 km/h; light alloy wheels; electrically-heated rear window; headrests.

124 Sport Spider

See 124 Sport Coupé, except for:

PRICE IN USA: $ 3,304.
PRICE EX WORKS: 1,790,000 liras.

PERFORMANCE power-weight ratio: 23.2 lb/hp, 10.5 kg/hp; max gradient in 1st gear: 45%; acceleration: standing ¼ mile 18.2 sec, 0-50 mph (0-80 km/h) 8.3 sec; fuel consumption: 27.4 m/imp gal, 22.8 m/US gal, 10.3 l x 100 km.

DIMENSIONS AND WEIGHT wheel base: 89.76 in, 2,280 mm; overall length: 156.34 in, 3,971 mm; overall width: 63.50 in, 1,613 mm; overall height: 49.21 in, 1,250 mm; ground clearance: 4.92 in, 125 mm; dry weight: 2,084 lb, 945 kg; distribution of weight: 56% front axle, 44% rear axle; turning circle (between walls): 36.1 ft, 11 m.

BODY sports; seats: 2 + 2.

PRACTICAL INSTRUCTIONS normal tyre pressure: rear 23 psi, 1.6 atm.

OPTIONAL ACCESSORIES only 5-speed mechanical gearbox; light alloy wheels, hardtop and headrests.

124 Sport Coupé 1600

See 124 Sport Coupé, except for:

PRICE IN GB: £ 1,335.
PRICE EX WORKS: 1,825,000 liras.

ENGINE bore and stroke: 3.15 x 3.15 in, 80 x 80 mm; engine capacity: 98.1 cu in, 1,608 cu cm; compression ratio: 9.8; max power (DIN): 110 hp at 6,400 rpm; max torque (DIN): 101 lb ft, 14 kg m at 3,800 rpm; specific power: 68.4 hp/l; carburation: 2 Weber 40 IDF or Solex C 40 PII downdraught twin barrel carburettors.

TRANSMISSION gears: 5 + reverse (standard); synchromesh gears: I, II, III, IV, V; gearbox ratios: I 3.667, II 2.100, III 1.361, IV 1, V 0.881, rev 3.526; axle ratio: 4.300.

PERFORMANCE max speeds: 28 mph, 45 km/h in 1st gear; 50 mph, 80 km/h in 2nd gear; 75 mph, 120 km/h in 3rd gear; 103 mph, 165 km/h in 4th gear; 112 mph, 180 km/h in 5th gear; power-weight ratio: 19.8 lb/hp, 9 kg/hp; max gradient in 1st gear: 45%; acceleration: standing ¼ mile 17 sec, 0-50 mph (0-80 km/h) 7.2 sec; speed in top at 1,000 rpm: 15.5 mph, 24.9 km/h; fuel consumption: 25.7 m/imp gal, 21.4 m/US gal, 11 l x 100 km.

ELECTRICAL EQUIPMENT headlamps: iodine long-distance lights.

DIMENSIONS AND WEIGHT dry weight: 2,194 lb, 995 kg.

PRACTICAL INSTRUCTIONS gearbox oil: 2.8 imp pt, 3.4 US pt, 1.6 l; normal tyre pressure: front 28 psi, 2 atm, rear 28 psi, 2 atm.

OPTIONAL ACCESSORIES electronic ignition.

FIAT 124 Special T Berlina

FIAT 124 Sport Coupé 1600

FIAT 125 Special Berlina

124 Sport Spider 1600

See 124 Sport Coupé 1600, except for:

PRICE EX WORKS: 1,870,000 liras.

PERFORMANCE power-weight ratio: 19.2 lb/hp, 8.7 kg/hp; max gradient in 1st gear: 50%; acceleration: standing ¼ mile 16.8 sec, 0-50 mph (0-80 km/h) 6.9 sec.

DIMENSIONS AND WEIGHT wheel base: 89.76 in, 2,280 mm; overall length: 156.34 in, 3,971 mm; overall width: 63.50 in, 1,613 mm; overall height: 49.21 in, 1,250 mm; ground clearance: 4.92 in, 125 mm; dry weight: 2,117 lb, 960 kg; distribution of weight: 57% front axle, 43% rear axle; turning circle (between walls): 36.1 ft, 11 m.

BODY sports; seats: 2 + 2.

PRACTICAL INSTRUCTIONS normal tyre pressure: front 26 psi, 1.8 atm, rear 26 psi, 1.8 atm.

OPTIONAL ACCESSORIES only electronic ignition, light alloy wheels, hardtop and headrests.

125 Berlina

PRICE IN GB: £ 925.
PRICE EX WORKS: 1,480,000 liras.

ENGINE front, 4 stroke; cylinders: 4, in line; bore and stroke: 3.15 x 3.15 in, 80 x 80 mm; engine capacity: 98.1 cu in, 1,608 cu cm; compression ratio: 8.8; max power (DIN): 90 hp at 5,600 rpm; max torque (DIN): 94 lb ft, 13 kg m at 3,500 rpm; max engine rpm: 6,200; specific power: 56 hp/l; cylinder block: cast iron; cylinder head: light alloy; crankshaft bearings: 5; valves: 2 per cylinder, overhead; camshafts: 2, overhead, cogged belt; lubrication: gear pump, centrifugal filter, cartridge on by-pass; lubricating system capacity: 8.6 imp pt, 10.4 US pt, 4.9 l; carburation: 1 Weber 34 DCHE or Solex C 34 PAIA/3 downdraught twin barrel carburettor; fuel feed: mechanical pump; cooling system: water, electric thermostatic fan; cooling system capacity: 13.2 imp pt, 15.9 US pt, 7.5 l.

TRANSMISSION driving wheels: rear; clutch: single dry plate; gearbox: mechanical; gears: 4 + reverse; synchromesh gears: I, II, III, IV; gearbox ratios: I 3.422, II 2.100, III 1.361, IV 1, rev 3.526; gear lever: central; final drive: hypoid bevel; axle ratio: 4.100; width of rims: 5''; tyres: 170/175 x 13.

PERFORMANCE max speeds: 31 mph, 50 km/h in 1st gear; 50 mph, 80 km/h in 2nd gear; 78 mph, 125 km/h in 3rd gear; 99 mph, 160 km/h in 4th gear; power-weight ratio: 24.7 lb/hp, 11.2 kg/hp; carrying capacity: 882 lb, 400 kg; max gradient in 1st gear: 40%; acceleration: standing ¼ mile 18.8 sec, 0-50 mph (0-80 km/h) 9.3 sec; speed in direct drive at 1,000 rpm: 16.3 mph, 26.3 km/h; fuel consumption: 28.5 m/imp gal, 23.8 m/US gal, 9.9 l x 100 km.

CHASSIS integral; front suspension: independent, wishbones, coil springs, anti-roll bar, telescopic dampers; rear suspension: rigid axle, semi-elliptic leafsprings, telescopic dampers.

STEERING worm and roller; turns of steering wheel lock to lock: 3.

BRAKES disc (diameter 8.94 in, 227 mm), dual circuit, rear compensator, servo; lining area: front 19.2 sq in, 124 sq cm, rear 19.2 sq in, 124 sq cm, total 38.4 sq in, 248 sq cm.

ELECTRICAL EQUIPMENT voltage: 12 V; battery: 45 Ah; generator type: alternator, 770 W; ignition distributor: Marelli; headlamps: 4.

DIMENSIONS AND WEIGHT wheel base: 98.62 in, 2,505 mm; front track: 51.69 in, 1,313 mm; rear track: 50.83 in, 1,291 mm; overall length: 166.26 in, 4,223 mm; overall width: 63.43 in, 1,611 mm; overall height: 56.69 in, 1,440 mm; ground clearance: 4.72 in, 120 mm; dry weight: 2,227 lb, 1,010 kg; distribution of weight: 54.5% front axle, 45.5% rear axle; turning circle (between walls): 37.7 ft, 11.5 m; fuel tank capacity: 9.9 imp gal, 11.9 US gal, 45 l.

BODY saloon/sedan; doors: 4; seats: 5; front seats: separate, reclining backrests.

PRACTICAL INSTRUCTIONS fuel: 98 oct petrol; engine sump oil: 6.5 imp pt, 7.8 US pt, 3.7 l, SAE 10W-30 (winter) 20W-40 (summer), change every 6,200 miles, 10,000 km; gearbox oil: 2.3 imp pt, 2.7 US pt, 1.3 l, SAE 90 EP, change every 18,600 miles, 30,000 km; final drive oil: 2.5 imp pt, 3 US pt, 1.4 l, SAE 90 EP, change every 18,600 miles, 30,000 km; greasing: none; tappet clearances: inlet 0.018 in, 0.45 mm, exhaust 0.020 in, 0.50 mm; valve timing: inlet opens 26° before tdc and closes 66° after bdc, exhaust opens 66° before bdc and closes 26° after tdc; normal tyre pressure: front 24 psi, 1.7 atm, rear 26 psi, 1.8 atm.

OPTIONAL ACCESSORIES GM automatic gearbox, hydraulic torque convertor and planetary gears with 3 ratios (I 2.400,

125 BERLINA

II 1.480, III 1, rev 1.920), possible manual selection, max speeds (I) 43 mph, 70 km/h, (II) 71 mph, 115 km/h, (III) 99 mph, 160 km/h; rev counter; electrically-heated rear window.

125 Special Berlina

See 125 Berlina, except for:

PRICE IN GB: £ 1,030.
PRICE EX WORKS: 1,590,000 liras.

ENGINE max power (DIN): 100 hp at 6,200 rpm; max torque (DIN): 96 lb ft, 13.3 kg m at 4,000 rpm; specific power: 62 hp/l; carburation: 1 Weber 34 DCHE or Solex C 34 PAIA downdraught twin barrel carburettor.

TRANSMISSION gears: 5 + reverse; synchromesh gears: I, II, III, IV, V; gearbox ratios: I 3.667, II 2.100, III 1.361, IV 1, V 0.881, rev 3.526.

PERFORMANCE max speeds: 28 mph, 45 km/h in 1st gear; 50 mph, 80 km/h in 2nd gear; 78 mph, 125 km/h in 3rd gear; 103 mph, 165 km/h in 4th gear; 106 mph, 170 km/h in 5th gear; power-weight ratio: 23.4 lb/hp, 10.6 kg/hp; max gradient in 1st gear: 42%; acceleration: standing ¼ mile 18.6 sec, 0-50 mph (0-80 km/h) 9 sec; speed in top at 1,000 rpm: 16.8 mph, 27 km/h; fuel consumption: 29.1 m/imp gal, 24.2 m/US gal, 9.7 l x 100 km.

ELECTRICAL EQUIPMENT headlamps: iodine long-distance lights.

DIMENSIONS AND WEIGHT overall length: 166.61 in, 4,232 mm; overall width: 63.86 in, 1,622 mm; overall height: 55.91 in, 1,420 mm; dry weight: 2,326 lb, 1,055 kg; distribution of weight: 54.1% front axle, 45.9% rear axle; fuel tank capacity: 11 imp gal, 13.2 US gal, 50 l.

PRACTICAL INSTRUCTIONS gearbox oil: 2.8 imp pt, 3.4 US pt, 1.6 l.

OPTIONAL ACCESSORIES GM automatic gearbox, hydraulic torque convertor and planetary gears with 3 ratios (I 2.400, II 1.480, III 1, rev 1.920), possible manual selection, max speeds (I) 43 mph, 70 km/h, (II) 71 mph, 115 km/h, (III) 103 mph, 165 km/h; electronic ignition; rev counter; electrically-heated rear window; air-conditioning system; light alloy wheels.

Dino Coupé 2400

PRICE EX WORKS: 4,450,000 liras.

ENGINE front, 4 stroke; cylinders: 6, Vee-slanted at 65°; bore and stroke: 3.64 x 2.36 in, 92.5 x 60 mm; engine capacity: 147.5 cu in, 2,418 cu cm; compression ratio: 9; max power (DIN): 180 hp at 6,600 rpm; max torque (DIN): 159 lb ft, 22 kg m at 4,600 rpm; max engine rpm: 8,000; specific power: 74.4 hp/l; cylinder block: cast iron; cylinder head: light alloy, hemispherical combustion chambers; crankshaft bearings: 4; valves: 2 per cylinder, overhead, Vee-slanted, thimble tappets; camshafts: 2 per cylinder block, overhead; lubrication: gear pump, cartridge filter; lubricating system capacity: 14.6 imp pt, 17.5 US pt, 8.3 l; carburation: 3 Weber 40 DCNF downdraught twin barrel carburettors; fuel feed: electric pump; cooling system: liquid, sealed circuit, electric thermostatic fan; cooling system capacity: 21.1 imp pt, 25.4 US pt, 12 l.

TRANSMISSION driving wheels: rear; clutch: single dry plate; gearbox: ZF mechanical; gears: 5 + reverse; synchromesh gears: I, II, III, IV, V; gearbox ratios: I 2.991, II 1.763, III 1.301, IV 1, V 0.874, rev 3.670; gear lever: central; final drive: hypoid bevel, limited slip; axle ratio: 4.778; width of rims: 6.5''; tyres: ER 70 VR x 14.

PERFORMANCE max speeds: 40 mph, 65 km/h in 1st gear; 68 mph, 110 km/h in 2nd gear; 93 mph, 150 km/h in 3rd gear; 121 mph, 195 km/h in 4th gear; over 127 mph, 205 km/h in 5th gear; power-weight ratio: 17 lb/hp, 7.7 kg/hp; carrying capacity: 706 lb, 320 kg; max gradient in 1st gear: 50%; acceleration: standing ¼ mile 16 sec, 0-50 mph (0-80 km/h) 6.1 sec; speed in top at 1,000 rpm: 15.3 mph, 24.6 km/h; fuel consumption: 18.7 m/imp gal, 15.6 m/US gal, 15.1 l x 100 km.

CHASSIS integral; front suspension: independent, wishbones (lower trailing links), coil springs, anti-roll bar, telescopic dampers; rear suspension: independent, wishbones, semi-axle as lower arm, transverse upper radius arms, oblique trailing arms, coil springs, anti-roll bar, telescopic dampers.

STEERING worm and roller; turns of steering wheel lock to lock: 3.

BRAKES disc (front diameter 10.63 in, 270 mm, rear 11.02 in, 280 mm), radial fins, dual circuit, rear compensator, servo; lining area: front 30.4 sq in, 196 sq cm, rear 30.4 sq in, 196 sq cm, total 60.8 sq in, 392 sq cm.

FIAT Dino Coupé 2400

FIAT Dino Spider 2400

FIAT 130 Berlina

ELECTRICAL EQUIPMENT voltage: 12 V; battery: 77 Ah; generator type: alternator, 980 W; ignition distributor: Marelli (electronic); headlamps: 4, iodine long-distance lights.

DIMENSIONS AND WEIGHT wheel base: 100.39 in, 2,550 mm; front track: 54.72 in, 1,390 mm; rear track: 54.37 in, 1,381 mm; overall length: 177.44 in, 4,507 mm; overall width: 66.77 in, 1,696 mm; overall height: 51.77 in, 1,315 mm; ground clearance: 4.72 in, 120 mm; dry weight: 3,087 lb, 1,400 kg; distribution of weight: 52% front axle, 48% rear axle; turning circle (between walls): 40.7 ft, 12.4 m; fuel tank capacity: 15.4 imp gal, 18.5 US gal, 70 l.

BODY coupé; doors: 2; seats: 4; front seats: separate, reclining backrests; details: electrically-controlled windows, electrically-heated rear window.

PRACTICAL INSTRUCTIONS fuel: 98 oct petrol; engine sump oil: 12.3 imp pt, 14.8 US pt, 7 l, SAE 30 (winter) 40 (summer), change every 3,100 miles, 5,000 km; gearbox oil: 2.1 imp pt, 2.5 US pt, 1.2 l, SAE 90 EP, change every 18,600 miles, 30,000 km; final drive oil: 5.5 imp pt, 6.6 US pt, 3.1 l, SAE 90 EP, change every 18,600 miles, 30,000 km; greasing: every 1,600 miles, 2,500 km, 2 points; tappet clearances: inlet 0.006-0.008 in, 0.15-0.20 mm, exhaust 0.016-0.018 in, 0.40-0.45 mm; valve timing: inlet opens 40° before tdc and closes 52° after bdc, exhaust opens 53° before bdc and closes 31° after tdc; normal tyre pressure: front 31 psi, 2.2 atm, rear 31 psi, 2.2 atm.

Dino Spider 2400

See Dino Coupé 2400, except for:

PRICE EX WORKS: 4,300,000 liras.

PERFORMANCE max speed: over 130 mph, 210 km/h; power-weight ratio: 15 lb/hp, 6.8 kg/hp; carrying capacity: 529 lb, 240 kg; max gradient in 1st gear: 55%; acceleration: standing ¼ mile 15.5 sec, 0-50 mph (0-80 km/h) 6 sec.

ELECTRICAL EQUIPMENT battery: 55 Ah; generator type: alternator, 810 W.

DIMENSIONS AND WEIGHT wheel base: 89.76 in, 2,280 mm; front track: 54.45 in, 1,383 mm; overall length: 162.76 in, 4,134 mm; overall width: 67.32 in, 1,710 mm; overall height: 50 in, 1,270 mm; dry weight: 2,734 lb, 1,240 kg; turning circle (between walls): 37.7 ft, 11.5 m.

BODY sports; seats: 2 + 1; details: none.

PRACTICAL INSTRUCTIONS normal tyre pressure: front 27 psi, 1.9 atm, rear 27 psi, 1.9 atm.

OPTIONAL ACCESSORIES electrically-controlled windows; hardtop; headrests.

130 Berlina

PRICE EX WORKS: 3,400,000 liras.

ENGINE front, 4 stroke; cylinders: 6, Vee-slanted at 60°; bore and stroke: 3.78 x 2.60 in, 96 x 66 mm; engine capacity: 174.9 cu in, 2,866 cu cm; compression ratio: 9; max power (DIN): 160 hp at 5,800 rpm; max torque (DIN): 161 lb ft, 22.2 kg m at 3,400 rpm; max engine rpm: 6,000; specific power: 55.8 hp/l; cylinder block: cast iron; cylinder head: light alloy, hemispherical combustion chambers; crankshaft bearings: 4; valves: 2 per cylinder, overhead, in line, thimble tappets; camshafts: 1 per cylinder block, overhead, cogged belt; lubrication: gear pump, cartridge filter; lubricating system capacity: 11.8 imp pt, 14.2 US pt, 6.7 l; carburation: 1 Weber 45 DFC downdraught twin barrel carburettor; fuel feed: electric pump; cooling system: liquid, sealed circuit, electric thermostatic fan; cooling system capacity: 27.3 imp pt, 32.8 US pt, 15.5 l.

TRANSMISSION driving wheels: rear; gearbox: Borg-Warner 35/3 automatic, hydraulic torque convertor and planetary gears with 3 ratios + reverse, max ratio of convertor at stall 2.1, possible manual selection; gearbox ratios: I 2.390, II 1.450, III 1, rev 2.090; selector lever: central; final drive: hypoid bevel; axle ratio: 3.727; width of rims: 6.5''; tyres: 185 x 14.

PERFORMANCE max speeds: 50 mph, 80 km/h in 1st gear; 84 mph, 135 km/h in 2nd gear; 115 mph, 185 km/h in 3rd gear; power-weight ratio: 20.7 lb/hp, 9.4 kg/hp; carrying capacity: 882 lb, 400 kg; max gradient in 1st gear: 45%; acceleration: standing ¼ mile 19.3 sec, 0-50 mph (0-80 km/h) 10.3 sec; speed in direct drive at 1,000 rpm: 19.5 mph, 31.4 km/h; fuel consumption: 18.8 m/imp gal, 15.7 m/US gal, 15 l x 100 km.

CHASSIS integral; front suspension: independent, wishbones, longitudinal torsion bars, anti-roll bar, telescopic dampers; rear suspension: independent, wishbones, semi-axle as lower arm, transverse upper radius arms, oblique trailing arms, coil springs, anti-roll bar, telescopic dampers.

STEERING worm and roller, servo; turns of steering wheel lock to lock: 4.25.

FIAT Dino Coupé 2400

FIAT Dino Spider 2400

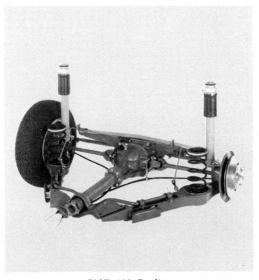

*FIAT 130 Berlina
(independent rear suspension)*

BRAKES disc (front diameter 10.83 in, 275 mm, rear 10.31 in, 262 mm), radial fins, dual circuit, rear compensator, servo; lining area: front 31 sq in, 200 sq cm, rear 21.7 sq in, 140 sq cm, total 52.7 sq in, 340 sq cm.

ELECTRICAL EQUIPMENT voltage: 12 V; battery: 55 Ah; generator type: alternator, 900 W; ignition distributor: Marelli; headlamps: 4, iodine long-distance lights.

DIMENSIONS AND WEIGHT wheel base: 107.09 in, 2,720 mm; front track: 57.01 in, 1,448 mm; rear track: 57.36 in, 1,457 mm; overall length: 187.01 in, 4,750 mm; overall width: 71.06 in, 1,805 mm; overall height: 58.07 in, 1,475 mm; ground clearance: 5.12 in, 130 mm; dry weight: 3,330 lb, 1,510 kg; distribution of weight: 53.3% front axle, 46.7% rear axle; turning circle (between walls): 38.7 ft, 11.8 m; fuel tank capacity: 17.6 imp gal, 21.1 US gal, 80 l.

BODY saloon/sedan; doors: 4; seats: 5; front seats: separate, reclining backrests; details: electrically-heated rear window.

PRACTICAL INSTRUCTIONS fuel: 98 oct petrol; engine sump oil: 9.9 imp pt, 11.8 US pt, 5.6 l, SAE 20W (winter) 30 (summer), change every 6.200 miles, 10,000 km; gearbox oil: 14.1 imp pt, 16.9 US pt, 8 l, G1/B; final drive oil: 3 imp pt, 3.6 US pt, 1.7 l, SAE 90, change every 18,600 miles, 30,000 km; greasing: none; sparking plug type: 240°; tappet clearances: inlet 0.016 in, 0.40 mm, exhaust 0.018 in, 0.45 mm; valve timing: inlet opens 26° before tdc and closes 66° after bdc, exhaust opens 66° before bdc and closes 26° after tdc; normal tyre pressure: front 28 psi, 2 atm, rear 31 psi, 2.2 atm.

OPTIONAL ACCESSORIES 5-speed mechanical gearbox (I 3.874, II 2.080, III 1.390, IV 1, V 0.874, rev 3.660), max speeds (I) 31 mph, 50 km/h, (II) 56 mph, 90 km/h, (III) 87 mph, 140 km/h, (IV) 115 mph, 185 km/h, (V) 112 mph, 180 km/h, acceleration standing ¼ mile 18.1 sec, 0-50 mph (0-80 km/h) 8.5 sec, speed in top at 1,000 rpm 19.6 mph, 31.5 km/h; air-conditioning system; electrically-controlled windows.

Campagnola A

PRICE EX WORKS: 2,050,000 liras.

ENGINE front, 4 stroke; cylinders: 4, in line; bore and stroke: 3.23 x 3.54 in, 82 x 90 mm; engine capacity: 116 cu in, 1,901 cu cm; compression ratio: 7.5; max power (DIN): 61 hp at 4,000 rpm; max torque (DIN): 94 lb ft, 13 kg m at 2,500 rpm; max engine rpm: 4,050; specific power: 32.1 hp/l; cylinder block: cast iron; cylinder head: light alloy; crankshaft bearings: 3; valves: 2 per cylinder, overhead, push-rods and rockers; camshafts: 1, side; lubrication: gear pump, cartridge, oil cooler; lubricating system capacity: 9.5 imp pt, 11.4 US pt, 5.4 l; carburation: 1 Solex 32 x 30 CBI downdraught carburettor; fuel feed: mechanical pump; cooling system: water; cooling system capacity: 16 imp pt, 19.2 US pt, 9.1 l.

TRANSMISSION driving wheels: front and rear; clutch: single dry plate; gearbox: mechanical; high gearbox ratios: I 4.181, II 2.425, III 1.594, IV 1.043, rev 4.181; low gearbox ratios: I 16.749, II 9.718, III 6.386, IV 4.180, rev 16.749; gear lever and transfer lever: central; final drive: hypoid bevel; axle ratio: 4.440; width of rims: 4.5'' K; tyres: 6.40 x 16.

PERFORMANCE max speeds: 17 mph, 28 km/h in 1st gear; 30 mph, 48 km/h in 2nd gear; 46 mph, 74 km/h in 3rd gear; over 68 mph, 110 km/h in 4th gear; power-weight ratio: 46.5 lb/hp, 21.1 kg/hp; carrying capacity: 1,058 lb, 480 kg; max gradient in high 1st gear: 30%, low 1st gear 90%; speed in top at 1,000 rpm: 17 mph, 28 km/h; fuel consumption: 22.2 m/imp gal, 18.5 m/US gal, 12.7 l x 100 km.

CHASSIS shaped long members linked X-ways and straight by cross members; front suspension: independent, swinging trailing arms, coil springs, rubber springs, anti-roll bar, telescopic dampers; rear suspension: rigid axle, semi-elliptic leafsprings, rubber springs, telescopic dampers.

STEERING screw and nut; turns of steering wheel lock to lock: 3.

BRAKES drum; lining area: front 80.2 sq in, 517 sq cm, rear 80.2 sq in, 517 sq cm, total 160.4 sq in, 1,034 sq cm.

ELECTRICAL EQUIPMENT voltage: 12 V; battery: 40 Ah; generator type: alternator, 400 W; ignition distributor: Marelli; headlamps: 4.

DIMENSIONS AND WEIGHT wheel base: 88.58 in, 2,250 mm; front track: 49.37 in, 1,254 mm; rear track: 49.61 in, 1,260 mm; overall length: 141.57 in, 3,596 mm; overall width: 61.81 in, 1,570 mm; overall height: 76.57 in, 1,945 mm; ground clearance: 7.99 in, 203 mm; dry weight: 2,844 lb, 1,290 kg; distribution of weight: 43% front axle, 57% rear axle; turning circle (between walls): 36.1 ft, 11 m; fuel tank capacity: 12.8 imp gal, 15.3 US gal, 58 l.

BODY open; doors: 2 + 1; seats: 6; front seats: separate; details: detachable canvas sunshine roof.

PRACTICAL INSTRUCTIONS fuel: 92 oct petrol; engine sump

CAMPAGNOLA A

oil: 9.5 imp pt, 11.4 US pt, 5.4 l, SAE 10W-40, change every 3,100 miles, 5,000 km; gearbox and transfer oil: 4.9 imp pt, 5.9 US pt, 2.8 l, SAE 90, change every 12,400 miles, 20,000 km; final drive oil: 2.1 imp pt, 2.5 US pt, 1.2 l, SAE 90 EP, change every 12,400 miles, 20,000 km; greasing: every 1,500 miles, 2,500 km, 18 points; sparking plug type: 225°; tappet clearances: inlet 0.006 in, 0.15 mm, exhaust 0.006 in, 0.15 mm; valve timing: inlet opens 10° before tdc and closes 51° after bdc, exhaust opens 48° before bdc and closes 11° after tdc; normal tyre pressure: front 23 psi, 1.6 atm, rear 28 psi, 2 atm.

OPTIONAL ACCESSORIES 6.50 x 16 tyres; independent heating; power take-off; limited slip final drive.

Campagnola C

See Campagnola A, except for:

PRICE EX WORKS: 2,450,000 liras.

ENGINE Diesel; bore and stroke: 3.35 x 3.29 in, 85 x 83.5 mm; engine capacity: 115.6 cu in, 1,895 cu cm; compression ratio: 22.5; max power (DIN): 47 hp at 3,700 rpm; max torque (DIN): 75 lb ft, 10.3 kg m at 2,200 rpm; specific power: 24.8 hp/l; cylinder head: cast iron; lubricating system capacity: 14.6 imp pt, 17.5 US pt, 8.3 l; carburation: Bosch injection pump; cooling system capacity: 16.7 imp pt, 20.1 US pt, 9.5 l.

TRANSMISSION high gearbox ratios: I 4.927, II 2.859, III 1.679, IV 1.043, rev 4.927; low gearbox ratios: I 19.738, II 11.452, III 6.726, IV 4.180, rev 19.738; axle ratio: 4.625; tyres: 6.50 x 16.

PERFORMANCE max speeds: 14 mph, 22 km/h in 1st gear; 24 mph, 38 km/h in 2nd gear; 40 mph, 64 km/h in 3rd gear; 59 mph, 95 km/h in 4th gear; power-weight ratio: 64.1 lb/hp, 29.1 kg/hp; speed in top at 1,000 rpm: 17.7 mph, 28.5 km/h; fuel consumption: 31 m/imp gal, 25.8 m/US gal, 9.1 l x 100 km.

ELECTRICAL EQUIPMENT voltage: 24 V; battery: 48 Ah; generator type: alternator, 26 A.

DIMENSIONS AND WEIGHT ground clearance: 8.39 in, 213 mm; dry weight: 3,021 lb, 1,370 kg; distribution of weight: 45% front axle, 55% rear axle.

PRACTICAL INSTRUCTIONS fuel: Diesel; engine sump oil: 14.6 imp pt, 17.5 US pt, 8.3 l, SAE 10W-40; final drive oil: 2.6 imp pt, 3.2 US pt, 1.5 l, SAE 90 EP; greasing: every 1,500 miles, 2,500 km, 16 points; tappet clearances: inlet 0.008 in, 0.20 mm, exhaust 0.008 in, 0.20 mm; valve timing: inlet opens 5° before tdc and closes 40° after bdc; exhaust opens 53° before bdc and closes 5° after tdc.

GIANNINI   ITALY

Fiat Giannini 500 TV

PRICE EX WORKS: 645,000 liras.

ENGINE rear, 4 stroke; cylinders: 2, vertical, in line; bore and stroke: 2.65 x 2.76 in, 67.4 x 70 mm; engine capacity: 30.4 cu in, 499 cu cm; compression ratio: 8.2; max power (DIN): 21.5 hp at 5,200 rpm; max torque (DIN): 26 lb ft, 3.6 kg m at 3,800 rpm; max engine rpm: 5,400; specific power: 43.1 hp/l; cylinder block: light alloy; cylinder head: light alloy; crankshaft bearings: 2; valves: 2 per cylinder, overhead, push-rods and rockers; camshafts: 1, side; lubrication: gear pump, full flow filter; lubricating system capacity: 4.8 imp pt, 5.7 US pt, 2.7 l; carburation: 1 Weber 26 IMB 4 downdraught carburettor; fuel feed: mechanical pump; cooling system: air-cooled.

TRANSMISSION driving wheels: rear; clutch: single dry plate; gearbox: mechanical; gears: 4 + reverse; silent claw coupling gears: II, III, IV; gearbox ratios: I 3.700, II 2.067, III 1.300, IV 0.875, rev 5.140; gear lever: central; final drive: spiral bevel; axle ratio: 5.125; width of rims: 3.5''; tyres: 125 x 12.

PERFORMANCE max speeds: 19 mph, 30 km/h in 1st gear; 31 mph, 50 km/h in 2nd gear; 50 mph, 80 km/h in 3rd gear; 71 mph, 115 km/h in 4th gear; power-weight ratio: 53.4 lb/hp, 24.2 kg/hp; carrying capacity: 706 lb, 320 kg; max gradient in 1st gear: 29%; speed in top at 1,000 rpm: 13.7 mph, 22 km/h; fuel consumption: 44.1 m/imp gal, 36.8 m/US gal, 6.4 l x 100 km.

CHASSIS integral; front suspension: independent, wishbones, transverse leafspring lower arms, telescopic dampers; rear suspension: independent, oblique semi-trailing arms, coil springs, telescopic dampers.

FIAT Campagnola A

GIANNINI Fiat Giannini 500 TV

GIANNINI Fiat Giannini 650 Coupé/Cabriolet

STEERING screw and sector; turns of steering wheel lock to lock: 3.

BRAKES drum; lining area: front 33.5 sq in, 216 sq cm, rear 33.5 sq in, 216 sq cm, total 67 sq in, 432 sq cm.

ELECTRICAL EQUIPMENT voltage: 12 V; battery: 32 Ah; generator type: dynamo, 230 W; ignition distributor: Marelli; headlamps: 2.

DIMENSIONS AND WEIGHT wheel base: 72.44 in, 1,840 mm; front track: 44.13 in, 1,121 mm; rear track: 44.68 in, 1,135 mm; overall length: 116.93 in, 2,970 mm; overall width: 51.97 in, 1,320 mm; overall height: 52.17 in, 1,325 mm; ground clearance: 4.92 in, 125 mm; dry weight: 1,147 lb, 520 kg; distribution of weight: 43% front axle, 57% rear axle; turning circle (between walls): 29.8 ft, 9.1 m; fuel tank capacity: 4.8 imp gal, 5.8 US gal, 22 l.

BODY saloon/sedan; doors: 2; seats: 4; front seats: separate; details: canvas sunshine roof.

PRACTICAL INSTRUCTIONS fuel: 98-100 oct petrol; engine sump oil: 4.4 imp pt, 5.3 US pt, 2.5 l, SAE 10W-40, change every 3,100 miles, 5,000 km; gearbox and final drive oil: 1.9 imp pt, 2.3 US pt, 1.1 l, SAE 90 EP, change every 18,600 miles, 30,000 km; greasing: every 1,600 miles, 2,500 km, 2 points; sparking plug type: 240°; tappet clearances: inlet 0.006 in, 0.15 mm, exhaust 0.006 in, 0.15 mm; valve timing: inlet opens 22° before tdc and closes 64° after bdc, exhaust opens 64° before bdc and closes 22° after tdc; normal tyre pressure: front 16 psi, 1.1 atm, rear 23 psi, 1.6 atm.

OPTIONAL ACCESSORIES special instrument panel with rev counter.

Fiat Giannini 500 TVL

See Fiat Giannini 500 TV, except for:

PRICE EX WORKS: 700,000 liras.

PERFORMANCE power-weight ratio: 54.5 lb/hp, 24.7 kg/hp.

DIMENSIONS AND WEIGHT overall length: 119.09 in, 3,025 mm; dry weight: 1,169 lb, 530 kg.

BODY details: luxury interior.

Fiat Giannini 500 Montecarlo

See Fiat Giannini 500 TV, except for:

PRICE EX WORKS: 795,000 liras.

ENGINE compression ratio: 10; max power (DIN): 39 hp at 7,500 rpm; max torque (DIN): 26 lb ft, 3.6 kg m at 6,000 rpm; max engine rpm: 8,000; specific power: 78.2 hp/l; lubricating system capacity: 6.2 imp pt, 7.4 US pt, 3.5 l; carburation: 1 Solex 34 PBIC downdraught carburettor or indirect injection system; fuel feed: electric pump.

TRANSMISSION axle ratio: 4.875.

PERFORMANCE max speeds: 34 mph, 55 km/h in 1st gear; 47 mph, 75 km/h in 2nd gear; 78 mph, 125 km/h in 3rd gear; 90 mph, 145 km/h in 4th gear; power-weight ratio: 27.8 lb/hp, 12.6 kg/hp; speed in top at 1,000 rpm: 11.8 mph, 19 km/h.

DIMENSIONS AND WEIGHT dry weight: 1,080 lb, 490 kg; distribution of weight: 42% front axle, 58% rear axle.

BODY special instrument panel with rev counter (standard).

PRACTICAL INSTRUCTIONS sparking plug type: 300°; tappet clearances: inlet 0.008 in, 0.20 mm, exhaust 0.008 in, 0.20 mm; valve timing: inlet opens 54° before tdc and closes 87° after bdc, exhaust opens 87° before bdc and closes 54° after tdc.

Fiat Giannini 590 GT

See Fiat Giannini 500 TV, except for:

PRICE EX WORKS: 705,000 liras.

ENGINE bore and stroke: 2.87 x 2.76 in, 73 x 70 mm; engine capacity: 36.5 cu in, 598 cu cm; compression ratio: 8.5; max power (DIN): 31 hp at 5,800 rpm; max torque (DIN): 33 lb ft, 4.6 kg m at 3,800 rpm; max engine rpm: 6,000; specific power: 51.8 hp/l; lubricating system capacity: 6.2 imp pt, 7.4 US pt, 3.5 l; carburation: 1 Solex 28 IB2 downdraught carburettor.

PERFORMANCE max speeds: 22 mph, 35 km/h in 1st gear; 36 mph, 58 km/h in 2nd gear; 56 mph, 90 km/h in 3rd gear;

FIAT Campagnola A

GIANNINI Fiat Giannini 500 TV

GIANNINI Fiat Giannini 590 Vallelunga

78 mph, 125 km/h in 4th gear; power-weight ratio: 34.8 lb/hp, 15.8 kg/hp; speed in top at 1,000 rpm: 14.3 mph, 23 km/h; fuel consumption: 43.5 m/imp gal, 36.2 m/US gal, 6.5 l x 100 km.

DIMENSIONS AND WEIGHT dry weight: 1,080 lb, 490 kg; distribution of weight: 42% front axle, 58% rear axle.

PRACTICAL INSTRUCTIONS valve timing: inlet opens 30° before tdc and closes 70° after bdc, exhaust opens 70° before bdc and closes 30° after tdc.

OPTIONAL ACCESSORIES special instrument panel with rev counter.

Fiat Giannini 590 GTL

See Fiat Giannini 590 GT, except for:

PRICE EX WORKS: 760,000 liras.

PERFORMANCE power-weight ratio: 37.7 lb/hp, 17.1 kg/hp.

DIMENSIONS AND WEIGHT overall length: 119.09 in, 3,025 mm; dry weight: 1,169 lb, 530 kg.

BODY details: luxury interior.

Fiat Giannini 590 Vallelunga

See Fiat Giannini 590 GT, except for:

PRICE EX WORKS: 795,000 liras.

ENGINE compression ratio: 10; max power (DIN): 41 hp at 7,500 rpm; max torque (DIN): 36 lb ft, 5 kg m at 6,000 rpm; max engine rpm: 8,000; specific power: 68.6 hp/l; carburation: 1 Solex 34 PBIC downdraught carburettor or indirect injection system; fuel feed: electric pump.

TRANSMISSION axle ratio: 4.555.

PERFORMANCE max speeds: 34 mph, 55 km/h in 1st gear; 47 mph, 75 km/h in 2nd gear; 81 mph, 130 km/h in 3rd gear; 93 mph, 150 km/h in 4th gear; power-weight ratio: 26.2 lb/hp, 11.9 kg/hp; max gradient in 1st gear: 36%; speed in top at 1,000 rpm: 11.8 mph, 19 km/h.

BODY special instrument panel with rev counter (standard).

PRACTICAL INSTRUCTIONS sparking plug type: 300°; tappet clearances: inlet 0.008 in, 0.20 mm, exhaust 0.008 in, 0.20 mm; valve timing: inlet opens 54° before tdc and closes 87° after bdc, exhaust opens 87° before bdc and closes 54° after tdc.

Fiat Giannini 650 NP

See Fiat Giannini 500 TV, except for:

PRICE EX WORKS: 725,000 liras.

ENGINE bore and stroke: 3.03 x 2.76 in, 77 x 70 mm; engine capacity: 39.8 cu in, 652 cu cm; compression ratio: 9; max power (DIN): 35 hp at 6,000 rpm; max torque (DIN): 38 lb ft, 5.2 kg m at 3,500 rpm; max engine rpm: 6,000; specific power: 53.7 hp/l; carburation: 1 Solex or Weber 34 PBIC or 30 DCI carburettor.

TRANSMISSION axle ratio: 4.875; tyres: 135 x 12.

PERFORMANCE max speeds: 22 mph, 35 km/h in 1st gear; 37 mph, 60 km/h in 2nd gear; 59 mph, 95 km/h in 3rd gear; 84 mph, 135 km/h in 4th gear; power-weight ratio: 30.9 lb/hp, 14 kg/hp; speed in top at 1,000 rpm: 14 mph, 22.5 km/h; fuel consumption: 43.5 m/imp gal, 36.2 m/US gal, 6.5 l x 100 km.

DIMENSIONS AND WEIGHT dry weight: 1,080 lb, 490 kg; distribution of weight: 42% front axle, 58% rear axle.

PRACTICAL INSTRUCTIONS valve timing: inlet opens 30° before tdc and closes 70° after bdc, exhaust opens 70° before bdc and closes 30° after tdc; normal tyre pressure: front 17 psi, 1.2 atm, rear 26 psi, 1.8 atm.

OPTIONAL ACCESSORIES light alloy wheels; special instrument panel with rev counter; Giannini special equipment.

Fiat Giannini 650 NPL

See Fiat Giannini 650 NP, except for:

PRICE EX WORKS: 780,000 liras.

PERFORMANCE power-weight ratio: 33.3 lb/hp, 15.1 kg/hp.

FIAT GIANNINI 650 NPL

DIMENSIONS AND WEIGHT overall length: 119.09 in, 3,025 mm; dry weight: 1,160 lb, 530 kg.

BODY details: luxury equipment.

Fiat Giannini 650 Coupé/Cabriolet

See Fiat Giannini 650 NP, except for:

PRICE EX WORKS: —

TRANSMISSION axle ratio: 4.333.

PERFORMANCE max speeds: 28 mph, 45 km/h in 1st gear; 47 mph, 75 km/h in 2nd gear; 68 mph, 110 km/h in 3rd gear; 99 mph, 160 km/h in 4th gear; max gradient in 1st gear: 30%; speed in top at 1,000 rpm: 15.5 mph, 25 km/h.

DIMENSIONS AND WEIGHT overall width: 58.27 in, 1,480 mm; overall height: 35.43 in, 900 mm.

BODY coupé/convertible in plastic material; seats: 2; details: detachable roof.

OPTIONAL ACCESSORIES only light alloy wheels.

Fiat Giannini 1000 Coupé Grand Prix

PRICE EX WORKS: 1,640,000 liras.

ENGINE rear, 4 stroke; cylinders: 4, vertical, in line; bore and stroke: 2.56 x 2.91 in, 65 x 74 mm; engine capacity: 59.9 cu in, 982 cu cm; compression ratio: 9; max power (DIN): 65 hp at 5,800 rpm; max torque (DIN): 54 lb ft, 7.5 kg m at 4,000 rpm; max engine rpm: 6,600; specific power: 66.2 hp/l; cylinder block: cast iron; cylinder head: light alloy; crankshaft bearings: 3; valves: 2 per cylinder, overhead, in line, push-rods and rockers; camshafts: 1, side; lubrication: gear pump; lubricating system capacity: 7.9 imp pt, 9.5 US pt, 4.5 l; carburation: 1 Weber 30 DCI downdraught twin barrel carburettor; fuel feed: mechanical pump; cooling system: liquid, sealed circuit; cooling system capacity: 13.2 imp pt, 15.9 US pt, 7.5 l.

TRANSMISSION driving wheels: rear; clutch: single dry plate; gearbox: mechanical; gears: 4 + reverse; synchromesh gears: I, II, III, IV; gearbox ratios: I 3.636, II 2.055, III 1.409, IV 0.963, rev 3.615; gear lever: central; final drive: hypoid bevel; axle ratio: 5.125; width of rims: 4.5''; tyres: 145 x 13.

PERFORMANCE max speeds: 31 mph, 50 km/h in 1st gear; 50 mph, 80 km/h in 2nd gear; 68 mph, 110 km/h in 3rd gear; 103 mph, 165 km/h in 4th gear; power-weight ratio: 21.2 lb/hp, 9.6 kg/hp; carrying capacity: 419 lb, 190 kg; max gradient in 1st gear: 38%; speed in top at 1,000 rpm: 15.5 mph, 25 km/h; fuel consumption: 34.9 m/imp gal, 29 m/US gal, 8.1 l x 100 km.

CHASSIS integral; front suspension: independent, wishbones, transverse leafspring lower arms, anti-roll bar, telescopic dampers; rear suspension: independent, semi-trailing arms, coil springs, anti-roll bar, telescopic dampers.

STEERING screw and sector; turns of steering wheel lock to lock: 3.75.

BRAKES front disc, rear drum; lining area: front 19.2 sq in, 124 sq cm, rear 33.5 sq in, 216 sq cm, total 52.7 sq in, 340 sq cm.

ELECTRICAL EQUIPMENT voltage: 12 V; battery: 45 Ah; generator type: alternator, 770 W; ignition distributor: Marelli; headlamps: 2, retractable.

DIMENSIONS AND WEIGHT wheel base: 79.80 in, 2,027 mm; front track: 45.20 in, 1,148 mm; rear track: 47.52 in, 1,207 mm; overall length: 140.75 in, 3,575 mm; overall width: 56.10 in, 1,425 mm; overall height: 54.53 in, 1,385 mm; ground clearance: 4.72 in, 120 mm; dry weight: 1,378 lb, 625 kg; distribution of weight: 36.1% front axle, 63.9% rear axle; turning circle (between walls): 33.5 ft, 10.2 m; fuel tank capacity: 6.6 imp gal, 7.9 US gal, 30 l.

BODY coupé; doors: 2; seats: 2.

PRACTICAL INSTRUCTIONS fuel: 98-100 oct petrol; engine sump oil: 7 imp pt, 8.5 US pt, 4 l, SAE 10W-40, change every 3,100 miles, 5,000 km; gearbox and final drive oil: 3.7 imp pt, 4.4 US pt, 2.1 l, SAE 90 EP, change every 18,600 miles, 30,000 km; greasing: every 1,600 miles, 2,500 km, 2 points; sparking plug type: 260°; tappet clearances: inlet 0.006 in, 0.15 mm, exhaust 0.006 in, 0.15 mm; valve timing: inlet opens 32° before tdc and closes 74° after bdc, exhaust opens 74° before bdc and closes 32° after tdc; normal tyre pressure: front 16 psi, 1.1 atm, rear 26 psi, 1.8 atm.

GIANNINI *Fiat Giannini 1000 Coupé Grand Prix*

GIANNINI *2-door Fiat Giannini 128 NP-S Berlina*

INNOCENTI *Mini Minor Mk 3*

2-door Fiat Giannini 128 NP Berlina

PRICE EX WORKS: 1,250,000 liras.

ENGINE front, 4 stroke; cylinders: 4, in line; bore and stroke: 3.15 x 2.19 in, 80 x 55.5 mm; engine capacity: 68.1 cu in, 1,116 cu cm; compression ratio: 9.8; max power (DIN): 66.2 hp at 6,500 rpm; max torque (DIN): 62 lb ft, 8.6 kg m at 4,000 rpm; max engine rpm: 7,000; specific power: 59.3 hp/l; cylinder block: cast iron; cylinder head: light alloy; crankshaft bearings: 5; valves: 2 per cylinder, overhead, thimble tappets; camshafts: 1, overhead; lubrication: gear pump, cartridge; lubricating system capacity: 7.2 imp pt, 8.7 US pt, 4.1 l; carburation: 1 Weber 32 ICEV downdraught carburettor; fuel feed: mechanical pump; cooling system: water; cooling system capacity: 11.4 imp pt, 13.7 US pt, 6.5 l.

TRANSMISSION driving wheels: front; clutch: single dry plate; gearbox: mechanical; gears: 4 + reverse; synchromesh gears: I, II, III, IV; gearbox ratios: I 3.583, II 2.235, III 1.454, IV 1.037, rev 3.714; gear lever: central; final drive: cylindrical gears; axle ratio: 4.077; width of rims: 4.5''; tyres: 145 x 13.

PERFORMANCE max speeds: 28 mph, 45 km/h in 1st gear; 44 mph, 71 km/h in 2nd gear; 68 mph, 110 km/h in 3rd gear; over 99 mph, 160 km/h in 4th gear; power-weight ratio: 26 lb/hp, 11.8 kg/hp; carrying capacity: 882 lb, 400 kg; speed in top at 1,000 rpm: 14.2 mph, 22.9 km/h; fuel consumption: 35.8 m/imp gal, 29.8 m/US gal, 7.9 l x 100 km.

CHASSIS integral; front suspension: independent, by McPherson, coil springs/telescopic damper struts, lower wishbones, anti-roll bar; rear suspension: independent, single wide based wishbone, transverse leafspring, telescopic dampers.

STEERING rack-and-pinion; turns of steering wheel lock to lock: 3.50.

BRAKES front disc (diameter 8.94 in, 227 mm), rear drum, dual circuit, rear compensator; lining area: front 19.2 sq in, 124 sq cm, rear 33.5 sq in, 216 sq cm, total 52.7 sq in, 340 sq cm.

ELECTRICAL EQUIPMENT voltage: 12 V; battery: 34 Ah; generator type: dynamo, 230 W; ignition distributor: Marelli; headlamps: 2.

DIMENSIONS AND WEIGHT wheel base: 96.38 in, 2,448 mm; front track: 51.50 in, 1,308 mm; rear track: 51.42 in, 1,306 mm; overall length: 151.81 in, 3,856 mm; overall width: 62.20 in, 1,590 mm; overall height: 55.91 in, 1,420 mm; ground clearance: 5.71 in, 145 mm; dry weight: 1,731 lb, 785 kg; distribution of weight: 61.5% front axle, 38.5% rear axle; turning circle (between walls): 35.8 ft, 10.9 m; fuel tank capacity: 8.4 imp gal, 10 US gal, 38 l.

BODY saloon/sedan; doors: 2; seats: 5; front seats: separate.

PRACTICAL INSTRUCTIONS fuel: 98 oct petrol; engine sump oil: 5.8 imp pt, 7 US pt, 3.3 l, SAE 20W-30, change every 6,200 miles, 10,000 km; gearbox and final drive oil: 5.5 imp pt, 6.6 US pt, 3.1 l, SAE 90, change every 18,600 miles, 30,000 km; greasing: none; normal tyre pressure: front 26 psi, 1.8 atm, rear 24 psi, 1.7 atm.

OPTIONAL ACCESSORIES special gearbox ratios; special final drive; light alloy wheels; instrument panel with rev counter; Giannini special equipment.

2-door Fiat Giannini 128 NP-S Berlina

See 2-door Fiat Giannini 128 NP Berlina, except for:

PRICE EX WORKS: 1,380,000 liras.

ENGINE max power (DIN): 76 hp at 7,000 rpm; max torque (DIN): 67 lb ft, 9.2 kg m at 4,800 rpm; max engine rpm: 7,500; specific power: 68.1 hp/l; carburation: 2 Weber 40 DCNF twin barrel carburettors.

PERFORMANCE max speed: over 106 mph, 170 km/h; power-weight ratio: 22.7 lb/hp, 10.3 kg/hp.

INNOCENTI   ITALY

Mini Minor Mk 3

PRICE EX WORKS: 998,000 liras.

ENGINE front, transverse, 4 stroke; cylinders: 4, in line; bore and stroke: 2.48 x 2.69 in, 62.9 x 68.3 mm; engine capacity: 51.7 cu in, 848 cu cm; compression ratio: 9; max power (SAE): 48 hp at 5,800 rpm; max torque (SAE): 48

GIANNINI *Fiat Giannini 1000 Coupé Grand Prix*

GIANNINI *2-door Fiat Giannini 128 NP-S Berlina*

INNOCENTI *Mini Minor Mk 3*

lb ft, 6.6 kg m at 3,000 rpm; max engine rpm: 6,000; specific power: 56.6 hp/l; cylinder block: cast iron; cylinder head: cast iron; crankshaft bearings: 3; valves: 2 per cylinder, overhead, in line, push-rods and rockers; camshafts: 1, side; lubrication: eccentric pump, full flow filter; lubricating system capacity: 8.8 imp pt, 10.6 US pt, 5 l; carburation: 1 SU type HS 4 AUD 263 carburettor; fuel feed: electric pump; cooling system: water; cooling system capacity: 6.2 imp pt, 7.4 US pt, 3.5 l.

TRANSMISSION driving wheels: front; clutch: single dry plate, hydraulically controlled; gearbox: mechanical, in unit with engine; gears: 4 + reverse: synchromesh gears: I, II, III, IV; gearbox ratios: I 3.525, II 2.218, III 1.433, IV 1, rev 3.544; gear lever: central; final drive: cylindrical gears, in unit with engine; axle ratio: 3.765; width of rims: 3.5''; tyres: 145 x 10.

PERFORMANCE max speeds: 19 mph, 30 km/h in 1st gear; 37 mph, 60 km/h in 2nd gear; 56 mph, 90 km/h in 3rd gear; 84 mph, 135 km/h in 4th gear; power-weight ratio: 28.9 lb/hp, 13.1 kg/hp; carrying capacity: 706 lb, 320 kg; max gradient in 1st gear: 25%; acceleration (medium load): standing ¼ mile 22.4 sec, 0-50 mph (0-80 km/h) 18.7 sec; speed in direct drive at 1,000 rpm: 14.7 mph, 23.6 km/h; fuel consumption: 44.1 m/imp gal, 36.8 m/US gal, 6.4 l x 100 km.

CHASSIS integral, front and rear auxiliary frames; front suspension: independent, wishbones, hydrolastic (liquid) rubber cone springs, hydraulic connecting pipes to rear wheels; rear suspension: independent, swinging longitudinal trailing arms, hydrolastic (liquid) rubber cone springs, hydraulic connecting pipes to front wheels, pitch control tension springs.

STEERING rack-and-pinion; turns of steering wheel lock to lock: 2.80.

BRAKES drum; lining area: front 40.6 sq in, 262 sq cm, rear 33.8 sq in, 218 sq cm, total 74.4 sq in, 480 sq cm.

ELECTRICAL EQUIPMENT voltage: 12 V; battery: 40 Ah; generator type: dynamo, 250 W; ignition distributor: Lucas; headlamps: 2.

DIMENSIONS AND WEIGHT wheel base: 80.16 in, 2,036 mm; front track: 47.44 in, 1,205 mm; rear track: 45.87 in, 1,165 mm; overall length: 120.28 in, 3,055 mm; overall width: 55.51 in, 1,410 mm; overall height: 52.76 in, 1,340 mm; ground clearance: 4.92 in, 125 mm; dry weight: 1,389 lb, 630 kg; distribution of weight: 61% front axle, 39% rear axle; turning circle (between walls): 28.2 ft, 8.6 m; fuel tank capacity: 5.5 imp gal, 6.6 US gal, 25 l.

BODY saloon/sedan; doors: 2; seats: 4; front seats: separate.

PRACTICAL INSTRUCTIONS fuel: 92 oct petrol; engine sump, gearbox and final drive oil: 8.8 imp pt, 10.6 US pt, 5 l, SAE 10W-40, change every 3,100 miles, 5,000 km; greasing: every 3,100 miles, 5,000 km, 7 points; tappet clearances: inlet 0.012 in, 0.30 mm, exhaust 0.012 in, 0.30 mm; valve timing: inlet opens 5° before tdc and closes 45° after bdc, exhaust opens 51° before bdc and closes 21° after tdc; normal tyre pressure: front 24 psi, 1.7 atm, rear 23 psi, 1.6 atm.

Mini T (all-metal body)

See Mini Minor Mk 3, except for:

PRICE EX WORKS: 1,005,000 liras.

PERFORMANCE power-weight ratio: 29.8 lb/hp, 13.5 kg/hp; fuel consumption: 41.5 m/imp gal, 34.6 m/US gal, 6.8 l x 100 km.

CHASSIS front and rear suspensions: rubber cone springs, telescopic dampers.

DIMENSIONS AND WEIGHT wheel base: 84.17 in, 2,138 mm; overall length: 128.66 in, 3,268 mm; overall width: 55.71 in, 1,415 mm; overall height: 53.54 in, 1,360 mm; ground clearance: 6.02 in, 153 mm; dry weight: 1,433 lb, 650 kg; distribution of weight: 57.5% front axle, 42.5% rear axle; turning circle (between walls): 28.9 ft, 8.8 m; fuel tank capacity: 6.4 imp gal, 7.7 US gal, 29 l.

BODY estate car/station wagon; doors: 2 + 1.

Mini T (wood-trimmed body)

See Mini T (all-metal body), except for:

PRICE EX WORKS: 1,065,000 liras.

PERFORMANCE power-weight ratio: 30.2 lb/hp, 13.7 kg/hp.

DIMENSIONS AND WEIGHT dry weight: 1,455 lb, 660 kg.

Mini Matic

See Mini Minor Mk 3, except for:

PRICE EX WORKS: 1,194,000 liras.

ENGINE bore and stroke: 2.54 x 3 in, 64.6 x 76.2 mm; engine capacity: 60.9 cu in, 998 cu cm; compression ratio: 8.9; max power (SAE): 46 hp at 4,800 rpm; max torque (SAE): 59 lb ft, 8.2 kg m at 2,400 rpm; specific power: 46.1 hp/l; lubricating system capacity: 13.2 imp pt, 15.9 US pt, 7.5 l; carburation: 1 SU type HS 4 AUD 460 carburettor.

TRANSMISSION gearbox: automatic, hydraulic torque convertor with 2 conic bevel gears (twin concentric differential-like gear clusters) with 4 ratios + reverse, max ratio of convertor at stall 2, possible manual selection; gearbox ratios: I 2.690, II 1.850, III 1.469, IV 1, rev 2.690; gear lever: central; axle ratio: 3.270.

PERFORMANCE max speeds: 22 mph, 35 km/h in 1st gear; 37 mph, 60 km/h in 2nd gear; 53 mph, 85 km/h in 3rd gear; over 78 mph, 125 km/h in 4th gear; power-weight ratio: 31.3 lb/hp, 14.2 kg/hp; speed in direct drive at 1,000 rpm: 14.6 mph, 23.5 km/h; fuel consumption: 38.7 m/imp gal, 32.2 m/US gal, 7.3 l x 100 km.

DIMENSIONS AND WEIGHT dry weight: 1,444 lb, 655 kg.

PRACTICAL INSTRUCTIONS valve timing: inlet opens 5° before tdc and closes 45° after bdc, exhaust opens 40° before bdc and closes 10° after tdc.

Mini Cooper Mk 3

See Mini Minor Mk 3, except for:

PRICE EX WORKS: 1,307,000 liras.

ENGINE bore and stroke: 2.54 x 3 in, 64.6 x 76.2 mm; engine capacity: 60.9 cu in, 998 cu cm; compression ratio: 9.5; max power (SAE): 60 hp at 6,000 rpm; max torque (SAE): 62 lb ft, 8.6 kg m at 3,000 rpm; max engine rpm: 6,200; specific power: 60.1 hp/l; carburation: 2 SU type HS 2 AUD 324 carburettors; cooling system capacity: 6.7 imp pt, 8 US pt, 3.8 l.

TRANSMISSION gearbox ratios: I 3.329, II 2.094, III 1.353, IV 1, rev 3.347; width of rims: 4.5''.

PERFORMANCE max speeds: 25 mph, 40 km/h in 1st gear; 43 mph, 70 km/h in 2nd gear; 62 mph, 100 km/h in 3rd gear; 93 mph, 150 km/h in 4th gear; power-weight ratio: 23.8 lb/hp, 10.8 kg/hp; max gradient in 1st gear: 33%; acceleration (medium load): standing ¼ mile 19.8 sec, 0-50 mph (0-80 km/h) 10 sec; fuel consumption: 36.7 m/imp gal, 30.5 m/US gal, 7.7 l x 100 km.

BRAKES front disc, rear drum, rear compensator, servo; lining area: front 16.1 sq in, 104 sq cm, rear 33.8 sq in, 218 sq cm, total 49.9 sq in, 322 sq cm.

DIMENSIONS AND WEIGHT front track: 49.02 in, 1,245 mm; rear track: 47.64 in, 1,210 mm; dry weight: 1,433 lb, 650 kg; distribution of weight: 60% front axle, 40% rear axle; turning circle (between walls): 28.9 ft, 8.8 m.

PRACTICAL INSTRUCTIONS valve timing: inlet opens 10° before tdc and closes 50° after bdc, exhaust opens 51° before bdc and closes 21° after tdc.

Austin J5

PRICE EX WORKS: 1,216,000 liras.

ENGINE front, transverse, 4 stroke; cylinders: 4, in line; bore and stroke: 2.54 x 3.30 in, 64.6 x 83.7 mm; engine capacity: 67 cu in, 1,098 cu cm; compression ratio: 8.9; max power (SAE): 58 hp at 5,500 rpm; max torque (SAE): 62 lb ft, 8.5 kg m at 2,500 rpm; max engine rpm: 5,800; specific power: 52.8 hp/l; cylinder block: cast iron; cylinder head: cast iron; crankshaft bearings: 3; valves: 2 per cylinder, overhead, in line, push-rods and rockers; camshafts: 1, side; lubrication: eccentric pump, full flow filter; lubricating system capacity: 8.8 imp pt, 10.6 US pt, 5 l; carburation: 2 SU type HS 2 AUD 132 carburettors; fuel feed: electric pump; cooling system: water; cooling system capacity: 6.7 imp pt, 8 US pt, 3.8 l.

TRANSMISSION driving wheels: front; clutch: single dry plate, hydraulically controlled; gearbox: mechanical; gears: 4 + reverse; synchromesh gears: I, II, III, IV; gearbox ratios: I 3.525, II 2.220, III 1.433, IV 1, rev 3.560; gear lever: central; final drive: cylindrical gears; axle ratio: 4.133; width of rims: 4''; tyres: 5.50 x 12 or 145 x 12.

PERFORMANCE max speeds: 22 mph, 35 km/h in 1st gear; 37 mph, 60 km/h in 2nd gear; 57 mph, 92 km/h in 3rd gear; 90 mph, 145 km/h in 4th gear; power-weight ratio: 32.2 lb/hp, 14.6 kg/hp; carrying capacity: 882 lb, 400 kg; acceleration: 0-50 mph (0-80 km/h) 16 sec; speed in direct drive at 1,000 rpm: 15 mph, 24.2 km/h; fuel consumption: 38.2 m/imp gal, 31.8 m/US gal, 7.4 l x 100 km.

CHASSIS integral, front and rear auxiliary frames; front suspension: independent, wishbones, hydrolastic (liquid) rubber cone springs, hydraulic connecting pipes to rear

INNOCENTI Mini Matic

INNOCENTI Austin J5

ISO Grifo 7-litre

wheels; rear suspension: independent, swinging longitudinal trailing arms, hydrolastic (liquid) rubber cone springs, hydraulic connecting pipes to front wheels, combined with transverse torsion bars, anti-roll bar.

STEERING rack-and-pinion; turns of steering wheel lock to lock: 3.30.

BRAKES front disc (diameter 8 in, 203 mm), rear drum, rear compensator, servo; lining area: front 16.1 sq in, 104 sq cm, rear 38.4 sq in, 248 sq cm, total 54.5 sq in, 352 sq cm.

ELECTRICAL EQUIPMENT voltage: 12 V; battery: 43 Ah; generator type: dynamo, 250 W; ignition distributor: Lucas; headlamps: 2.

DIMENSIONS AND WEIGHT wheel base: 93.50 in, 2,375 mm; front track: 51.57 in, 1,310 mm; rear track: 50.79 in, 1,290 mm; overall length: 146.26 in, 3,715 mm; overall width: 60.39 in, 1,534 mm; overall height: 54.13 in, 1,375 mm; ground clearance: 5.12 in, 130 mm; dry weight: 1,865 lb, 846 kg; distribution of weight: 59.5% front axle, 40.5% rear axle; turning circle (between walls): 33.8 ft, 10.3 m; fuel tank capacity: 8.4 imp gal, 10 US gal, 38 l.

BODY saloon/sedan; doors: 4; seats: 5; front seats: separate, reclining backrests.

PRACTICAL INSTRUCTIONS fuel: 98-100 oct petrol; engine sump, gearbox and final drive oil: 8.8 imp pt, 10.6 US pt, 5 l, SAE 10W-40, change every 3,100 miles, 5,000 km; greasing: every 3,100 miles, 5,000 km, 5 points; tappet clearances: inlet 0.012 in, 0.30 mm, exhaust 0.012 in, 0.30 mm; valve timing: inlet opens 5° before tdc and closes 45° after bdc, exhaust opens 51° before bdc and closes 21° after tdc; normal tyre pressure: front 27 psi, 1.9 atm, rear 24 psi, 1.7 atm.

ISO   ITALY

Fidia

PRICE IN GB: £ 5,436.
PRICE IN USA: $ 14,800.

ENGINE front, 4 stroke; cylinders: 8, Vee-slanted at 90°; bore and stroke: 4 x 3.25 in, 101.6 x 82.6 mm; engine capacity: 326.9 cu in, 5,358 cu cm; compression ratio: 10.5; max power (SAE): 300 hp at 5,000 rpm; max torque (SAE): 361 lb ft, 49.8 kg m at 3,200 rpm; max engine rpm: 5,000; specific power: 56 hp/l; cylinder block: cast iron; cylinder head: cast iron; crankshaft bearings: 5; valves: 2 per cylinder, overhead, push-rods and rockers, hydraulic tappets; camshafts: 1, at centre of Vee; lubrication: gear pump, full flow filter; lubricating system capacity: 15 imp pt, 18 US pt, 8.5 l; carburation: 1 Rochester 4 MV downdraught 4-barrel carburettor; fuel feed: mechanical pump; cooling system: water; cooling system capacity: 31.7 imp pt, 38.1 US pt, 18 l.

TRANSMISSION driving wheels: rear; clutch: single dry plate (diaphragm); gearbox: mechanical; gears: 4 + reverse; synchromesh gears: I, II, III, IV; gearbox ratios: I 2.200, II 1.640, III 1.280, IV 1, rev 2.270; gear lever: central; final drive: hypoid bevel, limited slip; axle ratio: 2.880; tyres: 205 VR x 15.

PERFORMANCE max speeds: 60 mph, 96 km/h in 1st gear; 81 mph, 130 km/h in 2nd gear; 102 mph, 164 km/h in 3rd gear; 137 mph, 220 km/h in 4th gear; power-weight ratio: 11 lb/hp, 5 kg/hp; carrying capacity: 882 lb, 400 kg; acceleration: standing ¼ mile 14 sec, 0-80 mph (0-80 km/h) 6.5 sec; speed in direct drive at 1,000 rpm: 27.3 mph, 44 km/h; fuel consumption: 15.7 m/imp gal, 13.1 m/US gal, 18 l x 100 km.

CHASSIS integral; front suspension: independent, wishbones, coil springs, anti-roll bar, telescopic dampers; rear suspension: de Dion rigid axle, twin trailing radius arms, transverse linkage bar, coil springs, telescopic dampers.

STEERING recirculating ball; turns of steering wheel lock to lock: 4.

BRAKES disc (front diameter 11.43 in, 290 mm, rear 10.87 in, 277 mm), dual circuit, servo; area rubbed by linings: front 288.1 sq in, 1,858 sq cm, rear 214.1 sq in, 1,381 sq cm, total 502.2 sq in, 3,239 sq cm.

ELECTRICAL EQUIPMENT voltage: 12 V; battery: 60 Ah; generator type: alternator, 500 W; ignition distributor: Delco-Remy; headlamps: 4, iodine.

DIMENSIONS AND WEIGHT wheel base: 112.20 in, 2,850 mm; front track: 55.51 in, 1,410 mm; rear track: 55.51 in, 1,410 mm; overall length: 195.67 in, 4,970 mm; overall width: 70.08 in, 1,780 mm; overall height: 51.97 in, 1,320 mm; ground clearance: 4.72 in, 120 mm; dry weight: 3,308 lb, 1,500 kg; turning circle (between walls): 41 ft, 12.5 m; fuel tank capacity: 20.9 imp gal, 25.1 US gal, 95 l.

BODY saloon/sedan; doors: 4; seats: 4-5; front seats: separate, reclining backrests.

INNOCENTI Mini T (all-metal body)

INNOCENTI Austin J5

ISO Grifo 7-litre

PRACTICAL INSTRUCTIONS fuel: 98-100 oct petrol; engine sump oil: 11.4 imp pt, 13.7 US pt, 6.5 l, SAE 10W-30, change every 3,100 miles, 5,000 km; gearbox oil: 2.6 imp pt, 3.2 US pt, 1.5 l, SAE 90, change every 12,400 miles, 20,000 km; final drive oil: 2.6 imp pt, 3.2 US pt, 1.5 l, SAE 90, change every 12,400 miles, 20,000 km; greasing: every 9,300 miles, 15,000 km, 12 points; sparking plug type: 225°; normal tyre pressure: front 31 psi, 2.2 atm, rear 34 psi, 2.4 atm.

VARIATIONS

ENGINE 11 compression ratio, max power (SAE) 350 hp at 5,800 rpm, max torque (SAE) 361 lb ft, 49.8 kg m at 3,600 rpm, max engine rpm 5,800, 65.3 hp/l specific power.
TRANSMISSION 3.070 axle ratio.
PERFORMANCE max speeds (I) 62 mph, 100 km/h, (II) 84 mph, 135 km/h, (III) 107 mph, 173 km/h, (IV) 143 mph, 230 km/h, power-weight ratio 9.5 lb/hp, 4.3 kg/hp, acceleration standing ¼ mile 12.8 sec, speed in direct drive at 1,000 rpm 25.5 mph, 41 km/h, fuel consumption 14.9 m/imp gal, 12.4 m/US gal, 19 l x 100 km.

OPTIONAL ACCESSORIES 3.070 or 3.310 axle ratio; 5-speed ZF mechanical gearbox; Powerglide automatic gearbox (only with 300 hp engine); wire or light alloy wheels; power-assisted steering; air-conditioning system.

Lele

See Fidia, except for:

PRICE IN GB: £ 5,704.
PRICE EX WORKS: 7,000,000 liras.

ENGINE bore and stroke: 4 x 3.48 in, 101.6 x 88.4 mm; engine capacity: 349.9 cu in, 5,735 cu cm; compression ratio: 10.2; max power (SAE): 300 hp at 4,800 rpm; max torque (SAE): 380 lb ft, 52.4 kg m at 3,200 rpm; specific power: 52.3 hp/l.

PERFORMANCE max speed: 143 mph, 230 km/h; power-weight ratio: 10.1 lb/hp, 4.6 kg/hp; carrying capacity: 706 lb, 320 kg; fuel consumption: 16.1 m/imp gal, 13.4 m/US gal, 17.5 l x 100 km.

DIMENSIONS AND WEIGHT wheel base: 106.30 in, 2,700 mm; overall length: 183.07 in, 4,650 mm; overall width: 68.90 in, 1,750 mm; overall height: 53.15 in, 1,350 mm; dry weight: 3,043 lb, 1,380 kg; turning circle (between walls): 39.4 ft, 12 m; fuel tank capacity: 22 imp gal, 26.4 US gal, 100 l.

BODY coupé; doors: 2; seats: 4.

VARIATIONS

(With 350 hp engine and 3.070 axle ratio).

PERFORMANCE max speed 155 mph, 250 km/h, power-weight ratio 8.6 lb/hp, 3.9 kg/hp, fuel consumption 14.9 m/imp gal, 12.4 m/US gal, 19 l x 100 km.

Grifo GL

See Fidia, except for:

PRICE IN GB: £ 5,589.
PRICE IN USA: $ 13,448.

PERFORMANCE max speeds: 62 mph, 100 km/h in 1st gear; 84 mph, 135 km/h in 2nd gear; 107 mph, 173 km/h in 3rd gear; 143 mph, 230 km/h in 4th gear; power-weight ratio: 10.1 lb/hp, 4.6 kg/hp; carrying capacity: 573 lb, 260 kg; acceleration: standing ¼ mile 13 sec, 0-50 mph (0-80 km/h) 6 sec; speed in direct drive at 1,000 rpm: 28.6 mph, 46 km/h; fuel consumption: 17.7 m/imp gal, 14.7 m/US gal, 16 l x 100 km.

DIMENSIONS AND WEIGHT wheel base: 98.42 in, 2,500 mm; overall length: 174.41 in, 4,430 mm; overall width: 69.68 in, 1,770 mm; overall height: 47.24 in, 1,200 mm; dry weight: 3,043 lb, 1,380 kg; distribution of weight: 48% front axle, 52% rear axle; turning circle (between walls): 39.4 ft, 12 m; fuel tank capacity: 22 imp gal, 26.4 US gal, 100 l.

BODY coupé; doors: 2; seats: 2; details: light alloy wheels (standard).

PRACTICAL INSTRUCTIONS normal tyre pressure: front 34 psi, 2.4 atm, rear 37 psi, 2.6 atm.

VARIATIONS

(With 350 hp engine (no extra charge) and 3.070 axle ratio).

PERFORMANCE max speeds (I) 68 mph, 109 km/h, (II) 92 mph, 148 km/h, (III) 117 mph, 188 km/h, (IV) 162 mph, 260 km/h, power-weight ratio 8.6 lb/hp, 3.9 kg/hp, acceleration standing ¼ mile 12 sec, 0-50 mph (0-80 km/h) 5 sec, speed in direct drive at 1,000 rpm 28 mph, 45 km/h, fuel consumption 15.7 m/imp gal, 13.1 m/US gal, 18 l x 100 km.

Grifo Spider

See Grifo GL, except for:

PRICE EX WORKS: 7,650,000 liras.

BODY convertible.

Grifo 7-litre

PRICE IN GB: £ 6,815.
PRICE IN USA: $ 15,500.

ENGINE front, 4 stroke; cylinders: 8, Vee-slanted at 90°; bore and stroke: 4.25 x 3.76 in, 107.9 x 95.9 mm; engine capacity: 427 cu in, 6,998 cu cm; compression ratio: 10.2; max power (SAE): 490 hp at 5,200 rpm; max torque (SAE): 460 lb ft, 63.5 kg m at 3,600 rpm; max engine rpm: 5,200; specific power: 55.7 hp/l; cylinder block: cast iron; cylinder head: cast iron; crankshaft bearings: 5; valves: 2 per cylinder, overhead, push-rods and rockers, hydraulic tappets; camshafts: 1, at centre of Vee; lubrication: gear pump, full flow filter; lubricating system capacity: 16.7 imp pt, 20.1 US pt, 9.5 l; carburation: 1 Rochester 4 MV downdraught 4-barrel carburettor; fuel feed: mechanical pump; cooling system: water; cooling system capacity: 31.7 imp pt, 38.1 US pt, 18 l.

TRANSMISSION driving wheels: rear; clutch: single dry plate; gearbox: mechanical; gears: 4 + reverse; synchromesh gears: I, II, III, IV; gearbox ratios: I 2.200, II 1.640, III 1.280, IV 1, rev 2.270; gear lever: central; final drive: hypoid bevel; axle ratio: 2.400; tyres: 205 VR x 15.

PERFORMANCE max speeds: 78 mph, 125 km/h in 1st gear; 104 mph, 168 km/h in 2nd gear; 133 mph, 214 km/h in 3rd gear; 171 mph, 275 km/h in 4th gear; power-weight ratio: 7.9 lb/hp, 3.6 kg/hp; carrying capacity: 573 lb, 260 kg; speed in direct drive at 1,000 rpm: 33 mph, 53 km/h; fuel consumption: 15.7 m/imp gal, 13.1 m/US gal, 18 l x 100 km.

CHASSIS integral; front suspension: independent, wishbones, coil springs, anti-roll bar, telescopic dampers; rear suspension: de Dion rigid axle, twin trailing radius arms, transverse linkage bar, coil springs, telescopic dampers.

STEERING recirculating ball; turns of steering wheel lock to lock: 4.

BRAKES disc (front diameter 11.43 in, 290 mm, rear 10.87 in, 277 mm), dual circuit, servo; area rubbed by linings: front 268.5 sq in, 1,732 sq cm, rear 243.1 sq in, 1,568 sq cm, total 511.6 sq in, 3,300 sq cm.

ELECTRICAL EQUIPMENT voltage: 12 V; battery: 60 Ah; generator type: alternator, 500 W; ignition distributor: Delco-Remy; headlamps: 4.

DIMENSIONS AND WEIGHT wheel base: 98.42 in, 2,500 mm; front track: 55.51 in, 1,410 mm; rear track: 55.51 in, 1,410 mm; overall length: 174.41 in, 4,430 mm; overall width: 69.68 in, 1,770 mm; overall height: 48.43 in, 1,230 mm; ground clearance: 4.72 in, 120 mm; dry weight: 3,087 lb, 1,400 kg; distribution of weight: 49% front axle, 51% rear axle; turning circle (between walls): 39.4 ft, 12 m; fuel tank capacity: 22 imp gal, 26.4 US gal, 100 l.

BODY coupé; doors: 2; seats: 2.

PRACTICAL INSTRUCTIONS fuel: 98-100 oct petrol; engine sump oil: 13.2 imp pt, 15.9 US pt, 7.5 l, SAE 10W-30, change every 3,100 miles, 5,000 km; gearbox oil: 2.6 imp pt, 3.2 US pt, 1.5 l, SAE 90, change every 12,400 miles, 20,000 km; final drive oil: 2.6 imp pt, 3.2 US pt, 1.5 l, SAE 90, change every 12,400 miles, 20,000 km; greasing: every 3,100 miles, 5,000 km, 12 points; sparking plug type: 250°; normal tyre pressure: front 34 psi, 2.4 atm, rear 37 psi, 2.6 atm.

OPTIONAL ACCESSORIES detachable roof; air-conditioning system.

LAMBORGHINI   ITALY

Urraco

PRICE EX WORKS: —

ENGINE rear, transverse, 4 stroke; cylinders: 8, Vee-slanted at 90°; bore and stroke: 3.39 x 2.09 in, 86 x 53 mm; engine capacity: 150.3 cu in, 2,463 cu cm; compression ratio: 10.5; max power (DIN): 220 hp at 7,800 rpm; max torque (DIN): 167 lb ft, 23 kg m at 5,750 rpm; max engine rpm: 8,000; specific power: 89.3 hp/l; cylinder block: light alloy, wet liners; cylinder head: light alloy; crankshaft bearings: 5; valves: 2 per cylinder, overhead, Vee-slanted at 45°, thimble tappets; camshafts: 2 per cylinder block, overhead; lubrication: gear pump, full flow filter; lubricating system capacity: 10.6 imp pt, 12.7 US pt, 6 l; carburation: 4 Weber 40 IDF 1 downdraught twin barrel carburettors; fuel feed: electric pump; cooling system: water, 2 front fans, 1 electric and 1 thermostatic fan; cooling system capacity: 21.1 imp pt, 25.4 US pt, 12 l.

LAMBORGHINI *Urraco*

LAMBORGHINI *Jarama*

LAMBORGHINI *Miura S*

TRANSMISSION driving wheels: rear; clutch: single dry plate (diaphragm), hydraulically controlled; gearbox: mechanical; gears: 5 + reverse; synchromesh gears: I, II, III, V, V, rev; gearbox ratios: I 2.687, II 2.105, III 1.565, V 1.185, V 0.903, rev 2.540; gear lever: central; final drive: helical spur gears; axle ratio: 4.250; width of rims: 7''; tyres: 205 VR x 14.

PERFORMANCE max speeds: 55 mph, 89 km/h in 1st gear; 71 mph, 114 km/h in 2nd gear; 95 mph, 153 km/h in 3rd gear; 126 mph, 202 km/h in 4th gear; over 149 mph, 240 km/h in 5th gear; power-weight ratio: 11 lb/hp, 5 kg/hp; carrying capacity: 882 lb, 400 kg; speed in top at 1,000 rpm: 19.2 mph, 30.9 km/h; fuel consumption: 23.5 m/imp gal, 19.6 m/US gal, 12 l x 100 km.

CHASSIS integral, rear auxiliary frame; front suspension: independent, by McPherson, coil springs/telescopic damper struts, lower wishbones (trailing links), anti-roll bar; rear suspension: independent, by McPherson, coil springs/telescopic damper struts, lower wishbones, anti-roll bar.

STEERING rack-and-pinion; turns of steering wheel lock to lock: 4.25.

BRAKES disc (diameter 10.94 in, 278 mm), internal radial fins, dual circuit.

ELECTRICAL EQUIPMENT voltage: 12 V; battery: 55 Ah; generator type: alternator, 770 W; ignition distributor: Marelli; headlamps: 2, retractable, iodine.

DIMENSIONS AND WEIGHT wheel base: 96.46 in, 2,450 mm; front track: 57.48 in, 1,460 mm; rear track: 57.48 in, 1,460 mm; overall length: 167.32 in, 4,250 mm; overall width: 69.29 in, 1,760 mm; overall height: 43.90 in, 1,115 mm; ground clearance: 4.92 in, 125 mm; dry weight: 2,426 lb, 1,100 kg; turning circle (between walls): 35.1 ft, 10.7 m; fuel tank capacity: 15.4 imp gal, 18.5 US gal, 70 l.

BODY coupé; doors: 2; seats: 4; front seats: separate.

PRACTICAL INSTRUCTIONS fuel: 98-100 oct petrol; engine sump oil: 10.6 imp pt, 12.7 US pt, 6 l, 20W-50, change every 2,500 miles, 4,000 km; gearbox and final drive oil: 10.6 imp pt, 12.7 US pt, 6 l, SAE 90, change every 6,200 miles, 10,000 km; tappet clearances: inlet 0.018 in, 0.45 mm, exhaust 0.018 in, 0.45 mm; valve timing: inlet opens 40° before tdc and closes 60° after bdc, exhaust opens 58° before bdc and closes 38° after bdc; normal tyre pressure: front 28 psi, 2 atm, rear 31 psi, 2.2 atm.

Espada

PRICE IN GB: £ 8,450.
PRICE EX WORKS: 8,300,000 liras.

ENGINE front, 4 stroke; cylinders: 12, Vee-slanted at 60°; bore and stroke: 3.23 x 2.44 in, 82 x 62 mm; engine capacity: 239.7 cu in, 3,929 cu cm; compression ratio: 10.7; max power (DIN): 350 hp at 7,500 rpm; max torque (DIN): 290 lb ft, 40 kg m at 5,500 rpm; max engine rpm: 8,000; specific power: 89.1 hp/l; cylinder block: light alloy, wet liners; cylinder head: light alloy; crankshaft bearings: 7; valves: 2 per cylinder, overhead, Vee-slanted at 70°, thimble tappets; camshafts: 2 per cylinder block, overhead; lubrication: gear pump, full flow filter; lubricating system capacity: 25.2 imp pt, 30.2 US pt, 14.3 l; carburation: 6 Weber 40 DCOE 20/21 horizontal twin barrel carburettors; fuel feed: electric pump; cooling system: water, 2 fans, 1 electric and 1 thermostatic fan; cooling system capacity: 24.6 imp pt, 29.6 US pt, 14 l.

TRANSMISSION driving wheels: rear; clutch: single dry plate (diaphragm), hydraulically controlled; gearbox: mechanical; gears: 5 + reverse; synchromesh gears: I, II, III, IV, V, rev; gearbox ratios: I 2.520, II 1.735, III 1.225, IV 1, V 0.815, rev 2.765; gear lever: central; final drive: hypoid bevel; axle ratio: 4.500; width of rims: 7''; tyres: 205 VR x 15.

PERFORMANCE max speeds: 47 mph, 75 km/h in 1st gear; 68 mph, 110 km/h in 2nd gear; 93 mph, 150 km/h in 3rd gear; 124 mph, 200 km/h in 4th gear; 155 mph, 250 km/h in 5th gear; power-weight ratio: 9.3 lb/hp, 4.2 kg/hp; carrying capacity: 926 lb, 420 kg; speed in top at 1,000 rpm: 21.2 mph, 34.1 km/h; fuel consumption: 16.6 m/imp gal, 13.8 m/US gal, 17 l x 100 km.

CHASSIS integral; front suspension: independent, wishbones, coil springs, anti-roll bar, telescopic dampers; rear suspension: independent, wishbones, coil springs, anti-roll bar, telescopic dampers.

STEERING ZF worm and wheel; turns of steering wheel lock to lock: 3.80.

BRAKES disc (front diameter 11.81 in, 300 mm, rear 11.02 in, 280 mm), internal radial fins, dual circuit, each with servo; area rubbed by linings: front 285.3 sq in, 1,840 sq cm, rear 206.2 sq in, 1,330 sq cm, total 491.5 sq in, 3,170 sq cm.

ELECTRICAL EQUIPMENT voltage: 12 V; battery: 72 Ah; generator type: alternator, 550 W; ignition distributor: Marelli; headlamps: 2, iodine; fog lamps: 2, iodine.

DIMENSIONS AND WEIGHT wheel base: 104.33 in, 2,650 mm; front track: 58.66 in, 1,490 mm; rear track: 58.66 in, 1,490 mm; overall length: 186.54 in, 4,738 mm; overall width: 73.23 in, 1,860 mm; overall height: 46.65 in, 1,185

LAMBORGHINI Urraco

LAMBORGHINI Jarama

LAMBORGHINI Miura S

mm; ground clearance: 4.92 in, 125 mm; dry weight: 3,230 lb, 1,465 kg; distribution of weight: 49.5% front axle, 50.5% rear axle; turning circle (between walls): 37.7 ft, 11.5 m; fuel tank capacity: 20.5 imp gal, 24.6 US gal, 93 l (2 separate tanks).

BODY coupé; doors: 2; seats: 4; front seats: separate, reclining backrests; details: air-conditioning system, electrically-controlled windows, electrically-heated rear window.

PRACTICAL INSTRUCTIONS fuel: 98-100 oct petrol; engine sump oil: 25.2 imp pt, 30.2 US pt, 14.3 l, SAE 20W-50, change every 2,500 miles, 4,000 km; gearbox oil: 7 imp pt, 8.5 US pt, 4 l, SAE 90, change every 6,200 miles, 10,000 km; final drive oil: 2.6 imp pt, 3.2 US pt, 1.5 l, SAE 90 EP, change every 6,200 miles, 10,000 km; greasing: every 3,100 miles, 5,000 km, 5 points; sparking plug type: 235°; tappet clearances: inlet 0.010 in, 0.25 mm, exhaust 0.010 in, 0.25 mm; valve timing: inlet opens 32° before tdc and closes 76° after bdc, exhaust opens 64° before bdc and closes 32° after tdc; normal tyre pressure: front 34 psi, 2.4 atm, rear 37 psi, 2.6 atm.

OPTIONAL ACCESSORIES 4.090 axle ratio; wire wheels.

Jarama

See Espada, except for:
PRICE EX WORKS: 8,000,000 liras.

PERFORMANCE max speeds: 50 mph, 80 km/h in 1st gear; 75 mph, 120 km/h in 2nd gear; 99 mph, 160 km/h in 3rd gear; 130 mph, 210 km/h in 4th gear; 162 mph, 260 km/h in 5th gear; power-weight ratio: 8.1 lb/hp, 3.7 kg/hp; carrying capacity: 617 lb, 280 kg; speed in top at 1,000 rpm: 24.9 mph, 40 km/h.

DIMENSIONS AND WEIGHT wheel base: 93.70 in, 2,380 mm; overall length: 176.57 in, 4,485 mm; overall width: 71.65 in, 1,820 mm; overall height: 46.85 in, 1,190 mm; dry weight: 2,822 lb, 1,280 kg.

BODY seats: 2 + 2; details: electrically-controlled windows, electrically-heated rear window.

OPTIONAL ACCESSORIES wire wheels and air-conditioning system.

Miura S

PRICE IN GB: £ 8,340.
PRICE EX WORKS: 8,150,000 liras.

ENGINE rear, transverse, 4 stroke; cylinders: 12, Vee-slanted at 60°; bore and stroke: 3.23 x 2.44 in, 82 x 62 mm; engine capacity: 239.7 cu in, 3,929 cu cm; compression ratio: 10.7; max power (DIN): 370 hp at 7,700 rpm; max torque (DIN): 286 lb ft, 39.5 kg m at 5,500 rpm; max engine rpm: 7,900; specific power: 94.2 hp/l; cylinder block: light alloy, wet liners; cylinder head: light alloy; crankshaft bearings: 7; valves: 2 per cylinder, overhead, Vee-slanted at 70°, thimble tappets; camshafts: 2 per cylinder block, overhead; lubrication: gear pump, full flow filter; lubricating system capacity: 22.2 imp pt, 26.6 US pt, 12.6 l; carburation: 4 Weber 40 IDL 3L downdraught 3-barrel carburettors; fuel feed: electric pump; cooling system: water, 2 fans, 1 electric and 1 thermostatic fan; cooling system capacity: 28.2 imp pt, 33.8 US pt, 16 l.

TRANSMISSION driving wheels: rear; clutch: single dry plate (diaphragm), hydraulically controlled; gearbox: mechanical, in unit with engine and final drive; gears: 5 + reverse; synchromesh gears: I, II, III, IV, V, rev; gearbox ratios: I 2.520, II 1.735, III 1.225, IV 1, V 0.815, rev 2.765; gear lever: central; final drive: helical spur gears; axle ratio: 4.090; width of rims: 7''; tyres: GR 70 VR x 15.

PERFORMANCE max speeds: 56 mph, 90 km/h in 1st gear; 84 mph, 135 km/h in 2nd gear; 115 mph, 185 km/h in 3rd gear; 146 mph, 235 km/h in 4th gear; over 174 mph, 280 km/h in 5th gear; power-weight ratio: 6.6 lb/hp, 3 kg/hp; carrying capacity: 617 lb, 280 kg; speed in top at 1,000 rpm: 22.8 mph, 36.7 km/h; fuel consumption: 15.7 m/imp gal, 13.1 m/US gal, 18 l x 100 km.

CHASSIS integral; front suspension: independent, wishbones, coil springs, anti-roll bar, telescopic dampers; rear suspension: independent, wide-based wishbones, coil springs, anti-roll bar, telescopic dampers.

STEERING rack-and-pinion; turns of steering wheel lock to lock: 3.50.

BRAKES disc (front diameter 11.81 in, 300 mm, rear 11.02 in, 280 mm), internal radial fins, dual circuit, rear brake compensator; area rubbed by linings: front 285.3 sq in, 1,840 sq cm, rear 227.6 sq in, 1,468 sq cm, total 512.9 sq in, 3,308 sq cm.

ELECTRICAL EQUIPMENT voltage: 12 V; battery: 72 Ah; generator type: alternator, 450 W; ignition distributors: 2, Marelli; headlamps: 2, retractable, iodine; fog lamps: 2, iodine.

DIMENSIONS AND WEIGHT wheel base: 98.58 in, 2,504

MIURA S

mm; front track: 55.59 in, 1,412 mm; rear track: 55.59 in, 1,412 mm; overall length: 172.83 in, 4,390 mm; overall width: 70.08 in, 1,780 mm; overall height: 43.31 in, 1,100 mm; ground clearance: 4.92 in, 125 mm; dry weight: 2,481 lb, 1,125 kg; distribution of weight: 41.6% front axle, 58.4% rear axle; turning circle (between walls): 36.7 ft, 11.2 m; fuel tank capacity: 16.9 imp gal, 20.3 US gal, 77 l.

BODY coupé; doors: 2; seats: 2; details: electrically-controlled windows.

PRACTICAL INSTRUCTIONS fuel: 98-100 oct petrol; engine sump, gearbox and final drive oil: 20.4 imp pt, 24.5 US pt, 11.6 l, SAE 20W-50, change every 3,100 miles, 5,000 km; greasing: every 3,100 miles, 5,000 km, 4 points; sparking plug type: 235°; tappet clearances: inlet 0.010 in, 0.25 mm, exhaust 0.010 in, 0.25 mm; valve timing: inlet opens 32° before tdc and closes 76° after bdc, exhaust opens 64° before bdc and closes 32° after tdc; normal tyre pressure: front 33 psi, 2.3 atm, rear 36 psi, 2.5 atm.

OPTIONAL ACCESSORIES air-conditioning system.

LANCIA   ITALY

Fulvia Berlina 2ª Serie

PRICE IN GB: £ 1,079.
PRICE IN USA: $ 2,950.

ENGINE front, 4 stroke; cylinders: 4, Vee-slanted at 12°53'28''; bore and stroke: 3.03 x 2.74 in, 77 x 69.7 mm; engine capacity: 79.2 cu in, 1,298 cu cm; compression ratio: 9; max power (DIN): 85 hp at 6,000 rpm; max torque (DIN): 83 lb ft, 11.5 kg m at 4,500 rpm; max engine rpm: 6,200; specific power: 65.4 hp/l; cylinder block: cast iron; cylinder head: light alloy, hemispherical combustion chambers; crankshaft bearings: 3; valves: 2 per cylinder, Vee-slanted at 60°, rockers; camshafts: 2, overhead; lubrication: rotary pump, full flow filter (cartridge); lubricating system capacity: 7.6 imp pt, 9.1 US pt, 4.3 l; carburation: 2 Solex C 35 PHH 18 horizontal twin barrel carburettors; fuel feed: mechanical pump; cooling system: liquid, electric thermo-static fan; cooling system capacity: 11.4 Imp pt, 13.7 US pt, 6.5 l.

TRANSMISSION driving wheels: front; clutch: single dry plate (diaphragm); gearbox: mechanical; gears: 5 + reverse; synchromesh gears: I, II, III, IV, V; gearbox ratios: I 4.159, II 2.698, III 1.793, IV 1.284, V 1, rev 4.239; gear lever: central; final drive: hypoid bevel; axle ratio: 4.100; width of rims: 4.5''; tyres: 155 x 14.

PERFORMANCE max speeds: 25 mph, 40 km/h in 1st gear; 39 mph, 62 km/h in 2nd gear; 58 mph, 93 km/h in 3rd gear; 81 mph, 131 km/h in 4th gear; over 99 mph, 160 km/h in 5th gear; power-weight ratio: 27.6 lb/hp, 12.5 kg/hp; carrying capacity: 882 lb, 400 kg; max gradient in 1st gear: 39.5% (max load); speed in direct drive at 1,000 rpm: 16.8 mph, 27 km/h; fuel consumption: 32.1 m/imp gal, 26.7 m/US gal, 8.8 l x 100 km.

CHASSIS integral, front auxiliary frame; front suspension: independent, wishbones, transverse upper leafspring, anti-roll bar, telescopic dampers; rear suspension: rigid axle, semi-elliptic leafsprings, transverse linkage bar, telescopic dampers.

STEERING worm and roller; turns of steering wheel lock to lock: 4.17.

BRAKES disc (front diameter 10.16 in, 258 mm, rear 10.51 in, 267 mm), dual circuit, rear compensator, servo; lining area: front 16.1 sq in, 104 sq cm, rear 16.1 sq in, 104 sq cm, total 32.2 sq in, 208 sq cm.

ELECTRICAL EQUIPMENT voltage: 12 V; battery: 45 Ah; generator type: alternator, 400 W; ignition distributor: Marelli; headlamps: 4, iodine long-distance lights.

DIMENSIONS AND WEIGHT wheel base: 98.43 in, 2,500 mm; front track: 51.18 in, 1,300 mm; rear track: 50.39 in, 1,280 mm; overall length: 163.58 in, 4,155 mm; overall width: 61.22 in, 1,555 mm; overall height: 55.12 in, 1,400 mm; ground clearance: 4.72 in, 120 mm; dry weight: 2,337 lb, 1,060 kg; distribution of weight: 62.9% front axle, 37.1% rear axle; turning circle (between walls): 36.4 ft, 11.1 m; fuel tank capacity: 9.2 imp gal, 11.1 US gal, 42 l.

BODY saloon/sedan; doors: 4; seats: 5; front seats: separate, reclining backrests.

PRACTICAL INSTRUCTIONS fuel: 92 oct petrol; engine sump oil: 7.6 imp pt, 9.1 US pt, 4.3 l, SAE 10W-40, change every 4,300 miles, 7,000 km; gearbox and final drive oil:

LANCIA Fulvia Berlina 2ª Serie

LANCIA Fulvia Coupé 1.3 S 2ª Serie

LANCIA Fulvia Sport 1.3 S 2ª Serie

4.4 imp pt, 5.3 US pt, 2.5 l, SAE 90, change every 8,70 miles, 14,000 km; greasing: every 4,300 miles, 7,000 km, 11 points; tappet clearances: inlet 0.006 in, 0.15 mm exhaust 0.010 in, 0.25 mm; valve timing: inlet opens 17 before tdc and closes 65° after bdc, exhaust opens 65 before bdc and closes 17° after tdc; normal tyre pressure front 24 psi, 1.7 atm, rear 24 psi, 1.7 atm.

OPTIONAL ACCESSORIES electrically-heated rear window

Fulvia Coupé 1.3 S 2ª Serie

See Fulvia Berlina 2ª Serie, except for:

PRICE IN GB: £ 1,432.
PRICE IN USA: $ 3,440.

ENGINE compression ratio: 9.5; max power (DIN): 90 hp at 6,000 rpm; max torque (DIN): 84 lb ft, 11.6 kg m at 5,000 rpm; specific power: 69.3 hp/l; lubrication: oil cooler carburation: 2 Solex C 35 PHH 19 horizontal twin barre carburettors; cooling system capacity: 11.1 imp pt, 13. US pt, 6.3 l.

TRANSMISSION axle ratio: 3.909; tyres: 165 x 14.

PERFORMANCE max speeds: 27 mph, 43 km/h in 1st gear 41 mph, 66 km/h in 2nd gear; 62 mph, 100 km/h in 3rd gear 87 mph, 140 km/h in 4th gear; over 106 mph, 170 km/h i 5th gear; power-weight ratio: 23.6 lb/hp, 10.7 kg/hp; carryin capacity: 706 lb, 320 kg; max gradient in 1st gear: 43% (max 'oad); speed in direct drive at 1,000 rpm: 18 mph 28.9 km/h; fuel consumption: 31.7 m/imp gal, 26.4 m/US gal, 8.9 l x 100 km.

CHASSIS rear suspension: anti-roll bar.

ELECTRICAL EQUIPMENT headlamps: 4, iodine.

DIMENSIONS AND WEIGHT wheel base: 91.73 in, 2,33 mm; overall length: 156.50 in, 3,975 mm; overall height 51.97 in, 1,320 mm; dry weight: 2,139 lb, 970 kg; distributio of weight: 63.3% front axle, 36.7% rear axle; turning circle (between walls): 34.4 ft, 10.5 m; fuel tank capacity: 8.4 imp gal, 10 US gal, 38 l.

BODY coupé; doors: 2; seats: 2 + 2.

PRACTICAL INSTRUCTIONS valve timing: inlet opens 28 before tdc and closes 66° after bdc, exhaust opens 66 before bdc and closes 28° after tdc; normal tyre pressure front 26 psi, 1.8 atm, rear 26 psi, 1.8 atm.

Fulvia Sport 1.3 S 2ª Serie

See Fulvia Coupé 1.3 S 2ª Serie, except for:

PRICE IN GB: £ 1,723.
PRICE IN USA: $ 4,150.

TRANSMISSION axle ratio: 3.700.

PERFORMANCE max speeds: 29 mph, 46 km/h in 1st gear 43 mph, 70 km/h in 2nd gear; 66 mph, 106 km/h in 3rd gear; 92 mph, 148 km/h in 4th gear; over 112 km/h in 5th gear; power-weight ratio: 23.4 lb/hp, 10.6 kg/hp carrying capacity: 529 lb, 240 kg; speed in direct drive at 1,000 rpm: 19 mph, 30.5 km/h; fuel consumption: 32.8 m/imp gal, 27.3 m/US gal, 8.6 l x 100 km.

ELECTRICAL EQUIPMENT headlamps: 2, iodine.

DIMENSIONS AND WEIGHT overall length: 161.02 in, 4,090 mm; overall width: 61.81 in, 1,570 mm; overall height 50.39 in, 1,280 mm; dry weight: 2,117 lb, 960 kg; distribution of weight: 67.8% front axle, 32.2% rear axle.

Fulvia Coupé 1600 HF 2ª Serie

PRICE IN GB: £ 2,064.
PRICE EX WORKS: 2,580,000 liras.

ENGINE front, 4 stroke; cylinders: 4, Vee-slanted at 12°35'; bore and stroke: 3.23 x 2.95 in, 82 x 75 mm; engine capacity: 96.7 cu in, 1,584 cu cm; compression ratio: 10.5; max power (DIN): 114 hp at 6,000 rpm; max torque (DIN): 113 lb ft, 15.6 kg m at 4,500 rpm; max engine rpm: 6,500; specific power: 72 hp/l; cylinder block: cast iron; cylinder head: light alloy, hemispherical combustion chambers; crankshaft bearings: 3; valves: 2 per cylinder, overhead, Vee-slanted at 60°, rockers; camshafts: 2, overhead; lubrication: rotary pump, full flow filter (cartridge), oil cooler; lubricating system capacity: 10.2 imp pt, 12.3 US pt, 5.8 l; carburation: 2 Solex, C 42 DDHF front, C 42 DDHF/1 rear, horizontal twin barrel carburettors; fuel feed: mechanical pump; cooling system: liquid, electric thermostatic fan; cooling system capacity: 12.3 imp pt, 14.8 US pt, 7 l.

TRANSMISSION driving wheels: front; clutch: single dry plate; gearbox: mechanical; gears: 5 + reverse; synchromesh gears: I, II, III, IV, V; gearbox ratios: I 3.646, II 2.473, III 1.719, IV 1.317, V 1, rev 4.062; gear lever: central; final drive: hypoid bevel; axle ratio: 3.909; width of rims: 6''; tyres: 175 x 14.

PERFORMANCE max speeds: 33 mph, 53 km/h in 1st gear;

48 mph, 78 km/h in 2nd gear; 70 mph, 112 km/h in 3rd gear; 91 mph, 146 km/h in 4th gear; over 112 mph, 180 km/h in 5th gear; power-weight ratio: 17.4 lb/hp, 7.9 kg/hp; carrying capacity: 706 lb, 320 kg; max gradient in 1st gear: 51% (max load); acceleration: standing ¼ mile 16.5 sec, 0-50 mph (0-80 km/h) 6.5 sec; speed in direct drive at 1,000 rpm: 18.4 mph, 29.6 km/h; fuel consumption: 26.2 m/imp gal, 21.8 m/US gal, 10.8 l x 100 km.

CHASSIS integral, front auxiliary frame; front suspension: independent, wishbones, lower transverse leafspring, anti-roll bar, telescopic dampers; rear suspension: rigid axle, semi-elliptic leafsprings, transverse linkage bar, anti-roll bar, telescopic dampers.

STEERING worm and roller; turns of steering wheel lock to lock: 4.17.

BRAKES disc (front diameter 10.16 in, 258 mm, rear 10.51 in, 267 mm), dual circuit, rear compensator, servo; lining area: front 16.1 sq in, 104 sq cm, rear 16.1 sq in, 104 sq cm, total 32.2 sq in, 208 sq cm.

ELECTRICAL EQUIPMENT voltage: 12 V; battery: 45 Ah; generator type: alternator, 400 W; ignition distributor: Marelli; headlamps: 4, iodine.

DIMENSIONS AND WEIGHT wheel base: 91.73 in, 2,330 mm; front track: 54.72 in, 1,390 mm; rear track: 52.56 in, 1,335 mm; overall length: 154.92 in, 3,935 mm; overall width: 61.81 in, 1,570 mm; overall height: 52.36 in, 1,330 mm; ground clearance: 4.72 in, 120 mm; dry weight: 1,958 lb, 900 kg; distribution of weight: 64.5% front axle, 35.5% rear axle; turning circle (between walls): 35.4 ft, 10.8 m; fuel tank capacity: 8.4 imp gal, 10 US gal, 38 l.

BODY coupé; doors: 2; seats: 2 + 2; front seats: separate, reclining backrests.

PRACTICAL INSTRUCTIONS fuel: 92 oct petrol; engine sump oil: 10.2 imp pt, 12.3 US pt, 5.8 l, SAE 10W-40, change every 4,300 miles, 7,000 km; gearbox and final drive oil: 4.8 imp pt, 5.7 US pt, 2.7 l, SAE 90, change every 8,700 miles, 14,000 km; greasing: every 4,300 miles, 7,000 km, 11 points; tappet clearances: inlet 0.008 in, 0.20 mm, exhaust 0.012 in, 0.30 mm; valve timing: inlet opens 28° before tdc and closes 66° after bdc, exhaust opens 66° before bdc and closes 28° after tdc; normal tyre pressure: front 21 psi, 1.5 atm, rear 21 psi, 1.5 atm.

OPTIONAL ACCESSORIES electrically-heated rear window; luxury version with biffers, deflectors and headrests.

Flavia Berlina 1.8

PRICE EX WORKS: 2,100,000 liras.

ENGINE front, 4 stroke; cylinders: 4, horizontally opposed; bore and stroke: 3.46 x 2.91 in, 88 x 74 mm; engine capacity: 109.8 cu in, 1,800 cu cm; compression ratio: 9; max power (SAE): 92 hp at 5,200 rpm; max torque (SAE): 108 lb ft, 14.9 kg m at 3,000 rpm; max engine rpm: 5,700; specific power: 51.1 hp/l; cylinder block: light alloy, wet liners; cylinder head: light alloy, hemispherical combustion chambers; crankshaft bearings: 3; valves: 2 per cylinder, overhead, Vee-slanted, push-rods and rockers; camshafts: 2, side, lower; lubrication: rotary pump, full flow filter (cartridge), oil cooler; lubricating system capacity: 12.5 imp pt, 15 US pt, 7.1 l; carburation: 1 Solex C 32 PAIA 8 downdraught twin barrel carburettor; fuel feed: mechanical pump; cooling system: liquid, electric thermostatic fan; cooling system capacity: 13.2 imp pt, 15.9 US pt, 7.5 l.

TRANSMISSION driving wheels: front; clutch: single dry plate; gearbox: mechanical; gears: 4 + reverse; synchromesh gears: I, II, III, IV; gearbox ratios: I 3.333, II 1.968, III 1.387, IV 1, rev 3.714; gear lever: steering column; final drive at 1,000 rpm: 18.1 mph, 29.2 km/h; fuel consumptyres: 165 x 15.

PERFORMANCE max speeds: 31 mph, 50 km/h in 1st gear; 53 mph, 85 km/h in 2nd gear; 75 mph, 120 km/h in 3rd gear; 103 mph, 165 km/h in 4th gear; power-weight ratio: 28.4 lb/hp, 12.9 kg/hp; carrying capacity: 1,058 lb, 480 kg; max gradient in 1st gear: 34% (max load); speed in direct drive at 1,000 rpm: 18.1 mph, 29.2 km/h; fuel consumption: 27.2 m/imp gal, 22.6 m/US gal, 10.4 l x 100 km.

CHASSIS integral, front auxiliary frame; front suspension: independent, wishbones, transverse upper leafspring, anti-roll bar, telescopic dampers; rear suspension: rigid axle, semi-elliptic leafsprings, transverse linkage bar, anti-roll bar, telescopic dampers.

STEERING worm and roller, steering check for snow chains; turns of steering wheel lock to lock: 4.50 (3.50 if checked for snow chains).

BRAKES disc (diameter 11.14 in, 283 mm), dual circuit, servo; lining area: front 16.1 sq in, 104 sq cm, rear 16.1 sq in, 104 sq cm, total 32.2 sq in, 208 sq cm.

ELECTRICAL EQUIPMENT voltage: 12 V; battery: 42 Ah; generator type: alternator, 400 W; ignition distributor: Marelli; headlamps: 4, iodine long-distance lights.

DIMENSIONS AND WEIGHT wheel base: 104.33 in, 2,650 mm; front track: 51.97 in, 1,320 mm; rear track: 50.39 in,

LANCIA Fulvia Berlina 2ª Serie

LANCIA Fulvia Coupé 1.3 S 2ª Serie

LANCIA Fulvia Sport 1.3 S 2ª Serie

FLAVIA BERLINA 1.8

1,280 mm; overall length: 180.31 in, 4,580 mm; overall width: 63.39 in, 1,610 mm; overall height: 59.06 in, 1,500 mm; ground clearance: 5.31 in, 135 mm; dry weight: 2,624 lb, 1,190 kg; distribution of weight: 61.7% front axle, 38.3% rear axle; turning circle (between walls): 36.1 ft, 11 m; fuel tank capacity: 12.1 imp gal, 14.5 US gal, 55 l.

BODY saloon/sedan; doors: 4; seats: 6; front seats: bench, reclining backrests.

PRACTICAL INSTRUCTIONS fuel: 92 oct petrol; engine sump oil: 12.5 imp pt, 15 US pt, 7.1 l, SAE 10W-40, change every 4,300 miles, 7,000 km; gearbox and final drive oil: 4.4 imp pt, 5.3 US pt, 2.5 l, SAE 90, change every 8,600 miles, 14,000 km; greasing: every 4,300 miles, 7,000 km, 11 points; tappet clearances: inlet 0.004 in, 0.10 mm, exhaust 0.008 in, 0.20 mm; valve timing: inlet opens 14° before tdc and closes 58° after bdc, exhaust opens 58° before bdc and closes 14° after tdc; normal tyre pressure: front 26 psi, 1.8 atm, rear 26 psi, 1.8 atm.

VARIATIONS

ENGINE (injection) max power (SAE) 102 hp at 5,200 rpm, max torque (SAE) 113 lb ft, 15.6 kg m at 3,500 rpm, max engine rpm 5,800, 56.7 hp/l specific power, injection pump in inlet pipes (Kugelfischer system).
TRANSMISSION 3.909 axle ratio.
PERFORMANCE max speeds (I) 33 mph, 53 km/h, (II) 55 mph, 89 km/h, (III) 79 mph, 127 km/h, (IV) 106 mph, 170 km/h, power-weight ratio 26 lb/hp, 11.8 kg/hp, speed in direct drive at 1,000 rpm 18.8 mph, 30.3 km/h, fuel consumption 26.9 m/imp gal, 22.4 m/US gal, 10.5 l x 100 km.
DIMENSIONS AND WEIGHT dry weight 2,646 lb, 1,200 kg.

OPTIONAL ACCESSORIES ZF hydraulic power-assisted steering (3.50 turns of steering wheel lock to lock); separate front seats with central gear lever.

Flavia Berlina 1.8 LX

See Flavia Berlina 1.8, except for:

PRICE IN GB: £ 1,586.
PRICE EX WORKS: 2,275,000 liras.

PERFORMANCE power-weight ratio: 28.7 lb/hp, 13 kg/hp.

STEERING ZF hydraulic servo (standard).

DIMENSIONS AND WEIGHT overall length: 181.50 in, 4,610 mm; dry weight: 2,646 lb, 1,200 kg.

BODY details: luxury interior, electrically-heated rear window.

Flavia Berlina 2000

PRICE IN GB: £ 1,651.
PRICE EX WORKS: 2,470,000 liras.

ENGINE front, 4 stroke; cylinders: 4, horizontally opposed; bore and stroke: 3.50 x 3.15 in, 89 x 80 mm; engine capacity: 121.5 cu in, 1,991 cu cm; compression ratio: 9; max power (SAE): 131 hp at 5,400 rpm; max torque (SAE): 133 lb ft, 18.3 kg m at 4,200 rpm; max engine rpm: 5,800; specific power: 65.8 hp/l; cylinder block: light alloy, wet liners; cylinder head: light alloy, hemispherical combustion chambers; crankshaft bearings: 3; valves: 2 per cylinder, overhead, Vee-slanted, push-rods and rockers; camshafts: 2, side, lower; lubrication: rotary pump, full flow filter (cartridge), oil cooler; lubricating system capacity: 15.5 imp pt, 18.6 US pt, 8.8 l; carburation: 1 Solex C 34 EIES downdraught twin barrel carburettor; fuel feed: mechanical pump; cooling system: liquid, sealed circuit, electric thermostatic fan; cooling system capacity: 13.2 imp pt, 15.9 US pt, 7.5 l.

TRANSMISSION driving wheels: front; clutch: single dry plate; gearbox: mechanical; gears: 4 + reverse; synchromesh gears: I, II, III, IV; gearbox ratios: I 3.785, II 2.264, III 1.467, IV 1, rev 4.367; gear lever: central; final drive: hypoid bevel; axle ratio: 3.818; width of rims: 5''; tyres: 165 x 15.

PERFORMANCE max speeds: 29 mph, 47 km/h in 1st gear; 49 mph, 79 km/h in 2nd gear; 76 mph, 122 km/h in 3rd gear; 109 mph, 175 km/h in 4th gear; power-weight ratio: 20.9 lb/hp, 9.5 kg/hp; carrying capacity: 882 lb, 400 kg; max gradient in 1st gear: 41% (max load); acceleration: standing ¼ mile 17 sec, 0-50 mph (0-80 km/h) 8.5 sec; speed in direct drive at 1,000 rpm: 19.2 mph, 30.9 km/h; fuel consumption 26.4 m/imp gal, 22 m/US gal, 10.7 l x 100 km.

CHASSIS integral, front auxiliary frame; front suspension: independent, wishbones, transverse upper leafspring, anti-roll bar, telescopic dampers; rear suspension: rigid axle,

LANCIA Flavia Berlina 2000 LX

LANCIA Flavia Coupé 2000

LMX Sirex 2300 HCS Coupe (210 hp)

semi-elliptic leafsprings, transverse linkage bar, anti-roll bar, telescopic dampers.

STEERING worm and roller, steering check for snow chains; turns of steering wheel lock to lock: 4.50 (3.50 if checked for snow chains).

BRAKES disc (diameter 11.14 in, 283 mm), dual circuit, rear compensator, servo; lining area: front 16.1 sq in, 104 sq cm, rear 16.1 sq in, 104 sq cm, total 32.2 sq in, 208 sq cm.

ELECTRICAL EQUIPMENT voltage: 12 V; battery: 45 Ah; generator type: alternator, 500 W; ignition distributor: Marelli; headlamps: 4, iodine long-distance lights.

DIMENSIONS AND WEIGHT wheel base: 104.33 in, 2,650 mm; front track: 51.97 in, 1,320 mm; rear track: 50.39 in, 1,280 mm; overall length: 180.31 in, 4,580 mm; overall width: 63.39 in, 1,610 mm; overall height: 59.06 in, 1,500 mm; ground clearance: 5.31 in, 135 mm; dry weight: 2,734 lb, 1,240 kg; distribution of weight: 62.5% front axle, 37.5% rear axle; turning circle (between walls): 36.1 ft, 11 m; fuel tank capacity: 12.1 imp gal, 14.5 US gal, 55 l.

BODY saloon/sedan; doors: 4; seats: 5; front seats: separate, reclining backrests.

PRACTICAL INSTRUCTIONS fuel: 92 oct petrol; engine sump oil: 15.5 imp pt, 18.6 US pt, 8.8 l, SAE 10W-40, change every 4,300 miles, 7,000 km; gearbox oil: 4.2 imp pt, 5.1 US pt, 2.4 l, SAE 90, change every 8,700 miles, 14,000 km; final drive oil: 3.9 imp pt, 4.7 US pt, 2.2 l, SAE 140, change every 8,700 miles, 14,000 km; greasing: every 4,300 miles, 7,000 km, 11 points; tappet clearances: inlet 0.004 in, 0.10 mm, exhaust 0.008 in, 0.20 mm; valve timing: inlet opens 24° before tdc and closes 68° after bdc, exhaust opens 68° before bdc and closes 24° after tdc; normal tyre pressure: front 26 psi, 1.8 atm, rear 26 psi, 1.8 atm.

VARIATIONS

ENGINE (injection) max power (SAE) 140 hp at 5,600 rpm, max torque (SAE) 142 lb ft, 19.6 kg m at 4,000 rpm, 70.3 hp/l specific power, injection pump in inlet pipes (Kugelfischer system).
TRANSMISSION 3.727 axle ratio.
PERFORMANCE max speeds (I) 30 mph, 49 km/h, (II) 50 mph, 81 km/h, (III) 78 mph, 126 km/h, (IV) 115 mph, 185 km/h, power-weight ratio 19.6 lb/hp, 8.9 kg/hp, speed in direct drive at 1,000 rpm 19.8 mph, 31.8 km/h, fuel consumption 26.9 m/imp gal, 22.4 m/US gal, 10.5 l x 100 km.
DIMENSIONS AND WEIGHT dry weight 2,756 lb, 1,250 kg.

OPTIONAL ACCESSORIES ZF hydraulic power-assisted steering (3.50 turns of steering wheel lock to lock).

Flavia Berlina 2000 LX

See Flavia Berlina 2000, except for:

PRICE IN GB: £ 1,763.
PRICE IN USA: $ 4,305.

PERFORMANCE power-weight ratio: 21.4 lb/hp, 9.7 kg/hp.

STEERING ZF hydraulic servo (standard).

DIMENSIONS AND WEIGHT overall length: 181.50 in, 4,610 mm; dry weight: 2,789 lb, 1,265 kg.

BODY details: luxury interior, electrically-heated rear window.

Flavia Coupé 2000

See Flavia Berlina 2000, except for:

PRICE IN GB: £ 2,288.
PRICE IN USA: $ 5,380.

TRANSMISSION axle ratio: 3.727; width of rims: 5.5''.

PERFORMANCE max speeds: 30 mph, 49 km/h in 1st gear; 50 mph, 81 km/h in 2nd gear; 78 mph, 126 km/h in 3rd gear; 115 mph, 185 km/h in 4th gear; power-weight ratio: 20.1 lb/hp, 9.1 kg/hp; carrying capacity: 706 lb, 320 kg; acceleration: standing ¼ mile 17.5 sec, 0-50 mph (0-80 km/h) 8 sec; speed in direct drive at 1,000 rpm: 19.8 mph, 31.8 km/h; fuel consumption: 28.2 m/imp gal, 23.5 m/US gal, 10 l x 100 km.

DIMENSIONS AND WEIGHT wheel base: 97.64 in, 2,480 mm; overall length: 178.74 in, 4,540 mm; overall width: 63.19 in, 1,605 mm; overall height: 52.36 in, 1,330 mm; ground clearance: 4.72 in, 120 mm; dry weight: 2,624 lb, 1,190 kg; distribution of weight: 61.3% front axle, 38.7% rear axle; turning circle (between walls): 35.4 ft, 10.8 m.

BODY coupé; doors: 2; seats: 4.

PRACTICAL INSTRUCTIONS normal tyre pressure: front 28 psi, 2 atm, rear 28 psi, 2 atm.

LANCIA Flavia Berlina 2000 LX

LANCIA Flavia Coupé 2000

LMX Sirex 2300 HCS Coupé (210 hp)

VARIATIONS

ENGINE (injection) max power (SAE) 140 hp at 5,600 rpm, max torque (SAE) 142 lb ft, 19.6 kg m at 4,000 rpm, 70.3 hp/l specific power, injection pump in inlet pipes (Kugelfischer system).
TRANSMISSION 3.545 axle ratio.
PERFORMANCE max speeds (I) 32 mph, 51 km/h, (II) 53 mph, 86 km/h, (III) 82 mph, 132 km/h, (IV) 118 mph, 190 km/h, power-weight ratio 19 lb/hp, 8.6 kg/hp, speed in direct drive at 1,000 rpm 20.8 mph, 33.4 km/h.
DIMENSIONS AND WEIGHT dry weight 2,646 lb, 1,200 kg.

LMX   ITALY

Sirex 2300 HCS Coupé

PRICE EX WORKS: 3,580,000 liras.

ENGINE front, 4 stroke; cylinders: 6, Vee-slanted at 60°; bore and stroke: 3.54 x 2.37 in, 90 x 60.1 mm; engine capacity: 139.9 cu in, 2,293 cu cm; compression ratio: 9; max power (SAE): 126 hp at 5,000 rpm; max torque (SAE): 138 lb ft, 19.1 kg m at 3,500 rpm; max engine rpm: 5,600; specific power: 54.9 hp/l; cylinder block: cast iron; cylinder head: cast iron; crankshaft bearings: 4; valves: 2 per cylinder, overhead, push-rods and rockers; camshafts: 1, at centre of Vee; lubrication: rotary pump, full-flow filter; lubricating system capacity: 8.4 imp pt, 10.1 US pt, 4.8 l; carburation: 1 Solex 32 DDIST downdraught twin barrel carburettor; fuel feed: mechanical pump; cooling system: water; cooling system capacity: 11.6 imp pt, 14 US pt, 6.6 l.

TRANSMISSION driving wheels: rear; clutch: single dry plate, hydraulically controlled; gearbox: mechanical; gears: 4 + reverse; synchromesh gears: I, II, III, IV; gearbox ratios: I 3.420, II 1.970, III 1.370, IV 1, rev 3.660; gear lever: central; final drive: hypoid bevel; axle ratio: 3.777; width of rims: 6.5''; tyres: 185 HR x 14.

PERFORMANCE max speeds 36 mph, 58 km/h in 1st gear; 63 mph, 101 km/h in 2nd gear; 91 mph, 146 km/h in 3rd gear; 124 mph, 200 km/h in 4th gear; power-weight ratio: 16.5 lb/hp, 7.5 kg/hp; carrying capacity: 397 lb, 180 kg; speed in direct drive at 1,000 rpm: 20.7 mph, 33.3 km/h; fuel consumption: 20.2 m/imp gal, 16.8 m/US gal, 14 l x 100 km.

CHASSIS central backbone; front suspension: independent, by McPherson, coil springs/telescopic damper struts, anti-roll bar, lower wishbones; rear suspension: independent, semi-trailing arms, swinging semi-axles, coil springs, telescopic dampers.

STEERING recirculating ball.

BRAKES disc, dual circuit, servo.

ELECTRICAL EQUIPMENT voltage: 12 V; battery: 45 Ah; generator type: alternator, 25 A; headlamps: 2.

DIMENSIONS AND WEIGHT wheel base: 90.55 in, 2,300 mm; front track: 59.84 in, 1,520 mm; rear track: 60.24 in, 1,530 mm; overall length: 155.91 in, 3,960 mm; overall width: 69.29 in, 1,760 mm; overall height: 44.49 in, 1,130 mm; ground clearance: 4.72 in, 120 mm; dry weight: 2,095 lb, 950 kg; turning circle (between walls): 28.2 ft, 8.6 m; fuel tank capacity: 13.2 imp gal, 15.8 US gal, 60 l.

BODY coupé in plastic material; doors: 2; seats: 2; details: electrically-controlled windows.

PRACTICAL INSTRUCTIONS fuel: 98-100 oct petrol; engine sump oil: 7.9 imp pt, 9.5 US pt, 4.5 l, SAE 20W-40, change every 6,200 miles, 10,000 km; gearbox oil: 2.3 imp pt, 2.7 US pt, 1.3 l, SAE 80, change every 12,400 miles, 20,000 km; final drive oil: 1.9 imp pt, 2.3 US pt, 1.1 l, SAE 90, change every 12,400 miles, 20,000 km; greasing: none; normal tyre pressure: front 28 psi, 2 atm, rear 31 psi, 2.2 atm.

VARIATIONS

ENGINE max power (SAE) 180 hp at 6,300 rpm, 78.5 hp/l specific power, Costantin 1-stage supercharger.
PERFORMANCE max speed 130 mph, 210 km/h, power-weight ratio 11.7 lb/hp, 5.3 kg/hp.

ENGINE max power (SAE) 210 hp at 6,100 rpm, 91.6 hp/l specific power, MAY turbo-supercharger.
PERFORMANCE max speed 137 mph, 220 km/h, power-weight ratio 9.9 lb/hp, 4.5 kg/hp.

Sirex 2300 HCS Spider

See Sirex 2300 HCS Coupé, except for:

PRICE EX WORKS: 3,780,000 liras.

BODY convertible.

OPTIONAL ACCESSORIES hardtop.

MASERATI   ITALY

Mexico

PRICE IN GB: £ 5,965.
PRICE EX WORKS: 7,390,000 liras.

ENGINE front, 4 stroke; cylinders: 8, Vee-slanted at 90°; bore and stroke: 3.46 x 3.35 in, 88 x 85 mm; engine capacity: 252.4 cu in, 4,136 cu cm; compression ratio: 8.5; max power (DIN): 260 hp at 5,500 rpm; max torque (DIN): 275 lb ft, 38 kg m at 3,800 rpm; max engine rpm: 6,000; specific power: 62.9 hp/l; cylinder block: light alloy, wet liners; cylinder head: light alloy, special combustion chambers; crankshaft bearings: 5; valves: 2 per cylinder, overhead, Vee-slanted, thimble tappets; camshafts: 2 per cylinder block, overhead; lubrication: gear pump, full flow filter; lubricating system capacity: 17.6 imp pt, 21.1 US pt, 10 l; carburation: 4 Weber 42 DCNF downdraught twin barrel carburettors; fuel feed: 2 electric pumps; cooling system: water; cooling system capacity: 24.6 imp pt, 29.6 US pt, 14 l.

TRANSMISSION driving wheels: rear; clutch: single dry plate, hydraulically controlled; gearbox: ZF mechanical; gears: 5 + reverse; synchromesh gears: I, II, III, IV, V, rev; gearbox ratios: I 3.000, II 1.705, III 1.240, IV 1, V 0.850, rev 3.170; gear lever: central; final drive: hypoid bevel; axle ratio: 3.540; width of rims: 6.5''; tyres: 205 x 15.

PERFORMANCE max speeds: 42 mph, 67 km/h in 1st gear; 74 mph, 119 km/h in 2nd gear; 101 mph, 163 km/h in 3rd gear; 126 mph, 202 km/h in 4th gear; 149 mph, 240 km/h in 5th gear; power-weight ratio: 12.8 lb/hp, 5.8 kg/hp; carrying capacity: 706 lb, 320 kg; speed in top at 1,000 rpm: 25.4 mph, 40.8 km/h; fuel consumption: 16.6 m/imp gal, 13.8 m/US gal, 17 l x 100 km.

CHASSIS integral; front suspension: independent, wishbones, coil springs, anti-roll bar, telescopic dampers; rear suspension: rigid axle, cantilever semi-elliptic leafsprings, flexible trailing radius arms, transverse linkage bar, anti-roll bar, telescopic dampers.

STEERING recirculating ball; turns of steering wheel lock to lock: 3.50.

BRAKES disc, internal radial fins, dual circuit, servo; area rubbed by linings: front 245.4 sq in, 1,583 sq cm, rear 188.5 sq in, 1,216 sq cm, total 433.9 sq in, 2,799 sq cm.

ELECTRICAL EQUIPMENT voltage: 12 V; battery: 72 Ah; generator type: alternator, 650 W; ignition distributor: Bosch; headlamps: 4, iodine.

DIMENSIONS AND WEIGHT wheel base: 103.94 in, 2,640 mm; front track: 54.72 in, 1,390 mm; rear track: 53.54 in, 1,360 mm; overall length: 187.40 in, 4,760 mm; overall width: 68.11 in, 1,730 mm; overall height: 53.15 in, 1,350 mm; ground clearance: 5.51 in, 140 mm; dry weight: 3,308 lb, 1,500 kg; turning circle (between walls): 36.1 ft, 11 m; fuel tank capacity: 20.9 imp gal, 25.1 US gal, 95 l (2 separate tanks).

BODY coupé; doors: 2; seats: 4; front seats: separate, reclining backrests; details: air-conditioning system, electrically-heated rear window.

PRACTICAL INSTRUCTIONS fuel: 98-100 oct petrol; engine sump oil: 15.8 imp pt, 19 US pt, 9 l, SAE 20W-50, change every 3,100 miles, 5,000 km; gearbox oil: 1.9 imp pt, 2.3 US pt, 1.1 l, SAE 90, change every 12,400 miles, 20,000 km; final drive oil: 2.5 imp pt, 3 US pt, 1.4 l, SAE 90, change every 12,400 miles, 20,000 km; greasing: every 3,700 miles, 6,000 km, 6 points; tappet clearances: inlet 0.006 in, 0.15 mm, exhaust 0.012 in, 0.30 mm; valve timing: inlet opens 42° before tdc and closes 60° after bdc, exhaust opens 65° before bdc and closes 35° after tdc; normal tyre pressure: front 33 psi, 2.3 atm, rear 36 psi, 2.5 atm.

VARIATIONS

ENGINE bore and stroke 3.70 x 3.35 in, 94 x 85 mm, engine capacity 288 cu in, 4,719 cu cm, max power (DIN) 290 hp at 5,500 rpm, max torque (DIN) 290 lb ft, 40 kg m at 3,800 rpm, 61.5 hp/l specific power.
TRANSMISSION gearbox ratios I 2.970, II 1.920, III 1.340, IV 1, V 0.900, rev 3.310, 3.310 axle ratio.
PERFORMANCE max speed 158 mph, 255 km/h, power-weight ratio 11.5 lb/hp, 5.2 kg/hp, fuel consumption 14.1 m/imp gal, 11.8 m/US gal, 20 l x 100 km.

OPTIONAL ACCESSORIES limited slip final drive, 4.090 3.770 3.310 axle ratios; power-assisted steering; Borg Warner automatic gearbox, hydraulic torque convertor and planetary gears with 3 ratios (I 2.400, II 1.470, III 1), max ratio of convertor at stall 2.7, possible manual selection.

Indy

See Mexico, except for:
PRICE IN GB: £ 6,271.
PRICE IN USA: $ 17,500.

TRANSMISSION width of rims: 7.5''; tyres: 205 x 14.

PERFORMANCE max speeds: 43 mph, 69 km/h in 1st gear; 77 mph, 124 km/h in 2nd gear; 104 mph, 168 km/h in 3rd gear; 134 mph, 216 km/h in 4th gear; 155 mph, 250 km/h in 5th gear.

ELECTRICAL EQUIPMENT headlamps: retractable.

MASERATI Indy

MASERATI Ghibli Spider

OTAS A 112 KL

DIMENSIONS AND WEIGHT wheel base: 102.36 in, 2,600 mm; front track: 58.27 in, 1,480 mm; rear track: 56.46 in, 1,434 mm; overall length: 186.61 in, 4,740 mm; overall width: 69.29 in, 1,760 mm; overall height: 48.03 in, 1,220 mm; ground clearance: 4.72 in, 120 mm; fuel tank capacity: 22 imp gal, 26.4 US gal, 100 l (2 separate tanks).

VARIATIONS

(With 288 cu in, 4,719 cu cm engine).

PERFORMANCE max speed 165 mph, 265 km/h.

Ghibli Coupé

PRICE IN GB: £ 6,727.
PRICE IN USA: $ 18,900.

ENGINE front, 4 stroke; cylinders: 8, Vee-slanted at 90°; bore and stroke: 3.70 x 3.35 in, 94 x 85 mm; engine capacity: 288 cu in, 4,719 cu cm; compression ratio: 8.8; max power (DIN): 330 hp at 5,500 rpm; max torque (DIN): 326 lb ft, 45 kg m at 4,000 rpm; max engine rpm: 6,300; specific power: 69.9 hp/l; cylinder block: light alloy, wet liners; cylinder head: light alloy, special combustion chambers; crankshaft bearings: 5; valves: 2 per cylinder, overhead, Vee-slanted, thimble tappets; camshafts: 2 per cylinder block, overhead; lubrication: gear pump, full flow filter, dry sump, separate oil tank; lubricating system capacity: 21.1 imp pt, 25.4 US pt, 12 l; carburation: 4 Weber 42 DCNF downdraught twin barrel carburettors; fuel feed: 2 electric pumps; cooling system: water; cooling system capacity: 26.4 imp pt, 31.7 US pt, 15 l.

TRANSMISSION driving wheels: rear; clutch: single dry plate, hydraulically controlled; gearbox: mechanical; gears 5 + reverse; synchromesh gears: I, II, III, IV, V, rev; gearbox ratios: I 2.970, II 1.920, III 1.340, IV 1, V 0.900, rev 3.310; gear lever: central; final drive: hypoid bevel; axle ratio: 3.310; width of rims: 7.5''; tyres: 205 x 15.

PERFORMANCE max speeds: 54 mph, 87 km/h in 1st gear; 85 mph, 136 km/h in 2nd gear; 121 mph, 194 km/h in 3rd gear; 161 mph, 259 km/h in 4th gear; 168 mph, 270 km/h in 5th gear; power-weight ratio: 8.6 lb/hp, 3.9 kg/hp; carrying capacity: 617 lb, 280 kg; acceleration: standing 1/4 mile 14.8 sec, 0-50 mph (0-80 km/h) 5.5 sec; speed in top at 1,000 rpm: 28.4 mph, 45.7 km/h; fuel consumption 14.1 m/imp gal, 11.8 m/US gal, 20 l x 100 km.

CHASSIS tubular; front suspension: independent, wishbones, coil springs, anti-roll bar, telescopic dampers; rear suspension: rigid axle, cantilever semi-elliptic leafsprings, flexible trailing radius arms, transverse linkage bar, anti-roll bar, telescopic dampers.

STEERING recirculating ball; turns of steering wheel lock to lock: 3.50.

BRAKES disc, internal radial fins, dual circuit, servo; area rubbed by linings: front 279.1 sq in, 1,800 sq cm, rear 209.3 sq in, 1,350 sq cm, total 488.4 sq in, 3,150 sq cm.

ELECTRICAL EQUIPMENT voltage: 12 V; battery: 72 Ah; generator type: alternator, 650 W; ignition distributor: Bosch; headlamps: 4, retractable, iodine.

DIMENSIONS AND WEIGHT wheel base: 100.39 in, 2,550 mm; front track: 56.69 in, 1,440 mm; rear track: 55.91 in, 1,420 mm; overall length: 184.65 in, 4,690 mm; overall width: 70.47 in, 1,790 mm; overall height: 45.67 in, 1,160 mm; ground clearance: 4.72 in, 120 mm; dry weight: 2,867 lb, 1,300 kg; distribution of weight: 50% front axle, 50% rear axle; turning circle (between walls): 36.1 ft, 11 m; fuel tank capacity: 20.9 imp gal, 25.1 US gal, 95 l (2 separate tanks).

BODY coupé; doors: 2; seats: 2; details: air-conditioning system, electrically-controlled windows, electrically-heated rear window.

PRACTICAL INSTRUCTIONS fuel: 100 oct petrol; engine sump oil: 21.1 imp pt, 25.4 US pt, 12 l, SAE 30 (winter) 50 (summer), change every 3,700 miles, 6,000 km; gearbox oil: 3.9 imp pt, 4.7 US pt, 2.2 l, SAE 90, change every 12,400 miles, 20,000 km; final drive oil: 2.3 imp pt, 2.7 US pt, 1.3 l, SAE 90, change every 12,400 miles, 20,000 km; greasing: every 3,700 miles, 6,000 km, 12 points; sparking plug type: 240°; tappet clearances: inlet 0.006 in, 0.15 mm, exhaust 0.018 in, 0.45 mm; valve timing: inlet opens 40° before tdc and closes 60° after bdc, exhaust opens 65° before bdc and closes 35° after tdc; normal tyre pressure: front 33 psi, 2.3 atm, rear 36 psi, 2.5 atm.

OPTIONAL ACCESSORIES limited slip final drive, 4.090 3.770 3.310 axle ratios; power-assisted steering; Borg-Warner automatic gearbox, hydraulic torque convertor and planetary gears with 3 ratios (I 2.400, II 1.470, III 1), max ratio of convertor at stall 2.7, possible manual selection.

Ghibli Spider

See Ghibli Coupé, except for:
PRICE IN GB: £ 7,117.
PRICE IN USA: $ 19,400.

PERFORMANCE max speed: 165 mph, 265 km/h; power-weight ratio: 8.4 lb/hp, 3.8 kg/hp.

DIMENSIONS AND WEIGHT dry weight: 2,767 lb, 1,255 kg.
BODY convertible.
OPTIONAL ACCESSORIES hardtop.

MASERATI Indy

MASERATI Ghibli Spider

OTAS A 112 KL

Ghibli SS Coupé

See Ghibli Coupé, except for:

PRICE EX WORKS: 8,690,000 liras.

ENGINE bore and stroke: 3.70 x 3.50 in, 93.9 x 89 mm; engine capacity: 300.8 cu in, 4,930 cu cm; compression ratio: 8.5; max power (DIN): 335 hp at 5,500 rpm; max torque (DIN): 355 lb ft, 49 kg m at 4,000 rpm; max engine rpm: 6,000; specific power: 67.9 hp/l; lubricating system capacity: 22.9 imp pt, 27.5 US pt, 13 l.

PERFORMANCE max speed: 174 mph, 280 km/h; power-weight ratio: 8.8 lb/hp, 4 kg/hp; acceleration: standing ¼ mile 14.3 sec, 0-50 mph (0-80 km/h) 5 sec; fuel consumption: 13.5 m/imp gal, 11.2 m/US gal, 21 l x 100 km.

DIMENSIONS AND WEIGHT dry weight: 2,977 lb, 1,350 kg; fuel tank capacity: 22 imp gal, 26.4 US gal, 100 l (2 separate tanks).

BODY seats: 2 + 2.

PRACTICAL INSTRUCTIONS engine sump oil: 22.9 imp pt, 27.5 US pt, 13 l; gearbox oil: 2.5 imp pt, 3 US pt, 1.4 l; final drive oil: 2.5 imp pt, 3 US pt, 1.4 l; greasing: every 3,700 miles, 6,000 km, 6 points; tappet clearances: inlet 0.006 in, 0.15 mm, exhaust 0.020 in, 0.50 mm; valve timing: inlet opens 45° before tdc and closes 60° after bdc, exhaust opens 63° before bdc and closes 37° after tdc; normal tyre pressure: front 31 psi, 2.2 atm, rear 34 psi, 2.4 atm.

Ghibli SS Spider

See Ghibli SS Coupé, except for:

PRICE EX WORKS: 8,990,000 liras.

PERFORMANCE max speed: 168 mph, 270 km/h; power-weight ratio: 8.6 lb/hp, 3.9 kg/hp.

DIMENSIONS AND WEIGHT dry weight: 2,867 lb, 1,300 kg.

BODY convertible.

OPTIONAL ACCESSORIES hardtop.

OTAS ITALY

A 112 KL

PRICE EX WORKS: 1,400,000 liras.

ENGINE front, 4 stroke, transverse; cylinders: 4, in line; bore and stroke: 2.56 x 2.68 in, 65 x 68 mm; engine capacity: 55.1 cu in, 903 cu cm; compression ratio: 9.5; max power (DIN): 59 hp at 6,800 rpm; max torque (DIN): 46 lb ft, 6.4 kg m at 4,000 rpm; specific power: 65.3 hp/l; cylinder block: cast iron; cylinder head: light alloy; crankshaft bearings: 3; valves: 2 per cylinder, overhead, push-rods and rockers; camshafts: 1, side; lubrication: gear pump, centrifugal filter; lubricating system capacity: 5.5 imp pt, 6.6 US pt, 3.1 l; carburation: 1 Solex C 34 PAIA 7 downdraught carburettor; fuel feed: mechanical pump; cooling system: water, electric thermostatic fan; cooling system capacity: 8.8 imp pt, 10.6 US pt, 5 l.

TRANSMISSION driving wheels: front; clutch: single dry plate; gearbox: mechanical; gears: 4 + reverse; synchromesh gears: I, II, III, IV; gearbox ratios: I 3.636, II 2.055, III 1.409, IV 0.963, rev 3.615; gear lever: central; final drive: cylindrical gears; axle ratio: 4.692; tyres: 135 x 13.

PERFORMANCE max speeds: 27 mph, 44 km/h in 1st gear; 48 mph, 78 km/h in 2nd gear; 71 mph, 114 km/h in 3rd gear; 99 mph, 160 km/h in 4th gear; power-weight ratio: 24.7 lb/hp, 11.2 kg/hp; carrying capacity: 617 lb, 280 kg; speed in top at 1,000 rpm: 14.2 mph, 22.9 km/h; fuel consumption: 35.3 m/imp gal, 29.4 m/US gal, 8 l x 100 km.

CHASSIS integral; front suspension: independent, by McPherson, coil springs/telescopic damper struts, anti-roll bar, lower semi-trailing arms (trailing links); rear suspension: independent wishbones, lower transverse anti-roll leafspring, telescopic dampers.

STEERING rack-and-pinion; turns of steering wheel lock to lock: 3.40.

BRAKES front disc (diameter 8.94 in, 227 mm), rear drum, dual circuit, rear compensator; lining area: front 22.5 sq in, 145 sq cm, rear 33.5 sq in, 216 sq cm, total 56 sq in, 361 sq cm.

ELECTRICAL EQUIPMENT voltage: 12 V; battery: 34 Ah; generator type: dynamo, 230 W; ignition distributor: Marelli; headlamps: 2.

DIMENSIONS AND WEIGHT wheel base: 79.96 in, 2,031 mm; front track: 49.21 in, 1,250 mm; rear track: 48.98 in, 1,244 mm; overall length: 131.89 in, 3,350 mm; overall width: 60.63 in, 1,540 mm; overall height: 44.88 in, 1,140 mm; ground clearance: 5.91 in, 150 mm; dry weight: 1,455 lb, 660 kg; turning circle (between walls): 29.2 ft, 8.9 m; fuel tank capacity: 6.6 imp gal, 7.9 US gal, 30 l.

BODY coupé; doors: 2, seats: 2.

PRACTICAL INSTRUCTIONS fuel: 98-100 oct petrol; engine sump oil: 5.5 imp pt, 6.6 US pt, 3.1 l, SAE 10W-40, change every 6,200 miles, 10,000 km; gearbox and final drive oil: 4 imp pt, 4.9 US pt, 2.3 l, SAE 90, change every 18,600 miles, 30,000 km; greasing: none; tappet clearances: inlet 0.008 in, 0.20 mm, exhaust 0.008 in, 0.20 mm; valve timing: inlet opens 22° before tdc and closes 59° after bdc, exhaust opens 58° before bdc and closes 21° after tdc; normal tyre pressure: front 24 psi, 1.7 atm, rear 27 psi, 1.9 atm.

POLSKI-FIAT   POLAND

125 P/1300

PRICE: —

ENGINE front, 4 stroke; cylinders: 4, in line; bore and stroke: 2.83 x 3.13 in, 72 x 79.5 mm; engine capacity: 79 cu in, 1,295 cu cm; compression ratio: 9; max power (SAE): 70 hp at 5,400 rpm; max torque (SAE): 76 lb ft, 10.5 kg m at 3,200 rpm; max engine rpm: 5,400; specific power: 54 hp/l; cylinder block: cast iron; cylinder head: light alloy; crankshaft bearings: 3; valves: 2 per cylinder, overhead, push-rods and rockers; camshafts: 1, side, in crankcase; lubrication: gear pump, centrifugal filter, cartridge; lubricating system capacity: 6.2 imp pt, 7.4 US pt, 3.5 l; carburation: 1 Weber 34 DCHD 1 downdraught twin barrel carburettor; fuel feed: mechanical pump; cooling system: water; cooling system capacity: 11.8 imp pt, 14.2 US pt, 6.7 l.

TRANSMISSION driving wheels: rear; clutch: single dry plate, hydraulically controlled; gearbox: mechanical; gears: 4 + reverse; synchromesh gears: I, II, III IV; gearbox ratios: I 3.750, II 2.300, III 1.490, IV 1, rev 3.870; gear lever: steering column; final drive: hypoid bevel; axle ratio: 4.100; width of rims: 4.5''; tyres: 5.60 x 13.

PERFORMANCE max speeds: 25 mph, 40 km/h in 1st gear; 40 mph, 65 km/h in 2nd gear; 62 mph, 100 km/h in 3rd gear; 87 mph, 140 km/h in 4th gear; power-weight ratio: 30.6 lb/hp, 13.9 kg/hp; carrying capacity: 882 lb, 400 kg; acceleration: 0-50 mph (0-80 km/h) 12.8 sec; speed in direct drive at 1,000 rpm: 17.8 mph, 28.7 km/h; fuel consumption: 29.7 m/imp gal, 24.8 m/US gal, 9.5 l x 100 km.

CHASSIS integral; front suspension: independent, wishbones, coil springs, anti-roll bar, telescopic dampers; rear suspension: rigid axle, semi-elliptic leafsprings, telescopic dampers.

STEERING worm and roller; turns of steering wheel lock to lock: 2.75.

BRAKES disc, servo.

ELECTRICAL EQUIPMENT voltage: 12 V; battery: 48 Ah; generator type: alternator, 558 W; ignition distributor: Marelli; headlamps: 4.

DIMENSIONS AND WEIGHT wheel base: 98.62 in, 2,505 mm; front track: 51.10 in, 1,298 mm; rear track: 50.20 in, 1,275 mm; overall length: 166.65 in, 4,233 mm; overall width: 63.98 in, 1,625 mm; overall height: 56.69 in, 1,440 mm; ground clearance: 5.51 in, 140 mm; dry weight: 2,139 lb, 970 kg; turning circle (between walls): 34.1 ft, 10.4 m; fuel tank capacity: 9.9 imp gal, 11.9 US gal, 45 l.

BODY saloon/sedan; doors: 4; seats: 5; front seats: separate.

PRACTICAL INSTRUCTIONS fuel: 92 oct petrol; engine sump oil: 6.2 imp pt, 7.4 US pt, 3.5 l, SAE 20W-30, change every 3,100 miles, 5,000 km; gearbox oil: 2.3 imp pt, 2.7 US pt, 1.3 l, SAE 90 EP, change every 18,600 miles, 30,000 km; final drive oil: 3.5 imp pt, 4.2 US pt, 2 l, SAE 90 EP, change every 18,600 miles, 30,000 km; greasing: none; sparking plug type: 240°; tappet clearances: inlet 0.008 in, 0.20 mm, exhaust 0.010 in, 0.25 mm; valve timing: inlet opens 9° before tdc and closes 61° after bdc, exhaust opens 49° before bdc and closes 21° after tdc; normal tyre pressure: front 23 psi, 1.6 atm, rear 27 psi, 1.9 atm.

125 P/1500

See 125 P/1300, except for:

PRICE: —

ENGINE bore and stroke: 3.03 x 3.13 in, 77 x 79.5 mm; engine capacity: 90.4 cu in, 1,481 cu cm; max power (SAE): 80 hp at 5,400 rpm; max torque (SAE): 89 lb ft, 12.3 kg m at 3,200 rpm; specific power: 54 hp/l.

PERFORMANCE max speed: 93 mph, 150 km/h; power-weight ratio: 26.7 lb/hp, 12.1 kg/hp; fuel consumption: 17.1 m/imp gal, 20.5 m/US gal, 9.7 l x 100 km.

SYRENA   POLAND

104

PRICE: —

ENGINE front, 2 stroke; cylinders: 3, vertical, in line; bore and stroke: 2.76 x 2.87 in, 70 x 73 mm; engine capacity: 51.4

POLSKI-FIAT 125 P/1300

SYRENA 104

WARSZAWA 223

cu in, 842 cu cm; compression ratio: 7-7.2; max power (SAE): 40 hp at 4,300 rpm; max torque (SAE): 58 lb ft, 8 kg m at 2,750 rpm; max engine rpm: 5,200; specific power: 47.5 hp/l; cylinder block: cast iron; cylinder head: light alloy; crankshaft bearings: 4, on ball bearings; lubrication: gear pump, mixture 1 : 30; carburation: 1 Jikov 35 POH/048 horizontal carburettor; fuel feed: mechanical pump; cooling system: water; cooling system capacity: 12.3 imp pt, 14.8 US pt, 7 l.

TRANSMISSION driving wheels: front; clutch: single dry plate; gearbox: mechanical; gears: 4 + reverse, free wheel; gearbox ratios: I 3.900, II 2.357, III 1.474, IV 0.958, rev 3.273; gear lever: steering column; final drive: spiral bevel; axle ratio: 4.875; width of rims: 4''; tyres: 5.60 x 15.

PERFORMANCE max speeds: 19 mph, 31 km/h in 1st gear; 32 mph, 51 km/h in 2nd gear; 50 mph, 81 km/h in 3rd gear; 75 mph, 120 km/h in 4th gear; power-weight ratio: 46.7 lb/hp, 21.2 kg/hp; carrying capacity: 706 lb, 320 kg; acceleration: 0-50 mph (0-80 km/h) 21 sec; speed in top at 1,000 rpm: 14.9 mph, 24 km/h; fuel consumption: 32.1 m/imp gal, 26.7 m/US gal, 8.8 l x 100 km.

CHASSIS box-type ladder frame; front suspension: independent, wishbones, transverse leafspring lower arms, lever dampers; rear suspension: rigid axle, transverse upper leafspring, trailing radius arms, lever dampers.

STEERING worm and roller; turns of steering wheel lock to lock: 2.80.

BRAKES drum; area rubbed by linings: front 136.4 sq in, 880 sq cm, rear 85.3 sq in, 550 sq cm, total 221.7 sq in, 1,430 sq cm.

ELECTRICAL EQUIPMENT voltage: 12 V; battery: 37.5 Ah; generator type: dynamo, 200 W; headlamps: 2.

DIMENSIONS AND WEIGHT wheel base: 90.55 in, 2,300 mm; front track: 47.24 in, 1,200 mm; rear track: 48.82 in, 1,240 mm; overall length: 159.05 in, 4,040 mm; overall width: 61.42 in, 1,560 mm; overall height: 59.65 in, 1,515 mm; ground clearance: 7.87 in, 200 mm; dry weight: 1,874 lb, 850 kg; distribution of weight: 48% front axle, 52% rear axle; turning circle (between walls): 34.1 ft, 10.4 m; fuel tank capacity: 7.5 imp gal, 9 US gal, 34 l.

BODY saloon/sedan; doors: 2; seats: 4; front seats: separate.

PRACTICAL INSTRUCTIONS fuel: mixture 1 : 30; gearbox and final drive oil: 4 imp pt, 4.9 US pt, 2.3 l, SAE 50, change every 7,500 miles, 12,000 km; greasing: every 7,500 miles, 12,000 km, 29 points; sparking plug type: 175° or 225°; normal tyre pressure: front 23 psi, 1.6 atm, rear 23 psi, 1.6 atm.

WARSZAWA   POLAND

223

PRICE: —

ENGINE front, 4 stroke; cylinders: 4, vertical, in line; bore and stroke: 3.23 x 3.94 in, 82.1 x 100 mm; engine capacity: 129.4 cu in, 2,120 cu cm; compression ratio: 7.5; max power (SAE): 77 hp at 4,000 rpm; max torque (SAE): 86 lb ft, 11.8 kg m at 2,200 rpm; max engine rpm: 4,800; specific power: 36.3 hp/l; cylinder block: cast iron; cylinder head: light alloy; crankshaft bearings: 5; valves: 2 per cylinder, overhead, push-rods and rockers; camshafts: 1, side; lubrication: gear pump, full flow filter and cartridge on by-pass; lubricating system capacity: 11.4 imp pt, 13.7 US pt, 6.5 l; carburation: 1 Jikov 40 SOP downdraught carburettor; fuel feed: mechanical pump; cooling system: water; cooling system capacity: 18.5 imp pt, 22.2 US pt, 10.5 l.

TRANSMISSION driving wheels: rear; clutch: single dry plate; gearbox: mechanical; gears: 4 + reverse; synchromesh gears: I, II, III, IV; gearbox ratios: I 3.753, II 2.372, III 1.482, IV 1, rev 3.753; gear lever: steering column; final drive: spiral bevel; axle ratio: 4.550; tyres: 6.40 x 15.

PERFORMANCE max speeds: 22 mph, 36 km/h in 1st gear; 35 mph, 57 km/h in 2nd gear; 57 mph, 91 km/h in 3rd gear; 84 mph, 135 km/h in 4th gear; power-weight ratio: 37.7 lb/hp, 17.1 kg/hp; carrying capacity: 1,058 lb, 480 kg; acceleration: standing ¼ mile 17 sec; speed in direct drive at 1,000 rpm: 18.3 mph, 29.5 km/h; fuel consumption: 27.7 m/imp gal, 23.1 m/US gal, 10.2 l x 100 km.

CHASSIS integral; front suspension: independent, wishbones, coil springs, telescopic dampers; rear suspension: rigid axle, semi-elliptic leafsprings, lever dampers.

STEERING worm and roller; turns of steering wheel lock to lock: 2.80.

POLSKI-FIAT 125 P/1300

SYRENA 104

WARSZAWA 223

BRAKES drum; area rubbed by linings: front 135.7 sq in, 875 sq cm, rear 135.7 sq in, 875 sq cm, total 271.4 sq in, 1,750 sq cm.

ELECTRICAL EQUIPMENT voltage: 12 V; battery: 56 Ah; generator type: dynamo, 220 W; ignition distributor: Zelmot; headlamps: 2.

DIMENSIONS AND WEIGHT wheel base: 106.30 in, 2,700 mm; front track: 54.92 in, 1,395 mm; rear track: 55.20 in, 1,402 mm; overall length: 186.61 in, 4,740 mm; overall width: 66.73 in, 1,695 mm; overall height: 62.80 in, 1,595 mm; ground clearance: 7.48 in, 190 mm; dry weight: 2,911 lb, 1,320 kg; distribution of weight: 46% front axle, 54% rear axle; turning circle (between walls): 43.3 ft, 13.2 m; fuel tank capacity: 12.1 imp gal, 14.5 US gal, 55 l.

BODY saloon/sedan; doors: 4; seats: 6; front seats: separate.

PRACTICAL INSTRUCTIONS fuel: 80 oct petrol; engine sump oil: 10.6 imp pt, 12.7 US pt, 6 l, SAE 20W (winter) 30W (summer), change every 3,700 miles, 6,000 km; gearbox oil: 2.8 imp pt, 3.4 US pt, 1.6 l, SAE 90, change every 7,500 miles, 12,000 km; final drive oil: 1.9 imp pt, 2.3 US pt, 1.1 l, SAE 90, change every 7,500 miles, 12,000 km; greasing: every 7,500 miles, 12,000 km, 42 points; sparking plug type: 225° or 240°; tappet clearances: inlet 0.009 in, 0.22 mm, exhaust 0.013 in, 0.32 mm; valve timing: inlet opens 33° before tdc and closes 59° after bdc, exhaust opens 68° before bdc and closes 24° after tdc; normal tyre pressure: front 24 psi, 1.7 atm, rear 26 psi, 1.8 atm.

223 K

See 223, except for:

PRICE: —

PERFORMANCE max speed: 81 mph, 130 km/h; power-weight ratio: 39.2 lb/hp, 17.8 kg/hp.

DIMENSIONS AND WEIGHT overall length: 187.01 in, 4,750 mm; overall height: 67.13 in, 1,705 mm; dry weight: 3,032 lb, 1,375 kg.

BODY estate car/station wagon; doors: 4 + 1.

SEAT   SPAIN

4-door 850 Especial

PRICE EX WORKS: 94,000 pesetas.

ENGINE rear, 4 stroke; cylinders: 4, vertical, in line; bore and stroke: 2.56 x 2.50 in, 65 x 63.5 mm; engine capacity: 51.4 cu in, 843 cu cm; compression ratio: 9.3; max power (DIN): 47 hp at 6,400 rpm; max torque (DIN): 43 lb ft, 6 kg m at 3,600 rpm; max engine rpm: 6,400; specific power: 55.8 hp/l; cylinder block: cast iron; cylinder head: light alloy; crankshaft bearings: 3; valves: 2 per cylinder, overhead, in line, push-rods and rockers; camshafts: 1, side; lubrication: gear pump, centrifugal filter; lubricating system capacity: 5.8 imp pt, 7 US pt, 3.3 l; carburation: 1 Weber 30 DIC downdraught single barrel carburettor; fuel feed: mechanical pump; cooling system: liquid, sealed circuit; cooling system capacity: 13.2 imp pt, 15.9 US pt, 7.5 l.

TRANSMISSION driving wheels: rear; clutch: single dry plate; gearbox: mechanical; gears: 4 + reverse; synchromesh gears: I, II, III, IV; gearbox ratios: I 3.636, II 2.055, III 1.409, IV 0.963, rev 3.615; gear lever: central; final drive: hypoid bevel; axle ratio: 5.125; width of rims: 4.5''; tyres: 5.50 x 13.

PERFORMANCE max speeds: 22 mph, 35 km/h in 1st gear; 40 mph, 65 km/h in 2nd gear; 59 mph, 95 km/h in 3rd gear; 85 mph, 137 km/h in 4th gear; power-weight ratio: 33.5 lb/hp, 15.2 kg/hp; carrying capacity: 882 lb, 400 kg; max gradient in 1st gear: 36%; acceleration (max load): standing ¼ mile 21 sec, 0-50 mph (0-80 km/h) 14.3 sec; speed in top at 1,000 rpm: 13.9 mph, 22.4 km/h; fuel consumption: 37.7 m/imp gal, 31.4 m/US gal, 7.5 l x 100 km.

CHASSIS integral; front suspension: independent, wishbones, transverse leafspring lower arms, anti-roll bar, telescopic dampers; rear suspension: independent, semi-trailing arms, coil springs, anti-roll bar, telescopic dampers.

STEERING screw and sector; turns of steering wheel lock to lock: 3.75.

263

4-DOOR 850 ESPECIAL

BRAKES front disc, rear drum; lining area: total 51.5 sq in, 332 sq cm.

ELECTRICAL EQUIPMENT voltage: 12 V; battery: 48 Ah; generator type: dynamo, 230 W; ignition distributor: Femsa; headlamps: 2.

DIMENSIONS AND WEIGHT wheel base: 79.80 in, 2,027 mm; front track: 45.12 in, 1,146 mm; rear track: 44.13 in, 1,121 mm; overall length: 146.65 in, 3,725 mm; overall width: 56.10 in, 1,425 mm; overall height: 52.95 in, 1,345 mm; ground clearance: 7.68 in, 195 mm; dry weight: 1,572 lb, 713 kg; distribution of weight: 39% front axle, 61% rear axle; turning circle (between walls): 33.1 ft, 10.1 m; fuel tank capacity: 6.6 imp gal, 7.9 US gal, 30 l.

BODY saloon/sedan; doors: 4; seats: 4-5; front seats: separate.

PRACTICAL INSTRUCTIONS fuel: 96 oct petrol; engine sump oil: 5.6 imp pt, 6.8 US pt, 3.2 l, SAE 20W (winter) 30 (summer), change every 3,100 miles, 5,000 km; gearbox and final drive oil: 3.7 imp pt, 4.4 US pt, 2.1 l, SAE 90 EP, change every 18,600 miles, 30,000 km; greasing: every 1,600 miles, 2,500 km, 2 points; sparking plug type: 260°; tappet clearances: inlet 0.006 in, 0.15 mm, exhaust 0.008 in, 0.20 mm; valve timing: inlet opens 25° before tdc and closes 51° after bdc, exhaust opens 64° before bdc and closes 12° after tdc; normal tyre pressure: front 16 psi, 1.1 atm, rear 26 psi, 1.8 atm.

1430

PRICE EX WORKS: 136,600 pesetas.

ENGINE front, 4 stroke; cylinders: 4, in line; bore and stroke: 3.15 x 2.81 in, 80 x 71.5 mm; engine capacity: 87.7 cu in, 1,438 cu cm; compression ratio: 9; max power (DIN): 70 hp at 5,400 rpm; max torque (DIN): 80 lb ft, 11 kg m at 3,400 rpm; max engine rpm: 6,000; specific power: 48.7 hp/l; cylinder block: cast iron; cylinder head: light alloy; crankshaft bearings: 5; valves: 2 per cylinder, overhead, push-rods and rockers; camshafts: 1, side; lubrication: gear pump, full flow filter; lubricating system capacity: 6.9 imp pt, 8.2 US pt, 3.9 l; carburation: 1 Weber 32 DHS 1 downdraught twin barrel carburettor; fuel feed: mechanical pump; cooling system: water; cooling system capacity: 13.2 imp pt, 15.9 US pt, 7.5 l.

TRANSMISSION driving wheels: rear; clutch: single dry plate; gearbox: mechanical; gears: 4 + reverse; synchromesh gears: I, II, III, IV; gearbox ratios: I 3.797, II 2.175, III 1.410, IV 1, rev 3.655; gear lever: central; final drive: hypoid bevel; axle ratio: 4.100; width of rims: 4.5''; tyres: 150 x 13.

PERFORMANCE max speeds: 25 mph, 40 km/h in 1st gear; 43 mph, 70 km/h in 2nd gear; 65 mph, 105 km/h in 3rd gear; 96 mph, 155 km/h in 4th gear; power-weight ratio: 28.7 lb/hp, 13 kg/hp; carrying capacity: 937 lb, 425 kg; max gradient in 1st gear: 40%; acceleration: standing ¼ mile 19.5 sec; speed in direct drive at 1,000 rpm: 15.7 mph, 25.3 km/h; fuel consumption: 33.2 m/imp gal, 27.7 m/US gal, 8.5 l x 100 km.

CHASSIS integral; front suspension: independent, wishbones, coil springs, anti-roll bar, telescopic dampers; rear suspension: rigid axle, twin trailing radius arms, transverse linkage bar, coil springs, telescopic dampers.

STEERING worm and roller; turns of steering wheel lock to lock: 2.75.

BRAKES disc; lining area: front 18 sq in, 116 sq cm, rear 18 sq in, 116 sq cm, total 36 sq in, 232 sq cm.

ELECTRICAL EQUIPMENT voltage: 12 V; battery: 48 Ah; generator type: alternator, 540 W; ignition distributor: Femsa; headlamps: 4.

DIMENSIONS AND WEIGHT wheel base: 95.28 in, 2,420 mm; front track: 52.36 in, 1,330 mm; rear track: 51.18 in, 1,300 mm; overall length: 159.57 in, 4,053 mm; overall width: 63.43 in, 1,611 mm; overall height: 55.91 in, 1,420 mm; ground clearance: 6.46 in, 164 mm; dry weight: 2,007 lb, 910 kg; distribution of weight: 53% front axle, 47% rear axle; turning circle (between walls): 35.1 ft, 10.7 m; fuel tank capacity: 8.6 imp gal, 10.3 US gal, 39 l.

BODY saloon/sedan; doors: 4; seats: 5; front seats: separate.

PRACTICAL INSTRUCTIONS fuel: 98 oct petrol; engine sump

SEAT 1430

SAAB 96 V4 and 95 V4

SAAB 95 V4

oil: 6.7 imp pt, 8 US pt, 3.8 l, SAE 30W-40, change every 6,200 miles, 10,000 km; gearbox oil: 2.3 imp pt, 2.7 US pt, 1.3 l, SAE 90 EP, change every 18,600 miles, 30,000 km; final drive oil: 1.2 imp pt, 1.5 US pt, 0.7 l, SAE 90 EP, change every 18,600 miles, 30,000 km; greasing: none; sparking plug type: 240°; tappet clearances: inlet 0.008 in, 0.20 mm, exhaust 0.008 in, 0.20 mm; valve timing: inlet opens 19° before tdc and closes 48° after bdc, exhaust opens 59° before bdc and closes 8° after tdc; normal tyre pressure: front 24 psi, 1.7 atm, rear 26 psi, 1.8 atm.

SAAB   SWEDEN

96 V4

PRICE IN GB: £ 780.
PRICE IN USA: $ 2,545.

ENGINE front, 4 stroke; cylinders: 4, Vee-slanted at 60°; bore and stroke: 3.54 x 2.32 in, 90 x 58.9 mm; engine capacity: 91.4 cu in, 1,498 cu cm; compression ratio: 9; max power (SAE): 73 hp at 5,000 rpm; max torque (SAE): 87 lb ft, 12 kg m at 2,700 rpm; max engine rpm: 5,400; specific power: 48.7 hp/l; cylinder block: cast iron; cylinder head: cast iron; crankshaft bearings: 3; valves: 2 per cylinder, overhead, push-rods and rockers; camshafts: 1, at centre of Vee; lubrication: rotary pump, full flow filter; lubricating system capacity: 5.8 imp pt, 7 US pt, 3.3 l; carburation: 1 Autolite 71 TW-IB downdraught carburettor; fuel feed: mechanical pump; cooling system: water; cooling system capacity: 12 imp pt, 14.4 US pt, 6.8 l.

TRANSMISSION driving wheels: front; clutch: single dry plate, hydraulically controlled; gearbox: mechanical; gears: 4 + reverse; synchromesh gears: I, II, III, IV; gearbox ratios: I 3.484, II 2.090, III 1.291, IV 0.840, rev 3.176; gear lever: steering column; final drive: spiral bevel; axle ratio: 4.880; width of rims: 4''; tyres: 155 x 15.

PERFORMANCE max speeds: 22 mph, 36 km/h in 1st gear; 37 mph, 60 km/h in 2nd gear; 61 mph, 98 km/h in 3rd gear; 90 mph, 145 km/h in 4th gear; power-weight ratio: 26.7 lb/hp, 12.1 kg/hp; carrying capacity: 948 lb, 430 kg; acceleration: standing ¼ mile 10.4 sec; speed in top at 1,000 rpm: 17.3 mph, 27.8 km/h; fuel consumption: 33.2 m/imp gal, 27.7 m/US gal, 8.5 l x 100 km.

CHASSIS integral; front suspension: independent, wishbones, coil springs, anti-roll bar, telescopic dampers; rear suspension: U-shaped tubular rigid axle (swept-back ends), swinging trailing lower radius levers, U-shaped central transverse linkage, coil springs, telescopic dampers.

STEERING rack-and-pinion; turns of steering wheel lock to lock: 2.70.

BRAKES front disc (diameter 10.51 in, 267 mm), rear drum, 2 separate X hydraulic circuits, servo; area rubbed by linings: front 179.8 sq in, 1,160 sq cm, rear 76 sq in, 490 sq cm, total 255.8 sq in, 1,650 sq cm.

ELECTRICAL EQUIPMENT voltage: 12 V; battery: 60 Ah; generator type: alternator, 375 W; ignition distributor: Bosch; headlamps: 2.

DIMENSIONS AND WEIGHT wheels base: 98.35 in, 2,498 mm; front track: 48.03 in, 1,220 mm; rear track: 48.03 in, 1,220 mm; overall length: 165.35 in, 4,200 mm; overall width: 62.60 in, 1,590 mm; overall height: 57.87 in, 1,470 mm; ground clearance: 7.09 in, 180 mm; dry weight: 1,943 lb, 881 kg; distribution of weight: 63% front axle, 37% rear axle; turning circle (between walls): 36.1 ft, 11 m; fuel tank capacity: 8.4 imp gal, 10 US gal, 38 l.

BODY saloon/sedan; doors: 2; seats: 5; front seats: separate.

PRACTICAL INSTRUCTIONS fuel: 97 oct petrol; engine sump oil: 5.3 imp pt, 6.3 US pt, 3 l, SAE 10W-30 (winter) 10W-40 (summer), change every 6,200 miles, 10,000 km; gearbox and final drive oil: 3 imp pt, 3.6 US pt, 1.7 l, SAE 80 EP, change every 12,400 miles, 20,000 km; greasing: every 6,200 miles, 10,000 km, 7 points; sparking plug type: 200°; tappet clearances: inlet 0.014 in, 0.35 mm, exhaust 0.016 in, 0.40 mm; valve timing: inlet opens 21° before tdc and closes 82° after bdc, exhaust opens 63° before bdc and closes 40° after tdc; normal tyre pressure: front 24 psi, 1.7 atm, rear 24 psi, 1.7 atm.

OPTIONAL ACCESSORIES sunshine roof.

SEAT 4-door 850 Especial

SAAB 96 V4

SAAB 95 V4

95 V4

See 96 V4, except for:

PRICE IN GB: £ 860.
PRICE IN USA: $ 2,799.

PERFORMANCE max speed: 87 mph, 140 km/h; power-weight ratio: 28.9 lb/hp, 13.1 kg/hp; carrying capacity: 1,191 lb, 540 kg; fuel consumption: 31.4 m/imp gal, 26.1 m/US gal, 9 l x 100 km.

CHASSIS rear suspension: lever dampers.

DIMENSIONS AND WEIGHT overall length: 169.29 in, 4,300 mm; overall height: 58.66 in, 1,490 mm; dry weight: 2,112 lb, 958 kg; distribution of weight: 58% front axle, 42% rear axle; turning circle (between walls): 37.7 ft, 11.5 m; fuel tank capacity: 9.2 imp gal, 11.1 US gal, 42 l.

BODY estate car/station wagon; doors: 2 + 1; seats: 7.

99 2-door Saloon

PRICE IN GB: £ 1,086.
PRICE IN USA: $ 3,100.

ENGINE front, 4 stroke; cylinders: 4, in line; bore and stroke: 3.29 x 3.07 in, 83.5 x 78 mm; engine capacity: 104.3 cu in, 1,709 cu cm; compression ratio: 9; max power (SAE): 87 hp at 5,500 rpm; max torque (SAE): 98 lb ft, 13.5 kg m at 3,000 rpm; max engine rpm: 5,700; specific power: 51 hp/l; cylinder block: cast iron; cylinder head: light alloy; crankshaft bearings: 5; valves: 2 per cylinder, overhead, thimble tappets; camshafts: 1, overhead; lubrication: gear pump, full flow filter; lubricating system capacity: 6.2 imp pt, 7.4 US pt, 3.5 l; carburation: 1 Zenith-Stromberg 175 CD horizontal carburettor; fuel feed: mechanical pump; cooling system: water; cooling system capacity: 15 imp pt, 18 US pt, 8.5 l.

TRANSMISSION driving wheels: front; clutch: single dry plate, hydraulically controlled; gearbox: mechanical; gears: 4 + reverse; synchromesh gears: I, II, III, IV; gearbox ratios: I 3.223, II 2.038, III 1.374, IV 0.948, rev 3.223; gear lever: central; final drive: hypoid bevel; axle ratio: 4.220; width of rims: 4.5''; tyres: 155 x 15.

PERFORMANCE max speeds: 30 mph, 48 km/h in 1st gear; 47 mph, 76 km/h in 2nd gear; 70 mph, 112 km/h in 3rd gear; 96 mph, 155 km/h in 4th gear; power-weight ratio: 26.4 lb/hp, 12 kg/hp; carrying capacity: 926 lb, 420 kg; acceleration: standing ¼ mile 19 sec; speed in top at 1,000 rpm: 17.7 mph, 28.5 km/h; fuel consumption: 29.7 m/imp gal, 24.8 m/US gal, 9.5 l x 100 km.

CHASSIS integral; front suspension: independent, wishbones, coil springs, telescopic dampers; rear suspension: rigid axle, twin swinging trailing radius arms, transverse linkage bar, coil springs, telescopic dampers.

STEERING rack-and-pinion; turns of steering wheel lock to lock: 3.33.

BRAKES disc, 2 separate X hydraulic circuits, servo; area rubbed by linings: front 186.2 sq in, 1,201 sq cm, rear 165 sq in, 1,064 sq cm, total 351.2 sq in, 2,265 sq cm.

ELECTRICAL EQUIPMENT voltage: 12 V; battery: 60 Ah; generator type: alternator, 420 W; ignition distributor: Delco; headlamps: 2.

DIMENSIONS AND WEIGHT wheel base: 97.36 in, 2,473 mm; front track: 54.72 in, 1,390 mm; rear track: 55.12 in, 1,400 mm; overall length: 171.26 in, 4,350 mm; overall width: 65.98 in, 1,676 mm; overall height: 56.69 in, 1,440 mm; ground clearance: 6.69 in, 170 mm; dry weight: 2,304 lb, 1,045 kg; distribution of weight: 61% front axle, 39% rear axle; turning circle (between walls): 33.5 ft, 10.2 m; fuel tank capacity: 10.6 imp gal, 12.7 US gal, 48 l.

BODY saloon/sedan; doors: 2; seats: 5; front seats: separate.

PRACTICAL INSTRUCTIONS fuel: 96 oct petrol; engine sump oil: 6.2 imp pt, 7.4 US pt, 3.5 l, SAE 10W-40, change every 6,200 miles, 10,000 km; gearbox and final drive oil: 5.3 imp pt, 6.3 US pt, 3 l, SAE 80, change every 6,200 miles, 10,000 km; greasing: every 6,200 miles, 10,000 km; tappet clearances: inlet 0.006-0.012 in, 0.15-0.30 mm, exhaust 0.014-0.020 in, 0.35-0.50 mm; valve timing: inlet opens 12° before tdc and closes 52° after bdc, exhaust opens 52° before bdc and closes 12° after tdc; normal tyre pressure: front 24 psi, 1.7 atm, rear 24 psi, 1.7 atm.

99 2-DOOR SALOON

VARIATIONS

ENGINE bore and stroke 3.43 x 3.07 in, 87 x 78 mm, engine capacity 112.9 cu in, 1,850 cu cm, max power (SAE) 93 hp at 5,500 rpm, max torque (SAE) 109 lb ft, 15 kg m at 3,000 rpm, 50.3 hp/l specific power.
PERFORMANCE max speed 99 mph, 160 km/h, power-weight ratio 24.7 lb/hp, 11.2 kg/hp.

ENGINE (injection) bore and stroke 3.43 x 3.07 in, 87 x 78 mm; engine capacity 112.9 cu in, 1,850 cu cm, max power (SAE) 103 hp at 5,500 rpm, max torque (SAE) 106 lb ft, 14.6 kg m at 3,200 rpm, 55.7 hp/l specific power, electronically controlled Bosch injection system.
PERFORMANCE max speed 103 mph, 165 km/h, power-weight ratio 22.3 lb/hp, 10.1 kg/hp.

OPTIONAL ACCESSORIES Borg-Warner 35/3 automatic gearbox, hydraulic torque convertor and planetary gears with 3 ratios (I 2.393, II 1.450, III 1, rev 2.090), max ratio of convertor at stall 2, possible manual selection, axle ratio 3.820 (only with injection engine).

99 4-door Saloon

See 99 2-door Saloon, except for:

PRICE IN GB: £ 1,143.

VOLVO   SWEDEN

142 Saloon

PRICE IN USA: $ 3,095.

ENGINE front, 4 stroke; cylinders: 4, in line; bore and stroke: 3.50 x 3.15 in, 88.9 x 80 mm; engine capacity: 121.2 cu in, 1,986 cu cm; compression ratio: 8.7; max power (SAE): 90 hp at 4,800 rpm; max torque (SAE): 120 lb ft, 16.5 kg m at 3,000 rpm; max engine rpm: 5,800; specific power: 45.3 hp/l; cylinder block: cast iron; cylinder head: cast iron; crankshaft bearings: 5; valves: 2 per cylinder, overhead, push-rods and rockers; camshafts: 1, side; lubrication: gear pump, full flow filter; lubricating system capacity: 6.5 imp pt, 7.8 US pt, 3.7 l; carburation: 1 Zenith-Stromberg 175 CD-25 horizontal carburettor; fuel feed: mechanical pump; cooling system: liquid, sealed circuit; cooling system capacity: 17.6 imp pt, 21.1 US pt, 10 l.

TRANSMISSION driving wheels: rear; clutch: single dry plate (diaphragm); gearbox: mechanical; gears: 4 + reverse; synchromesh gears: I, II, III, IV; gearbox ratios: I 3.130, II 1.990, III 1.360, IV 1, rev 3.250; gear lever: central; final drive: hypoid bevel; axle ratio: 4.100; width of rims: 5''; tres: 165 x 15.

PERFORMANCE max speeds: 33 mph, 53 km/h in 1st gear; 52 mph, 83 km/h in 2nd gear; 75 mph, 121 km/h in 3rd gear; 98 mph, 158 km/h in 4th gear; power-weight ratio: 28.9 lb/hp, 13.1 kg/hp; carrying capacity: 1,147 lb, 520 kg; acceleration: 0-50 mph (0-80 km/h) 9.8 sec; fuel consumption: 31.4 m/imp gal, 26.1 m/US gal, 9 l x 100 km.

CHASSIS integral; front suspension: independent, wishbones, coil springs, anti-roll bar, telescopic dampers; rear suspension: rigid axle, twin trailing radius arms, transverse linkage bar, coil springs, telescopic dampers.

STEERING worm and roller; turns of steering wheel lock to lock: 4.

BRAKES disc (diameter 10.91 in, 277 mm), dual circuit, rear compensator, servo; lining area: front 20 sq in, 129 sq cm, rear 15.5 sq in, 100 sq cm, total 35.5 sq in, 229 sq cm.

ELECTRICAL EQUIPMENT voltage: 12 V; battery: 60 Ah; generator type: alternator, 490 W; ignition distributor: Bosch; headlamps: 2.

DIMENSIONS AND WEIGHT wheel base: 103.15 in, 2,620 mm; front track: 53.15 in, 1,350 mm; rear track: 53.15 in, 1,350 mm; overall length: 182.68 in, 4,640 mm; overall width: 68.50 in, 1,740 mm; overall height: 56.69 in, 1,440 mm; ground clearance: 7.09 in, 180 mm, dry weight: 2,602 lb, 1,180 kg; turning circle (between walls): 30.2 ft, 9.2 m; fuel tank capacity: 12.8 imp gal, 15.3 US gal, 58 l.

SAAB 99 4-door Saloon

VOLVO 144 Grand Luxe Saloon

VOLVO 145 De Luxe Station Wagon

BODY saloon/sedan; doors: 2; seats: 5; front seats: separate, reclining backrests; details: built-in adjustable headrests, electrical-heated rear window.

PRACTICAL INSTRUCTIONS fuel: 98-100 oct petrol; engine sump oil: 5.6 imp pt, 6.8 US pt, 3.2 l, SAE 10W-30, change every 3,100 miles, 5,000 km; gearbox oil: 1.2 imp pt, 1.5 US pt, 0.7 l, SAE 80, change every 24,900 miles, 40,000 km; final drive oil: 2.3 imp pt, 2.7 US pt, 1.3 l, SAE 80, change every 24,900 miles, 40,000 km; greasing: none; normal tyre pressure: front 20 psi, 1.4 atm, rear 23 psi, 1.6 atm.

OPTIONAL ACCESSORIES limited slip final drive; Borg-Warner 35 automatic gearbox, hydraulic torque convertor and planetary gears with 3 ratios (I 2.390, II 1.450, III 1, rev 2.090), max ratio of convertor at stall 2, central selector lever.

142 De Luxe Saloon

See 142 Saloon, except for:

PRICE: —

BODY details; L equipment.

142 S Saloon

See 142 Saloon, except for:

PRICE: —

ENGINE compression ratio: 9.3; max power (SAE): 118 hp at 5,800 rpm; max torque (SAE): 123 lb ft, 17 kg m at 3,500 rpm; max engine rpm: 6,000; specific power: 59.4 hp/l; carburation: 2 SU type HS 6 horizontal carburettors.

PERFORMANCE max speeds: 35 mph, 56 km/h in 1st gear; 54 mph, 87 km/h in 2nd gear; 80 mph, 128 km/h in 3rd gear; 106 mph, 170 km/h in 4th gear; power-weight ratio: 22 lb/hp, 10 kg/hp; acceleration: 0-50 mph (0-80 km/h) 9 sec; speed in direct drive at 1,000 rpm: 17.7 mph, 28.5 km/h; fuel consumption: 26.9 m/imp gal, 22.4 m/US gal, 10.5 l x 100 km.

DIMENSIONS AND WEIGHT dry weight: 2,613 lb, 1,185 kg.

PRACTICAL INSTRUCTIONS tappet clearances: inlet 0.020 in, 0.50 mm, exhaust 0.020 in, 0.50 mm; valve timing: inlet opens 32° before tdc and closes 72° after bdc, exhaust opens 20° before bdc and closes 32° after tdc.

OPTIONAL ACCESSORIES only limited slip final drive and Laycock-de Normanville overdrive/top (0.797 ratio) with 4.300 axle ratio.

142 S De Luxe Saloon

See 142 S Saloon, except for:

PRICE: —

BODY details: L equipment.

142 Grand Luxe Saloon

See 142 Saloon, except for:

PRICE: —

ENGINE compression ratio: 10.5; max power (SAE): 130 hp at 6,000 rpm; max torque (SAE): 130 lb ft, 18 kg m at 3,500 rpm; max engine rpm: 6,000; specific power: 65.4 hp/l; carburation: Bosch electronically-controlled injection system: fuel feed: electric pump; cooling system: automatic fan.

PERFORMANCE max speeds: 38 mph, 61 km/h in 1st gear; 60 mph, 96 km/h in 2nd gear; 87 mph, 140 km/h in 3rd gear; 116 mph, 186 km/h in 4th gear; power-weight ratio: 20.1 lb/hp, 9.1 kg/hp; carrying capacity: 1,125 lb, 510 kg.

BRAKES lining area: front 26.7 sq in, 172 sq cm.

DIMENSIONS AND WEIGHT dry weight: 2,624 lb, 1,190 kg.

SAAB 99 Saloon

VOLVO 142 and 144 Grand Luxe Saloon

VOLVO 142 and 144 Grand Luxe Saloon

BODY details: L equipment.

OPTIONAL ACCESSORIES limited slip final drive, Laycock-de Normanville overdrive/top (0.797 ratio) with 4.300 axle ratio, Borg-Warner 35 automatic gearbox.

144 Saloon

See 142 Saloon, except for:

PRICE IN USA: $ 3,195.

PERFORMANCE power-weight ratio: 29.5 lb/hp, 13.4 kg/hp.

DIMENSIONS AND WEIGHT dry weight: 2,657 lb, 1,205 kg.

BODY doors: 4.

144 De Luxe Saloon

See 144 Saloon, except for:

PRICE IN GB: £ 1,241.

BODY details: L equipment.

144 S Saloon

See 142 S Saloon, except for:

PRICE: —

PERFORMANCE power-weight ratio: 22.7 lb/hp, 10.3 kg/hp.

DIMENSIONS AND WEIGHT dry weight: 2,668 lb, 1,210 kg.

BODY doors: 4.

144 S De Luxe Saloon

See 144 S Saloon, except for:

PRICE IN GB: £ 1,314.

BODY details: L equipment.

144 Grand Luxe Saloon

See 142 Grand Luxe Saloon, except for:

PRICE IN GB: £ 1,476.

PERFORMANCE power-weight ratio: 20.5 lb/hp, 9.3 kg/hp.

DIMENSIONS AND WEIGHT dry weight: 2,679 lb, 1,215 kg.

BODY doors: 4.

145 Station Wagon

See 142 Saloon, except for:

PRICE IN USA: $ 3,495.

TRANSMISSION axle ratio: 4.300.

PERFORMANCE max speeds: 31 mph, 50 km/h in 1st gear; 49 mph, 79 km/h in 2nd gear; 72 mph, 116 km/h in 3rd gear; 95 mph, 153 km/h in 4th gear; power-weight ratio: 32 lb/hp, 14.5 kg/hp; carrying capacity: 1,180 lb, 535 kg; acceleration: 0-50 mph (0-80 km/h) 11.5 sec.

DIMENSIONS AND WEIGHT overall width: 68.11 in, 1,730 mm; overall height: 57.09 in, 1,450 mm; dry weight: 2,789 lb, 1,265 kg.

BODY estate car/station wagon; doors: 4 + 1.

145 De Luxe Station Wagon

See 145 Station Wagon, except for:

PRICE IN GB: £ 1,382.

BODY details: L equipment.

145 S Station Wagon

See 142 S Saloon, except for:

PRICE: —

TRANSMISSION axle ratio: 4.300.

PERFORMANCE max speeds: 34 mph, 54 km/h in 1st gear; 53 mph, 86 km/h in 2nd gear; 78 mph, 125 km/h in 3rd gear; 103 mph, 165 km/h in 4th gear; power-weight ratio: 23.8 lb/hp, 10.8 kg/hp; carrying capacity: 1,169 lb, 530 kg; speed in direct drive at 1,000 rpm: 16.8 mph, 27.1 km/h.

DIMENSIONS AND WEIGHT overall width: 68.11 in, 1,730 mm; overall height: 57.09 in, 1,450 mm; dry weight: 2,800 lb, 1,270 kg.

BODY estate car/station wagon; doors: 4 + 1.

145 S De Luxe Station Wagon

See 145 S Station Wagon, except for:

PRICE IN GB: £ 1,437.

BODY details: L equipment.

1800 E Coupé

PRICE IN GB: £ 1,725.
PRICE IN USA: $ 4,495.

ENGINE front, 4 stroke; cylinders: 4, in line; bore and stroke: 3.50 x 3.15 in, 88.9 x 80 mm; engine capacity: 121.2 cu in, 1,986 cu cm; compression ratio: 10.5; max power (SAE): 130 hp at 6,000 rpm; max torque (SAE): 130 lb ft, 18 kg m at 3,500 rpm; max engine rpm: 6,000; specific power: 65.5 hp/l; cylinder block: cast iron; cylinder head: cast iron; crankshaft bearings: 5; valves: 2 per cylinder, overhead, push-rods and rockers; camshafts: 1, side; lubrication: gear pump, full flow filter; lubricating system capacity: 6.7 imp pt, 8 US pt, 3.8 l; carburation: Bosch electronically-controlled injection system; fuel feed: electric pump; cooling system: liquid, sealed circuit, automatic fan; cooling system capacity: 15 imp pt, 18 US pt, 8.5 l.

TRANSMISSION driving wheels: rear; clutch: single dry plate (diaphragm); gearbox: mechanical; gears: 4 + reserse and Laycock-de Normanville overdrive/top; synchromesh gears: I, II, III, IV; gearbox ratios: I 3.130, II 1.990, III 1.360, IV 1, overdrive/top 0.797, rev 3.250; gear lever: central; final drive: hypoid bevel; axle ratio: 4.300; width of rims: 5''; tyres: 165 x 15.

PERFORMANCE max speed: 121 mph, 195 km/h; power-weight ratio: 19.4 lb/hp, 8.8 kg/hp; carrying capacity: 662 lb, 300 kg; fuel consumption: 31.4 m/imp gal, 26.1 m/US gal, 9 l x 100 km.

CHASSIS integral; front suspension: independent, wishbones, coil springs, anti-roll bar, telescopic dampers; rear suspension: rigid axle, swinging longitudinal trailing arms, torque arms, coil springs, transverse linkage bar, telescopic dampers.

STEERING worm and roller; turns of steering wheel lock to lock: 3.25.

BRAKES disc, dual circuit, rear compensator, servo.

ELECTRICAL EQUIPMENT voltage: 12 V; battery: 60 Ah; generator type: alternator, 490 W; ignition distributor: Bosch; headlamps: 2.

DIMENSIONS AND WEIGHT wheel base: 96.46 in, 2,450 mm; front track: 51.69 in, 1,315 mm; rear track: 51.69 in, 1,315 mm; overall length: 173.23 in, 4,400 mm; overall width: 66.93 in, 1,700 mm; overall height: 50.59 in, 1,285 mm; ground clearance: 4.33 in, 110 mm; dry weight: 2,536 lb, 1,150 kg; turning circle (between walls): 32.8 ft, 10 m; fuel tank capacity: 9.9 imp gal, 11.9 US gal, 45 l.

VOLVO 1800 E Coupé (automatic)

VOLVO 164 Saloon

MONTEVERDI High Speed 375 L

BODY coupé; doors: 2; seats: 2 + 2; front seats: separate; details: built-in adjustable headrest, electrically-heated rear window.

PRACTICAL INSTRUCTIONS fuel: 98-100 oct petrol; engine sump oil: 6 imp pt, 7.2 US pt, 3.4 l, SAE 10W-30, change every 3,100 miles, 5,000 km; gearbox oil: 3.2 imp pt, 3.8 US pt, 1.8 l, SAE 80, change every 12,400 miles, 20,000 km; final drive oil: 2.3 imp pt, 2.7 US pt, 1.3 l, SAE 90, change every 24,900 miles, 40,000 km; normal tyre pressure: front 26 psi, 1.8 atm, rear 28 psi, 2 atm.

OPTIONAL ACCESSORIES limited slip final drive; Borg-Warner 35 automatic gearbox, hydraulic torque convertor and planetary gears with 3 ratios (I 2.390, II 1.450, III 1, rev 2.090), max ratio of convertor at stall 2, central selector lever.

164 Saloon

PRICE IN GB: £ 1,720 (with overdrive and power-assisted steering).
PRICE IN USA: $ 4,070 (with power-assisted steering).

ENGINE front, 4 stroke; cylinders: 6, in line; bore and stroke: 3.50 x 3.15 in, 88.9 x 80 mm; engine capacity: 181.7 cu in, 2,978 cu cm; compression ratio: 9.3; max power (SAE): 145 hp at 5,500 rpm; max torque (SAE): 163 lb ft, 22.5 kg m at 3,000 rpm; max engine rpm: 6,000; specific power: 48.7 hp/l; cylinder block: cast iron; cylinder head: cast iron; crankshaft bearings: 7; valves: 2 per cylinder, overhead, push-rods and rockers; camshafts: 1, side; lubrication: gear pump, full flow filter; lubricating system capacity: 9.2 imp pt, 11 US pt, 5.2 l; carburation: 2 Zenith-Stromberg horizontal carburettors; fuel feed: mechanical pump; cooling system: liquid, sealed circuit; cooling system capacity: 22.9 imp pt, 27.5 US pt, 13 l.

TRANSMISSION driving wheels: rear; clutch: single dry plate (diaphragm); gearbox: mechanical; gears: 4 + reverse; synchromesh gears: I, II, III, IV; gearbox ratios: I 3.140, II 1.970, III 1.340, IV 1, rev 3.540; gear lever: central; final drive: hypoid bevel; axle ratio: 3.730; width of rims: 5''; tyres: 165 x 15.

PERFORMANCE max speeds: 37 mph, 60 km/h in 1st gear; 59 mph, 95 km/h in 2nd gear; 87 mph, 140 km/h in 3rd gear; 115 mph, 185 km/h in 4th gear; power-weight ratio: 20.3 lb/hp, 9.2 kg/hp; carrying capacity: 1,080 lb, 490 kg; speed in direct drive at 1,000 rpm: 19.4 mph, 31.2 km/h; fuel consumption: 23.5 m/imp gal, 19.6 m/US gal, 12 l x 100 km.

CHASSIS integral; front suspension: independent, wishbones, coil springs, anti-roll bar, telescopic dampers; rear suspension: rigid axle, twin trailing radius arms, transverse linkage bar, coil springs, telescopic dampers.

STEERING recirculating ball; turns of steering wheel lock to lock: 3.70.

BRAKES disc, dual circuit, rear compensator, servo.

ELECTRICAL EQUIPMENT voltage: 12 V; battery: 60 Ah; generator type: alternator, 770 W; ignition distributor: Bosch; headlamps: 4, 2 fog lamps.

DIMENSIONS AND WEIGHT wheel base: 107.9 in, 2,720 mm; front track: 53.15 in, 1,350 mm; rear track: 53.15 in, 1,350 mm; overall length: 185.43 in, 4,710 mm; overall width: 68.11 in, 1,730 mm; overall height: 56.69 in, 1,440 mm; ground clearance: 7.09 in, 180 mm; dry weight: 2,944 lb, 1,335 kg; turning circle (between walls): 31.5 ft, 9.6 m; fuel tank capacity: 12.8 imp gal, 15.3 US gal, 58 l.

BODY saloon/sedan; doors: 4; seats: 5; front seats: separate, reclining backrests; details: built-in adjustable headrests, electrically-heated rear window.

PRACTICAL INSTRUCTIONS fuel: 98-100 oct petrol; engine sump oil: 9.2 imp pt, 11 US pt, 5.2 l, SAE 10W-30, change every 3,100 miles, 5,000 km; gearbox oil: 1.2 imp pt, 1.5 US pt, 0.7 l, SAE 90, change every 12,400 miles, 20,000 km; final drive oil: 2.3 imp pt, 2.7 US pt, 1.3 l, SAE 90 EP, change every 24,900 miles, 40,000 km; greasing: none; tappet clearances: inlet 0.020-0.022 in, 0.50-0.55 mm, exhaust 0.020-0.022 in, 0.50-0.55 mm; valve timing: inlet opens 32° before tdc and closes 72° after bdc, exhaust opens 20° before bdc and closes 32° after tdc; normal tyre pressure: front 26 psi, 1.8 atm, rear 28 psi, 2 atm.

OPTIONAL ACCESSORIES limited slip final drive; power-assisted steering; Laycock-de Normanville overdrive/top, 0.797 ratio; Borg-Warner 35 automatic gearbox, hydraulic torque convertor and planetary gears with 3 ratios (I 2.390, II 1.450, III 1, rev 2.090), max ratio of convertor at stall 2, 3.310 axle ratio.

VOLVO 1800 E Coupé

VOLVO 164 Saloon

MONTEVERDI High Speed 375 L

MONTEVERDI   SWITZERLAND

High Speed 375 S

PRICE EX WORKS: 71,000 francs.

ENGINE front, 4 stroke; cylinders: 8, Vee-slanted at 90°; bore and stroke: 4.32 x 3.75 in, 109.7 x 95.2 mm; engine capacity: 439.7 cu in, 7,206 cu cm; compression ratio: 10.1; max power (SAE): 375 hp at 4,600 rpm; max torque (SAE): 481 lb ft, 66.4 kg m at 3,200 rpm; max engine rpm: 5,600; specific power: 52 hp/l; cylinder block: cast iron; cylinder head: cast iron; crankshaft bearings: 5; valves: 2 per cylinder, overhead, in line, push-rods and rockers; camshafts: 1, at centre of Vee; lubrication: rotary pump, full flow filter; lubricating system capacity: 12.3 imp pt, 14.8 US pt, 7 l; carburation: 1 Carter AVS downdraught 4-barrel carburettor; fuel feed: mechanical pump; cooling system: water; cooling system capacity: 38.7 imp pt, 46.5 US pt, 22 l.

TRANSMISSION driving wheels: rear; gearbox: Torqueflite automatic, hydraulic torque convertor and planetary gears with 3 ratios + reverse, max ratio of convertor at stall 2.2, possible manual selection; gearbox ratios: I 2.450, II 1.450, III 1, rev 2.200; selector lever: central; final drive: hypoid bevel, limited slip; axle ratio: 2.880; width of rims: 7''; tyres: GR 70 x VR 15.

PERFORMANCE max speeds: 66 mph, 106 km/h in 1st gear; 111 mph, 179 km/h in 2nd gear; 162 mph, 260 km/h in 3rd gear; power-weight ratio: 9 lb/hp, 4.1 kg/hp; carrying capacity: 706 lb, 320 kg; speed in direct drive at 1,000 rpm: 28.9 mph, 46.5 km/h; fuel consumption: 15.7 m/imp gal, 13.1 m/US gal, 18 l x 100 km.

CHASSIS tubular; front suspension: independent, wishbones, coil springs, anti-roll bar, adjustable telescopic dampers; rear suspension: de Dion rigid axle, Watt transverse linkage bar, twin trailing arms, coil springs, anti-roll bar, adjustable telescopic dampers.

STEERING ZF worm and roller, servo.

BRAKES disc, internal radial fins, dual circuit, servo.

ELECTRICAL EQUIPMENT voltage: 12 V; battery: 48 Ah; generator: alternator, 60 A; headlamps: 2, iodine.

DIMENSIONS AND WEIGHT wheel base: 99.21 in, 2,520 mm; front track: 57.48 in, 1,460 mm; rear track: 56.30 in, 1,430 mm; overall length: 181.10 in, 4,600 mm; overall width: 70.67 in, 1,795 mm; overall height: 47.64 in, 1,210 mm; ground clearance: 5.51 in, 140 mm; dry weight: 3,352 lb, 1,520 kg; turning circle (between walls): 39 ft, 11.9 m; fuel tank capacity: 27.5 imp gal, 33 US gal, 125 l.

BODY coupé; doors: 2; seats: 2; details: air-conditioning system, electrically-heated rear window.

OPTIONAL ACCESSORIES 4-speed mechanical gearbox (I 2.650, II 1.900, III 1.390, IV 1, rev 2.200).

High Speed 375 L

See High Speed 375 S, except for:

PRICE EX WORKS: 73,000 francs.

PERFORMANCE max speed: 155 mph, 250 km/h; power-weight ratio: 9.5 lb/hp, 4.3 kg/hp.

DIMENSIONS AND WEIGHT wheel base: 104.72 in 2,660 mm; front track: 59.06 in, 1,500 mm; rear track: 57.48 in, 1,460 mm; overall length: 188.98 in, 4,800 mm; overall height: 50 in, 1,270 mm; ground clearance: 5.91 in, 150 mm; dry weight: 3,528 lb, 1,600 kg; fuel tank capacity: 28.6 imp gal, 34.3 US gal, 130 l.

BODY seats: 4.

Hai 450 SS

PRICE EX WORKS: —

ENGINE front, 4 stroke; cylinders: 8, Vee-slanted at 90°; bore and stroke: 4.32 x 3.75 in, 107.9 x 95.2 mm; engine capacity: 425.9 cu in, 6,980 cu cm; compression ratio: 10.2; max power (SAE): 450 hp at 5,000 rpm; max torque (SAE): 491 lb ft, 67.7 kg m at 4,000 rpm; max engine rpm: 6,200; specific power: 64.5 hp/l; cylinder block: cast iron; cylinder head: cast iron; crankshaft bearings: 5; valves: 2 per cylinder, overhead, in line, push-rods and rockers; camshafts: 1, at centre of Vee; lubrication: rotary pump, full flow filter; lubricating system capacity: 12.3 imp pt, 14.8 US pt, 7 l; carburation: 2 Carter downdraught 4-barrel carburettors; fuel feed: mechanical pump; cooling system: water; cooling system capacity: 40.5 imp pt, 48.6 US pt, 23 l.

HAI 450 SS

TRANSMISSION driving wheels: rear; clutch: single dry plate, hydraulically controlled; gearbox: ZF mechanical; gears: 5 + reverse; synchromesh gears: I, II, III, IV, V; gearbox ratios: I 2.400, II 1.400, III 1, IV 0.900, V 0.800, rev 2.800; gear lever: central; final drive: hypoid bevel, limited slip; axle ratio: 3.560; width of rims: 7''; tyres: GR 70 x VR 15.

PERFORMANCE max speeds: 61 mph, 98 km/h in 1st gear; 104 mph, 168 km/h in 2nd gear; 147 mph, 236 km/h in 3rd gear; 163 mph, 262 km/h in 4th gear; 180 mph, 290 km/h in 5th gear; power-weight ratio: 6.4 lb/hp, 2.9 kg/hp; carrying capacity: 397 lb, 180 kg; speed in top at 1,000 rpm: 29.5 mph, 47.5 km/h; fuel consumption: 15.7 m/imp gal, 13.1 m/US gal, 18 l x 100 km.

CHASSIS tubular; front suspension: independent, wishbones, coil springs, anti-roll bar, adjustable telescopic dampers; rear suspension: de Dion rigid axle, Watt transverse linkage bar, twin trailing arms, coil springs, anti-roll bar, adjustable telescopic dampers.

STEERING ZF worm and roller.

BRAKES disc, dual circuit, rear compensator, servo.

ELECTRICAL EQUIPMENT voltage: 12 V; battery: 48 Ah; generator type: alternator, 60 A; headlamps: 2, retractable, iodine.

DIMENSIONS AND WEIGHT wheel base: 100.39 in, 2,550 mm; front track: 59.06 in, 1,500 mm; rear track: 57.48 in, 1,460 mm; overall length: 168.50 in, 4,280 mm; overall width: 70.67 in, 1,795 mm; overall height: 42.91 in, 1,090 mm; ground clearance: 5.12 in, 130 mm; dry weight: 2,844 lb, 1,290 kg; turning circle (between walls): 35.8 ft, 10.9 m; fuel tank capacity: 28.6 imp gal, 34.3 US gal, 130 l.

BODY coupé; doors: 2; seats: 2; details: air-conditioning system, electrically-heated rear window.

MONTEVERDI Hai 450 SS

AZLK   USSR

Moskvich 408

PRICE IN GB: £ 572.

ENGINE front, 4 stroke; cylinders: 4, vertical, in line; bore and stroke: 2.99 x 2.95 in, 76 x 75 mm; engine capacity: 82.99 cu in, 1,360 cu cm; compression ratio: 7; max power (SAE): 60.5 hp at 4,750 rpm; max torque (SAE): 80 lb ft, 11 kg m at 2,750 rpm; max engine rpm: 5,200; specific power: 44.5 hp/l; cylinder block: cast iron; cylinder head: light alloy; crankshaft bearings: 3; valves: 2 per cylinder, overhead, parallel, push-rods and rockers; camshafts: 1, side; lubrication: gear pump, full flow filter; lubricating system capacity: 7.5 imp pt, 9.1 US pt, 4.3 l; carburation: 1 K-59 downdraught carburettor; fuel feed: mechanical pump; cooling system: water; cooling system capacity: 12.3 imp pt, 14.8 US pt, 7 l.

TRANSMISSION driving wheels: rear; clutch: single dry plate; gearbox: mechanical; gears: 4 + reverse; synchromesh gears: I, II, III, IV; gearbox ratios: I 3.8:0, II 2.420, III 1.450, IV 1, rev 4.710; gear lever: steering column; final drive: hypoid bevel; axle ratio: 4.710; width of rims: 4.5''; tyres: 6.00 x 13.

PERFORMANCE max speeds: 22 mph, 36 km/h in 1st gear; 35 mph, 56 km/h in 2nd gear; 58 mph, 94 km/h in 3rd gear; 81 mph, 130 km/h in 4th gear; power-weight ratio: 35.1 lb/hp, 15.9 kg/hp; carrying capacity: 882 lb, 400 kg; max gradient in 1st gear: 33%; acceleration: standing ¼ mile 22.7 sec, 0-50 mph (0-80 km/h) 17.8 sec; speed in direct drive at 1,000 rpm: 16.2 mph, 26.1 km/h; fuel consumption: 35.3 m/imp gal, 29.4 m/US gal, 8 l x 100 km.

CHASSIS integral; front suspension: independent, wishbones, coil springs, anti-roll bar, telescopic dampers; rear suspension: rigid axle, semi-elliptic leafsprings, telescopic dampers.

STEERING worm and double roller; turns of steering wheel lock to lock: 3.50.

BRAKES drum, 2 front leading shoes; lining area: front 60 sq in, 387 sq cm, rear 60 sq in, 387 sq cm, total 120 sq in, 774 sq cm.

ELECTRICAL EQUIPMENT voltage: 12 V; battery: 42 Ah; generator type: dynamo, 250 W; ignition distributor: P 107; headlamps: 4.

DIMENSIONS AND WEIGHT wheel base: 94.49 in, 2,400 mm; front track: 48.70 in, 1,237 mm; rear track: 48.31 in, 1,227 mm; overall length: 161.02 in, 4,090 mm; overall width: 61.02 in, 1,550 mm; overall height: 58.27 in, 1,480 mm; ground

AZLK Moskvich 412

GAZ Volga 24

clearance: 7.01 in, 178 mm; dry weight: 2,117 lb, 960 kg; distribution of weight: 54% front axle, 46% rear axle; turning circle (between walls): 32.8 ft, 10 m; fuel tank capacity: 10.1 imp gal, 12.1 US gal, 46 l.

BODY saloon/sedan; doors: 4; seats: 4-5; front seats: bench, separate backrests.

PRACTICAL INSTRUCTIONS fuel: 72 oct petrol; engine sump oil: 7.5 imp pt, 9.1 US pt, 4.3 l, SAE 10W-30, change every 2,500 miles, 4,000 km; gearbox oil: 0.9 imp pt, 1.1 US pt, 0.5 l, SAE 80-90, change every 15,000 miles, 24,000 km; final drive oil: 1.2 imp pt, 1.5 US pt, 0.7 l, SAE 80-90, change every 15,000 miles, 24,000 km; greasing: every 2,500 miles, 4,000 km, 15 points; sparking plug type: 175°; tappet clearances: inlet 0.006 in, 0.15 mm, exhaust 0.008 in, 0.20 mm; valve timing: inlet opens 21° before tdc and closes 55° after bdc, exhaust opens 57° before bdc and closes 19° after tdc; normal tyre pressure: front 24 psi, 1.7 atm, rear 24 psi, 1.7 atm.

Moskvich 426

See Moskvich 408, except for:

PRICE: —

TRANSMISSION axle ratio: 4.550.

PERFORMANCE power-weight ratio: 38.6 lb/hp, 17.5 kg/hp.

DIMENSIONS AND WEIGHT dry weight: 2,337 lb, 1,060 kg; distribution of weight: 52% front axle, 48% rear axle.

ELECTRICAL EQUIPMENT headlamps: 2.

BODY estate car/station wagon; doors: 4 + 1.

Moskvich 412

See Moskvich 408, except for:

PRICE: —

ENGINE bore and stroke: 3.23 x 2.76 in, 82 x 70 mm; engine capacity: 90.3 cu in, 1,480 cu cm; compression ratio: 8.8; max power (SAE): hp 80 at 5,800 rpm; max torque (SAE): 86 lb ft, 11.8 kg m at 3,400 rpm; max engine rpm: 6,500; specific power: 54 hp/l; crankshaft bearings: 5; valves: 2 per cylinder, overhead, rockers; lubricating system capacity: 9.2 imp pt, 11 US pt, 5.2 l; carburation: 1 K-126 H downdraught twin barrel carburettor; cooling system capacity: 13.2 imp pt, 15.9 US pt, 7.5 l.

TRANSMISSION gearbox ratios: I 3.490, II 2.040, III 1.330, IV 1, rev 3.390; gear lever: central; axle ratio: 4.220; tyres: 6.45 x 13.

PERFORMANCE max speeds: 27 mph, 43 km/h in 1st gear; 45 mph, 73 km/h in 2nd gear; 70 mph, 113 km/h in 3rd gear; 93 mph, 149 km/h in 4th gear; power-weight ratio: 26.7 lb/hp, 12.1 kg/hp; carrying capacity: 915 lb, 415 kg; speed in direct drive at 1,000 rpm: 16 mph, 25.8 km/h; fuel consumption: 32.1 m/imp gal, 26.7 m/US gal, 8.8 l x 100 km.

BRAKES servo; lining area: front 59.5 sq in, 384 sq cm, rear 59.5 sq in, 384 sq cm, total 119 sq in, 768 sq cm.

ELECTRICAL EQUIPMENT generator type: dynamo, 350 W; ignition distributor: ATE-2; headlamps: 2.

DIMENSIONS AND WEIGHT overall length: 162.20 in, 4,120 mm; dry weight: 2,128 lb, 965 kg.

BODY front seats: separate.

PRACTICAL INSTRUCTIONS fuel: 93 oct petrol; engine sump oil: 9.2 imp pt, 11 US pt, 5.2 l; gearbox oil: 1.6 imp pt, 1.9 US pt, 0.9 l; final drive oil: 2.3 imp pt, 2.7 US pt, 1.3 l; greasing: 8 points; sparking plug type: 240°; valve timing: inlet opens 30° before tdc and closes 72° after bdc, exhaust opens 72° before bdc and closes 30° after tdc; normal tyre pressure: front 28 psi, 2 atm, rear 28 psi, 2 atm.

Moskvich 427

See Moskvich 412, except for:

PRICE IN GB: £ 610.

TRANSMISSION axle ratio: 4.550.

PERFORMANCE power-weight ratio: 28 lb/hp, 12.7 kg/hp.

ELECTRICAL EQUIPMENT headlamps: 2 or 4.

MONTEVERDI Hai 450 SS

AZLK Moskvich 412

GAZ Volga 21

DIMENSIONS AND WEIGHT front track: 49.09 in, 1,247 mm; rear track: 48.70 in, 1,237 mm; overall length: 161.02 in, 4,090 mm; overall height: 60.04 in, 1,525 mm; dry weight: 2,249 lb, 1,020 kg.

BODY estate car/station wagon; doors: 4 + 1.

GAZ   USSR

Volga 21

PRICE: —

ENGINE front, 4 stroke; cylinders: 4, in line; bore and stroke: 3.62 x 3.62 in, 92 x 92 mm; engine capacity: 149.2 cu in, 2,445 cu cm; compression ratio: 7.6; max power (SAE): 95 hp at 4,000 rpm; max torque (SAE): 146 lb ft, 20.2 kg m at 2,000 rpm; max engine rpm: 5,200; specific power: 38.9 hp/l; cylinder block: light alloy, wet liners; cylinder head: light alloy; crankshaft bearings: 5; valves: 2 per cylinder, overhead, push-rods and rockers; camshafts: 1, side; lubrication: gear pump, filter on by-pass; lubricating system capacity: 11 imp pt, 13.1 US pt, 6.2 l; carburation: 1 type K-105 downdraught carburettor; fuel feed: mechanical pump; cooling system: water; cooling system capacity: 20.2 imp pt, 24.3 US pt, 11.5 l.

TRANSMISSION driving wheels: rear; clutch: single dry plate, hydraulically controlled; gearbox: mechanical; gears: 3 + reverse; synchromesh gears: II and III; gearbox ratios: I 3.115, II 1.772, III 1, rev 3.738; gear lever: central; final drive: hypoid bevel; axle ratio: 4.550; width of rims: 5''; tyres: 6.70 x 15.

PERFORMANCE max speeds: 29 mph, 47 km/h in 1st gear; 51 mph, 82 km/h in 2nd gear; 85 mph, 137 km/h in 3rd gear; power-weight ratio: 31.3 lb/hp, 14.2 kg/hp; carrying capacity: 1,058 lb, 480 kg; max gradient in 1st gear: 29%; acceleration: standing ¼ mile 22.9 sec, 0-50 mph (0-80 km/h) 18 sec; speed in direct drive at 1,000 rpm: 17.4 mph, 28 km/h; fuel consumption: 31.4 m/imp gal, 26.1 m/US gal, 9 l x 100 km.

CHASSIS integral; front suspension: independent, wishbones, coil springs, anti-roll bar, telescopic dampers; rear suspension: rigid axle, semi-elliptic leafsprings, telescopic dampers.

STEERING worm and double roller; turns of steering wheel lock to lock: 3.50.

BRAKES drum, 2 front leading shoes; lining area: front 94.4 sq in, 609 sq cm, rear 80.5 sq in, 519 sq cm, total 174.9 sq in, 1,128 sq cm.

ELECTRICAL EQUIPMENT voltage: 12 V; battery: 54 Ah; generator type: dynamo, 250 W; ignition distributor: P 3-B; headlamps: 2.

DIMENSIONS AND WEIGHT wheel base: 106.30 in, 2,700 mm; front track: 55.51 in, 1,410 mm; rear track: 55.90 in, 1,420 mm; overall length: 189.37 in, 4,810 mm; overall width: 70.87 in, 1,800 mm; overall height: 63.78 in, 1,620 mm; ground clearance: 7.48 in, 190 mm; dry weight: 2,977 lb, 1,350 kg; distribution of weight: 52% front axle, 48% rear axle; turning circle (between walls): 44 ft, 13.4 m; fuel tank capacity: 13.2 imp gal, 15.8 US gal, 60 l.

BODY saloon/sedan; doors: 4; seats: 5-6; front seats: bench.

PRACTICAL INSTRUCTIONS fuel: 80 oct petrol; engine sump oil: 10 imp pt, 12 US pt, 5.7 l, SAE 10W-30, change every 1,900 miles, 3,000 km; gearbox oil: 1.4 imp pt, 1.7 US pt, 0.8 l, SAE 90, change every 9,900 miles, 16,000 km; final drive oil: 1.6 imp pt, 1.9 US pt, 0.9 l, SAE 80-90, change every 9,900 miles, 16,000 km; greasing: every 1,200 miles, 2,000 km, 11 points; sparking plug type: 175°; tappet clearances: inlet 0.011 in, 0.28 mm, exhaust 0.011 in, 0.28 mm; valve timing: inlet opens 24° before tdc and closes 64° after bdc, exhaust opens 50° before bdc and closes 22° after tdc; normal tyre pressure: front 24 psi, 1.7 atm, rear 24 psi, 1.7 atm.

Volga 22 G

See Volga 21, except for:

PRICE: —

PERFORMANCE max speed: 83 mph, 134 km/h; power-weight ratio: 34.4 lb/hp, 15.6 kg/hp; fuel consumption: 28.2 m/imp gal, 23.5 m/US gal, 10 l x 100 km.

DIMENSIONS AND WEIGHT dry weight: 3,263 lb, 1,480 kg.

BODY estate car/station wagon; doors: 4 + 1.

Volga 24

See Volga 21, except for:

PRICE: —

ENGINE compression ratio: 8.2; max power (SAE): 110 hp at 4,500 rpm; max torque (SAE): 138 lb ft, 19 kg m at 2,400 rpm; max engine rpm: 4,500; specific power: 45 hp/l; carburation: 1 downdraught twin barrel carburettor.

TRANSMISSION gears: 4 + reverse; synchromesh gears: I, II, III, IV; gearbox ratios: I 3.500, II 2.260, III 1.450, IV 1, rev 3.540; tyres: 7.35 x 14.

PERFORMANCE max speeds: 25 mph, 41 km/h in 1st gear; 40 mph, 64 km/h in 2nd gear; 62 mph, 100 km/h in 3rd gear; 90 mph, 145 km/h in 4th gear; power-weight ratio: 26 lb/hp, 11.8 kg/hp; speed in direct drive at 1,000 rpm: 20.2 mph, 32.5 km/h.

ELECTRICAL EQUIPMENT generator type: alternator, 350 W; ignition distributor: R 119-B.

DIMENSIONS AND WEIGHT wheel base: 110.24 in, 2,800 mm; front track: 57.87 in, 1,470 mm; overall length: 186.42 in, 4,735 mm; overall height: 58.66 in, 1,490 mm; ground clearance: 7.09 in, 180 mm; dry weight: 2,866 lb, 1,300 kg; turning circle (between walls): 36.1 ft, 11 m; fuel tank capacity: 12.1 imp gal, 14.5 US gal, 55 l.

BODY front seats: separate.

69AM

PRICE: —

ENGINE front, 4 stroke; cylinders: 4, vertical, in line; bore and stroke: 3.46 x 3.94 in, 88 x 100 mm; engine capacity: 148.3 cu in, 2,430 cu cm; compression ratio: 6.7; max power (SAE): 72 hp at 3,800 rpm; max torque (SAE): 130 lb ft, 18 kg m at 2,000 rpm; max engine rpm: 4,500; specific power: 29.6 hp/l; cylinder block: cast iron; cylinder head: light alloy; crankshaft bearings: 4; valves: 2 per cylinder, side, push-rods and tappets; camshafts: 1, side; lubrication: gear pump, full flow filter; lubricating system capacity: 9.7 imp pt, 11.6 US pt, 5.5 l; carburation: 1 type K-22D downdraught single barrel carburettor; fuel feed: mechanical pump; cooling system: water; cooling system capacity: 21.1 imp pt, 25.4 US pt, 12 l.

TRANSMISSION driving wheels: front and rear; clutch: single dry plate; gearbox: mechanical with transfer box; gears: 3 + reverse and 2-ratio transfer box; synchromesh gears: II and III; gearbox ratios: I 3.115, II 1.772, III 1, rev 3.738; transfer box ratios: I 1.150, II 2.780; gear lever and transfer lever: central; final drive: spiral bevel; axle ratio: 5.125; width of rims: 4.5''; tyres: 6.50 x 16.

PERFORMANCE max speeds: 20 mph, 32 km/h in 1st gear; 35 mph, 56 km/h in 2nd gear; 59 mph, 95 km/h in 3rd gear; power-weight ratio: 42.8 lb/hp, 19.4 kg/hp; carrying capacity: 882 lb, 400 kg; max gradient in 1st gear: 57.5%; speed in direct drive at 1,000 rpm: 13.8 mph, 22.2 km/h; fuel consumption: 20.2 m/imp gal, 16.8 m/US gal, 14 l x 100 km.

CHASSIS ladder frame; front suspension: rigid axle, semi-elliptic leafsprings, lever dampers; rear suspension: rigid axle, semi-elliptic leafsprings, lever dampers.

STEERING worm and double roller; turns of steering wheel lock to lock: 3.50.

BRAKES drum; lining area: total 153.5 sq in, 990 sq cm.

ELECTRICAL EQUIPMENT voltage: 12 V; battery: 54 Ah; generator type: dynamo, 220 W; ignition distributor: P-23 B; headlamps: 2.

DIMENSIONS AND WEIGHT wheel base: 90.55 in, 2,300 mm; front track: 56.69 in, 1,440 mm; rear track: 56.69 in, 1,440 mm; overall length: 151.57 in, 3,850 mm; overall width: 68.90 in, 1,750 mm; overall height: 79.92 in, 2,030 mm; ground clearance: 8.27 in, 210 mm; dry weight: 3,076 lb, 1,395 kg; distribution of weight: 56% front axle, 44% rear axle; turning circle (between walls): 42.6 ft, 13 m; fuel tank capacity: 13.2 imp gal, 15.8 US gal, 60 l.

BODY open; doors: 4; seats: 5; front seats: separate.

PRACTICAL INSTRUCTIONS fuel: 72 oct petrol; engine sump oil: 9 imp pt, 10.8 US pt, 5.1 l, SAE 20-30, change every 1,900 miles, 3,000 km; gearbox oil: 1.4 imp pt, 1.7 US pt, 0.8 l, SAE 80-90, change every 7,500 miles, 12,000 km; final drive oil: 1.4 imp pt, 1.7 US pt, 0.8 l, SAE 80-90, change every 7,500 miles, 12,000 km; greasing: every 1,200 miles, 2,000 km, 20 points; sparking plug type: 145°; tappet clearances: inlet 0.009 in, 0.23 mm, exhaust 0.011 in, 0.28 mm; valve

VAZ 2101

ZAZ Zaporozhets 966 Limousine

ZIL 114 Limousine

timing: inlet opens 9° before tdc and closes 51° after bdc exhaust opens 47° before bdc and closes 13° after tdc; normal tyre pressure: front 28 psi, 2 atm, rear 31 psi, 2.2 atm.

VAZ — USSR

2101

PRICE: —

ENGINE front, 4 stroke; cylinders: 4, in line; bore and stroke: 2.99 x 2.60 in, 76 x 66 mm; engine capacity: 73.1 cu in, 1,198 cu cm; compression ratio: 8.8; max power (DIN): 60 hp at 5,600 rpm; max torque (DIN): 64 lb ft, 8.9 kg m at 3,400 rpm; max engine rpm: 5,800; specific power: 50.1 hp/l; cylinder block: cast iron; cylinder head: light alloy; crankshaft bearings: 5; valves: 2 per cylinder, overhead, rockers; camshafts: 1, overhead; lubrication: gear pump, full flow filter; lubricating system capacity: 7.7 imp pt, 9.3 US pt, 4.4 l; carburation: 1 Weber downdraught carburettor; fuel feed: mechanical pump; cooling system: water; cooling system capacity: 15 imp pt, 18 US pt, 8.5 l.

TRANSMISSION driving wheels: rear; clutch: single dry plate, hydraulically controlled; gearbox: mechanical; gears: 4 + reverse; synchromesh gears: I, II, III, IV; gearbox ratios: I 3.753, II 2.303, III 1.493, IV 1, rev 3.867; gear lever: central; final drive: hypoid bevel; axle ratio: 4.300; width of rims: 4.5''; tyres: 155 x 13.

PERFORMANCE max speeds: 19 mph, 30 km/h in 1st gear; 31 mph, 50 km/h in 2nd gear; 43 mph, 70 km/h in 3rd gear; 87 mph, 140 km/h in 4th gear; power-weight ratio: 32.6 lb/hp, 14.8 kg/hp; carrying capacity: 882 lb, 400 kg; speed in direct drive at 1,000 rpm: 15 mph, 24.1 km/h; fuel consumption: 35.3 m/imp gal, 29.4 m/US gal, 8 l x 100 km.

CHASSIS integral; front suspension: independent, wishbones, coil springs, anti-roll bar, telescopic dampers; rear suspension: rigid axle, twin trailing radius arms, transverse linkage bar, coil springs, telescopic dampers.

STEERING worm and roller; turns of steering wheel lock to lock: 2.75.

BRAKES front disc, rear drum, dual circuit, rear compensator.

ELECTRICAL EQUIPMENT voltage: 12 V; battery: 55 Ah; generator type: alternator, 480 W; headlamps: 2.

DIMENSIONS AND WEIGHT wheel base: 95.43 in, 2,424 mm; front track: 52.95 in, 1,345 mm; rear track: 51.34 in, 1,304 mm; overall length: 160.31 in, 4,072 mm; overall width: 63.42 in, 1,611 mm; overall height: 56.69 in, 1,440 mm; ground clearance: 6.69 in, 170 mm; dry weight: 1,962 lb, 890 kg; turning circle (between walls): 37.4 ft, 11.4 m; fuel tank capacity: 8.6 imp gal, 10.3 US gal, 39 l.

BODY saloon/sedan; doors: 4; seats: 5; front seats: separate.

ZAZ — USSR

Zaporozhets 966 Limousine

PRICE: —

ENGINE rear, 4 stroke; cylinders: 4, Vee-slanted at 90°; bore and stroke: 2.99 x 2.60 in, 76 x 66 mm; engine capacity: 73 cu in, 1,196 cu cm; compression ratio: 7.2; max power (SAE): 48 hp at 4,400 rpm; max torque (SAE): 62 lb ft, 8.6 kg m at 2,900 rpm; max engine rpm: 4,400; specific power: 40.1 hp/l; cylinder block: light alloy; cylinder head: light alloy; crankshaft bearings: 3; valves: 2 per cylinder, overhead, push-rods and rockers; camshafts: 1, at centre of Vee; lubrication: mechanical pump, full flow filter; lubricating system capacity: 5.8 imp pt, 7 US pt, 3.3 l; carburation: 1 K-125 downdraught carburettor; fuel feed: mechanical pump; cooling system: air cooled.

TRANSMISSION driving wheels: rear; clutch: single dry plate; gearbox: mechanical; gears: 4 + reverse; synchromesh gears: I, II, III, IV; gearbox ratios: I 3.800, II 2.120, III 1.409, IV 0.964, rev 4.165; gear lever: central; final drive: spiral bevel; axle ratio: 4.125; tyres: 5.20 x 13.

PERFORMANCE max speeds: 17 mph, 27 km/h in 1st gear; 27 mph, 44 km/h in 2nd gear; 45 mph, 73 km/h in 3rd gear; 75 mph, 120 km/h in 4th gear; power-weight ratio: 33 lb/hp, 15 kg/hp; carrying capacity: 750 lb, 340 kg; speed in direct

VAZ 2101

ZAZ Zaporozhets 966 Limousine

ZIL 114 Limousine

drive at 1,000 rpm: 15.7 mph, 25.2 km/h; fuel consumption: 37.7 m/imp gal, 31.4 m/US gal, 7.5 l x 100 km.

CHASSIS integral; front suspension: independent, swinging longitudinal trailing arms, transverse torsion bars, telescopic dampers; rear suspension: independent, semi-trailing arms, coil springs, telescopic dampers.

STEERING worm and double roller.

BRAKES drum; lining area: total 78.9 sq in, 509 sq cm.

ELECTRICAL EQUIPMENT voltage: 12 V; battery: 42 Ah; generator type: alternator, 250 W; headlamps: 2.

DIMENSIONS AND WEIGHT wheel base: 85.04 in, 2,160 mm; front track: 48.03 in, 1,220 mm; rear track: 47.24 in, 1,200 mm; overall length: 146.85 in, 3,730 mm; overall width: 60.43 in, 1,535 mm; overall height: 53.94 in, 1,370 mm; ground clearance: 7.48 in, 190 mm; dry weight: 1,588 lb, 720 kg; distribution of weight: 43% front axle, 57% rear axle; turning circle (between walls): 36.1 ft, 11 m; fuel tank capacity: 6.6 imp gal, 7.9 US gal, 30 l.

BODY saloon/sedan; doors: 2; seats: 4; front seats: separate.

PRACTICAL INSTRUCTIONS fuel: 76 oct petrol; engine sump oil: 4.6 imp pt, 5.5 US pt, 2.6 l, SAE 20W-30, change every 2,500 miles, 4,000 km; gearbox and final drive oil: 2.5 imp pt, 3 US pt, 1.4 l, SAE 80-90, change every 15,000 miles, 24,000 km; greasing: every 3,700 miles, 6,000 km, 10 points; tappet clearances: inlet 0.003 in, 0.08 mm, exhaust 0.004 in, 0.10 mm; normal tyre pressure: front 21 psi, 1.5 atm, rear 24 psi, 1.7 atm.

ZIL   USSR

114 Limousine

PRICE: —

ENGINE front, 4 stroke; cylinders: 8, Vee-slanted at 90°; engine capacity: 427.1 cu in, 7,000 cu cm; compression ratio: 9; max power (SAE): 300 hp at 4,300 rpm; max torque (SAE): 413 lb ft, 57 kg m at 2,750 rpm; max engine rpm: 4,500; specific power: 42.9 hp/l; cylinder block: cast iron, wet liners; cylinder head: light alloy; crankshaft bearings: 5; valves: 2 per cylinder, overhead, push-rods and rockers, hydraulic tappets; camshafts: 1, at centre of Vee; lubrication: gear pump, full flow filter; lubricating system capacity: 13.2 imp pt, 15.9 US pt, 7.5 l; carburation: 1 K 85 downdraught 4-barrel carburettor; fuel feed: electric pump; cooling system: water; cooling system capacity: 39.9 imp pt, 48 US pt, 22.7 l.

TRANSMISSION driving wheels: rear; gearbox: automatic, hydraulic torque convertor and planetary gears with 2 ratios, max ratio of convertor at stall 2.5; gearbox ratios: I 1.720, II 1, rev 2.930; push button control; final drive: hypoid bevel; axle ratio: 3.540; width of rims: 6.5''; tyres: 8.90 x 15.

PERFORMANCE max speed: 118 mph, 190 km/h; power-weight ratio: 23.4 lb/hp, 10.6 kg/hp; carrying capacity: 1,411 lb, 640 kg; fuel consumption: 11.3 m/imp gal, 9.4 m/US gal, 25 l x 100 km.

CHASSIS box-type ladder frame and X cross members; front suspension: independent, wishbones, coil springs, anti-roll bar, lever dampers; rear suspension: rigid axle, semi-elliptic leafsprings, telescopic dampers.

STEERING recirculating ball, servo; turns of steering wheel lock to lock: 4.30.

BRAKES drum, servo.

ELECTRICAL EQUIPMENT voltage: 12 V; battery: 54 x 2 Ah; generator type: dynamo, 500 W; ignition distributor: P-4; headlamps: 4; fog lamps: 2.

DIMENSIONS AND WEIGHT wheel base: 148.03 in, 3,760 mm; front track: 65.75 in, 1,570 mm; rear track: 64.92 in, 1,649 mm; overall length: 247.44 in, 6,285 mm; overall width: 81.50 in, 2,070 mm; overall height: 59.45 in, 1,510 mm; ground clearance: 7.09 in, 180 mm; dry weight: 7,001 lb, 3,175 kg; turning circle (between walls): 51.8 ft, 15.8 m; fuel tank capacity: 26.4 imp gal, 31.7 US gal, 120 l.

BODY limousine; doors: 4; seats: 7; front seats: separate, adjustable backrests; details: air-conditioning system.

PRATICAL INSTRUCTIONS fuel: 95 oct petrol; engine sump oil: 12.3 imp pt, 14.8 US pt, 7 l, SAE 10W-30, change every 2,500 miles, 4,000 km; gearbox oil: 22 imp pt, 26.4 US pt, 12.5 l, A type automatic transmission fluid, change every 12 months; final drive oil: 6 imp pt, 7.2 US pt, 3.4 l, SAE 80-90, change every 7,500 miles, 12,000 km; normal tyre pressure: front 31 psi, 2.2 atm, rear 31 psi, 2.2 atm.

The Americas

Models now in production

Illustrations and technical information

ANDINO   ARGENTINA

GT 1100

PRICE EX WORKS: 1,850,000 old pesos.

ENGINE rear, 4 stroke; cylinders: 4, vertical, in line; bore and stroke: 2.68 x 3.03 in, 68 x 77 mm; engine capacity: 68.2 cu in, 1,118 cu cm; compression ratio: 8.5; max power (SAE): 56 hp at 5,500 rpm; max torque (SAE): 62 lb ft, 8.5 kg m at 3,500 rpm; max engine rpm: 6,200; specific power: 50.1 hp/l; cylinder block: cast iron, wet liners; cylinder head: light alloy; crankshaft bearings: 5; valves: 2 per cylinder, overhead, push-rods and rockers; camshafts: 1, side; lubrication: gear pump, full flow filter; lubricating system capacity: 5.3 imp pt, 6.3 US pt, 3 l; carburation: 1 Solex F 32 PDIS-3 carburettor; fuel feed: mechanical pump; cooling system: water; cooling system capacity: 9.7 imp pt, 11.6 US pt, 5.5 l.

TRANSMISSION driving wheels: rear; clutch: single dry plate; gearbox: mechanical; gears: 4 + reverse; synchromesh gears: I, II, III, IV; gearbox ratios: I 3.615, II 2.263, III 1.480, IV 1.032, rev 3.080; gear lever: central; final drive: hypoid bevel; axle ratio: 3.875; tyres: 690 x 14.

PERFORMANCE max speeds: 29 mph, 47 km/h in 1st gear; 47 mph, 75 km/h in 2nd gear; 71 mph, 115 km/h in 3rd gear; 106 mph, 170 km/h in 4th gear; power-weight ratio: 24 lb/hp, 10.9 kg/hp; carrying capacity: 397 lb, 180 kg; speed in top at 1,000 rpm: 17 mph, 27.4 km/h; fuel consumption: 40.4 m/imp gal, 33.6 m/US gal, 7 l x 100 km.

CHASSIS tubular backbone; front suspension: independent, wishbones, coil springs, anti-roll bar, telescopic dampers; rear suspension: independent, swinging semi-axles, swinging longitudinal trailing arms articulated at centre, coil springs, anti-roll bar, telescopic dampers.

STEERING rack-and-pinion; turns of steering wheel lock to lock: 3.

BRAKES disc (diameter 10.28 in, 261 mm); area rubbed by linings: total 342.9 sq in, 2,212 sq cm.

ELECTRICAL EQUIPMENT voltage: 12 V; battery: 55 Ah; generator type: alternator, 500 W; headlamps: 2.

DIMENSIONS AND WEIGHT wheel base: 89.37 in, 2,270 mm; front track: 50.39 in, 1,280 mm; rear track: 51.18 in, 1,300 mm; overall length: 155.51 in, 3,950 mm; overall width: 62.99 in, 1,600 mm; overall height: 41.73 in, 1,060 mm; ground clearance: 6.30 in, 160 mm; dry weight: 1,345 lb, 610 kg; distribution of weight: 46% front axle, 54% rear axle; turning circle (between walls): 32.8 ft, 10 m; fuel tank capacity: 8.4 imp gal, 10 US gal, 38 l.

BODY coupé in plastic material; doors: 2; seats: 2.

PRACTICAL INSTRUCTIONS fuel: 90-95 oct petrol; engine sump oil: 4.4 imp pt, 5.3 US pt, 2.5 l, SAE 10W-40, change every 1,600 miles, 2,500 km; gearbox and final drive oil: 3.3 imp pt, 4 US pt, 1.9 l, SAE 80, change every 6,200 miles, 10,000 km; greasing: every 12,400 miles, 20,000 km, 1 point; tappet clearances: inlet 0.006-0.007 in, 0.15-0.18 mm, exhaust 0.007-0.009 in, 0.18-0.22 mm; normal tyre pressure: front 21 psi, 1.5 atm, rear 23 psi, 1.6 atm.

VARIATIONS

ENGINE capacity 79.3 cu in, 1,300 cu cm, max power (SAE) 80 hp at 7,000 rpm.
PERFORMANCE max speed 121 mph, 195 km/h.

CHEVROLET   ARGENTINA

Chevy Super Sport

PRICE: —

ENGINE front, 4 stroke; cylinders: 6, in line; bore and stroke: 3.87 x 3.53 in, 98.4 x 89.7 mm; engine capacity: 250 cu in, 4,097 cu cm; compression ratio: 8.1; max power (SAE): 150 hp at 4,400 rpm; max torque (SAE): 225 lb ft, 31.1 kg m at 1,800 rpm; max engine rpm: 4,600; specific power: 36.3 hp/l; cylinder block: cast iron; cylinder head: cast iron; crankshaft bearings: 7; valves: 2 per cylinder, overhead, in line; camshafts: 1, side; lubrication: gear pump; lubricating system capacity: 7.4 imp pt, 8.9 US pt, 4.2 l; carburation: 1 Holley carburettor; fuel feed: mechanical pump; cooling system: water; cooling system capacity: 20.1 imp pt, 24.1 US pt, 11.4 l.

TRANSMISSION driving wheels: rear; clutch: single dry plate; gearbox: mechanical; gears: 4 + reverse; synchromesh gears: I, II, III, IV; gearbox ratios: I 3.110, II 2.200, III 1.470, IV 1, rev 3.110; gear lever: central; final drive: hypoid bevel; axle ratio: 3.080; tyres: 6.40 x 13.

PERFORMANCE max speeds: 32 mph, 51 km/h 1st gear; 45 mph, 73 km/h in 2nd gear; 68 mph, 109 km/h in 3rd gear; 99 mph, 160 km/h in 4th gear; power-weight ratio: 20.5 lb/hp, 9.3 kg/hp; carrying capacity: 1.058 lb, 480 kg; speed in direct drive at 1,000 rpm: 21.6 mph, 34.8 km/h; fuel consumption: 18.8 m/imp gal, 15.7 m/US gal, 15 l x 100 km.

ANDINO GT 1100

CHEVROLET Chevy Super Sport

DODGE GTX

CHASSIS perimeter box type ladder frame; front suspension: independent, wishbones, coil springs, anti-roll bar, telescopic dampers; rear suspension: rigid axle, trailing lower radius arms, upper torque arms, coil springs, telescopic dampers.

STEERING recirculating ball.

BRAKES drum; lining area: total 128.1 sq in, 826 sq cm.

ELECTRICAL EQUIPMENT voltage: 12 V; battery: 55 Ah; generator type: dynamo, 420 W; ignition distributor: Delco-Remy; headlamps: 4.

DIMENSIONS AND WEIGHT wheel base: 110 in, 2,794 mm; front track: 56.50 in, 1,435 mm; rear track: 55.98 in, 1,422 mm; overall length: 185.39 in, 4,709 mm; overall width: 70.47 in, 1,790 mm; overall height: 55.79 in, 1,417 mm; ground clearance: 5.51 in, 140 mm; dry weight: 3,087 lb, 1,400 kg; turning circle (between walls): 38.4 ft, 11.7 m; fuel tank capacity: 13.2 imp gal, 15.8 US gal, 60 l.

BODY saloon/sedan; doors: 4; seats: 5; front seats: separate.

DODGE   ARGENTINA

Dodge

PRICE: —

ENGINE front, 4 stroke; cylinders: 6, in line; bore and stroke: 3.40 x 4.13 in, 86.4 x 104.8 mm; engine capacity: 225 cu in, 3,688 cu cm; compression ratio: 7.3; max power (SAE): 137 hp at 4,000 rpm; max torque (SAE): 206 lb ft, 28.4 kg m at 2,400 rpm; max engine rpm: 4,000; specific power: 37.1 hp/l; cylinder block: cast iron; cylinder head: cast iron; crankshaft bearings: 4; valves: 2 per cylinder, overhead, push-rods and rockers; camshafts: 1, side; lubrication: rotary pump, filter on by-pass; lubricating system capacity: 8.3 imp pt, 9.9 US pt, 4.7 l; carburation: 1 Holley 1922 downdraught single barrel carburettor; fuel feed: mechanical pump; cooling system: water; cooling system capacity: 22.4 imp pt, 26.8 US pt, 12.7 l.

TRANSMISSION driving wheels: rear; clutch: single dry plate; gearbox: mechanical; gears: 4 + reverse; synchromesh gears: I, II, III, IV; gearbox ratios: I 3.090, II 2.100, III 1.450, IV 1, rev 2.680; gear lever: central; final drive: hypoid bevel; axle ratio: 3.070; tyres: 6.40 x 13.

PERFORMANCE max speeds: 32 mph, 51 km/h in 1st gear; 47 mph, 76 km/h in 2nd gear; 68 mph, 110 km/h in 3rd gear; 99 mph, 159 km/h in 4th gear; power-weight ratio: 22.3 lb/hp, 10.1 kg/hp; carrying capacity: 1,125 lb, 510 kg; max gradient in 1st gear: 39%; speed in direct drive at 1,000 rpm: 24.7 mph, 39.7 km/h; fuel consumption: 23.5 m/imp gal, 19.6 m/US gal, 12 l x 100 km.

CHASSIS integral; front suspension: independent, wishbones, lower trailing links, longitudinal torsion bars, telescopic dampers; rear suspension: rigid axle, semi-elliptic leafsprings, telescopic dampers.

STEERING recirculating ball; turns of steering wheel lock to lock: 5.30.

BRAKES drum; lining area: front 48.2 sq in, 311 sq cm, rear 55 sq in, 355 sq cm, total 103.2 sq in, 666 sq cm.

ELECTRICAL EQUIPMENT voltage: 12 V; battery: 59 Ah; generator type: alternator, 480 W; ignition distributor: Chrysler; headlamps: 4.

DIMENSIONS AND WEIGHT wheel base: 110.98 in, 2,819 mm; front track: 56.69 in, 1,440 mm; rear track: 57.72 in, 1,466 mm; overall length: 196.61 in, 4,994 mm; overall width: 73.39 in, 1,864 mm; overall height: 55.12 in, 1,400 mm; ground clearance: 6.18 in, 157 mm; dry weight: 3,054 lb, 1,385 kg; distribution of weight: 57% front axle, 43% rear axle; turning circle (between walls): 41.7 ft, 12.7 m; fuel tank capacity: 15 imp gal, 18 US gal, 68 l.

BODY saloon/sedan; doors: 4; seats: 5; front seats: separate.

PRACTICAL INSTRUCTIONS fuel: 75 oct petrol; engine sump oil: 6.7 imp pt, 8 US pt, 3.8 l, SAE 20W-40, change every 3,700 miles, 6,000 km; gearbox oil: 4.2 imp pt, 5.1 US pt, 2.4 l, change every 22,000 miles, 36,000 km; final drive oil: 1.8 imp pt, 2.1 US pt, 1 l, SAE 90, change every 22,000 miles, 36,000 km; greasing: every 22,000 miles, 36,000 km, 1 point; tappet clearances: inlet 0.010 in, 0.25 mm, exhaust 0.010 in, 0.50 mm; valve timing: inlet opens 10° before tdc and closes 50° after bdc, exhaust opens 50° before bdc and closes 6° after tdc; normal tyre pressure: front 26 psi, 1.8 atm, rear 27 psi, 1.9 atm.

Polara

See Dodge, except for:

PRICE: —

ENGINE compression ratio: 8.4; max power (SAE): 145 hp at 4,400 rpm; max torque (SAE): 218 lb ft, 30.1 kg m at 2,400 rpm; specific power: 39.3 hp/l.

ANDINO GT 1100

CHEVROLET Chevy Super Sport

DODGE GTX

TRANSMISSION gears: 3 + reverse; gearbox ratios: I 2.830, II 1.560, III 1, rev 2.660; gear lever: steering column; tyres: 7.30 x 14.

PERFORMANCE max speeds: 34 mph, 55 km/h in 1st gear; 59 mph, 95 km/h in 2nd gear; 103 mph, 166 km/h in 3rd gear; power-weight ratio: 21.8 lb/hp, 9.9 kg/hp; speed in direct drive at 1,000 rpm: 23.4 mph, 37.7 km/h; fuel consumption: 22.6 m/imp gal, 18.8 m/US gal, 12.5 l x 100 km.

BRAKES front disc, rear drum; lining area: front 24.8 sq in, 160 sq cm.

DIMENSIONS AND WEIGHT overall length: 197.50 in, 5,019 mm; dry weight: 3,175 lb, 1,440 kg.

BODY seats: 6; front seats: bench.

Coronado Automatic

See Polara, except for:

PRICE: —

TRANSMISSION gearbox: Torqueflite automatic, hydraulic torque convertor and planetary gears with 3 ratios + reverse, max ratio of convertor at stall 2.7, possible manual selection; gearbox ratios: I 2.450, II 1.450, III 1, rev 2.200; axle ratio: 3.310.

PERFORMANCE power-weight ratio: 22 lb/hp, 10 kg/hp.

DIMENSIONS AND WEIGHT dry weight: 3,187 lb, 1,450 kg.

GTX

See Dodge, except for:

PRICE: —

ENGINE compression ratio: 8.4; max power (SAE): 155 hp at 4,500 rpm; max torque (SAE): 221 lb ft, 30.5 kg m at 2,400 rpm; specific power: 42 hp/l; lubricating system capacity: 9.9 imp pt, 11.8 US pt, 5.6 l; carburation: 1 Carter BBD downdraught twin barrel carburettor.

TRANSMISSION tyres: E70 x 14.

PERFORMANCE max speeds: 35 mph, 57 km/h in 1st gear; 50 mph, 80 km/h in 2nd gear; 68 mph, 110 km/h in 3rd gear; 106 mph, 170 km/h in 4th gear; power-weight ratio: 21.3 lb/hp, 9.7 kg/hp; fuel consumption: 21.6 m/imp gal, 18 m/US gal, 13.1 l x 100 km.

BRAKES front disc, rear drum; lining area: front 24.8 sq in, 160 sq cm.

DIMENSIONS AND WEIGHT overall length: 197.60 in, 5,019 mm; overall width: 74.61 in, 1,895 mm; overal height: 53.78 in, 1,366 mm; ground clearance: 6.69 in, 170 mm; dry weight: 3,308 lb, 1,500 kg.

BODY hardtop; door : 2.

PRACTICAL INSTRUCTIONS valve timing: inlet opens 12° before tdc and closes 52° after bdc, exhaust opens 50° before bdc and closes 14° after tdc.

VARIATIONS

ENGINE 8 Vee-slanted at 90° cylinders, bore and stroke 3.91 x 3.31 in, 99.3 x 84 mm, engine capacity 318 cu in, 5,211 cu cm, max power (SAE) 212 hp at 4,400 rpm, max torque (SAE) 290 lb ft, 40 kg m at 2,600 rpm, 40.7 hp/l specific power, 5 crankshaft bearings, cooling system capacity 27.8 imp pt, 33.4 US pt, 15.8 l.
TRANSMISSION 2.870 axle ratio.
PERFORMANCE max speed 116 mph, 186 km/h, power-weight ratio 16.3 lb/hp, 7.4 kg/hp, speed in direct drive at 1,000 rpm 26.3 mph, 42.3 km/h, fuel consumption 20.2 m/imp gal, 16.8 m/US gal, 14 l x 100 km.
DIMENSIONS AND WEIGHT dry weight 3,440 lb, 1,560 kg.
PRACTICAL INSTRUCTIONS valve timing 10° 50° 58° 10°.

FIAT   ARGENTINA

1600 Sport

PRICE EX WORKS: 17,950 new pesos.

ENGINE front, 4 stroke; cylinders: 4, vertical, in line; bore and stroke: 3.07 x 3.35 in, 78 x 85 mm; engine capacity: 99.2 cu in, 1,625 cu cm; compression ratio: 8.8; max power (SAE): 92 hp at 5,300 rpm; max torque (SAE): 105 lb ft, 14.5 kg m at 3,500 rpm; max engine rpm: 5,500; specific power: 56.6 hp/l; cylinder block: cast iron; cylinder head: light alloy; crankshaft bearings: 3; valves: 2 per cylinder, overhead, Vee-slanted, push-rods and rockers; camshafts: 1, side; lubrication: gear pump; lubricating system capacity: 7.6 imp pt, 9.1 US pt, 4.3 l; carburation: 1 Weber 34 DCHD or Solex C 34 PAIA 2 downdraught twin barrel carburettor; fuel feed: mechanical pump; cooling system: water, sealed circuit; cooling system capacity: 15.3 imp pt, 18.4 US pt, 8.7 l.

TRANSMISSION driving wheels: rear; clutch: single dry plate, hydraulically controlled; gearbox; mechanical; gears:

1600 SPORT

4 + reverse; synchromesh gears: I, II, III, IV; gearbox ratios: I 3.750, II 2.300, III 1.490, IV 1, rev 3.870; gear lever: central; final drive: hypoid bevel; axle ratio: 4.100; width of rims: 5.5''; tyres: 175S/695S x 13.

PERFORMANCE max speeds: 26 mph, 42 km/h in 1st gear; 43 mph, 70 km/h in 2nd gear; 65 mph, 105 km/h in 3rd gear; over 99 mph, 160 km/h in 4th gear; power-weight ratio: 22.7 lb/hp, 10.3 kg/hp; carrying capacity: 728 lb, 330 kg; max gradient in st gear: 40%; speed in direct drive at 1,000 rpm: 16.7 mph, 26.8 km/h; fuel consumption: 27.4 m/imp gal, 22.8 m/US gal, 10.3 l x 100 km.

CHASSIS integral; front suspension: independent, wishbones, lower trailing links, coil springs, anti-roll bar, telescopic dampers; rear suspension: rigid axle, semi-elliptic leaf-springs, telescopic dampers.

STEERING worm and roller; turns of steering wheel lock to lock: 3.

BRAKES front disc, rear drum, servo; area rubbed by linings: front 22 sq in, 142 sq cm, rear 70.7 sq in, 456 sq cm, total 92.7 sq in, 598 sq cm.

ELECTRICAL EQUIPMENT voltage: 12 V; battery: 48 Ah; generator type: alternator, 550 W; ignition distributor: Ga-ref; headlamps: 4, iodine long-distance lights.

DIMENSIONS AND WEIGHT wheel base: 98.74 in, 2,508 mm; front track: 52.48 in, 1,333 mm; rear track: 51.10 in, 1,298 mm; overall length: 168.11 in, 4,270 mm; overall width: 60.24 in, 1,530 mm; overall height: 54.33 in, 1,380 mm; ground clearance: 5.91 in, 150 mm; dry weight: 2,095 lb, 950 kg; distribution of weight: 55% front axle, 45% rear axle; turning circle (between walls): 40.3 ft, 12.3 m; fuel tank capacity: 9.9 imp gal, 11.9 US gal, 45 l.

BODY coupé; doors: 2; seats: 4; front seats: separate, reclining backrests.

PRACTICAL INSTRUCTIONS fuel: 92 act petrol; engine sump oil: 6.2 imp pt, 7.4 US pt, 3.5 l, SAE 10W-40, change every 2,200 miles, 3,500 km; gearbox oil: 2.3 imp pt, 2.7 US pt, 1.3 l, SAE 90, change every 18,600 miles, 30,000 km; final drive oil: 3.5 imp pt, 4.2 US pt, 2 l, SAE 90, change every 18,600 miles, 30,000 km; greasing: every 3,100 miles, 5,000 km, 8 points; sparking plug type: 240°; tappet clearances: inlet 0.008 in, 0.20 mm, exhaust 0.008 in, 0.20 mm; valve timing: inlet opens 5° before tdc and closes 44° after bdc exhaust opens 47° before bdc and closes 2° after tdc; normal tyre pressure: front 21 psi, 1.5 atm, rear 24 psi, 1.7 atm.

IKA   ARGENTINA

Torino L

PRICE EX WORKS: 17,412 new pesos.

ENGINE front 4, stroke; cylinders: 6, in line; bore and stroke: 3.34 x 4.37 in, 84.9 x 111.1 mm; engine capacity: 230 cu in, 3,770 cu cm; compression ratio: 7.5; max power (SAE): 140 hp at 4,200 rpm; max torque (SAE): 196 lb ft, 27 kg m at 2,200 rpm; max engine rpm: 4,600; specific power: 37.1 hp/l; cylinder block: cast iron; cylinder head: cast iron; crankshaft bearings: 4; valves: 2 per cylinder, overhead, rockers; camshafts: 1, overhead; lubrication: gear pump, full flow filter; lubricating system capacity: 7.9 imp pt, 9.5 US pt, 4.5 l; carburation: 1 Carter RBS downdraught carburettor; fuel feed: mechanical pump; cooling system: water; cooling system capacity: 19.9 imp pt, 23.9 US pt, 11.3 l.

TRANSMISSION driving wheels: rear; clutch: single drv plate; gearbox: ZF mechanical; gears: 4 + reverse; synchro-mesh gears: I, II, III, IV; gearbox ratios: I 2.830, II 1.850, III 1.320, IV 1, rev 3.150; gear lever: central; final drive: hypoid bevel; axle ratio: 3.310; width of rims: 5.5''; tyres: 6.85 x 15.

PERFORMANCE max speeds: 36 mph, 58 km/h in 1st gear; 55 mph, 89 km/h in 2nd gear; 78 mph, 125 km/h in 3rd gear; 103 mph, 165 km/h in 4th gear; power-weight ratio: 21.6 lb/hp, 9.8 kg/hp; carrying capacity: 882 lb, 400 kg; acceleration: 0-50 mph (0-80 km/h) 8.2 sec; speed in direct drive at 1,000 rpm: 22.3 mph, 35.9 km/h; fuel consumption: 26.6 m/imp gal, 22.2 m/US gal, 10.6 l x 100 km.

CHASSIS integral; front suspension: independent, wishbones, coil springs, anti-roll bar, telescopic dampers; rear suspension: rigid axle, trailing lower radius arms, oblique upper torque arms, coil springs, telescopic dampers.

STEERING recirculating ball; turns of steering wheel lock to lock: 5.50.

BRAKES drum; lining area: front 78.9 sq in, 509 sq cm, rear 62.6 sq in, 404 sq cm, total 141.5 sq in, 913 sq cm.

ELECTRICAL EQUIPMENT voltage: 12 V; battery: 55 Ah;

FIAT 1600 Sport

IKA Torino TS Coupé

CHEVROLET Opala 2500 De Luxo

generator type: alternator, 480 W; ignition distributor: Prestolite; headlamps: 2.

DIMENSIONS AND WEIGHT wheel base: 107.20 in, 2,723 mm; front track: 56.69 in, 1,440 mm; rear track: 56.38 in, 1,432 mm; overall length: 186.46 in, 4,736 mm; overall width: 70.87 in, 1,800 mm; overall height: 56.69 in, 1,440 mm; ground clearance: 5.98 in, 152 mm; dry weight: 3,014 lb, 1,367 kg; distribution of weight: 56.5% front axle, 43.5% rear axle; turning circle (between walls): 39 ft, 11.9 m; fuel tank capacity: 14.1 imp gal, 16.9 US gal, 64 l.

BODY saloon/sedan; doors: 4; seats: 5; front seats: bench.

PRACTICAL INSTRUCTIONS fuel: 83-85 oct petrol; engine sump oil: 6.9 imp pt, 8.2 US pt, 3.9 l, SAE 30, change every 3,100 miles, 5,000 km; gearbox oil: 2.1 imp pt, 2.5 US pt, 1.2 l, SAE 90 EP, change every 12,400 miles, 20,000 km; final drive oil: 2.1 imp pt, 2.5 US pt, 1.2 l, SAE 90 EP change every 12,400 miles, 20,000 km; greasing: every 3,100 miles, 5,000 km, 16 points; tappet clearances: inlet 0.007 in, 0.18 mm, exhaust 0.008 in, 0.20 mm; valve timing: inlet opens 20° before tdc and closes 52° after bdc, exhaust opens 50° before bdc and closes 10° after tdc; normal tyre pressure: front 24 psi, 1.7 atm, rear 28 psi, 2 atm.

OPTIONAL ACCESSORIES electrically-heated rear window.

Torino S

See Torino L, except for:

PRICE EX WORKS: 19,950 new pesos.

PERFORMANCE power-weight ratio: 22.3 lb/hp, 10.1 kg/hp.

BRAKES front disc, rear drum, servo; area rubbed by linings: front 27.9 sq in, 180 sq cm, rear 76.6 sq in, 494 sq cm, total 104.5 sq in, 674 sq cm.

ELECTRICAL EQUIPMENT headlamps: 4.

DIMENSIONS AND WEIGHT dry weight: 3,122 lb, 1,416 kg; distribution of weight: 56.4% front axle, 43.6% rear axle.

BODY front seats: separate, reclining backrests.

Torino TS Berlina

See Torino S, except for:

PRICE EX WORKS: 22,000 new pesos.

ENGINE max power (SAE): 155 hp at 4,300 rpm; max torque (SAE): 217 lb ft, 30 kg m at 2,200 rpm; specific power: 41.1 hp/l; carburation: 1 Holley 2300 C downdraught twin barrel carburettor.

PERFORMANCE max speed: 106 mph, 170 km/h; power-weight ratio: 20.5 lb/hp, 9.3 kg/hp; fuel consumption: 25.4 m/imp gal, 21.2 m/US gal, 11.1 l x 100 km.

DIMENSIONS AND WEIGHT dry weight: 3,171 lb, 1,438 kg.

OPTIONAL ACCESSORIES air-conditioning system.

Torino TS Coupé

See Torino TS Berlina, except for:

PRICE EX WORKS: 23,561 new pesos.

TRANSMISSION tyres: 7.35 x 15.

PERFORMANCE power-weight ratio: 20.9 lb/hp, 9.5 kg/hp; acceleration: 0-50 mph (0-80 km/h) 8 sec; speed in direct drive at 1,000 rpm: 22.9 mph, 36.9 km/h.

DIMENSIONS AND WEIGHT overall height: 55.91 in, 1,420 mm; dry weight: 3,244 lb, 1,471 kg.

BODY hardtop; doors: 2.

Torino GS Coupé

See Torino TS Coupé, except for:

PRICE EX WORKS: 25,679 new pesos.

ENGINE max power (SAE): 176 hp at 4,500 rpm; max torque (SAE): 232 lb ft, 32 kg m at 3,500 rpm; max engine rpm: 4,800; specific power: 46.7 hp/l; carburation: 3 Weber 45 DCOE 17 horizontal twin barrel carburettors.

TRANSMISSION axle ratio: 3.070; tyres: 7.75 x 15.

PERFORMANCE max speed: 124 mph, 199 km/h; power-weight ratio: 18.7 lb/hp, 8.5 kg/hp; acceleration: 0-50 mph (0-80 km/h) 7.4 sec; speed in direct drive at 1,000 rpm: 25.5 mph, 41 km/h.

DIMENSIONS AND WEIGHT dry weight: 3,301 lb, 1,497 kg; distribution of weight: 53.2% front axle, 46.8% rear axle.

FIAT 1600 Sport

IKA Torino TS and GS Coupé

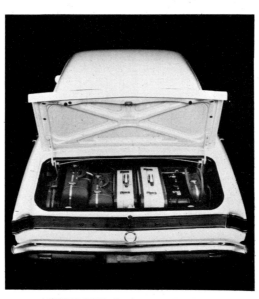

CHEVROLET Opala 2500 De Luxo

CHEVROLET BRAZIL

Opala 2500

PRICE: —

ENGINE front, 4 stroke; cylinders: 4, in line; bore and stroke: 3.87 x 3.25 in, 98.4 x 82.5 mm; engine capacity: 153 cu in, 2,507 cu cm; compression ratio: 7; max power (SAE): 80 hp at 4,000 rpm; max torque (SAE): 130 lb ft, 17.9 kg m at 2,600 rpm; max engine rpm: 4,400; specific power: 31.9 hp/l; cylinder block: cast iron; cylinder head: cast iron; crankshaft bearings: 5; valves: 2 per cylinder, overhead, push-rods and rockers, hydraulic tappets; camshafts: 1, side; lubrication: gear pump, full flow filter; lubricating system capacity: 7.6 imp pt, 9.1 US pt, 4.3 l; carburation: 1 Solex 40 DIS single barrel carburettor; fuel feed: mechanical pump; cooling system: water; cooling system capacity: 15.1 imp pt, 18.2 US pt, 8.6 l.

TRANSMISSION driving wheels: rear; clutch: single dry plate; gearbox: mechanical; gears: 3 + reverse; synchromesh gears: I, II, III; gearbox ratios: I 2.790, II 1.680, III 1, rev 3.570; gear lever: steering column; final drive: hypoid bevel; axle ratio: 3.730; width of rims: 4.5''; tyres: 5.90 x 14.

PERFORMANCE max speed: 90 mph, 145 km/h; power-weight ratio: 28.2 lb/hp, 12.8 kg/hp; carrying capacity: 882 lb, 400 kg; fuel consumption: 26.9 m/imp gal, 22.4 m/US gal, 10.5 l x 100 km.

CHASSIS integral; front suspension: independent, wishbones, coil springs, anti-roll bar, telescopic dampers; rear suspension: rigid axle, twin trailing radius arms, transverse linkage bar, telescopic dampers.

STEERING screw and sector; turns of steering wheel lock to lock: 3.20.

BRAKES drum; lining area: total 123.6 sq in, 797 sq cm.

ELECTRICAL EQUIPMENT voltage: 12 V; battery: 44 Ah; generator type: alternator, 32 A; ignition distributor: Arno; headlamps: 2.

DIMENSIONS AND WEIGHT wheel base: 105.04 in, 2,668 mm; front track: 55.51 in, 1,410 mm; rear track: 55.51 in, 1,410 mm; overall length: 180.12 in, 4,575 mm; overall width: 69.21 in, 1,758 mm; overall height: 54.49 in, 1,384 mm; ground clearance: 5.79 in, 147 mm; dry weight: 2,254 lb, 1,022 kg; turning circle (between walls): 38.7 ft, 11.8 m; fuel tank capacity: 12.1 imp gal, 14.5 US gal, 55 l.

BODY saloon/sedan; doors: 4; seats: 6; front seats: bench.

PRACTICAL INSTRUCTIONS fuel: 73 oct petrol; engine sump oil: 6.2 imp pt, 7.4 US pt, 3.5 l, SAE 20W-30, change every 3,100 miles, 5,000 km; gearbox oil: 1.4 imp pt, 1.7 US pt, 0.8 l; final drive oil: 1.2 imp pt, 1.5 US pt, 0.7 l; greasing: none; valve timing: inlet opens 16° before tdc and closes 48° after bdc, exhaust opens 46°30' before bdc and closes 17°30' after tdc; normal tyre pressure: front 20 psi, 1.4 atm, rear 21 psi, 1.5 atm.

OPTIONAL ACCESSORIES 6.45 x 14 tyres.

Opala 2500 De Luxo

See Opala 2500, except for:

PRICE: —

BODY details: L equipment.

Opala 3800

See Opala 2500, except for:

PRICE: —

ENGINE cylinders: 6, in line; engine capacity: 223.8 cu in, 3,668 cu cm; max power (SAE): 125 hp at 4,000 rpm; max torque (SAE): 190 lb ft, 26.2 kg m at 2,400 rpm; specific power: 34.1 hp/l; crankshaft bearings: 7; lubricating system capacity: 8.3 imp pt, 9.9 US pt, 4.7 l; cooling system capacity: 18 imp pt, 21.6 US pt, 10.2 l.

TRANSMISSION axle ratio: 3.080.

PERFORMANCE max speed: 111 mph, 178 km/h; power-weight ratio: 19.2 lb/hp, 8.7 kg/hp; fuel consumption: 16.8 m/imp gal, 15.7 m/US gal, 15 l x 100 km.

DIMENSIONS AND WEIGHT dry weight: 2,397 lb, 1,087 kg.

Opala 3800 De Luxo

See Opala 3800, except for:

PRICE: —

BODY details: L equipment.

FNM   BRAZIL

2150

PRICE EX WORKS: 20,000 cruzeiros.

ENGINE front, 4 stroke; cylinders: 4, in line; bore and stroke: 3.33 x 3.74 in, 84.5 x 95 mm; engine capacity: 130.1 cu in, 2,132 cu cm; compression ratio: 8.2; max power (SAE): 125 hp at 5,700 rpm; max torque (SAE): 133 lb ft, 18.3 kg m at 3,900 rpm; max engine rpm: 5,700; specific power: 58.6 hp/l; cylinder block: cast iron; cylinder head: light alloy; crankshaft bearings: 5; valves: 2 per cylinder, Vee-slanted; camshafts: 2, overhead; lubrication: mechanical pump, filter on by-pass; lubricating system capacity: 12.3 imp pt, 14.8 US pt, 7 l; carburation: 1 Solex APAI-G downdraught twin barrel carburettor; fuel feed: mechanical pump; cooling system: water; cooling system capacity: 19.4 imp pt, 23.3 US pt, 11 l.

TRANSMISSION driving wheels: rear; clutch: single dry plate; gearbox: mechanical; gears: 5 + reverse; synchromesh gears: I, II, III, IV, V; gearbox ratios: I 3.258, II 1.985, III 1.357, IV 1, V 0.854, rev 3.252; gear lever: steering column; final drive: hypoid bevel; axle ratio: 5.123; tyres: 175 x 400.

PERFORMANCE max speeds: 25 mph, 40 km/h in 1st gear; 42 mph, 67 km/h in 2nd gear; 60 mph, 97 km/h in 3rd gear; 82 mph, 132 km/h in 4th gear; 103 mph, 165 km/h in 5th gear; power-weight ratio: 24 lb/hp, 10.9 kg/hp; carrying capacity: 1,014 lb, 460 km; max gradient in 1st gear: 36%; acceleration: 0-50 mph (0-80 km/h) 9 sec; speed in top at 1,000 rpm: 17.4 mph, 28 km/h; fuel consumption: 23.5 m/imp gal, 19.6 m/US gal, 12 l x 100 km.

CHASSIS integral; front suspension: independent, wishbones, coil springs, anti-roll bar, telescopic dampers; rear suspension: rigid axle, trailing lower radius arms, upper A-bracket, coil springs, telescopic dampers.

STEERING worm and roller; turns of steering wheel lock to lock: 4.50.

BRAKES drum, servo; area rubbed by linings: front 120.2 sq in, 775.50 sq cm, rear 120.2 sq in, 775.50 sq cm, total 240.4 sq in, 1,551 sq cm.

ELECTRICAL EQUIPMENT voltage: 12 V; battery: 50 Ah; generator type: alternator, 360 W; ignition distributor: Bosch; headlamps: 2.

DIMENSIONS AND WEIGHT wheel base: 107.09 in, 2,720 mm; front track: 55.12 in, 1,400 mm; rear track: 53.94 in, 1,370 mm; overall length: 185.63 in, 4,715 mm; overall width: 66.93 in, 1,700 mm; overall height: 57.17 in, 1,452 mm; ground clearance: 5.91 in, 150 mm; dry weight: 2,999 lb, 1,360 kg; distribution of weight: 53% front axle, 47% rear axle; turning circle (between walls): 34.1 ft, 10.4 m; fuel tank capacity: 13.2 imp gal, 15.8 US gal, 60 l.

BODY saloon/sedan; doors: 4; seats: 6; front seats: bench.

PRACTICAL INSTRUCTIONS fuel: 98-100 oct petrol; engine sump oil: 11.4 imp pt, 13.7 US pt, 6.5 l, SAE 40, change every 2,500 miles, 4,000 km; gearbox oil: 3 imp pt, 3.6 US pt, 1.7 l, SAE 90, change every 5,000 miles, 8,000 km; final drive oil: 5.1 imp pt, 6.1 US pt, 2.9 l, SAE 90, change every 5,000 miles, 8,000 km; greasing: every 2,500 miles, 4,000 km, 25 points; tappet clearances: inlet 0.018 in, 0.45 mm, exhaust 0.020 in, 0.50 mm; valve timing: inlet opens 5°25' before tdc and closes 52°33' after bdc, exhaust opens 52°33' before bdc and closes 5°25' after tdc; normal tyre pressure: front 24 psi, 1.7 atm, rear 26 psi, 1.8 atm.

OPTIONAL ACCESSORIES front disc brakes.

2150 Luxo

See 2150, except for:

PRICE EX WORKS: 22,000 cruzeiros.

TRANSMISSION gear lever: central.

BODY seats: 5; front seats: separate.

FORD   BRAZIL

4-door Corcel Sedan

PRICE: —

ENGINE front, 4 stroke; cylinders: 4, vertical, in line; bore and stroke: 2.87 x 3.03 in, 73 x 77 mm; engine capacity: 78.7 cu in, 1,289 cu cm; compression ratio: 7.8; max power (SAE): 68 hp at 5,200 rpm; max torque (SAE): 71 lb ft, 9.8

FNM 2150 Luxo

FORD Corcel Coupé Luxo

FORD Corcel GT Coupé

kg m at 3,200 rpm; max engine rpm: 5,200; specific power 52.5 hp/l; cylinder block: cast iron; cylinder head: light alloy; crankshaft bearings: 5; valves: 2 per cylinder, overhead, push-rods and rockers; camshafts: 1, side; lubrication gear pump, full flow filter; lubricating system capacity: 5.3 imp pt, 6.3 US pt, 3 l; carburation: 1 Solex 32 PDIS-1 downdraught single barrel carburettor; fuel feed: mechanical pump; cooling system: water; cooling system capacity: 7.9 imp pt, 9.5 US pt, 4.5 l.

TRANSMISSION driving wheels: front; clutch: single dry plate; gearbox: mechanical; gears: 4 + reverse; synchromesh gears: I, II, III, IV; gearbox ratios: I 3.615, II 2.263 III 1.480, IV 1.032, rev 3.077; gear lever: central; final drive: hypoid bevel; axle ratio: 4.125; width of rims: 4.5''; tyres 6.45 x 13.

PERFORMANCE max speeds: 23 mph, 37 km/h in 1st gear; 37 mph, 59 km/h in 2nd gear; 57 mph, 91 km/h in 3rd gear; 83 mph, 134 km/h in 4th gear; power-weight ratio: 30.4 lb/hp 13.8 kg/hp; carrying capacity: 827 lb, 375 kg; max gradient in 1st gear: 30%; acceleration: standing ¼ mile 22 sec; speed in top at 1,000 rpm: 15.7 mph, 25.2 km/h; fuel consumption: 33.6 m/imp gal, 28 m/US gal, 8.4 l x 100 km.

CHASSIS integral; front suspension: independent, wishbones, upper trailing arms, coil springs, anti-roll bar, telescopic dampers; rear suspension: rigid axle, trailing lower radius arms, upper Vee bracket, coil springs, telescopic dampers.

STEERING rack-and-pinion; turns of steering wheel lock to lock: 3.50.

BRAKES front disc, rear drum; lining area: front 64.7 sq in, 417 sq cm, rear 36.7 sq in, 237 sq cm, total 101.4 sq in, 654 sq cm.

ELECTRICAL EQUIPMENT voltage: 12 V; battery: 40 Ah; generator type: alternator, 380 W; ignition distributor: Bosch; headlamps: 2.

DIMENSIONS AND WEIGHT wheel base: 95.98 in, 2,438 mm; front track: 51.65 in, 1,312 mm; rear track: 50.39 in, 1,280 mm; overall length: 173.62 in, 4,410 mm; overall width: 64.76 in, 1,645 mm; overall height: 54.09 in, 1,374 mm; ground clearance: 6.50 in, 165 mm; dry weight: 2,077 lb, 942 kg; distribution of weight: 56.3% front axle, 43.7% rear axle; turning circle (between walls): 35.4 ft, 10.8 m; fuel tank capacity: 11.2 imp gal, 13.5 US gal, 51 l.

BODY saloon/sedan; doors: 4; seats: 5; front seats: separate.

PRACTICAL INSTRUCTIONS fuel: 70 oct petrol; engine sump oil: 4.4 imp pt, 5.3 US pt, 2.5 l, SAE 30, change every 3,100 miles, 5,000 km; gearbox and final drive oil: 2.8 imp pt, 3.4 US pt, 1.6 l, SAE 90, change every 6,200 miles, 10,000 km; greasing: every 31,100 miles, 50,000 km, 2 points; tappet clearances: inlet 0.006 in, 0.15 mm, exhaust 0.008 in, 0.20 mm; valve timing: inlet opens 20° before tdc and closes 60° after bdc, exhaust opens 60° before bdc and closes 20° after tdc; normal tyre pressure: front 17 psi, 1.2 atm, rear 17 psi, 1.2 atm.

4-door Corcel Sedan Luxo

See 4-door Corcel Sedan, except for:

PRICE: —

BODY details: L equipment.

Corcel Coupé

See 4-door Corcel Sedan, except for:

PRICE: —

PERFORMANCE power-weight ratio: 30.2 lb/hp, 13.7 kg/hp.

DIMENSIONS AND WEIGHT dry weight: 2,051 lb, 930 kg; distribution of weight: 56.7% front axle, 43.3% rear axle.

BODY coupé; doors: 2.

OPTIONAL ACCESSORIES reclining backrests.

Corcel Coupé Luxo

See 4-door Corcel Sedan, except for:

PRICE: —

PERFORMANCE power-weight ratio: 30.2 lb/hp, 13.7 kg/hp.

DIMENSIONS AND WEIGHT dry weight: 2,051 lb, 930 kg; distribution of weight: 56.7% front axle, 43.3% rear axle.

BODY coupé; doors: 2; details: L equipment.

OPTIONAL ACCESSORIES reclining backrests.

FNM 2150 Luxo

FORD 4-door Corcel Sedan Luxo

FORD Aero Willys

Corcel GT Coupé

See 4-door Corcel Sedan, except for:

PRICE: —

ENGINE compression ratio: 8; max power (SAE): 80 hp at 5,200 rpm; max torque (SAE): 77 lb ft, 10.6 kg m at 3,200 rpm; max engine rpm: 6,000; specific power: 62 hp/l; carburation: 1 Solex 35 DIDS-2 downdraught twin barrel carburettor.

PERFORMANCE max speeds: 30 mph, 48 km/h in 1st gear; 43 mph, 69 km/h in 2nd gear; 70 mph, 113 km/h in 3rd gear; 88 mph, 141 km/h in 4th gear; power-weight ratio: 26 lb/hp, 11.8 kg/hp; max gradient in 1st gear: 31.5%; acceleration: standing ¼ mile 21.5 sec; fuel consumption: 29.7 m/imp gal, 24.8 m/US gal, 9.5 l x 100 km.

ELECTRICAL EQUIPMENT generator type: alternator, 560 W.

DIMENSIONS AND WEIGHT dry weight: 2,082 lb, 944 kg; distribution of weight: 56.7% front axle, 43.3% rear axle.

BODY coupé; doors: 2.

Corcel Station Wagon

See 4-door Corcel Sedan, except for:

PRICE: —

ENGINE max engine rpm: 6,000.

PERFORMANCE power-weight ratio: 32.1 lb/hp, 14.6 kg/hp; carrying capacity: 926 lb, 420 kg; fuel consumption: 25.4 m/imp gal, 21.2 m/US gal, 11.1 l x 100 km.

DIMENSIONS AND WEIGHT overall height: 55.20 in, 1,402 mm; dry weight: 2,190 lb, 993 kg; distribution of weight: 52.7% front axle, 47.3% rear axle.

BODY estate car/station wagon; doors: 2 + 1.

Aero Willys

PRICE: —

ENGINE front, 4 stroke; cylinders: 6, vertical, in line; bore and stroke: 3.12 x 3.50 in, 79.3 x 88.9 mm; engine capacity: 161 cu in, 2,638 cu cm; compression ratio: 7.6; max power (SAE): 130 hp at 4,800 rpm; max torque (SAE): 141 lb ft, 19.4 kg m at 2,000 rpm; max engine rpm: 4,800; specific power: 49.3 hp/l; cylinder block: cast iron; cylinder head: cast iron; crankshaft bearings: 4; valves: 2 per cylinder, overhead, push-rods and rockers; camshafts: 1, side; lubrication: gear pump, filter on by-pass; lubricating system capacity: 12.3 imp pt, 14.8 US pt, 7 l; carburation: 2 D.F. Vasconcelos downdraught single barrel carburettors; fuel feed: mechanical pump; cooling system: water; cooling system capacity: 18.3 imp pt, 22 US pt, 10.4 l.

TRANSMISSION driving wheels: rear; clutch: single dry plate; gearbox: mechanical; gears: 4 + reverse; synchromesh gears: I, II, III, IV; gearbox ratios: I 2.991, II 1.992, III 1.390, IV 1, rev 3.544; gear lever: steering column; final drive: hypoid bevel; axle ratio: 4.090; width of rims: 5''; tyres: 6.40 x 15.

PERFORMANCE max speeds: 28 mph, 45 km/h in 1st gear; 42 mph, 67 km/h in 2nd gear; 60 mph, 96 km/h in 3rd gear; 86 mph, 138 km/h in 4th gear; power-weight ratio: 24.9 lb/hp, 11.3 kg/hp; carrying capacity: 992 lb, 450 kg; max gradient in 1st gear: 24%; acceleration: standing ¼ mile 22.5 sec; speed in direct drive at 1,000 rpm: 18.9 mph, 30.4 km/h; fuel consumption: 18.8 m/imp gal, 15.7 m/US gal, 15 l x 100 km.

CHASSIS integral; front suspension: independent, wishbones, coil springs, telescopic dampers; rear suspension: rigid axle, semi-elliptic leafsprings, telescopic dampers.

STEERING worm and roller; turns of steering wheel lock to lock: 4.30.

BRAKES drum; area rubbed by linings: front 138.1 sq in, 891 sq cm, rear 138.1 sq in, 891 sq cm, total 276.2 sq in, 1,782 sq cm.

ELECTRICAL EQUIPMENT voltage: 12 V; battery: 54 Ah; generator type: alternator, 380 W; ignition distributor: Bosch or Autolite; headlamps: 2.

DIMENSIONS AND WEIGHT wheel base: 107.80 in, 2,738 mm; front track: 58.19 in, 1,478 mm; rear track: 57.87 in, 1,470 mm; overall length: 189.41 in, 4,811 mm; overall width: 72.40 in, 1,839 mm; overall height: 59.96 in, 1,523 mm; ground clearance: 7.32 in, 186 mm; dry weight: 3,241 lb, 1,470 kg; distribution of weight: 54.6% front axle, 45.4% rear axle; turning circle (between walls): 41 ft, 12.5 m; fuel tank capacity: 15.8 imp gal, 19 US gal, 72 l.

BODY saloon/sedan; doors: 4; seats: 6; front seats: bench.

PRACTICAL INSTRUCTIONS fuel: 70 oct petrol; engine sump oil: 10.6 imp pt, 12.7 US pt, 6 l, SAE 30, change every 1,900 miles, 3,000 km; gearbox oil: 3 imp pt, 3.6 US pt, 1.7 l, SAE 90, change every 12,100 miles, 19,500 km; final drive oil: 2.6 imp pt, 3.2 US pt, 1.5 l, SAE 90, change every 12,100

AERO WILLYS

miles, 19,500 km; greasing: every 900 miles, 1,500 km, 25 points, every 12,100 miles, 19,500 km, 4 points; tappet clearances (hot): inlet 0.018 in, 0.46 mm, exhaust 0.016 in, 0.41 mm; valve timing: inlet opens 9° before tdc and closes 50° after bdc, exhaust opens 47° before bdc and closes 12° after tdc; normal tyre pressure: front 23 psi, 1.6 atm, rear 23 psi, 1.6 atm.

VARIATIONS

ENGINE bore and stroke 3.12 x 4 in, 79.3 x 101.6 mm, engine capacity 183.9 cu in, 3,014 cu cm, max power (SAE) 140 hp at 4,600 rpm, max torque (SAE) 162 lb ft, 22.3 kg m at 2,000 rpm, max engine rpm 4,600, 46.4 hp/l specific power.
PERFORMANCE power-weight ratio 23.2 lb/hp, 10.5 kg/hp.

OPTIONAL ACCESSORIES limited slip final drive; 7.35 x 15 tyres.

Itamaraty

See Aero Willys, except for:

PRICE: —

ENGINE bore and stroke: 3.12 x 4 in, 79.3 x 101.6 mm; engine capacity: 183.9 cu in, 3,014 cu cm; max power (SAE): 140 hp at 4,600 rpm; max torque (SAE): 162 lb ft, 22.3 kg m at 2,000 rpm; max engine rpm: 4,600; specific power: 46.4 hp/l; lubricating system capacity: 11.4 imp pt, 13.7 US pt, 6.5 l; carburation: 1 D.F. Vasconcelos downdraught twin barrel carburettor; cooling system capacity: 18.8 imp pt, 22.6 US pt, 10.7 l.

TRANSMISSION axle ratio: 3.920.

PERFORMANCE max speeds: 29 mph, 46 km/h in 1st gear; 43 mph, 70 km/h in 2nd gear; 62 mph, 100 km/h in 3rd gear; 91 mph, 146 km/h in 4th gear; power-weight ratio: 24 lb/hp, 10.9 kg/hp; max gradient in 1st gear: 29%; acceleration: standing ¼ mile 21 sec; speed in direct drive at 1,000 rpm: 19.7 mph, 31.7 km/h; fuel consumption: 18.1 m/imp gal, 15.1 m/US gal, 15.6 l x 100 km.

ELECTRICAL EQUIPMENT ignition distributor: Walita.

DIMENSIONS AND WEIGHT dry weight: 3,358 lb, 1,523 kg; distribution of weight: 54% front axle, 46% rear axle.

PRACTICAL INSTRUCTIONS engine sump oil: 9.7 imp pt, 11.6 US pt, 5.5 l.

OPTIONAL ACCESSORIES 4.090 axle ratio.

Galaxie 500

PRICE: —

ENGINE front, 4 stroke; cylinders: 8, Vee-slanted at 90°; bore and stroke: 3.62 x 3.30 in, 92 x 83.8 mm; engine capacity: 272 cu in, 4,458 cu cm; compression ratio: 7.8; max power (SAE): 170 hp at 4,400 rpm; max torque (SAE): 251 lb ft, 34.6 kg m at 2,200 rpm; max engine rpm: 4,400; specific power: 38.1 hp/l; cylinder block: cast iron; cylinder head: cast iron; crankshaft bearings: 5; valves: 2 per cylinder, overhead, push-rods and rockers; camshafts: 1, at centre of Vee; lubrication: gear pump, full flow filter; lubricating system capacity: 9.2 imp pt, 11 US pt, 5.2 l; carburation: 1 D.F. Vasconcelos downdraught twin barrel carburettor; fuel feed: mechanical pump; cooling system: water; cooling system capacity: 25.7 imp pt, 30.9 US pt, 14.6 l.

TRANSMISSION driving wheels: rear; clutch: single dry plate; gearbox: mechanical; gears: 3 + reverse; synchromesh gears: I, II, III; gearbox ratios: I 2.667, II 1.602, III 1, rev 3.437; gear lever: steering column; final drive: hypoid bevel; axle ratio: 3.540; width of rims: 5''; tyres: 7.75 x 15.

PERFORMANCE max speeds: 37 mph, 59 km/h in 1st gear; 62 mph, 99 km/h in 2nd gear; 93 mph, 150 km/h in 3rd gear; power-weight ratio: 21.4 lb/hp, 9.7 kg/hp; carrying capacity: 1,069 lb, 485 kg; max gradient in 1st gear: 29%; speed in direct drive at 1,000 rpm: 22.4 mph, 36 km/h; fuel consumption: 18.3 m/imp gal, 15.3 m/US gal, 15.4 l x 100 km.

CHASSIS perimeter box-type; front suspension: independent, wishbones, lower trailing arms, coil springs, anti-roll bar, telescopic dampers; rear suspension: rigid axle, lower trailing arms, upper torque arms, transverse linkage bar, coil springs, telescopic dampers.

STEERING worm and roller; turns of steering wheel lock to lock: 6.60.

BRAKES drum, dual circuit; area rubbed by linings: front 180.6 sq in, 1,165 sq cm, rear 163.9 sq in, 1,057 sq cm, total 344.5 sq in, 2,222 sq cm.

ELECTRICAL EQUIPMENT voltage: 12 V; battery: 40 Ah; generator type: alternator, 560 W; ignition distributor: Autolite; headlamps: 4.

FORD Itamaraty

PUMA GTE 1600

ACADIAN Acadian 2-door Coupé

DIMENSIONS AND WEIGHT wheel base: 119.02 in, 3,023 mm; front track: 62.01 in, 1,575 mm; rear track: 62.01 in, 1,575 mm; overall length: 210 in, 5,334 mm; overall width: 79.02 in, 2,007 mm; overall height: 55.59 in, 1,412 mm; ground clearance: 5.51 in, 140 mm; dry weight: 3,638 lb, 1,650 kg; distribution of weight: 54.4% front axle, 45.6% rear axle; turning circle (between walls): 38.7 ft, 11.8 m; fuel tank capacity: 16.7 imp gal, 20.1 US gal, 76 l.

BODY saloon/sedan; doors: 4; seats: 6; front seats: bench.

PRACTICAL INSTRUCTIONS fuel: 70 oct petrol; engine sump oil: 7.7 imp pt, 9.3 US pt, 4.4 l, SAE 20W-40, change every 6,200 miles, 10,000 km; gearbox oil: 3.3 imp pt, 4 US pt, 1.9 l, SAE 90, change every 9,300 miles, 15,000 km; final drive oil: 3 imp pt, 3.6 US pt, 1.7 l, SAE 90, change every 6,200 miles, 10,000 km; greasing: every 6,200 miles, 10,000 km, 2 points, every 31,100 miles, 50,000 km, 3 points; tappet clearances (cold): inlet 0.019 in, 0.48 mm, exhaust 0.019 in, 0.48 mm; valve timing: inlet opens 12° before tdc and closes 54° after bdc, exhaust opens 58° before bdc and closes 8° after tdc; normal tyre pressure: front 26 psi, 1.8 atm, rear 27 psi, 1.9 atm.

VARIATIONS

ENGINE capacity 289.8 cu in, 4,750 cu cm, max power (SAE) 190 hp at 4,400 rpm, max torque (SAE) 269 lb ft, 37.1 kg m at 2,400 rpm, 40 hp/l specific power.
PERFORMANCE power-weight ratio 19.2 lb/hp, 8.7 kg/hp.

OPTIONAL ACCESSORIES Cruise-o-Matic automatic gearbox, hydraulic torque convertor and planetary gears with 3 ratios (I 2.460, II 1.460, III 1, rev 2.200), max ratio of convertor at stall 2, possible manual selection, 3.310 axle ratio; power-assisted steering; servo brake; air-conditioning system.

LTD

See Galaxie 500, except for:

PRICE: —

ENGINE bore and stroke: 3.74 x 3.30 in, 95 x 83.8 mm; engine capacity: 289.8 cu in, 4,750 cu cm; max power (SAE): 190 hp at 4,400 rpm, max torque (SAE): 269 lb ft, 37.1 kg m at 2,400 rpm; max engine rpm: 4,800; specific power: 40 hp/l.

PERFORMANCE max speeds: 43 mph, 69 km/h in 1st gear; 72 mph, 116 km/h in 2nd gear; 106 mph, 170 km/h in 3rd gear; power-weight ratio: 20.7 lb/hp, 9.4 kg/hp; max gradient in 1st gear: 27.5%; fuel consumption: 17.5 m/imp gal, 14.6 m/US gal, 16.1 l x 100 km.

STEERING servo (standard); turns of steering wheel lock to lock: 4.

DIMENSIONS AND WEIGHT dry weight: 3,940 lb, 1,787 kg.

PUMA BRAZIL

GTE 1600

PRICE EX WORKS: 22,310 cruzeiros.

ENGINE rear, 4 stroke; cylinders: 4, horizontally opposed; bore and stroke: 3.37 x 2.72 in, 85.5 x 69 mm; engine capacity: 96.7 cu in, 1,584 cu cm; compression ratio: 7.2; max power (SAE): 70 hp at 4,700 rpm; max torque (SAE): 89 lb ft, 12.3 kg m at 3,000 rpm; max engine rpm: 5,500; specific power: 44.2 hp/l; cylinder block: cast iron liners with light alloy fins; cylinder head: light alloy; crankshaft bearings: 4; valves: 2 per cylinder, overhead, push-rods and rockers; camshafts: 1, central, lower; lubrication: gear pump, filter in sump, oil cooler; lubricating system capacity: 4.4 imp pt, 5.3 US pt, 2.5 l; carburation: 2 Solex-Brosol 32 PDI downdraught carburettors; fuel feed: mechanical pump; cooling system: air cooled.

TRANSMISSION driving wheels: rear; clutch: single dry plate; gearbox: mechanical; gears: 4 + reverse; synchromesh gears: I, II, III, IV; gearbox ratios: I 3.800, II 2.060, III 1.320, IV 0.890, rev 3.880; gear lever: central; final drive: spiral bevel; axle ratio: 4.125; width of rims: 5.5''; tyres: 185 x 14.

PERFORMANCE max speeds: 26 mph, 42 km/h in 1st gear; 47 mph, 76 km/h in 2nd gear; 75 mph, 120 km/h in 3rd gear; 103 mph, 165 km/h in 4th gear; power-weight ratio: 21.4 lb/hp, 9.7 kg/hp; carrying capacity: 551 lb, 250 kg; max gradient in 1st gear: 44.6%; acceleration: 0-50 mph (0-80 km/h) 12.5 sec; speed in top at 1,000 rpm: 19.9 mph, 32 km/h; fuel consumption: 37.2 m/imp gal, 30.9 m/US gal, 7.6 l x 100 km.

CHASSIS backbone platform, rear auxiliary frame; front suspension: independent, twin swinging longitudinal trailing arms, transverse torsion bars, anti-roll bar, telescopic dampers; rear suspension: independent, semi-trailing arms, transverse linkage by oblique swinging trailing arms, transverse torsion bars, telescopic dampers.

FORD LTD

PUMA GTE 1600

ACADIAN Acadian 2-door Coupé

STEERING worm and roller; turns of steering wheel lock to lock: 3.

BRAKES front disc, rear drum; lining area: front 11.2 sq in, 72 sq cm, rear 52.6 sq in, 339 sq cm, total 63.8 sq in, 411 sq cm.

ELECTRICAL EQUIPMENT voltage: 12 V; battery: 36 Ah; generator type: dynamo, 160 W; ignition distributor: Bosch; headlamps: 2.

DIMENSIONS AND WEIGHT wheel base: 84.65 in, 2,150 mm; front track: 51.81 in, 1,316 mm; rear track: 53.46 in, 1,358 mm; overall length: 156.10 in, 3,965 mm; overall width: 62.40 in, 1,585 mm; overall height: 44.88 in, 1,140 mm; ground clearance: 5.98 in, 152 mm; dry weight: 1,499 lb, 680 kg; distribution of weight: 40% front axle, 60% rear axle; turning circle (between walls): 32.5 ft, 9.9 m; fuel tank capacity: 8.8 imp gal, 10.6 US gal, 40 l.

BODY coupé in plastic material; doors: 2; seats: 2.

PRACTICAL INSTRUCTIONS fuel: 72 oct petrol; engine sump oil: 4.4 imp pt, 5.3 US pt, 2.5 l, SAE 20W-40, change every 1,600 miles, 2,500 km; gearbox and final drive oil: 4.4 imp pt, 5.3 US pt, 2.5 l, SAE 90, change every 6,200 miles, 10,000 km; greasing: every 1,600 miles, 2,500 km, 7 points; tappet clearances: inlet 0.004 in, 0.10 mm, exhaust 0.004 in, 0.10 mm; valve timing: inlet opens 4° before tdc and closes 36° after bdc, exhaust opens 41° before bdc and closes 2° after tdc; normal tyre pressure: front 20 psi, 1.4 atm, rear 23 psi, 1.6 atm.

ACADIAN CANADA

Acadian Series

PRICES EX WORKS:

Acadian	2-door Coupé	$ —
Acadian	4-door Sedan	$ —

145 hp power team

(standard for both models).

ENGINE front, 4 stroke; cylinders: 6, in line; bore and stroke: 3.87 x 3.53 in, 98.2 x 89.6 mm; engine capacity: 250 cu in, 4,097 cu cm; compression ratio: 8.5; max power (SAE): 145 hp at 4,200 rpm; max torque (SAE): 230 lb ft, 31.8 kg m at 1,600 rpm; max engine rpm: 4,400; specific power: 35.4 hp/l; cylinder block: cast iron; cylinder head: cast iron; crankshaft bearings: 7; valves: 2 per cylinder, overhead, in line, push-rods and rockers; hydraulic tappets; camshafts: 1, side; lubrication: gear pump, full flow filter; lubricating system capacity: 7.2 imp pt, 8.7 US pt, 4.1 l; carburation: 1 Rochester 7041017 downdraught single barrel carburettor; fuel feed: mechanical pump; cooling system: water; cooling system capacity: 16.7 imp pt, 20.1 US pt, 9.5 l.

TRANSMISSION driving wheels: rear; clutch: single dry plate (diaphragm); gearbox: mechanical; gears: 3 + reverse; synchromesh gears: I, II, III; gearbox ratios: I 2.850, II 1.680, III 1, rev 2.950; gear lever: steering column; final drive: hypoid bevel; axle ratio: 3.080; width of rims: 5''; tyres: E78 x 14.

PERFORMANCE max speed: about 93 mph, 149 km/h; power-weight ratio: coupé 21 lb/hp, 9.5 kg/hp — sedan 21.1 lb/hp, 9.6 kg/hp; speed in direct drive at 1,000 rpm: 21.5 mph, 34.6 km/h; fuel consumption: 18.6 m/imp gal, 15.5 m/US gal, 15.2 l x 100 km.

CHASSIS integral, front ladder frame; front suspension: independent, wishbones, coil springs, telescopic dampers; rear suspension: rigid axle, single leaf semi-elliptic spring, telescopic dampers.

STEERING recirculating ball; turns of steering wheel lock to lock: 4.80.

BRAKES drum, dual circuit; area rubbed by linings: total 268.8 sq in, 1,734 sq cm.

ELECTRICAL EQUIPMENT voltage: 12 V; battery: 45 Ah; generator type: alternator, 37 A; ignition distributor: Delco-Remy; headlamps: 2.

DIMENSIONS AND WEIGHT wheel base: 111 in, 2,819 mm; front track: coupé 58.90 in, 1,496 mm — sedan 59 in, 1,498 mm; rear track: 58.90 in, 1,496 mm; overall length: 189.40 in, 4,811 mm; overall width: 72.40 in, 1,839 mm; overall height: coupé 52.50 in, 1,333 mm — sedan 53.90 in, 1,369 mm; ground clearance: 5.10 in, 130 mm; dry weight: Acadian 2-door Coupé 3,042 lb, 1,379 kg — Acadian 4-door Sedan 3,066 lb, 1,391 kg; turning circle (between walls): 43.3 ft, 13.2 m; fuel tank capacity: 11 imp gal, 13.3 US gal, 50 l.

OPTIONAL ACCESSORIES Torque Drive semi-automatic gearbox with 2 ratios (I 1.820, II 1, rev 1.820), max ratio of convertor at stall 2.10, 3.080 axle ratio; Powerglide automatic gearbox with 2 ratios (I 1.820, II 1, rev 1.820), max ratio of convertor at stall 2.10, 3.080 axle ratio; limited slip final drive; power-assisted steering; front disc brakes with servo.

200 hp power team

(standard for both models).

See 145 hp power team, except for:

ENGINE cylinders: 8, Vee-slanted at 90°; bore and stroke: 3.87 x 3.25 in, 98.2 x 82.5 mm; engine capacity: 307 cu in, 5,031 cu cm; max power (SAE): 200 hp at 4,600 rpm; max torque (SAE): 300 lb ft, 41.4 kg m at 2,400 rpm; max engine rpm: 5,000; specific power: 39.7 hp/l; crankshaft bearings: 5; camshafts: 1, at centre of Vee; carburation: 1 Rochester 7041101 downdraught twin barrel carburettor; cooling system capacity: 20.8 imp pt, 24.9 US pt, 11.8 l.

PERFORMANCE max speed: about 106 mph, 170 km/h; power-weight ratio: coupé 15.8 lb/hp, 7.1 kg/hp — sedan 15.9 lb/hp, 7.2 kg/hp; fuel consumption: 17.4 m/imp gal, 14.5 m/US gal, 16.2 l x 100 km.

CHASSIS front suspension: anti-roll bar.

ELECTRICAL EQUIPMENT battery: 61 Ah.

DIMENSIONS AND WEIGHT dry weight: Acadian 2-door Coupé 3,160 lb, 1,433 kg — Acadian 4-door Sedan 3,184 lb, 1,444 kg.

OPTIONAL ACCESSORIES Torque Drive semi-automatic gearbox not available; Turbo Hydramatic automatic gearbox with 3 ratios (I 2.520, II 1.520, III 1, rev 1.930), max ratio of convertor at stall 2.10, 2.560 axle ratio; air-conditioning system.

245 hp power team

(optional for both models).

See 145 hp power team, except for:

ENGINE cylinders: 8, Vee-slanted at 90°; bore and stroke: 4 x 3.48 in, 101.6 x 88.3 mm; engine capacity: 350 cu in, 5,736 cu cm; max power (SAE): 245 hp at 4,800 rpm; max torque (SAE): 350 lb ft, 48.3 kg m at 2,800 rpm; max engine rpm: 5,200; specific power: 42.7 hp/l; crankshaft bearings: 5; camshafts: 1, at centre of Vee; carburation: 1 Rochester 7041113 downdraught 4-barrel carburettor; cooling system capacity: 22.2 imp pt, 26.6 US pt, 12.6 l.

TRANSMISSION clutch: centrifugal; gears: 4 + reverse; synchromesh gears: I, II, III, IV; gearbox ratios: I 2.540, II 1.800, III 1.440, IV 1, rev 2.540; gear lever: central.

PERFORMANCE max speed: about 108 mph, 174 km/h; power-weight ratio: coupé 13.1 lb/hp, 5.9 kg/hp — sedan 13.2 lb/hp, 6 kg/hp; fuel consumption: 16.1 m/imp gal, 13.4 m/US gal, 17.5 l x 100 km.

CHASSIS front suspension: anti-roll bar; rear suspension: multi leaf semi-elliptic spring.

ELECTRICAL EQUIPMENT battery: 61 Ah.

DIMENSIONS AND WEIGHT (see 200 hp power team) dry weight: plus 38 lb, 17 kg.

OPTIONAL ACCESSORIES Torque Drive semi-automatic and Powerglide automatic gearboxes not available; Turbo Hydramatic automatic gearbox with 3 ratios (I 2.520, II 1.520, III 1, rev 1.930), max ratio of convertor at stall 2.10, 2.560 axle ratio; air-conditioning system.

270 hp power team

(optional for Acadian 2-door Coupé; not available for the other model).

See 145 hp power team, except for:

ENGINE cylinders: 8, Vee-slanted at 90°; bore and stroke: 4 x 3.48 in, 101.6 x 88.3 mm; engine capacity: 350 cu in, 5,736 cu cm; max power (SAE): 270 hp at 4,800 rpm; max torque (SAE): 360 lb ft, 49.7 kg m at 3,200 rpm; max engine rpm: 5,200; specific power: 47.1 hp/l; crankshaft bearings: 5; camshafts: 1, at centre of Vee; carburation: 1 Rochester 7041203 downdraught 4-barrel carburettor; cooling system capacity: 22.2 imp pt, 26.6 US pt, 12.6 l.

TRANSMISSION clutch: centrifugal; gears: 4 + reverse; synchromesh gears: I, II, III, IV; gearbox ratios: I 2.520, II 1.880, III 1.460, IV 1, rev 2.590; gear lever: central; axle ratio: 3.310; width of rims: 7''; tyres: E70 x 14.

PERFORMANCE max speed: about 110 mph, 177 km/h; power-weight ratio: 12.1 lb/hp, 5.5 kg/hp; speed in direct drive at 1,000 rpm: 21.3 mph, 34.3 km/h; fuel consumption: 13.3 m/imp gal, 12.9 m/US gal, 18.3 l x 100 km.

CHASSIS front suspension: anti-roll bar; rear suspension: multi leaf semi-elliptic spring.

BRAKES front disc, rear drum, dual circuit, servo; area rubbed by linings: total 332.4 sq in, 2,144 sq cm.

ELECTRICAL EQUIPMENT battery: 61 Ah.

DIMENSIONS AND WEIGHT (see 200 hp power team) dry weight: plus 122 lb, 55 kg.

PONTIAC Laurentian 4-door Sedan

PONTIAC Catalina 4-door Sedan

AMERICAN MOTORS Gremlin 2-passenger Sedan

OPTIONAL ACCESSORIES Torque Drive semi-automatic an Powerglide automatic gearboxes not available; Turbo Hy dramatic automatic gearbox with 3 ratios (I 2.520, II 1.520 III 1, rev 1.930), max ratio of convertor at stall 2.10, 3.070 axle ratio; air-conditioning system.

FORD   CANADA

Meteor Rideau - Meteor Rideau 500 - Meteor Montcalm Series

PRICES EX WORKS:

Meteor Rideau	4-door Pillared Hardtop	$ —
Meteor Rideau 500	2-door Hardtop	$ —
Meteor Rideau 500	4-door Hardtop	$ —
Meteor Rideau 500	Station Wagon	$ —
Meteor Montcalm	2-door Hardtop	$ —
Meteor Montcalm	4-door Hardtop	$ —
Meteor Montcalm	Station Wagon	$ —
Meteor Montcalm	4-door Pillared Hardtop	$ —

260 hp power team

(optional for all Series).

ENGINE front, 4 stroke; cylinders: 8, Vee-slanted at 90° bore and stroke: 4 x 4 in, 101.6 x 101.6 mm; engine capacity 400 cu in, 6,555 cu cm; compression ratio: 9; max powe (SAE): 260 hp at 4,400 rpm; max torque (SAE): 400 lb ft 55.2 kg m at 2,200 rpm; max engine rpm: 4,600; specific power: 39.7 hp/l; cylinder block: cast iron; cylinder head cast iron; crankshaft bearings: 5; valves: 2 per cylinder overhead, in line, push-rods and rockers, hydraulic tappets camshafts: 1, at centre of Vee; lubrication: rotary pump full flow filter; lubricating system capacity: 8.3 imp pt 9.9 US pt, 4.7 l; carburation: 1 downdraught twin barre carburettor; fuel feed: mechanical pump; cooling system water; cooling system capacity: 29.2 imp pt, 35.1 US pt 16.6 l.

TRANSMISSION driving wheels: rear; gearbox: Select Shif Cruise-o-Matic automatic, hydraulic torque convertor and planetary gears with 3 ratios + reverse, max ratio o convertor at stall 2.05, possible manual selection; gearbox ratios: I 2.460, II 1.460, III 1, rev 2.180; selector lever steering column; final drive: hypoid bevel; axle ratio: 2.750 width of rims: 5''; tyres: G78 x 15.

PERFORMANCE max speed: about 102 mph, 164 km/h speed in direct drive at 1,000 rpm: 22.3 mph, 35.9 km/h fuel consumption: 15.6 m/imp gal, 13 m/US gal, 18.1 l x 100 km.

CHASSIS perimeter box-type with cross members; fron suspension: independent, wishbones, lower leading arms coil springs, anti-roll bar, telescopic dampers; rear sus pension: rigid axle, lower trailing arm, upper torque arms transverse linkage bar, coil springs, telescopic dampers.

STEERING recirculating ball; turns of steering wheel to lock: 5.64.

BRAKES drum, dual circuit; lining area: front 42.8 sq in 276 sq cm, rear 95.5 sq in, 616 sq cm, total 138.3 sq in 892 sq cm.

ELECTRICAL EQUIPMENT voltage: 12 V; battery: 45 Ah; ge nerator type: alternator, 42 A; ignition distributor: Autolite headlamps: 4.

DIMENSIONS AND WEIGHT wheel base: 124 in, 3,149 mm front track: 63.30 in, 1,608 mm; rear track: 64.30 in, 1,633 mm; overall length: 224.70 in, 5,707 mm; overall width 79.30 in, 2,014 mm; overall height: 53.80 in, 1,366 mm ground clearance: 4.90 in, 124 mm; turning circle (between walls): 42.8 ft, 13 m; fuel tank capacity: 16.7 imp gal 20 US gal, 76 l.

VARIATIONS

ENGINE capacity 302 cu in, 4,949 cu cm (standard for Meteor Rideau and Meteor Rideau 500).

ENGINE capacity 351 cu in, 5,752 cu cm (standard for Meteor Montcalm).

ENGINE capacity 429 cu in, 7,030 cu cm, 1 downdraught twin barrel carburettor (optional for Meteor Rideau and Meteor Rideau 500).

ENGINE capacity 429 cu in, 7,030 cu cm, 1 downdraught 4-barrel carburettor (optional for Meteor Rideau and Meteor Rideau 500).

OPTIONAL ACCESSORIES limited slip final drive; automatic levelling control; power-assisted steering; servo brake; air conditioning system.

FORD Meteor Rideau 500 2-door Hardtop

PONTIAC Parisienne Brougham 2-door Hardtop

AMERICAN MOTORS Gremlin 2-passenger Sedan

PONTIAC   CANADA

Laurentian - Catalina - Parisienne Brougham Series

PRICES EX WORKS:

Laurentian	2-door Hardtop	$	—
Laurentian	4-door Hardtop	$	—
Laurentian	4-door Sedan	$	—
Catalina	2-door Hardtop	$	—
Catalina	4-door Hardtop	$	—
Catalina	4-door Sedan	$	—
Parisienne Brougham	2-door Hardtop	$	—
Parisienne Brougham	4-door Hardtop	$	—
Parisienne Brougham	4-door Sedan	$	—

145 hp power team

(standard for Laurentian Series; not available for other Series).

ENGINE front, 4 stroke; cylinders: 6, in line; bore and stroke: 3.87 x 3.52 in, 98.2 x 89.3 mm; engine capacity: 250 cu in, 4,097 cu cm; compression ratio: 8.5; max power (SAE): 145 hp at 4,200 rpm; max torque (SAE): 230 lb ft, 31.8 kg m at 1,600 rpm; max engine rpm: 4,400; specific power: 35.4 hp/l; cylinder block: cast iron; cylinder head: cast iron; crankshaft bearings: 7; valves: 2 per cylinder, overhead, in line, push-rods and rockers, hydraulic tappets; camshafts: 1, side; lubrication: gear pump, full flow filter; lubricating system capacity: 7 imp pt, 8.5 US pt, 4 l; carburation: 1 Rochester downdraught single barrel carburettor; fuel feed: mechanical pump; cooling system: water; cooling system capacity: 16.7 imp pt, 20.1 US pt, 9.5 l.

TRANSMISSION driving wheels: rear; clutch: single dry plate; gearbox: mechanical; gears: 3 + reverse; synchromesh gears: I, II, III; gearbox ratios: I 2.850, II 1.680, III 1, rev 2.950; gear lever: steering column; final drive: hypoid bevel; axle ratio: 3.080; width of rims: 6''; tyres: G78 x 15.

PERFORMANCE max speed: about 92 mph, 148 km/h; speed in direct drive at 1,000 rpm: 21 mph, 33.8 km/h; fuel consumption: 19.5 m/imp gal, 16.2 m/US gal, 14.5 l x 100 km.

CHASSIS perimeter; front suspension: independent, wishbones, coil springs, telescopic dampers; rear suspension: rigid axle, lower trailing radius arms, upper torque arms, coil springs, telescopic dampers.

STEERING recirculating ball; turns of steering wheel lock to lock: 5.60.

BRAKES front disc, rear drum, dual circuit; area rubbed by linings: total 374.7 sq in, 2,417 sq cm.

ELECTRICAL EQUIPMENT voltage: 12 V; battery: 45 Ah; generator type: alternator, 37 A; ignition distributor: Delco-Remy; headlamps: 4.

DIMENSIONS AND WEIGHT wheel base: 123.50 in, 3,137 mm; front track: 64 in, 1,625 mm; rear track: 64 in, 1,625 mm; overall length: 220.20 in, 5,593 mm; overall width: 79.50 in, 2,019 mm; overall height: 2-door hardtop 53.40 in, 1,356 mm — 4-door hardtop 53.60 in, 1,361 mm — 4-door sedan 54.30 in, 1,379 mm; ground clearance: 5.10 in, 130 mm; fuel tank capacity: 17.4 imp gal, 20.8 US gal, 79 l.

BODY seats: 6; front seats: bench.

OPTIONAL ACCESSORIES limited slip final drive; power-assisted steering; servo brake.

245 hp power team

(standard for all Series).

See 145 hp power team, except for:

ENGINE cylinders: 8, Vee-slanted at 90°; bore and stroke: 4 x 3.48 in, 101.6 x 88.3 mm; engine capacity: 350 cu in, 5,736 cu cm; max power (SAE): 245 hp at 4,800 rpm; max torque (SAE): 350 lb ft, 48.3 kg m at 2,800 rpm; max engine rpm: 5,000; specific power: 42.7 hp/l; crankshaft bearings: 5; camshafts: 1, at centre of Vee; carburation: 1 Rochester downdraught twin barrel carburettor; cooling system capacity: 22.2 imp pt, 26.6 US pt, 12.6 l.

TRANSMISSION gearbox ratios: I 2.540, II 1.500, III 1, rev 2.630.

PERFORMANCE max speed: about 99 mph, 159 km/h; speed in direct drive at 1,000 rpm: 21 mph, 33.8 km/h; fuel consumption: 16.1 m/imp gal, 13.4 m/US gal, 17.5 l x 100 km.

CHASSIS front suspension: anti-roll bar.

ELECTRICAL EQUIPMENT battery: 61 Ah.

AMERICAN MOTORS   USA

Gremlin Series

PRICES IN USA:

| Gremlin | 2-passenger Sedan | $ 1,899 |
| Gremlin | 4-passenger Sedan | $ 1,999 |

135 hp power team

(standard for both models).

ENGINE front, 4 stroke; cylinders: 6, in line; bore and stroke: 3.75 x 3.50 in, 95.2 x 88.9 mm; engine capacity: 232 cu in, 3,802 cu cm; compression ratio: 8; max power (SAE): 135 hp at 4,000 rpm; max torque (SAE): 210 lb ft, 29 kg m at 1,600 rpm; max engine rpm: 4,500; specific power: 35.5 hp/l; cylinder block: cast iron; cylinder head: cast iron; crankshaft bearings: 7; valves: 2 per cylinder, overhead, in line, push-rods and rockers, hydraulic tappets; camshafts: 1, side; lubrication: gear pump, full flow filter; lubricating system capacity: 8.3 imp pt, 9.9 US pt, 4.7 l; carburation: 1 Carter YF 6093S downdraught single barrel carburettor; fuel feed: mechanical pump; cooling system: water; cooling system capacity: 17.4 imp pt, 20.9 US pt, 9.9 l.

TRANSMISSION driving wheels: rear; clutch: single dry plate; gearbox: mechanical; gears: 3 + reverse, synchromesh gears: II and III; gearbox ratios: I 2.605, II 1.630, III 1, rev 3.536; gear lever: central or steering column; final drive: hypoid bevel; axle ratio: 2.730; width of rims: 4.5''; tyres: 6.00 x 13.

PERFORMANCE max speed: about 102 mph, 164 km/h; power-weight ratio: Gremlin 2-passenger 19.1 lb/hp, 8.7 kg/hp — Gremlin 4-passenger 19.5 lb/hp, 8.8 kg/hp; speed in direct drive at 1,000 rpm: 22.7 mph, 36.5 km/h; fuel consumption: 20.6 m/imp gal, 17.2 m/US gal, 13.7 l x 100 km.

CHASSIS integral; front suspension: independent, wishbones, coil springs, telescopic dampers; rear suspension: rigid axle, torque tube, semi-elliptic leafsprings, telescopic dampers.

STEERING recirculating ball; turns of steering wheel lock to lock: 6.

BRAKES drum, dual circuit; area rubbed by linings: total 254.5 sq in, 1,641 sq cm.

ELECTRICAL EQUIPMENT voltage: 12 V; battery: 50 Ah; generator type: alternator, 35 A; ignition distributor: Delco-Remy; headlamps: 2.

DIMENSIONS AND WEIGHT wheel base: 96 in, 2,438 mm; front track: 57.46 in, 1,459 mm; rear track: 57 in, 1,448 mm; overall length: 161.25 in, 4,096 mm; overall width: 70.53 in, 1,793 mm; overall height: 51.80 in, 1,316 mm; ground clearance: 5.01 in, 127 mm; dry weight: Gremlin 2-passenger 2,581 lb, 1,170 kg — Gremlin 4-passenger 2,630 lb, 1,193 kg; turning circle (between walls): 34.8 ft, 10.6 m; fuel tank capacity: 17.6 imp gal, 21 US gal, 80 l.

BODY saloon/sedan; doors: 2; seats: 2 or 4; front seats: separate, reclining backrests; details: back seat folding down to luggage table only for 4-passenger model.

OPTIONAL ACCESSORIES Shift-Command automatic gearbox (I 2.390, II 1.450, III 1, rev 2.090), max ratio of convertor at stall 2, 2.370 axle ratio; limited slip final drive; power-assisted steering; servo brake; air-conditioning system; X equipment.

150 hp power team

(optional for both models).

See 135 hp power team, except for:

ENGINE bore and stroke: 3.75 x 3.90 in, 95.2 x 99 mm; engine capacity: 258 cu in, 4,229 cu cm; max power (SAE): 150 hp at 3,800 rpm; max torque (SAE): 240 lb ft, 33.1 kg m at 1,800 rpm; max engine rpm: 4,900; specific power: 35.5 hp/l; carburation: 1 Carter YF 6095S downdraught single barrel carburettor.

TRANSMISSION synchromesh gears: I, II, III; gearbox ratios: I 2.636, II 1.605, III 1, rev 2.636; gear lever: central.

PERFORMANCE max speed: about 110 mph, 177 km/h; power-weight ratio: Gremlin 2-passenger 17.2 lb/hp, 7.8 kg/hp — Gremlin 4-passenger 17.5 lb/hp, 7.9 kg/hp; fuel consumption: 19 m/imp gal, 15.8 m/US gal, 14.9 l x 100 km.

OPTIONAL ACCESSORIES Shift-Command automatic gearbox with 2.730 axle ratio.

AMERICAN MOTORS Gremlin 4-passenger Sedan

AMERICAN MOTORS Hornet 2-door Sedan

AMERICAN MOTORS Hornet Sportabout Station Wagon

Hornet - Hornet SST - Hornet SC/360 - Hornet Sportabout Series

PRICES IN USA:

Hornet	2-door Sedan	$ 2,174
Hornet	4-door Sedan	$ 2,234
Hornet SST	2-door Sedan	$ 2,274
Hornet SST	4-door Sedan	$ 2,334
Hornet SC/360	2-door Sedan	$ 2,663
Hornet Sportabout	Station Wagon	$ 2,594

For V8 engines add $ 129.

135 hp power team

standard for Hornet, Hornet SST and Hornet Sportabout Series; not available for Hornet SC/360).

ENGINE front, 4 stroke; cylinders: 6, in line; bore and stroke: 3.75 x 3.50 in, 95.2 x 88.9 mm; engine capacity: 232 cu in, 3,802 cu cm; compression ratio: 8; max power (SAE): 135 hp at 4,000 rpm; max torque (SAE): 210 lb ft, 29 kg m at 1,600 rpm; max engine rpm: 4,500; specific power: 35.5 hp/l; cylinder block: cast iron; cylinder head: cast iron; crankshaft bearings: 7; valves: 2 per cylinder, overhead, in line, push-rods and rockers, hydraulic tappets; camshafts: 1, side; lubrication: gear pump, full flow filter; lubricating system capacity: 8.3 imp pt, 9.9 US pt, 4.7 l; carburation: 1 Carter 6093S downdraught single barrel carburettor; fuel feed: mechanical pump; cooling system: water; cooling system capacity: 17.4 imp pt, 20.9 US pt, 9.9 l.

TRANSMISSION driving wheels: rear; clutch: single dry plate; gearbox: mechanical; gears: 3 + reverse; synchromesh gears: II and III; gearbox ratios: I 2.605, II 1.630, III 1, rev 3.536; gear lever: steering column; final drive: hypoid bevel; axle ratio: 3.080; width of rims: 4.5''; tyres: 6.45 x 14 (station wagon 6.95 x 14).

PERFORMANCE max speed: about 94 mph, 151 km/h; power-weight ratio: Hornet 4-door Sedan and Hornet SST 4-door Sedan 20.6 lb, 9.3 kg; speed in direct drive at 1,000 rpm: 22.2 mph, 35.7 km/h; fuel consumption: 20.5 m/imp gal, 17 m/US gal, 13.8 l x 100 km.

CHASSIS integral; front suspension: independent, wishbones, coil springs, telescopic dampers; rear suspension: rigid axle, torque tube, semi-elliptic leafsprings, telescopic dampers.

STEERING recirculating ball; turns of steering wheel lock to lock: 6.

BRAKES drum, dual circuit; area rubbed by linings: total 254.5 sq in, 1,641 sq cm.

ELECTRICAL EQUIPMENT voltage: 12 V; battery: 50 Ah; generator type: alternator, 35 A; ignition distributor: Delco-Remy; headlamps: 2.

DIMENSIONS AND WEIGHT wheel base: 108 in, 2,743 mm; front track: 57.46 in, 1,459 mm; rear track: 57 in, 1,448 mm; overall length: 179.26 in, 4,553 mm; overall width: 70.58 in, 1,793 mm; overall height: 52.40 in, 1,331 mm — station wagon 52.90 in, 1,344 mm; ground clearance: 5.21 in, 132 mm; dry weight: Hornet 2-door Sedan 2,702 lb, 1,225 kg — Hornet 4-door Sedan 2,779 lb, 1,260 kg — Hornet SST 2-door Sedan 2,739 lb, 1,242 kg — Hornet SST 4-door Sedan 2,739 lb, 1,242 kg — Hornet Sportabout Station Wagon 2,875 lb, 1,304 kg; turning circle (between walls): 38 ft, 11.6 m; fuel tank capacity: 13.2 imp gal, 16 US gal, 60 l.

BODY seats: 5; front seats: bench.

OPTIONAL ACCESSORIES Shift-Command automatic gearbox (I 2.390, II 1.450, III 1, rev 2.090), max ratio of convertor at stall 2, 2.370 axle ratio; limited slip final drive; power-assisted steering; servo brake; air-conditioning system; de luxe equipment only for Hornet Sportabout.

150 hp power team

(optional for Hornet, Hornet SST and Hornet Sportabout Series; not available for Hornet SC/360).

See 135 hp power team, except for:

ENGINE bore and stroke: 3.75 x 3.90 in, 95.2 x 99 mm; engine capacity: 258 cu in, 4,229 cu cm; max power (SAE): 150 hp at 3,800 rpm; max torque (SAE): 240 lb ft, 33.1 kg m at 1,800 rpm; max engine rpm: 4,600; carburation: 1 Carter YF 6095S downdraught single barrel carburettor.

TRANSMISSION synchromesh gears: I, II, III; gearbox ratios: I 2.636, II 1.605, III 1, rev 2.636; gear lever: central.

PERFORMANCE max speed: about 101 mph, 162 km/h; power-weight ratio: Hornet 4-door Sedan and Hornet SST 4-door Sedan 18.5 lb/hp, 8.4 kg/hp; fuel consumption: 18.8 m/imp gal, 15.7 m/US gal, 15 l x 100 km.

OPTIONAL ACCESSORIES Shift-Command automatic gearbox with 2.730 axle ratio.

AMERICAN MOTORS Gremlin 4-passenger Sedan

AMERICAN MOTORS Hornet Sedan

AMERICAN MOTORS
Hornet Sportabout Station Wagon

210 hp power team

(optional for Hornet SST and Hornet Sportabout Series; not available for other Series).

See 135 hp power team, except for:

ENGINE cylinders: 8, Vee-slanted at 90°; bore and stroke: 3.75 x 3.44 in, 95.2 x 87.3 mm; engine capacity: 304 cu in, 4,982 cu cm; compression ratio: 8.4; max power (SAE): 210 hp at 4,400 rpm; max torque (SAE): 300 lb ft, 41.4 kg m at 2,600 rpm; max engine rpm: 4,800; specific power: 42.1 hp/l; crankshaft bearings: 5; camshafts: 1, at centre of Vee; carburation: 1 AM (FAL) 2100D 1DA2 downdraught twin barrel carburettor; cooling system capacity: 23.2 imp pt, 25.8 US pt, 13.2 l.

TRANSMISSION gearbox: Shift-Command automatic (standard); selector lever: steering column; axle ratio: 2.870; tyres: 6.95 x 14.

PERFORMANCE max speed: about 106 mph, 170 km/h; power-weight ratio: Hornet SST 4-door Sedan 13.2 lb/hp, 6 kg/hp; speed in direct drive at 1,000 rpm: 23.2 mph, 37.3 km/h; fuel consumption: 17.8 m/imp gal, 14.8 m/US gal, 15.9 l x 100 km.

CHASSIS front suspension: anti-roll bar.

BRAKES area rubbed by linings: total 267 sq in, 1,722 sq cm.

DIMENSIONS AND WEIGHT front track: 57.24 in, 1,454 mm; rear track: 56.60 in, 1,438 mm.

OPTIONAL ACCESSORIES front disc brakes with servo.

245 hp power team

(standard for Hornet SC/360; not available for other Series).

See 135 hp power team, except for:

ENGINE cylinders: 8, Vee-slanted at 90°; bore and stroke: 4.08 x 3.44 in, 103.6 x 87.3 mm; engine capacity: 360 cu in, 5,900 cu cm; compression ratio: 8.5; max power (SAE): 245 hp at 4,400 rpm; max torque (SAE): 365 lb ft, 50.4 kg m at 2,600 rpm; max engine rpm: 5,000; specific power: 41.5 hp/l; crankshaft bearings: 5; camshafts: 1, at centre of Vee; carburation: 1 AM (FAL) 2100D 1DM2 downdraught twin barrel carburettor; cooling system capacity: 21.6 imp pt, 26 US pt, 12.3 l.

TRANSMISSION synchromesh gears: I, II, III; gearbox ratios: I 2.548, II 1.558, III 1, rev 2.548; gear lever: central; axle ratio: 3.150; width of rims: 6''; tyres: D70 x 14.

PERFORMANCE max speed: about 116 mph, 186 km/h; power-weight ratio: 12.7 lb/hp, 5.8 kg/hp; speed in direct drive at 1,000 rpm: 23.1 mph, 37.1 km/h; fuel consumption: 16.2 m/imp gal, 13.5 m/US gal, 17.4 l x 100 km.

CHASSIS front suspension: anti-roll bar.

STEERING turns of steering wheel lock to lock: 5.10.

BRAKES area rubbed by linings: total 267 sq in, 1,722 sq cm.

ELECTRICAL EQUIPMENT battery: 60 Ah.

DIMENSIONS AND WEIGHT front track: 57.24 in, 1,454 mm; rear track: 56.60 in, 1,438 mm; dry weight: 3,105 lb, 1,408 kg.

OPTIONAL ACCESSORIES Shift-Command automatic gearbox with 2.870 axle ratio; front disc brakes with servo.

285 hp power team

(optional for Hornet SC/360; not available for other Series).

See 135 hp power team, except for:

ENGINE cylinders: 8, Vee-slanted at 90°; bore and stroke: 4.08 x 3.44 in, 103.6 x 87.3 mm; engine capacity: 360 cu in, 5,900 cu cm; compression ratio: 8.5; max power (SAE): 285 hp at 4,800 rpm; max torque (SAE): 330 lb ft, 45.5 kg m at 5,000 rpm; max engine rpm: 5,200; specific power: 48.3 hp/l; crankshaft bearings: 5; camshafts: 1, at centre of Vee; carburation: 1 AM (FAL) 4300 1TM4 downdraught 4-barrel carburettor; cooling system capacity: 21.6 imp pt, 26 US pt, 12.3 l.

TRANSMISSION synchromesh gears: I, II, III; gearbox ratios: I 2.548, II 1.558, III 1, rev 2.548; gear lever: central; axle ratio: 3.150; width of rims: 6''; tyres: D70 x 14.

PERFORMANCE max speed: about 120 mph, 193 km/h; power-weight ratio: 10.9 lb/hp, 4.9 kg/hp; speed in direct drive at 1,000 rpm: 23.1 mph, 37.1 km/h; fuel consumption: 15.3 m/imp gal, 12.7 m/US gal, 18.5 l x 100 km.

CHASSIS front suspension: anti-roll bar.

285 HP POWER TEAM

STEERING turns of steering wheel lock to lock: 5.10.

BRAKES area rubbed by linings: total 267 sq in, 1,722 sq cm.

ELECTRICAL EQUIPMENT battery: 60 Ah.

DIMENSIONS AND WEIGHT front track: 57.24 in, 1,454 mm; rear track: 56.60 in, 1,438 mm; dry weight: 3,105 lb, 1,408 kg.

OPTIONAL ACCESSORIES Shift-Command automatic gearbox with 3.150 axle ratio; 4-sped fully synchronized mechanical gearbox (I 2.230, II 1.770, III 1.350, IV 1, rev 2.160), 3.540 axle ratio; front disc brakes with servo.

Javelin Series

PRICES IN USA:

Javelin	2-door Hardtop	$ 2,879
Javelin SST	2-door Hardtop	$ 2,999
Javelin AMX	2-door Hardtop	$ 3,432

For V8 engines add $ 101.

135 hp power team

(standard for Javelin and Javelin SST; not available for Javelin AMX).

ENGINE front, 4 stroke; cylinders: 6, in line; bore and stroke: 3.75 x 3.50 in, 95.2 x 88.9 mm; engine capacity: 232 cu in, 3,802 cu cm; compression ratio: 8; max power (SAE): 135 hp at 4,000 rpm; max torque (SAE): 210 lb ft, 29 kg m at 1,600 rpm; max engine rpm: 4,500; specific power: 35.5 hp/l; cylinder block: cast iron; cylinder head: cast iron; crankshaft bearings: 7; valves: 2 per cylinder, overhead, in line, push-rods and rockers, hydraulic tappets; camshafts: 1, side; lubrication: gear pump, full flow filter; lubricating system capacity: 8.3 imp pt, 9.9 US pt, 4.7 l; carburation: 1 Carter YF 6095S downdraught single barrel carburettor; fuel feed: mechanical pump; cooling system: water; cooling system capacity: 17.4 imp pt, 20.9 US pt, 9.9 l.

TRANSMISSION driving wheels: rear; clutch: single dry plate; gearbox: mechanical; gears: 3 + reverse; synchromesh gears: I, II, III; gearbox ratios: I 2.636, II 1.605, III 1, rev 2.636; gear lever: central; final drive: hypoid bevel; axle ratio: 3.080; width of rims: 5''; tyres: C78 x 14.

PERFORMANCE max speed: about 93 mph, 149 km/h; power-weight ratio: Javelin 2-door Hardtop 21.7 lb/hp, 9.8 kg/hp — Javelin SST 2-door Hardtop 21.8 lb/hp, 9.9 kg/hp; speed in direct drive at 1,000 rpm: 22.8 mph, 36.7 km/h; fuel consumption: 20.5 m/imp gal, 17 m/US gal, 13.8 l x 100 km.

CHASSIS integral; front suspension: independent, wishbones, coil springs, telescopic dampers; rear suspension: rigid axle, torque tube, semi-elliptic leafsprings, telescopic dampers.

STEERING recirculating ball; turns of steering wheel lock to lock: 5.10.

BRAKES drum, dual circuit; area rubbed by linings: total 254.5 sq in, 1,641 sq cm.

ELECTRICAL EQUIPMENT voltage: 12 V; battery: 50 Ah; generator type: alternator, 35 A; ignition distributor: Delco-Remy; headlamps: 2.

DIMENSIONS AND WEIGHT wheel base: 110 in, 2,794 mm; front track: 59.30 in, 1,506 mm; rear track: 60 in, 1,524 mm; overall length: 191.77 in, 4,871 mm; overall width: 75.20 in, 1,910 mm; overall height: 50.87 in, 1,292 mm; ground clearance: 5.48 in, 139 mm; dry weight: Javelin 2-door Hardtop 2,935 lb, 1,331 kg — Javelin SST 2-door Hardtop 2,938 lb, 1,332 kg; turning circle (between walls): 38.3 ft, 11.7 m; fuel tank capacity: 13.4 imp gal, 16 US gal, 61 l.

BODY hardtop; doors: 2; seats: 4; front seats: separate.

OPTIONAL ACCESSORIES Shift-Command automatic gearbox (I 2.390, II 1.450, III 1, rev 2.090), max ratio of convertor at stall 2, 3.080 axle ratio; limited slip final drive; power-assisted steering; servo brake; air-conditioning system.

150 hp power team

(optional for Javelin and Javelin SST; not available for Javelin AMX).

See 135 hp power team, except for:

ENGINE bore and stroke: 3.75 x 3.90 in, 95.2 x 99 mm; engine capacity: 258 cu in, 4,229 cu cm; max power (SAE): 150 hp at 3,800 rpm; max torque (SAE): 240 lb ft, 33.1 kg m at 1,800 rpm; max engine rpm: 4,300; carburation: 1 Carter 6038S downdraught single barrel carburettor.

TRANSMISSION gearbox: Shift-Command automatic (standard); selector lever: steering column.

PERFORMANCE max speed: about 98 mph, 157 km/h; power-weight ratio: Javelin 2-door Hardtop and Javelin SST 2-door Hardtop 19.6 lb/hp, 8.9 kg/hp; fuel consumption: 18.7 m/imp gal, 15.6 m/US gal, 15.1 l x 100 km.

AMERICAN MOTORS
Javelin SST 2-door Hardtop (front disc brake)

AMERICAN MOTORS
Javelin AMX 2-door Hardtop

AMERICAN MOTORS Matador 2-door Hardtop

210 hp power team

(optional for Javelin and Javelin SST; not available for Javelin AMX).

See 135 hp power team, except for:

ENGINE cylinders: 8, Vee-slanted at 90°; bore and stroke 3.75 x 3.44 in, 95.2 x 87.3 mm; engine capacity: 304 cu in 4,982 cu cm; compression ratio: 8.4; max power (SAE): 21 hp at 4,400 rpm; max torque (SAE): 300 lb ft, 41.4 kg r at 2,600 rpm; max engine rpm; 5,000; specific power: 42. hp/l; crankshaft bearings: 5; camshafts: 1, at centre of Vee carburation: 1 AM (FAL) 2100D 1DM2 downdraught twi barrel carburettor; cooling system capacity: 23.2 imp p 25.8 US pt, 13.2 l.

TRANSMISSION axle ratio: 3.150; tyres: D78 x 14.

PERFORMANCE max speed: about 112 mph, 180 km/h; powe weight ratio: Javelin 2-door Hardtop and Javelin SST 2-doo Hardtop 14 lb/hp, 6.3 kg/hp; speed in direct drive at 1,00 rpm: 22.5 mph, 36.2 km/h; fuel consumption: 17.7 m/im gal, 14.7 m/US gal, 16 l x 100 km.

CHASSIS front suspension: anti-roll bar.

BRAKES area rubbed by linings: total 267 sq in, 1,72 sq cm.

DIMENSIONS AND WEIGHT front track: 59.70 in, 1,516 mm

OPTIONAL ACCESSORIES Shift-Command automatic gear box with 2.870 axle ratio; front disc brakes with servo.

245 hp power team

(standard for Javelin AMX; optional for Javelin and Jave lin SST).

See 135 hp power team, except for:

ENGINE cylinders: 8, Vee-slanted at 90°; bore and stroke 4.08 x 3.44 in, 103.6 x 87.3 mm; engine capacity: 360 cu in, 5,900 cu cm; compression ratio: 8.5; max power (SAE) 245 hp at 4,400 rpm; max torque (SAE): 365 lb ft, 50.4 kg m at 2,600 rpm; max engine rpm: 5,000; specific power 41.5 hp/l; crankshaft bearings: 5; camshafts: 1, at centre of Vee; carburation: 1 AM (FAL) 2100D 1DM2 downdraugh twin barrel carburettor; cooling system capacity: 21.6 imp pt, 26 US pt, 12.3 l.

TRANSMISSION gearbox ratios: I 2.548, II 1.558, III 1, rev 2.548; axle ratio: 3.150; width of rims: 5.5'' — Javelin AMX 6''; tyres: Javelin AMX E70 x 14 — Javelin and Javelin SST D78 x 14.

PERFORMANCE max speed: about 115 mph, 185 km/h; power-weight ratio: Javelin 2-door Hardtop and Javelin SST 2-door Hardtop 12 lb/hp, 5.4 kg/hp; speed in direct drive at 1,000 rpm: 23 mph, 37 km/h; fuel consumption: 16.2 m/imp gal 13.5 m/US gal, 17.4 l x 100 km.

CHASSIS front suspension: anti-roll bar.

BRAKES area rubbed by linings: total 267 sq in, 1,722 sq cm.

ELECTRICAL EQUIPMENT battery: 60 Ah.

DIMENSIONS AND WEIGHT front track: 59.70 in, 1,516 mm.

OPTIONAL ACCESSORIES Shift-Command automatic gearbox with 2.870 axle ratio; front disc brakes with servo.

285 hp power team

(optional for all models).

See 135 hp power team, except for:

ENGINE cylinders: 8, Vee-slanted at 90°; bore and stroke: 4.08 x 3.44 in, 103.6 x 87.3 mm; engine capacity: 360 cu in, 5,900 cu cm; compression ratio: 8.5; max power (SAE): 285 hp at 4,800 rpm; max torque (SAE): 330 lb ft, 45.5 kg m at 5,000 rpm; max engine rpm: 5,200; specific power: 48.3 hp/l; crankshaft bearings: 5; camshafts: 1, at centre of Vee; carburation: 1 AM (FAL) 4300 1TM4 downdraught 4-barrel carburettor; cooling system capacity: 21.6 imp pt, 26 US pt, 12.3 l.

TRANSMISSION gearbox ratios: I 2.548, II 1.558, III 1, rev 2.548; axle ratio: 3.150; width of rims: 5.5'' — Javelin AMX 6''; tyres: Javelin AMX E70 x 14 — Javelin and Javelin SST D78 x 14.

PERFORMANCE max speed: about 117 mph, 188 km/h; power-weight ratio: Javelin 2-door Hardtop and Javelin SST 2-door Hardtop 10.3 lb/hp, 4.7 kg/hp; speed in direct drive at 1,000 rpm: 23 mph, 37 km/h; fuel consumption: 15.3 m/imp gal, 12.7 m/US gal, 18.5 l x 100 km.

BRAKES area rubbed by linings: total 167 sq in, 1,722 sq cm.

ELECTRICAL EQUIPMENT battery: 60 Ah.

DIMENSIONS AND WEIGHT front track: 59.70 in, 1,516 mm.

OPTIONAL ACCESSORIES Shift-Command automatic gearbox with 2.870 axle ratio; 4-speed fully synchronized mechanical gearbox (I 2.230, II 1.770, III 1.350, IV 1, rev 2.160), 3.540 axle ratio; front disc brakes with servo.

AMERICAN MOTORS Javelin SST 2-door Hardtop

AMERICAN MOTORS Javelin AMX 2-door Hardtop

330 hp power team

(Optional for all models).

See 135 hp power team, except for:

ENGINE cylinders: 8, Vee-slanted at 90°; bore and stroke: 4.16 x 3.68 in, 105.6 x 93.4 mm; engine capacity: 401 cu in, 6,571 cu cm; compression ratio: 9.5; max power (SAE): 430 lb ft, 59.3 kg m at 3,400 rpm; max engine rpm: 5,600; specific power: 50.2 hp/l; crankshaft bearings: 5; camshafts: 1, at centre of Vee; carburation: 1 AM (FAL) 4300 1TM4 downdraught 4-barrel carburettor; cooling system capacity: 21.6 imp pt, 26 US pt, 12.3 l.

TRANSMISSION gears: 4 + reverse; synchromesh gears: I, II, III, IV; gearbox ratios: I 2.230, II 1.770, III 1.350, IV 1, rev 2.160; axle ratio: 3.540; width of rims: 5.5'' — Javelin AMX 6''; tyres: Javelin AMX E70 x 14 — Javelin SST D78 x 14.

PERFORMANCE max speed: about 123 mph, 198 km/h; power-weight ratio: Javelin 2-door Hardtop and Javelin SST 2-door Hardtop 8.9 lb/hp, 4 kg/hp; speed in direct drive at 1,000 rpm: 22 mph, 35.4 km/h; fuel consumption: 14.3 m/imp gal, 11.9 m/US gal, 19.7 l x 100 km.

CHASSIS front suspension: anti-roll bar.

BRAKES area rubbed by linings: total 267 sq in, 1,722 sq cm.

ELECTRICAL EQUIPMENT battery: 60 Ah.

DIMENSIONS AND WEIGHT front track: 59.70 in, 1,516 mm.

OPTIONAL ACCESSORIES Shift-Command automatic gearbox with 2.870 axle ratio; front disc brakes with servo.

Matador Series

PRICES IN USA:

Matador	2-door Hardtop	$ 2,799
Matador	4-door Sedan	$ 2,770
Matador	Station Wagon	$ 3,163

For V8 engines add $ 101.

135 hp power team

(standard for all models).

ENGINE front, 4 stroke; cylinders: 6, in line; bore and stroke: 3.75 x 3.50 in, 95.2 x 88.9 mm; engine capacity: 232 cu in, 3 802 cu cm; compression ratio: 8; max power (SAE): 135 hp at 4,000 rpm; max torque (SAE): 210 lb ft, 29 kg m at 1,600 rpm; max engine rpm: 4,500; specific power: 35.5 np/l; cylinder block: cast iron; cylinder head: cast iron; crankshaft bearings: 7; valves: 2 per cylinder, overhead, in line, push-rods and rockers, hydraulic tappets; camshafts: 1, side; lubrication: gear pump, full flow filter; lubricating system capacity: 8.3 imp pt, 9.9 US pt, 4.7 l; carburation: 1 Carter YF 6095S downdraught single barrel carburettor; fuel feed: mechanical pump; cooling system: water; cooling system capacity: 17.4 imp pt, 20.9 US pt, 9.9 l.

TRANSMISSION driving wheels: rear; clutch: single dry plate; gearbox: mechanical; gears: 3 + reverse; synchromesh gears: I, II, III; gearbox ratios: I 2.636, II 1.605, III 1, rev 2.636; gear lever: steering column; final drive: hypoid bevel; axle ratio: 3.150; width of rims: 5.5'' — station wagon 6''; tyres: E78 x 14 — station wagon G78 x 14.

PERFORMANCE max speed: about 92 mph, 148 km/h; power-weight ratio: Matador 4-door Sedan 23.9 lb/hp, 10.8 kg/hp; speed in direct drive at 1,000 rpm: 22.6 mph, 36.3 km/h; fuel consumption: 19.9 m/imp gal, 16.6 m/US gal, 14.2 l x 100 km.

CHASSIS integral; front suspension: independent, wishbones, coil springs, anti-roll bar, telescopic dampers; rear suspension: rigid axle, lower trailing radius arms, upper oblique torque arms, coil springs, telescopic dampers.

STEERING recirculating ball; turns of steering wheel lock to lock: 6.

BRAKES drum, dual circuit; area rubbed by linings: total 267 sq in, 1,722 sq cm (station wagon 314 sq in, 2,025 sq cm).

ELECTRICAL EQUIPMENT voltage: 12 V; battery: 50 Ah; generator type: alternator, 35 A; ignition distributor: Delco-Remy; headlamps: 4.

DIMENSIONS AND WEIGHT wheel base: 118 in, 2,997 mm; front track: 59.94 in, 1,522 mm; rear track: 60 in, 1,524 mm; overall length: 206.05 in, 5,234 mm — station wagon 205 in, 5,207 mm; overall width: 77.24 in, 1,962 mm; overall height: 2-door hardtop 53.82 in, 1,367 mm — 4-door sedan 55.35 in, 1,406 mm — station wagon 56.39 in, 1,432 mm; ground clearance: 2-door hardtop 5.20 in, 132 mm — 4-door sedan 6.08 in, 154 mm — station wagon 6.60 in, 167 mm; dry weight: Matador 2-door Hardtop 3,270 lb, 1,483 kg — Matador 4-door Sedan 3,234 lb, 1,462 kg — Matador Station Wagon 3,560 lb, 1,590 kg; turning circle (between walls): 41 ft, 12 m; fuel tank capacity: 16.3 imp gal, 19.5 US gal, 74 l (station wagon 14.1 imp gal, 17 US gal, 64 l).

OPTIONAL ACCESSORIES Shift-Command automatic gearbox (I 2.390, II 1.450, III 1, rev 2.090), max ratio of convertor at stall 2, 3.150 axle ratio; limited slip final drive; anti-roll bar on rear suspension; power-assisted steering; servo brake; air-conditioning system.

AMERICAN MOTORS Matador 2-door Hardtop

150 hp power team

(optional for all models).

See 135 hp power team, except for:

ENGINE bore and stroke: 3.75 x 3.90 in, 95.2 x 99 mm; engine capacity: 258 cu in, 4,229 cu cm; max power (SAE): 150 hp at 3,800 rpm; max torque (SAE): 240 lb ft, 33.1 kg m at 1,800 rpm; max engine rpm: 4,300; carburation: 1 Carter YF 6038S downdraught single barrel carburettor.

TRANSMISSION gearbox: Shift-Command automatic (standard); selector lever: steering column.

PERFORMANCE max speed: about 99 mph, 159 km/h; power-weight ratio: Matador 4-door Sedan 21.5 lb/hp, 9.7 kg/hp; fuel consumption: 18.1 m/imp gal, 15.1 m/US gal, 15.6 l x 100 km.

210 hp power team

(optional for all models).

See 135 hp power team, except for:

ENGINE cylinders: 8 Vee-slanted at 90°; bore and stroke: 3.75 x 3.44 in, 95.2 x 87.3 mm; engine capacity: 304 cu in, 4,982 cu cm; compression ratio: 8.4; max power (SAE): 210 hp at 4,400 rpm; max torque (SAE): 300 lb ft, 41.4 kg m at 2,600 rpm; max engine rpm: 5,000; specific power: 42.1 hp/l; crankshaft bearings: 5; camshafts: 1, at centre of Vee; carburation: 1 AM (FAL) 2100D 1DA2 downdraught twin barrel carburettor; cooling system capacity: 23.2 imp pt, 25.8 US pt, 13.2 l.

TRANSMISSION gearbox: Shift-Command automatic (standard); selector lever: central; axle ratio: 2.870.

PERFORMANCE max speed: about 105 mph, 169 km/h; power-weight ratio: Matador 4-door Sedan 15.4 lb/hp, 7 kg/hp; speed in direct drive at 1,000 rpm: 22.7 mph, 36.5 km/h; fuel consumption: 17.2 m/imp gal, 14.3 m/US gal, 16.4 l x 100 km.

ELECTRICAL EQUIPMENT battery: 60 Ah.

DIMENSIONS AND WEIGHT front track: 59.72 in, 1,517 mm.

OPTIONAL ACCESSORIES front disc brakes with servo.

245 hp power team

(optional for all models).

See 135 hp power team, except for:

ENGINE cylinders: 8, Vee-slanted at 90°; bore and stroke: 4.08 x 3.44 in, 103.6 x 87.3 mm; engine capacity: 360 cu in, 5,900 cu cm; compression ratio: 8.5; max power (SAE): 245 hp at 4,400 rpm; max torque (SAE): 365 lb ft, 50.4 kg m at 2,600 rpm; max engine rpm: 5,000; specific power: 41.5 hp/l; crankshaft bearings: 5; camshafts: 1, at centre of Vee; carburation: 1 AM (FAL) 2100D 1RA2 downdraught twin barrel carburettor; cooling system capacity: 21.6 imp pt, 26 US pt, 12.3 l.

TRANSMISSION gearbox: Shift-Command automatic (standard); gearbox ratios: I 2.400, II 1.470, III 1, rev 2; selector lever: central; axle ratio: 2.870.

PERFORMANCE max speed: about 107 mph, 172 km/h; power-weight ratio: Matador 4-door Sedan 13.2 lb/hp, 6 kg/hp; speed in direct drive at 1,000 rpm: 22.7 mph, 36.5 km/h; fuel consumption: 16 m/imp gal, 13.3 m/US gal, 17.7 l x 100 km.

ELECTRICAL EQUIPMENT battery: 60 Ah.

DIMENSIONS AND WEIGHT front track: 59.72 in, 1,517 mm.

OPTIONAL ACCESSORIES front disc brakes with servo.

285 hp power team

(optional for all models).

See 135 hp power team, except for:

ENGINE cylinders: 8, Vee-slanted at 90°; bore and stroke: 4.08 x 3.44 in, 103.6 x 87.3 mm; engine capacity: 360 cu in, 5,900 cu cm; compression ratio: 8.5; max power (SAE): 285 hp at 4,800 rpm; max torque (SAE): 330 lb ft, 45.5 kg m at 5,000 rpm; max engine rpm: 5,200; specific power: 48.3 hp/l; crankshaft bearings: 5; camshafts: 1, at centre of Vee; carburation: 1 AM (FAL) 4300 1RA4 downdraught 4-barrel carburettor; cooling system capacity: 21.6 imp pt, 26 US pt, 12.3 l.

TRANSMISSION gearbox: Shift-Command automatic (standard); gearbox ratios: I 2.400, II 1.470, III 1, rev 2; selector lever: central; axle ratio: 2.870.

PERFORMANCE max speed: about 111 mph, 178 km/h; power-weight ratio: Matador 4-door Sedan 11.3 lb/hp, 5.1 kg/hp; speed in direct drive at 1,000 rpm: 22.7 mph, 36.5 km/h; fuel consumption: 15 m/imp gal, 12.5 m/US gal, 18.8 l x 100 km.

AMERICAN MOTORS Matador Station Wagon

AMERICAN MOTORS Ambassador SST 4-door Sedan

AMERICAN MOTORS Ambassador Brougham Station Wagon

ELECTRICAL EQUIPMENT battery: 60 Ah.

DIMENSIONS AND WEIGHT front track: 59.72 in, 1,517 mm.

OPTIONAL ACCESSORIES front disc brakes with servo; 4-speed fully synchronized mechanical gearbox (I 2.230, II 1.770, III 1.350, IV 1, rev 2.160) with 3.540 axle ratio only for Matador 2-door Hardtop.

330 hp power team

(optional for all models).

See 135 hp power team, except for:

ENGINE cylinders: 8, Vee-slanted at 90°; bore and stroke: 4.16 x 3.68 in, 105.6 x 93.4 mm; engine capacity: 401 cu in, 6,571 cu cm; compression ratio: 9.5; max power (SAE): 330 hp at 5,000 rpm; max torque (SAE): 430 lb ft, 59.3 kg m at 3,400 rpm; max engine rpm: 5,300; specific power: 50.2 hp/l; crankshaft bearings: 5; camshafts: 1, at centre of Vee; carburation: 1 AM (FAL) 4300 1TM4 downdraught 4-barrel carburettor; cooling system capacity: 21.6 imp pt, 26 US pt, 12.3 l.

TRANSMISSION gearbox: Shift-Command automatic (standard); gearbox ratios: I 2.400, II 1.470, III 1, rev 2; selector lever: central; axle ratio: 2.870.

PERFORMANCE max speed: about 116 mph, 186 km/h; power-weight ratio: Matador 4-door Sedan 9.8 lb/hp, 4.4 kg/hp; speed in direct drive at 1,000 rpm: 22.7 mph, 36.5 km/h; fuel consumption: 14.3 m/imp gal, 11.9 m/US gal, 19.7 l x 100 km.

ELECTRICAL EQUIPMENT battery: 60 Ah.

DIMENSIONS AND WEIGHT front track: 59.72 in, 1,517 mm.

OPTIONAL ACCESSORIES front disc brakes with servo; 4-speed fully synchronized mechanical gearbox (I 2.230, II 1.770, III 1.350, IV 1, rev 2.160) with 3.540 axle ratio only for Matador 2-door Hardtop.

Ambassador DPL - Ambassador SST - Ambassador Brougham Series

PRICES IN USA:

Ambassador DPL	4-door Sedan	$ 3,616
Ambassador SST	2-door Hardtop	$ 3,870
Ambassador SST	4-door Sedan	$ 3,852
Ambassador SST	Station Wagon	$ 4,430
Ambassador Brougham	2-door Hardtop	$ 3,999
Ambassador Brougham	4-door Sedan	$ 3,983
Ambassador Brougham	Station Wagon	$ 4,430

For V8 engines add $ 101.

150 hp power team

(standard for Ambassador DPL; not available for other Series).

ENGINE front, 4 stroke; cylinders: 6, in line; bore and stroke: 3.75 x 3.90 in, 95.2 x 99 mm; engine capacity: 258 cu in, 4,229 cu cm; compression ratio: 8; max power (SAE): 150 hp at 3,800 rpm; max torque (SAE): 240 lb ft, 33.1 kg m at 1,800 rpm; max engine rpm: 4,300; specific power: 35.5 hp/l; cylinder block: cast iron; cylinder head: cast iron; crankshaft bearings: 7; valves: 2 per cylinder, overhead, in line, push-rods and rockers, hydraulic tappets; camshafts: 1, side; lubrication: gear pump, full flow filter; lubricating system capacity: 8.3 imp pt, 9.9 US pt, 4.7 l; carburation: 1 Carter YF 6038 downdraught single barrel carburettor; fuel feed: mechanical pump; cooling system: water; cooling system capacity: 17.4 imp pt, 20.9 US pt, 9.9 l.

TRANSMISSION driving wheels: rear; gearbox: Shift-Command automatic, hydraulic torque convertor and planetary gears with 3 ratios + reverse, max ratio of convertor at stall 2, possible manual selection; gearbox ratios: I 2.390, II 1.450, III 1, rev 2.090; selector lever: steering column; final drive: hypoid bevel; axle ratio: 3.150; width of rims: 5.5''; tyres: E78 x 14.

PERFORMANCE max speed: about 97 mph, 156 km/h; power-weight ratio: 22.5 lb/hp, 10.2 kg/hp; speed in direct drive at 1,000 rpm: 22.6 mph, 36.4 km/h; fuel consumption: 17.9 m/imp gal, 14.9 m/US gal, 15.8 l x 100 km.

CHASSIS integral; front suspension: independent, wishbones, coil springs, anti-roll bar, telescopic dampers; rear suspension: rigid axle, lower trailing radius arms, upper oblique torque arms, coil springs, telescopic dampers.

STEERING recirculating ball; turns of steering wheel lock to lock: 6.

BRAKES drum, dual circuit; area rubbed by linings: total 267 sq in, 1,722 sq cm.

ELECTRICAL EQUIPMENT voltage: 12 V; battery: 50 Ah; generator type: alternator, 35 A; ignition distributor: Delco-Remy; headlamps: 4.

DIMENSIONS AND WEIGHT wheel base: 122 in, 3,099 mm; front track: 59.94 in, 1,522 mm; rear track: 60 in, 1,524 mm;

AMERICAN MOTORS Matador Station Wagon

AMERICAN MOTORS Ambassador SST 4-door Sedan

AMERICAN MOTORS Ambassador Brougham Station Wagon

overall length: 210.78 in, 5,354 mm; overall width: 77.24 in, 1,962 mm; overall height: 55.54 in, 1,411 mm; ground clearance: 6.29 in, 160 mm; dry weight: 3,384 lb, 1,535 kg; turning circle (between walls): 42.5 ft, 13 m; fuel tank capacity: 23.2 imp gal, 19.5 US gal, 88 l.

BODY saloon/sedan; doors: 4; seats: 6; front seats: bench; details: air-conditioning system.

OPTIONAL ACCESSORIES limited slip final drive; power-assisted steering; servo brake.

210 hp power team

(standard for Ambassador SST and Ambassador Brougham Series; optional for Ambassador DPL).

See 150 hp power team, except for:

ENGINE cylinders: 8, Vee-slanted at 90°; bore and stroke: 3.75 x 3.44 in, 95.2 x 87.3 mm; engine capacity: 304 cu in, 4,982 cu cm; compression ratio: 8.4; max power (SAE): 210 hp at 4,400 rpm; max torque (SAE): 300 lb ft, 41.4 kg m at 2,600 rpm; max engine rpm: 5,000; specific power: 42.1 hp/l; crankshaft bearings: 5; camshafts: 1, at centre of Vee; carburation: 1 AM (FAL) 2100D 1DA2 downdraught twin barrel carburettor; cooling system capacity: 23.2 imp pt, 25.8 US pt, 13.2 l.

TRANSMISSION selector lever: central; axle ratio: 2.870; width of rims: station wagons 6''; tyres: station wagons H78 x 14.

PERFORMANCE max speed: about 104 mph, 167 km/h; power-weight ratio: Ambassador SST 4-door Sedan 17.1 lb/ hp, 7.7 kg/hp — Ambassador Brougham 4-door Sedan 17.2 lb/hp, 7.8 kg/hp; speed in direct drive at 1,000 rpm: 24 mph, 38.6 km/h; fuel consumption: 17 m/imp gal, 14.2 m/US gal, 16.6 l x 100 km.

BRAKES area rubbed by linings: station wagons total 314.2 sq in, 2,026 sq cm.

DIMENSIONS AND WEIGHT front track: 59.72 in, 1,517 mm; overall length: station wagons 209.73 in, 5,327 mm; overall height: 2-door hardtops 54.86 in, 1,393 mm — station wagons 56.70 in, 1,440 mm; ground clearance: station wagons 7 in, 178 mm; dry weight: Ambassador SST 2-door Hardtop 3,630 lb, 1,646 kg — Ambassador SST 4-door Sedan 3,589 lb, 1,627 kg — Ambassador SST Station Wagon 3,869 lb, 1,754 kg — Ambassador Brougham 2-door Hardtop 3,649 lb, 1,655 kg — Ambassador Brougham 4-door Sedan 3,610 lb, 1,637 kg — Ambassador Brougham Station Wagon 3,916 lb, 1,776 kg; fuel tank capacity: station wagons 20.3 imp gal, 17 US gal, 77 l.

OPTIONAL ACCESSORIES front disc brakes with servo.

245 hp power team

(optional for all Series).

See 150 hp power team, except for:

ENGINE cylinders: 8, Vee-slanted at 90°; bore and stroke: 4.08 x 3.44 in, 103.6 x 87.3 mm; engine capacity: 360 cu in, 5,900 cu cm; compression ratio: 8.5; max power (SAE): 245 hp at 4,400 rpm; max torque (SAE): 365 lb ft, 50.4 kg m at 2,600 rpm; max engine rpm: 5,000; specific power: 41.5 hp/l; crankshaft bearings: 5; camshafts: 1, at centre of Vee; carburation: 1 AM (FAL) 2100D 1RA2 downdraught twin barrel carburettor; cooling system capacity: 21.6 imp pt, 26 US pt, 12.3 l.

TRANSMISSION gearbox ratios: I 2.400, II 1.470, III 1, rev 2; selector lever: central; axle ratio: 2.870; width of rims: station wagon 6''; tyres: F78 x 14 — station wagons H78 x 14.

PERFORMANCE max speed: about 107 mph, 172 km/h; power-weight ratio: Ambassador SST 4-door Sedan 14.6 lb/hp, 6.6 kg/hp — Ambassador Brougham 4-door Sedan 14.7 lb/hp, 6.7 kg/hp; speed in direct drive at 1,000 rpm: 24.1 mph, 38.8 km/h; fuel consumption: 17 m/imp gal, 14.2 m/US gal, 16.6 l x 100 km.

BRAKES area rubbed by linings: station wagons total 314.2 sq in, 2,026 sq cm.

ELECTRICAL EQUIPMENT battery: 60 Ah.

DIMENSIONS AND WEIGHT (see 210 hp power team).

OPTIONAL ACCESSORIES front disc brakes with servo.

285 hp power team

(optional for all Series).

See 150 hp power team, except for:

ENGINE cylinders: 8, Vee-slanted at 90°; bore and stroke: 4.08 x 3.44 in, 103.6 x 87.3 mm; engine capacity: 360 cu in, 5,900 cu cm; compression ratio: 8.5; max power (SAE): 285 hp at 4,800 rpm; max torque (SAE): 330 lb ft, 45.5 kg m at 5,000 rpm; max engine rpm: 5,200; specific power: 48.3 hp/l; crankshaft bearings: 5; camshafts: 1, at centre of Vee; carburation: 1 AM (FAL) 4300 1RA4 downdraught 4-barrel

285 HP POWER TEAM

carburettor; cooling system capacity: 21.6 imp gal, 26 US pt, 12.3 l.

TRANSMISSION gearbox ratios: I 2.400, II 1.470, III 1, rev 2; selector lever: central; axle ratio: 2.870; width of rims: station wagon 6''; tyres: F78 x 14 — station wagons H78 x 14.

PERFORMANCE max speed: about 112 mph, 180 km/h; power-weight ratio: Ambassador SST 4-door Sedan 12.6 lb/hp, 5.7 kg/hp — Ambassador Brougham 4-door Sedan 12.7 lb/hp, 5.8 kg/hp; speed in direct drive at 1,000 rpm: 24.1 mph, 38.8 km/h; fuel consumption: 14.9 m/imp gal, 12.4 m/US gal, 19 l x 100 km.

BRAKES area rubbed by linings: station wagons total 314.2 sq in, 2,026 sq cm.

ELECTRICAL EQUIPMENT battery: 60 Ah.

DIMENSIONS AND WEIGHT (see 210 hp power team).

OPTIONAL ACCESSORIES front disc brakes with servo.

330 hp power team

(optional for Ambassador SST and Ambassador Brougham Series; not available for Ambassador DPL).

See 150 hp power team, except for:

ENGINE cylinders: 8, Vee-slanted at 90°; bore and stroke: 4.16 x 3.68 in, 105.6 x 93.4 mm; engine capacity: 401 cu in, 6,571 cu cm; compression ratio: 9.5; max power (SAE): 330 hp at 5,000 rpm; max torque (SAE): 430 lb ft, 59.3 kg m at 3,400 rpm; max engine rpm: 5,300; specific power: 50.2 hp/l; crankshaft bearings: 5; camshafts: 1, at centre of Vee; carburation: 1 AM (FAL) 4300 1TA4 downdraught 4-barrel carburettor; cooling system capacity: 21.6 imp pt, 26 US pt, 12.3 l.

TRANSMISSION gearbox ratios: I 2.400, II 1.470, III 1, rev 2; selector lever: central; axle ratio: 2.870; width of rims: station wagon 6''; tyres: F78 x 14 — station wagons H78 x 14.

PERFORMANCE max speed: about 115 mph, 185 km/h; power-weight ratio: Ambassador SST 4-door Sedan and Ambassador Brougham 4-door Sedan 10.9 lb/hp, 4.9 kg/hp; speed in direct drive at 1,000 rpm: 24.1 mph, 38.8 km/h; fuel consumption: 14.3 m/imp gal, 11.9 m/US gal, 19.8 l x 100 km.

BRAKES area rubbed by linings: station wagons total 314.2 sq in, 2,026 sq cm.

ELECTRICAL EQUIPMENT battery: 60 Ah.

DIMENSIONS AND WEIGHT (see 210 hp power team).

OPTIONAL ACCESSORIES front disc brakes with servo.

AVANTI   USA

Avanti II

PRICE IN USA:

Avanti II	Coupé	$ 7,645

270 hp power team

(standard).

ENGINE front, 4 stroke; cylinders: 8, Vee-slanted at 90°; bore and stroke: 4 x 3.48 in, 101.6 x 88.4 mm; engine capacity: 350 cu in, 5,736 cu cm; compression ratio: 8.7; max power (SAE): 270 hp at 4,800 rpm; max torque (SAE): 380 lb ft, 52.4 kg m at 3,200 rpm; max engine rpm: 5,600; specific power: 47.1 hp/l; cylinder block: cast iron; cylinder head: cast iron; crankshaft bearings: 5; valves: 2 per cylinder, overhead, in line, push-rods and rockers, hydraulic tappets; camshafts: 1, at centre of Vee; lubrication: gear pump, full flow filter; lubricating system capacity: 8.3 imp pt, 10 US pt, 4.7 l; carburation: 1 Rochester downdraught 4-barrel carburettor; fuel feed: mechanical pump; cooling system: water; cooling system capacity: 28.3 imp pt, 34 US pt, 16.1 l.

TRANSMISSION driving wheels: rear; clutch: single dry plate; gearbox: mechanical; gears: 4 + reverse; synchromesh gears: I, II, III, IV; gearbox ratios: I 2.430, II 1.760, III 1.470, IV 1, rev 2.350; gear lever: central; final drive: hypoid bevel; axle ratio: 3.310; width of rims: 5''; tyres: F78 x 15.

PERFORMANCE max speeds: 52 mph, 83 km/h in 1st gear; 70 mph, 112 km/h in 2nd gear; 90 mph, 145 km/h in 3rd

AVANTI Avanti II Coupé

BUICK Skylark Custom 2-door Hardtop Coupé

BUICK G.S. 2-door Hardtop Coupé

gear; 130 mph, 209 km/h in 4th gear; power-weight ratio: 11.5 lb/hp, 5.2 kg/hp; carrying capacity: 772 lb, 350 kg; acceleration: standing ¼ mile 15.5 sec, 0-50 mph (0-80 km/h) 5.9 sec; speed in direct drive at 1,000 rpm: 22.3 mph, 35.9 km/h; fuel consumption: 16.8 m/imp gal, 14 m/US gal, 16.8 l x 100 km.

CHASSIS box-type ladder frame, X cross members; front suspension: independent, wishbones, coil springs, anti-roll bar, telescopic dampers; rear suspension: rigid axle, semi-elliptic leafsprings, upper torque arms, anti-roll bar, telescopic dampers.

STEERING recirculating ball; turns of steering wheel lock to lock: 3.50.

BRAKES front disc, internal radial fins, rear drum, servo.

ELECTRICAL EQUIPMENT voltage: 12 V; battery: 61 Ah; generator type: alternator; ignition distributor: Delco-Remy; headlamps: 2, halogen.

DIMENSIONS AND WEIGHT wheel base: 109 in, 2,768 mm; front track: 57.37 in, 1,457 mm; rear track: 56.56 in, 1,437 mm; overall length: 192.44 in, 4,888 mm; overall width: 70.40 in, 1,788 mm; overall height: 54 in, 1,371 mm; ground clearance: 7.50 in, 190 mm; dry weight: 3,100 lb, 1,406 kg; distribution of weight: 59% front axle, 41% rear axle; turning circle (between walls): 37.5 ft, 11.4 m; fuel tank capacity: 17.6 imp gal, 21 US gal, 80 l.

BODY coupé in plastic material; doors: 2; seats: 4; front seats: separate.

OPTIONAL ACCESSORIES 6'' or 6.5'' wide rims; 205 x 15 tyres; Borg-Warner automatic gearbox (I 2.400, II 1.470, III 1, rev 2), max ratio of convertor at stall 2.2, possible manual selection, central selector lever; limited slip final drive; power-assisted steering; electrically-controlled windows; electrically-heated rear window; air-conditioning system.

BUICK   USA

Skylark - Skylark Custom - G.S. Series

PRICES IN USA:

Skylark	2-door Coupé	$ 2,846
Skylark	2-door Hardtop Coupé	$ 2,917
Skylark	4-door Sedan	$ 2,896
Skylark Custom	2-door Hardtop Coupé	$ 3,316
Skylark Custom	4-door Hardtop Sedan	$ 3,396
Skylark Custom	2-door Convertible	$ 3,437
Skylark Custom	4-door Sedan	$ 3,287
G. S.	2-door Hardtop Coupé	$ 3,284
G. S.	2-door Convertible	$ 3,475

For V8 engines add $ 121.

145 hp power team

(standard for Skylark Series; not available for other Series).

ENGINE front, 4 stroke; cylinders: 6, in line; bore and stroke: 3.87 x 3.53 in, 98.3 x 89.6 mm; engine capacity: 250 cu in, 4,097 cu cm; compression ratio: 8.5; max power (SAE): 145 hp at 4,000 rpm; max torque (SAE): 235 lb ft, 32.4 kg m at 2,400 rpm; max engine rpm: 4,400; specific power: 35.4 hp/l; cylinder block: cast iron; cylinder head: cast iron; crankshaft bearings: 7; valves: 2 per cylinder, overhead, in line, push-rods and rockers, hydraulic tappets; camshafts: 1, side; lubrication: gear pump, full flow filter; lubricating system capacity: 8.3 imp pt, 9.9 US pt, 4.7 l; carburation: 1 Rochester 1 MV downdraught single barrel carburettor; fuel feed: mechanical pump; cooling system: water; cooling system capacity: 27.3 imp pt, 32.8 US pt, 15.5 l.

TRANSMISSION driving wheels: rear; clutch: single dry plate; gearbox: mechanical; gears: 3 + reverse; synchromesh gears: I, II, III; gearbox ratios: I 2.850, II 1.680, III 1, rev 2.950; gear lever: steering column; final drive: hypoid bevel; axle ratio: 3.080; width of rims: 6''; tyres: F78 x 14.

PERFORMANCE max speed: about 95 mph, 153 km/h; power-weight ratio: Skylark 4-door Sedan 23.1 lb/hp, 10.5 kg/hp; speed in direct drive at 1,000 rpm: 22.5 mph, 36.2 km/h; fuel consumption: 20.2 m/imp gal, 16.8 m/US gal, 14 l x 100 km.

CHASSIS perimeter box-type; front suspension: independent, wishbones, lower trailing radius arms, coil springs, anti-roll bar, telescopic dampers; rear suspension: rigid axle, lower trailing radius arms, upper oblique torque arms, coil springs, telescopic dampers.

STEERING recirculating ball; turns of steering wheel lock to lock: 6.64.

BRAKES drum, dual circuit; area rubbed by linings: total 268.6 sq in, 1,732 sq cm.

AVANTI Avanti II Coupé

BUICK Skylark Custom 2-door Hardtop Coupé

BUICK G.S. 2-door Hardtop Coupé

ELECTRICAL EQUIPMENT voltage: 12 V; battery: 45 Ah; generator type: alternator, 37 A; ignition distributor: Delco-Remy; headlamps: 4.

DIMENSIONS AND WEIGHT wheel base: 112 in, 2,845 mm — 4-door sedan 116 in, 2,946 mm; front track: 59 in, 1,498 mm; rear track: 59 in, 1,498 mm; overall length: 203.22 in, 5,162 mm — 4-door sedan 207.22 in, 5,263 mm; overall width: 77.34 in, 1,964 mm; overall height: 53.33 in, 1,354 mm — 4-door sedan 54.05 in, 1,373 mm; ground clearance: 5.63 in, 143 mm — 4-door sedan 5.25 in, 133 mm; dry weight: Skylark 2-door Coupé 3,290 lb, 1,492 kg — Skylark 2-door Hardtop Coupé 3,321 lb, 1,506 kg — Skylark 4-door Sedan 3,349 lb, 1,519 kg; turning circle (between walls): 45.5 ft, 13.9 m — 4-door sedan 45.3 ft, 13.8 m; fuel tank capacity: 16.7 imp gal, 20 US gal, 76 l.

OPTIONAL ACCESSORIES Turbo Hydramatic automatic gearbox with 3 ratios (I 2.520, II 1.520, III 1, rev 1.930), max ratio of convertor at stall 2.05; limited slip final drive; power-assisted steering; servo brake; front disc brakes with servo; air-conditioning system.

230 hp power team

(standard for Skylark and Skylark Custom Series; not available for G.S. Series).

See 145 hp power team, except for:

ENGINE cylinders: 8, Vee-slanted at 90°; bore and stroke: 3.80 x 3.85 in, 96.5 x 97.8 mm; engine capacity: 350 cu in, 5,736 cu cm; max power (SAE): 230 hp at 4,400 rpm; max torque (SAE): 350 lb ft, 48.3 kg m at 2,400 rpm; max engine rpm: 4,600; specific power: 40.1 hp/l; crankshaft bearings: 5; camshafts: 1, at centre of Vee; carburation: 1 Rochester 2GV downdraught twin barrel carburettor.

TRANSMISSION gearbox ratios: I 2.540, II 1.500, III 1, rev 2.630; tyres: G78 x 14.

PERFORMANCE max speed: about 106 mph, 170 km/h; power-weight ratio: Skylark 4-door Sedan 15.4 lb/hp, 7 kg/hp — Skylark Custom 4-door Sedan 15.8 lb/hp, 7.2 kg/hp; speed in direct drive at 1,000 rpm: 23.3 mph, 37.5 km/h; fuel consumption: 15.7 m/imp gal, 13.1 m/US gal, 18 l x 100 km.

ELECTRICAL EQUIPMENT battery: 61 Ah.

DIMENSIONS AND WEIGHT overall height: Skylark Custom 2-door Hardtop Coupé 53.53 in, 1,360 mm — Skylark Custom 2-door Convertible 53.85 in, 1,368 mm — Skylark Custom 2-door Hardtop Coupé and 4-door Sedan 54.25 in, 1,378 mm; ground clearance: Skylark Custom 2-door Hardtop Coupé and 2-door Convertible 5.83 in, 148 mm — Skylark Custom 4-door Hardtop Sedan and 4-door Sedan 5.45 in, 138 mm; dry weight: plus 203 lb, 92 kg — Skylark Custom 2-door Hardtop Coupé 3,556 lb, 1,613 kg — Skylark Custom 4-door Hardtop Sedan 3,686 lb, 1,763 kg — Skylark Custom 2-door Convertible 3,633 lb, 1,647 kg — Skylark Custom 4-door box with 2.560 axle ratio.

OPTIONAL ACCESSORIES Turbo Hydramatic automatic gearbox with 2.560 axle ratio.

260 hp power team

(standard for G.S. Series; optional for Skylark and Skylark Custom Series).

See 145 hp power team, except for:

ENGINE cylinders: 8, Vee-slanted at 90°; bore and stroke: 3.80 x 3.85 in, 96.5 x 97.8 mm; engine capacity: 350 cu in, 5,736 cu cm; max power (SAE): 260 hp at 4,600 rpm; max torque (SAE): 360 lb ft, 49.7 kg m at 3,000 rpm; max engine rpm: 5,000; specific power: 45.3 hp/l; crankshaft bearings: 5; camshafts: 1, at centre of Vee; carburation: 1 Rochester 4MV downdraught 4-barrel carburettor.

TRANSMISSION gearbox ratios: I 2.540, II 1.500, III 1, rev 2.630; tyres: G78 x 14.

PERFORMANCE max speed: about 110 mph, 177 km/h; power-weight ratio: G.S. 2-door Hardtop Coupé 13.7 lb/hp, 6.2 kg/hp — G.S. 2-door Convertible 13.9 lb/hp, 6.3 kg/hp; speed in direct drive at 1,000 rpm: 22 mph, 35.4 km/h; fuel consumption: 15.5 m/imp gal, 12.9 m/US gal, 18.2 l x 100 km.

ELECTRICAL EQUIPMENT battery: 61 Ah.

DIMENSIONS AND WEIGHT front track: 59.36 in, 1,508 mm; overall height: 2-door hardtop coupé 53.53 in, 1,360 mm — 2-door convertible 53.85 in, 1,368 mm; ground clearance: 5.83 in, 148 mm; dry weight: Skylark plus 235 lb, 106 kg — Skylark Custom plus 32 lb, 14 kg — G.S. 2-door Hardtop Coupé 3,570 lb, 1,619 kg — G.S. 2-door Convertible 3,626 lb, 1,644 kg.

OPTIONAL ACCESSORIES Turbo Hydramatic automatic gearbox with 2.730 axle ratio only for Skylark and Skylark Custom (with 3.080 axle ratio only for G.S.).

315 hp power team

(optional for G.S. Series; not available for other Series).

See 145 hp power team, except for:

ENGINE cylinders: 8, Vee-slanted at 90°; bore and stroke: 4.31 x 3.90 in, 109.4 x 99 mm; engine capacity: 455 cu in, 7,456 cu cm; max power (SAE): 315 hp at 4,400 rpm; max torque (SAE): 450 lb ft, 62.1 kg m at 2,800 rpm; max engine rpm: 5,250; specific power: 42.2 hp/l; crankshaft bearings: 5; camshafts: 1 centre of Vee; carburation: 1 Rochester 4MV downdraught 4-barrel carburettor.

TRANSMISSION gears: 4 + reverse; synchromesh gears: I, II, III, IV; gearbox ratios: I 2.200, II 1.640, III 1.280, IV 1, rev 2.270; axle ratio: 3.420; tyres: G78 x 14.

PERFORMANCE max speed: about 115 mph, 185 km/h; power-weight ratio: G.S. 2-door Hardtop Coupé 11.3 lb/hp, 5.1 kg/hp — G.S. 2-door Convertible 11.5 lb/hp, 5.2 kg/hp; speed in direct drive at 1,000 rpm: 22 mph, 35.4 km/h; fuel consumption: 14.6 m/imp gal, 12.2 m/US gal, 19.3 l x 100 km.

ELECTRICAL EQUIPMENT battery: 61 Ah.

DIMENSIONS AND WEIGHT (see 260 hp power team).

345 hp power team

(optional for G.S. Series; not available for other Series).

See 145 hp power team, except for:

ENGINE cylinders: 8, Vee-slanted at 90°; bore and stroke: 4.31 x 3.90 in, 109.4 x 99 mm; engine capacity: 455 cu in, 7,456 cu cm; max power (SAE): 345 hp at 5,000 rpm; max torque (SAE): 460 lb ft, 63.5 kg m at 3,000 rpm; max engine rpm: 5,400; specific power: 46.3 hp/l; crankshaft bearings: 5; camshafts: 1, at centre of Vee; carburation: 1 Rochester 4MV downdraught 4-barrel carburettor.

TRANSMISSION gears: 4 + reverse; synchromesh gears: I, II, III, IV; gearbox ratios: I 2.200, II 1.640, III 1.280, IV 1, rev 2.270; axle ratio: 3.420; tyres: G78 x 14.

PERFORMANCE max speed: about 118 mph, 190 km/h; power-weight ratio: G.S. 2-door Hardtop Coupé 10.3 lb/hp, 4.7 kg/hp — G.S. 2-door Convertible 10.5 lb/hp, 4.8 kg/hp; speed in direct drive at 1,000 rpm: 22 mph, 35.4 km/h; fuel consumption: 14.2 m/imp gal, 11.8 m/US gal, 19.9 l x 100 km.

ELECTRICAL EQUIPMENT battery: 61 Ah.

DIMENSIONS AND WEIGHT (see 260 hp power team).

OPTIONAL ACCESSORIES Turbo Hydramatic automatic gearbox with 3.420 axle ratio.

Sportwagon - Estate Wagon Series

PRICES IN USA:

Sportwagon	6-passenger	$ 3,514
Estate Wagon	6-passenger	$ 4,403
Estate Wagon	9-passenger	$ 4,549

230 hp power team

(standard for Sportwagon; not available for Estate Wagon Series).

ENGINE front, 4 stroke; cylinders: 8, Vee-slanted at 90°; bore and stroke: 3.80 x 3.85 in, 96.5 x 97.8 mm; engine capacity: 350 cu in, 5,736 cu cm; compression ratio: 8.5; max power (SAE): 230 hp at 4,400 rpm: max torque (SAE): 350 lb ft, 48.3 kg m at 2,400 rpm; max engine rpm: 4,600; specific power: 40.1 hp/l; cylinder block: cast iron; cylinder head: cast iron; crankshaft bearings: 5; valves: 2 per cylinder, overhead, in line, push-rods and rockers, hydraulic tappets; camshafts: 1, at centre of Vee; lubrication: gear pump, full flow filter; lubricating system capacity: 8.3 imp pt, 9.9 US pt, 4.7 l; carburation: 1 Rochester 2GV downdraught twin barrel carburettor; fuel feed: mechanical pump; cooling system: water; cooling system capacity: 27.3 imp pt, 32.8 US pt, 15.5 l.

TRANSMISSION driving wheels: rear; clutch: single dry plate; gearbox: mechanical; gears: 3 + reverse; synchromesh gears: I, II, III; gearbox ratios: I 2.540, II 1.500, III 1, rev 2.630; gear lever: steering column; final drive: hypoid bevel; axle ratio: 3.080; width of rims: 6''; tyres: H78 x 14.

PERFORMANCE max speed: about 106 mph, 170 km/h;

BUICK Estate Wagon 9-passenger

BUICK Le Sabre Custom 4-door Hardtop Sedan

BUICK Centurion 2-door Hardtop Coupé

power-weight ratio: 17.7 lb/hp, 8 kg/hp; speed in direct drive at 1,000 rpm: 23.5 mph, 37.8 km/h; fuel consumption: 15.6 m/imp gal, 13 m/US gal, 18.1 l x 100 km.

CHASSIS perimeter box-type; front suspension: independent, wishbones, lower trailing links, coil springs, anti-roll bar, telescopic dampers; rear suspension: rigid axle, lower trailing radius arms, upper oblique torque arms, coil springs, telescopic dampers.

STEERING recirculating ball; turns of steering wheel lock to lock: 6.64.

BRAKES front disc, rear drum, dual circuit, servo; area rubbed by linings: total 332.4 sq in, 2,144 sq cm.

ELECTRICAL EQUIPMENT voltage: 12 V; battery: 61 Ah; generator type: alternator, 37 A; ignition distributor: Delco-Remy; headlamps: 4.

DIMENSIONS AND WEIGHT wheel base: 116 in, 2,946 mm; front track: 59 in, 1,498 mm; rear track: 59 in, 1,498 mm; overall length: 212.73 in, 5,403 mm; overall width: 77.34 in, 1,964 mm; overall height: 54.78 in, 1,391 mm; ground clearance: 5.90 in, 150 mm; dry weight: 4,063 lb, 1,842 kg; turning circle (between walls): 45.3 ft, 13.8 m; fuel tank capacity: 19.1 imp gal, 23 US gal, 87 l.

BODY estate car/station wagon; doors: 4 + 1; seats: 6.

OPTIONAL ACCESSORIES Turbo Hydramatic automatic gearbox with 3 ratios (I 2.520, II 1.520, III 1, rev 1.930), max ratio of convertor at stall 2.5; limited slip final drive; power-assisted steering; air-conditioning system.

260 hp power team

(optional for Sportwagon; not available for Estate Wagon Series).

See 230 hp power team, except for:

ENGINE max power (SAE): 260 hp at 4,600 rpm; max torque (SAE): 360 lb ft, 49.7 kg m at 3,000 rpm; max engine rpm: 5,000; specific power: 45.3 hp/l; carburation: 1 Rochester 4MV downdraught 4-barrel carburettor.

PERFORMANCE max speed: about 110 mph, 177 km/h; power-weight ratio: 15.5 lb/hp, 7 kg/hp; fuel consumption: 15.4 m/imp gal, 12.8 m/US gal, 18.4 l x 100 km.

315 hp power team

(standard for Estate Wagon Series; not available for Sportwagon).

See 230 hp power team, except for:

ENGINE bore and stroke: 4.31 x 3.90 in, 109.4 x 99 mm; engine capacity: 455 cu in, 7,456 cu cm; max power (SAE): 315 hp at 4,400 rpm; max torque (SAE): 450 lb ft, 62.1 kg m at 2,800 rpm; max engine rpm: 4,900; specific power: 42.2 hp/l; carburation: 1 Rochester 4MV downdraught 4-barrel carburettor; cooling system capacity: 31.2 imp pt, 37.4 US pt, 17.7 l.

TRANSMISSION gearbox ratios: I 2.420, II 1.610, III 1, rev 2.330; axle ratio: 3.420; tyres: L78 x 15.

PERFORMANCE max speed: about 115 mph, 185 km/h; power-weight ratio: Estate Wagon 6-passenger 15.8 lb/hp, 7.2 kg/hp — Estate Wagon 9-passenger 16 lb/hp, 7.3 kg/hp; speed in direct drive at 1,000 rpm: 23.6 mph, 38 km/h; fuel consumption: 14.5 m/imp gal, 12.1 m/US gal, 19.5 l x 100 km.

CHASSIS rear suspension: rigid axle, semi-elliptic leaf-springs, telescopic dampers.

STEERING recirculating ball, servo; turns of steering wheel lock to lock: 3.

BRAKES area rubbed by linings: total 385.6 sq in, 2,487 sq cm.

ELECTRICAL EQUIPMENT battery: 70 Ah; generator type: alternator, 42 A.

DIMENSIONS AND WEIGHT wheel base: 127 in, 3,226 mm; front track: 64.10 in, 1,628 mm; rear track: 64 in, 1,625 mm; overall length: 226.82 in, 5,761 mm; overall width: 79.72 in, 2,025 mm; overall height: 57.32 in, 1,456 mm; ground clearance: 5.48 in, 139 mm; dry weight: Estate Wagon 6-passenger 4,972 lb, 2,255 kg — Estate Wagon 9-passenger 5,020 lb, 2,276 kg; turning circle (between walls): 46.8 ft, 14.3 m.

BODY seats: 6 or 9.

OPTIONAL ACCESSORIES Turbo Hydramatic automatic gearbox with 3 ratios (I 2.480, II 1.480, III 1, rev 2.080).

BUICK Estate Wagon 9-passenger

BUICK Le Sabre Custom 4-door Hardtop Sedan

BUICK Centurion 2-door Hardtop Coupé

Le Sabre - Le Sabre Custom Series

PRICES IN USA:

Le Sabre	4-door Hardtop Sedan	$ 3,904
Le Sabre	2-door Hardtop Coupé	$ 3,846
Le Sabre	4-door Sedan	$ 3,777
Le Sabre Custom	4-door Hardtop Sedan	$ 3,998
Le Sabre Custom	2-door Hardtop Coupé	$ 3,934
Le Sabre Custom	2-door Convertible	$ 4,127
Le Sabre Custom	4-door Sedan	$ 3,870

230 hp power team

(standard for both Series).

ENGINE front, 4 stroke; cylinders: 8, Vee-slanted at 90°; bore and stroke: 3.80 x 3.85 in, 96.5 x 97.8 mm; engine capacity: 350 cu in, 5,736 cu cm; compression ratio: 8.5; max power (SAE): 230 hp at 4,400 rpm; max torque (SAE): 350 lb ft, 48.3 kg m at 2,400 rpm; max engine rpm: 4,600; specific power: 40.1 hp/l; cylinder block: cast iron; cylinder head: cast iron; crankshaft bearings: 5; valves: 2 per cylinder, overhead, in line, push-rods and rockers, hydraulic tappets; camshafts: 1, at centre of Vee; lubrication: gear pump, full flow filter; lubricating system capacity: 8.3 imp pt, 9.9 US pt, 4.7 l; carburation: 1 Rochester 2GV downdraught twin barrel carburettor; fuel feed: mechanical pump; cooling system: water; cooling system capacity: 27.3 imp pt, 32.8 US pt, 15.5 l.

TRANSMISSION driving wheels: rear; clutch: single dry plate; gearbox: mechanical; gears: 3 + reverse; synchromesh gears: I, II, III; gearbox ratios: I 2.420, II 1.610, III 1, rev 2.330; gear lever: steering column; final drive: hypoid bevel; axle ratio: 3.420; width of rims: 6''; tyres: H78 x 15.

PERFORMANCE max speed: about 104 mph, 167 km/h; power-weight ratio: Le Sabre 4-door Sedan and Le Sabre Custom 4-door Sedan 18.3 lb/hp, 8.3 kg/hp; speed in direct drive at 1,000 rpm: 23.7 mph, 38.1 km/h; fuel consumption: 15.2 m/imp gal, 12.6 m/US gal, 18.6 l x 100 km.

CHASSIS perimeter box-type; front suspension: independent, wishbones, lower trailing links, coil springs, anti-roll bar, telescopic dampers; rear suspension: rigid axle, lower trailing radius arms, upper oblique torque arms, coil springs, telescopic dampers.

STEERING recirculating ball, servo; turns of steering wheel lock to lock: 2.99.

BRAKES front disc, rear drum, dual circuit, servo; area rubbed by linings: total 373.1 sq in, 2,406 sq cm.

ELECTRICAL EQUIPMENT voltage: 12 V; battery: 61 Ah; generator type: alternator, 42 A; ignition distributor: Delco-Remy; headlamps: 4.

DIMENSIONS AND WEIGHT wheel base: 124 in, 3,149 mm; front track: 63.64 in, 1,616 mm; rear track: 64 in, 1,625 mm; overall length: 220.74 in, 5,607 mm; overall width: 79.72 in, 2,025 mm; overall height: 2-door hardtop coupés 53.57 in, 1,361 mm — 4-door hardtop sedans 53.77 in, 1,366 mm — 4-door sedans 54.39 in, 1,381 mm — 2-door convertible 53.89 in, 1,369 mm; ground clearance: 5.45 in, 138 mm; dry weight: Le Sabre 4-door Hardtop Sedan 4,234 lb, 1,920 kg — Le Sabre 2-door Hardtop Coupé 4,170 lb, 1,891 kg — Le Sabre 4-door Sedan 4,207 lb, 1,908 kg — Le Sabre Custom 4-door Hardtop Sedan 4,243 lb, 1,924 kg — Le Sabre Custom 2-door Hardtop Coupé 4,186 lb, 1,898 kg — Le Sabre Custom 2-door Convertible 4,227 lb, 1,917 kg — Le Sabre Custom 4-door Sedan 4,219 lb, 1,913 kg; turning circle (between walls): 44.1 ft, 13.4 m; fuel tank capacity: 20.9 imp gal, 25 US gal, 95 l.

OPTIONAL ACCESSORIES Turbo Hydramatic automatic gearbox with 3 ratios (I 2.520, II 1.520, III 1, rev 1.930), max ratio of convertor at stall 2.05, 3.080 axle ratio; limited slip final drive; air-conditioning system.

260 hp power team

(optional for both Series).

See 230 hp power team, except for:

ENGINE max power (SAE): 260 hp at 4,600 rpm; max torque (SAE): 360 lb ft, 49.7 kg m at 3,000 rpm; max engine rpm: 5,000; specific power: 45.3 hp/l; carburation: 1 Rochester 4MV downdraught 4-barrel carburettor.

TRANSMISSION gearbox: Turbo Hydramatic automatic (standard); axle ratio: 3.080.

PERFORMANCE max speed: about 107 mph, 172 km/h; power-weight ratio: Le Sabre 4-door Sedan 16.3 lb/hp, 7.4 kg/hp — Le Sabre Custom 4-door Sedan 16.4 lb/hp, 7.5 kg/hp; speed in direct drive at 1,000 rpm: 22.9 mph, 36.8 km/h; fuel consumption: 14.9 m/imp gal, 12.4 m/US gal, 18.9 l x 100 km.

DIMENSIONS AND WEIGHT dry weight: plus 45 lb, 20 kg.

315 hp power team

(optional for both Series).

See 230 hp power team, except for:

ENGINE bore and stroke: 4.31 x 3.90 in, 109.4 x 99 mm; engine capacity: 455 cu in, 7,456 cu cm; max power (SAE): 315 hp at 4,400 rpm; max torque (SAE): 450 lb ft, 62.1 kg m at 2,800 rpm; max engine rpm: 4,600; specific power: 42.2 hp/l; carburation: 1 Rochester 4MV downdraught 4-barrel carburettor.

TRANSMISSION gearbox: Turbo Hydramatic automatic (standard); axle ratio: 2.930.

PERFORMANCE max speed: about 112 mph, 180 km/h; power-weight ratio: Le Sabre 4-door Sedan and Le Sabre Custom 4-door Sedan 13.8 lb/hp, 6.3 kg/hp; speed in direct drive at 1,000 rpm: 24.4 mph, 39.2 km/h; fuel consumption: 14.1 m/imp gal, 11.7 m/US gal, 20.1 l x 100 km.

STEERING turns of steering wheel lock to lock: 2.94.

DIMENSIONS AND WEIGHT dry weight: plus 134 lb, 61 kg.

Centurion - Electra 225 - Electra 225 Custom - Riviera Series

PRICES IN USA:

Centurion	4-door Hardtop Sedan	$ 4,332
Centurion	2-door Hardtop Coupé	$ 4,407
Centurion	2-door Convertible	$ 4,416
Electra 225	2-door Hardtop Coupé	$ 4,839
Electra 225	4-door Hardtop Sedan	$ 4,953
Electra 225 Custom	2-door Hardtop Coupé	$ 5,018
Electra 225 Custom	4-door Hardtop Sedan	$ 5,131
Riviera	2-door Hardtop Coupé	$ 5,290

315 hp power team

(standard for all Series).

ENGINE front, 4 stroke; cylinders: 8, Vee-slanted at 90°; city: 455 cu in, 7,456 cu cm; compression ratio: 8.5; max power (SAE): 315 hp at 4,400 rpm; max torque (SAE): 450 lb ft, 62.1 kg m at 2,800 rpm; max engine rpm: 4,850; specific power: 42.2 hp/l; cylinder block: cast iron; cylinder head: cast iron; crankshaft bearings: 5; valves: 2 per cylinder, overhead, in line, push-rods and rockers, hydraulic tappets; camshafts: 1, at centre of Vee; lubrication: gear pump, full flow filter; lubricating system capacity: 6.7 imp pt, 8 US pt, 3.8 l; carburation: 1 Rochester 4MV downdraught 4-barrel carburettor; fuel feed: mechanical pump; cooling system: water; cooling system capacity: 31.2 imp pt, 37.4 US pt, 17.7 l.

TRANSMISSION driving wheels: rear; clutch: single dry plate; gearbox: mechanical (Electra 225, Electra 225 Custom and Riviera only automatic standard); gears: 3 + reverse; synchromesh gears: I, II, III; gearbox ratios: I 2.420, II 1.610, III 1, rev 2.330; gear lever: steering column; final drive: hypoid bevel; axle ratio: Centurion 3.420 — Electra 225 and Electra 225 Custom 2.730 — Riviera 2.930; width of rims: 6''; tyres: H78 x 15 — Electra 225 and Electra 225 Custom J78 x 15.

PERFORMANCE max speed: about 111 mph, 178 km/h; power-weight ratio: Centurion 4-door Hardtop Sedan 14.1 lb/hp, 6.4 kg/hp — Electra 225 4-door Hardtop Sedan 14.5 lb/hp, 6.5 kg/hp — Electra 225 Custom 4-door Hardtop Sedan 14.6 lb/hp, 6.6 kg/hp — Riviera 2-door Hardtop Coupé 14 lb/hp, 6.3 kg/hp; speed in direct drive at 1,000 rpm: 23 mph, 37 km/h; fuel consumption: 14.1 m/imp gal, 11.7 m/US gal, 20.1 l x 100 km.

CHASSIS perimeter box-type; front suspension: independent, wishbones, lower trailing links, coil springs, anti-roll bar, telescopic dampers; rear suspension: rigid axle, lower trailing radius arms, upper oblique torque arms, coil springs, telescopic dampers.

STEERING recirculating ball, servo; turns of steering wheel lock to lock: 2.94.

BRAKES front disc, rear drum, dual circuit, servo; area rubbed by linings: total 373.1 sq in, 2,406 sq cm.

ELECTRICAL EQUIPMENT voltage: 12 V; battery: 70 Ah; generator type: alternator, 42 A; ignition distributor: Delco-Remy; headlamps: 2.

DIMENSIONS AND WEIGHT wheel base: Centurion 124 in, 3,149 mm — Electra 225 and Electra 225 Custom 127 in, 3,226 mm — Riviera 122 in, 3,099 mm; front track: 63.64 in, 1,616 mm; rear track: 64 in, 1,625 mm; overall length: Centurion 220.74 in, 5,607 mm — Electra 225 and Electra 225 Custom 226.18 in, 5,745 mm — Riviera 217.41 in, 5,522 mm;

BUICK Electra 225 Custom 2-door Hardtop Coupé

BUICK Riviera 2-door Hardtop Coupé

CADILLAC De Ville Coupé

overall width: 79.72 in, 2,025 mm — Riviera 79.90 in, 2,029 mm; overall height: Centurion 4-door Hardtop Sedan 53.57 in, 1,361 mm — Centurion 2-door Hardtop Coupé 53.77 in, 1,366 mm — Centurion 2-door Convertible 53.89 in, 1,369 mm — Electra 225 2-door Hardtop Coupé and Electra 225 Custom 2-door Hardtop Coupé 54.44 in, 1,383 mm — Electra 225 4-door Hardtop Sedan and Electra 225 Custom 4-door Hardtop Sedan 54.94 in, 1,395 mm — Riviera 53.97 in, 1,371 mm; ground clearance: 5.45 in, 138 mm — Electra 225 and Electra 225 Custom 5.60 in, 142 mm; dry weight: Centurion 4-door Hardtop Sedan 4,453 lb, 2,020 kg — Centurion 2-door Hardtop Coupé 4,363 lb, 1,979 kg — Centurion 2-door Convertible 4,397 lb, 1,994 kg — Electra 225 2-door Hardtop Coupé 4,488 lb, 2,035 kg — Electra 225 4-door Hardtop Sedan 4,569 lb, 2,072 kg — Electra 225 Custom 2-door Hardtop Coupé 4,526 lb, 2,052 kg — Electra 225 Custom 4-door Hardtop Sedan 4,597 lb, 2,085 kg — Riviera 2-door Hardtop Coupé 4,428 lb, 2,008 kg; turning circle (between walls): Centurion 44.1 ft, 13.4 m — Electra 225 and Electra 225 Custom 46.8 ft, 14.3 m — Riviera 46.5 ft, 14.2 m; fuel tank capacity: 20.9 imp gal, 25 US gal, 95 l.

OPTIONAL ACCESSORIES Turbo Hydramatic automatic gearbox with 3 ratios (I 2.480, II 1.480, III 1, rev 2.080) and max ratio of convertor at stall 2.05 only for Centurion Series; dual exhaust engines; limited slip final drive; air-conditioning system.

330 hp power team

(optional for Centurion and Riviera Series; not available for other Series).

See 315 hp power team, except for:

ENGINE max power (SAE): 330 hp at 4,600 rpm; max torque (SAE): 455 lb ft, 62.8 kg m at 2,800 rpm; max engine rpm: 5,000; specific power: 44.3 hp/l.

TRANSMISSION gearbox: Turbo Hydramatic automatic (standard); selector lever: steering column; axle ratio: 2.930 — Riviera 3.420.

PERFORMANCE max speed: about 115 mph, 185 km/h; power-weight ratio: Centurion 4-door Hardtop Sedan 13.5 lb/hp, 6.1 kg/hp — Riviera 2-door Hardtop Coupé 13.4 lb/hp, 6 kg/hp; speed in direct drive at 1,000 rpm: 24 mph, 38.6 km/h; fuel consumption: 13.8 m/imp gal, 11.5 m/US gal, 20.4 l x 100 km.

CADILLAC USA

Calais - De Ville - Fleetwood Series

PRICES IN USA:

Calais	Coupé	$ 5,934
Calais	Hardtop Sedan	$ 6,110
De Ville	Coupé	$ 6,299
De Ville	Hardtop Sedan	$ 6,533
Fleetwood Sixty	Special Brougham	$ 7,821
Fleetwood Seventy-Five	Sedan	$ 11,955
Fleetwood Seventy-Five	Limousine	$ 12,094

345 hp power team

(standard for all Series).

ENGINE front, 4 stroke; cylinders: 8, Vee-slanted at 90°; bore and stroke: 4.30 x 4.06 in, 109.2 x 103.1 mm; engine capacity: 472 cu in, 7,735 cu cm; compression ratio: 8.5; max power (SAE): 345 hp at 4,400 rpm; max torque (SAE): 500 lb ft, 69 kg m at 4,000 rpm; max engine rpm: 4,600; specific power: 44.6 hp/l; cylinder block: cast iron; cylinder head: cast iron; crankshaft bearings: 5; valves: 2 per cylinder, overhead, in line, push-rods and rockers, hydraulic tappets; camshafts: 1, at centre of Vee; lubrication: gear pump, full flow filter; lubricating system capacity: 8.3 imp pt, 9.9 US pt, 4.7 l; carburation: 1 Rochester 4MV downdraught 4-barrel carburettor; fuel feed: mechanical pump; cooling system: water, glexible blade cooling fan; cooling system capacity: 35.2 imp pt, 42.3 US pt, 20 l (Fleetwood Seventy-Five Limousine 40.5 imp pt, 69.8 US pt, 23 l).

TRANSMISSION driving wheels: rear; gearbox: Turbo Hydramatic automatic, hydraulic torque convertor and planetary gears with 3 ratios + reverse, max ratio of convertor at stall 2.03, possible manual selection; gearbox ratios: I 2.480, II 1.480, III 1, rev 2.080; selector lever: steering column; final drive: hypoid bevel; axle ratio: 2.930 — Fleetwood Seventy-Five Limousine 3.150; width of rims: 6''; tyres: L78 x 15.

PERFORMANCE max speed: about 120 mph, 193 km/h — Fleetwood Seventy-Five Limousine 116 mph, 186 km/h;

power-weight ratio: Calais Hardtop Sedan 14 lb/hp, 6.4 kg/hp — Calais Coupé and De Ville Coupé 13.9 lb/hp, 6.3 kg/hp — De Ville Hardtop Sedan 14.1 lb/hp, 6.5 kg/hp — Fleetwood Sixty Special Brougham 14.6 lb/hp, 6.6 kg/hp — Fleetwood Seventy-Five Sedan 16.2 lb/hp, 7.3 kg/hp — Fleetwood Seventy-Five Limousine 16.6 lb/hp, 7.5 kg/hp; carrying capacity: 1,058 lb, 480 kg — Fleetwood Seventy-Five Sedan and Limousine 1,588 lb, 720 kg; speed in direct drive at 1,000 rpm: 25.9 mph, 41.7 km/hp; fuel consumption: 13.3 m/imp gal, 11.1 m/US gal, 21.2 l x 100 km (Fleetwood Seventy-Five Limousine 12.1 m/imp gal, 10.1 m/US gal, 23.3 l x 100 km).

CHASSIS perimeter box-type; front suspension: independent, wishbones, coil springs, anti-roll bar, telescopic dampers; rear suspension: rigid axle, lower trailing arms, upper oblique torque arms, coil springs, telescopic dampers (for Fleetwood Special Brougham and Fleetwood Seventy-Five Limousine automatic levelling control as standard).

STEERING recirculating ball, variable ratio, servo; turns of steering wheel lock to lock: 2.75.

BRAKES front disc (diameter 11.90 in, 302 mm), internal radial fins, rear drum, dual circuit, servo; area rubbed by linings: front 240 sq in, 1,548 sq cm, rear 188.5 sq in, 1,216 sq cm, total 428.5 sq in, 2,764 sq cm.

ELECTRICAL EQUIPMENT voltage: 12 V; battery: 74 Ah; generator type: alternator, 42 A (Fleetwood Seventy-Five Limousine 63 A); ignition distributor: Delco-Remy; headlamps: 4.

DIMENSIONS AND WEIGHT wheel base: Calais and De Ville 130 in, 3,302 mm — Fleetwood Sixty Special Brougham 133 in, 3,378 mm — Fleetwood Seventy-Five Sedan and Limousine 151.50 in, 3,848 mm; front track: 63.60 in, 1,615 mm; rear track: 63.30 in, 1,608 mm; overall length: Calais and De Ville 225.80 in, 5,735 mm — Fleetwood Sixty Special Brougham 228.80 in, 5,812 mm — Fleetwood Seventy-Five Sedan and Limousine 247.30 in, 6,281 mm; overall width: 79.80 in, 2,027 mm; overall height: Calais and De Ville 54.10 in, 1,374 mm — Fleetwood Sixty Special Brougham 56.50 in, 1,435 mm — Fleetwood Seventy-Five Sedan and Limousine 58.10 in, 1,476 mm; ground clearance: Calais and De Ville 5.90 in, 150 mm — Fleetwood Sixty Special Brougham 6.30 in, 160 mm — Fleetwood Seventy-Five Sedan and Limousine 6.90 in, 175 mm; dry weight: Calais Coupé 4,785 lb, 2,170 kg — Calais Hardtop Sedan 4,843 lb, 2,196 kg — De Ville Coupé 4,810 lb, 2,181 kg — De Ville Hardtop Sedan 4,881 lb, 2,213 kg — Fleetwood Sixty Special Brougham 5,051 lb, 2,290 kg — Fleetwood Seventy-Five Sedan 5,603 lb, 2,541 kg — Fleetwood Seventy-Five Limousine 5,744 lb, 2,605 kg; turning circle (between walls): 48 ft, 14.6 m — Fleetwood Sixty Special Brougham 48.4 ft, 14.8 m — Fleetwood Seventy-Five Sedan and Limousine 61.8 ft, 18.8 m; fuel tank capacity: 22.9 imp gal, 27.5 US gal, 104 l.

BODY doors: 4 (coupés and convertibles 2); seats: 6 (Fleetwood Seventy-Five Sedan and Limousine 9); front seats: bench, separate reclining backrests, built-in headrests; details: electrically-controlled windows (Fleetwood Seventy-Five Sedan and Limousine with air-conditioning system).

OPTIONAL ACCESSORIES limited slip final drive; automatic levelling control on rear suspension only for Calais, De Ville and Fleetwood Seventy-Five Sedan; electrically-heated rear window; air-conditioning system.

Fleetwood Eldorado Series

PRICES IN USA:

Fleetwood Eldorado	Coupé	$ 7,416
Fleetwood Eldorado	Convertible	$ 7,784

365 hp power team

(standard for both models).

ENGINE front, 4 stroke; cylinders: 8, Vee-slanted at 90°; bore and stroke: 4.30 x 4.30 in, 109.2 x 109.2 mm; engine capacity: 500 cu in, 8,193 cu cm; compression ratio: 10.5; max power (SAE): 365 hp at 4,400 rpm; max torque (SAE): 535 lb ft, 73.8 kg m at 2,800 rpm; max engine rpm: 4,700; specific power: 44.6 hp/l; cylinder block: cast iron; cylinder head: cast iron; crankshaft bearings: 5; valves: 2 per cylinder, overhead, in line, push-rods and rockers, hydraulic tappets; camshafts: 1, at centre of Vee; lubrication: gear pump, full flow filter; lubricating system capacity: 10 imp pt, 12 US pt, 5.7 l; carburation: 1 Rochester 4MV downdraught 4-barrel carburettor; fuel feed: mechanical pump; cooling system: water, flexible blade cooling fan; cooling system capacity: 35.2 imp pt, 42.3 US pt, 20 l.

TRANSMISSION driving wheels: front; gearbox: Turbo Hydramatic automatic, hydraulic torque convertor and planetary gears (chain torque by engine-mounted convertor) with 3 ratios + reverse, max ratio of convertor at stall 2.03, possible manual selection; gearbox ratios: I 2.480, II 1.480, III 1, rev 2.090; selector lever: steering column; axle ratio: 3.070; width of rims: 6''; tyres: L78 x 15.

BUICK Electra 225 Custom 2-door Hardtop Coupé

BUICK Riviera 2-door Hardtop Coupé

CADILLAC De Ville Hardtop Sedan

365 HP POWER TEAM

PERFORMANCE max speed: about 121 mph, 194 km/h; power-weight ratio: Fleetwood Eldorado Coupé 13.2 lb/hp, 5.9 kg/hp — Fleetwood Eldorado Convertible 13.3 lb/hp, 6 kg/hp; carrying capacity: 1,058 lb, 480 kg; speed in direct drive at 1,000 rpm: 25.8 mph, 41.5 km/h; fuel consumption: 12.5 m/imp gal, 10.4 m/US gal, 22.6 l x 100 km.

CHASSIS perimeter box-type; front suspension: independent, wishbones, longitudinal torsion bars, anti-roll bar, telescopic dampers; rear suspension: rigid axle, automatic levelling control, coil springs, telescopic dampers.

STEERING recirculating ball, variable ratio, servo; turns of steering wheel lock to lock: 3.

BRAKES front disc (diameter 11 in, 279 mm), internal radial fins, rear drum, dual circuit, servo; area rubbed by linings: front 224 sq in, 1,445 sq cm, rear 148 sq in, 890 sq cm, total 372 sq in, 2,335 sq cm.

ELECTRICAL EQUIPMENT voltage: 12 V; battery: 74 Ah; generator type: alternator, 42 A; ignition distributor: Delco-Remy; headlamps: 4.

DIMENSIONS AND WEIGHT wheel base: 126.30 in, 3,208 mm; front track: 63.66 in, 1,617 mm; rear track: 63.60 in, 1,615 mm; overall length: 221.60 in, 5,629 mm; overall width: 79.80 in, 2,027 mm; overall height: coupé 53.90 in, 1,369 mm — convertible 54.30 in, 1,379 mm; ground clearance: 5.80 in, 147 mm; dry weight: Fleetwood Eldorado Coupé 4,811 lb, 2,182 kg — Fleetwood Eldorado Convertible 4,870 lb, 2,208 kg; turning circle (between walls): 46.8 ft, 14.3 m; fuel tank capacity: 22.9 imp gal, 27.5 US gal, 104 l.

BODY doors: 2; seats: 6.

OPTIONAL ACCESSORIES computerized rear wheel skid-control braking system; air-conditioning system.

CHECKER   USA

Marathon Series

PRICES IN USA:

Marathon	Sedan	$ —
Marathon	6-passenger De Luxe Sedan	$ —
Marathon	8-passenger De Luxe Sedan	$ —
Marathon	De Luxe Limousine	$ —
Marathon	6-passenger Station Wagon	$ —
Marathon	8-passenger Station Wagon	$ —

155 hp power team

(standard for all models).

ENGINE front, 4 stroke; cylinders: 6, in line; bore and stroke: 3.87 x 3.53 in, 98.3 x 89.7 mm; engine capacity: 250 cu in, 4,097 cu cm; compression ratio: 8.5; max power (SAE): 155 hp at 4,200 rpm; max torque (SAE): 235 lb ft, 32.4 kg m at 1,600 rpm; max engine rpm: 4,400; specific power: 37.8 hp/l; cylinder block: cast iron; cylinder head: cast iron; crankshaft bearings: 7; valves: 2 per cylinder, overhead, in line, push-rods and rockers, hydraulic tappets; camshafts: 1, side; lubrication: gear pump, full flow filter; lubricating system capacity: 8.3 imp pt, 9.9 US pt, 4.7 l; carburation: 1 Rochester 7040014 downdraught single barrel carburettor; fuel feed: mechanical pump; cooling system: water; cooling system capacity: 20.1 imp pt, 24.1 US pt, 11.4 l.

TRANSMISSION driving wheels: rear; gearbox: Dual Range automatic, hydraulic torque convertor and planetary gears with 3 ratios + reverse, max ratio of convertor at stall 2.1, possible manual selection; gearbox ratios: I 2.400, II 1.470, III 1, rev 2; selector lever: steering column; final drive: hypoid bevel; axle ratio: 3.310; width of rims: 6''; tyres: 8.25 x 15.

PERFORMANCE max speed: about 92 mph, 148 km/h; power-weight ratio: Marathon Sedan 21.1 lb/hp, 9.6 kg/hp; speed in direct drive at 1,000 rpm: 21 mph, 33.8 km/h; fuel consumption: 19.6 m/imp gal, 16.3 m/US gal, 14.4 l x 100 km.

CHASSIS box-type ladder frame, X reinforcements; front suspension: independent, wishbones, coil springs, anti-roll bar, telescopic dampers; rear suspension: rigid axle, semi-elliptic leafsprings, telescopic dampers.

STEERING recirculating ball; turns of steering wheel lock to lock: 6.14.

BRAKES drum, dual circuit; area rubbed by linings: total 326.9 sq in, 2,108 sq cm.

CADILLAC Fleetwood Eldorado Coupé

CHECKER Marathon Sedan

CHEVROLET Vega 2300 2-door Sedan

ELECTRICAL EQUIPMENT voltage: 12 V; battery: 50 Ah; generator type: alternator, 35 A; ignition distributor: Delco-Remy; headlamps: 4, halogen.

DIMENSIONS AND WEIGHT wheel base: 120 in, 3,048 mm; front track: 63.64 in, 1,616 mm; rear track: 63 in, 1,600 mm; overall length: 230 in, 5,842 mm; overall width: 76 in, 1,930 mm; overall height: 62.75 in, 1,594 mm; ground clearance: 6.50 in, 165 mm; dry weight: Marathon Sedan and Marathon 6-passenger De Luxe Sedan 3,268 lb, 1,482 kg — Marathon 8-passenger De Luxe Sedan 3,374 lb, 1,530 kg — Marathon De Luxe Limousine 3,578 lb, 1,622 kg — Marathon 6-passenger Station Wagon 3,470 lb, 1,574 kg — Marathon 8-passenger Station Wagon 3,580 lb, 1,623 kg; turning circle (between walls): 42 ft, 12.8 m; fuel tank capacity: 19.1 imp gal, 23 US gal, 87 l.

OPTIONAL ACCESSORIES limited slip final drive; power-assisted steering, 3.98 turns of steering wheel lock to lock; servo brake; front disc brakes (diameter 11.68 in, 297 mm), servo, total area rubbed by linings 374.7 sq in, 2,417 sq cm.

CHEVROLET USA

Vega 2300 Series

PRICES IN USA:

Vega 2300	2-door Sedan	$ 2,091
Vega 2300	2-door Coupé	$ 2,197
Vega 2300	Station Wagon	$ 2,329

90 hp power team

(standard).

ENGINE front, 4 stroke; cylinders: 4, in line; bore and stroke: 3.50 x 3.62 in, 88.8 x 91.9 mm; engine capacity: 140 cu in, 2,294 cu cm; compression ratio: 8; max power (SAE): 90 hp at 4,600-4,800 rpm; max torque (SAE): 136 lb ft, 18.7 kg m at 2,400 rpm; max engine rpm: 5,000; specific power: 39.2 hp/l; cylinder block: light alloy; cylinder head: light alloy; crankshaft bearings: 5; valves: 2 per cylinder, overhead, in line, push-rods and rockers; camshafts: 1, overhead; lubrication: gear pump, full flow filter; lubricating system capacity: 6.7 imp pt, 8 US pt, 3.8 l; carburation: 1 Rochester 7041023 downdraught single barrel carburettor; fuel feed: electric pump; cooling system: water; cooling system capacity: 10.7 imp pt, 12.9 US pt, 6.1 l.

TRANSMISSION driving wheels: rear; clutch: single dry plate (diaphragm); gearbox: mechanical; gears: 3 + reverse; synchromesh gears: I, II, III; gearbox ratios: I 3.240, II 1.680, III 1, rev 3.470; gear lever: central; final drive: hypoid bevel; axle ratio: 2.530; width of rims: 5''; tyres: A78 x 13.

PERFORMANCE max speed: about 88 mph, 141 km/h; power-weight ratio: sedan 24.5 lb/hp, 11.1 kg/hp — coupé 24.9 lb/hp, 11.3 kg/hp; speed in direct drive at 1,000 rpm: 20 mph, 32.2 km/h; fuel consumption: 21.6 m/imp gal, 18 m/US gal, 13.1 l x 100 km.

CHASSIS integral; front suspension: independent, wishbones, coil springs, telescopic dampers; rear suspension: rigid axle, lower trailing radius arms, upper torque arms, coil springs, telescopic dampers.

STEERING recirculating ball; turns of steering wheel lock to lock: 4.40.

BRAKES front disc, rear drum, dual circuit; area rubbed by linings: total 228.4 sq in, 1,473 sq cm.

ELECTRICAL EQUIPMENT voltage: 12 V; battery: 45 Ah; generator type: alternator, 32 A; ignition distributor: Delco-Remy; headlamps: 2.

DIMENSIONS AND WEIGHT wheel base: 97 in, 2,464 mm; front track: 55.10 in, 1,399 mm; rear track: 54.10 in, 1,374 mm; overall length: 169.70 in, 4,310 mm; overall width: 65.40 in, 1,661 mm; overall height: sedan 51.90 in, 1,318 mm — coupé 50 in, 1,270 mm — station wagon 52 in, 1,321 mm; ground clearance: 4.50 in, 114 mm; dry weight: Vega 2300 2-door Sedan 2,202 lb, 998 kg — Vega 2300 Coupé 2,246 lb, 1,018 kg — Vega 2300 Station Wagon 2,286 lb, 1,037 kg; turning circle (between walls): 34.7 ft, 10.6 m; fuel tank capacity: 9.2 imp gal, 11 US gal, 42 l.

BODY doors: 2; seats: 4; front seats: separate.

OPTIONAL ACCESSORIES Torque Drive semi-automatic gearbox with 2 ratios (I 1.820, II 1, rev 1.820), max ratio of convertor at stall 2.40, 2.920 axle ratio; Powerglide automatic gearbox with 2 ratios (I 1.820, II 1, rev 1.820), max ratio of convertor at stall 2.10, 2.920 axle ratio; 4-speed fully synchronized mechanical gearbox (I 3.430, II 2.160, III 1.370, IV 1, rev 3.320), 2.920 axle ratio; limited slip final drive; power-assisted steering; anti-roll bar on front and rear suspensions; air-conditioning system.

CADILLAC Fleetwood Eldorado Convertible

CHECKER Marathon Sedan

CHEVROLET Vega 2300 2-door Sedan

110 hp power team

(optional).

See 90 hp power team, except for:

ENGINE max power (SAE): 110 hp at 4,800 rpm; max torque (SAE): 138 lb ft, 19 kg m at 3,200 rpm; max engine rpm: 5,200; specific power: 48.6 hp/l; carburation: 1 Rochester 7041181 downdraught twin barrel carburettor.

TRANSMISSION axle ratio: 2.920.

PERFORMANCE max speed: about 94 mph, 151 km/h; power-weight ratio: sedan 20 lb/hp, 9.1 kg/hp — coupé 20.4 lb/hp, 9.3 kg/hp; speed in direct drive at 1,000 rpm: 19 mph, 30.5 km/h; fuel consumption: 20.3 m/imp gal, 16.9 m/US gal, 13.9 l x 100 km.

OPTIONAL ACCESSORIES 4-speed fully synchronized mechanical gearbox with 3.360 axle ratio.

Nova - Nova SS Series

PRICES IN USA:

Nova	2-door Coupé	$ 2,378
Nova	4-door Sedan	$ 2,407
Nova SS	2-door Coupé	$ —

For V8 engines add $ 95.

145 hp power team

(standard).

ENGINE front, 4 stroke; cylinders: 6, in line; bore and stroke: 3.87 x 3.53 in, 98.2 x 89.6 mm; engine capacity: 250 cu in, 4,097 cu cm; compression ratio: 8.5; max power (SAE): 145 hp at 4,200 rpm; max torque (SAE): 230 lb ft, 31.8 kg m at 1,600 rpm; max engine rpm: 4,500; specific power: 35.4 hp/l; cylinder block: cast iron; cylinder head: cast iron; crankshaft bearings: 7; valves: 2 per cylinder, overhead, in line, push-rods and rockers, hydraulic tappets; camshafts: 1, side; lubrication: gear pump, full flow filter; lubricating system capacity: 8.3 imp pt, 9.9 US pt, 4.7 l; carburation: 1 Rochester 7041017 downdraught single barrel carburettor; fuel feed: mechanical pump; cooling system: water; cooling system capacity: 22.2 imp pt, 26.6 US pt, 12.6 l.

TRANSMISSION driving wheels: rear; clutch: single dry plate (diaphragm); gearbox: mechanical; gears: 3 + reverse; synchromesh gears: I, II, III; gearbox ratios: I 2.850, II 1.680, III 1, rev 2.950; gear lever: steering column; final drive: hypoid bevel; axle ratio: 3.080; width of rims: 5''; tyres: E78 x 14.

PERFORMANCE max speed: about 95 mph, 153 km/h; power-weight ratio: Nova 2-door Coupé 20.9 lb/hp, 9.5 kg/hp — Nova 4-door Sedan 21.1 lb/hp, 9.6 kg/hp; speed in direct drive at 1,000 rpm: 21.5 mph, 34.6 km/h; fuel consumption: 21.2 m/imp gal, 16.4 m/US gal, 14.3 l x 100 km.

CHASSIS integral, front box-type ladder frame; front suspension: independent, wishbones, coil springs, telescopic dampers; rear suspension: rigid axle, single leaf semi-elliptic springs, telescopic dampers.

STEERING recirculating ball; turns of steering wheel lock to lock: 4.60.

BRAKES drum, dual circuit; area rubbed by linings: total 268.8 sq in, 1,734 sq cm.

ELECTRICAL EQUIPMENT voltage: 12 V; battery: 45 Ah; generator type: alternator, 37 A; ignition distributor: Delco-Remy; headlamps: 2.

DIMENSIONS AND WEIGHT wheel base: 111 in, 2,819 mm; front track: 59 in, 1,499 mm; rear track: 58.90 in, 1,496 mm; overall length: 189.40 in, 4,811 mm; overall width: 72.40 in, 1,839 mm; overall height: 2-door coupés 52.50 in, 1,333 mm — 4-door sedan 53.90 in, 1,369 mm; ground clearance: 4.90 in, 124 mm; dry weight: Nova 2-door Coupé 3,036 lb, 1,377 kg — Nova 4-door Sedan 3,060 lb, 1,388 kg; turning circle (between walls): 43.3 ft, 13.2 m; fuel tank capacity: 19.3 imp gal, 16 US gal, 73 l.

BODY seats: 5-6.

OPTIONAL ACCESSORIES Torque Drive semi-automatic gearbox with 2 ratios (I 1.820, II 1, rev 1.820); Powerglide automatic gearbox with 2 ratios (I 1.820, II 1, rev 1.820), max ratio of convertor at stall 2.10; limited slip final drive; power-assisted steering; servo brake; front disc brakes with servo; air-conditioning system.

200 hp power team

(standard).

See 145 hp power team, except for:

ENGINE cylinders: 8, Vee-slanted at 90°; bore and stroke: 3.87 x 3.25 in, 98.2 x 82.5 mm; engine capacity: 307 cu in, 5,031 cu cm; max power (SAE): 200 hp at 4,600 rpm; max torque (SAE): 300 lb ft, 41.4 kg m at 2,400 rpm; max engine rpm: 4,800; specific power: 39.8 hp/l; crankshaft bearings: 5; camshafts: 1, at centre of Vee; carburation: 1 Rochester 7041101 downdraught twin barrel carburettor; cooling system capacity: 25 imp pt, 30 US pt, 14.2 l.

PERFORMANCE max speed: about 102 mph, 164 km/h; power-weight ratio: Nova 2-door Coupé 18.5 lb/hp, 8.4 kg/hp — Nova 4-door Sedan 16 lb/hp, 7.3 kg/hp; fuel consumption: 17.9 m/imp gal, 14.9 m/US gal, 15.8 l x 100 km.

CHASSIS front suspension: anti-roll bar.

ELECTRICAL EQUIPMENT battery: 61 Ah.

DIMENSIONS AND WEIGHT dry weight: plus 32 lb, 15 kg.

OPTIONAL ACCESSORIES Turbo Hydramatic automatic gearbox with 3 ratios (I 2.520, II 1.520, III 1, rev 1.930), 2.560 axle ratio; Torque Drive semi-automatic gearbox not available.

245 hp power team

(optional).

See 145 hp power team, except for:

ENGINE cylinders: 8, Vee-slanted at 90°; bore and stroke: 4 x 3.48 in, 101.6 x 88.3 mm; engine capacity: 350 cu in, 5,736 cu cm; max power (SAE): 245 hp at 4,800 rpm; max torque (SAE): 350 lb ft, 48.3 kg m at 2,800 rpm; max engine rpm: 5,200; specific power: 42.7 hp/l; crankshaft bearings: 5; camshafts: 1, at centre of Vee; carburation: 1 Rochester 7041113 downdraught twin barrel carburettor; cooling system capacity: 26.6 imp pt, 31.9 US pt, 15.1 l.

TRANSMISSION clutch: centrifugal; gearbox ratios: I 2.540, II 1.500, III 1, rev 2.630.

PERFORMANCE max speed: about 104 mph, 167 km/h; power-weight ratio: Nova 2-door Coupé 12.9 lb/hp, 5.8 kg/hp — Nova 4-door Sedan 13 lb/hp, 5.9 kg/hp; fuel consumption: 16.6 m/imp gal, 13.8 m/US gal, 17 l x 100 km.

CHASSIS front suspension: anti-roll bar.

ELECTRICAL EQUIPMENT battery: 61 Ah.

DIMENSIONS AND WEIGHT dry weight: plus 32 lb, 15 kg.

OPTIONAL ACCESSORIES Turbo Hydramatic automatic gearbox with 3 ratios (I 2.520, II 1.520, III 1, rev 1.930), 2.560 axle ratio; Torque Drive semi-automatic gearbox and Powerglide automatic gearbox not available.

270 hp power team

(optional for Nova SS 2-door Coupé; not available for Nova 2-door Coupé and 4-door Sedan).

See 145 hp power team, except for:

ENGINE cylinders: 8, Vee-slanted at 90°; bore and stroke: 4 x 3.48 in, 101.6 x 88.3 mm; engine capacity: 350 cu in, 5,736 cu cm; max power (SAE): 270 hp at 4,800 rpm; max torque (SAE): 360 lb ft, 49.7 kg m at 3,200 rpm; max engine rpm: 5,200; specific power: 47 hp/l; crankshaft bearings: 5; camshafts: 1, at centre of Vee; carburation: 1 Rochester 7041203 downdraught 4-barrel carburettor; cooling system capacity: 26.6 imp pt, 31.9 US pt, 15.1 l.

TRANSMISSION clutch: centrifugal; gears: 4 + reverse; synchromesh gears: I, II, III, IV; gearbox ratios: I 2.520, II 1.880, III 1.460, IV 1, rev 2.590; gear lever: central; axle ratio: 3.310; width of rims: 7''; tyres: E70 x 14.

PERFORMANCE max speed: about 107 mph, 172 km/h; power-weight ratio: 11.7 lb/hp, 5.3 kg/hp; speed in direct drive at 1,000 rpm: 20.5 mph, 33 km/h; fuel consumption: 15.8 m/imp gal, 13.1 m/US gal, 17.9 l x 100 km.

CHASSIS front suspension: anti-roll bar; rear suspension: multiple leaf semi-elliptic springs.

BRAKES front disc, rear drum, dual circuit; area rubbed by linings: total 323.4 sq in, 2,086 sq cm.

ELECTRICAL EQUIPMENT battery: 61 Ah.

DIMENSIONS AND WEIGHT dry weight: plus 32 lb, 15 kg.

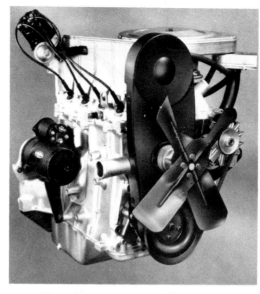

CHEVROLET Vega 2300 2-door Coupé (140 cu in engine)

CHEVROLET Vega 2300 Station Wagon

CHEVROLET Nova 2-door Coupé

BODY coupé; doors: 2; seats: 4; front seats: separate.

OPTIONAL ACCESSORIES Turbo Hydramatic automatic gearbox with 3 ratios (I 2.520, II 1.520, III 1, rev 1.930); Torque Drive semi-automatic gearbox and Powerglide automatic gearbox not available.

Monte Carlo - Monte Carlo SS Series

PRICES IN USA:

Monte Carlo	2-door-Sport Coupé	$ 3,304
Monte Carlo SS	2-door-Sport Coupé	$ —

245 hp power team

(standard for Monte Carlo; not available for Monte Carlo SS).

ENGINE front, 4 stroke; cylinders: 8, Vee-slanted at 90°; bore and stroke: 4 x 3.48 in, 101.6 x 88.3 mm; engine capacity: 350 cu in, 5,736 cu cm; compression ratio: 8.5; max power (SAE): 245 hp at 4,800 rpm; max torque (SAE): 350 lb ft, 48.3 kg m at 2,800 rpm; max engine rpm: 5,200; specific power: 42.7 hp/l; cylinder block: cast iron; cylinder head: cast iron; crankshaft bearings: 5; valves: 2 per cylinder, overhead, in line, push-rods and rockers, hydraulic tappets; camshafts: 1, at centre of Vee; lubrication: gear pump, full flow filter; lubricating system capacity: 8.3 imp pt, 9.9 US pt, 4.7 l; carburation: 1 Rochester 7041113 downdraught twin barrel carburettor; fuel feed: mechanical pump; cooling system: water; cooling system capacity: 22.2 imp pt, 26.6 US pt, 15.1 l.

TRANSMISSION driving wheels: rear; clutch: single dry plate (diaphragm); gearbox: mechanical; gears: 3 + reverse; synchromesh gears: I, II, III; gearbox ratios: I 2.540, II 1.500, III 1, rev 2.630; gear lever: steering column; final drive: hypoid bevel; axle ratio: 3.080; width of rims: 6''; tyres: G78 x 15.

PERFORMANCE max speed: about 111 mph, 178 km/h; power-weight ratio: 14.6 lb/hp, 6.6 kg/hp; carrying capacity: 882 lb, 400 kg; speed in direct drive at 1,000 rpm: 22.2 mph, 35.7 km/h; fuel consumption: 16 m/imp gal, 13.3 m/US gal, 17.7 l x 100 km.

CHASSIS perimeter box-type with cross members; front suspension: independent, wishbones, coil springs, anti-roll bar, telescopic dampers; rear suspension: rigid axle, lower trailing radius arms, upper oblique torque arms, coil springs, telescopic dampers.

STEERING recirculating ball; turns of steering wheel lock to lock: 5.20.

BRAKES front disc (diameter 11 in, 279 mm), rear drum, dual circuit, servo; area rubbed by linings: total 332.4 sq in, 2,144 sq cm.

ELECTRICAL EQUIPMENT voltage: 12 V; battery: 61 Ah; generator type: alternator, 37 A; ignition distributor: Delco-Remy; headlamps: 2.

DIMENSIONS AND WEIGHT wheel base: 116 in, 2,946 mm; front track: 60.20 in, 1,529 mm; rear track: 59.30 in, 1,506 mm; overall length: 206.50 in, 5,245 mm; overall width: 75.60 in, 1,920 mm; overall height: 52.90 in, 1,344 mm; ground clearance: 4.70 in, 119 mm; dry weight: 3,586 lb, 1,626 kg; turning circle (between walls): 45.5 ft, 13.9 m; fuel tank capacity: 15.8 imp gal, 19 US gal, 72 l.

BODY doors: 2; seats: 5; front seats: separate.

OPTIONAL ACCESSORIES Powerglide automatic gearbox with 2 ratios (I 1.820, II 1, rev 1.820), max ratio of convertor at stall 2.10; Turbo Hydramatic automatic gearbox with 3 ratios (I 2.520, II 1.520, III 1, rev 1.930), max ratio of convertor at stall 2.10, 2.730 axle ratio; limited slip final drive; power-assisted steering; air-conditioning system.

270 hp power team

(optional for Monte Carlo; not available for Monte Carlo SS).

See 245 hp power team, except for:

ENGINE max power (SAE): 270 hp at 4,800 rpm; max torque (SAE): 360 lb ft, 49.7 kg m at 3,200 rpm; max engine rpm: 5,200; specific power: 47 hp/l; carburation: 1 Rochester 7041203 downdraught 4-barrel carburettor.

TRANSMISSION gears: 4 + reverse; synchromesh gears: I, II, III, IV; gearbox ratios: I 2.520, II 1.880, III 1.460, IV 1, rev 2.590; gear lever: central; axle ratio: 3.310.

PERFORMANCE max speed: about 112 mph, 180 km/h; power-weight ratio: 13.3 lb/hp, 6 kg/hp; speed in direct drive at

CHEVROLET Vega 2300 2-door Coupé

CHEVROLET Vega 2300 Station Wagon

CHEVROLET Nova 2-door Coupé

1,000 rpm: 21.9 mph, 35.2 km/h; fuel consumption: 15.6 m/imp gal, 13 m/US gal, 18.1 l x 100 km.

DIMENSIONS AND WEIGHT dry weight: plus 18 lb, 8 kg.

OPTIONAL ACCESSORIES Powerglide automatic gearbox not available.

300 hp power team

(optional for Monte Carlo; not available for Monte Carlo SS).

See 245 hp power team, except for:

ENGINE bore and stroke: 4.13 x 3.76 in, 104.8 x 95.4 mm; engine capacity: 402 cu in, 6,588 cu cm; max power (SAE): 300 hp at 4,800 rpm; max torque (SAE): 400 lb ft, 55.2 kg m at 3,200 rpm; max engine rpm: 5,300; specific power: 45.5 hp/l; carburation: 1 Rochester 7041201 downdraught 4-barrel carburettor; cooling system capacity: 38.7 imp pt, 46.5 US pt, 22 l.

TRANSMISSION gears: 4 + reverse; synchromesh gears: I, II, III, IV; gearbox ratios: I 2.520, II 1.880, III 1.460, IV 1, rev 2.590; gear lever: central; axle ratio: 3.310.

PERFORMANCE max speed: about 115 mph, 185 km/h; power-weight ratio: 12 lb/hp, 5.4 kg/hp; speed in direct drive at 1,000 rpm: 21.9 mph, 35.2 km/h; fuel consumption: 14.7 m/imp gal, 12.3 m/US gal, 19.2 l x 100 km.

DIMENSIONS AND WEIGHT dry weight: plus 18 lb, 8 kg.

OPTIONAL ACCESSORIES Powerglide automatic gearbox not available.

365 hp power team

(standard for Monte Carlo SS; not available for Monte Carlo).

See 245 hp power team, except for:

ENGINE bore and stroke: 4.25 x 4 in, 107.9 x 101.6 mm; engine capacity: 454 cu in, 7,440 cu cm; max power (SAE): 365 hp at 4,800 rpm; max torque (SAE): 465 lb ft, 64.2 kg m at 3,200 rpm; max engine rpm: 5,500; specific power: 49.1 hp/l; carburation: 1 Rochester 7041200 downdraught 4-barrel carburettor; cooling system capacity: 38.7 imp pt, 46.5 US pt, 22 l.

TRANSMISSION gearbox: Turbo Hydramatic automatic (standard), max ratio of convertor at stall 2.10; gearbox ratios: I 2.480, II 1.480, III 1, rev 2.080; selector lever: steering column or central; axle ratio: 3.310; width of rims: 7''; tyres: G70 x 15.

PERFORMANCE max speed: about 122 mph, 196 km/h; power-weight ratio: 10.4 lb/hp, 4.7 kg/hp; speed in direct drive at 1,000 rpm: 22 mph, 35.4 km/h; fuel consumption: 13.5 m/imp gal, 11.2 m/US gal, 21 l x 100 km.

ELECTRICAL EQUIPMENT battery: 80 Ah.

DIMENSIONS AND WEIGHT dry weight: plus 210 lb, 95 kg.

OPTIONAL ACCESSORIES Powerglide automatic gearbox not available.

425 hp power team

(optional for Monte Carlo SS; not available for Monte Carlo).

See 245 hp power team, except for:

ENGINE bore and stroke: 4.25 x 4 in, 107.9 x 101.6 mm; engine capacity: 454 cu in, 7,440 cu cm; compression ratio: 9; max power (SAE): 425 hp at 5,600 rpm; max torque (SAE): 475 lb ft, 65.5 kg m at 4,000 rpm; max engine rpm: 5,800; specific power: 57.1 hp/l; carburation: 1 Holley 3986195 downdraught 4-barrel carburettor; cooling system capacity: 38.7 imp pt, 46.5 US pt, 22 l.

TRANSMISSION gears: 4 + reverse; synchromesh gears: I, II, III, IV; gearbox ratios: I 2.200, II 1.640, III 1.270, IV 1, rev 2.260; gear lever: central; axle ratio: 3.310; width of rims: 7''; tyres: G70 x 15.

PERFORMANCE max speed: about 124 mph, 200 km/h; power-weight ratio: 8.9 lb/hp, 4 kg/hp; speed in direct drive at 1,000 rpm: 22 mph, 35.4 km/h; fuel consumption: 12.7 m/imp gal, 10.5 m/US gal, 22.3 l x 100 km.

ELECTRICAL EQUIPMENT battery: 80 Ah.

DIMENSIONS AND WEIGHT dry weight: plus 200 lb, 91 kg.

OPTIONAL ACCESSORIES Turbo Hydramatic automatic gearbox with 3.310 axle ratio; Powerglide automatic gearbox not available.

Chevelle - Chevelle SS - Malibu - Malibu SS - Nomad - Greenbrier - Concours - Concours Estate Series

PRICES IN USA:

Chevelle	2-door Sport Coupé	$ 2,707
Chevelle	4-door Sedan	$ 2,672
Chevelle SS	2-door Sport Coupé	$ —
Malibu	2-door Sport Coupé	$ 2,880
Malibu	4-door Sedan	$ 3,047
Malibu	2-door Convertible	$ 3,245
Malibu	4-door Sedan	$ 2,846
Malibu SS	2-door Sport Coupé	$ —
Nomad	6-passenger Station Wagon	$ 2,997
Greenbrier	6-passenger Station Wagon	$ 3,223
Greenbrier	9-passenger Station Wagon	$ 3,335
Concours	6-passenger Station Wagon	$ 3,332
Concours	9-passenger Station Wagon	$ 3,445
Concours Estate	6-passenger Station Wagon	$ 3,500
Concours Estate	9-passenger Station Wagon	$ 3,621

For V8 engines add $ 95.

145 hp power team

(standard for Chevelle, Malibu, Nomad, Greenbrier, Concours and Concours Estate Series; not available for Chevelle SS and Malibu SS).

ENGINE front, 4 stroke; cylinders: 6, in line; bore and stroke: 3.87 x 3.53 in, 98.2 x 89.6 mm; engine capacity: 250 cu in, 4,097 cu cm; compression ratio: 8.5; max power (SAE): 145 hp at 4,200 rpm; max torque (SAE): 230 lb ft, 31.8 kg m at 1,600 rpm; max engine rpm: 4,500; specific power: 35.4 hp/l; cylinder block: cast iron; cylinder head: cast iron; crankshaft bearings: 7; valves: 2 per cylinder, overhead, in line, push-rods and rockers, hydraulic tappets; camshafts: 1, side; lubrication: gear pump, full flow filter; lubricating system capacity: 8.3 imp pt, 9.9 US pt, 4.7 l; carburation: 1 Rochester 7041107 downdraught single barrel carburettor; fuel feed: mechanical pump; cooling system: water; cooling system capacity: 20.1 imp pt, 24.1 US pt, 11.4 l.

TRANSMISSION driving wheels: rear; clutch: single dry plate (diaphragm); gearbox: mechanical; gears: 3 + reverse; synchromesh gears: I, II, III; gearbox ratios: I 2.850, II 1.680, III 1, rev 2.950; gear lever: steering column; final drive: hypoid bevel; axle ratio: 3.080 — station wagons 3.360; width of rims: 5'' — station wagons 6''; tyres: E78 x 14 — station wagons G78 x 14.

PERFORMANCE max speed: about 93 mph, 149 km/h; power-weight ratio: Chevelle 4-door Sedan 22.8 lb/hp, 10.3 kg/hp — Malibu 4-door Sedan 23.1 lb/hp, 10.5 kg/hp; speed in direct drive at 1,000 rpm: 21.6 mph, 34.7 km/h; fuel consumption: 18.6 m/imp gal, 15.5 m/US gal, 15.2 l x 100 km.

CHASSIS perimeter box-type with cross members; front suspension: independent, wishbones, coil springs, anti-roll bar, telescopic dampers; rear suspension: rigid axle, lower trailing radius arms, upper oblique torque arms, coil springs, telescopic dampers.

STEERING recirculating ball; turns of steering wheel lock to lock: 5.50.

BRAKES drum, dual circuit; area rubbed by linings: total 268.8 sq in, 1,734 sq cm.

ELECTRICAL EQUIPMENT voltage: 12 V; battery: 45 Ah; generator type: alternator, 37 A; ignition distributor: Delco-Remy; headlamps: 2.

DIMENSIONS AND WEIGHT wheel base: 116 in, 2,946 mm — 2-door sport coupés and 2-door convertible 112 in, 2,845 mm; front track: 60 in, 1,524 mm — station wagons 59.30 in, 1,506 mm; rear track: 59.30 in, 1,506 mm — station wagons 59.20 in, 1,504 mm; overall length: 201.50 in, 5,118 mm — 2-door sport coupés and 2-door convertible 197.50 in, 5,016 mm — station wagons 206.80 in, 5,253 mm; overall width: 75.40 in, 1,915 mm; overall height: 53.30 in, 1,354 mm — 2-door sport coupés 52.70 in, 1,338 mm — 2-door convertible 52.90 in, 1,344 mm — station wagons 54.40 in, 1,382 mm; ground clearance: 4.70 in, 119 mm — 2-door sport coupés and 2-door convertible 4.60 in, 117 mm — station wagons 6.20 in, 157 mm; dry weight: Chevelle 2-door Sport Coupé 3,264 lb, 1,472 kg — Chevelle 4-door Sedan 3,308 lb, 1,500 kg — Malibu 2-door Sport Coupé 3,310 lb, 1,501 kg — Malibu 4-door Sedan 3,348 lb, 1,519 kg — Nomad 6-passenger Station Wagon 3,726 lb, 1,690 kg; turning circle (between walls): 45.5 ft, 13.9 m; fuel tank capacity: 15.8 imp gal, 19 US gal, 72 l (station wagons 15 imp gal, 18 US gal, 68 l).

OPTIONAL ACCESSORIES Powerglide automatic gearbox with 2 ratios (I 1.820, II 1, rev 1.820), max ratio of convertor at stall 2.10; limited slip final drive; power-assisted steering; servo brake; front disc brakes with servo.

CHEVROLET Nova 4-door Sedan

CHEVROLET Monte Carlo 2-door Sport Coupé

CHEVROLET Chevelle SS 2-door Sport Coupé

200 hp power team

standard for Chevelle, Malibu, Nomad, Greenbrier, Concours and Concours Estate Series; not available for Chevelle SS and Malibu SS).

See 145 hp power team, except for:

ENGINE cylinders: 8, Vee-slanted at 90°; bore and stroke: 3.87 x 3.25 in, 98.2 x 82.5 mm; engine capacity: 307 cu in, 5,031 cu cm; max power (SAE): 200 hp at 4,600 rpm; max torque (SAE): 300 lb ft, 41.4 kg m at 2,400 rpm; max engine rpm: 4,900; specific power: 39.8 hp/l; crankshaft bearings: 5; camshafts: 1, at centre of Vee; carburation: 1 Rochester 7040101 downdraught twin barrel carburettor; cooling system capacity: 26.4 imp pt, 31.7 US pt, 15 l.

PERFORMANCE max speed: about 107 mph, 172 km/h; power-weight ratio: Chevelle 4-door Sedan 17.2 lb/hp, 7.8 kg/hp — Malibu 4-door Sedan 17.4 lb/hp, 7.9 kg/hp; fuel consumption: 17.3 m/imp gal, 14.4 m/US gal, 16.3 l x 100 km.

ELECTRICAL EQUIPMENT battery: 61 Ah.

DIMENSIONS AND WEIGHT dry weight: Chevelle 2-door Sport Coupé 3,394 lb, 1,539 kg — Chevelle 4-door Sedan 3,436 lb, 1,558 kg — Malibu 2-door Sport Coupé 3,440 lb, 1,560 kg — Malibu 4-door Sport Sedan 3,548 lb, 1,609 kg — Malibu 2-door Convertible 3,488 lb, 1,582 kg — Malibu 4-door Sedan 3,478 lb, 1,577 kg — Nomad 6-passenger Station Wagon 3,480 lb, 1,578 kg — Greenbrier 6-passenger Station Wagon 3,914 lb, 1,775 kg — Greenbrier 9-passenger Station Wagon 3,976 lb, 1,803 kg — Concours 6-passenger Station Wagon 3,958 lb, 1,795 kg — Concours 9-passenger Station Wagon 4,002 lb, 1,815 kg — Concours Estate 6-passenger Station Wagon 3,986 lb, 1,808 kg — Concours Estate 9-passenger Station Wagon 4,038 lb, 1,831 kg.

OPTIONAL ACCESSORIES Turbo Hydramatic automatic gearbox with 3 ratios (I 2.520, II 1.520, III 1, rev 1.930), 2.730 axle ratio (station wagons 3.080); air-conditioning system.

245 hp power team

(optional for Chevelle, Malibu, Nomad, Greenbrier, Concours and Concours Estate Series; not available for Chevelle SS and Malibu SS).

See 145 hp power team, except for:

ENGINE cylinders: 8, Vee-slanted at 90°; bore and stroke: 4 x 3.48 in, 101.6 x 88.3 mm; engine capacity: 350 cu in, 5,736 cu cm; max power (SAE): 245 hp at 4,800 rpm; max torque (SAE): 350 lb ft, 48.3 kg m at 2,800 rpm; max engine rpm: 5,200; specific power: 42.7 hp/l; crankshaft bearings: 5; camshafts: 1, at centre of Vee; carburation: 1 Rochester 7041113 downdraught twin barrel carburettor; cooling system capacity: 26.6 imp pt, 31.9 US pt, 15.1 l.

TRANSMISSION clutch: centrifugal; gearbox ratios: I 2.540, II 1.500, III 1, rev 2.630.

PERFORMANCE max speed: about 109 mph, 175 km/h; power-weight ratio: Chevelle 4-door Sedan 14.1 lb/hp, 6.4 kg/hp — Malibu 4-door Sedan 14.3 lb/hp, 6.5 kg/hp; fuel consumption: 16 m/imp gal, 13.4 m/US gal, 17.6 l x 100 km.

ELECTRICAL EQUIPMENT battery: 61 Ah.

DIMENSIONS AND WEIGHT (see 200 hp power team) dry weight: plus 26 lb, 12 kg.

OPTIONAL ACCESSORIES Turbo Hydramatic automatic gearbox with 3 ratios (I 2.520, II 1.520, III 1, rev 1.930), 2.560 axle ratio; 4-speed fully synchronized mechanical gearbox (I 2.540, II 1.800, III 1.440, IV 1, rev 2.540) with central gear lever and 3.360 axle ratio; air-conditioning system; Powerglide automatic gearbox not available.

270 hp power team

(optional for Chevelle, Malibu, Nomad, Greenbrier, Concours and Concours Estate Series; not available for Chevelle SS and Malibu SS).

See 145 hp power team, except for:

ENGINE cylinders: 8, Vee-slanted at 90°; bore and stroke: 4 x 3.48 in, 101.6 x 88.3 mm; engine capacity: 350 cu in, 5,736 cu cm; max power (SAE): 270 hp at 4,800 rpm; max torque (SAE): 360 lb ft, 49.7 kg m at 3,200 rpm; max engine rpm: 5,200; specific power: 47 hp/l; crankshaft bearings: 5; camshafts: 1, at centre of Vee; carburation: 1 Rochester 7041203 downdraught 4-barrel carburettor; cooling system capacity: 26.6 imp pt, 31.9 US pt, 15.1 l.

TRANSMISSION clutch: centrifugal; gearbox ratios: I 2.540, II 1.500, III 1, rev 2.630; axle ratio: station wagons 3.080.

PERFORMANCE max speed: about 112 mph, 180 km/h; power-weight ratio: Chevelle 4-door Sedan 12.8 lb/hp, 5.8 kg/hp — Malibu 4-door Sedan 13 lb/hp, 5.9 kg/hp; fuel consumption: 15.4 m/imp gal, 12.8 m/US gal, 18.4 l x 100 km.

CHEVROLET Nova 4-door Sedan

CHEVROLET Monte Carlo 2-door Sport Coupé

CHEVROLET Chevelle SS 2-door Sport Coupé

ELECTRICAL EQUIPMENT battery: 61 Ah.

DIMENSIONS AND WEIGHT (see 200 hp power team) dry weight: plus 29 lb, 13 kg.

OPTIONAL ACCESSORIES Turbo Hydramatic automatic gearbox with 3 ratios (I 2.520, II 1.520, III 1, rev 1.930), 2.730 axle ratio; 4-speed fully synchronized mechanical gearbox (I 2.520, II 1.880, III 1.460, IV 1, rev 2.590) with central gear lever and 3.310 axle ratio; air-conditioning system; Powerglide automatic gearbox not available.

300 hp power team

(optional for Chevelle, Malibu, Nomad, Greenbrier, Concours and Concours Estate Series; not available for Chevelle SS and Malibu SS).

See 145 hp power team, except for:

ENGINE cylinders: 8, Vee-slanted at 90°; bore and stroke: 4.13 x 3.76 in, 104.8 x 95.4 mm; engine capacity: 402 cu in, 6,588 cu cm; max power (SAE): 300 hp at 4,800 rpm; max torque (SAE): 400 lb ft, 55.2 kg m at 3,200 rpm; max engine rpm: 5,300; specific power: 45.5 hp/l; crankshaft bearings: 5; camshafts: 1, at centre of Vee; carburation: 1 Rochester 7041201 downdraught 4-barrel carburettor; cooling system capacity: 38.7 imp pt, 46.5 US pt, 22 l.

TRANSMISSION clutch: centrifugal; gearbox ratios: I 2.420, II 1.580, III 1, rev 2.410; axle ratio: station wagons 3.080; width of rims: 6''; tyres: F78 x 14.

PERFORMANCE max speed: about 115 mph, 185 km/h; power-weight ratio: Chevelle 4-door Sedan and Malibu 4-door Sedan 12.3 lb/hp, 5.6 kg/hp; speed in direct drive at 1,000 rpm: 22.5 mph, 36.2 km/h; fuel consumption: 14.3 m/imp gal, 11.9 m/US gal, 19.7 l x 100 km.

ELECTRICAL EQUIPMENT battery: 61 Ah.

DIMENSIONS AND WEIGHT (see 200 hp power team) dry weight: plus 229 lb, 104 kg.

OPTIONAL ACCESSORIES Turbo Hydramatic automatic gearbox with 3 ratios (I 2.480, II 1.480, III 1, rev 2.080); 4-speed fully synchronized mechanical gearbox (I 2.520, II 1.880, III 1.460, IV 1, rev 2.590) with central gear lever; air-conditioning system; Powerglide automatic gearbox not avail-

365 hp power team

(standard for Chevelle SS and Malibu SS; optional for Malibu 2-door Convertible; not available for other models).

See 145 hp power team, except for:

ENGINE cylinders: 8, Vee-slanted at 90°; bore and stroke: 4.25 x 4 in, 107.9 x 101.6 mm; engine capacity: 454 cu in, 7,440 cu cm; max power (SAE): 365 hp at 4,800 rpm; max torque (SAE): 465 lb ft, 64.2 kg m at 3,200 rpm; max engine rpm: 5,500; specific power: 49.1 hp/l; crankshaft bearings: 5; camshafts: 1, at centre of Vee; carburation: 1 Rochester 7041201 downdraught 4-barrel carburettor; cooling system capacity: 38.7 imp pt, 46.5 US pt, 22 l.

TRANSMISSION clutch: centrifugal; gears: 4 + reverse; synchromesh gears: I, II, III, IV; gearbox ratios: I 2.200, II 1.640, III 1.270, IV 1, rev 2.260; gear lever: central; axle ratio: 3.310; with of rims: 7''; tyres: F60 x 15.

PERFORMANCE max speed: about 117 mph, 188 km/h; power-weight ratio: Chevelle SS 2-door Sport Coupé 9.9 lb/hp, 4.4 kg/hp — Malibu SS 2-door Sport Coupé 10 lb/hp, 4.5 kg/hp; speed in direct drive at 1,000 rpm: 21.3 mph, 34.2 km/h; fuel consumption: 13.3 m/imp gal, 11.1 m/US gal, 21.2 l x 100 km.

ELECTRICAL EQUIPMENT battery: 80 Ah.

DIMENSIONS AND WEIGHT (see 200 hp power team) dry weight: plus 237 lb, 107 kg — Chevelle SS 2-door Sport Coupé 3,631 lb, 1,647 kg — Malibu SS 2-door Sport Coupé 3,677 lb, 1,667 kg.

BODY doors: 2; seats: 5; front seats: separate.

OPTIONAL ACCESSORIES Turbo Hydramatic automatic gearbox with 3 ratios (I 2.480, II 1.480, III 1, rev 2.080); air-conditioning system; Powerglide automatic gearbox not available.

425 hp power team

(optional for Chevelle SS, Malibu 2-door Convertible and Malibu SS; not available for other models).

See 145 hp power team, except for:

ENGINE cylinders: 8, Vee-slanted at 90°; bore and stroke: 4.25 x 4 in, 107.9 x 101.6 mm; engine capacity: 454 cu in,

425 HP POWER TEAM

7,440 cu cm; compression ratio: 9; max power (SAE): 425 hp at 5,600 rpm; max torque (SAE): 475 lb ft, 65.5 kg m at 4,000 rpm; max engine rpm: 5,800; specific power: 57.1 hp/l; nrankshaft bearings: 5; camshafts: 1, at centre of Vee; carburation: 1 Holley 3986195 downdraught 4-barrel carburettor; cooling system capacity: 37 imp pt, 44.4 US pt, 21 l.

TRANSMISSION clutch: centrifugal; gears: 4 + reverse; synchromesh gears: I, II, III, IV; gearbox ratios: I 2.200, II 1.640, III 1.270, IV 1, rev 2.260; gear lever: central: axle ratio: 3.310; width of rims: 7''; tyres: F60 x 15.

PERFORMANCE max speed: about 122 mph, 196 km/h; power-weight ratio: Chevelle SS 2-door Sport Coupé 8.5 lb/hp, 3.8 kg/hp — Malibu SS 2-door Sport Coupé 8.6 lb/hp, 3.9 kg/hp; speed in direct drive at 1,000 rpm: 21.3 mph, 34.2 km/h; fuel consumption: 12.6 m/imp gal, 10.5 m/US gal, 22.5 l x 100 km.

ELECTRICAL EQUIPMENT battery: 80 Ah.

DIMENSIONS AND WEIGHT (see 200 hp power team) dry weight: plus 237 lb, 107 kg — Chevelle SS 2-door Sport Coupé 3,631 lb, 1,647 kg — Malibu SS 2-door Sport Coupé 3,677 lb, 1,667 kg.

OPTIONAL ACCESSORIES Turbo Hydramatic automatic gearbox with 3 ratios (I 2.480, II 1.480, III 1, rev 2.080); air-conditioning system; Powerglide automatic gearbox not avail.

Camaro - Camaro SS - Camaro Z28 Series

PRICES IN USA:

Camaro	2-door Sport Coupé	$ 2,916
Camaro SS	2-door Sport Coupé	$ —
Camaro Z28	2-door Sport Coupé	$ —

For V8 engines add $ 95.

145 hp power team

(standard for Camaro; not available for Camaro SS and Camaro Z28).

ENGINE front, 4 stroke; cylinders: 6, in line; bore and stroke: 3.87 x 3.53 in, 98.2 x 89.6 mm; engine capacity: 250 cu in, 4,097 cu cm; compression ratio: 8.5; max power (SAE): 145 hp at 4,200 rpm; max torque (SAE): 230 lb ft, 31.8 kg m at 1,600 rpm; max engine rpm: 4,500; specific power: 35.4 hp/l; cylinder block: cast iron; cylinder head: cast iron; crankshaft bearings: 7; valves: 2 per cylinder, overhead, in line, push-rods and rockers, hydraulic tappets; camshafts: 1, side; lubrication: gear pump, full flow filter; lubricating system capacity: 8.3 imp pt, 9.9 US pt, 4.7 l; carburation: 1 Rochester 7041107 downdraught single barrel carburettor; fuel feed: mechanical pump; cooling system: water; cooling system capacity: 20.1 imp pt, 24.1 US pt, 11.4 l.

TRANSMISSION driving wheels: rear; clutch: single dry plate (diaphragm); gearbox: mechanical; gears: 3 + reverse; synchromesh gears: I, II, III; gearbox ratios: I 2.850, II 1.680, III 1, rev 2.950; gear lever: central; final drive: hypoid bevel; axle ratio: 3.080; width of rims: 6''; tyres: E78 x 14.

PERFORMANCE max speed: about 99 mph, 159 km/h; power-weight ratio: 22 lb/hp, 10 kg/hp; carrying capacity: 882 lb, 400 kg; speed in direct drive at 1,000 rpm: 22.4 mph, 36 km/h; fuel consumption: 19.8 m/imp gal, 16.4 m/US gal, 14.3 l x 100 km.

CHASSIS integral, front box-type ladder frame; front suspension: independent, wishbones, coil springs, anti-roll bar, telescopic dampers; rear suspension: rigid axle, semi-elliptic leafsprings, anti-roll bar, telescopic dampers.

STEERING recirculating ball; turns of steering wheel lock to lock: 6.19.

BRAKES front disc, rear drum, dual circuit; area rubbed by linings: total 332.4 sq in, 2,144 sq cm.

ELECTRICAL EQUIPMENT voltage: 12, V; battery: 45 Ah; generator type: alternator, 37 A; ignition distributor: Delco-Remy; headlamps: 2.

DIMENSIONS AND WEIGHT wheel base: 108 in, 2,743 mm; front track: 61.30 in, 1,557 mm; rear track: 60 in, 1,524 mm; overall length: 188 in, 4,775 mm; overall width: 74.40 in, 1,690 mm; overall height: 49.10 in, 1,247 mm; ground clearance: 4.20 in, 107 mm; dry weight: 3,186 lb, 1,445 kg; turning circle (between walls): 41 ft, 12.5 m; fuel tank capacity: 14.1 imp gal, 17 US gal, 64 l.

CHEVROLET Malibu 2-door Sport Coupé

CHEVROLET Camaro SS 2-door Sport Coupé

CHEVROLET Caprice 4-door Sedan

BODY coupé; doors: 2; seats: 4; front seats: separate.

OPTIONAL ACCESSORIES Powerglide automatic gearbox with 2 ratios (I 1.820, II 1, rev 1.820), max ratio of converter at stall 2.10; limited slip final drive; power-assisted steering; servo brake; aic-conditioning system; RS equipment.

200 hp power team

(standard for Camaro; not available for Camaro SS and Camaro Z28).

See 145 hp power team, except for:

ENGINE cylinders: 8, Vee-slanted at 90°; bore and stroke: 3.87 x 3.25 in, 98.2 x 82.5 mm; engine capacity: 307 cu in, 5,031 cu cm; max power (SAE): 200 hp at 4,600 rpm; max torque (SAE): 300 lb ft, 41.4 kg m at 2,400 rpm; max engine rpm: 5,000; specific power: 39.8 hp/l; crankshaft bearings: 5; camshafts: 1, at centre of Vee; carburation: 1 Rochester 7041101 downdraught twin barrel carburettor; cooling system capacity: 25 imp pt, 30 US pt, 14.2 l.

PERFORMANCE max speed: about 113 mph, 182 km/h; power-weight ratio: 16.5 lb/hp, 7.5 kg/hp; fuel consumption: 18 m/imp gal, 15 m/US gal, 15.7 l x 100 km.

ELECTRICAL EQUIPMENT battery: 61 Ah.

DIMENSIONS AND WEIGHT dry weight: 3,310 lb, 1,501 kg.

OPTIONAL ACCESSORIES Turbo Hydramatic automatic gearbox with 3 ratios (I 2.520, II 1.520, III 1, rev 1.930), 2.73 axle ratio.

245 hp power team

(optional for Camaro; not available for Camaro SS and Camaro Z28).

See 145 hp power team, except for:

ENGINE cylinders: 8, Vee-slanted at 90°; bore and stroke: 4 x 3.48 in, 101.6 x 88.3 mm; engine capacity: 350 cu in, 5,736 cu cm; max power (SAE): 245 hp at 4,800 rpm; max torque (SAE): 350 lb ft, 48.3 kg m at 2,800 rpm; max engine rpm: 5,200; specific power: 42.7 hp/l; crankshaft bearings: 5; camshafts: 1, at centre of Vee; carburation: 1 Rochester 7041113 downdraught twin barrel carburettor; cooling system capacity: 26.6 imp pt, 31.9 US pt, 15.1 l.

TRANSMISSION clutch: centrifugal; gears: 4 + reverse; synchromesh gears: I, II, III, IV; gearbox ratios: I 2.540, II 1.800, III 1.440, IV 1, rev 2.540.

PERFORMANCE max speed: about 115 mph, 185 km/h; power-weight ratio: 13.6 lb/hp, 6.7 kg/hp; fuel consumption: 16.6 m/imp gal, 13.8 m/US gal, 17 l x 100 km.

ELECTRICAL EQUIPMENT battery: 61 Ah.

DIMENSIONS AND WEIGHT (see 200 hp power team) dry weight: plus 15 lb, 7 kg.

OPTIONAL ACCESSORIES Turbo Hydramatic automatic gearbox with 3 ratios (I 2.520, II 1.520, III 1, rev 1.930); Powerglide automatic gearbox not available.

270 hp power team

(standard for Camaro SS; not available for other models).

See 145 hp power team, except for:

ENGINE cylinders: 8, Vee-slanted at 90°; bore and stroke: 4 x 3.48 in, 101.6 x 88.3 mm; engine capacity: 350 cu in, 5,736 cu cm; max power (SAE): 270 hp at 4,800 rpm; max torque (SAE): 360 lb ft, 49.7 kg m at 3,200 rpm; max engine rpm: 5,300; specific power: 47 hp/l; crankshaft bearings: 5; camshafts: 1, at centre of Vee; carburation: 1 Rochester 7041203 downdraught 4-barrel carburettor; cooling system capacity: 26.6 imp pt, 31.9 US pt, 15.1 l.

TRANSMISSION clutch: centrifugal; gears: 4 + reverse; synchromesh gears: I, II, III, IV; gearbox ratios: I 2.520, II 1.880, III 1.460, IV 1, rev 2.590; axle ratio: 3.420; width of rims: 7''; tyres: F70 x 14.

PERFORMANCE max speed: about 116 mph, 186 km/h; power-weight ratio: 12.4 lb/hp, 5.6 kg/hp; speed in direct drive at 1,000 rpm: 22 mph, 35.4 km/h; fuel consumption: 15.9 m/imp gal, 13.2 m/US gal, 17.8 l x 100 km.

ELECTRICAL EQUIPMENT battery: 61 Ah.

DIMENSIONS AND WEIGHT (see 200 hp power team) dry weight: plus 53 lb, 24 kg.

OPTIONAL ACCESSORIES Turbo Hydramatic automatic gearbox with 3 ratios (I 2.520, II 1.520, III 1, rev 1.930); Powerglide automatic gearbox not available.

CHEVROLET Malibu 2-door Sport Coupé

CHEVROLET Camaro SS 2-door Sport Coupé

CHEVROLET Caprice 4-door Sedan

300 hp power team

(optional for Camaro SS; not available for other models).

See 145 hp power team, except for:

ENGINE cylinders: 8, Vee-slanted at 90°; bore and stroke: 4.13 x 3.76 in, 104.8 x 95.4 mm; engine capacity: 402 cu in, 6,588 cu cm; max power (SAE): 300 hp at 4,800 rpm; max torque (SAE): 400 lb ft, 55.2 kg m at 3,200 rpm; max engine rpm: 5,400; specific power: 45.5 hp/l; crankshaft bearings: 5; camshafts: 1, at centre of Vee; carburation: 1 Rochester 7041201 downdraught 4-barrel carburettor; cooling system capacity: 40.5 imp pt, 48.6 US pt, 23 l.

TRANSMISSION clutch: centrifugal; gears: 4 + reverse; synchromesh gears: I, II, III, IV; gearbox ratios: I 2.520, II 1.880, III 1.460, IV 1, rev 2.590; axle ratio: 3.420; width of rims: 7''; tyres: F70 x 14.

PERFORMANCE max speed: about 118 mph, 190 km/h; power-weight ratio: 11.7 lb/hp, 5.3 kg/hp; speed in direct drive at 1,000 rpm: 22 mph, 35.4 km/h; fuel consumption: 14.9 m/imp gal, 12.4 m/US gal, 19 l x 100 km.

CHASSIS rear suspension: anti-roll bar.

ELECTRICAL EQUIPMENT battery: 61 Ah.

DIMENSIONS AND WEIGHT (see 200 hp power team) dry weight: plus 207 lb, 94 kg.

OPTIONAL ACCESSORIES Turbo Hydramatic automatic gearbox with 3 ratios (I 2.480, II 1.480, III 1, rev 2.080); Powerglide automatic gearbox not available.

330 hp power team

(standard for Camaro Z28; not available for other models).

See 145 hp power team, except for:

ENGINE cylinders: 8, Vee-slanted at 90°; bore and stroke: 4 x 3.48 in, 101.6 x 88.3 mm; engine capacity: 350 cu in, 5,736 cu cm; compression ratio: 9; max power (SAE): 330 hp at 5,600 rpm; max torque (SAE): 360 lb ft, 49.7 kg m at 4,000 rpm; max engine rpm: 5,800; specific power: 57.5 hp/l; crankshaft bearings: 5; camshafts: 1, at centre of Vee; carburation: 1 Holley 3989021 downdraught 4-barrel carburettor; cooling system capacity: 26.6 imp pt, 31.9 US pt, 15.1 l.

TRANSMISSION clutch: centrifugal; gears: 4 + reverse; synchromesh gears: I, II, III, IV; gearbox ratios: I 2.520, II 1.880, III 1.460, IV 1, rev 2.590; axle ratio: 3.730; width of rims: 7''; tyres: F60 x 15.

PERFORMANCE max speed: about 121 mph, 194 km/h; power-weight ratio: 10.4 lb/hp, 4.7 kg/hp; speed in direct drive at 1,000 rpm: 20.9 mph, 33.6 km/h; fuel consumption: 14.5 m/imp gal, 12.1 m/US gal, 19.5 l x 100 km.

CHASSIS rear suspension: anti-roll bar.

ELECTRICAL EQUIPMENT battery: 61 Ah.

DIMENSIONS AND WEIGHT (see 200 hp power team) dry weight: plus 117 lb, 53 kg.

OPTIONAL ACCESSORIES Turbo Hydramatic automatic gearbox with 3 ratios (I 2.480, II 1.480, III 1, rev 2.080); Powerglide automatic gearbox not available.

Biscayne - Bel Air - Impala - Caprice - Brookwood - Townsman - Kingswood - Kingswood Estate Series

PRICES IN USA:

Biscayne	4-door Sedan	$ 2,985
Bel Air	4-door Sedan	$ 3,122
Impala	2-door Sport Coupé	$ 3,297
Impala	2-door Custom Coupé	$ 3,484
Impala	4-door Sport Sedan	$ 3,472
Impala	2-door Convertible	$ 3,680
Impala	4-door Sedan	$ 3,280
Caprice	4-door Sedan	$ 3,793
Caprice	2-door Coupé	$ 3,740
Brookwood	6-passenger Station Wagon	$ 3,587
Townsman	6-passenger Station Wagon	$ 3,679
Townsman	9-passenger Station Wagon	$ 3,794
Kingswood	6-passenger Station Wagon	$ 3,771
Kingswood	9-passenger Station Wagon	$ 3,885
Kingswood Estate	6-passenger Station Wagon	$ 4,042
Kingswood Estate	9-passenger Station Wagon	$ 4,157

For V8 engines add $ 121.

145 hp power team

(standard for Biscayne, Bel Air, Impala 2-door Sport Coupé and 4-door Sedan; not available for other models).

ENGINE front, 4 stroke; cylinders: 6, in line; bore and stroke: 3.87 x 3.53 in, 98.2 x 89.6 mm; engine capacity: 250 cu in, 4,097 cu cm; compression ratio: 8.5; max power (SAE): 145 hp at 4,200 rpm; max torque (SAE): 230 lb ft, 31.8 kg m at 1,600 rpm; max engine rpm: 4,500; specific power: 35.4 hp/l; cylinder block: cast iron; cylinder head: cast iron; crankshaft bearings: 7; valves: 2 per cylinder, overhead, in line, push-rods and rockers, hydraulic tappets; camshafts: 1, side; lubrication: gear pump, full flow filter; lubricating system capacity: 8.3 imp pt, 9.9 US pt, 4.7 l; carburation: 1 Rochester 7041017 downdraught single barrel carburettor; fuel feed: mechanical pump; cooling system: water; cooling system capacity: 20.1 imp pt, 24.1 US pt, 11.4 l.

TRANSMISSION driving wheels: rear; clutch: single dry plate (diaphragm); gearbox: mechanical; gears: 3 + reverse; synchromesh gears: I, II, III; gearbox ratios: I 2.850, II 1.680, III 1, rev 2.950; gear lever: steering column; final drive: hypoid bevel; axle ratio: 3.080; width of rims: 6''; tyres: F78 x 15.

PERFORMANCE max speed: about 91 mph, 146 km/h; power-weight ratio: Biscayne 4-door Sedan and Bel Air 4-door Sedan 26.6 lb/hp, 12.1 kg/hp — Impala 4-door Sedan 26.8 lb/hp, 12.2 kg/hp; speed in direct drive at 1,000 rpm: 21.8 mph, 35.1 km/h; fuel consumption: 18.6 m/imp gal, 15.5 m/US gal, 15.2 l x 100 km.

CHASSIS perimeter box-type with cross members; front suspension: independent, wishbones, coil springs, anti-roll bar, telescopic dampers; rear suspension: rigid axle, lower trailing radius arms, upper oblique torque arms, coil springs, telescopic dampers.

STEERING recirculating ball; turns of steering wheel lock to lock: 6.33.

BRAKES front disc, rear drum, dual circuit, servo; area rubbed by linings: total 379.1 sq in, 2,445 sq cm.

ELECTRICAL EQUIPMENT voltage: 12 V; battery: 45 Ah; generator type: alternator, 37 A; ignition distributor: Delco-Remy; headlamps: 4.

DIMENSIONS AND WEIGHT wheel base: 121.50 in, 3.086 mm; front track: 64.10 in, 1,628 mm; rear track: 64 in, 1,625 mm; overall length: 216.80 in, 5,507 mm; overall width: 79.50 in, 2,019 mm; overall height: 4-door sedans 54.10 in, 1,374 mm — 2-door sport coupé 53.40 in, 1,356 mm; dry weight: Biscayne 4-door Sedan and Bel Air 4-door Sedan 3,858 lb, 1,749 kg — Impala 4-door Sedan 3,886 lb, 1,762 kg — Impala 2-door Sport Coupé 3,868 lb, 1,754 kg; turning circle (between walls): 45.2 ft, 13.8 m; fuel tank capacity: 20 imp gal, 24 US gal, 91 l.

OPTIONAL ACCESSORIES Powerglide automatic gearbox with 2 ratios (I 1.820, II 1, rev 1.820), max ratio of convertor at stall 2.10; limited slip final drive; power-assisted steering; air-conditioning system.

245 hp power team

(standard for Biscayne, Bel Air, Impala, Brookwood, Townsman and Kingswood Series; not available for other Series).

See 145 hp power team, except for:

ENGINE cylinders: 8, Vee-slanted at 90°; bore and stroke: 4 x 3.48 in, 101.6 x 88.3 mm; engine capacity: 350 cu in, 5,736 cu cm; max power (SAE): 245 hp at 4,800 rpm; max torque (SAE): 350 lb ft, 48.3 kg m at 2,800 rpm; max engine rpm: 5,200; specific power: 42.7 hp/l; crankshaft bearings: 5; camshafts: 1, at centre of Vee; carburation: 1 Rochester 7041113 downdraught twin barrel carburettor; cooling system capacity: 26.6 imp pt, 31.9 US pt, 15.1 l.

TRANSMISSION gearbox ratios: I 2.540, II 1.500, III 1, rev 2.630; axle ratio: station wagons 2.730; tyres: G78 x 15 — station wagons L78 x 15.

PERFORMANCE max speed: about 105 mph, 169 km/h; power-weight ratio: Biscayne 4-door Sedan and Bel Air 4-door Sedan 16.4 lb/hp, 7.4 kg/hp — Impala 4-door Sedan 16.5 lb/hp, 7.5 kg/hp; speed in direct drive at 1,000 rpm: 22.6 mph, 36.3 km/h; fuel consumption: 15.8 m/imp gal, 13.1 m/US gal, 17.9 l x 100 km.

CHASSIS (for station wagons only) rear suspension: rigid axle, semi-elliptic leafsprings, telescopic dampers.

BRAKES area rubbed by linings: station wagons total 391.6 sq in, 2,526 sq cm.

ELECTRICAL EQUIPMENT battery: 61 Ah.

DIMENSIONS AND WEIGHT wheel base: station wagons 125 in, 3,175 mm; overall length: 223.20 in, 5,669 mm; overall height: 2-door custom coupé 53.50 in, 1,359 mm — 2-door

CHEVROLET Caprice 2-door Coupé

CHEVROLET Kingswood 9-passenger Station Wagon

CHEVROLET Kingswood Estate 6-passenger Station Wagon

convertible 53.40 in, 1,356 mm — station wagons 57.10 in, 1,450 mm; dry weight: Biscayne 4-door Sedan and Bel Air 4-door Sedan 4,014 lb, 1,821 kg — Impala 2-door Sport Coupé 4,022 lb, 1,824 kg — Impala 2-door Custom Coupé 4,038 lb, 1,831 kg — Impala 4-door Sport Sedan 4,014 lb, 1,821 kg — Impala 2-door Convertible 4,086 lb, 1,853 kg — Impala 4-door Sedan 4,040 lb, 1,832 kg — Brookwood 6-passenger Station Wagon 4,646 lb, 2,107 kg — Townsman 6-passenger Station Wagon 4,648 lb, 2,108 kg — Townsman 9-passenger Station Wagon 4,702 lb, 2,132 kg — Kingswood 6-passenger Station Wagon 4,692 lb, 2,128 kg — Kingswood 9-passenger Station Wagon 4,752 lb, 2,155 kg; fuel tank capacity: station wagons 19.1 imp gal, 23 US gal, 87 l.

OPTIONAL ACCESSORIES Powerglide automatic gearbox with 2 ratios (I 1.760, II 1, rev 1.760), 2.730 axle ratio, only for Biscayne, Bel Air and Impala Series; Turbo Hydramatic automatic gearbox with 3 ratios (I 2.520, II 1.520, III 1, rev 1.930), max ratio of convertor at stall 2.10, 2.730 axle ratio.

255 hp power team

(standard for Caprice and Kingswood Estate Series: optional for other Series).

See 145 hp power team, except for:

ENGINE cylinders: 8, Vee-slanted at 90°; bore and stroke: 4.12 x 3.75 in, 104.6 x 95.2 mm; engine capacity: 400 cu in, 6,555 cu cm; max power (SAE): 255 hp at 4,400 rpm; max torque (SAE): 390 lb ft, 53.8 kg m at 2,400 rpm; max engine rpm: 4,800; specific power: 38.9 hp/l; crankshaft bearings: 5; camshafts: 1, at centre of Vee; carburation: 1 Rochester 7041118 downdraught twin barrel carburettor; cooling system capacity: 26.6 imp pt, 31.9 US pt, 15.1 l.

TRANSMISSION gearbox ratios: I 2.540, II 1.500, III 1, rev 2.630; axle ratio: 2.730; tyres: G78 x 15 — station wagons L78 x 15.

PERFORMANCE max speed: about 106 mph, 170 km/h; power-weight ratio: Biscayne 4-door Sedan and Bel Air 4-door Sedan 15.9 lb/hp, 7.2 kg/hp — Impala 4-door Sedan 16 lb/hp, 7.3 kg/hp — Caprice 4-door Sedan 16.3 lb/hp, 7.4 kg/hp; speed in direct drive at 1,000 rpm: 22.6 mph, 36.3 km/h; fuel consumption: 14.1 m/imp gal, 11.7 m/US gal, 20.1 l x 100 km.

CHASSIS (for station wagons only) rear suspension: rigid axle, semi-elliptic leafsprings, telescopic dampers.

BRAKES area rubbed by linings: station wagons total 391.6 sq in, 2,526 sq cm.

ELECTRICAL EQUIPMENT battery: 61 Ah.

DIMENSIONS AND WEIGHT (see 245 hp power team) dry weight: plus 46 lb, 21 kg — Caprice 4-door Sedan 4,166 lb, 1,890 kg — Caprice 2-door Coupé 4,090 lb, 1,855 kg — Kingswood Estate 6-passenger Station Wagon 4,782 lb, 2,169 kg — Kingswood Estate 9-passenger Station Wagon 4,882 lb, 2,214 kg.

OPTIONAL ACCESSORIES Turbo Hydramatic automatic gearbox with 3 ratios (I 2.480, II 1.480, III 1, rev 2.080); Powerglide automatic gearbox not available.

270 hp power team

(optional for Biscayne, Bel Air, Impala, Caprice, Brookwood, Townsman and Kingswood Series; not available for Kingswood Estate Series).

See 145 hp power team, except for:

ENGINE cylinders: 8, Vee-slanted at 90°; bore and stroke: 4 x 3.48 in, 101.6 x 88.3 mm; engine capacity: 350 cu in, 5,736 cu cm; max power (SAE): 270 hp at 4,800 rpm; max torque (SAE): 360 lb ft, 49.7 kg m at 3,200 rpm; max engine rpm: 5,200; specific power: 47 hp/l; crankshaft bearings: 5; camshafts: 1, at centre of Vee; carburation: 1 Rochester 7041202 downdraught 4-barrel carburettor; cooling system capacity: 26.6 imp pt, 31.9 US pt, 15.1 l.

TRANSMISSION gearbox: Turbo Hydramatic automatic, hydraulic torque convertor and planetary gears with 3 ratios + reverse, max ratio of convertor at stall 2.10, possible manual selection; gearbox ratios: I 2.520, II 1.520, III 1, rev 1.930; selector lever: steering column; axle ratio: 2.730; tyres: G78 x 15 — station wagons L78 x 15.

PERFORMANCE max speed: about 109 mph, 175 km/h; power-weight ratio: Biscayne 4-door Sedan and Bel Air 4-door Sedan 14.7 lb/hp, 6.6 kg/hp — Impala 4-door Sedan 14.8 lb/hp, 6.7 kg/hp — Caprice 4-door Sedan 15.4 lb/hp, 7 kg/hp; speed in direct drive at 1,000 rpm: 22.6 mph, 36.3 km/h; fuel consumption: 14.7 m/imp gal, 12.3 m/US gal, 19.2 l x 100 km.

CHASSIS (for station wagons only) rear suspension: rigid axle, semi-elliptic leafsprings, telescopic dampers.

BRAKES area rubbed by linings: stations wagons total 391.6 sq in, 2,526 sq cm.

CHEVROLET Caprice 2-door Coupé

CHEVROLET Kingswood 9-passenger Station Wagon

CHEVROLET Kingswood Estate 6-passenger Station Wagon

ELECTRICAL EQUIPMENT battery: 61 Ah.

DIMENSIONS AND WEIGHT (see 245 hp power team) dry weight: minus 52 lb, 24 kg — Caprice 4-door Sedan 4,166 lb, 1,890 kg — Caprice 2-door Coupé 4,090 lb, 1,855 kg.

OPTIONAL ACCESSORIES Powerglide automatic gearbox not available.

300 hp power team

(optional for all Series).

See 145 hp power team, except for:

ENGINE cylinders: 8, Vee-slanted at 90°; bore and stroke: 4.13 x 3.76 in, 104.8 x 95.4 mm; engine capacity: 402 cu in, 6,588 cu cm; max power (SAE): 300 hp at 4,800 rpm; max torque (SAE): 400 lb ft, 55.2 kg m at 3,200 rpm; max engine rpm: 5,200; specific power: 45.5 hp/l; crankshaft bearings: 5; camshafts: 1, at centre of Vee; carburation: 1 Rochester 7041200 downdraught 4-barrel carburettor; cooling system capacity: 38.7 imp pt, 46.5 US pt, 22 l.

TRANSMISSION gearbox: Turbo Hydramatic automatic, hydraulic torque convertor and planetary gears with 3 ratios + reverse, max ratio of convertor at stall 2.10, possible manual selection; gearbox ratios: I 2.480, II 1.480, III 1, rev 2.080; selector lever: steering column; axle ratio: 2.730; tyres: G78 x 15 — station wagons L78 x 15.

PERFORMANCE max speed: about 113 mph, 182 km/h; power-weight ratio: Biscayne 4-door Sedan and Bel Air 4-door Sedan 13.7 lb/hp, 6.2 kg/hp — Impala 4-door Sedan 13.8 lb/hp, 6.3 kg/hp — Caprice 4-door Sedan 14.3 lb/hp, 6.5 kg/hp; speed in direct drive at 1,000 rpm: 22.6 mph, 36.3 km/h; fuel consumption: 14 m/imp gal, 11.6 m/US gal, 20.2 l x 100 km.

CHASSIS (for station wagons only) rear suspension: rigid axle, semi-elliptic leafsprings, telescopic dampers.

BRAKES area rubbed by linings: station wagons total 391.6 sq in, 2,526 sq cm.

ELECTRICAL EQUIPMENT battery: 61 Ah.

DIMENSIONS AND WEIGHT (see 245 hp power team) dry weight: plus 113 lb, 51 kg — station wagons plus 104 lb, 47 kg — Caprice 4-door Sedan 4,279 lb, 1,940 kg — Caprice 2-door Coupé 4,203 lb, 1,906 kg — Kingswood Estate 6-passenger Station Wagon 4,886 lb, 2,216 kg — Kingswood Estate 9-passenger Station Wagon 4,986 lb, 2,261 kg.

OPTIONAL ACCESSORIES Powerglide automatic gearbox not available.

365 hp power team

(optional for all Series).

See 145 hp power team, except for:

ENGINE cylinders: 8, Vee-slanted at 90°; bore and stroke: 4.25 x 4 in, 107.9 x 101.6 mm; engine capacity: 454 cu in, 7,440 cu cm; max power (SAE): 365 hp at 4,800 rpm; max torque (SAE): 465 lb ft, 64.2 kg m at 3,200 rpm; max engine rpm: 5,200; specific power: 49.1 hp/l; crankshaft bearings: 5; camshafts: 1, at centre of Vee; carburation: 1 Rochester 7041200 downdraught 4-barrel carburettor; cooling system capacity: 37 imp pt, 44.4 US pt, 21 l.

TRANSMISSION gearbox: Turbo Hydramatic automatic, hydraulic torque convertor and planetary gears with 3 ratios + reverse, max ratio of convertor at stall 2.10, possible manual selection; gearbox ratios: I 2.480, II 1.480, III 1, rev 2.080; selector lever: steering column; axle ratio: 2.730; tyres: H78 x 15/— station wagons L78 x 15.

PERFORMANCE max speed: about 115 mph, 185 km/h; power-weight ratio: Biscayne 4-door Sedan and Bel Air 4-door Sedan 11.3 lb/hp, 5.1 kg/hp — Impala 4-door Sedan 11.4 lb/hp, 5.2 kg/hp — Caprice 4-door Sedan 11.7 lb/hp, 5.3 kg/hp; speed in direct drive at 1,000 rpm: 23.1 mph, 37.1 km/h; fuel consumption: 12.8 m/imp gal, 10.6 m/US gal, 22.1 l x 100 km.

CHASSIS (for station wagons only) rear suspension: rigid axle, semi-elliptic leafsprings, telescopic dampers.

BRAKES area rubbed by linings: station wagons total 391.6 sq in, 2,526 sq cm.

ELECTRICAL EQUIPMENT battery: 80 Ah.

DIMENSIONS AND WEIGHT (see 245 hp power team) dry weight: plus 108 lb, 49 kg — station wagons plus 127 lb, 58 kg — Caprice 4-door Sedan 4,274 lb, 1,838 kg — Caprice 2-door Coupé 4,198 lb, 1,904 kg — Kingswood Estate 6-passenger Station Wagon 4,909 lb, 2,226 kg — Kingswood Estate 9-passenger Station Wagon 5,009 lb, 2,272 kg.

OPTIONAL ACCESSORIES Powerglide automatic gearbox not available.

Corvette Series

270 hp power team

(standard for both models).

ENGINE front, 4 stroke; cylinders: 8, Vee-slanted at 90°; bore and stroke: 4 x 3.48 in, 101.6 x 88.3 mm; engine capacity: 350 cu in, 5,736 cu cm; compression ratio: 8.5; max power (SAE): 270 hp at 4,800 rpm; max torque (SAE): 360 lb ft, 49.7 kg m at 3,200 rpm; max engine rpm: 5,200; specific power: 47 hp/l; cylinder block: cast iron; cylinder head: cast iron; crankshaft bearings: 5; valves: 2 per cylinder, overhead, in line, push-rods and rockers, hydraulic tappets; camshafts: 1, at centre of Vee; lubrication: gear pump, full flow filter; lubricating system capacity: 8.3 imp pt, 9.9 US pt, 4.7 l; carburation: 1 Rochester 7041213 downdraught 4-barrel carburettor; fuel feed: mechanical pump; cooling system: water; cooling system capacity: 25 imp pt, 30 US pt, 14.2 l.

TRANSMISSION driving wheels: rear; clutch: single dry plate, semi-centrifugal; gearbox: mechanical; gears: 4 + reverse; synchromesh gears: I, II, III, IV; gearbox ratios: I 2.520, II 1.880, III 1.460, IV 1, rev 2.590; gear lever: central; final drive: hypoid bevel; axle ratio: 3.360; width of rims: 8''; tyres: F70 x 15.

PERFORMANCE max speed: about 120 mph, 193 km/h; power-weight ratio: 2-door sport coupé 12.2 lb/hp, 5.5 kg/hp — 2-door convertible 13.4 lb/hp, 6.1 kg/hp; speed in direct drive at 1,000 rpm: 23 mph, 37 km/h; fuel consumption: 14.9 m/imp gal, 12.4 m/US gal, 18.9 l x 100 km.

CHASSIS box-type ladder frame; front suspension: independent, wishbones, coil springs, anti-roll bar, telescopic dampers; rear suspension: independent, wishbones, semi-axle as upper arm, transverse semi-elliptic leafsprings, trailing radius arms, anti-roll bar, telescopic dampers.

STEERING recirculating ball; turns of steering wheel lock to lock: 3.40.

BRAKES disc, dual circuit; area rubbed by linings: total 461.2 sq in, 2,975 sq cm.

ELECTRICAL EQUIPMENT voltage: 12 V; battery: 62 Ah; generator type: alternator, 42 A; ignition distributor: Delco-Remy; headlamps: 4, retractable.

DIMENSIONS AND WEIGHT wheel base: 98 in, 2,489 mm; front track: 58.70 in, 1,491 mm; rear track: 59.40 in, 1,509 mm; overall length: 182.50 in, 4,635 mm; overall width: 69 in, 1,753 mm; overall height: 2-door sport coupé 47.80 in, 1,214 mm — 2-door convertible 47.90 in, 1,217 mm; ground clearance: 2-door sport coupé 4.80 in, 122 mm — 2-door convertible 4.50 in, 114 mm; dry weight: Corvette 2-door Sport Coupé 3,292 lb, 1,493 kg — Corvette 2-door Convertible 3,306 lb, 1,499 kg; turning circle (between walls): 39 ft, 11.9 m; fuel tank capacity: 15 imp gal, 18 US gal, 68 l.

BODY in plastic material; doors: 2; seats: 2; front seats: separate, built-in headrests.

OPTIONAL ACCESSORIES Turbo Hydramatic automatic gearbox with 3 ratios (I 2.480, II 1.480, III 1, rev 2.080), max ratio of convertor at stall 2.10, 3.080 axle ratio; limited slip final drive; power-assisted steering; servo brake; air-conditioning system.

330 hp power team

(optional for both models).

See 270 hp power team, except for:

ENGINE compression ratio: 9; max power (SAE): 330 hp at 5,600 rpm; max torque (SAE): 360 lb ft, 49.7 kg m at 4,000 rpm; max engine rpm: 5,800; specific power: 57.5 hp/l; carburation: 1 Holley 3989014 downdraught 4-barrel carburettor; cooling system capacity: 29.9 imp pt, 35.9 US pt, 17 l.

TRANSMISSION axle ratio: 3.550.

PERFORMANCE max speed: about 128 mph, 206 km/h; power-weight ratio: 10 lb/hp, 4.5 kg/hp; speed in direct drive at 1,000 rpm: 22.3 mph, 35.9 km/h; fuel consumption: 13.8 m/imp gal, 11.5 m/US gal, 20.4 l x 100 km.

OPTIONAL ACCESSORIES 4-speed fully synchronized mechanical gearbox (I 2.200, II 1.640, III 1.270, IV 1, rev 2.260), 3.700 or 3.360 axle ratio; Turbo Hydramatic automatic gearbox not available.

CHEVROLET Corvette 2-door Sport Coupé

CHEVROLET Corvette 2-door Convertible

CHRYSLER Newport 2-door Hardtop

365 hp power team

(optional for both models).

See 270 hp power team, except for:

ENGINE bore and stroke: 4.25 x 4 in, 107.9 x 101.6 mm; engine capacity: 454 cu in, 7,440 cu cm; max power (SAE): 365 hp at 4,800 rpm; max torque (SAE): 465 lb ft, 64.2 kg m at 3,200 rpm; max engine rpm: 5,500; specific power: 49.1 hp/l; lubricating system capacity: 10 imp pt, 12 US pt, 5.7 l; carburation: 1 Rochester 7041205 downdraught 4-barrel carburettor; cooling system capacity: 37 imp pt, 44.4 US pt, 21 l.

TRANSMISSION axle ratio: 3.080.

PERFORMANCE max speed: about 132 mph, 212 km/h; power-weight ratio: 2-door sport coupé 9.3 lb/hp, 4.2 kg/hp — 2-door convertible 9.7 lb/hp, 4.4 kg/hp; speed in direct drive at 1,000 rpm: 24 mph, 38.6 km/h; fuel consumption: 13.6 m/imp gal, 11.3 m/US gal, 20.8 l x 100 km.

ELECTRICAL EQUIPMENT battery: 80 Ah.

DIMENSIONS AND WEIGHT dry weight: plus 220 lb, 100 kg.

OPTIONAL ACCESSORIES 4-speed fully synchronized mechanical gearbox (I 2.200, II 1.640, III 1.270, IV 1, rev 2.260), 3.360 axle ratio.

425 hp power team

(optional for both models).

See 270 hp power team, except for:

ENGINE bore and stroke: 4.25 x 4 in, 107.9 x 101.6 mm; engine capacity: 454 cu in, 7,440 cu cm; compression ratio: 9; max power (SAE): 425 hp at 5,600 rpm; max torque (SAE): 475 lb ft, 65.5 kg m at 4,000 rpm; max engine rpm: 5,800; specific power: 57.1 hp/l; lubricating system capacity: 10 imp pt, 12 US pt, 5.7 l; carburation: 1 Holley 3986195 downdraught 4-barrel carburettor; cooling system capacity: 33.3 imp pt, 40 US pt, 18.9 l.

TRANSMISSION gearbox ratios: I 2.200, II 1.640, III 1.270, IV 1, rev 2.260.

PERFORMANCE max speed: about 126 mph, 202 km/h; power-weight ratio: 2-door sport coupé 7.9 lb/hp, 3.5 kg/hp — 2-door convertible 8 lb/hp, 3.6 kg/hp; speed in direct drive at 1,000 rpm: 24 mph, 38.6 km/h; fuel consumption: 12.6 m/imp gal, 10.5 m/US gal, 22.4 l x 100 km.

ELECTRICAL EQUIPMENT battery: 80 Ah.

DIMENSIONS AND WEIGHT dry weight: plus 82 lb, 37 kg.

CHRYSLER   USA

Newport - Newport Custom - 300 - New Yorker - Town and Country Series

275 hp power team

(standard for Newport, Newport Custom and Town and Country Series; not available for 300 and New Yorker Series).

ENGINE front, 4 stroke; cylinders: 8, Vee-slanted at 90°; bore and stroke: 4.25 x 3.38 in, 107.9 x 85.8 mm; engine capacity: 383 cu in, 6,277 cu cm; compression ratio: 8.5; max power (SAE): 275 hp at 4,400 rpm; max torque (SAE): 375 lb ft, 51.7 kg m at 2,800 rpm; max engine rpm: 4,800; specific power: 43.8 hp/l; cylinder block: cast iron; cylinder head: cast iron; crankshaft bearings: 5; valves: 2 per cylinder, overhead, in line, push-rods and rockers, hydraulic

CHEVROLET Corvette 2-door Sport Coupé

CHEVROLET Corvette 2-door Convertible

CHRYSLER Newport 2-door Hardtop

tappets; camshafts: 1, at centre of Vee; lubrication: rotary pump, full flow filter; lubricating system capacity: 8.3 imp pt, 9.9 US pt, 4.7 l; carburation: 1 Carter BBD 4961S down-draught twin barrel carburettor; fuel feed: mechanical pump; cooling system: water; cooling system capacity: 24.1 imp pt, 29 US pt, 13.7 l.

TRANSMISSION driving wheels: rear; clutch: single dry plate; gearbox: mechanical (station wagons only automatic standard); gears: 3 + reverse; synchromesh gears: I, II, III; gearbox ratios: I 2.550, II 1.490, III 1, rev 3.340; gear lever: steering column; final drive: hypoid bevel; axle ratio: 3.230; width of rims: 5.5'' — station wagons 6.5''; tyres: H78 x 15 — station wagons L84 x 15.

PERFORMANCE max speed: about 106 mph, 170 km/h; power-weight ratio: Newport 4-door Sedan and Newport Custom 4-door Sedan 15.4 lb/hp, 7 kg/hp; speed in direct drive at 1,000 rpm: 22.6 mph, 36.3 km/h; fuel consumption: 15.4 m/imp gal, 12.9 m/US gal, 18.3 l x 100 km.

CHASSIS integral; front suspension: independent, wishbones, lower trailing arms, longitudinal torsion bars, telescopic dampers; rear suspension: rigid axle, semi-elliptic leaf-springs, telescopic dampers.

STEERING recirculating ball; turns of steering wheel lock to lock: 5.80.

BRAKES drum, dual circuit, servo (station wagons front disc standard); area rubbed by linings: total 362.8 sq in, 2,340 sq cm (station wagons 393.6 sq in, 2,539 sq cm).

ELECTRICAL EQUIPMENT voltage: 12 V; battery: 59 Ah; generator type: alternator, 37 A; ignition distributor: Chrysler; headlamps: 4.

DIMENSIONS AND WEIGHT wheel base: 124 in, 3,149 mm — station wagons 122 in, 3,099 mm; front track: 62.10 in, 1,577 mm; rear track: 62 in, 1,575 mm — station wagons 63.40 in, 1,610 mm; overall length: 224.60 in, 5,705 mm — station wagons 224.80 in, 5,710 mm; overall width: 79 in, 2,006 mm — 4-door sedans and 4-door hardtops 79.10 in, 2,009 mm; overall height: 2-door hardtops 54.80 in, 1,392 mm — 4-door sedans and 4-door hardtops 55.20 in, 1,402 mm — station wagons 57.40 in, 1,453 mm; ground clearance: 5.90 in, 150 mm; dry weight: Newport 2-door Hardtop 4,190 lb, 1,900 kg — Newport 4-door Sedan 4,240 lb, 1,923 kg — Newport 4-door Hardtop 4,260 lb, 1,932 kg — Newport Custom 2-door Hardtop 4,195 lb, 1,902 kg — Newport Custom 4-door Sedan 4,250 lb, 1,927 kg — Newport Custom 4-door Hardtop 4,280 lb, 1,941 kg — Town and Country 6-passenger Station Wagon 4,695 lb, 2,129 kg — Town and Country 9-passenger Station Wagon 4,760 lb, 2,159 kg; turning circle (between walls): 47.5 ft, 14.5 m — station wagons 46.5 ft, 14.2 m; fuel tank capacity: 19.1 imp gal, 23 US gal, 87 l.

OPTIONAL ACCESSORIES Torqueflite automatic gearbox with 3 ratios (I 2.450, II 1.450, III 1, rev 2.200), max ratio of convertor at stall 2.02, 2.760 axle ratio; power-assisted steering; front disc brakes with servo; air-conditioning system; electrically-controlled sunshine roof only for 2-door hardtops.

300 hp power team

(optional for Newport, Newport Custom and Town and Country Series; not available for 300 and New Yorker Series).

See 275 hp power team, except for:

ENGINE max power (SAE): 300 hp at 4,800 rpm; max torque (SAE): 410 lb ft, 56.6 kg m at 3,400 rpm; max engine rpm: 5,000; specific power: 47.8 hp/l; carburation: 1 Holley R 4668A downdraught 4-barrel carburettor.

TRANSMISSION gearbox: Torqueflite automatic (standard), max ratio of convertor at stall 2.16; axle ratio: 3.230.

PERFORMANCE max speed: about 111 mph, 178 km/h; power-weight ratio: Newport 4-door Sedan 14.1 lb/hp, 6.3 kg/hp — Newport Custom 4-door Sedan 14.2 lb/hp, 6.4 kg/hp; fuel consumption: 14.7 m/imp gal, 12.3 m/US gal, 19.2 l x 100 km.

335 hp power team

(standard for 300 and New Yorker Series; optional for Town and Country Series; not available for Newport and Newport Custom Series).

See 275 hp power team, except for:

ENGINE bore and stroke: 4.32 x 3.75 in, 109.7 x 95.2 mm; engine capacity: 440 cu in, 7,211 cu cm; compression ratio: 8.8; max power (SAE): 335 hp at 4,400 rpm; max torque (SAE): 460 lb ft, 63.5 kg m at 3,200 rpm; max engine rpm: 4,600; specific power: 46.5 hp/l; lubricating system capacity: 10 imp pt, 12 US pt, 5.7 l; carburation: 1 Carter AVS 4968S downdraught 4-barrel carburettor; cooling system capacity: 25.9 imp pt, 31.1 US pt, 14.7 l.

335 HP POWER TEAM

TRANSMISSION gearbox: Torqueflite automatic (standard); axle ratio: 2.760 — station wagons 3.230; width of rims: 6'' — station wagons 6.5''; tyres: J78 x 15 — station wagons L84 x 15.

PERFORMANCE max speed: about 116 mph, 186 km/h; power-weight ratio: 300 4-door Hardtop 13.1 lb/hp, 5.9 kg/hp — New Yorker 4-door Sedan 13.3 lb/hp, 6 kg/hp; speed in direct drive at 1,000 rpm: 26 mph, 41.8 km/h; fuel consumption: 14.1 m/imp gal, 11.7 m/US gal, 20.1 l x 100 km.

BRAKES area rubbed by linings: total 393.6 sq in, 2,539 sq cm.

ELECTRICAL EQUIPMENT battery: 70 Ah.

DIMENSIONS AND WEIGHT overall height: New Yorker 4-door Sedan 55 in, 1,397 mm — New Yorker 4-door Hardtop 55.40 in, 1,407 mm; dry weight: 300 2-door Hardtop 4,315 lb, 1,957 kg — 300 4-door Hardtop 4,390 lb, 1,991 kg — New Yorker 4-door Sedan 4,455 lb, 2,020 kg — New Yorker 4-door Hardtop 4,475 lb, 2,030 kg; turning circle (between walls): New Yorker 47.4 ft, 14.4 m.

370 hp power team

(optional for Newport, Newport Custom, 300 and New Yorker Series; not available for Town and Country Series).

See 275 hp power team, except for:

ENGINE bore and stroke: 4.32 x 3.75 in, 109.7 x 95.2 mm; engine capacity: 440 cu in, 7,211 cu cm; compression ratio: 9.5; max power (SAE): 370 hp at 4,600 rpm; max torque (SAE): 480 lb ft, 66.2 kg m at 3,200 rpm; max engine rpm: 4,800; specific power: 51.3 hp/l; lubricating system capacity: 10 imp pt, 12 US pt, 5.7 l; carburation: 1 Carter AVS 4968S downdraught 4-barrel carburettor; cooling system capacity: 25.9 imp pt, 31.1 US pt, 14.7 l.

TRANSMISSION gearbox: Torqueflite automatic (standard); width of rims: 6''; tyres: J78 x 15.

PERFORMANCE max speed: about 121 mph, 194 km/h; power-weight ratio: Newport 4-door Sedan and Newport Custom 4-door Sedan 11.4 lb/hp, 5.2 kg/hp — 300 4-door Hardtop 11.8 lb/hp, 5.3 kg/hp — New Yorker 4-door Sedan 12 lb/hp, 5.4 kg/hp; speed in direct drive at 1,000 rpm: 26 mph, 41.8 km/h; fuel consumption: 12.8 m/imp gal, 10.7 m/US gal, 22 l x 100 km.

ELECTRICAL EQUIPMENT battery: 70 Ah.

DIMENSIONS AND WEIGHT overall height: New Yorker 55 in, 1,397 mm — New Yorker 4-door Hardtop 55.40 in, 1,407 mm; dry weight: 300 2-door Hardtop 4,315 lb, 1,957 kg — 300 4-door Hardtop 4,390 lb, 1,991 kg — New Yorker 2-door Hardtop 4,370 lb, 1,981 kg — New Yorker 4-door Sedan 4,455 lb, 2,020 kg — New Yorker 4-door Hardtop 4,475 lb, 2,030 kg; turning circle (between walls): New Yorker 47.4 ft, 14.4 m.

DODGE   USA

Dart - Demon - Demon 340 - Dart Swinger - Dart Custom Series

PRICES IN USA:

Dart	4-door Sedan	$ 2,450
Demon	2-door Coupé	$ 2,343
Demon 340	2-door Coupé	$ 2,721
Dart Swinger	2-door Hardtop	$ 2,561
Dart Custom	4-door Sedan	$ 2,609

For V8 engines add $ 124.

125 hp power team

(standard for Dart, Demon, Dart Swinger and Dart Custom; not available for Demon 340).

ENGINE front, 4 stroke; cylinders: 6, in line; bore and stroke: 3.40 x 3.64 in, 86.4 x 92.4 mm; engine capacity: 198 cu in, 3,245 cu cm; compression ratio: 8.4; max power (SAE): 125 hp at 4,400 rpm; max torque (SAE): 180 lb ft, 24.8 kg m at 2,000 rpm; max engine rpm: 4,600; specific power: 38.5 hp/l; cylinder block: cast iron; cylinder head: cast iron; crankshaft bearings: 4; valves: 2 per cylinder, overhead, in line, push-rods and rockers; camshafts: 1, side; lubrication: rotary pump, full flow filter; lubricating system capacity: 8.3 imp pt, 9.9 US pt, 4.7 l; carburation:

DODGE Demon 2-door Coupé

DODGE Demon 340 2-door Coupé

DODGE Dart Custom 4-door Sedan

Carter BB-4955S downdraught single barrel carburettor; fuel feed: mechanical pump; cooling system: water; cooling system capacity: 21.6 imp pt, 26 US pt, 12.3 l.

TRANSMISSION driving wheels: rear; clutch: single dry plate; gearbox: mechanical; gears: 3 + reverse; synchromesh gears: II and III; gearbox ratios: I 2.950, II 1.830, III 1, rev 3.800; gear lever: steering column or central; final drive: hypoid bevel; axle ratio: 3.230; width of rims: 4.5''; tyres: 6.45 x 14.

PERFORMANCE max speed: about 92 mph, 148 km/h; power-weight ratio: Dart 4-door Sedan, Dart Swinger 2-door Hardtop and Dart Custom 4-door Sedan 23.9 lb/hp, 10.8 kg/hp — Demon 2-door Coupé 23.4 lb/hp, 10.6 kg/hp; speed in direct drive at 1,000 rpm: 20.2 mph, 32.5 km/h; fuel consumption: 21.2 m/imp gal, 17.7 m/US gal, 13.3 l x 100 km.

CHASSIS integral; front suspension: independent, wishbones, longitudinal torsion bars, telescopic dampers; rear suspension: rigid axle, semi-elliptic leafsprings, telescopic dampers.

STEERING recirculating ball; turns of steering wheel lock to lock: 5.30.

BRAKES drum, dual circuit; area rubbed by linings: total 254.5 sq in, 1,641 sq cm.

ELECTRICAL EQUIPMENT voltage: 12 V; battery: 40 Ah; generator type: alternator, 34 A; ignition distributor: Chrysler; headlamps: 2.

DIMENSIONS AND WEIGHT wheel base: 111 in, 2,819 mm — Demon 108 in, 2,743 mm; front track: 57.40 in, 1,458 mm — Demon 57.50 in, 1,460 mm; rear track: 55.50 in, 1,410 mm; overall length: 196.20 in, 4,983 mm — Demon 192.50 in, 4,889 mm; overall width: 69.70 in, 1,770 mm — Demon 69.70 in, 1,819 mm; overall height: Dart and Dart Custom 71.60 in, 1,819 mm — Demon 52 in, 1,321 mm — Dart Swinger 52.60 in, 1,336 mm; dry weight: Dart 4-door Sedan, Dart Swinger 2-door Hardtop and Dart Custom 4-door Sedan 2,985 lb, 1,354 kg — Demon 2-door Coupé 2,930 lb, 1,329 kg; turning circle (between walls): 40.4 ft, 12.3 m; fuel tank capacity: 14.1 imp gal, 17 US gal, 64 l.

BODY seats: 4-5; front seats: bench, separate backrests, built-in headrests.

OPTIONAL ACCESSORIES Torqueflite automatic gearbox with 3 ratios (I 2.450, II 1.450, III 1, rev 2.200), max ratio of convertor at stall 2.16, 2.760 axle ratio; limited slip final drive; anti-roll bar on front suspension; power-assisted steering; servo brake; front disc brakes with servo.

145 hp power team

(optional for Dart, Demon, Dart Swinger and Dart Custom; not available for Demon 340).

See 125 hp power team, except for:

ENGINE bore and stroke: 3.40 x 4.12 in, 86.4 x 104.6 mm; engine capacity: 225 cu in, 3,688 cu cm; max power (SAE): 145 hp at 4,000 rpm; max torque (SAE): 215 lb ft, 29.7 kg m at 2,400 rpm; max engine rpm: 4,500; specific power: 39.3 hp/l; carburation: 1 Holley R-4655A downdraught single barrel carburettor.

TRANSMISSION tyres: 6.95 x 14.

PERFORMANCE max speed: about 98 mph, 157 km/h; power-weight ratio: Dart 4-door Sedan, Dart Swinger 2-door Hardtop and Dart Custom 4-door Sedan 20.6 lb/hp, 9.3 kg/hp — Demon 2-door Coupé 20.2 lb/hp, 9.2 kg/hp; speed in direct drive at 1,000 rpm: 21.9 mph, 35.2 km/h; fuel consumption: 20 m/imp gal, 16.7 m/US gal, 14.1 l x 100 km.

OPTIONAL ACCESSORIES air-conditioning system.

230 hp power team

(standard for Dart, Demon, Dart Swinger and Dart Custom; not available for Demon 340).

See 125 hp power team, except for:

ENGINE cylinders: 8, Vee-slanted at 90°; bore and stroke: 3.91 x 3.31 in, 99.3 x 84.1 mm; engine capacity: 318 cu in, 5,212 cu cm; compression ratio: 8.6; max power (SAE): 230 hp at 4,400 rpm; max torque (SAE): 320 lb ft, 44.1 kg m at 2,000 rpm; max engine rpm: 5,000; specific power: 44.1 hp/l; crankshaft bearings: 5; valves: hydraulic tappets; camshafts: 1, at centre of Vee; carburation: 1 Carter BBD-4957S downdraught twin barrel carburettor; cooling system capacity: 26.6 imp pt, 31.9 US pt, 15.1 l.

PERFORMANCE max speed: about 109 mph, 175 km/h; power-weight ratio: Dart 4-door Sedan, Dart Swinger 2-door Hardtop and Dart Custom 4-door Sedan 13.3 lb/hp, 6 kg/hp — Demon 2-door Coupé 13.1 lb/hp, 5.9 kg/hp; speed in direct drive at 1,000 rpm: 21.9 mph, 35.2 km/h; fuel consumption: 16.7 m/imp gal, 13.9 m/US gal, 16.9 l x 100 km.

DODGE Demon 2-door Coupé

DODGE Demon 340 2-door Coupé

DODGE Dart Custom 4-door Sedan

BRAKES area rubbed by linings: total 251.4 sq in, 1,621 sq cm.

ELECTRICAL EQUIPMENT generator type: alternator, 37 A.

DIMENSIONS AND WEIGHT overall height: Dart and Dart Custom 53.90 in, 1,369 mm — Demon 52.20 in, 1,326 mm; dry weight: Dart 4-door Sedan, Dart Swinger 2-door Hardtop and Dart Custom 4-door Sedan 3,070 lb, 1,392 kg — Demon 2-door Coupé 3,020 lb, 1,369 kg.

OPTIONAL ACCESSORIES air-conditioning system.

275 hp power team

(standard for Demon 340; not available for other models).

See 125 hp power team, except for:

ENGINE cylinders: 8, Vee-slanted at 90°; bore and stroke: 4.04 x 3.31 in, 102.5 x 84.1 mm; engine capacity: 340 cu in, 5,572 cu cm; compression ratio: 10.2; max power (SAE): 275 hp at 5,000 rpm; max torque (SAE): 340 lb ft, 46.9 kg m at 3,200 rpm; max engine rpm: 5,300; specific power: 49.4 hp/l; crankshaft bearings: 5; valves: hydraulic tappets; camshafts: 1, at centre of Vee; carburation: 1 Carter TQ-4972S downdraught 4-barrel carburettor; cooling system capacity: 25 imp pt, 30 US pt, 14.2 l.

TRANSMISSION synchromesh gears: I, II, III; gearbox ratios: I 2.550, II 1.490, III 1, rev 3.340; width of rims: 5.5''; tyres: E70 x 14.

PERFORMANCE max speed: about 116 mph, 186 km/h; power-weight ratio: 11.8 lb/hp, 5.3 kg/hp; speed in direct drive at 1,000 rpm: 22 mph, 35.4 km/h; fuel consumption: 15.6 m/imp gal, 13 m/US gal, 18.1 l x 100 km.

CHASSIS front suspension: anti-roll bar (standard).

BRAKES area rubbed by linings: total 251.4 sq in, 1,621 sq cm.

ELECTRICAL EQUIPMENT generator type: alternator, 37 A.

DIMENSIONS AND WEIGHT overall height: 52.60 in, 1,336 mm; dry weight: 3,250 lb, 1,474 kg.

OPTIONAL ACCESSORIES Torqueflite automatic gearbox with 3.230 axle ratio; 4-speed fully synchronized mechanical gearbox (I 2.470, II 1.770, III 1.340, IV 1, rev 2.400), 3.230 axle ratio; air-conditioning system.

Challenger Coupé - Challenger - Challenger T/A - Challenger R/T Series

PRICES IN USA:

Challenger Coupé	2-door Coupé	$ 2,706
Challenger	2-door Hardtop	$ 2,827
Challenger	2-door Convertible	$ 3,084
Challenger T/A	2-door Hardtop	$
Challenger R/T	2-door Hardtop	$ 3,252

For V8 engines add $ 102 (for Challenger Coupé add $ 126).

125 hp power team

(standard for Challenger Coupé; not available for other models).

ENGINE front, 4 stroke; cylinders: 6, in line; bore and stroke: 3.40 x 3.64 in, 86.4 x 92.4 mm; engine capacity: 198 cu in, 3,245 cu cm; compression ratio: 8.4; max power (SAE): 125 hp at 4,400 rpm; max torque (SAE): 180 lb ft, 24.8 kg m at 2,000 rpm; max engine rpm: 4,600; specific power: 38.5 hp/l; cylinder block: cast iron; cylinder head: cast iron; crankshaft bearings: 4; valves: 2 per cylinder, overhead, in line, push-rods and rockers; camshafts: 1, side; lubrication: rotary pump, full flow filter; lubricating system capacity: 8.3 imp pt, 9.9 US pt, 4.7 l; carburation: 1 Carter BBS-4955S downdraught single barrel carburettor; fuel feed: mechanical pump; cooling system: water; cooling system capacity: 21.6 imp pt, 26 US pt, 12.3 l.

TRANSMISSION driving wheels: rear; clutch: single dry plate; gearbox: mechanical; gears: 3 + reverse, synchromesh gears: I, II, III; gearbox ratios: I 3.080, II 1.700, III 1, rev 2.900; gear lever: central; final drive: hypoid bevel; axle ratio: 3.230; width of rims: 5''; tyres: 7.35 x 14.

PERFORMANCE max speed: about 89 mph, 143 km/h; power-weight ratio: 24.9 lb/hp, 11.3 kg/hp; speed in direct drive at 1,000 rpm: 21.1 mph, 34 km/h; fuel consumption: 20.2 m/imp gal, 16.8 m/US gal, 14 l x 100 km.

CHASSIS integral; front suspension: independent, wishbones, longitudinal torsion bars, telescopic dampers; rear

suspension: rigid axle, semi-elliptic leafsprings, telescopic dampers.

STEERING recirculating ball; turns of steering wheel lock to lock: 5.30.

BRAKES drum, dual circuit; area rubbed by linings: total 314.2 sq in, 2,026 sq cm.

ELECTRICAL EQUIPMENT voltage: 12 V; battery: 46 Ah; generator type: alternator, 37 A; ignition distributor: Chrysler; headlamps: 4.

DIMENSIONS AND WEIGHT wheel base: 110 in, 2,794 mm; front track: 59.70 in, 1,516 mm; rear track: 61.60 in, 1,565 mm; overall length: 191.30 in, 4,859 mm; overall width: 76.10 in, 1,933 mm; overall height: 50.60 in, 1,285 mm; ground clearance: 4.90 in, 124 mm; dry weight: 3,110 lb, 1,410 kg; turning circle (between walls): 42.8 ft, 13 m; fuel tank capacity: 15 imp gal, 18 US gal, 68 l.

BODY seats: 4; front seats: separate.

OPTIONAL ACCESSORIES Torqueflite automatic gearbox with 3 ratios (I 2.450, II 1.450, III 1, rev 2.200), max ratio of convertor at stall 2.16, 2.760 axle ratio; limited slip final drive; anti-roll bar on front suspension; power-assisted steering; servo brake; front disc brakes with servo.

145 hp power team

(standard for Challenger Series; optional for Challenger Coupé; not available for other models).

See 125 hp power team, except for:

ENGINE bore and stroke: 3.40 x 4.12 in, 86.4 x 104.6 mm; engine capacity: 225 cu in, 3,688 cu cm; max power (SAE): 145 hp at 4,000 rpm; max torque (SAE): 215 lb ft, 29.7 kg m at 2,400 rpm; max engine rpm: 4,500; specific power: 39.3 hp/l; carburation: 1 Holley R-4655A downdraught single barrel carburettor.

PERFORMANCE max speed: about 94 mph, 151 km/h; power-weight ratio: Challenger Coupé 21.4 lb/hp, 9.7 kg/hp — Challenger 2-door Hardtop 21.8 lb/hp, 9.9 kg/hp — Challenger 2-door Convertible 22.3 lb/hp, 10.1 kg/hp; fuel consumption: 19.6 m/imp gal, 16.3 m/US gal, 14.4 l x 100 km.

DIMENSIONS AND WEIGHT overall height: 50.80 in, 1,290 mm; dry weight: Challenger 2-door Hardtop 3,155 lb, 1,431 kg — Challenger 2-door Convertible 3,240 lb, 1,469 kg.

OPTIONAL ACCESSORIES air-conditioning system.

230 hp power team

(standard for Challenger Coupé and Challenger Series; not available for other models).

See 125 hp power team, except for:

ENGINE cylinders: 8, Vee-slanted at 90°; bore and stroke: 3.91 x 3.31 in, 99.3 x 84.1 mm; engine capacity: 318 cu in, 5,212 cu cm; compression ratio: 8.6; max power (SAE): 230 hp at 4,400 rpm; max torque (SAE): 320 lb ft, 44.1 kg m at 2,000 rpm; max engine rpm: 5,000; specific power: 44.1 hp/l; crankshaft bearings: 5; valves: hydraulic tappets; camshafts: 1, at centre of Vee; carburation: 1 Carter BBD-4957S downdraught twin barrel carburettor; cooling system capacity: 26.6 imp pt, 31.9 US pt, 15.1 l.

PERFORMANCE max speed: about 105 mph, 169 km/h; power-weight ratio: Challenger Coupé 13.8 lb/hp, 6.2 kg/hp — Challenger 2-door Hardtop 13.9 lb/hp, 6.3 kg/hp — Challenger 2-door Convertible 14.3 lb/hp, 6.5 kg/hp; fuel consumption: 17 m/imp gal, 14.2 m/US gal, 16.6 l x 100 km.

DIMENSIONS AND WEIGHT rear track: 60.70 in, 1,542 mm; overall height: 50.90 in, 1,293 mm; dry weight: Challenger Coupé 3,170 lb, 1,438 kg — Challenger 2-door Hardtop 3,210 lb, 1,456 kg — Challenger 2-door Convertible 3,300 lb, 1,496 kg.

OPTIONAL ACCESSORIES air-conditiong system.

275 hp power team

(optional for Challenger and Challenger R/T Series; not available for other models).

See 125 hp power team, except for:

ENGINE cylinders: 8, Vee-slanted at 90°; bore and stroke: 4.04 x 3.31 in, 102.5 x 84.1 mm; engine capacity: 340 cu in,

DODGE 300 hp engine

DODGE Challenger R/T 2-door Hardtop

DODGE Charger Super Bee 2-door Hardtop

5,572 cu cm; compression ratio: 10.2; max power (SAE): 275 hp at 5,000 rpm; max torque (SAE): 340 lb ft, 46.9 kg m at 3,200 rpm; max engine rpm: 5,300; specific power: 49.4 hp/l; crankshaft bearings: 5; valves: hydraulic tappets; camshafts: 1, at centre of Vee; carburation: 1 Carter TQ-4972S downdraught 4-barrel carburettor; cooling system capacity: 25 imp pt, 30 US pt, 14.2 l.

TRANSMISSION gearbox ratios: I 2.550, II 1.480, III 1, rev 3.340; width of rims: 5.5''; tyres: F70 x 14.

PERFORMANCE max speed: about 111 mph, 178 km/h; power-weight ratio: Challenger 2-door Hardtop 11.7 lb/hp, 5.3 kg/hp — Challenger 2-door Convertible 12 lb/hp, 5.4 kg/hp — Challenger R/T 2-door Hardtop 12.7 lb/hp, 5.8 kg/hp; fuel consumption: 15.4 m/imp gal, 12.9 m/US gal, 18.3 l x 100 km.

CHASSIS front suspension: anti-roll bar (standard).

BRAKES area rubbed by linings: total 380.1 sq in, 2,451 sq cm.

ELECTRICAL EQUIPMENT battery: 59 Ah.

DIMENSIONS AND WEIGHT front track: Challenger R/T 60.20 in, 1,529 mm; rear track: Challenger R/T 60.70 in, 1,542 mm; overall height: 50.90 in, 1,293 mm — Challenger R/T 51.20 in, 1,300 mm; dry weight: Challenger 2-door Hardtop 3,210 lb, 1,456 kg — Challenger 2-door Convertible 3,300 lb, 1,496 kg — Challenger R/T 2-door Hardtop 3,485 lb, 1,580 kg.

OPTIONAL ACCESSORIES Torqueflite automatic gearbox with 3.230 axle ratio; 4-speed fully synchronized mechanical gearbox (I 2.470, II 1.770, III 1.340, IV 1, rev 2.400), 3.230 axle ratio; air-conditioning system.

275 hp power team

(optional for Challenger Coupé and Challenger Series; not available for other models).

See 125 hp power team, except for:

ENGINE cylinders: 8, Vee-slanted at 90°; bore and stroke: 4.25 x 3.38 in, 107.9 x 85.8 mm; engine capacity: 383 cu in, 6,276 cu cm; compression ratio: 8.5; max power (SAE): 275 hp at 4,400 rpm; max torque (SAE): 375 lb ft, 51.7 kg m at 2,800 rpm; max engine rpm: 4,700; specific power: 43.8 hp/l; crankshaft bearings: 5; valves: hydraulic tappets; camshafts: 1, at centre of Vee; carburation: 1 Carter BBD-4962S downdraught twin barrel carburettor; cooling system capacity: 24.1 imp pt, 29 US pt, 13.7 l.

TRANSMISSION gearbox: Torqueflite automatic (standard), max ratio of convertor at stall 2.02; width of rims: 5.5''; tyres: F78 x 14.

PERFORMANCE max speed: about 109 mph, 175 km/h; power-weight ratio: Challenger Coupé 11.5 lb/hp, 5.2 kg/hp — Challenger 2-door Hardtop 11.7 lb/hp, 5.3 kg/hp — Challenger 2-door Convertible 12 lb/hp, 5.4 kg/hp; speed in direct drive at 1,000 rpm: 23 mph, 37 km/h; fuel consumption: 15.7 m/imp gal, 13.1 m/US gal, 18 l x 100 km.

CHASSIS front suspension: anti-roll bar (standard).

ELECTRICAL EQUIPMENT battery: 59 Ah.

DIMENSIONS AND WEIGHT (see 230 hp power team).

OPTIONAL ACCESSORIES air-conditioning system.

290 hp power team

(standard for Challenger T/A; not available for other models).

See 125 hp power team, except for:

ENGINE cylinders: 8, Vee-slanted at 90°; bore and stroke: 4.04 x 3.31 in, 102.5 x 84.1 mm; engine capacity: 340 cu in, 5,572 cu cm; compression ratio: 10.2; max power (SAE): 290 hp at 5,000 rpm; max torque (SAE): 340 lb ft, 46.9 kg m at 3,200 rpm; max engine rpm: 5,300; specific power: 52 hp/l; crankshaft bearings: 5; valves: hydraulic tappets; camshafts: 1, at centre of Vee; carburation: 3 Holley R-4789A-4790A-4791A downdraught twin barrel carburettors; cooling system capacity: 25 imp pt, 30 US pt, 14.2 l.

TRANSMISSION gears: 4 + reverse; synchromesh gears: I, II, III, IV; gearbox ratios: I 2.470, II 1.770, III 1.340, IV 1, rev 2.400; axle ratio: 3.550; width of rims: 7''; tyres: E60 x 15 front, G60 x 15 rear.

PERFORMANCE max speed: about 113 mph, 182 km/h; speed in direct drive at 1,000 rpm: 21.4 mph, 34.4 km/h; fuel consumption: 14.9 m/imp gal, 12.4 m/US gal, 18.9 l x 100 km.

CHASSIS front suspension: anti-roll bar (standard).

DODGE Challenger 2-door Hardtop

DODGE Challenger R/T 2-door Hardtop

DODGE Charger Super Bee 2-door Hardtop

BRAKES area rubbed by linings: total 380.1 sq in, 2,451 sq cm.

ELECTRICAL EQUIPMENT battery: 59 Ah.

DIMENSIONS AND WEIGHT front track: 60.70 in, 1,542 mm; rear track: 61.20 in, 1,554 mm; overall height: 51.70 in, 1,313 mm.

OPTIONAL ACCESSORIES Torqueflite automatic gearbox with 3.550 axle ratio; air-conditioning system.

300 hp power team

(standard for Challenger R/T; optional for Challenger Coupé and Challenger Series; not available for Challenger T/A).

See 125 hp power team, except for:

ENGINE cylinders: 8, Vee-slanted at 90°; bore and stroke: 4.25 x 3.38 in, 107.9 x 85.8 mm; engine capacity: 383 cu in, 6,276 cu cm; compression ratio: 8.5; max power (SAE): 300 hp at 4,800 rpm; max torque (SAE): 410 lb ft, 56.6 kg m at 3,400 rpm; max engine rpm: 5,200; specific power: 47.8 hp/l; crankshaft bearings: 5; valves: hydraulic tappets; camshafts: 1, at centre of Vee; carburation: 1 Holley R-4667A downdraught 4-barrel carburettor; cooling system capacity: 24.1 imp pt, 29 US pt, 13.7 l.

TRANSMISSION gearbox ratios: I 2.550, II 1.480, III 1, rev 3.340; width of rims: 5.5''; tyres: F78 x 14 — Challenger R/T F70 x 14.

PERFORMANCE max speed: about 114 mph, 183 km/h; power-weight ratio: Challenger Coupé 10.6 lb/hp, 4.8 kg/hp — Challenger 2-door Hardtop 10.7 lb/hp, 4.9 kg/hp — Challenger 2-door Convertible 11 lb/hp, 5 kg/hp — Challenger R/T 2-door Hardtop 11.9 lb/hp, 5.4 kg/hp; speed in direct drive at 1,000 rpm: 21.9 mph, 35.2 km/h; fuel consumption: 14.8 m/imp gal, 12.3 m/US gal, 19.1 l x 100 km.

CHASSIS front suspension: anti-roll bar (standard).

BRAKES area rubbed by linings: total 380.1 sq in, 2,451 sq cm.

ELECTRICAL EQUIPMENT battery: 59 Ah.

DIMENSIONS AND WEIGHT (see 230 hp power team) front track: Challenger R/T 60.20 in, 1,529 mm; rear track: Challenger R/T 60.70 in, 1,542 mm; overall height: Challenger R/T 51.20 in, 1,300 mm; dry weight: Challenger R/T 2-door Hardtop 3,585 lb, 1,626 kg.

OPTIONAL ACCESSORIES Torqueflite automatic gearbox with 2.760 axle ratio; 4-speed fully synchronized mechanical gearbox (I 2.470, II 1.770, III 1.340, IV 1, rev 2.400), 3.230 axle ratio; air-conditioning system.

385 hp power team

(optional for Challenger R/T; not available for other models).

See 125 hp power team, except for:

ENGINE cylinders: 8, Vee-slanted at 90°; bore and stroke: 4.32 x 3.75 in, 109.7 x 95.2 mm; engine capacity: 440 cu in, 7,210 cu cm; compression ratio: 10.3; max power (SAE): 385 hp at 4,700 rpm; max torque (SAE): 490 lb ft, 67.6 kg m at 3,200 rpm; max engine rpm: 5,500; specific power: 53.4 hp/l; crankshaft bearings: 5; valves: hydraulic tappets; camshafts: 1, at centre of Vee; lubricating system capacity: 10 imp pt, 12 US pt, 5.7 l; carburation: 3 Holley R-4671A-4672A-4669A downdraught twin barrel carburettors; cooling system capacity: 28.3 imp pt, 34 US pt, 16.1 l.

TRANSMISSION gears: 4 + reverse; synchromesh gears: I, II, III, IV; gearbox ratios: I 2.440, II 1.770, III 1.340, IV 1, rev 2.360, axle ratio: 3.540; width of rims: 6''; tyres: F70 x 14.

PERFORMANCE max speed: about 120 mph, 193 km/h; power-weight ratio: 9.3 lb/hp, 4.2 kg/hp; speed in direct drive at 1,000 rpm: 21.8 mph, 35.1 km/h; fuel consumption: 12.4 m/imp gal, 10.3 m/US gal, 22.8 l x 100 km.

CHASSIS front suspension: anti-roll bar (standard).

BRAKES area rubbed by linings: total 380.1 sq in, 2,451 sq cm.

ELECTRICAL EQUIPMENT battery: 70 Ah.

DIMENSIONS AND WEIGHT front track: 60.20 in, 1,529 mm; rear track: 60.70 in, 1,542 mm; overall height: 51.20 in, 1,300 mm; dry weight: 3,585 lb, 1,626 kg.

OPTIONAL ACCESSORIES Torqueflite automatic gearbox with max ratio of convertor at stall 2.02, 3.230 axle ratio; air-conditioning system.

425 hp power team

(optional for Challenger R/T; not available for other models).

See 125 hp power team, except for:

ENGINE cylinders: 8, Vee-slanted at 90°; bore and stroke: 4.25 x 3.75 in, 107.9 x 95.2 mm; engine capacity: 426 cu in, 6,981 cu cm; compression ratio: 10.2; max power (SAE): 425 hp at 5,000 rpm; max torque (SAE): 490 lb ft, 67.6 kg m at 4,000 rpm; max engine rpm: 5,700; specific power: 60.9 hp/l; crankshaft bearings: 5; valves: hydraulic tappets; camshafts: 1, at centre of Vee; lubricating system capacity: 10 imp pt, 12 US pt, 5.7 l; carburation: 2 Carter AFB-4971S-4969S downdraught 4-barrel carburettors; cooling system capacity: 26.6 imp pt, 31.9 US pt, 15.1 l.

TRANSMISSION gears: 4 + reverse; synchromesh gears: I, II, III, IV; gearbox ratios: I 2.440, II 1.770, III 1.340, IV 1, rev 2.360; axle ratio: 3.540; width of rims: 7''; tyres: F60 x 15.

PERFORMANCE max speed: about 123 mph, 198 km/h; power-weight ratio: 8.4 lb/hp, 3.8 kg/hp; speed in direct drive at 1,000 rpm: 21.8 mph, 35.1 km/h; fuel consumption: 12.6 m/imp gal, 10.5 m/US gal, 22.4 l x 100 km.

CHASSIS front suspension: anti-roll bar (standard).

BRAKES area rubbed by linings: total 380.1 sq in, 2,451 sq cm.

ELECTRICAL EQUIPMENT battery: 70 Ah.

DIMENSIONS AND WEIGHT front track: 60.20 in, 1,529 mm; rear track: 60.70 in, 1,542 mm; overall height: 51.20 in, 1,300 mm; dry weight: 3,585 lb, 1,626 kg.

OPTIONAL ACCESSORIES Torqueflite automatic gearbox with 3.230 axle ratio; air-conditioning system.

Charger Coupé - Coronet - Charger Super Bee - Coronet Custom - Charger - Charger 500 - Charger S.E. - Coronet Brougham - Coronet Crestwood - Charger R/T Series

PRICES IN USA:

Charger Coupé	2-door Coupé	$ 2,707
Coronet	4-door Sedan	$ 2,777
Coronet	6-passenger Station Wagon	$ 3,075
Charger Super Bee	2-door Hardtop	$ 3,245
Coronet Custom	4-door Sedan	$ 2,925
Coronet Custom	6-passenger Station Wagon	$ 3,296
Coronet Custom	9-passenger Station Wagon	$ 3,472
Charger	2-door Hardtop	$ 2,948
Charger 500	2-door Hardtop	$ 3,196
Charger S.E.	2-door Hardtop	$ 3,396
Coronet Brougham	4-door Sedan	$ 3,206
Coronet Crestwood	6-passenger Station Wagon	$ 3,575
Coronet Crestwood	9-passenger Station Wagon	$ 3,655
Charger R/T	2-door Hardtop	$ 3,750

For V8 engines add $ 95.

145 hp power team

(standard for Charger Coupé, Coronet and Charger Series, and all Coronet Custom Series except 9-passenger Station Wagon model; not available for other Series).

ENGINE front, 4 stroke; cylinders: 6, in line; bore and stroke: 3.40 x 4.12 in, 86.4 x 104.6 mm; engine capacity: 225 cu in, 3,688 cu cm; compression ratio: 8.4; max power (SAE): 145 hp at 4,000 rpm; max torque (SAE): 215 lb ft, 29.7 kg m at 2,400 rpm; max engine rpm: 4,500; specific power: 39.3 hp/l; cylinder block: cast iron; cylinder head: cast iron; crankshaft bearings: 4; valves: 2 per cylinder, overhead, in line, push-rods and rockers; camshafts: 1, side; lubrication: rotary pump, full flow filter; lubricating system capacity: 8.3 imp pt, 9.9 US pt, 4.7 l; carburation: 1 Holley R-4655A downdraught single barrel carburettor; fuel feed: mechanical pump; cooling system: water; cooling system capacity: 21.6 imp pt, 26 US pt, 12.3 l.

TRANSMISSION driving wheels: rear; clutch: single dry plate; gearbox: mechanical; gears: 3 + reverse; synchromesh gears: II and III; gearbox ratios: I 2.950, II 1.830, III 1, rev 3.800; gear lever: steering column or central; final drive: hypoid bevel; axle ratio: 3.230 — station wagons 3.550; width of rims: 5'' — station wagons 5.5''; tyres: E78 x 14 — station wagons H78 x 14.

PERFORMANCE max speed: about 94 mph, 151 km/h; power-weight ratio: Coronet Custom 4-door Sedan and Coronet 4-door Sedan 23.1 lb/hp, 10.5 kg/hp; speed in direct drive at

DODGE Charger 500 2-door Hardtop

DODGE Charger S.E. 2-door Hardtop

DODGE Coronet Brougham 4-door Sedan

000 rpm: 21 mph, 33.8 km/h; fuel consumption: 19.5 m/imp
al, 16.2 m/US gal, 14.5 l x 100 km.

HASSIS integral; front suspension: independent, wishbones,
ngitudinal torsion bars, telescopic dampers (anti-roll bar
n station wagons only); rear suspension: rigid axle, semi-
liptic leafsprings, telescopic dampers.

TEERING recirculating ball; turns of steering wheel lock
o lock: 5.30.

RAKES drum, dual circuit; area rubbed by linings: total
14.2 sq in, 2,026 sq cm (station wagons 380.1 sq in, 2,451
q cm).

LECTRICAL EQUIPMENT voltage: 12 V; battery: 46 Ah;
enerator type: alternator, 37 A; ignition distributor: Chrys-
er; headlamps: 4.

IMENSIONS AND WEIGHT wheel base: 115 in, 2,921 mm
- 4-door sedans and station wagons 118 in, 2,997 mm; front
rack: 59.70 in, 1,516 mm — station wagons 60.10 in, 1,526
mm; rear track: 61.60 in, 1,565 mm — 2-door hardtop 62 in,
,575 mm — station wagons 63.40 in, 1,610 mm; overall
ength: 205.40 in, 5,217 mm — 4-door sedans 207 in, 5,258
mm — station wagons 213.40 in, 5,420 mm; overall width:
6.90 in, 1,953 mm — 4-door sedans 77.70 in, 1,973 mm —
tation wagons 78.70 in, 1,999 mm; overall height: 52.30 in,
,328 mm — 2-door hardtop 52.60 in, 1,336 mm — 4-door
edans 53.80 in, 1,366 mm — station wagons 56.40 in, 1,432
mm; ground clearance: 4.70 in, 119 mm; dry weight: Coro-
et 4-door sedan 3,355 lb, 1,521 kg — Coronet 6-passenger
Station Wagon 3,855 lb, 1,748 kg — Coronet Custom 4-door
Sedan 3,360 lb, 1,524 kg — Coronet Custom 6-passenger
Station Wagon 3,860 lb, 1,750 kg — Charger 2-door Hard-
op 3,350 lb, 1,519 kg; fuel tank capacity: 17.4 imp gal, 21
US gal, 79 l.

OPTIONAL ACCESSORIES Torqueflite automatic gearbox with
ratios (I 2.450, II 1.450, III 1, rev 2.200), max ratio of
onvertor at stall 2.16, 2.930 axle ratio; limited slip final
drive; power-assisted steering; servo brake; front disc
brakes with servo; air-conditioning system.

230 hp power team

(standard for Charger Coupé, Coronet, Coronet Custom,
Charger, Charger 500, Charger S.E., Coronet Brougham and
Coronet Crestwood Series; not available for other Series).

See 145 hp power team, except for:

ENGINE cylinders: 8, Vee-slanted at 90°; bore and stroke:
3.91 x 3.31 in, 99.3 x 84.1 mm; engine capacity: 318 cu in,
5,212 cu cm; compression ratio: 8.6; max power (SAE): 230
hp at 4,400 rpm; max torque (SAE): 320 lb ft, 44.1 kg m
at 2,000 rpm; max engine rpm: 5,000; specific power: 44.1
hp/l; crankshaft bearings: 5; valves: hydraulic tappets; camshafts: 1, at centre of Vee; carburation: 1 Carter BBD-4957S
downdraught twin barrel carburettor; cooling system capacity: 26.6 imp pt, 31.9 US pt, 15.1 l.

TRANSMISSION synchromesh gears: I, II, III; gearbox
ratios: I 3.080, II 1.700, III 1, rev 2.900; axle ratio: 2.940 —
station wagons 3.230; width of rims: 5.5''; tyres: F78 x 14
— station wagons H78 x 14.

PERFORMANCE max speed: about 106 mph, 170 km/h; power-
weight ratio: Coronet 4-door Sedan 15 lb/hp, 6.8 kg/hp —
Coronet Custom 4-door Sedan and Coronet Brougham 4-door
Sedan 15.1 lb/hp, 6.9 kg/hp; speed in direct drive at 1,000
rpm: 22.5 mph, 36.2 km/h; fuel consumption: 16 m/imp gal,
13.3 m/US gal, 17.7 l x 100 km.

DIMENSIONS AND WEIGHT rear track: 62 in, 1,575 mm —
station wagons 63.40 in, 1,610 mm; overall height: 52.20 in,
1,326 mm — 4-door sedans 54.10 in, 1,374 mm; dry weight:
Coronet 4-door Sedan 3,470 lb, 1,574 kg — Coronet 6-
passenger Station Wagon 3,920 lb, 1,778 kg — Coronet
Custom 4-door Sedan 3,475 lb, 1,576 kg — Coronet
Custom 6-passenger Station Wagon 3,925 lb, 1,780 kg — Coronet
Custom 9-passenger Station Wagon 4,000 lb, 1,814 kg —
Charger 2-door Hardtop 3,460 lb, 1,569 kg — Charger 500
2-door Hardtop 3,460 lb, 1,569 kg — Charger S.E. 2-door
Hardtop 3,485 lb, 1,580 kg — Coronet Brougham 4-door Sedan
3,485 lb, 1,580 kg — Coronet Crestwood 6-passenger Station
Wagon 3,955 lb, 1,793 kg — Coronet Crestwood 9-passenger
Station Wagon 4,010 lb, 1,819 kg.

OPTIONAL ACCESSORIES Torqueflite automatic gearbox with
2.710 axle ratio (station wagons 2.940); electric headlamp
washer system only for Charger S.E.

275 hp power team

(optional for Charger Coupé, Coronet, Coronet Custom,
Charger, Charger 500, Charger S.E., Coronet Brougham and
Coronet Crestwood Series; not available for other Series).

See 145 hp power team, except for:

ENGINE cylinders: 8, Vee-slanted at 90°; bore and stroke:

DODGE Charger 500 2-door Hardtop

DODGE Charger S.E. 2-door Hardtop

DODGE Coronet Brougham 4-door Sedan

4.25 x 3.38 in, 107.9 x 85.8 mm; engine capacity: 383 cu in,
6,276 cu cm; compression ratio: 8.5; max power (SAE):
275 hp at 4,400 rpm; max torque (SAE): 375 lb ft, 51.7 kg
m at 2,800 rpm; max engine rpm: 4,700; specific power:
43.8 hp/l; crankshaft bearings: 5; valves: hydraulic tappets;
camshafts: 1, at centre of Vee; carburation: 1 Carter BBD-
4962S downdraught twin barrel carburettor; cooling system
capacity: 24.1 imp pt, 29 US pt, 13.7 l.

TRANSMISSION gearbox: Torqueflite automatic (standard),
max ratio of convertor at stall 2.02; axle ratio: 2.450 —
station wagons 2.760; width of rims: 5.5''; tyres: F78 x 14
— station wagons H78 x 14.

PERFORMANCE max speed: about 110 mph, 177 km/h; power-
weight ratio: Coronet 4-door Sedan, Coronet Custom 4-door
Sedan and Coronet Brougham 4-door Sedan 13.2 lb/hp, 6
kg/hp; speed in direct drive at 1,000 rpm: 24 mph, 38.6
km/h; fuel consumption: 15.4 m/imp gal, 12.8 m/US gal,
18.4 l x 100 km.

ELECTRICAL EQUIPMENT battery: 59 Ah.

DIMENSIONS AND WEIGHT (see 230 hp power team) dry
weight: plus 155 lb, 70 kg.

OPTIONAL ACCESSORIES electric headlamp washer system
only for Charger S.E.

300 hp power team

(standard for Charger Super Bee; optional for Charger Coupé, Coronet, Coronet Custom, Charger, Charger 500, Charger
S.E., Coronet Brougham and Coronet Crestwood Series; not
available for Charger R/T).

See 145 hp power team, except for:

ENGINE cylinders: 8, Vee-slanted at 90°; bore and stroke:
4.25 x 3.38 in, 107.9 x 85.8 mm; engine capacity: 383 cu in,
6,276 cu cm; compression ratio: 8.5; max power (SAE): 300
hp at 4,800 rpm; max torque (SAE): 410 lb ft, 56.6 kg m at
3,400 rpm; max engine rpm: 5,200; specific power: 47.8
hp/l; crankshaft bearings: 5; valves: hydraulic tappets; camshafts: 1, at centre of Vee; carburation: 1 Holley R-4667A
downdraught 4-barrel carburettor; cooling system capacity:
24.1 imp pt, 29 US pt, 13.7 l.

TRANSMISSION synchromesh gears: I, II, III; gearbox
ratios: I 2.550, II 1.490, III 1, rev 3.340; width of rims: 5.5''
— Charger Super Bee 6''; tyres: F78 x 14 — station wagons
H78 x 14 — Charger Super Bee F70 x 14.

PERFORMANCE max speed: about 114 mph, 183 km/h; power-
weight ratio: Charger Super Bee 12.5 lb/hp, 5.7 kg/hp —
Coronet 4-door Sedan and Coronet Custom 4-door Sedan
12.3 lb/hp, 5.5 kg/hp — Coronet Brougham 4-door Sedan 12.4
lb/hp, 5.6 kg/hp; speed in direct drive at 1,000 rpm: 22.2
mph, 35.7 km/h; fuel consumption: 14.9 m/imp gal, 12.4
m/US gal, 18.9 l x 100 km.

CHASSIS front suspension: anti-roll bar.

BRAKES area rubbed by linings: total 380.1 sq in, 2,451
sq cm.

ELECTRICAL EQUIPMENT battery: 59 Ah.

DIMENSIONS AND WEIGHT (see 230 hp power team) front
track: 60.10 in, 1,526 mm; overall height: 52.70 in, 1,338
mm; dry weight: plus 224 lb, 102 kg — Charger Super Bee
2-door Hardtop 3,750 lb, 1,701 kg.

OPTIONAL ACCESSORIES Torqueflite automatic gearbox with
max ratio of convertor at stall 2.16, 3.230 axle ratio; 4-speed
fully synchronized mechanical gearbox (I 2.470, II 1.770,
III 1.340, IV 1, rev 2.400), 3.230 axle ratio; electric headlamp washer system only for Charger S.E.

370 hp power team

(standard for Charger R/T; optional for Charger Super Bee
and Charger S.E.; not available for other Series).

See 145 hp power team, except for:

ENGINE cylinders: 8, Vee-slanted at 90°; bore and stroke:
4.32 x 3.75 in, 109.7 x 95.2 mm; engine capacity: 440 cu in,
7,210 cu cm; compression ratio: 9.5; max power (SAE): 370
hp at 4,600 rpm; max torque (SAE): 480 lb ft, 66.2 kg m
at 3,200 rpm; max engine rpm: 5,400; specific power: 51.3
hp/l; crankshaft bearings: 5; valves: hydraulic tappets; camshafts: 1, at centre of Vee; lubricating system capacity: 10
imp pt, 12 US pt, 5.7 l; carburation: 1 Carter AVS-4967S
downdraught 4-barrel carburettor; cooling system capacity:
25.9 imp pt, 31.1 US pt, 14.7 l.

TRANSMISSION gears: 4 + reverse; synchromesh gears: I,
II, III, IV; gearbox ratios: I 2.440, II 1.770, III 1.340, IV 1,
rev 2.360; gear lever: central; axle ratio: 3.540; width of
rims: 6''; tyres: G70 x 14.

370 HP POWER TEAM

PERFORMANCE max speed: about 117 mph, 188 km/h; power-weight ratio: Charger R/T 10.2 lb/hp, 4.6 kg/hp — Charger Super Bee 10.1 lb/hp, 4.5 kg/hp — Charger S.E. 9.4 lb/hp, 4.3 kg/hp; speed in direct drive at 1,000 rpm: 21.7 mph, 34.9 km/h; fuel consumption: 13.1 m/imp gal, 10.9 m/US gal, 21.6 l x 100 km.

CHASSIS front suspension: anti-roll bar.

BRAKES area rubbed by linings: total 380.1 sq in, 2,451 sq cm.

ELECTRICAL EQUIPMENT battery: 70 Ah.

DIMENSIONS AND WEIGHT front track: 60.10 in, 1,526 mm; overall height: Charger R/T 53 in, 1,346 mm — Charger Super Bee 52.70 in, 1,338 mm — Charger S.E. 52.20 in, 1,326 mm; dry weight: Charger R/T 3,795 lb, 1,721 kg — Charger Super Bee 3,750 lb, 1,701 kg — Charger S.E. 3,485 lb, 1,580 kg.

OPTIONAL ACCESSORIES Torqueflite automatic gearbox with max ratio of convertor at stall 2.02, 3.230 axle ratio; electric headlamp washer system only for Charger S.E.

385 hp power team

(optional for Charger Super Bee and Charger R/T; not available for other Series).

See 145 hp power team, except for:

ENGINE cylinders: 8, Vee-slanted at 90°; bore and stroke: 4.32 x 3.75 in, 109.7 x 95.2 mm; engine capacity: 440 cu in, 7,210 cu cm; compression ratio: 10.3; max power (SAE): 385 hp at 4,700 rpm; max torque (SAE): 490 lb ft, 67.6 kg m at 3,200 rpm; max engine rpm: 5,600; specific power: 53.4 hp/l; crankshaft bearings: 5; valves: hydraulic tappets; camshafts: 1, at centre of Vee; lubricating system capacity: 10 imp pt, 12 US pt, 5.7 l; carburation: 3 Holley R-4671A-4672A-4669A downdraught twin barrel carburettors; cooling system capacity: 25.9 imp pt, 31.1 US pt, 14.7 l.

TRANSMISSION gears: 4 + reverse; synchromesh gears: I, II, III, IV; gearbox ratios: I 2.440, II 1.770, III 1.340, IV 1, rev 2.360; gear lever: central; axle ratio: 3.540; width of rims: 6''; tyres: G70 x 14.

PERFORMANCE max speed: about 121 mph, 194 km/h; power-weight ratio: Charger Super Bee 9.7 lb/hp, 4.3 kg/hp — Charger R/T 9.8 lb/hp, 4.4 kg/hp; speed in direct drive at 1,000 rpm: 21.7 mph, 34.9 km/h; fuel consumption: 12.9 m/imp gal, 10.7 m/US gal, 21.9 l x 100 km.

CHASSIS front suspension: anti-roll bar.

BRAKES area rubbed by linings: total 380.1 sq in, 2,451 sq cm.

ELECTRICAL EQUIPMENT battery: 70 Ah.

DIMENSIONS AND WEIGHT front track: 60.10 in, 1,526 mm; rear track: 62 in, 1,575 mm; overall height: Charger Super Bee 52.70 in, 1,338 mm — Charger R/T 53 in, 1,346 mm; dry weight: Charger Super Bee 3,750 lb, 1,700 kg — Charger R/T 3,795 lb, 1,721 kg.

OPTIONAL ACCESSORIES Torqueflite automatic gearbox with max ratio of convertor at stall 2.02, 3.230 axle ratio.

425 hp power team

(optional for Charger Super Bee and Charger R/T; not available for other Series).

See 145 hp power team, except for:

ENGINE cylinders: 8, Vee-slanted at 90°; bore and stroke: 4.25 x 3.75 in, 107.9 x 95.2 mm; engine capacity: 426 cu in, 6,981 cu cm; compression ratio: 10.2; max power (SAE): 425 hp at 5,000 rpm; max torque (SAE): 490 lb ft, 67.6 kg m at 4,000 rpm; max engine rpm: 5,700; specific power: 60.9 hp/l; crankshaft bearings: 5; valves: hydraulic tappets; camshafts: 1, at centre of Vee; lubricating system capacity: 10 imp pt, 12 US pt, 5.7 l; carburation: 2 Carter AFB-4971S-4969S downdraught 4-barrel carburettors; cooling system capacity: 26.6 imp pt, 31.9 US pt, 15.1 l.

TRANSMISSION gears: 4 + reverse; synchromesh gears: I, II, III, IV; gearbox ratios: I 2.440, II 1.770, III 1.340, IV 1, rev 2.360; gear lever: central; axle ratio: 3.540; width of rims: 6''; tyres: G70 x 14.

PERFORMANCE max speed: about 122 mph, 196 km/h; power-weight ratio: Charger Super Bee 9.2 lb/hp, 4.1 kg/hp — Charger R/T 9.3 lb/hp, 4.2 kg/hp; speed in direct drive at 1,000 rpm: 21.7 mph, 34.9 km/h; fuel consumption: 12.6 m/imp gal, 10.5 m/US gal, 22.5 l x 100 km.

DODGE Coronet Crestwood 6-passenger Station Wagon

DODGE Charger R/T 2-door Hardtop

DODGE 255 hp engine

CHASSIS front suspension: anti-roll bar.

BRAKES area rubbed by linings: total 380.1 sq in, 2,45 sq cm.

ELECTRICAL EQUIPMENT battery: 70 Ah.

DIMENSIONS AND WEIGHT (see 370 hp power team) dr weight: plus 146 lb, 66 kg.

OPTIONAL ACCESSORIES Torqueflite automatic gearbox wit 3.230 axle ratio.

Polara - Polara Custom - Polara Brougham - Monaco Series

PRICE IN USA:

Polara	2-door Hardtop	$ 2,98
Polara	4-door Sedan	$ 2,96
Polara Custom	2-door Hardtop	$ 3,25
Polara Custom	4-door Sedan	$ 3,23
Polara Custom	4-door Hardtop	$ 3,32
Polara Custom	6-passenger Station Wagon	$ 3,66
Polara Custom	9-passenger Station Wagon	$ 3,76
Polara Brougham	2-door Hardtop	$ 3,46
Polara Brougham	4-door Hardtop	$ 3,52
Monaco	2-door Hardtop	$ 3,85
Monaco	4-door Sedan	$ 3,78
Monaco	4-door Hardtop	$ 3,91
Monaco	6-passenger Station Wagon	$ 4,31
Monaco	9-passenger Station Wagon	$ 4,44

For V8 engines add $ 111.

145 hp power team

(standard for Polara Series; not available for other Series)

ENGINE front, 4 stroke; cylinders: 6, in line; bore and stroke: 3.40 x 4.12 in, 86.4 x 104.6 mm; engine capacity: 22 cu in, 3,688 cu cm; compression ratio: 8.4; max power (SAE): 145 hp at 4,000 rpm; max torque (SAE): 215 lb ft 29.7 kg m at 2,400 rpm; max engine rpm: 4,500; specifi power: 39.3 hp/l; cylinder block: cast iron; cylinder head cast iron; crankshaft bearings: 4; valves: 2 per cylinder overhead, in line, push-rods and rockers; camshafts: 1, side lubrication: rotary pump, full flow filter; lubricating system capacity: 8.3 imp pt, 9.9 US pt, 4.7 l; carburation: 1 Holle R-4655A downdraught single barrel carburettor; fuel feed mechanical pump; cooling system: water; cooling system capacity: 21.6 imp pt, 26 US pt, 12.3 l.

TRANSMISSION driving wheels: rear; clutch: single dry plate; gearbox: mechanical; gears: 3 + reverse; synchro mesh gears: I, II, III; gearbox ratios: I 3.080, II 1.700 III 1, rev 2.900; gear lever: steering column; final drive hypoid bevel; axle ratio: 3.550; width of rims: 5.5''; tyres G78 x 15.

PERFORMANCE max speed: about 88 mph, 141 km/h; power-weight ratio: Polara 2-door Hardtop 26.4 lb/hp, 12 kg/hp — Polara 4-door Sedan 26.7 lb/hp, 12.1 kg/hp; speed in direc drive at 1,000 rpm: 19.5 mph, 31.4 km/h; fuel consumption 18.8 m/imp gal, 15.7 m/US gal, 15 l x 100 km.

CHASSIS integral, front auxiliary frame; front suspension independent, wishbones, longitudinal torsion bars, anti-rol bar (not available for station wagons), telescopic dampers rear suspension: rigid axle, semi-elliptic leafsprings, tele scopic dampers.

STEERING recirculating ball; turns of steering wheel lock to lock: 5.80.

BRAKES drum, dual circuit; area rubbed by linings: total 362.9 sq in, 2,341 sq cm.

ELECTRICAL EQUIPMENT voltage: 12 V; battery: 46 Ah generator type: alternator, 37 A; ignition distributor: Chrys ler; headlamps: 4.

DIMENSIONS AND WEIGHT wheel base: 122 in, 3,099 mm front track: 62.10 in, 1,577 mm; rear track: 62 in, 1,575 mm overall length: 220.20 in, 5,593 mm; overall width: 79.20 in 2,012 mm — 2-door hardtop 79.30 in, 2,014 mm; overall height: 2-door hardtop 54.60 in, 1,387 mm — 4-door sedan 55 in, 1,397 mm; ground clearance: 5.70 in, 145 mm; dry weight: Polara 2-door Hardtop 3,835 lb, 1,739 kg — Polara 4-door Sedan 3,875 lb, 1,757 kg; turning circle (between walls): 49 ft, 14.9 m; fuel tank capacity: 19.1 imp gal, 23 US gal, 87 l.

OPTIONAL ACCESSORIES Torqueflite automatic gearbox with 3 ratios (I 2.450, II 1.450, III 1, rev 2.200), max ratio of convertor at stall 2.16, 3.210 axle ratio; limited slip final drive; power-assisted steering; servo brake; front disc brakes with servo.

DODGE Coronet Crestwood 6-passenger Station Wagon

DODGE Charger R/T 2-door Hardtop

DODGE Polara Brougham 4-door Hardtop

230 hp power team

(standard for Polara and Polara Custom Series; not available for other Series).

See 145 hp power team, except for:

ENGINE cylinders: 8, Vee-slanted at 90°; bore and stroke: 3.91 x 3.31 in, 99.3 x 84.1 mm; engine capacity: 318 cu in, 5,212 cu cm; compression ratio: 8.6: max power (SAE): 230 hp at 4,400 rpm; max torque (SAE): 320 lb ft, 44.1 kg m at 2,000 rpm; max engine rpm: 5,000; specific power: 44.1 hp/l; crankshaft bearings: 5; valves: hydraulic tappets; camshafts: 1, at centre of Vee; carburation: 1 Carter BBD-4957S downdraught twin barrel carburettor; cooling system capacity: 26.6 imp pt, 31.9 US pt, 15.1 l.

TRANSMISSION axle ratio: 3.230; width of rims: station wagons 6''; tyres: station wagons J78 x 15.

PERFORMANCE max speed: about 103 mph, 165 km/h; power-weight ratio: Polara 4-door Sedan 17.1 lb/hp, 7.7 kg/hp — Polara Custom 4-door Sedan 17.2 lb/hp, 7.8 kg/hp; speed in direct drive at 1,000 rpm: 20.6 mph, 33.1 km/h; fuel consumption: 15.8 m/imp gal, 13.1 m/US gal, 17.9 l x 100 km.

BRAKES area rubbed by linings: total 380.1 sq in, 2,451 sq cm.

DIMENSIONS AND WEIGHT rear track: 63.40 in, 1,610 mm; overall length: station wagons 223.50 in, 5,677 mm; overall height: 2-door hardtops 54.50 in, 1,384 mm — 4-door sedans and 4-door hardtop 54.90 in, 1,394 mm — station wagons 57.10 in, 1,450 mm — dry weight: Polara 2-door Hardtop 3,915 lb, 1,775 kg — Polara 4-door Sedan 3,940 lb, 1,787 kg — Polara Custom 2-door Hardtop 3,925 lb, 1,780 kg — Polara Custom 4-door Sedan, 3,955 lb, 1,793 kg — Polara Custom 4-door Hardtop 3,995 lb, 1,812 kg — Polara Custom 6-passenger Station Wagon 4,400 lb, 1,995 kg — Polara Custom 9-passenger Station Wagon 4,455 lb, 2,021 kg.

OPTIONAL ACCESSORIES Torqueflite automatic gearbox with max ratio of convertor at stall 2.16, 2.710 axle ratio (station wagons 2.940); air-conditioning system.

255 hp power team

(standard for Polara and Polara Custom Series; not available for other Series).

See 145 hp power team, except for:

ENGINE cylinders: 8, Vee-slanted at 90°; bore and stroke: 4 x 3.53 in, 101.6 x 89.6 mm; engine capacity: 360 cu in, 5,900 cu cm; compression ratio: 8.7; max power (SAE): 255 hp at 4,400 rpm; max torque (SAE): 360 lb ft, 49.7 kg m at 2,400 rpm; max engine rpm: 5,000; specific power: 43.2 hp/l; crankshaft bearings: 5; valves: hydraulic tappets; camshafts: 1, at centre of Vee; carburation: 1 Holley R-4665A downdraught twin barrel carburettor; cooling system capacity: 25 imp pt, 30 US pt, 14.2 l.

TRANSMISSION gearbox ratios: I 2.550, II 1.490, III 1, rev 3.340; axle ratio: 3.230; width of rims: 9-passenger station wagon 6.5''; tyres: 9-passenger station wagon L84 x 15.

PERFORMANCE max speed: about 106 mph, 170 km/h; power-weight ratio: Polara 4-door Sedan 15.7 lb/hp, 7.1 kg/hp — Polara Custom 4-door Sedan 15.8 lb/hp, 7.2 kg/hp; speed in direct drive at 1,000 rpm: 21.2 mph, 34.1 km/h; fuel consumption: 15.5 m/imp gal, 12.9 m/US gal, 18.2 l x 100 km.

BRAKES area rubbed by linings: total 380.1 sq in, 2,451 sq cm.

ELECTRICAL EQUIPMENT battery: 50 Ah.

DIMENSIONS AND WEIGHT (see 230 hp power team) dry weight: plus 65 lb, 29 kg.

OPTIONAL ACCESSORIES Torqueflite automatic gearbox with max ratio of convertor at stall 2.16, 2.710 axle ratio (station wagons 2.760); air-conditioning system.

275 hp power team

(standard for Polara Brougham and Monaco Series; optional for Polara and Polara Custom Series).

See 145 hp power team, except for:

ENGINE cylinders: 8, Vee-slanted at 90°; bore and stroke: 4.25 x 3.38 in, 107.9 x 85.8 mm; engine capacity: 383 cu in, 6,276 cu cm; compression ratio: 8.5; max power (SAE): 275 hp at 4,400 rpm; max torque (SAE): 375 lb ft, 51.7 kg m at 2,800 rpm; max engine rpm: 4,700; specific power: 43.8 hp/l; crankshaft bearings: 5; valves: hydraulic tappets; camshafts: 1, at centre of Vee; carburation: 1 Carter BBD-4961S or BBD-4962S downdraught twin barrel carburettor; cooling system capacity: 24.1 imp pt, 29 US pt, 13.7 l.

TRANSMISSION gearbox: mechanical (station wagons only automatic standard); gearbox ratios: I 2.550, II 1.490, III 1, rev 3.340; axle ratio: 3.230 — station wagons 2.760; width of rims: 5.5'' — 9-passenger station wagons 6.5''; tyres: 9-passenger station wagons L84 x 15.

PERFORMANCE max speed: about 110 mph, 177 km/h; power-weight ratio: Polara 4-door Sedan 14.3 lb/hp, 6.4 kg/hp —

275 HP POWER TEAM

Polara Custom 4-door Sedan 14.4 lb/hp, 6.5 kg/hp — Monaco 4-door Sedan 15.2 lb/hp, 6.9 kg/hp; speed in direct drive at 1,000 rpm: 23.4 mph, 37.6 km/h; fuel consumption: 15.2 m/imp gal, 12.6 m/US gal, 18.6 l x 100 km.

BRAKES area rubbed by linings: total 393.6 sq in, 2,539 sq cm.

ELECTRICAL EQUIPMENT battery: 50 Ah.

DIMENSIONS AND WEIGHT rear track: 63.40 in, 1,610 mm; overall length: station wagons 223.50 in, 5,677 mm; overall height: 2-door hardtops 54.50 in, 1,384 mm — 4-door sedans and 4-door hardtops 54.90 in, 1,394 mm — station wagons 57.10 in, 1,450 mm; dry weight: Polara 2-door Hardtop 3,915 lb, 1,775 kg — Polara 4-door Sedan 3,940 lb, 1,787 kg — Polara Custom 2-door Hardtop 3,925 lb, 1,780 kg — Polara Custom 4-door Sedan 3,955 lb, 1,793 kg — Polara Custom 4-door Hardtop 3,995 lb, 1,812 kg — Polara Custom 6-passenger Station Wagon 4,400 lb, 1,995 kg — Polara Custom 9-passenger Station Wagon 4,455 lb, 2,020 kg — Polara Brougham 2-door Hardtop 4,085 lb, 1,852 kg — Polara Brougham 4-door Hardtop 4,155 lb, 1,884 kg — Monaco 2-door Hardtop 4,120 lb, 1,869 kg — Monaco 4-door Sedan 4,170 lb, 1,891 kg — Monaco 4-door Hardtop 4,200 lb, 1,905 kg — Monaco 6-passenger Station Wagon 4,645 lb, 2,106 kg — Monaco 9-passenger Station Wagon 4,705 lb, 2,134 kg.

OPTIONAL ACCESSORIES Torqueflite automatic gearbox with max ratio of convertor at stall 2.02, 2.760 axle ratio; air-conditioning system.

300 hp power team

(optional for all Series).

See 145 hp power team, except for:

ENGINE cylinders: 8, Vee-slanted at 90°; bore and stroke: 4.25 x 3.38 in, 107.9 x 85.8 mm; engine capacity: 383 cu in, 6,276 cu cm; compression ratio: 8.5; max power (SAE): 300 hp at 4,800 rpm; max torque (SAE): 410 lb ft, 56.6 kg m at 3,400 rpm; max engine rpm: 5,200; specific power: 47.8 hp/l; crankshaft bearings: 5; valves: hydraulic tappets; camshafts: 1, at centre of Vee; carburation: 1 Holley R-4668A or Carter AVS 6125S downdraught 4-barrel carburettor; cooling system capacity: 24.1 imp pt, 29 US pt, 13.7 l.

TRANSMISSION gearbox: Torqueflite automatic (standard), max ratio of convertor at stall 2.16; selector lever: steering column or central; axle ratio: 2.760; width of rims: 5.5'' — 9-passenger station wagons 6.5''; tyres: H78 x 15 — 9-passenger station wagons L84 x 15.

PERFORMANCE max speed: about 117 mph, 188 km/h; power-weight ratio: Polara 4-door Sedan and Polara Custom 4-door Sedan 13.1 lb/hp, 5.9 kg/hp — Monaco 4-door Sedan 14.1 lb/hp, 6.4 kg/hp; speed in direct drive at 1,000 rpm: 23.7 mph, 38.1 km/h; fuel consumption: 14.9 m/imp gal, 12.4 m/US gal, 19 l x 100 km.

BRAKES area rubbed by linings: total 393.6 sq in, 2,539 sq cm.

ELECTRICAL EQUIPMENT battery: 50 Ah.

DIMENSIONS AND WEIGHT (see 275 hp power team) dry weight: Polara Brougham and Monaco 4-door Sedan plus 52 lb, 24 kg — Monaco station wagons plus 21 lb, 9 kg.

OPTIONAL ACCESSORIES air-conditioning system.

335 hp power team

(optional for all Series).

See 145 hp power team, except for:

ENGINE cylinders: 8, Vee-slanted at 90°; bore and stroke: 4.23 x 3.75 in, 109.7 x 95.2 mm; engine capacity: 440 cu in, 7,210 cu cm; compression ratio: 8.8; max power (SAE): 335 hp at 4,400 rpm; max torque (SAE): 460 lb ft, 63.5 kg m at 3,200 rpm; max engine rpm: 5,000; specific power: 46.5 hp/l; crankshaft bearings: 5; valves: hydraulic tappets; camshafts: 1, at centre of Vee; carburation: 1 Carter AVS 4966S downdraught 4-barrel carburettor; cooling system capacity: 25.9 imp pt, 31.1 US pt, 14.7 l.

TRANSMISSION gearbox: Torqueflite automatic (standard), max ratio of convertor at stall 2.02; selector lever: steering column or central; axle ratio: 2.760; width of rims: 5.5'' — 9-passenger station wagons 6.5''; tyres: H78 x 15 — 9-passenger station wagons L84 x 15.

PERFORMANCE max speed: about 119 mph, 191 km/h; power-weight ratio: Polara 4-door Sedan 11.7 lb/hp, 5.3 kg/hp — Polara Custom 4-door Sedan 11.8 lb/hp, 5.4 kg/hp — Monaco 4-door Sedan 12.6 lb/hp, 5.7 kg/hp; speed in direct drive

EXCALIBUR SS Roadster

EXCALIBUR SS Phaeton

FORD Pinto 2-door Sedan

at 1,000 rpm: 23.7 mph, 38.1 km/h; fuel consumption: 14.5 m/imp gal, 12.1 m/US gal, 19.5 l x 100 km.

BRAKES area rubbed by linings: total 393.6 sq in, 2,539 sq cm.

ELECTRICAL EQUIPMENT battery: 70 Ah.

DIMENSIONS AND WEIGHT (see 275 hp power team) dry weight: Polara Brougham and Monaco 4-door Sedan plus 52 lb, 23 kg — Monaco station wagons plus 43 lb, 19 kg.

OPTIONAL ACCESSORIES air-conditioning system.

EXCALIBUR　　USA

SSK - SS Series

PRICES IN USA:

SSK	Roadster	$ 12,000
SS	Roadster	$ 12,000
SS	Phaeton	$ 12,900

300 hp power team

(standard for both Series).

ENGINE front, 4 stroke; cylinders: 8; Vee-slanted at 90°; bore and stroke: 4 x 3.48 in, 101.6 x 88.3 mm; engine capacity: 349.9 cu in, 5,735 cu cm; compression ratio: 10.2; max power (SAE): 300 hp at 4,800 rpm; max torque (SAE): 380 lb ft, 52.4 kg m at 3,200 rpm; max engine rpm: 5,800; specific power: 52.3 hp/l; cylinder block: cast iron; cylinder head: cast iron; crankshaft bearings: 5; valves: 2 per cylinder, overhead, in line, push-rods and rockers, hydraulic tappets; camshafts: 1, at centre of Vee; lubrication: gear pump, full flow filter; lubricating system capacity: 8.3 imp pt, 9.9 US pt, 4.7 l; carburation: 1 Rochester downdraught 4-barrel carburettor; fuel feed: mechanical pump; cooling system: water; cooling system capacity: 33.3 imp pt, 40 US pt, 18.9 l.

TRANSMISSION driving wheels: rear; clutch: single dry plate; gearbox: mechanical; gears: 4 + reverse; synchromesh gears: I, II, III, IV; gearbox ratios: I 2.200, II 1.640, III 1.270, IV 1, rev 2.260; gear lever: central; final drive: hypoid bevel, limited slip; axle ratio: 3.360; width of rims: 7.5''; tyres: G70 x 15.

PERFORMANCE max speeds: 72 mph, 116 km/h in 1st gear; 97 mph, 156 km/h in 2nd gear; 126 mph, 203 km/h in 3rd gear; 155 mph, 250 km/h in 4th gear; power-weight ratio: 9.2 lb/hp, 4.2 kg/hp; acceleration: standing ¼ mile 14 sec, 0-50 mph (0-80 km/h) 5 sec; speed in direct drive at 1,000 rpm: 25 mph, 40.2 km/h; fuel consumption: 18 m/imp gal, 15 m/US gal, 15.7 l x 100 km.

CHASSIS box-type ladder frame; front suspension: independent, wishbones, coil springs, anti-roll bar, telescopic dampers; rear suspension: independent, wishbones, semi-axle as upper arm, transverse semi-elliptic leafsprings, trailing radius arms, coil springs, anti-roll bar, telescopic dampers.

STEERING recirculating ball, servo; turns of steering wheel lock to lock: 2.50.

BRAKES disc, servo; area rubbed by linings: total 461.2 sq in, 2,975 sq cm.

ELECTRICAL EQUIPMENT voltage: 12 V; battery: 70 Ah; generator type: alternator, 37 A; ignition distributor: Delco-Remy; headlamps: 2.

DIMENSIONS AND WEIGHT wheel base: 111 in, 2,819 mm; front track: 62.50 in, 1,587 mm; rear track: 62.50 in, 1,587 mm; overall length: 170 in, 4,318 mm; overall width: 72 in, 1,829 mm; overall height: 53 in, 1,346 mm; ground clearance: 6 in, 153 mm; dry weight: 2,750 lb, 1,247 kg; turning circle (between walls): 38 ft, 11.6 m; fuel tank capacity: 16.7 imp gal, 20 US gal, 76 l.

OPTIONAL ACCESSORIES Turbo Hydramatic automatic gearbox with 3 ratios (I 2.480, II 1.480, III 1, rev 2.077), max ratio of convertor at stall 2.2; hardtop; air-conditioning system.

FORD　　USA

Pinto

PRICE IN USA:

Pinto	2-door Sedan	$ 1,919

EXCALIBUR SS Roadster

*EXCALIBUR SSK-SS Series
(independent rear suspension)*

FORD Pinto 2-door Sedan

75 hp power team

(standard).

ENGINE front, 4 stroke; cylinders: 4, in line; bore and stroke: 3.19 x 3.06 in, 80.9 x 77.6 mm; engine capacity: 97.6 cu in, 1,599 cu cm; compression ratio: 8.4; max power (SAE): 75 hp at 5,000 rpm; max torque (SAE): 96 lb ft, 13.2 kg m at 3,000 rpm; max engine rpm: 5,200; specific power: 46.9 hp/l; cylinder block: cast iron; cylinder head: cast iron; crankshaft bearings: 5; valves: 2 per cylinder, overhead, in line, push-rods and rockers; camshafts: 1, side; lubrication: gear pump, full flow filter; lubricating system capacity: 5.8 imp pt, 7 US pt, 3.3 l; carburation: 1 Autolite downdraught single barrel carburettor; fuel feed: mechanical pump; cooling system: water; cooling system capacity: 11.6 imp pt, 14 US pt, 6.6 l.

TRANSMISSION driving wheels: rear; clutch: single dry plate; gearbox: mechanical; gears: 4 + reverse; synchromesh gears: I, II, III, IV; gearbox ratios: I 3.650, II 1.970, III 1.370, IV 1, rev 3.660; gear lever: central; final drive: hypoid bevel; axle ratio: 3.550; width of rims: 4''; tyres: 6.00 x 13.

PERFORMANCE max speed: about 82 mph, 132 km/h; power-weight ratio: 27 lb/hp, 12.2 kg/hp; speed in direct drive at 1,000 rpm: 16.7 mph, 26.8 km/h; fuel consumption: 25.2 m/imp gal, 21 m/US gal, 11.2 l x 100 km.

CHASSIS integral; front suspension: independent, wishbones, lower leading arms, coil springs, telescopic dampers; rear suspension: rigid axle, semi-elliptic leafsprings, telescopic dampers.

STEERING rack-and-pinion; turns of steering wheel lock to lock: 4.15.

BRAKES drum, dual circuit; area rubbed by linings: total 191 sq in, 1,232 sq cm.

ELECTRICAL EQUIPMENT voltage: 12 V; battery: 45 Ah; generator type: alternator, 38 A; ignition distributor: Autolite; headlamps: 2.

DIMENSIONS AND WEIGHT wheel base: 94 in, 2,388 mm; front track: 55 in, 1,397 mm; rear track: 55 in, 1,397 mm; overall length: 163 in, 4,140 mm; overall width: 69.40 in, 1,763 mm; overall height: 50.10 in, 1,272 mm; ground clearance: 5.10 in, 129 mm; dry weight: 2,030 lb, 921 kg; turning circle (between walls): 34.6 ft, 10.5 m; fuel tank capacity: 9.2 imp gal, 11 US gal, 42 l.

BODY saloon/sedan; doors: 2; seats: 4; front seats: separate.

OPTIONAL ACCESSORIES 4-speed fully synchronized mechanical gearbox (I 3.540, II 2.400, III 1.410, IV 1, rev 3.960); front disc brakes.

100 hp power team

(optional).

See 75 hp power team, except for:

ENGINE bore and stroke: 3.57 x 3.03 in, 90.6 x 76.9 mm; engine capacity: 122 cu in, 2,000 cu cm; compression ratio: 9; max power (SAE): 100 hp at 5,600 rpm; max torque (SAE): 120 lb ft, 16.5 kg m at 3,600 rpm; max engine rpm: 5,800; specific power: 50 hp/l; camshafts: 1, overhead; lubricating system capacity: 5.8 imp pt, 7 US pt, 3.3 l; carburation: 1 Weber 32/36 DFAV downdraught twin barrel carburettor

PERFORMANCE max speed: about 90 mph, 145 km/h; power-weight ratio: 20.6 lb/hp, 9.3 kg/hp; fuel consumption: 21.7 m/imp gal, 18.1 m/US gal, 13 l x 100 km.

DIMENSIONS AND WEIGHT dry weight: plus 34 lb, 15 kg.

OPTIONAL ACCESSORIES Select Shift Cruise-o-Matic automatic gearbox with 3 ratios (I 2.460, II 1.460, III 1, rev 2.200), max ratio of convertor at stall 2.6, 3.180 axle ratio; air-conditioning system.

Maverick - Maverick Grabber Series

PRICES IN USA:

Maverick	2-door Sedan	$ 2,175
Maverick	4-door Sedan	$ 2,235
Maverick Grabber	2-door Sports Sedan	$ 2,354

100 hp power team

(standard for all models).

ENGINE front, 4 stroke; cylinders: 6, in line; bore and stroke: 3.50 x 2.94 in, 88.8 x 74.6 mm; engine capacity:

100 HP POWER TEAM

170 cu in, 2,786 cu cm; compression ratio: 8.7; max power (SAE): 100 hp at 4,200 rpm; max torque (SAE): 148 lb ft, 20.4 kg m at 2,600 rpm; max engine rpm: 4,600; specific power: 35.9 hp/l; cylinder block: cast iron; cylinder head: cast iron; crankshaft bearings: 4; valves: 2 per cylinder, overhead, in line, push-rods and rockers, hydraulic tappets; camshafts: 1, side; lubrication: rotary pump, full flow filter; lubricating system capacity: 5.8 imp pt, 7 US pt, 3.3 l; carburation: 1 Carter 9510 D1DF-EA downdraught single barrel carburettor; fuel feed: mechanical pump; cooling system: water; cooling system capacity: 17.8 imp pt, 21.4 US pt, 10.1 l.

TRANSMISSION driving wheels: rear; clutch: single dry plate, semi-centrifugal; gearbox: mechanical; gears: 3 + reverse; synchromesh gears: I, II, III; gearbox ratios: I 3.410, II 1.860, III 1, rev 3.510; gear lever: steering column; final drive: hypoid bevel; axle ratio: 2.790; width of rims: 4.5''; tyres: 6.45 x 14.

PERFORMANCE max speed: about 88 mph, 141 km/h; power-weight ratio: Maverick 4-door Sedan 27.2 lb/hp, 12.3 kg/hp; speed in direct drive at 1,000 rpm: 22.2 mph, 35.7 km/h; fuel consumption: 21.4 m/imp gal, 17.8 m/US gal, 13.2 l x 100 km.

CHASSIS integral; front suspension: independent, wishbones, lower leading arms, coil springs, telescopic dampers; rear suspension: rigid axle, semi-elliptic leafsprings, telescopic dampers.

STEERING recirculating ball; turns of steering wheel lock to lock: 5.20.

BRAKES drum, dual circuit; area rubbed by linings: total 212 sq in, 1,367 sq cm.

ELECTRICAL EQUIPMENT voltage: 12 V; battery: 45 Ah; generator type: alternator, 38 A; ignition distributor: Autolite; headlamps: 2.

DIMENSIONS AND WEIGHT wheel base: 103 in, 2,616 mm — 4-door sedan 109.90 in, 2,791 mm; front track: 56.50 in, 1,435 mm; rear track: 56.50 in, 1,435 mm; overall length: 179.40 in, 4,557 mm — 4-door sedan 186.30 in, 4,732 mm; overall width: 70.50 in, 1,791 mm — 4-door sedan 70.60 in, 1,793 mm; overall height: 53 in, 1,343 mm — 4-door sedan 53.10 in, 1,349 mm; ground clearance: 6.10 in, 155 mm; dry weight: Maverick 2-door Sedan 2,624 lb, 1,190 kg — Maverick 4-door Sedan 2,719 lb, 1,233 kg — Maverick Grabber 2-door Sports Sedan 2,679 lb, 1,215 kg; turning circle (between walls): 39.5 ft, 12 m; fuel tank capacity: 12.5 imp gal, 15 US gal, 57 l.

BODY saloon/sedan; seats: 4-5.

OPTIONAL ACCESSORIES power-assisted steering.

115 hp power team

(optional for all models).

See 100 hp power team, except for:

ENGINE bore and stroke: 3.68 x 3.13 in, 93.5 x 79.5 mm; engine capacity: 200 cu in, 3,277 cu cm; max power (SAE): 115 hp at 4,000 rpm; max torque (SAE): 180 lb ft, 24.8 kg m at 2,200 rpm; max engine rpm: 4,400; specific power: 35.1 hp/l; crankshaft bearings: 7; carburation: 1 Carter 9510 D1DF-GA downdraught single barrel carburettor; cooling system capacity: 18 imp pt, 21.6 US pt, 10.2 l.

TRANSMISSION gearbox ratios: I 2.990, II 1.750, III 1, rev 3.170; axle ratio: 3.000.

PERFORMANCE max speed: about 96 mph, 154 km/h; power-weight ratio: Maverick 4-door Sedan 23.6 lb/hp, 10.7 kg/hp; speed in direct drive at 1,000 rpm: 21.9 mph, 35.2 km/h; fuel consumption: 20 m/imp gal, 16.7 m/US gal, 14.1 l x 100 km.

OPTIONAL ACCESSORIES Select Shift Cruise-o-Matic automatic gearbox with 3 ratios (I 2.460, II 1.460, III 1, rev 2.200), max ratio of convertor at stall 2.10, 2.790 axle ratio; air-conditioning system.

145 hp power team

(optional for all models).

See 100 hp power team, except for:

ENGINE bore and stroke: 3.68 x 3.91 in, 93.5 x 99.3 mm; engine capacity: 250 cu in, 4,095 cu cm; compression ratio: 9; max power (SAE): 145 hp at 4,000 rpm; max torque (SAE): 232 lb ft, 32 kg m at 1,600 rpm; max engine rpm: 4,500; specific power: 35.4 hp/l; crankshaft bearings: 7;

FORD Maverick 4-door Sedan

FORD Mustang 2-door Convertible

FORD Mustang Mach 1 2-door Fastback

carburation: 1 Carter 9510 D1ZF-JA downdraught single barrel carburettor; cooling system capacity: 19.5 imp pt, 23.5 US pt, 11.1 l.

TRANSMISSION gearbox: Select Shift Cruise-o-Matic automatic, hydraulic torque convertor and planetary gears with 3 ratios + reverse, max ratio of convertor at stall 2.02, possible manual selection; gearbox ratios: I 2.460, II 1.460, III 1, rev 2.200; selector lever: steering column; axle ratio: 3.000.

PERFORMANCE max speed: about 98 mph, 157 km/h; power-weight ratio: Maverick 4-door Sedan, 19.4 lb/hp, 8.8 kg/hp; speed in direct drive at 1,000 rpm: 21.9 mph, 35.2 km/h; fuel consumption: 19.8 m/imp gal, 16.4 m/US gal, 14.3 l x 100 km.

BRAKES area rubbed by linings: total 267.2 sq in, 1,723 sq cm.

ELECTRICAL EQUIPMENT generator type: alternator, 55 A.

DIMENSIONS AND WEIGHT dry weight: plus 100 lb, 45 kg.

OPTIONAL ACCESSORIES central selector lever; air-conditioning system.

Mustang Series

PRICES IN USA:

Mustang	2-door Hardtop	$ 2,911
Mustang	2-door Fastback	$ 2,973
Mustang	2-door Convertible	$ 3,227
Mustang Mach 1	2-door Fastback	$ 3,268
Mustang Grandé	2-door Hardtop	$ 3,117

For V8 engines add $ 95.

145 hp power team

(standard for Mustang models and Mustang Grandé; not available for Mustang Mach 1).

ENGINE front, 4 stroke; cylinders: 6, in line; bore and stroke: 3.68 x 3.91 in, 93.5 x 99.3 mm; engine capacity: 250 cu in, 4,095 cu cm; compression ratio: 9; max power (SAE): 145 hp at 4,000 rpm; max torque (SAE): 232 lb ft, 32 kg m at 1,600 rpm; max engine rpm: 4,500; specific power: 35.4 hp/l; cylinder block: cast iron; cylinder head: cast iron; crankshaft bearings: 7; valves: 2 per cylinder, overhead, in line, push-rods and rockers, hydraulic tappets; camshafts: 1, side; lubrication: rotary pump, full flow filter; lubricating system capacity: 8.3 imp pt, 9.9 US pt, 4.7 l; carburation: 1 Carter 9510 D1ZF-HA downdraught single barrel carburettor; fuel feed: mechanical pump; cooling system: water; cooling system capacity: 18.7 imp pt, 22.4 US pt, 10.6 l.

TRANSMISSION driving wheels: rear; clutch: single dry plate, semi-centrifugal; gearbox: mechanical; gears: 3 + reverse; synchromesh gears: I, II, III; gearbox ratios: I 2.990, II 1.750, III 1, rev 3.170; gear lever: central; final drive: hypoid bevel; axle ratio: 3.000; width of rims: 6''; tyres: E78 x 14.

PERFORMANCE max speed: about 99 mph, 159 km/h; power-weight ratio: Mustang 2-door Hardtop 21.1 lb/hp, 9.6 kg/hp — Mustang Grandé 2-door Hardtop 21.3 lb/hp, 9.7 kg/hp; speed in direct drive at 1,000 rpm: 22 mph, 35.4 km/h; fuel consumption: 19 m/imp gal, 15.8 m/US gal, 14.9 l x 100 km.

CHASSIS integral; front suspension: independent, wishbones, lower leading arms, coil springs, anti-roll bar, telescopic dampers; rear suspension: rigid axle, semi-elliptic leafsprings, telescopic dampers.

STEERING recirculating ball; turns of steering wheel lock to lock: 5.10.

BRAKES drum, dual circuit; area rubbed by linings: total 251.2 sq in, 1,620 sq cm.

ELECTRICAL EQUIPMENT voltage: 12 V; battery: 45 Ah; generator type: alternator, 38 A; ignition distributor: Autolite; headlamps: 2.

DIMENSIONS AND WEIGHT wheel base: 109 in, 2,769 mm; front track: 61.50 in, 1,562 mm; rear track: 61 in, 1,550 mm; overall length: 189.50 in, 4,813 mm; overall width: 74.10 in, 1,882 mm; overall height: 2-door hardtops 50.80 in, 1,290 mm — 2-door fastback 50.10 in, 1,272 mm — 2-door convertible 50.50 in, 1,283 mm; ground clearance: 4.60 in, 117 mm; dry weight: Mustang 2-door Hardtop 3,058 lb, 1,387 kg — Mustang 2-door Fastback 3,028 lb, 1,373 kg — Mustang 2-door Convertible 3,180 lb, 1,442 kg — Mustang Grandé 2-door Hardtop 3,084 lb, 1,398 kg; turning circle (between walls): 42 ft, 12.8 m; fuel tank capacity: 16.7 imp gal, 20 US gal, 76 l.

BODY doors: 2; seats: 4; front seats: separate.

OPTIONAL ACCESSORIES Select Shift Cruise-o-Matic automatic gearbox with 3 ratios (I 2.460, II 1.460, III 1, rev 2.200), max ratio of convertor at stall 2.10, 2.790 axle ratio; limited slip final drive; power-assisted steering; front disc brakes with servo; air-conditioning system.

210 hp power team

(standard for Mustang Mach 1; optional for other models).

See 145 hp power team, except for:

ENGINE cylinders: 8, Vee-slanted at 90°; bore and stroke: 4 x 3 in, 101.6 x 76.2 mm; engine capacity: 302 cu in, 4,950 cu cm; max power (SAE): 210 hp at 4,600 rpm; max torque (SAE): 296 lb ft, 40.8 kg m at 2,600 rpm; max engine rpm: 5,000; specific power: 42.4 hp/l; crankshaft bearings: 5; camshafts: 1, at centre of Vee; carburation: 1 Autolite 9510 D10F-ABA downdraught twin barrel carburettor; cooling system capacity: 25.2 imp pt, 30.2 US pt, 14.3 l.

PERFORMANCE max speed: about 112 mph, 180 km/h; power-weight ratio: Mustang 2-door Hardtop 15 lb/hp, 6.8 kg/hp — Mustang Mach 1 2-door Fastback 15.1 lb/hp, 6.9 kg/hp; fuel consumption: 16.8 m/imp gal, 14 m/US gal, 16.8 l x 100 km.

DIMENSIONS AND WEIGHT dry weight: plus 92 lb, 42 kg — Mustang Mach 1 2-door Fastback 3,167 lb, 1,436 kg.

240 hp power team

(optional for all models).

See 145 hp power team, except for:

ENGINE cylinders: 8, Vee-slanted at 90°; bore and stroke: 4 x 3.50 in, 101.6 x 88.8 mm; engine capacity: 351 cu in, 5,752 cu cm; max power (SAE): 240 hp at 4,600 rpm; max torque (SAE): 350 lb ft, 48.3 kg m at 2,600 rpm; max engine rpm: 5,000; specific power: 41.7 hp/l; crankshaft bearings: 5; camshafts: 1, at centre of Vee; carburation: 1 Autolite 9510 D10F-ZA downdraught twin barrel carburettor; cooling system capacity: 26.2 imp pt, 31.5 US pt, 14.9 l.

TRANSMISSION gearbox ratios: I 2.420, II 1.610, III 1, rev 2.330; axle ratio: 2.750.

PERFORMANCE max speed: about 115 mph, 185 km/h; power-weight ratio: Mustang 2-door Hardtop 13.8 lb/hp, 6.2 kg/hp; speed in direct drive at 1,000 rpm: 23.7 mph, 38.1 km/h; fuel consumption: 16.2 m/imp gal, 13.5 m/US gal, 17.4 l x 100 km.

BRAKES area rubbed by linings: total 282.8 sq in, 1,824 sq cm.

DIMENSIONS AND WEIGHT (see 210 hp power team) dry weight: plus 163 lb, 74 kg.

OPTIONAL ACCESSORIES Select Shift Cruise-o-Matic automatic gearbox with 2.750 axle ratio.

285 hp power team

(optional for all models).

See 145 hp power team, except for:

ENGINE cylinders: 8, Vee-slanted at 90°; bore and stroke: 4 x 3.50 in, 101.6 x 88.8 mm; engine capacity: 351 cu in, 5,752 cu cm; compression ratio: 10.7; max power (SAE): 285 hp at 5,400 rpm; max torque (SAE): 370 lb ft, 51 kg m at 3,400 rpm; max engine rpm: 5,600; specific power: 49.5 hp/l; crankshaft bearings: 5; camshafts: 1, at centre of Vee; carburation: 1 Autolite 9510 D10F-EA downdraught 4-barrel carburettor; cooling system capacity: 26.2 imp pt, 31.5 US pt, 14.9 l.

TRANSMISSION gears: 4 + reverse; synchromesh gears: I, II, III, IV; gearbox ratios: I 2.780, II 1.930, III 1.360, IV 1, rev 2.780; axle ratio: 3.250.

PERFORMANCE max speed: about 118 mph, 190 km/h; power-weight ratio: Mustang 2-door Hardtop 11.8 lb/hp, 5.3 kg/hp; speed in direct drive at 1,000 rpm: 21,6 mph, 34.7 km/h; fuel consumption: 15.3 m/imp gal, 12.7 m/US gal, 18.5 l x 100 km.

BRAKES area rubbed by linings: total 282.8 sq in, 1,824 sq cm.

ELECTRICAL EQUIPMENT battery: 55 Ah.

DIMENSIONS AND WEIGHT (see 210 hp power team) dry weight: plus 220 lb, 100 kg.

OPTIONAL ACCESSORIES Select Shift Cruise-o-Matic automatic gearbox with 3.000 axle ratio.

FORD Maverick 4-door Sedan

FORD Mustang 2-door Convertible

FORD Mustang Mach 1 2-door Fastback

370 hp power team

(optional for all models).

See 145 hp power team, except for:

ENGINE cylinders: 8, Vee-slanted at 90°; bore and stroke: 4.36 x 3.59 in, 110.7 x 91.2 mm; engine capacity: 429 cu in, 7,030 cu cm; compression ratio: 11.3; max power (SAE): 370 hp at 5,400 rpm; max torque (SAE): 450 lb ft, 62.1 kg m at 3,400 rpm; max engine rpm: 5,600; specific power: 52.6 hp/l; crankshaft bearings: 5; camshafts: 1, at centre of Vee; lubrication: gear pump, full flow filter; lubricating system capacity: 11.6 imp pt, 14 US pt, 6.6 l; carburation: 1 Rochester 9510 D10F-KA downdraught 4-barrel carburettor; cooling system capacity: 32.4 imp pt, 38.9 US pt, 18.4 l.

TRANSMISSION gears: 4 + reverse; synchromesh gears: I, II, III, IV; gearbox ratios: I 2.320, II 1.690, III 1.290, IV 1, rev 2.320; axle ratio: 3.250; width of rims: 7''; tyres: F70 x 14.

PERFORMANCE max speed: about 124 mph, 200 km/h; power-weight ratio: Mustang 2-door Hardtop 9.6 lb/hp, 4.3 kg/hp; speed in direct drive at 1,000 rpm: 22.1 mph, 35.5 km/h; fuel consumption: 12.8 m/imp gal, 10.7 m/US gal, 22 l x 100 km.

CHASSIS rear suspension: anti-roll bar.

BRAKES area rubbed by linings: total 282.8 sq in, 1,824 sq cm.

ELECTRICAL EQUIPMENT battery: 80 Ah; generator type: alternator, 55 A.

DIMENSIONS AND WEIGHT (see 210 hp power team) dry weight: plus 421 lb, 190 kg.

OPTIONAL ACCESSORIES Select Shift Cruise-o-Matic automatic gearbox with 3.250 axle ratio.

375 hp power team

(optional for all models).

See 145 hp power team, except for:

ENGINE cylinders: 8, Vee-slanted at 90°; bore and stroke: 4.36 x 3.59 in, 110.7 x 91.2 mm; engine capacity: 429 cu in, 7,030 cu cm; compression ratio: 11.3; max power (SAE): 375 hp at 5,600 rpm; max torque (SAE): 450 lb ft, 62.1 kg m at 3,400 rpm; max engine rpm: 6,000; specific power: 53.3 hp/l; crankshaft bearings: 5; camshafts: 1, at centre of Vee; lubrication: gear pump, full flow filter; lubricating system capacity: 11.6 imp pt, 14 US pt, 6.6 l; carburation: 1 Holley 9510 D10F-SA downdraught 4-barrel carburettor; cooling system capacity: 32.4 imp pt, 38.9 US pt, 18.4 l.

TRANSMISSION gears: 4 + reverse; synchromesh gears: I, II, III, IV; gearbox ratios: I 2.780, II 1.930, III 1.360, IV 1, rev 2.780; final drive: hypoid bevel, limited slip (standard); axle ratio: 3.910; width of rims: 7''; tyres: F70 x 14.

PERFORMANCE max speed: about 130 mph, 209 km/h; power-weight ratio: Mustang 2-door Hardtop 9.6 lb/hp, 4.3 kg/hp; speed in direct drive at 1,000 rpm: 21.7 mph, 34.9 km/h; fuel consumption: 12.6 m/imp gal, 10.5 m/US gal, 22.4 l x 100 km.

CHASSIS rear suspension: anti-roll bar.

BRAKES area rubbed by linings: total 282.8 sq in, 1,824 sq cm.

ELECTRICAL EQUIPMENT battery: 80 Ah; generator type: alternator, 55 A.

DIMENSIONS AND WEIGHT (see 210 hp power team) dry weight: plus 456 lb, 207 kg.

OPTIONAL ACCESSORIES Select Shift Cruise-o-Matic automatic gearbox with 3.910 axle ratio.

Torino - Torino Ranch Wagon - Torino Squire - Torino 500 - Torino GT - Torino Brougham - Torino Cobra Series

PRICES IN USA:

Torino	2-door Hardtop	$ 2,706
Torino	4-door Sedan	$ 2,672
Torino Ranch Wagon	Station Wagon	$ 3,560
Torino Squire	Station Wagon	$ 3,023
Torino 500	2-door Hardtop	$ 2,887
Torino 500	2-door Fastback	$ 2,943
Torino 500	4-door Sedan	$ 2,855
Torino 500	4-door Hardtop	$ 2,959
Torino 500	Station Wagon	$ 3,170
Torino GT	2-door Hardtop	$ 3,150
Torino GT	2-door Convertible	$ 3,408
Torino Brougham	2-door Hardtop	$ 3,175
Torino Brougham	4-door Hardtop	$ 3,248
Torino Cobra	2-door Hardtop	$ 3,295

For V8 engines add $ 95.

322

FORD Mustang Grandé 2-door Hardtop

FORD Torino 4-door Sedan

FORD Torino Squire Station Wagon

145 hp power team

(standard for Torino and Torino 500 Series; not available for other Series).

ENGINE front, 4 stroke; cylinders: 6, in line; bore and stroke: 3.68 x 3.91 in, 93.5 x 99.3 mm; engine capacity: 250 cu in, 4,097 cu cm; compression ratio: 9; max power (SAE): 145 hp at 4,000 rpm; max torque (SAE): 232 lb ft, 32 kg m at 1,600 rpm; max engine rpm: 4,400; specific power: 35.4 hp/l; cylinder block: cast iron; cylinder head: cast iron; crankshaft bearings: 7; valves: 2 per cylinder, overhead, in line, push-rods and rockers, hydraulic tappets; camshafts: 1, side; lubrication: rotary pump, full flow filter; lubricating system capacity: 8.3 imp pt, 9.9 US pt, 4.7 l; carburation: 1 Carter 9510 DOZF-C downdraught single barrel carburettor; fuel feed: mechanical pump; cooling system: water; cooling system capacity: 19 imp pt, 22.8 US pt, 10.8 l.

TRANSMISSION driving wheels: rear; clutch: single dry plate, semi-centrifugal; gearbox: mechanical; gears: 3 + reverse, synchromesh gears: I, II, III; gearbox ratios: I 2.990, II 1.750, III 1, rev 3.170; gear lever: steering column; final drive: hypoid bevel; axle ratio: 3.000 — station wagon 3.250; width of rims: 5''; tyres: E78 x 14 — station wagon G78 x 14.

PERFORMANCE max speed: about 92 mph, 148 km/h; speed in direct drive at 1,000 rpm: 21.7 mph, 34.9 km/h; fuel consumption: 18.8 m/imp gal, 15.7 m/US gal, 15 l x 100 km.

CHASSIS integral; front suspension: independent, wishbones, lower leading arms, coil springs, anti-roll bar, telescopic dampers; rear suspension: rigid axle, semi-elliptic leafsprings, telescopic dampers.

STEERING recirculating ball; turns of steering wheel lock to lock: 4.90.

BRAKES drum, dual circuit; area rubbed by linings: total 267.2 sq in, 1,723 sq cm (station wagon 282.8 sq in, 1,824 sq cm).

ELECTRICAL EQUIPMENT voltage: 12 V; battery: 45 Ah; generator type: alternator, 38 A; ignition distributor: Autolite; headlamps: 4.

DIMENSIONS AND WEIGHT wheel base: 117 in, 2,972 mm — station wagon 114 in, 2,896 mm; front track: 60.50 in, 1,537 mm; rear track: 60 in, 1,524 mm; overall length: 206.20 in, 5,238 mm — station wagon 209 in, 5,308 mm; overall width: 76.50 in, 1,943 mm — 2-door hardtops 76.80 in, 1,951 mm — station wagon 75.40 in, 1,915 mm; overall height: 53.10 in, 1,349 mm — 2-door hardtops 52.30 in, 1,328 mm — 2-door fastback 51.10 in, 1,298 mm — station wagon 55.70 in, 1,415 mm; fuel tank capacity: 16.7 imp gal, 20 US gal, 76 l (station wagon 15 imp gal, 18 US gal, 68 l).

OPTIONAL ACCESSORIES Select Shift Cruise-o-Matic automatic gearbox with 3 ratios (I 2.460, II 1.460, III 1, rev 2.200), max ratio of convertor at stall 2.10, 2.790 axle ratio (station wagon 3.000); limited slip final drive; power-assisted steering; servo brake; front disc brakes; air-conditioning system.

210 hp power team

(standard for Torino GT, Torino Brougham, Torino Ranch Wagon and Torino Squire Series; optional for Torino and Torino 500 Series; not available for Torino Cobra).

See 145 hp power team, except for:

ENGINE cylinders: 8, Vee-slanted at 90°; bore and stroke: 4 x 3 in, 101.6 x 76.2 mm; engine capacity: 302 cu in, 4,950 cu cm; max power (SAE): 210 hp at 4,600 rpm; max torque (SAE): 296 lb ft, 40.8 kg m at 2,600 rpm; max engine rpm: 5,000; specific power: 42.4 hp/l; crankshaft bearings: 5; camshafts: 1, at centre of Vee; carburation: 1 Autolite 9510 DOAF-C downdraught twin barrel carburettor; cooling system capacity: 25.3 imp pt, 30.4 US pt, 14.4 l.

TRANSMISSION axle ratio: 2.790 — station wagons 3.000; width of rims: Torino GT 7''; tyres: Torino GT E70 x 14 — station wagons G78 x 14.

PERFORMANCE max speed: about 100 mph, 161 km/h; power-weight ratio: Torino 4-door Sedan and Torino 500 4-door Sedan 16.1 lb/hp, 7.3 kg/hp; speed in direct drive at 1,000 rpm: 22.3 mph, 35.9 km/h; fuel consumption: 16.7 m/imp gal, 13.9 m/US gal, 16.9 l x 100 km.

BRAKES area rubbed by linings: Torino GT 2-door Convertible total 282.8 sq in, 1,824 sq cm.

DIMENSIONS AND WEIGHT overall height: Torino GT 2-door Convertible 52.70 in, 1,338 mm; dry weight: Torino 2-door Hardtop 3,388 lb, 1,514 kg — Torino 4-door Sedan 3,380 lb, 1,533 kg — Torino Ranch Wagon Station Wagon 3,725 lb, 1,689 kg — Torino Squire Station Wagon 3,809 lb, 1,728 kg — Torino 500 2-door Hardtop 3,395 lb, 1,540 kg — Torino 500 2-door Fastback 3,451 lb, 1,565 kg — Torino 500 4-door Sedan 3,385 lb, 1,535 kg — Torino 500 4-door Hardtop 3,449 lb, 1,564 kg — Torino 500 Station Wagon 3,787 lb,

FORD Mustang Mach 1 2-door Fastback

FORD Torino 4-door Sedan

FORD Torino Squire Station Wagon

1,717 kg — Torino GT 2-door Hardtop 3,506 lb, 1,590 kg — Torino GT 2-door Convertible 3,646 lb, 1,653 kg — Torino Brougham 2-door Hardtop 3,448 lb, 1,564 kg — Torino Brougham 4-door Hardtop 3,503 lb, 1,588 kg.

240 hp power team

(optional for Torino, Torino Ranch Wagon, Torino Squire, Torino 500, Torino GT and Torino Brougham Series; not available for Torino Cobra).

See 145 hp power team, except for:

ENGINE cylinders: 8, Vee-slanted at 90°; bore and stroke: 4 x 3.50 in, 101.6 x 88.8 mm; engine capacity: 351 cu in, 5,752 cu cm; max power (SAE): 240 hp at 4,600 rpm; max torque (SAE): 350 lb ft, 48.3 kg m at 2,600 rpm; max engine rpm: 5,000; specific power: 41.7 hp/l; crankshaft bearings: 5; camshafts: 1, at centre of Vee; carburation: 1 Autolite 9510 DOOF-L downdraught twin barrel carburettor; cooling system capacity: 25.7 imp pt, 30.9 US pt, 14.6 l.

TRANSMISSION gearbox: Select Shift Cruise-o-Matic automatic (standard), max ratio of convertor at stall 2.10; gearbox ratios: I 2.460, II 1.460, III 1, rev 2.200; selector lever: steering column; axle ratio: 2.750 — station wagons 3.000; width of rims: Torino GT 7''; tyres: Torino GT E70 x 14 — station wagons G78 x 14.

PERFORMANCE max speed: about 106 mph, 170 km/h; power-weight ratio: Torino 4-door Sedan and Torino 500 4-door Sedan 14.7 lb/hp, 6.7 kg/hp; speed in direct drive at 1,000 rpm: 22.4 mph, 36 km/h; fuel consumption: 16 m/imp gal, 13.4 m/US gal, 17.6 l x 100 km.

BRAKES area rubbed by linings: total 282.8 sq in, 1,824 sq cm (station wagons 314 sq in, 2,025 sq cm).

ELECTRICAL EQUIPMENT battery: 55 Ah.

DIMENSIONS AND WEIGHT (see 210 hp power team) dry weight: plus 148 lb, 67 kg.

285 hp power team

(standard for Torino Cobra; optional for other Series).

See 145 hp power team, except for:

ENGINE cylinders: 8, Vee-slanted at 90°; bore and stroke: 4 x 3.50 in, 101.6 x 88.8 mm; engine capacity: 351 cu in, 5,752 cu cm; compression ratio: 10.7; max power (SAE): 285 hp at 5,400 rpm; max torque (SAE): 370 lb ft, 51 kg m at 3,400 rpm; max engine rpm: 5,600; specific power: 49.5 hp/l; crankshaft bearings: 5; camshafts: 1, at centre of Vee; carburation: 1 Autolite 9510 DOOF-AB downdraught 4-barrel carburettor; cooling system capacity: 25.7 imp pt, 30.9 US pt, 14.6 l.

TRANSMISSION gearbox: mechanical (station wagons only, automatic standard); gears: 4 + reverse; synchromesh gears: I, II, III, IV; gearbox ratios: I 2.780, II 1.930, III 1.360, IV 1, rev 2.780; gear lever: central; axle ratio: 3.250 — station wagons 3.000; width of rims: Torino Cobra 7''; tyres: Torino Cobra E70 x 14 — Torino GT 2-door Convertible F70 x 14 — station wagons G78 x 14.

PERFORMANCE max speed: about 110 mph, 177 km/h; power-weight ratio: Torino 4-door Sedan and Torino 500 4-door Sedan 12.7 lb/hp, 5.8 kg/hp — Torino Cobra 2-door Hardtop 13.7 lb/hp, 6.2 kg/hp; speed in direct drive at 1,000 rpm: 20.9 mph, 33.6 km/h; fuel consumption: 14.9 m/imp gal, 12.4 m/US gal, 18.9 l x 100 km.

BRAKES area rubbed by linings: total 282.8 sq in, 1,824 sq cm (station wagons 314 sq in, 2,025 sq cm).

ELECTRICAL EQUIPMENT battery: 55 Ah.

DIMENSIONS AND WEIGHT (see 210 hp power team) dry weight: plus 239 lb, 108 kg — Torino Cobra 2-door Hardtop 3,900 lb, 1,769 kg.

OPTIONAL ACCESSORIES Select Shift Cruise-o-Matic automatic gearbox with 3 ratios (I 2.460, II 1.460, III 1, rev 2.180), max ratio of convertor at stall 2.10, 2.750 axle ratio.

370 hp power team

(optional for all Series).

See 145 hp power team, except for:

ENGINE cylinders: 8, Vee-slanted at 90°; bore and stroke: 4.36 x 3.59 in, 110.7 x 91.2 mm; engine capacity: 429 cu in, 7,030 cu cm; compression ratio: 11.3; max power (SAE): 370 hp at 5,400 rpm; max torque (SAE): 450 lb ft, 62.1 kg m at 3,400 rpm; max engine rpm: 5,600; specific power: 52.6 hp/l; crankshaft bearings: 5; camshafts: 1, at centre

370 HP POWER TEAM

of Vee; lubrication: gear pump, full flow filter; lubricating system capacity: 13.4 imp pt, 16.1 US pt, 7.6 l; carburation: 1 Rochester 9510 DOOF-A downdraught 4-barrel carburettor; cooling system capacity: 32.6 imp pt, 39.1 US pt, 18.5 l.

TRANSMISSION gearbox: mechanical (station wagons only, automatic standard); gears: 4 + reverse; synchromesh gears: I, II, III, IV; gearbox ratios: I 2.320, II 1.690, III 1.290, IV 1, rev 2.320; gear lever: central; axle ratio: 3.250; width of rims: Torino GT and Torino Cobra 7''; tyres: F78 x 14 — Torino GT and Torino Cobra F70 x 14 — Torino GT 2-door Convertible G70 x 14 — station wagons G78 x 14.

PERFORMANCE max speed: about 117 mph, 188 km/h; power-weight ratio: Torino 4-door Sedan and Torino 500 4-door Sedan 10.4 lb/hp, 4.7 kg/hp — Torino Cobra 2-door Hardtop 10.5 lb/hp, 4.8 kg/hp; speed in direct drive at 1,000 rpm: 20.9 mph, 33.6 km/h; fuel consumption: 12.7 m/imp gal, 10.6 m/US gal, 22.2 l x 100 km.

BRAKES area rubbed by linings: total 282.8 sq in, 1,824 sq cm (station wagons 314 sq in, 2,025 sq cm).

ELECTRICAL EQUIPMENT battery: 80 Ah; generator type: alternator, 55 A.

DIMENSIONS AND WEIGHT (see 210 hp power team) dry weight: plus 459 lb, 208 kg — Torino Cobra 2-door Hardtop 3,900 lb, 1,769 kg.

OPTIONAL ACCESSORIES Select Shift Cruise-o-Matic automatic gearbox with 3 ratios (I 2.460, II 1.460, III 1, rev 2.180), max ratio of convertor at stall 2.10, 3.250 axle ratio.

Custom - Custom 500 - Galaxie 500 - LTD - LTD Brougham - Station Wagon Series

PRICES IN USA:

Custom	4-door Sedan	$ 2,940
Custom 500	4-door Sedan	$ 3,078
Galaxie 500	4-door Sedan	$ 3,246
Galaxie 500	2-door Hardtop	$ 3,280
Galaxie 500	4-door Hardtop	$ 3,317
LTD	2-door Hardtop	$ 3,575
LTD	2-door Convertible	$ 3,746
LTD	4-door Sedan	$ 3,583
LTD	4-door Hardtop	$ 3,621
LTD Brougham	4-door Sedan	$ 3,746
LTD Brougham	2-door Hardtop	$ 3,749
LTD Brougham	4-door Hardtop	$ 3,792
Station Wagons:		
4-door Ranch Wagon		$ —
4-door Custom Ranch Wagon		$ 3,542
4-door Country Sedan		$ 3,726
4-door Country Squire		$ 4,032

For V8 engines add $ 75 (for Galaxie 500 add $ 121).

140 hp power team

(standard for Custom, Custom 500 and Galaxie 500 Series; not available for other Series).

ENGINE front, 4 stroke; cylinders: 6, in line; bore and stroke: 4 x 3.18 in, 101.6 x 80.7 mm; engine capacity: 240 cu in, 3,933 cu cm; compression ratio: 8.9; max power (SAE): 140 hp at 4,000 rpm; max torque (SAE): 230 lb ft, 31.7 kg m at 2,200 rpm; max engine rpm: 4,400; specific power: 35.6 hp/l; cylinder block: cast iron; cylinder head: cast iron; crankshaft bearings: 7; valves: 2 per cylinder, overhead, in line, push-rods and rockers, hydraulic tappets; camshafts: 1, side; lubrication: rotary pump, full flow filter; lubricating system capacity: 8.3 imp pt, 9.9 US pt, 4.7 l; carburation: 1 Carter D1AF-PA downdraught single barrel carburettor; fuel feed: mechanical pump; cooling system: water; cooling system capacity: 23.9 imp pt, 28.8 US pt, 13.6 l.

TRANSMISSION driving wheels: rear; clutch: single dry plate, semi-centrifugal; gearbox: mechanical; gears: 3 + reverse; synchromesh gears: I, II, III; gearbox ratios: I 2.990, II 1.750, III 1, rev 3.170; gear lever: steering column; final drive: hypoid bevel; axle ratio: 3.250; width of rims: 5''; tyres: F78 x 15.

PERFORMANCE max speed: about 92 mph, 148 km/h; power-weight ratio: Custom 4-door Sedan and Custom 500 4-door Sedan 27.5 lb/hp, 12.4 kg/hp — Galaxie 500 4-door Sedan 27.6 lb/hp, 12.5 kg/hp; speed in direct drive at 1,000 rpm: 21 mph, 33.8 km/h; fuel consumption: 18.1 m/imp gal, 15.1 m/US gal, 15.6 l x 100 km.

CHASSIS perimeter box-type with cross members; front suspension: independent, wishbones, lower leading arms,

FORD Torino Brougham 4-door Hardtop

FORD Torino Cobra 2-door Hardtop

FORD Custom 500 4-door Sedan

coil springs, anti-roll bar, telescopic dampers; rear suspension: rigid axle, longitudinal lower trailing arms, upper torque arm, transverse linkage bar, coil springs, telescopic dampers.

STEERING recirculating ball; turns of steering wheel lock to lock: 5.64.

BRAKES drum, dual circuit; area rubbed by linings: total 329.2 sq in, 2,123 sq cm.

ELECTRICAL EQUIPMENT voltage: 12 V; battery: 45 Ah; generator type: alternator, 42 A; ignition distributor: Autolite; headlamps: 4.

DIMENSIONS AND WEIGHT wheel base: 121 in, 3,073 mm; front track: 63.30 in, 1,608 mm; rear track: 64.30 in, 1,633 mm; overall length: 216.20 in, 5,491 mm; overall width: 79.30 in, 2,014 mm — 2-door hardtop and 4-door hardtop 79.70 in, 2,024 mm; overall height: 4-door sedans 54.90 in, 1,394 mm — 2-door hardtop 53 in, 1,346 mm — 4-door hardtop 53.80 in, 1,366 mm; ground clearance: 4-door sedans 5 in, 127 mm — 2-door hardtop 4.70 in, 119 mm — 4-door hardtop 4.80 in, 122 mm; dry weight: Custom 4-door Sedan 3,849 lb, 1,745 kg — Custom 500 4-door Sedan 3,854 lb, 1,748 kg — Galaxie 500 4-door Sedan and 2-door Hardtop 3,859 lb, 1,750 kg — Galaxie 500 4-door Hardtop 3,914 lb, 1,775 kg; turning circle (between walls): 45.3 ft, 13.8 m; fuel tank capacity: 18.7 imp gal, 22.5 US gal, 85 l.

OPTIONAL ACCESSORIES Select Shift Cruise-o-Matic automatic gearbox with 3 ratios (I 2.460, II 1.460, III 1, rev 2.200), max ratio of convertor at stall 2.05, 3.250 axle ratio (Galaxie 500 3.000); limited slip final drive; power-assisted steering; servo brake; front disc brakes with servo; air-conditioning system.

210 hp power team

(optional for Custom and Custom 500 Series; not available for other Series).

See 140 hp power team, except for:

ENGINE cylinders: 8, Vee-slanted at 90°; bore and stroke: 4 x 3 in, 101.6 x 76.2 mm; engine capacity: 302 cu in, 4,950 cu cm; compression ratio: 9; max power (SAE): 210 hp at 4,600 rpm; max torque (SAE): 296 lb ft, 40.8 kg m at 2,600 rpm; max engine rpm: 5,000; specific power: 42.4 hp/l; crankshaft bearings: 5; camshafts: 1, at centre of Vee; carburation: 1 Autolite D10F-ABA downdraught twin barrel carburettor; cooling system capacity: 25.7 imp pt, 30.9 US pt, 14.6 l.

PERFORMANCE max speed: about 97 mph, 156 km/h; power-weight ratio: Custom 4-door Sedan and Custom 500 4-door Sedan 18.5 lb/hp, 8.4 kg/hp; fuel consumption: 16.4 m/imp gal, 13.7 m/US gal, 17.2 l x 100 km.

DIMENSIONS AND WEIGHT dry weight: Custom 4-door Sedan 3,880 lb, 1,759 kg — Custom 500 4-door Sedan 3,885 lb, 1,762 kg.

OPTIONAL ACCESSORIES Select Shift Cruise-o-Matic automatic gearbox with 2.750 axle ratio; automatic levelling system.

240 hp power team

(standard for LTD, LTD Brougham and Station Wagon Series; optional for other Series).

See 140 hp power team, except for:

ENGINE cylinders: 8, Vee-slanted at 90°; bore and stroke: 4 x 3.50 in, 101.6 x 88.8 mm; engine capacity: 351 cu in, 5,752 cu cm; compression ratio: 9; max power (SAE): 240 hp at 4,600 rpm; max torque (SAE): 350 lb ft, 48.3 kg m at 2,600 rpm; max engine rpm: 5,000; specific power: 41.7 hp/l; crankshaft bearings: 5; camshafts: 1, at centre of Vee; carburation: 1 Autolite D1AF-FA downdraught twin barrel carburettor; cooling system capacity: 27.5 imp pt, 33 US pt, 15.6 l.

TRANSMISSION gearbox ratios: I 2.420, II 1.610, III 1, rev 2.330; width of rims: 5'' — station wagons 7.5''; tyres: G78 x 15 — station wagons H78 x 15.

PERFORMANCE max speed: about 102 mph, 164 km/h; power-weight ratio: Custom 4-door Sedan 16.5 lb/hp, 7.4 kg/hp — Custom 500 4-door Sedan and Galaxie 500 4-door Sedan 16.6 lb/hp, 7.5 kg/hp — LTD 4-door Sedan 17.1 lb/hp, 7.7 kg/hp — LTD Brougham 4-door Sedan 17.2 lb/hp, 7.8 kg/hp; speed in direct drive at 1,000 rpm: 21.1 mph, 34 km/h; fuel consumption: 15.7 m/imp gal, 13.1 m/US gal, 18 l x 100 km.

BRAKES area rubbed by linings: station wagons total 363.8 sq in, 2,346 sq cm.

ELECTRICAL EQUIPMENT battery: 55 Ah.

DIMENSIONS AND WEIGHT (see 210 hp power team) overall length: station wagons 219.20 in, 5,568 mm; overall

FORD Torino Brougham 4-door Hardtop

FORD Torino Cobra 2-door Hardtop

FORD Custom 500 4-door Sedan

width: 79.70 in, 2,024 mm — station wagons 79.30 in, 2,014 mm — 4-door Country Squire 79.90 in, 2,029 mm; overall height: 4-door sedans 53.80 in, 1,366 mm — 2-door convertible 54.10 in, 1,374 mm — station wagons 57 in, 1,448 mm; ground clearance: 2-door convertible 4.80 in, 122 mm — station wagons 6.40 in, 163 mm; dry weight: plus 88 lb, 40 kg — Galaxie 500 4-door Sedan and 2-door Hardtop 3,978 lb, 1,804 kg — Galaxie 500 4-door Hardtop 4,033 lb, 1,829 kg — LTD 2-door Hardtop 4,043 lb, 1,833 kg — LTD 2-door Convertible 4,304 lb, 1,952 kg — LTD 4-door Sedan 4,109 lb, 1,863 kg — LTD 4-door Hardtop 4,104 lb, 1,861 kg — LTD Brougham 4-door Sedan 4,139 lb, 1,877 kg — LTD Brougham 2-door Hardtop 4,079 lb, 1,850 kg — LTD Brougham 4-door Hardtop 4,134 lb, 1,875 kg — 4-door Ranch Wagon 4,375 lb, 1,984 kg — 4-door Custom Ranch Wagon 4,400 lb, 1,996 kg — 4-door Country Sedan 4,426 lb, 2,007 kg — 4-door Country Squire 4,493 lb, 2,037 kg; fuel tank capacity: station wagons 26.4 imp gal, 22 US gal, 100 l.

OPTIONAL ACCESSORIES Select Shift Cruise-o-Matic automatic gearbox with 3 ratios (I 2.400, II 1.470, III 1, rev 2), max ratio of convertor at stall 2.05, 2.750 axle ratio; automatic levelling system.

255 hp power team

(optional for all Series).

See 140 hp power team, except for:

ENGINE cylinders: 8, Vee-slanted at 90°; bore and stroke: 4.05 x 3.78 in, 102.8 x 95.9 mm; engine capacity: 390 cu in, 6,391 cu cm; compression ratio: 8.6; max power (SAE): 255 hp at 4,400 rpm; max torque (SAE): 376 lb ft, 51.9 kg m at 2,600 rpm; max engine rpm: 4,600; specific power: 39.9 hp/l; crankshaft bearings: 5; camshafts: 1, at centre of Vee; carburation: 1 Autolite D1YF-DA downdraught twin barrel carburettor; cooling system capacity: 33.4 imp pt, 40.2 US pt, 19 l.

TRANSMISSION gearbox: Select Shift Cruise-o-Matic automatic (standard), max ratio of convertor at stall 2.05; gearbox ratios: I 2.460, II 1.460, III 1, rev 2.180; axle ratio: 2.750; width of rims: 5'' — station wagons 7.5''; tyres: G78 x 15 — station wagons H78 x 15.

PERFORMANCE max speed: about 103 mph, 166 km/h; power-weight ratio: Custom 4-door Sedan, Custom 500 4-door Sedan and Galaxie 500 4-door Sedan 16 lb/hp, 7.3 kg/hp — LTD 4-door Sedan 16.9 lb/hp, 7.6 kg/hp — LTD Brougham 4-door Sedan 17 lb/hp, 7.7 kg/hp; speed in direct drive at 1,000 rpm: 23 mph, 37 km/h; fuel consumption: 15.5 m/imp gal, 12.9 m/US gal, 18.2 l x 100 km.

BRAKES area rubbed by linings: station wagons total 363.8 sq in, 2,346 sq cm.

ELECTRICAL EQUIPMENT battery: 55 Ah.

DIMENSIONS AND WEIGHT (see 240 hp power team) dry weight: plus 201 lb, 91 kg — Galaxie 500 plus 113 lb, 51 kg.

OPTIONAL ACCESSORIES automatic levelling system.

260 hp power team

(optional for all Series).

See 140 hp power team, except for:

ENGINE cylinders: 8, Vee-slanted at 90°; bore and stroke: 4 x 4 in, 101.6 x 101.6 mm; engine capacity: 400 cu in, 6,555 cu cm; compression ratio: 9; max power (SAE): 260 hp at 4,400 rpm; max torque (SAE): 400 lb ft, 55.2 kg m at 2,200 rpm; max engine rpm: 4,600; specific power: 39.7 hp/l; crankshaft bearings: 5; camshafts: 1, at centre of Vee; carburation: 1 Autolite D1MF-KA downdraught twin barrel carburettor; cooling system capacity: 29.2 imp pt, 35.1 US pt, 16.6 l.

TRANSMISSION gearbox: Select Shift Cruise-o-Matic automatic (standard); max ratio of convertor at stall 2.05; gearbox ratios: I 2.460, II 1.460, III 1, rev 2.180; axle ratio: 2.750; width of rims: 5.5'' — station wagons 7.5''; tyres: station wagons H78 x 15.

PERFORMANCE max speed: about 103 mph, 165 km/h; power-weight ratio: Custom 4-door Sedan 15.7 lb/hp, 7.1 kg/hp — Custom 500 4-door Sedan and Galaxie 500 4-door Sedan 15.8 lb/hp, 7.2 kg/hp — LTD 4-door Sedan 16.6 lb/hp, 7.5 kg/hp — LTD Brougham 16.7 lb/hp, 7.6 kg/hp; speed in direct drive at 1,000 rpm: 23 mph, 37 km/h; fuel consumption: 15.5 m/imp gal, 12.9 m/US gal, 18.2 l x 100 km.

BRAKES area rubbed by linings: station wagons total 363.8 sq in, 2,346 sq cm.

ELECTRICAL EQUIPMENT battery: 70 Ah.

DIMENSIONS AND WEIGHT (see 240 hp power team) dry weight: plus 215 lb, 97 kg — Galaxie 500 plus 127 lb, 58 kg.

OPTIONAL ACCESSORIES automatic levelling system.

320 hp power team

(optional for all Series).

See 140 hp power team, except for:

ENGINE cylinders: 8, Vee-slanted at 90°; bore and stroke: 4.36 x 3.59 in, 110.7 x 91.2 mm; engine capacity: 429 cu in, 7,030 cu cm; compression ratio: 10.5; max power (SAE): 320 hp at 4,400 rpm; max torque (SAE): 460 lb ft, 63.5 kg m at 2,200 rpm; max engine rpm: 4,600; specific power: 45.5 hp/l; crankshafts bearings: 5; camshafts: 1, at centre of Vee; lubricating system capacity: 10 imp pt, 12 US pt, 5.7 l; carburation: 1 Autolite D1MF-FA downdraught twin barrel carburettor; cooling system capacity: 31 imp pt, 37.2 US pt, 17.6 l.

TRANSMISSION gearbox: Select Shift Cruise-o-Matic automatic (standard), max ratio of convertor at stall 2.05; gearbox ratios: I 2.460, II 1.460, III 1, rev 2.180; axle ratio: 2.750; width of rims: 5.5'' — station wagons 7.5''; tyres: H78 x 15.

PERFORMANCE max speed: about 116 mph, 186 km/h; power-weight ratio: Custom 4-door Sedan and Custom 500 4-door Sedan 13 lb/hp, 5.8 kg/hp — Galaxie 500 4-door Sedan 13.1 lb/hp, 5.9 kg/hp — LTD 4-door Sedan 13.8 lb/hp, 6.2 kg/hp — LTD Brougham 4-door Sedan 13.9 lb/hp, 6.3 kg/hp; speed in direct drive at 1,000 rpm: 25.3 mph, 40.7 km/h; fuel consumption: 13 m/imp gal, 10.8 m/US gal, 21.7 l x 100 km.

BRAKES area rubbed by linings: station wagons total 363.8 sq in, 2,346 sq cm.

ELECTRICAL EQUIPMENT battery: 80 Ah.

DIMENSIONS AND WEIGHT (see 240 hp power team) dry weight: plus 296 lb, 134 kg — Galaxie 500 plus 208 lb, 94 kg.

OPTIONAL ACCESSORIES automatic levelling system.

360 hp power team

(optional for all Series).

See 140 hp power team, except for:

ENGINE cylinders: 8, Vee-slanted at 90°; bore and stroke: 4.36 x 3.59 in, 110.7 x 91.2 mm; engine capacity: 429 cu in, 7.030 cu cm; compression ratio: 10.5; max power (SAE): 360 hp at 4,600 rpm; max torque (SAE): 480 lb ft, 66.2 kg m at 2,800 rpm; max engine rpm: 5,000; specific power: 51.2 hp/l; crankshaft bearings: 5; camshafts: 1, at centre of Vee; lubricating system capacity: 10 imp pt, 12 US pt, 5.7 l; carburation: 1 Autolite D1AF-MA downdraught 4-barrel carburettor; cooling system capacity: 31 imp pt, 37.2 US pt, 17.6 l.

TRANSMISSION gearbox: Select Shift Cruise-o-Matic automatic (standard), max ratio of convertor at stall 2.05; gearbox ratios: I 2.460, II 1.460, III 1, rev 2.180; axle ratio: 2.750; width of rims: 5.5'' — station wagons 7.5''; tyres: H78 x 15.

PERFORMANCE max speed: about 118 mph, 190 km/h; power-weight ratio: Custom 4-door Sedan, Custom 500 4-door Sedan 11.9 lb/hp, 5.4 kg/hp — LTD 4-door Sedan 12.5 lb/hp, 5.6 kg/hp — LTD Brougham 4-door Sedan 12.6 lb/hp, 5.7 kg/hp; speed in direct drive at 1,000 rpm: 25.3 mph, 40.7 km/h; fuel consumption: 12.6 m/imp gal, 10.5 m/US gal, 22.5 l x 100 km.

BRAKES area rubbed by linings: station wagons total 363.8 sq in, 2,346 sq cm.

ELECTRICAL EQUIPMENT battery: 80 Ah.

DIMENSIONS AND WEIGHT (see 240 hp power team) dry weight: plus 398 lb, 180 kg — Galaxie 500 plus 310 lb, 141 kg.

OPTIONAL ACCESSORIES automatic levelling system.

Thunderbird - Thunderbird Landau Series

PRICES IN USA:

Thunderbird	2-door Hardtop	$ 5,295
Thunderbird Landau	2-door Hardtop	$ 5,438
Thunderbird Landau	4-door Hardtop	$ 5,516

360 hp power team

(standard for both Series).

ENGINE front, 4 stroke; cylinders: 8, Vee-slanted at 90°; bore and stroke: 4.36 x 3.59 in, 110.7 x 91.2 mm; engine

FORD LTD Brougham 4-door Hardtop

FORD Thunderbird 2-door Hardtop

GLASSIC Phaeton

capacity: 429 cu in, 7,030 cu cm; compression ratio: 10; max power (SAE): 360 hp at 4,600 rpm; max torque (SAE): 480 lb ft, 66.2 kg m at 2,800 rpm; max engine rpm: 5,000; specific power: 51.2 hp/l; cylinder block: cast iron; cylinder head: cast iron; crankshaft bearings: 5; valves: 2 per cylinder, overhead, in line, push-rods and rockers, hydraulic tappets; camshafts: 1, at centre of Vee; lubrication: rotary pump, full flow filter; lubricating system capacity: 8.3 imp pt, 9.9 US pt, 4.7 l; carburation: 1 Autolite 9510 D1SF-AA downdraught 4-barrel carburettor; fuel feed: mechanical pump; cooling system: water; cooling system capacity: 32.4 imp pt, 38.9 US pt, 18.4 l.

TRANSMISSION driving wheels: rear; gearbox: Select Shift Cruise-o-Matic automatic, hydraulic torque convertor and planetary gears with 3 ratios + reverse, max ratio of convertor at stall 2.05, possible manual selection; gearbox ratios: I 2.460, II 1.460, III 1, rev 2.175; selector lever: steering column; final drive: hypoid bevel; axle ratio: 2.750; width of rims: 6''; tyres: H78 x 15.

PERFORMANCE max speed: about 124 mph, 200 km/h; power-weight ratio: Thunderbird 2-door Hardtop 12.8 lb/hp, 5.8 kg/hp — Thunderbird Landau 2-door Hardtop 12.7 lb/hp, 5.7 kg/hp — Thunderbird Landau 4-door Hardtop 13.1 lb/hp, 5.9 kg/hp; speed in direct drive at 1,000 rpm: 25.6 mph, 41.2 km/h; fuel consumption: 14 m/imp gal, 11.6 m/US gal, 20.2 l x 100 km.

CHASSIS perimeter box-type; front suspension: independent, wishbones, lower leading arms, coil springs, anti-roll bar, telescopic dampers; rear suspension: rigid axle, lower trailing radius arms, upper torque arm, transverse linkage bar, coil springs, telescopic dampers.

STEERING recirculating ball, servo; turns of steering wheel lock to lock: 3.72.

BRAKES front disc (diameter 11.72 in, 298 mm), rear drum, dual circuit, servo; area rubbed by linings; front 217.3 sq in, 1,401 sq cm, rear 155.9 sq in, 1,005 sq cm, total 373.2 sq in, 2,406 sq cm.

ELECTRICAL EQUIPMENT voltage: 12 V; battery: 80 Ah; generator type: alternator, 55 A; ignition distributor: Autolite; headlamps: 4.

DIMENSIONS AND WEIGHT wheel base: 114.70 in, 2,913 mm — 4-door hardtop 117.20 in, 2,977 mm; front track: 62.30 in, 1,582 mm; rear track: 62.30 in, 1,582 mm; overall length: 212.50 in, 5,937 mm — 4-door hardtop 215 in, 5,461 mm; overall width: 78 in, 1,981 mm — 4-door hardtop 77.40 in, 1,966 mm; overall height: 51.90 in, 1,318 mm — 4-door hardtop 53.70 in, 1,364 mm; ground clearance: 4.80 in, 122 mm — 4-door hardtop 4.70 in, 119 mm; dry weight: Thunderbird 2-door Hardtop 4,601 lb, 2,086 kg — Thunderbird Landau 2-door Hardtop 4,572 lb, 2,073 kg — Thunderbird Landau 4-door Hardtop 4,712 lb, 2,137 kg; fuel tank capacity: 26.9 imp pt, 22.5 US pt, 102 l.

BODY seats: 4-5; front seats: separate, high-backed seats.

OPTIONAL ACCESSORIES limited slip final drive; brakes with anti-skid device; air-conditioning system.

FORD LTD Brougham 2-door Hardtop

FORD Thunderbird 2-door Hardtop

GLASSIC USA

Glassic Series

PRICES IN USA:

Glassic	Sport Phaeton	$ 5,995
Glassic	Sport Roadster	$ 5,995

111 hp power team

(standard for both models).

ENGINE front, 4 stroke; cylinders: 4, in line; bore and stroke: 4.13 x 3.66 in, 104.8 x 92.9 mm; engine capacity: 195.4 cu in, 3,203 cu cm; compression ratio: 8.1; max power (SAE): 111 hp at 4,000 rpm; max torque (SAE): 180 lb ft, 24.8 kg m at 2,000 rpm; max engine rpm: 4,600; specific power: 34.7 hp/l; cylinder block: cast iron; cylinder head: cast iron; crankshaft bearings: 5; valves: 2 per cylinder, overhead, in line, push-rods and rockers; camshafts: 1, side; lubrication: gear pump, full flow filter; lubricating system capacity: 6.7 imp pt, 8 US pt, 3.8 l; carburation: 1 Holley downdraught single barrel carburettor; fuel feed: mechanical pump; cooling system: water; cooling system capacity: 19.4 imp pt, 23.3 US pt, 11 l.

TRANSMISSION driving wheels: rear; clutch: single dry plate; gearbox: mechanical; gears: 3 + reverse; synchro-

GLASSIC Roadster

mesh gears: I, II, III; gearbox ratios: I 3.340, II 1.850, III 1, rev 4.530; gear lever: central; final drive: hypoid bevel; axle ratio: 3.730; width of rims: 5.5''; tyres: 7.35 x 15.

PERFORMANCE max speed: about 76 mph, 122 km/h; carrying capacity: 882 lb, 400 kg; speed in direct drive at 1,000 rpm: 20.5 mph, 33 km/h; fuel consumption: 15.4 m/imp gal, 12.8 m/US gal, 18.4 l x 100 km.

CHASSIS ladder frame; front suspension: rigid axle, semi-elliptic leafsprings, telescopic dampers; rear suspension: rigid axle, semi-elliptic leafsprings, telescopic dampers.

STEERING worm and roller.

BRAKES drum, dual circuit; lining area: total 160.5 sq in, 1,035 sq cm.

ELECTRICAL EQUIPMENT voltage: 12 V; battery: 40 Ah; generator type: alternator, 32 A; headlamps: 2.

DIMENSIONS AND WEIGHT wheel base: 100 in, 2,540 mm; front track: 55.71 in, 1,415 mm; rear track: 55.71 in, 1,415 mm; turning circle (between walls): 40 ft, 12.2 m; fuel tank capacity: 14.1 imp gal, 16.9 US gal, 64 l.

IMPERIAL USA

Le Baron Series

PRICES IN USA:

Le Baron	2-door Hardtop	$ 6,005
Le Baron	4-door Hardtop	$ 6,237

335 hp power team

(standard for both models).

ENGINE front, 4 stroke; cylinders: 8, Vee-slanted at 90°; bore and stroke: 4.32 x 3.75 in, 109.7 x 95.2 mm; engine capacity: 440 cu in, 7,211 cu cm; compression ratio: 8.8; max power (SAE): 335 hp at 4,400 rpm; max torque (SAE): 460 lb ft, 63.5 kg m at 3,200 rpm; max engine rpm: 4,600; specific power: 46.4 hp/l; cylinder block: cast iron; cylinder head: cast iron; crankshaft bearings: 5; valves: 2 per cylinder, overhead, in line, push-rods and rockers, hydraulic tappets; camshafts: 1, at centre of Vee; lubrication: rotary pump, full flow filter; lubricating system capacity: 8.3 imp pt, 9.9 US pt, 4.7 l; carburation: 1 Carter AVS 4966S downdraught 4-barrel carburettor; fuel feed: mechanical pump; cooling system: water; cooling system capacity: 29.2 imp pt, 35.1 US pt, 16.6 l.

TRANSMISSION driving wheels: rear; gearbox: Torqueflite automatic, hydraulic torque convertor and planetary gears with 3 ratios + reverse, max ratio of convertor at stall 2.02, possible manual selection; gearbox ratios: I 2.450, II 1.450, III 1, rev 2.200; selector lever: steering column; final drive: hypoid bevel; axle ratio: 2.940; width of rims: 6''; tyres: L84 x 15.

PERFORMANCE max speed: about 114 mph, 183 km/h; power-weight ratio: 2-door hardtop 14.4 lb/hp, 6.5 kg/hp — 4-door hardtop 14.8 lb/hp, 6.7 kg/hp; carrying capacity: 882 lb, 400 kg; speed in direct drive at 1,000 rpm: 24.8 mph, 39.9 km/h; fuel consumption: 14 m/imp gal, 11.6 m/US gal, 20.2 l x 100 km.

CHASSIS integral, front box-type frame; front suspension: independent, wishbones, longitudinal torsion bars, anti-roll bar, telescopic dampers; rear suspension: rigid axle, semi-elliptic leafsprings, telescopic dampers.

STEERING recirculating ball, servo; turns of steering wheel lock to lock: 3.50.

BRAKES front disc, rear drum, dual circuit, servo; area rubbed by linings: total 428.1 sq in, 2,761 sq cm.

ELECTRICAL EQUIPMENT voltage: 12 V; battery: 70 Ah; generator type: alternator, 37 A; ignition distributor: Chrysler; headlamps: 4, retractable.

DIMENSIONS AND WEIGHT wheel base: 127 in, 3,226 mm; front track: 62.40 in, 1,585 mm; rear track: 62 in, 1,575 mm; overall length: 229.70 in, 5,834 mm; overall width: 2-door hardtop 79 in, 2,007 mm — 4-door hardtop 79.10 in, 2,009 mm; overall height: 2-door hardtop 55.60 in, 1,412 mm — 4-door hardtop 56.10 in, 1,425 mm; ground clearance: 6.70 in, 170 mm; dry weight: Le Baron 2-door Hardtop 4,825 lb, 2,188 kg — Le Baron 4-door Hardtop 4,975 lb, 2,257 kg; turning circle (between walls): 47.7 ft, 14.5 m; fuel tank capacity: 19.1 imp gal, 23 US gal, 87 l.

335 HP POWER TEAM

BODY hardtop; seats: 5; front seats: bench, separate backrests, built-in headrests.

OPTIONAL ACCESSORIES Sure-Brake anti-skid device; electric headlamps washer system; air-conditioning system.

INTERNATIONAL HARVESTER   USA

Scout Series

PRICES IN USA:

Scout 800A	$ —
Scout 800B	$ —

111 hp power team

(standard).

ENGINE front, 4 stroke; cylinders: 4, in line; bore and stroke: 4.13 x 3.66 in, 104.8 x 92.9 mm; engine capacity: 195.4 cu in, 3,203 cu cm; compression ratio: 8.1; max power (SAE): 111 hp at 4,000 rpm; max torque (SAE): 180 lb ft, 24.8 kg m at 2,000 rpm; max engine rpm: 4,600; specific power: 34.7 hp/l; cylinder block: cast iron; cylinder head: cast iron; crankshaft bearings: 5; valves: 2 per cylinder, overhead, in line, push-rods and rockers; camshafts: 1, side; lubrication: gear pump, full flow filter; lubricating system capacity: 6.7 imp pt, 8 US pt, 3.8 l; carburation: 1 Holley downdraught single barrel carburettor; fuel feed: mechanical pump; cooling system: water; cooling system capacity: 19.4 imp pt, 23.3 US pt, 11 l.

TRANSMISSION driving wheels: rear; clutch: single dry plate; gearbox: mechanical; gears: 3 + reverse; synchromesh gears: I, II, III; gearbox ratios: I 3.340, II 1.850, III 1, rev 4.530; gear lever: central; final drive: hypoid bevel; axle ratio: 3.730; width of rims: 5.5''; tyres: 7.35 x 15.

PERFORMANCE max speed: about 76 mph, 122 km/h; power-weight ratio: 28.8 lb/hp, 13.1 kg/hp; carrying capacity: 882 lb, 400 kg; speed in direct drive at 1,000 rpm: 20.5 mph, 33 km/h; fuel consumption: 15.4 m/imp gal, 12.8 m/US gal, 18.4 l x 100 km.

CHASSIS ladder frame; front suspension: rigid axle, semi-elliptic leafsprings, telescopic dampers; rear suspension: rigid axle, semi-elliptic leafsprings, telescopic dampers.

STEERING worm and roller.

BRAKES drum, dual circuit; lining area: total 160.5 sq in, 1,035 sq cm.

ELECTRICAL EQUIPMENT voltage: 12 V; battery: 40 Ah; generator type: alternator, 37 A; headlamps: 2, halogen.

DIMENSIONS AND WEIGHT wheel base: 100 in, 2,540 mm; front track: 55.70 in, 1,415 mm; rear track: 55.70 in, 1,415 mm; overall length: 154 in, 3,912 mm; overall width: 68.60 in, 1,742 mm; ground clearance: 8.70 in, 221 mm; dry weight: 3,200 lb, 1,451 kg; turning circle (between walls): 40 ft, 12.2 m: fuel tank capacity: 8.4 imp gal, 10 US gal, 38 l.

BODY estate car/station wagon; doors: 2 + 1; seats: 5; front seats: separate; details: fixed or detachable roof.

OPTIONAL ACCESSORIES 3-speed automatic gearbox; 4-wheel drive, gearbox with transfer box (2.030 ratio); limited slip final drive; 3.310 or 4.270 axle ratio; 60 Ah battery; 52 A alternator.

145 hp power team

(optional).

See 111 hp power team, except for:

ENGINE cylinders: 6, in line; bore and stroke: 3.75 x 3.50 in, 95.2 x 88.8 mm; engine capacity: 232 cu in, 3,802 cu cm; compression ratio: 8.5; max power (SAE): 145 hp at 4,300 rpm; max torque (SAE): 215 lb ft, 29.7 kg m at 1,600 rpm; max engine rpm: 4,500; specific power: 38.1 hp/l; crankshaft bearings: 7; valves: hydraulic tappets; lubricating system capacity: 8.3 imp pt, 10 US pt, 4.7 l; cooling system capacity: 28.3 imp pt, 34 US pt, 16.1 l.

TRANSMISSION axle ratio: 3.310.

PERFORMANCE max speed: about 81 mph, 130 km/h; power-weight ratio: 22 lb/hp, 10 kg/hp; speed in direct drive at

IMPERIAL Le Baron 4-door Hardtop

INTERNATIONAL HARVESTER Scout 800A

INTERNATIONAL HARVESTER 145 hp engine

1,000 rpm: 18 mph, 28.9 km/h; fuel consumption: 20 m/imp gal, 16.8 m/US gal, 14 l x 100 km.

BRAKES lining area: total 169.2 sq in, 1,092 sq cm.

ELECTRICAL EQUIPMENT battery: 50 Ah.

193 hp power team

(optional).

See 111 hp power team, except for:

ENGINE cylinders: 8, Vee-slanted at 90°; bore and stroke 3.87 x 3.22 in, 98.4 x 81.7 mm; engine capacity: 304 cu in 4,982 cu cm; compression ratio: 8.2; max power (SAE) 193 hp at 4,400 rpm; max torque (SAE): 272 lb ft, 37.5 k m at 2,800 rpm; specific power: 38.7 hp/l; valves: hydrauli tappets; camshafts: 1, at centre of Vee; carburation: 1 Holle downdraught twin barrel carburettor.

TRANSMISSION tyres: 7.75 x 15.

PERFORMANCE max speed: about 90 mph, 145 km/h; powe weight ratio: 16.1 lb/hp, 7.3 kg/hp; fuel consumption: 13. m/imp gal, 11.7 m/US gal, 20.1 l x 100 km.

BRAKES lining area: total 169.5 sq in, 1,093 sq cm.

Travelall 1000D

PRICE IN USA:

Travelall 1000D	$ —

145 hp power team

(standard).

ENGINE front, 4 stroke; cylinders: 6, in line; bore an stroke: 3.75 x 3.50 in, 95.2 x 88.8 mm; engine capacity: 23 cu in, 3,802 cu cm; compression ratio: 8.5; max powe (SAE): 145 hp at 4,300 rpm; max torque (SAE): 215 lb ft 29.7 kg m at 1,600 rpm; max engine rpm: 4,600; specifi power: 38.1 hp/l; cylinder block: cast iron; cylinder head cast iron; crankshaft bearings: 7; valves: 2 per cylinder overhead, in line, push-rods and rockers, hydraulic tappets camshafts: 1, side; lubrication: gear pump, full flow filter lubricating system capacity: 8.3 imp pt, 10 US pt, 4.7 l carburation: 1 Holley downdraught single barrel carburettor fuel feed: mechanical pump; cooling system: water; coolin system capacity: 20.1 imp pt, 24.1 US pt, 11.4 l.

TRANSMISSION driving wheels: rear; clutch: single dr plate; gearbox: mechanical; gears: 3 + reverse; synchro mesh gears: I, II, III; gearbox ratios: I 3.060, II 1.550, III 1 rev 3.060; gear lever: steering column; final drive: hypoi bevel; axle ratio: 3.310; width of rims: 5.5''; tyres 8.25 x 15.

PERFORMANCE max speed: about 82 mph, 132 km/h; power weight ratio: 22 lb/hp, 10 kg/hp; carrying capacity: 1,058 lb, 480 kg; speed in direct drive at 1,000 rpm: 23 mph, 37 km/h; fuel consumption: 14.1 m/imp gal, 11.8 m/US gal 20 l x 100 km.

CHASSIS box-type ladder frame; front suspension: inde pendent, wishbones, longitudinal torsion bars, telescopic dampers; rear suspension: rigid axle, semi-elliptic leaf springs, telescopic dampers.

STEERING recirculating ball; turns of steering wheel lock to lock: 3.50.

BRAKES drum, dual circuit; lining area: 237.4 sq in, 1,531 sq cm.

ELECTRICAL EQUIPMENT voltage: 12 V; battery: 50 Ah; generator type: alternator, 37 A; headlamps: 2, halogen.

DIMENSIONS AND WEIGHT wheel base: 119 in, 3,023 mm; front track: 63 in, 1,600 mm; rear track: 61.40 in, 1,560 mm; overall length: 186.80 in, 4,745 mm; overall width: 77.60 in 1,971 mm; overall height: 66.50 in, 1,689 mm; ground clear ance: 7.30 in, 185 mm; dry weight: 3,200 lb, 1,451 kg; turning circle (between walls): 44.5 ft, 13.6 m; fuel tank capacity: 14.1 imp gal, 17 US gal, 64 l.

BODY estate car/station wagon; doors: 4 + 1; seats: 6; front seats: bench.

OPTIONAL ACCESSORIES automatic gearbox; 4-speed mechanical gearbox; limited slip final drive; 3.070 3.540 3.730 4.090 axle ratios; power-assisted steering; servo brake.

154.8 hp power team

(optional).

See 145 hp power team, except for:

ENGINE cylinders: 8, Vee-slanted at 90°; engine capacity: 266 cu in, 4,360 cu cm; compression ratio: 8.4; max power

IMPERIAL Le Baron 4-door Hardtop

INTERNATIONAL HARVESTER Scout 800B

INTERNATIONAL HARVESTER Travelall 1000D

(SAE): 154.8 hp at 4,400 rpm; max torque (SAE): 227 lb ft, 31.3 kg m at 2,800 rpm; max engine rpm: 4,600; specific power: 35.5 hp/l; crankshaft bearings: 5; camshafts: 1, at centre of Vee.

TRANSMISSION axle ratio: 3.540; width of rims: 6''; tyres: 8.00 x 16.5.

PERFORMANCE max speed: about 82 mph, 132 km/h; speed in direct drive at 1,000 rpm: 17.8 mph, 28.7 km/h.

BRAKES lining area: total 245.5 sq in, 1,583 sq cm.

JEEP CORPORATION   USA

Jeep Wagoneer Series

PRICES IN USA:

Jeep Wagoneer	Standard	$ 4,447
Jeep Wagoneer	Custom	$ 4,697

135 hp power team

(standard)

ENGINE front, 4 stroke; cylinders: 6, in line; bore and stroke: 3.75 x 3.50 in, 95.2 x 88.8 mm; engine capacity: 232 cu in, 3,802 cu cm; compression ratio: 8.5; max power (SAE): 135 hp at 4,300 rpm; max torque (SAE): 215 lb ft, 29.7 kg m at 1,600 rpm; max engine rpm: 4,500; specific power: 35.5 hp/l; cylinder block: cast iron; cylinder head: cast iron; crankshaft bearings: 7; valves: 2 per cylinder, overhead, in line, push-rods and rockers, hydraulic tappets; camshafts: 1, side; lubrication: gear pump, full flow filter; lubricating system capacity: 8.3 imp pt, 10 US pt, 4.7 l; carburation: 1 Carter downdraught single barrel carburettor; fuel feed: mechanical; cooling system: water; cooling system capacity: 17.6 imp pt, 21 US pt, 10 l.

TRANSMISSION driving wheels: front (automatically engaged with transfer box low ratio) and rear; clutch: single dry plate; gearbox: mechanical; gears: 3 with high and low ratios + reverse; synchromesh gears: I, II, III; gearbox ratios: I 3.100 (low 5.80), II 1.612 (low 4.01), III 1 (low 2.46), rev 3.100 (low 6.26); gear and low ratio levers: steering column; final drive: hypoid bevel; axle ratio: 4.090; width of rims: 6''; tyres: 7.75 x 15.

PERFORMANCE max speed: about 88 mph, 141 km/h; power-weight ratio: 27.4 lb/hp, 12.4 kg/hp; speed in direct drive at 1,000 rpm: 18.8 mph, 30.2 km/h; fuel consumption: 18.8 m/imp gal, 15.7 m/US gal, 15 l x 100 km.

CHASSIS box-type ladder frame; front suspension: rigid axle, semi-elliptic leafsprings, telescopic dampers; rear suspension: rigid axle, semi-elliptic leafsprings, telescopic dampers.

STEERING recirculating ball; turns of steering wheel lock to lock: 5.25.

BRAKES drum, dual circuit; lining area: front 90.4 sq in, 583 sq cm, rear 90.4 sq in, 583 sq cm, total 180.8 sq in, 1,166 sq cm.

ELECTRICAL EQUIPMENT voltage: 12 V; battery: 50 Ah; generator type: alternator, 35 A; ignition distributor: Delco-Remy; headlamps: 2.

DIMENSIONS AND WEIGHT wheel base: 110 in, 2,794 mm; front track: 57 in, 1,448 mm; rear track: 57 in, 1,448 mm; overall length: 183.66 in, 4,665 mm; overall width: 75.60 in, 1,920 mm; overall height: 63.50 in, 1,613 mm; ground clearance: front axle 8.54 in, 217 mm — rear axle 7.75 in, 197 mm; dry weight: 3,699 lb, 1,677 kg; distribution of weight: 51.9% front axle, 48.1% rear axle; turning circle (between walls): 47.9 ft, 14.6 m; fuel tank capacity: 18.3 imp gal, 22 US gal, 83 l.

BODY estate car/station wagon; doors: 4; seats: 2; front seats: bench.

OPTIONAL ACCESSORIES 3-speed Turbo Hydramatic automatic gearbox; 4-speed fully synchronized mechanical gearbox; limited slip final drive; power-assisted steering; servo brake; air-conditioning system.

230 hp power team

(optional).

See 135 hp power team, except for:

ENGINE cylinders: 8, Vee-slanted at 90°; bore and stroke: 3.80 x 3.85 in, 96.4 x 97.7 mm; engine capacity: 350 cu in,

230 HP POWER TEAM

5,736 cu cm; compression ratio: 9; max power (SAE): 230 hp at 4,600 rpm; max torque (SAE): 350 lb ft, 48.3 kg m at 2,400 rpm; max engine rpm: 4,800; specific power: 40.1 hp/l; crankshaft bearings: 5; camshafts: 1, at centre of Vee; carburation: 1 Carter downdraught twin barrel carburettor; cooling system capacity: 25 imp pt, 30 US pt, 14.2 l.

PERFORMANCE max speed: about 103 mph, 165 km/h; power-weight ratio: 16 lb/hp, 7.3 kg/hp; speed in direct drive at 1,000 rpm: 18.7 mph, 30.1 km/h; fuel consumption: 16.6 m/imp gal, 13.8 m/US gal, 17 l x 100 km.

ELECTRICAL EQUIPMENT battery: 60 Ah.

Jeepster Commando Series

PRICES IN USA:

Jeepster Commando	Convertible	$ 3,291
Jeepster Commando	Roadster	$ 3,197
Jeepster Commando	Station Wagon	$ 3,447

For V6 engines add $ 201.

75 hp power team

(standard).

ENGINE front, 4 stroke; cylinders: 4, in line; bore and stroke: 3.12 x 4.37 in, 79.2 x 111 mm; engine capacity: 134 cu in, 2,199 cu cm; compression ratio: 6.7; max power (SAE): 75 hp at 4,000 rpm; max torque (SAE): 114 lb ft, 15.7 kg m at 2,000 rpm; max engine rpm: 4,600; specific power: 34.1 hp/l; cylinder block: cast iron; cylinder head: cast iron; crankshaft bearings: 3; valves: 2 per cylinder, overhead, in line, push-rods and rockers; camshafts: 1, side; lubrication: gear pump, full flow filter; lubricating system capacity: 8.3 imp pt, 10 US pt, 4.7 l; carburation: 1 Carter downdraught single barrel carburettor; fuel feed: mechanical pump; cooling system: water; cooling system capacity: 16.5 imp pt, 20 US pt, 9.4 l.

TRANSMISSION driving wheels: front (automatically engaged with transfer box low ratio) and rear; clutch: single dry plate; gearbox: mechanical; gears: 3 with high and low ratios + reverse; synchromesh gears: I, II, III; gearbox ratios: I 3.100 (low 5.80), II 1.612 (low 4.01), III 1 (low 2.46), rev 3.100 (low 6.26); gear and low ratio levers: central; final drive: hypoid bevel; axle ratio: 3.730; width of rims: 5.5''; tyres: 7.35 x 15.

PERFORMANCE max speed: about 78 mph, 125 km/h; speed in direct drive at 1,000 rpm: 19.3 mph, 31 km/h; fuel consumption: 25.7 m/imp gal, 21.4 m/US gal, 11 l x 100 km.

CHASSIS box-type ladder frame; front suspension: rigid axle, semi-elliptic leafsprings, anti-roll bar, telescopic dampers; rear suspension: rigid axle, semi-elliptic leafsprings, telescopic dampers.

STEERING worm and roller; turns of steering wheel lock to lock: 4.50.

BRAKES drum, dual circuit; lining area: front 78 sq in, 503 sq cm, rear 78 sq in, 503 sq cm, total 156 sq in, 1,006 sq cm.

ELECTRICAL EQUIPMENT voltage: 12 V; battery: 50 Ah; generator type: alternator, 35 A; ignition distributor: Prestolite; headlamps: 2.

DIMENSIONS AND WEIGHT wheel base: 101 in, 2,566 mm; front track: 50 in, 1,270 mm; rear track: 50 in, 1,270 mm; overall length: 168.40 in, 4,277 mm; overall width: 65.20 in, 1,656 mm; overall height: 62.40 in, 1,585 mm — station wagon 65 in, 1,651 mm; ground clearance: 7.50 in, 190 mm; fuel tank capacity: 12.5 imp gal, 15 US gal, 57 l.

OPTIONAL ACCESSORIES 3-speed Turbo Hydramatic automatic gearbox; 4-speed fully synchronized mechanical gearbox; limited slip final drive; power-assisted steering; servo brake; sunshine roof only for station wagon.

160 hp power team

(optional).

See 75 hp power team, except for:

ENGINE cylinders: 6, Vee-slanted at 90°; bore and stroke: 3.75 x 3.40 in, 95.2 x 86.4 mm; engine capacity: 225 cu in,

JEEP CORPORATION Jeep Wagoneer Custom

JEEP CORPORATION Jeep Universal

LINCOLN Continental 4-door Sedan

3,685 cu cm; compression ratio: 9; max power (SAE): 160 hp at 4,200 rpm; max torque (SAE): 235 lb ft, 32.4 kg m at 2,400 rpm; max engine rpm: 4,400; specific power: 43.4 hp/l; crankshaft bearings: 4; valves: hydraulic tappets; camshafts: 1, at centre of Vee; carburation: 1 Carter YF-4002-S downdraught twin barrel carburettor.

PERFORMANCE max speed: about 90 mph, 145 km/h; speed in direct drive at 1,000 rpm: 22.3 mph, 35.9 km/h; fuel consumption: 20.2 m/imp gal, 16.8 m/US gal, 14 l x 100 km.

STEERING recirculating ball.

Jeep Universal

PRICE IN USA:

Jeep Universal $ 2,886

For V6 engine add $ 100.

75 hp power team

(standard).

ENGINE front, 4 stroke; cylinders: 4, in line; bore and stroke: 3.12 x 4.37 in, 79.2 x 111 mm; engine capacity: 134 cu in, 2,199 cu cm; compression ratio: 6.7; max power (SAE): 75 hp at 4,000 rpm; max torque (SAE): 114 lb ft, 15.7 kg m at 2,000 rpm; max engine rpm: 4,600; specific power: 34.1 hp/l; crankshaft bearings: 3; valves: 2 per cylinder, overhead, in line, push-rods and rockers; camshafts: 1, side; lubrication: gear pump, full flow filter; lubricating system capacity: 8.3 imp pt, 10 US pt, 4.7 l; carburation: 1 Carter downdraught single barrel carburettor; cooling system: water; cooling system capacity: 16.5 imp pt, 20 US pt, 9.4 l.

TRANSMISSION driving wheels: front (automatically engaged with transfer box low ratio) and rear; clutch: single dry plate; gearbox: mechanical; gears: 3 with high and low ratios + reverse; synchromesh gears: II and III; gearbox ratios: I 3.100 (low 5.80), II 1.612 (low 4.01), III 1 (low 2.46), rev 3.100 (low 6.26); gear and low ratio levers: central; final drive: hypoid bevel; axle ratio: 3.730; width of rims: 4.5''; tyres: 6.00 x 16.

PERFORMANCE max speed: about 78 mph, 125 km/h; power-weight ratio: 50 lb/hp, 22.7 kg/hp; speed in direct drive at 1,000 rpm: 19.3 mph, 31 km/h; fuel consumption: 25.7 m/imp gal, 21.4 m/US gal, 11 l x 100 km.

CHASSIS ladder frame; front suspension: rigid axle, semi-elliptic leafsprings, telescopic dampers; rear suspension: rigid axle, semi-elliptic leafsprings, telescopic dampers.

STEERING cam and lever; turns of steering wheel lock to lock: 3.52.

BRAKES drum, dual circuit; lining area: front 78 sq in, 503 sq cm, rear 78 sq in, 503 sq cm, total 156 sq in, 1,006 sq cm.

ELECTRICAL EQUIPMENT voltage: 12 V; battery: 50 Ah; generator type: alternator, 35 A; ignition distributor: Presto-lite; headlamps: 2.

DIMENSIONS AND WEIGHT wheel base: 81 in, 2,057 mm; front track: 48.40 in, 1,229 mm; rear track: 48.40 in, 1,229 mm; overall length: 135.60 in, 3,444 mm; overall width: 71.75 in, 1,822 mm; overall height: 69.50 in, 1,765 mm; ground clearance: 8.60 in, 219 mm; dry weight: 3,750 lb, 1,700 kg; turning circle (between walls): 36.3 ft, 11.1 m; fuel tank capacity: 8.8 imp gal, 10.5 US gal, 40 l.

BODY open; doors: none; seats: 4-5; front seats: separate.

OPTIONAL ACCESSORIES 4-speed fully synchronized mechanical gearbox also with front limited slip final drive; rear limited slip final drive; wheel base 101 in, 2,566 mm, overall length 155.60 in, 5,952 mm, overall height 68.30 in, 1,735 mm, dry weight 3,900 lb, 1,769 kg.

160 hp power team

(optional).

See 75 hp power team, except for:

ENGINE cylinders: 6, Vee-slanted at 90°; bore and stroke: 3.75 x 3.40 in, 95.2 x 86.4 mm; engine capacity: 225 cu in, 3,687 cu cm; compression ratio: 9; max power (SAE): 160 hp at 4,200 rpm; max torque (SAE): 235 lb ft, 32.4

JEEP CORPORATION Jeepster Commando Station Wagon

JEEP CORPORATION Jeep Universal

LINCOLN Continental 4-door Sedan

kg m at 2,400 rpm; max engine rpm: 4,400; specific power: 43.4 hp/l; crankshaft bearings: 4; valves: hydraulic tappets; camshafts: 1, at centre of Vee; carburation: 1 Carter YF-4002-S downdraught twin barrel carburettor.

TRANSMISSION synchromesh gears: I, II, III; width of rims: 6''; tyres: 7.35 x 15.

PERFORMANCE max speed: about 95 mph, 153 km/h; power-weight ratio: 23.4 lb/hp, 10.6 kg/hp; speed in direct drive at 1,000 rpm: 22.1 mph, 35.5 km/h; fuel consumption: 20.2 m/imp gal, 16.8 m/US gal, 14 l x 100 km.

LINCOLN   USA

Continental - Continental Mk III Series

PRICES IN USA:

Continental	4-door Sedan	$ 7,213
Continental	2-door Hardtop Coupé	$ 6,966
Continental Mk III	2-door Hardtop	$ 8,421

365 hp power team

(standard).

ENGINE front, 4 stroke; cylinders: 8, Vee-slanted at 90°; bore and stroke: 4.36 x 3.85 in, 110.7 x 97.8 mm; engine capacity: 460 cu in, 7,538 cu cm; compression ratio: 10; max power (SAE): 365 hp at 4,600 rpm; max torque (SAE): 500 lb ft, 69 kg m at 2,800 rpm; max engine rpm: 5,000; specific power: 48.4 hp/l; cylinder block: cast iron; cylinder head: cast iron; crankshaft bearings: 5; valves: 2 per cylinder, overhead, in line, push-rods and rockers, hydraulic tappets; camshafts: 1, at centre of Vee; lubrication: rotary pump, full flow filter; lubricating system capacity: 8.3 imp pt, 9.9 US pt, 4.7 l; carburation: 1 Autolite 9510 D1VF-AA downdraught 4-barrel carburettor; fuel feed: mechanical pump; cooling system: water; cooling system capacity: 32.6 imp pt, 39.1 US pt, 18.5 l (Continental Mk III 32.4 imp pt, 38.9 US pt, 18.4 l).

TRANSMISSION driving wheels: rear; gearbox: Select-Shift automatic, hydraulic torque convertor and planetary gears with 3 ratios + reverse, max ratio of convertor at stall 2.05, possible manual selection; gearbox ratios: I 2.460, II 1.460, III 1, rev 2.170; selector lever: steering column; final drive: hypoid bevel; axle ratio: 2.800; width of rims: 6''; tyres: 225 x 15.

PERFORMANCE max speed: about 112 mph, 180 km/h; power-weight ratio: Continental 4-door Sedan 13.9 lb/hp, 6.3 kg/hp; speed in direct drive at 1,000 rpm: 22.4 mph, 36 km/h; fuel consumption: 12.8 m/imp gal, 10.6 m/US gal, 22.1 l x 100 km.

CHASSIS box-type ladder frame; front suspension: independent, wishbones, coil springs, anti-roll bar, telescopic dampers; rear suspension: rigid axle, lower trailing radius arms, upper torque arm, transverse linkage bar, coil springs, automatic levelling control, telescopic dampers.

STEERING recirculating ball, servo; turns of steering wheel lock to lock: 3.61.

BRAKES front disc, rear drum, dual circuit, servo; area rubbed by linings: front 217.3 sq in, 1,401 sq cm, rear 173.3 sq in, 1,118 sq cm (Continental Mk III 155.9 sq in, 1,005 sq cm), total 390.6 sq in, 2,519 sq cm (Continental Mk III 373.2 sq in, 2,406 sq cm).

ELECTRICAL EQUIPMENT voltage: 12 V; battery: 85 Ah; generator type: alternator, 61 A (Continental Mk III 55 A); ignition distributor: Autolite; headlamps: 4, retractable.

DIMENSIONS AND WEIGHT wheel base: 127 in, 3,226 mm — Continental Mk III 117.20 in, 2,977 mm; front track: 64.30 in, 1,633 mm — Continental Mk III 62.30 in, 1,582 mm; rear track: 64.30 in, 1,633 mm — Continental Mk III 62.30 in, 1,582 mm; overall length: 225 in, 5,715 mm — Continental Mk III 216.10 in, 5,489 mm; overall width: 79.60 in, 2,022 mm — Continental Mk III 79.40 in, 2,017 mm; overall height: sedan 55.50 in, 1,410 mm — hardtop coupé 54.50 in, 1,384 mm — Continental Mk III 53 in, 1,346 mm; dry weight: Continental 4-door Sedan 5,062 lb, 2,296 kg — Continental 2-door Hardtop Coupé 5,022 lb, 2,277 kg — Continental Mk III 2-door Hardtop 5,003 lb, 2,269 kg; turning circle (between walls): 49.9 ft, 15.2 m — Continental Mk III 48.3 ft, 14.7 m; fuel tank capacity: 18.7 imp gal, 22.5 US gal, 85 l.

BODY seats: 6; front seats: built-in headrests; details: air-conditioning system.

365 HP POWER TEAM

OPTIONAL ACCESSORIES limited slip final drive; 3.000 axle ratio; adjustable tilt of steering wheel; 65 A alternator; electrically-heated rear window.

MERCURY   USA

Comet - Comet GT Series

PRICES IN USA:

Comet	2-door Sedan	$ 2,217
Comet	4-door Sedan	$ 2,276
Comet GT	2-door Sedan	$ 2,396

For V8 engine add $ 163.

100 hp power team

(standard for all models).

ENGINE front, 4 stroke; cylinders: 6, in line; bore and stroke: 3.50 x 2.94 in, 88.8 x 74.6 mm; engine capacity: 170 cu in, 2,786 cu cm; compression ratio: 8.7; max power (SAE): 100 hp at 4,200 rpm; max torque (SAE): 148 lb ft, 20.4 kg m at 2,600 rpm; max engine rpm: 4,400; specific power: 35.9 hp/l; cylinder block: cast iron; cylinder head: cast iron; crankshaft bearings: 4; valves: 2 per cylinder, overhead, in line, push-rods and rockers, hydraulic tappets; camshafts: 1, side; lubrication: rotary pump, full flow filter; lubricating system capacity: 8.3 imp pt, 9.9 US pt, 4.7 l; carburation: 1 Carter 910 D1DF-EA downdraught single barrel carburettor; fuel feed: mechanical pump; cooling system: water; cooling system capacity: 14.8 imp pt, 17.8 US pt, 8.4 l.

TRANSMISSION driving wheels: rear; clutch: single dry plate, semi-centrifugal; gearbox: mechanical; gears: 3 + reverse; synchromesh gears: I, II, III; gearbox ratios: I 3.410, II 1.860, III 1, rev 3.510; gear lever: steering column; final drive: hypoid bevel; axle ratio: 2.790; width of rims: 4.5''; tyres: 6.45 x 14.

PERFORMANCE max speed: about 95 mph, 153 km/h; power-weight ratio: 2-door sedan 26.1 lb/hp, 11.8 kg/hp — 4-door sedan 27.1 lb/hp, 12.3 kg/hp; speed in direct drive at 1,000 rpm: 22.2 mph, 35.7 km/h; fuel consumption: 20.8 m/imp gal, 17.3 m/US gal, 13.6 l x 100 km.

CHASSIS integral; front suspension: independent, wishbones, lower leading arm, coil springs, anti-roll bar, telescopic dampers; rear suspension: rigid axle, semi-elliptic leafsprings, telescopic dampers.

STEERING recirculating ball; turns of steering wheel lock to lock: 5.20.

BRAKES drum, dual circuit; area rubbed by linings: total 212 sq in, 1,367 sq cm.

ELECTRICAL EQUIPMENT voltage: 12 V; battery: 45 Ah; generator type: alternator, 38 A; ignition distributor: Autolite; headlamps: 2.

DIMENSIONS AND WEIGHT wheel base: 103 in, 2,616 mm — 4-door sedan 109.90 in, 2,791 mm; front track: 56.50 in, 1,435 mm; rear track: 56.50 in, 1,435 mm; overall length: 181.70 in, 4,615 mm — 4-door sedan 188.60 in, 4,790 mm; overall width: 70.60 in, 1,793 mm — 4-door sedan 70.70 in, 1,796 mm; overall height: 53 in, 1,346 mm — 4-door sedan 53.10 in, 1,349 mm; ground clearance: 6.10 in, 155 mm; dry weight: Comet 2-door Sedan 2,614 lb, 1,185 kg — Comet 4-door Sedan 2,714 lb, 1,231 kg; turning circle (between walls): 39.6 ft, 12.1 m; fuel tank capacity: 12.5 imp gal, 15 US gal, 57 !.

BODY saloon/sedan; seats: 4-5; front seats: bench.

OPTIONAL ACCESSORIES power-assisted steering; air-conditioning system.

115 hp power team

(optional for all models).

See 100 hp power team, except for:

ENGINE bore and stroke: 3.68 x 3.13 in, 93.4 x 79.4 mm; engine capacity: 200 cu in, 3,277 cu cm; max power (SAE): 115 hp at 4,000 rpm; max torque (SAE): 180 lb ft, 24.8 kg m at 2,200 rpm; max engine rpm: 4,300; specific power: 35.1 hp/l; crankshaft bearings: 7; carburation: 1 Carter 9510 D1DF-GA downdraught single barrel carburettor; cooling system capacity: 15 imp pt, 18 US pt, 8.5 l.

TRANSMISSION gearbox ratios: I 2.990, II 1.750, III 1, rev 3.170; axle ratio: 3.000.

PERFORMANCE max speed: about 98 mph, 157 km/h; power-

LINCOLN Continental Mk III 2-door Hardtop

MERCURY Comet 4-door Sedan

MERCURY Montego 2-door Hardtop

weight ratio: 2-door sedan 22.8 lb/hp, 10.3 kg/hp — 4-door sedan 23.6 lb/hp, 10.7 kg/hp; speed in direct drive at 1,00 rpm: 25 mph, 40.3 km/h; fuel consumption: 20 m/imp ga 16.7 m/US gal, 14.1 l x 100 km.

DIMENSIONS AND WEIGHT dry weight: plus 5 lb, 2 k

OPTIONAL ACCESSORIES Select Shift Cruise-o-Matic automatic gearbox with 3 ratios (I 2.460, II 1.460, III 1, re 2.200), max ratio of convertor at stall 2.10, 2.790 axle rati

145 hp power team

(optional for all models).

See 100 hp power team, except for:

ENGINE bore and stroke: 3.68 x 3.91 in, 93.5 x 99.3 mm engine capacity: 250 cu in, 4,097 cu cm; compression ratio 9; max power (SAE): 145 hp at 4,000 rpm; max torque (SAE): 232 lb ft, 32 kg m at 1,600 rpm; max engine rpm 4,300; specific power: 35.4 hp/l; crankshaft bearings: carburation: 1 Carter 9510 D1ZF-JA downdraught single barre carburettor; cooling system capacity: 16.4 imp pt, 19 US pt, 9.3 l.

TRANSMISSION gearbox: Select Shift Cruise-o-Matic auto matic, hydraulic torque convertor and planetary gears wit 3 ratios + reverse, max ratio of convertor at stall 2.0 possible manual selection; gearbox ratios: I 2.460, II 1.46 III 1, rev 2.200; selector lever: steering column; axl ratio: 3.000.

PERFORMANCE max speed: about 100 mph, 161 km/h; powe weight ratio: 2-door sedan 18.7 lb/hp, 8.5 kg/hp — 4-doo sedan 19.4 lb/hp, 8.8 kg/hp; speed in direct drive at 1,00 rpm: 25 mph, 40.3 km/h; fuel consumption: 19.2 m/imp ga 16 m/US gal, 14.7 l x 100 km.

ELECTRICAL EQUIPMENT generator type: alternator, 55 A

DIMENSIONS AND WEIGHT dry weight: plus 105 lb, 48 kg

210 hp power team

(optional for all models).

See 100 hp power team, except for:

ENGINE cylinders: 8, Vee-slanted at 90°; bore and stroke 4 x 3 in, 101.6 x 76.1 mm; engine capacity: 302 cu in, 4,94 cu cm; compression ratio: 9; max power (SAE): 210 hp a 4,600 rpm; max torque (SAE): 296 lb ft, 40.8 kg m at 2,60 rpm; max engine rpm: 4,800; specific power: 42.4 hp/ crankshaft bearings: 5; camshafts: 1, at centre of Vee carburation: 1 Autolite 9510 D10F-ABA downdraught twi barrel carburettor; cooling system capacity: 22.5 imp p 27.1 US pt, 12.8 l.

TRANSMISSION gearbox ratios: I 2.990, II 1.750, III 1 rev 3.170.

PERFORMANCE max speed: about 103 mph, 165 km/h; powe weight ratio: 2-door sedan 13.4 lb/hp, 6.1 kg/hp — 4-doo sedan 13.8 lb/hp, 6.3 kg/hp; speed in direct drive at 1,00 rpm: 25 mph, 40.3 km/h; fuel consumption: 17.3 m/imp ga 14.4 m/US gal, 16.3 l x 100 km.

BRAKES area rubbed by linings: total 267.2 sq in, 1,72 sq cm.

ELECTRICAL EQUIPMENT generator type: alternator, 55 A

DIMENSIONS AND WEIGHT dry weight: plus 194 lb, 88 kg

OPTIONAL ACCESSORIES Select Shift Cruise-o-Matic auto matic gearbox with 3 ratios (I 2.460, II 1.460, III 1, re 2.200), max ratio of convertor at stall 2.02, 2.790 axle ratio

Montego - Montego MX - Montego MX Brougham - Montego MX Villager - Cyclone - Cyclone GT - Cyclone Spoiler Series

PRICES IN USA:

Montego	2-door Hardtop	$ 2,77
Montego	4-door Sedan	$ 2,77
Montego MX	2-door Hardtop	$ 2,89
Montego MX	4-door Sedan	$ 2,87
Montego MX	Station Wagon	$ 3,21
Montego MX Brougham	2-door Hardtop	$ 3,08
Montego MX Brougham	4-door Sedan	$ 3,07
Montego MX Brougham	4-door Hardtop	$ 3,15
Montego MX Villager	Station Wagon	$ 3,45
Cyclone	2-door Hardtop	$ 3,36
Cyclone GT	2-door Hardtop	$ 3,68
Cyclone Spoiler	2-door Hardtop	$ 3,80

For V8 engines add $ 116.

LINCOLN Continental Mk III 2-door Hardtop

MERCURY Comet 4-door Sedan

MERCURY Montego 2-door Hardtop

145 hp power team

(standard for Montego, Montego MX, Montego MX Brougham and Montego MX Villager Series; not available for other models).

ENGINE front, 4 stroke; cylinders: 6, in line; bore and stroke: 3.68 x 3.91 in, 93.5 x 99.3 mm; engine capacity: 250 cu in, 4,097 cu cm; compression ratio: 9; max power (SAE): 145 hp at 4,000 rpm; max torque (SAE): 232 lb ft, 32 kg m at 1,600 rpm; max engine rpm: 4,300; specific power: 35.4 hp/l; cylinder block: cast iron; cylinder head: cast iron; crankshaft bearings: 7; valves: 2 per cylinder, overhead, in line, push-rods and rockers, hydraulic tappets; camshafts: 1, side; lubrication: rotary pump, full flow filter; lubricating system capacity: 8.3 imp pt, 9.9 US pt, 4.7 l; carburation: 1 Carter 9510 D1ZF-HA downdraught single barrel carburettor; fuel feed: mechanical pump; cooling system: water; cooling system capacity: 19 imp pt, 22.8 US pt, 10.8 l.

TRANSMISSION driving wheels: rear; clutch: single dry plate, semi-centrifugal; gearbox: mechanical; gears: 3 + reverse; synchromesh gears: I, II, III; gearbox ratios: I 2.990, II 1.750, III 1, rev 3.170; gear lever: steering column; final drive: hypoid bevel; axle ratio: 3.000 — station wagons 3.250; width of rims: 5''; tyres: E78 x 14 — station wagons G78 x 14.

PERFORMANCE max speed: about 99 mph, 160 km/h; speed in direct drive at 1,000 rpm: 23 mph, 37 km/h; fuel consumption: 19.9 m/imp gal, 16.6 m/US gal, 14.2 l x 100 km.

CHASSIS integral; front suspension: independent, wishbones, lower leading arms, coil springs, anti-roll bar, telescopic dampers; rear suspension: rigid axle, semi-elliptic leafsprings, telescopic dampers.

STEERING recirculating ball; turns of steering wheel lock to lock: 4.90.

BRAKES drum, dual circuit; area rubbed by linings: total 267.2 sq in, 1,722 sq cm (station wagons 282.8 sq in, 1,824 sq cm).

ELECTRICAL EQUIPMENT voltage: 12 V; battery: 45 Ah; generator type: alternator, 38 A; ignition distributor: Autolite; headlamps: 4.

DIMENSIONS AND WEIGHT wheel base: 117 in, 2,972 mm — station wagons 114 in, 2,895 mm; front track: 60.50 in, 1,537 mm; rear track: 60 in, 1,524 mm; overall length: 209.90 in, 5,331 mm — station wagons 211.80 in, 5,380 mm; overall width: 4-door sedans and 4-door hardtop 77.40 in, 1,966 mm — 2-door hardtops 77.30 in, 1,963 mm — station wagon 75.40 in, 1,915 mm; overall height: 4-door sedans and 4-door hardtop 53.60 in, 1,361 mm — 2-door hardtops 52.50 in, 1,333 mm — station wagons 56.10 in, 1,425 mm; ground clearance: 5 in, 127 mm — station wagons 6 in, 152 mm; turning circle (between walls): 43.7 ft, 13.3 m; fuel tank capacity: 16.7 imp gal, 20 US gal, 76 l (station wagons 15 imp gal, 18 US gal, 68 l).

OPTIONAL ACCESSORIES Select Shift Cruise-o-Matic automatic gearbox with 3 ratios (I 2.460, II 1.460, III 1, rev 2.200), max ratio of convertor at stall 2.10, 2.790 axle ratio (station wagons 3.000); limited slip final drive; anti-roll bar on front suspension; power-assisted steering; servo brake: front disc brakes with servo; air-conditioning system.

210 hp power team

(standard for Cyclone GT; optional for Montego, Montego MX, Montego MX Brougham and Montego MX Villager Series; not available for other models).

See 145 hp power team, except for:

ENGINE cylinders: 8, Vee-slanted at 90°; bore and stroke: 4 x 3 in, 101.6 x 76.1 mm; engine capacity: 302 cu in, 4,949 cu cm; max power (SAE): 210 hp at 4,600 rpm; max torque (SAE): 296 lb ft, 40.8 kg m at 2,600 rpm; max engine rpm: 4,800; specific power: 42.4 hp/l; crankshaft bearings: 5; camshafts: 1, at centre of Vee; carburation: 1 Autolite 9510 D10F-ABA downdraught twin barrel carburettor; cooling system capacity: 25.7 imp pt, 30.9 US pt, 14.6 l.

TRANSMISSION axle ratio: station wagons 3.000; width of rims: Cyclone GT 7''; tyres: Cyclone GT G78 x 14.

PERFORMANCE max speed: about 102 mph, 164 km/h; speed in direct drive at 1,000 rpm: 23.3 mph, 37.5 km/h; fuel consumption: 17.2 m/imp gal, 14.3 m/US gal, 16.4 l x 100 km.

ELECTRICAL EQUIPMENT headlamps: 4, retractable.

OPTIONAL ACCESSORIES Select Shift Cruise-o-Matic automatic gearbox with max ratio of convertor at stall 2.02.

240 hp power team

(optional for Montego, Montego MX, Montego MX Brougham, Montego MX Villager and Cyclone GT Series; not available for other models).

See 145 hp power team, except for:

ENGINE cylinders: 8, Vee-slanted at 90°; bore and stroke: 4 x 3.50 in, 101.6 x 88.8 mm; engine capacity: 351 cu in, 5,752 cu cm; max power (SAE): 240 hp at 4,600 rpm; max torque (SAE): 350 lb ft, 48.3 kg m at 2,600 rpm; max engine rpm: 4,800; specific power: 41.7 hp/l; crankshaft bearings: 5; camshafts: 1, at centre of Vee; carburation: 1 Autolite 9510 D1ZF-UA downdraught twin barrel carburettor; cooling system capacity: 25.7 imp pt, 30.9 US pt, 14.6 l.

TRANSMISSION gearbox: Select Shift Cruise-o-Matic automatic (standard), max ratio of convertor at stall 2.14; gearbox ratios: I 2.460, II 1.460, III 1, rev 2.200; selector lever: central; axle ratio: 2.750 — station wagons 3.000; width of rims: Cyclone GT 7''; tyres: Cyclone GT G78 x 14.

PERFORMANCE max speed: about 107 mph, 172 km/h; speed in direct drive at 1,000 rpm: 23.6 mph, 38 km/h; fuel consumption: 17.3 m/imp gal, 14.4 m/US gal, 16.3 l x 100 km.

BRAKES area rubbed by linings: total 282.8 sq in, 1,824 sq cm (station wagons 314 sq in, 2,025 sq cm).

285 hp power team

(standard for Cyclone; optional for Montego, Montego MX, Montego MX Brougham, Montego MX Villager and Cyclone GT Series; not available for Cyclone Spoiler).

See 145 hp power team, except for:

ENGINE cylinders: 8, Vee-slanted at 90°; bore and stroke: 4 x 3.50 in, 101.6 x 88.8 mm; engine capacity: 351 cu in, 5,752 cu cm; compression ratio: 10.7; max power (SAE): 285 hp at 5,400 rpm; max torque (SAE): 370 lb ft, 51 kg m at 3,400 rpm; max engine rpm: 5,600; specific power: 49.5 hp/l; crankshaft bearings: 5; camshafts: 1, at centre of Vee; carburation: 1 Autolite 9510 D10F-EA downdraught 4-barrel carburettor; cooling system capacity: 25.7 imp pt, 30.9 US pt, 14.6 l.

TRANSMISSION gears: 4 + reverse; synchromesh gears: I, II, III, IV; gearbox ratios: I 2.780, II 1.930, III 1.360, IV 1, rev 2.780; gear lever: central; axle ratio: 3.250; width of rims: Cyclone and Cyclone GT 7''; tyres: Cyclone F70 x 14 — Cyclone GT G78 x 14.

PERFORMANCE max speed: about 113 mph, 182 km/h; speed in direct drive at 1,000 rpm: 20.3 mph, 32.6 km/h; fuel consumption: 15.5 m/imp gal, 12.9 m/US gal, 18.2 l x 100 km.

BRAKES area rubbed by linings: total 282.8 sq in, 1,824 sq cm (station wagons 314 sq in, 2,025 sq cm).

ELECTRICAL EQUIPMENT battery: 55 Ah.

OPTIONAL ACCESSORIES Select Shift Cruise-o-Matic automatic gearbox with 3 ratios (I 2.460, II 1.460, III 1, rev 2.180), max ratio of convertor at stall 2.14, 2.750 axle ratio (station wagons 3.250).

370 hp power team

(standard for Cyclone Spoiler; optional for Cyclone and Cyclone GT; not available for other models).

See 145 hp power team, except for:

ENGINE cylinders: 8, Vee-slanted at 90°; bore and stroke: 4.36 x 3.59 in, 110.7 x 91.2 mm; engine capacity: 429 cu in, 7,030 cu cm; compression ratio: 11.3; max power (SAE): 370 hp at 5,400 rpm; max torque (SAE): 450 lb ft, 62.1 kg m at 3,400 rpm; max engine rpm: 5,600; specific power: 52.6 hp/l; crankshaft bearings: 5; camshafts: 1, at centre of Vee; lubrication: gear pump, full flow filter; lubricating system capacity: 11.6 imp pt, 14 US pt, 6.6 l; carburation: 1 Rochester 9510 D10F-KA downdraught 4-barrel carburettor; cooling system capacity: 32.6 imp pt, 39.1 US pt, 18.5 l.

TRANSMISSION gears: 4 + reverse; synchromesh gears: I, II, III, IV; gearbox ratios: I 2.320, II 1.690, III 1.290, IV 1, rev 2.320; gear lever: central; axle ratio: 3.250; width of rims: Cyclone Spoiler 7''; tyres: Cyclone Spoiler G70 x 14.

PERFORMANCE max speed: about 118 mph, 190 km/h; speed in direct drive at 1,000 rpm: 21 mph, 33.8 km/h; fuel consumption: 14.1 m/imp gal, 11.7 m/US gal, 20.1 l x 100 km.

CHASSIS front suspension: anti-roll bar (standard).

BRAKES area rubbed by linings: total 282.8 sq in, 1,824 sq cm.

ELECTRICAL EQUIPMENT battery: 80 Ah.

MERCURY Montego MX Brougham 4-door Hardtop

MERCURY Cyclone Spoiler 2-door Hardtop

MERCURY Cougar 2-door Hardtop

Cougar - Cougar XR-7 - Cougar GT Series

PRICES IN USA:

Cougar	2-door Hardtop	$ 3,289
Cougar	2-door Convertible	$ 3,681
Cougar XR-7	2-door Hardtop	$ 3,629
Cougar XR-7	2-door Convertible	$ 3,877
Cougar GT	2-door Hardtop	$ 3,398

240 hp power team

(standard for all models).

ENGINE front, 4 stroke; cylinders: 8, Vee-slanted at 90°; bore and stroke: 4 x 3.50 in, 101.6 x 88.8 mm; engine capacity: 351 cu in, 5,752 cu cm; compression ratio: 9; max power (SAE): 240 hp at 4,600 rpm; max torque (SAE): 350 lb ft, 48.3 kg m at 2,600 rpm; max engine rpm: 4,800; specific power: 41.7 hp/l; cylinder block: cast iron; cylinder head: cast iron; crankshaft bearings: 5; valves: 2 per cylinder, overhead, in line, push-rods and rockers, hydraulic tappets; camshafts: 1, at centre of Vee; lubrication: rotary pump, full flow filter; lubricating system capacity: 8.3 imp pt, 9.9 US pt, 4.7 l; carburation: 1 Autolite 9510 D10F-ZA downdraught twin barrel carburettor; fuel feed: mechanical pump; cooling system: water; cooling system capacity: 25.7 imp pt, 30.9 US pt, 14.6 l.

TRANSMISSION driving wheels: rear; clutch: single dry plate, semi-centrifugal; gearbox: 3 + reverse, synchromesh gears: I, II, III; gearbox ratios: I 2.420, II 1.610, III 1, rev 2.330; gear lever: central; final drive: hypoid bevel; axle ratio: 2.750 — GT 3.000; width of rims: 6''; tyres: E78 x 14.

PERFORMANCE max speed: about 115 mph, 185 km/h; power-weight ratio: Cougar 2-door Hardtop 14.5 lb/hp, 6.5 kg/hp — Cougar XR-7 2-door Hardtop 14.6 lb/hp, 6.6 kg/hp; speed in direct drive at 1,000 rpm: 24 mph, 38.6 km/h; fuel consumption: 17.1 m/imp gal, 14.3 m/US gal, 16.5 l x 100 km.

CHASSIS integral; front suspension: independent, wishbones, lower leading arms, coil springs, anti-roll bar, telescopic dampers; rear suspension: rigid axle, semi-elliptic leafsprings, telescopic dampers.

STEERING recirculating ball; turns of steering wheel lock to lock: 4.46.

BRAKES drum, dual circuit; area rubbed by linings: total 282.8 sq in, 1,824 sq cm.

ELECTRICAL EQUIPMENT voltage: 12 V; battery: 45 Ah; generator type: alternator, 42 A; ignition distributor: Autolite; headlamps: 4.

DIMENSIONS AND WEIGHT wheel base: 112.10 in, 2,847 mm; front track: 61.50 in, 1,562 mm; rear track: 61 in, 1,549 mm; overall length: 196.70 in, 4,996 mm; overall width: 75.10 in, 1,907 mm; overall height: hardtops 50.80 in, 1,290 mm — convertibles 50.50 in, 1,283 mm; ground clearance: 4.50 in, 114 mm; dry weight: Cougar 2-door Hardtop 3,485 lb, 1,580 kg — Cougar 2-door Convertible 3,615 lb, 1,639 kg — Cougar XR-7 2-door Hardtop 3,514 lb, 1,593 kg — Cougar XR-7 2-door Convertible 3,634 lb, 1,648 kg; turning circle (between walls): 43.7 ft, 12.3 m; fuel tank capacity: 16.7 imp gal, 20 US gal, 76 l.

OPTIONAL ACCESSORIES Select Shift Cruise-o-Matic automatic gearbox with 3 ratios (I 2.400, II 1.470, III 1, rev 2.000), max ratio of convertor at stall 2.10, 2.750 axle ratio (GT 3.000); limited slip final drive; competition suspension; power-assisted steering; front disc brakes with servo; air-conditioning system.

285 hp power team

(optional for all models).

See 240 hp power team, except for:

ENGINE compression ratio: 10.7; max power (SAE): 285 hp at 5,400 rpm; max torque (SAE): 370 lb ft, 51 kg m at 3,500 rpm; max engine rpm: 5,600; specific power: 49.5 hp/l; carburation: 1 Autolite 9510 D10F-AAA downdraught 4-barrel carburettor.

TRANSMISSION gearbox: Select Shift Cruise-o-Matic automatic (standard), max ratio of convertor at stall 2.10; gearbox ratios: I 2.460, II 1.460, III 1, rev 2.180; axle ratio: 3.000 — GT 3.250.

MERCURY Montego MX Brougham 4-door Hardtop

MERCURY Cyclone Spoiler 2-door Hardtop

MERCURY Cougar 2-door Hardtop

PERFORMANCE max speed: about 120 mph, 193 km/h; power-weight ratio: Cougar 2-door Hardtop 12.4 lb/hp, 5.6 kg/hp — Cougar XR-7 2-door Hardtop 12.5 lb/hp, 5.7 kg/hp; speed in direct drive at 1,000 rpm: 22 mph, 35.4 km/h; fuel consumption: 14.6 m/imp gal, 12.1 m/US gal, 19.4 l x 100 km.

ELECTRICAL EQUIPMENT battery: 55 Ah; generator type: alternator, 55 A.

DIMENSIONS AND WEIGHT dry weight: plus 63 lb, 29 kg.

OPTIONAL ACCESSORIES 4-speed fully synchronized mechanical gearbox (I 2.780, II 1.930, III 1.360, IV 1, rev 2.780), 3.250 axle ratio.

370 hp power team

(optional for all models).

See 240 hp power team, except for:

ENGINE bore and stroke: 4.36 x 3.59 in, 110.7 x 91.2 mm; engine capacity: 429 cu in, 7,030 cu cm; compression ratio: 11.3; max power (SAE): 370 hp at 5,400 rpm; max torque (SAE): 450 lb ft, 62.1 kg m at 3,400 rpm; max engine rpm: 5,600; specific power: 52.6 hp/l; lubrication: gear pump, full flow filter; lubricating system capacity: 11.6 imp pt, 14 US pt, 6.6 l; carburation: 1 Rochester 9510 D10F-AA downdraught 4-barrel carburettor; cooling system capacity: 32.6 imp pt, 39.1 US pt, 18.5 l.

TRANSMISSION gearbox: Select Shift Cruise-o-Matic automatic (standard), max ratio of convertor at stall 2.10; gearbox ratios: I 2.460, II 1.460, III 1, rev 2.180; axle ratio: 3.250; width of rims: 7''; tyres: F70 x 14.

PERFORMANCE max speed: about 129 mph, 207 km/h; power-weight ratio: Cougar 2-door Hardtop 10 lb/hp, 4.5 kg/hp — Cougar XR-7 2-door Hardtop 10.2 lb/hp, 4.6 kg/hp; speed in direct drive at 1,000 rpm: 23.1 mph, 37.1 km/h; fuel consumption: 13.4 m/imp gal, 11.1 m/US gal, 21.1 l x 100 km.

CHASSIS rear suspension: anti-roll bar.

BRAKES front disc, rear drum, dual circuit, servo.

ELECTRICAL EQUIPMENT battery: 80 Ah; generator type: alternator, 55 A.

DIMENSIONS AND WEIGHT dry weight: plus 248 lb, 112 kg.

OPTIONAL ACCESSORIES 4-speed fully synchronized mechanical gearbox (I 2.320, II 1.690, III 1.290, IV 1, rev 2.320); axle ratio: 3.250.

Monterey - Monterey Custom - Marquis - Marquis Brougham - Colony Park Series

PRICES IN USA:

Monterey	4-door Sedan	$ 3,423
Monterey	2-door Hardtop	$ 3,465
Monterey	4-door Hardtop	$ 3,533
Monterey	Station Wagon	$ 4,283
Monterey Custom	4-door Sedan	$ 3,958
Monterey Custom	2-door Hardtop	$ 4,041
Monterey Custom	4-door Hardtop	$ 4,113
Marquis	4-door Sedan	$ 4,474
Marquis	2-door Hardtop	$ 4,557
Marquis	4-door Hardtop	$ 4,624
Marquis	Station Wagon	$ 4,547
Marquis Brougham	4-door Sedan	$ 4,880
Marquis Brougham	2-door Hardtop	$ 4,963
Marquis Brougham	4-door Hardtop	$ 5,033
Colony Park	Station Wagon	$ 4,806

240 hp power team

(standard for Monterey 4-door Sedan, 2- and 4-door Hardtop; not available for Monterey Station Wagon and other Series).

ENGINE front, 4 stroke; cylinders: 8, Vee-slanted at 90°; bore and stroke: 4 x 3.50 in, 101.6 x 88.8 mm; engine capacity: 351 cu in, 5,752 cu cm; compression ratio: 9; max power (SAE): 240 hp at 4,600 rpm; max torque (SAE): 350 lb ft, 48.3 kg m at 2,600 rpm; max engine rpm: 4,800; specific power: 41.7 hp/l; cylinder block: cast iron; cylinder head: cast iron; crankshaft bearings: 5; valves: 2 per cylinder, overhead, in line, push-rods and rockers, hydraulic tappets; camshafts: 1, at centre of Vee; lubrication: rotary pump, full flow filter; lubricating system capacity: 8.3

240 HP POWER TEAM

imp pt, 9.9 US pt, 4.7 l; carburation: 1 Autolite 9510 D1AF-FA downdraught twin barrel carburettor; fuel feed: mechanical pump; cooling system: water; cooling system capacity: 30.6 imp pt, 36.8 US pt, 17.4 l.

TRANSMISSION driving wheels: rear; clutch: single dry plate, semi-centrifugal; gearbox: mechanical; gears: 3 + reverse; synchromesh gears: I, II, III; gearbox ratios: I 2.420, II 1.610, III 1, rev 2.330; gear lever: steering column; final drive: hypoid bevel; axle ratio: 3.250; width of rims: 5''; tyres: G78 x 15.

PERFORMANCE max speed: about 111 mph, 178 km/h; power-weight ratio: Monterey 4-door Sedan 17.5 lb/hp, 7.9 kg/hp; speed in direct drive at 1,000 rpm: 23.4 mph, 37.6 km/h; fuel consumption: 16.9 m/imp gal, 14.1 m/US gal, 16.7 l x 100 km.

CHASSIS perimeter; front suspension: independent, wishbones, lower leading arms, coil springs, anti-roll bar, telescopic dampers; rear suspension: rigid axle, lower trailing radius arms, upper torque arm, transverse linkage bar, coil springs, telescopic dampers.

STEERING recirculating ball; turns of steering wheel lock to lock: 5.64.

BRAKES drum, dual circuit; area rubbed by linings: total 363.8 sq in, 2,346 sq cm.

ELECTRICAL EQUIPMENT voltage: 12 V; battery: 45 Ah; generator type: alternator, 42 A; ignition distributor: Autolite; headlamps: 4.

DIMENSIONS AND WEIGHT wheel base: 124 in, 3,150 mm; front track: 63.30 in, 1,608 mm; rear track: 64.30 in, 1,633 mm; overall length: 224.70 in, 5,707 mm; overall width: 79.30 in, 2,014 mm; overall height: 54 in, 1,371 mm — 2-door hardtop 53.20 in, 1,351 mm; ground clearance: 5 in, 127 mm — 2-door hardtop 4.90 in, 124 mm; dry weight: Monterey 4-door Sedan 4,199 lb, 1,904 kg — Monterey 2-door Hardtop 4,129 lb, 1,872 kg — Monterey 4-door Hardtop 4,194 lb, 1,902 kg; turning circle (between walls): 46.5 ft, 14.2 m; fuel tank capacity: 18.7 imp gal, 22.5 US gal, 85 l.

OPTIONAL ACCESSORIES Select Shift Merc-o-Matic automatic gearbox with 3 ratios (I 2.400, II 1.470, III 1, rev 2.000), max ratio of convertor at stall 2.05, 2.750 axle ratio; limited slip final drive; automatic levelling control on rear suspension; power-assisted steering; front disc brakes with servo; air-conditioning system.

260 hp power team

(standard for Monterey Station Wagon, Colony Park Station Wagon and Monterey Custom Series; optional for Monterey 4-door Sedan and 2- and 4-door Hardtop; not available for Marquis and Marquis Brougham Series).

See 240 hp power team, except for:

ENGINE bore and stroke: 4 x 4 in, 101.6 x 101.6 mm; engine capacity: 400 cu in, 6,555 cu cm; max power (SAE): 260 hp at 4,400 rpm; max torque (SAE): 400 lb ft, 55.2 kg m at 2,200 rpm; max engine rpm: 4,600; specific power: 39.7 hp/l; carburation: 1 Autolite 9510 D1MF-KA downdraught twin barrel carburettor; cooling system capacity: 29.2 imp pt, 35.1 US pt, 16.6 l.

TRANSMISSION gearbox: Select Shift Merc-o-Matic automatic (standard), max ratio of convertor at stall 2.05; gearbox ratios: I 2.460, II 1.460, III 1, rev 2.800; selector lever: steering column; axle ratio: 2.750; width of rims: station wagons 6.5''; tyres: station wagons H78 x 15.

PERFORMANCE max speed: about 113 mph, 182 km/h; power-weight ratio: Monterey 4-door Sedan and Monterey Custom 4-door Sedan 16.4 lb/hp, 7.4 kg/hp; speed in direct drive at 1,000 rpm: 25.6 mph, 41.2 km/h; fuel consumption: 16 m/imp gal, 13.3 m/US gal, 17.7 l x 100 km.

ELECTRICAL EQUIPMENT battery: 70 Ah.

DIMENSIONS AND WEIGHT wheel base: station wagons 121 in, 3,073 mm; overall length: station wagons 220.40 in, 5,598 mm; overall width: station wagons 79.40 in, 2,017 mm; overall height: station wagons 56.90 in, 1,445 mm; ground clearance: station wagons 6.20 in, 157 mm; dry weight: plus 77 lb, 35 kg — Monterey Station Wagon 4,534 lb, 2,056 kg — Colony Park Station Wagon 4,645 lb, 2,106 kg — Monterey Custom 4-door Sedan 4,282 lb, 1,942 kg — Monterey Custom 2-door Hardtop 4,212 lb, 1,910 kg — Monterey Custom 4-door Hardtop 4,277 lb, 1,940 kg; fuel tank capacity: station wagon 18 imp gal, 21.5 US gal, 82 l.

MERCURY Monterey 2-door Hardtop

OLDSMOBILE Cutlass Town Sedan

OLDSMOBILE Cutlass 'S' Hardtop Coupé

320 hp power team

(standard for Marquis and Marquis Brougham Series; optional for other Series).

See 240 hp power team, except for:

ENGINE bore and stroke: 4.36 x 3.59 in, 110.7 x 91.2 mm; engine capacity: 429 cu in, 7,030 cu cm; compression ratio: 10.5; max power (SAE): 320 hp at 4,400 rpm; max torque (SAE): 460 lb ft, 63.5 kg m at 2,200 rpm; max engine rpm: 4,600; specific power: 45.5 hp/l; carburation: 1 Autolite 9510 D1MF-FA downdraught twin barrel carburettor; cooling system capacity: 31 imp pt, 37.2 US pt, 17.6 l.

TRANSMISSION gearbox: Select Shift Merc-o-Matic automatic (standard), max ratio of convertor at stall 2.05; gearbox ratios: I 2.460, II 1.460, III 1, rev 2.180; selector lever: steering column; axle ratio: 2.750; width of rims: station wagons 6.5''; tyres: station wagons H78 x 15.

PERFORMANCE max speed: about 116 mph, 186 km/h; power-weight ratio: Monterey 4-door Sedan 13.6 lb/hp, 6.2 kg/hp — Monterey Custom 4-door Sedan 13.8 lb/hp, 6.3 kg/hp — Marquis 4-door Sedan 14.6 lb/hp, 6.6 kg/hp — Marquis Brougham 4-door Sedan 14.1 lb/hp, 6.4 kg/hp; speed in direct drive at 1,000 rpm: 25.6 mph, 41.2 km/h; fuel consumption: 14.3 m/imp gal, 11.9 m/US gal, 19.8 l x 100 km.

ELECTRICAL EQUIPMENT battery: 80 Ah.

DIMENSIONS AND WEIGHT (see 260 hp power team) dry weight: plus 150 lb, 68 kg — Marquis 4-door Sedan 4,487 lb, 2,035 kg — Marquis 2-door Hardtop 4,417 lb, 2,003 kg — Marquis 4-door Hardtop 4,482 lb, 2,032 kg — Marquis Station Wagon 4,584 lb, 2,078 kg — Marquis Brougham 4-door Sedan 4,522 lb, 2,051 kg — Marquis Brougham 2-door Hardtop 4,452 lb, 2,019 kg — Marquis Brougham 4-door Hardtop 4,517 lb, 2,048 kg.

360 hp power team

(optional for all Series).

See 240 hp power team, except for:

ENGINE bore and stroke: 4.36 x 3.59 in, 110.7 x 91.2 mm; engine capacity: 429 cu in, 7,030 cu cm; compression ratio: 10.5; max power (SAE): 360 hp at 4,600 rpm; max torque (SAE): 480 lb ft, 66.2 kg m at 2,800 rpm; max engine rpm: 4,800; specific power: 51.2 hp/l; carburation: 1 Autolite 9510 D1AF-MA downdraught 4-barrel carburettor; cooling system capacity: 31 imp pt, 37.2 US pt, 17.6 l.

TRANSMISSION gearbox: Select Shift Merc-o-Matic automatic (standard), max ratio of convertor at stall 2.05; gearbox ratios: I 2.460, II 1.460, III 1, rev 2.180; selector lever: steering column; axle ratio: 2.750; width of rims: station wagons 6.5''; tyres: station wagons H78 x 15.

PERFORMANCE max speed: about 118 mph, 190 km/h; power-weight ratio: Monterey 4-door Sedan 12.2 lb/hp, 5.5 kg/hp — Monterey Custom 4-door Sedan and Marquis 4-door Sedan 12.4 lb/hp, 5.6 kg/hp — Marquis Brougham 4-door Sedan 12.5 lb/hp, 5.7 kg/hp; speed in direct drive at 1,000 rpm: 25.6 mph, 41.2 km/h; fuel consumption: 13.9 m/imp gal, 11.6 m/US gal, 20.3 l x 100 km.

ELECTRICAL EQUIPMENT battery: 80 Ah.

DIMENSIONS AND WEIGHT (see 260 hp power team) dry weight: plus 197 lb, 89 kg — Marquis 4-door Sedan 4,487 lb, 2,035 kg — Marquis 2-door Hardtop 4,417 lb, 2,002 kg — Marquis 4-door Hardtop 4,482 lb, 2,032 kg — Marquis Station Wagon 4,584 lb, 2,079 kg — Marquis Brougham 4-door Sedan 4,522 lb, 2,051 kg — Marquis Brougham 2-door Hardtop 4,452 lb, 2,019 kg — Marquis Brougham 4-door Hardtop 4,517 lb, 2,048 kg.

OLDSMOBILE   USA

F-85 - Cutlass - Cutlass 'S' - Cutlass Supreme Series

PRICE IN USA:

F-85	Town Sedan	$ 2,884
F-85	Sports Coupé	$ —
Cutlass	Town Sedan	$ 2,998
Cutlass	Sports Coupé	$ 2,900
Cutlass 'S'	Sports Coupé	$ 2,957
Cutlass 'S'	Hardtop Coupé	$ 3,020
Cutlass Supreme	Hardtop Sedan	$ 3,322
Cutlass Supreme	Hardtop Coupé	$ 3,322
Cutlass Supreme	Convertible	$ 3,506

For V8 engines add $ 121.

MERCURY Monterey 2-door Hardtop

OLDSMOBILE Cutlass Town Sedan

OLDSMOBILE Cutlass 'S' Hardtop Coupé

145 hp power team

(standard for F-85, Cutlass and Cutlass 'S' Series; not available for Cutlass Supreme Series).

ENGINE front, 4 stroke; cylinders: 6, in line; bore and stroke: 3.87 x 3.53 in, 98.2 x 89.6 mm; engine capacity: 250 cu in, 4,097 cu cm; compression ratio: 8; max power (SAE): 145 hp at 4,200 rpm; max torque (SAE): 230 lb ft, 31.8 kg m at 2,000 rpm; max engine rpm: 4,400; specific power: 35.4 hp/l; cylinder block: cast iron; cylinder head: cast iron; crankshaft bearings: 7; valves: 2 per cylinder, overhead, in line, push-rods and rockers, hydraulic tappets; camshafts: 1, side; lubrication: gear pump, full flow filter; lubricating system capacity: 8.3 imp pt, 9.9 US pt, 4.7 l; carburation: 1 Rochester 1BV downdraught single barrel carburettor; fuel feed: mechanical pump; cooling system: water; cooling system capacity: 20.2 imp pt, 24.3 US pt, 11.5 l.

TRANSMISSION driving wheels: rear; clutch: single dry plate; gearbox: mechanical; gears: 3 + reverse; synchromesh gears: I, II, III; gearbox ratios: I 2.850, II 1.680, III 1, rev 2.950; gear lever: steering column; final drive: hypoid bevel; axle ratio: 2.730; width of rims: 6''; tyres: F78 x 14.

PERFORMANCE max speed: about 103 mph, 165 km/h; power-weight ratio: F-85 Town Sedan 23.1 lb/hp, 10.4 kg/hp — Cutlass Town Sedan 23.4 lb/hp, 10.5 kg/hp; speed in direct drive at 1,000 rpm: 24.3 mph, 39.2 km/h; fuel consumption: 19.5 m/imp gal, 16.2 m/US gal, 14.5 l x 100 km.

CHASSIS channel section ladder frame; front suspension: independent, wishbones, coil springs, anti-roll bar, telescopic dampers; rear suspension: rigid axle, lower trailing radius arms, upper oblique torque arms, coil springs, telescopic dampers.

STEERING recirculating ball; turns of steering wheel lock to lock: 6.64.

BRAKES drum, dual circuit; area rubbed by linings: total 268.8 sq in, 1,734 sq cm.

ELECTRICAL EQUIPMENT voltage: 12 V; battery: 45 Ah; generator type: alternator, 37 A; ignition distributor: Delco-Remy; headlamps: 4.

DIMENSIONS AND WEIGHT wheel base: 116 in, 2,946 mm — sports coupés and hardtop coupé 112 in, 2,845 mm; front track: 59.70 in, 1,516 mm; rear track: 59 in, 1,498 mm; overall length: 207.60 in, 5,273 mm — sports coupés and hardtop coupé 203.60 in, 5,171 mm; overall width: 76.80 in, 1,951 mm — hardtop coupé 76.30 in, 1,938 mm; overall height: 53.50 in, 1,359 mm — sports coupés and hardtop coupé 52.90 in, 1,344 mm; ground clearance: 4.70 in, 119 mm; dry weight: F-85 Town Sedan 3,358 lb, 1,523 kg — F-85 Sports Coupé 3,339 lb, 1,514 kg — Cutlass Town Sedan 3,396 lb, 1,540 kg — Cutlass 'S' Sports Coupé 3,334 lb, 1,512 kg — Cutlass 'S' Hardtop Coupé 3,340 lb, 1,515 kg; turning circle (between walls): 44.5 ft, 13.6 m; fuel tank capacity: 16.7 imp gal, 20 US gal, 76 l.

OPTIONAL ACCESSORIES Turbo Hydramatic 350 automatic gearbox with 3 ratios (I 2.520, II 1.520, III 1, rev 1.930), max ratio of convertor at stall 2.25, 2.730 axle ratio; limited slip final drive; power-assisted steering; front disc brakes with servo; air-conditioning system.

240 hp power team

(standard for F-85, Cutlass and Cutlass 'S' Series; optional for Cutlass Supreme Series).

See 145 hp power team, except for:

ENGINE cylinders: 8, Vee-slanted at 90°; bore and stroke: 4.06 x 3.38 in, 103.1 x 85.8 mm; engine capacity: 350 cu in, 5,736 cu cm; compression ratio: 8.5; max power (SAE): 240 hp at 4,200 rpm; max torque (SAE): 350 lb ft, 48.3 kg m at 2,400 rpm; max engine rpm: 4,600; specific power: 41.8 hp/l; crankshaft bearings: 5; camshafts: 1, at centre of Vee; carburation: 1 Rochester 2GC downdraught twin barrel carburettor; cooling system capacity: 25.3 imp pt, 30.4 US pt, 14.4 l.

TRANSMISSION gearbox ratios: I 2.540, II 1.500, III 1, rev 2.630; axle ratio: 3.080; tyres: G78 x 14.

PERFORMANCE max speed: about 108 mph, 174 km/h; power-weight ratio: F-85 Town Sedan 14.9 lb/hp, 6.7 kg/hp — Cutlass Town Sedan 15 lb/hp, 6.8 kg/hp — Cutlass Supreme Hardtop Sedan 15.4 lb/hp, 7 kg/hp; speed in direct drive at 1,000 rpm: 23.9 mph, 38.4 km/hp; fuel consumption: 17.4 m/imp gal, 14.5 m/US gal, 16.2 l x 100 km.

DIMENSIONS AND WEIGHT dry weight: F-85 Town Sedan 3,569 lb, 1,618 kg — F-85 Sports Coupé 3,553 lb, 1,611 kg — Cutlass Town Sedan 3,595 lb, 1,630 kg — Cutlass 'S' Sports Coupé 3,550 lb, 1,610 kg — Cutlass 'S' Hardtop Coupé 3,561 lb, 1,615 kg — Cutlass Supreme Hardtop Sedan 3,690 lb, 1,673 kg — Cutlass Supreme Hardtop Coupé 3,562 lb, 1,615 kg — Cutlass Supreme Convertible 3,631 lb, 1,647 kg.

260 hp power team

(standard for Cutlass Supreme Series; optional for other Series).

See 145 hp power team, except for:

ENGINE cylinders: 8, Vee-slanted at 90°; bore and stroke: 4.06 x 3.38 in, 103.1 x 85.8 mm; engine capacity: 350 cu in, 5,736 cu cm; compression ratio: 8.5; max power (SAE): 260 hp at 4,600 rpm; max torque (SAE): 360 lb ft, 49.7 kg m at 3,200 rpm; max engine rpm: 5,000; specific power: 45.3 hp/l; crankshaft bearings: 5; camshafts: 1, at centre or Vee; carburation: 1 Rochester 4MC downdraught 4-barrel carburettor; cooling system capacity: 25.3 imp pt, 30.4 US pt, 14.4 l.

TRANSMISSION gearbox ratios: I 2.540, II 1.500, III 1, rev 2.630; axle ratio: 3.230; tyres: G78 x 14.

PERFORMANCE max speed: about 115 mph, 185 km/h; power-weight ratio: F-85 Town Sedan 13.7 lb/hp, 6.2 kg/hp — Cutlass Town Sedan 13.8 lb/hp, 6.3 kg/hp — Cutlass Supreme Hardtop Sedan 14.2 lb/hp, 6.4 kg/hp; speed in direct drive at 1,000 rpm: 23.5 mph, 37.8 km/h; fuel consumption: 16 m/imp gal, 13.4 m/US gal, 17.6 l x 100 km.

ELECTRICAL EQUIPMENT generator type: alternator, 55 A.

DIMENSIONS AND WEIGHT (see 240 hp power team).

320 hp power team

(optional for Cutlass Supreme Hardtop Coupé and Convertible; not available for other models).

See 145 hp power team, except for:

ENGINE cylinders: 8, Vee-slanted at 90°; bore and stroke: 4.12 x 4.25 in, 104.6 x 107.9 mm; engine capacity: 455 cu in, 7,456 cu cm; compression ratio: 8.5; max power (SAE): 320 hp at 4,400 rpm; max torque (SAE): 460 lb ft, 49.7 kg m at 2,800 rpm; max engine rpm: 4,600; specific power: 42.9 hp/l; crankshaft bearings: 5; camshafts: 1, at centre of Vee; carburation: 1 Rochester 4MC downdraught 4-barrel carburettor; cooling system capacity: 26.9 imp pt, 32.3 US pt, 15.3 l.

TRANSMISSION gearbox: Turbo Hydramatic 400 automatic, hydraulic torque convertor and planetary gears with 3 ratios + reverse, max ratio of convertor at stall 2.25, possible manual selection; gearbox ratios: I 2.480, II 1.480, III 1, rev 2.080; selector lever: steering column; axle ratio: 2.560; tyres: G78 x 14.

PERFORMANCE max speed: about 118 mph, 190 km/h; power-weight ratio: Cutlass Supreme Hardtop Coupé 11.4 lb/hp, 5.2 kg/hp — Cutlass Supreme Convertible 11.6 lb/hp, 5.3 kg/hp; speed in direct drive at 1,000 rpm: 26.6 mph, 42.8 km/h; fuel consumption: 14.9 m/imp gal, 12.4 m/US gal, 19 l x 100 km.

STEERING recirculating ball, servo; turns of steering wheel lock to lock: 2.94.

BRAKES front disc, rear drum, dual circuit, servo; area rubbed by linings: total 386.2 sq in, 2,491 sq cm.

ELECTRICAL EQUIPMENT battery: 74 Ah; generator type: alternator, 42 A.

DIMENSIONS AND WEIGHT (see 240 hp power team) dry weight: plus 77 lb, 35 kg; turning circle (between walls): 48 ft, 14.6 m.

OPTIONAL ACCESSORIES Turbo Hydramatic 350 automatic gearbox not available.

4-4-2 Series

PRICES IN USA:

4-4-2	Hardtop Coupé	$ 3,551
4-4-2	Convertible	$ 3,742

340 hp power team

(standard for both models).

ENGINE front, 4 stroke; cylinders: 8, Vee-slanted at 90°; bore and stroke: 4.12 x 4.25 in, 104.6 x 107.9 mm; engine capacity: 455 cu in, 7,456 cu cm; compression ratio: 8.5; max power (SAE): 340 hp at 4,600 rpm; max torque (SAE): 460 lb ft, 63.5 kg m at 3,200 rpm; max engine rpm: 4,800; specific power: 45.6 hp/l; cylinder block: cast iron; cylinder head: cast iron; crankshaft bearings: 5; valves: 2 per cylinder, overhead, in line, push-rods and rockers, hydraulic tappets; camshafts: 1, at centre of Vee; lubrication: gear pump, full flow filter; lubricating system capacity: 8.3 imp pt, 9.9 US pt, 4.7 l; carburation: 1 Rochester 4MC down-

OLDSMOBILE Cutlass Supreme Hardtop Coupé

OLDSMOBILE 4-4-2 Convertible

OLDSMOBILE Custom Cruiser 6-passenger Station Wagon

draught 4-barrel carburettor; fuel feed: mechanical pump; cooling system: water; cooling system capacity: 26.9 imp pt, 32.3 US pt, 15.3 l.

TRANSMISSION driving wheels: rear; clutch: single dry plate; gearbox: mechanical; gears: 3 + reverse; synchromesh gears: I, II, III; gearbox ratios: I 2.420, II 1.580, III 1, rev 2.410; gear lever: central; final drive: hypoid bevel; axle ratio: 3.230; width of rims: 7''; tyres: G70 x 14.

PERFORMANCE max speed: about 119 mph, 191 km/h; power-weight ratio: hardtop coupé 11.1 lb/hp, 5 kg/hp — convertible 11.3 lb/hp, 5.1 kg/hp; speed in direct drive at 1,000 rpm: 24.8 mph, 39.9 km/h; fuel consumption: 13.5 m/imp gal, 11.3 m/US gal, 20.9 l x 100 km.

CHASSIS channel section ladder frame; front suspension: independent. wishbones, coil springs, anti-roll bar, telescopic dampers; rear suspension: rigid axle, lower trailing radius arms, upper torque arms, coil springs, anti-roll bar, telescopic dampers.

STEERING recirculating ball; turns of steering wheel lock to lock: 6.64.

BRAKES drum, dual circuit; area rubbed by linings: total 268.8 sq in, 1,734 sq cm.

ELECTRICAL EQUIPMENT voltage: 12 V; battery: 74 Ah; generator type: alternator, 37 A; ignition distributor: Delco-Remy; headlamps: 4.

DIMENSIONS AND WEIGHT wheel base: 112 in, 2,845 mm; front track: 59.70 in, 1,516 mm; rear track: 59 in, 1,499 mm; overall length: 203.60 in, 5,171 mm; overall width: 76.80 in, 1,951 mm; overall height: hardtop coupé 52.70 in, 1,338 mm — convertible 53.20 in, 1,351 mm; ground clearance: 4.20 in, 107 mm; dry weight: 4-4-2 Hardtop Coupé 3,792 lb, 1,720 kg — 4-4-2 Convertible 3,835 lb, 1,739 kg; turning circle (between walls): 43.3 ft, 13.2 m; fuel tank capacity: 16.7 imp gal, 20 US gal, 76 l.

OPTIONAL ACCESSORIES 4-speed fully synchronized mechanical gearbox; Turbo Hydramatic 400 automatic gearbox with 3 ratios (I 2.480, II 1.480, III 1, rev 2.080), max ratio of convertor at stall 2.20, 3.230 axle ratio; limited slip final drive; power-assisted steering; front disc brakes with servo; air-conditioning system.

350 hp power team

(optional for 4-4-2 Convertible; not available for 4-4-2 Hardtop Coupé).

See 340 hp power team, except for:

ENGINE max power (SAE): 350 hp at 4,700 rpm; max engine rpm: 5,000; specific power: 46.9 hp/l.

TRANSMISSION gears: 4 + reverse; synchromesh gears: I, II, III, IV; axle ratio: 3.420.

PERFORMANCE max speed: about 120 mph, 193 km/h; power-weight ratio: 10.9 lb/hp, 4.9 kg/hp; speed in direct drive at 1,000 rpm: 24 mph, 38.6 km/h; fuel consumption: 13.4 m/imp gal, 11.1 m/US gal, 21.1 l x 100 km.

OPTIONAL ACCESSORIES Turbo Hydramatic 400 automatic gearbox with 3.420 axle ratio.

Cutlass - Vista Cruiser - Custom Cruiser Series

PRICES IN USA:

Cutlass	6-passenger Station Wagon	$ 3,453
Vista Cruiser	6-passenger Station Wagon	$ 3,865
Vista Cruiser	9-passenger Station Wagon	$ 4,007
Custom Cruiser	6-passenger Station Wagon	$ 4,539
Custom Cruiser	9-passenger Station Wagon	$ 4,680

For V8 engines add $ 121.

145 hp power team

(standard for Cutlass; not available for other Series).

ENGINE front, 4 stroke; cylinders: 6, in line; bore and stroke: 3.87 x 3.53 in, 98.2 x 89.6 mm; engine capacity: 250 cu in, 4,907 cu cm; compression ratio: 8; max power (SAE): 145 hp at 4,200 rpm; max torque (SAE): 230 lb ft, 31.8 kg m at 2,000 rpm; max engine rpm: 4,400; specific power: 35.4 hp/l; cylinder block: cast iron; cylinder head: cast iron; crankshaft bearings: 7; valves: 2 per cylinder, overhead, in line, push-rods and rockers, hydraulic tappets; camshafts: 1, side; lubrication: gear pump, full flow filter; lubricating system capacity: 8.3 imp pt, 9.9 US pt, 4.7 l; carburation: 1 Rochester 1BV downdraught single barrel carburettor; fuel feed: mechanical pump; cooling system: water; cooling system capacity: 20.2 imp pt, 24.3 US pt, 11.5 l.

OLDSMOBILE Cutlass Supreme Hardtop Coupé (steering gear)

OLDSMOBILE 4-4-2 Series (4-speed mechanical gearbox)

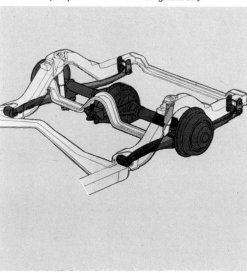

OLDSMOBILE Custom Cruiser Series (rear suspension)

TRANSMISSION driving wheels: rear; clutch: single dry plate; gearbox: mechanical; gears: 3 + reverse; synchromesh gears: I, II, III; gearbox ratios: I 2.540, II 1.500, III 1, rev 2.630; gear lever: steering column; final drive: hypoid bevel; axle ratio: 2.730; width of rims: 6''; tyres: H78 x 14.

PERFORMANCE max speed: about 91 mph, 146 km/h; power-weight ratio: 23.3 lb/hp, 10.6 kg/hp; speed in direct drive at 1,000 rpm: 23 mph, 37 km/h; fuel consumption: 19.3 m/imp gal, 16.1 m/US gal, 14.6 l x 100 km.

CHASSIS channel section ladder frame (perimeter type); front suspension: independent, wishbones, coil springs, telescopic dampers; rear suspension: rigid axle, lower trailing radius arms, upper oblique torque arms, coil springs, telescopic dampers.

STEERING recirculating ball; turns of steering wheel lock to lock: 6.64.

BRAKES front disc, rear drum, dual circuit; area rubbed by linings: total 375.6 sq in, 2,422 sq cm.

ELECTRICAL EQUIPMENT voltage: 12 V; battery: 61 Ah; generator type: alternator, 37 A; ignition distributor: Delco-Remy; headlamps: 4.

DIMENSIONS AND WEIGHT wheel base: 116 in, 2,946 mm; front track: 59.70 in, 1,516 mm; rear track: 59 in, 1,499 mm; overall length: 213.30 in, 5,418 mm; overall width: 76.80 in, 1,951 mm; overall height: 54.40 in, 1,382 mm; ground clearance: 5.20 in, 132 mm; dry weight: 3,380 lb, 1,533 kg; turning circle (between walls): 41.3 ft, 12.6 m; fuel tank capacity: 19.1 imp gal, 23 US gal, 87 l.

OPTIONAL ACCESSORIES Turbo Hydramatic 350 automatic gearbox with 3 ratios (I 2.520, II 1.520, III 1, rev 1.930), max ratio of convertor at stall 2.25, 2.730 axle ratio; limited slip final drive; power-assisted steering; servo brake; air-conditioning system.

240 hp power team

(standard for Cutlass and Vista Cruiser Series; not available for Custom Cruiser Series).

See 145 hp power team, except for:

ENGINE cylinders: 8, Vee-slanted at 90°; bore and stroke: 4.06 x 3.38 in, 103.1 x 85.8 mm; engine capacity: 350 cu in, 5,736 cu cm; compression ratio: 8.5; max power (SAE): 240 hp at 4,200 rpm; max torque (SAE): 350 lb ft, 48.3 kg m at 2,400 rpm; max engine rpm: 4,400; specific power: 41.8 hp/l; crankshaft bearings: 5; camshafts: 1, at centre of Vee; carburation: 1 Rochester 2GC downdraught twin barrel carburettor; cooling system capacity: 25.3 imp pt, 30.4 US pt, 14.4 l.

TRANSMISSION axle ratio: 3.080 — Vista Cruiser 3.230.

PERFORMANCE max speed: about 95 mph, 153 km/h; power-weight ratio: Cutlass 6-passenger Station Wagon 16.8 lb/hp, 7.6 kg/hp — Vista Cruiser 6-passenger Station Wagon 17.9 lb/hp, 8.1 kg/hp; speed in direct drive at 1,000 rpm: 22.4 mph, 36 km/h; fuel consumption: 16.9 m/imp gal, 14.1 m/US gal, 16.7 l x 100 km.

BRAKES area rubbed by linings: Vista Cruiser total 345.6 sq in, 2,229 sq cm.

DIMENSIONS AND WEIGHT wheel base: Vista Cruiser 121 in, 3,073 mm; overall length: Vista Cruiser 218.30 in, 5,545 mm; overall height: Vista Cruiser 58.50 in, 1,486 mm; ground clearance: Vista Cruiser 6.70 in, 170 mm; dry weight: Cutlass 6-passenger Station Wagon 4,027 lb, 1,826 kg — Vista Cruiser 6-passenger Station Wagon 4,293 lb, 1,947 kg — Vista Cruiser 9-passenger Station Wagon 4,412 lb, 2,001 kg; turning circle (between walls): Vista Cruiser 42.8 ft, 13 m.

OPTIONAL ACCESSORIES Turbo Hydramatic 350 automatic gearbox with 2.560 axle ratio; only for Vista Cruiser 3-speed fully synchronized mechanical gearbox with 3.230 axle ratio or Turbo Hydramatic 400 automatic gearbox with 3 ratios (I 2.480, II 1.480, III 1, rev 2.080), max ratio of convertor at stall 2.20, 2.730 axle ratio.

260 hp power team

(optional for Cutlass; not available for Vista Cruiser and Custom Cruiser Series).

See 145 hp power team, except for:

ENGINE cylinders: 8, Vee-slanted at 90°; bore and stroke: 4.06 x 3.38 in, 103.1 x 85.8 mm; engine capacity: 350 cu in, 5,736 cu cm; compression ratio: 8.5; max power (SAE): 260 hp at 4,600 rpm; max torque (SAE): 360 lb ft, 49.7 kg m at 3,200 rpm; max engine rpm: 5,000; specific power: 45.3 hp/l; crankshaft bearings: 5; camshafts: 1, at centre of Vee; car-

260 HP POWER TEAM

buration: 1 Rochester 4MC downdraught 4-barrel carburettor; cooling system capacity: 25.3 imp pt, 30.4 US pt, 14.4 l.

TRANSMISSION max speed: about 99 mph, 159 km/h; power-weight ratio: 15.5 lb/hp, 7 kg/hp; speed in direct drive at 1,000 rpm: 21.4 mph, 34.4 km/h; fuel consumption: 16.5 m/imp gal, 13.8 m/US gal, 17.1 l x 100 km.

DIMENSIONS AND WEIGHT (see 240 hp power team).

OPTIONAL ACCESSORIES Turbo Hydramatic 350 automatic gearbox with 2.730 axle ratio.

280 hp power team

(standard for Custom Cruiser Series; optional for Vista Cruiser Series; not available for Cutlass).

See 145 hp power team, except for:

ENGINE cylinders: 8, Vee-slanted at 90°; bore and stroke: 4.12 x 4.25 in, 104.6 x 107.9 mm; engine capacity: 455 cu in, 7,456 cu cm; compression ratio: 8.5; max power (SAE): 280 hp at 4,000 rpm; max torque (SAE): 445 lb ft, 61.4 kg m at 2,000 rpm; max engine rpm: 4,400; specific power: 37.6 hp/l; crankshaft bearings: 5; camshafts: 1, at centre of Vee; carburation: 1 Rochester 2GC downdraught twin barrel carburettor; cooling system capacity: 38 imp pt, 45.4 US pt, 21.5 l.

TRANSMISSION gearbox: Turbo Hydramatic 400 automatic, hydraulic torque convertor and planetary gears with 3 ratios + reverse, max ratio of convertor at stall 2.20, possible manual selection; gearbox ratios: I 2.480, II 1.480, III 1, rev 2.080; selector lever: steering column; axle ratio: 2.730 — Vista Cruiser 2.560; tyres: L78 x 15.

PERFORMANCE max speed: about 102 mph, 164 km/h; power-weight ratio: Custom Cruiser 6-passenger Station Wagon 17.8 lb/hp, 8.1 kg/hp; speed in direct drive at 1,000 rpm: 24.6 mph, 39.6 km/h; fuel consumption: 15.5 m/imp gal, 12.9 m/US gal, 18.2 l x 100 km.

CHASSIS rear suspension (for Custom Cruiser only): rigid axle, semi-elliptic leafsprings, telescopic dampers.

STEERING recirculating ball, servo; turns of steering wheel lock to lock: 2.94.

BRAKES front disc, rear drum, dual circuit, servo; area rubbed by linings: total 399.6 sq in, 2,578 sq cm.

ELECTRICAL EQUIPMENT battery: 73 Ah; generator type: alternator, 42 A.

DIMENSIONS AND WEIGHT wheel base: 127 in, 3,226 mm; front track: 63.80 in, 1,620 mm; rear track: 63.70 in, 1,618 mm; overall length: 225.30 in, 5,723 mm; overall width: 79.50 in, 2,019 mm; overall height: 57.20 in, 1,453 mm; ground clearance: 5.30 in, 135 mm; dry weight: Custom Cruiser 6-passenger Station Wagon 4,987 lb, 2,262 kg — Custom Cruiser 9-passenger Station Wagon 5,107 lb, 2,316 kg; turning circle (between walls): 53.8 ft, 16.4 m; fuel tank capacity: 18.9 imp gal, 22.7 US gal, 86 l.

OPTIONAL ACCESSORIES only limited slip final drive and air-conditioning system.

320 hp power team

(optional for Vista Cruiser and Custom Cruiser Series; not available for Cutlass).

See 145 hp power team, except for:

ENGINE cylinders: 8, Vee-slanted at 90°; bore and stroke: 4.12 x 4.25 in, 104.6 x 107.9 mm; engine capacity: 455 cu in, 7,456 cu cm; compression ratio: 8.5; max power (SAE): 320 hp at 4,400 rpm; max torque (SAE): 460 lb ft, 49.7 kg m at 2,800 rpm; max engine rpm: 4,800; specific power: 42.9 hp/l; crankshaft bearings: 5; camshafts: 1, at centre of Vee; carburation: 1 Rochester 4MC downdraught 4-barrel carburettor; cooling system capacity: 38 imp pt, 45.4 US pt, 21.5 l.

TRANSMISSION gearbox: Turbo Hydramatic 400 automatic, hydraulic torque convertor and planetary gears with 3 ratios + reverse, max ratio of convertor at stall 2.20, possible manual selection; gearbox ratios: I 2.480, II 1.480, III 1, rev 2.080; selector lever: steering column; axle ratio: 2.730 — Vista Cruiser 2.560; tyres: L78 x 15.

PERFORMANCE max speed: about 109 mph, 175 km/h; power-weight ratio: Custom Cruiser 6-passenger Station Wagon 15.6 lb/hp, 7.1 kg/hp; speed in direct drive at 1,000 rpm: 24.6 mph, 39.6 km/h; fuel consumption: 14.3 m/imp gal, 11.9 m/US gal, 19.7 l x 100 km.

CHASSIS rear suspension (for Custom Cruiser only): rigid axle, semi-elliptic leafsprings, telescopic dampers.

OLDSMOBILE Delta 88 Custom Holiday Sedan

OLDSMOBILE Ninety-Eight Hardtop Coupé

OLDSMOBILE Ninety-Eight Luxury Sedan

STEERING recirculating ball, servo; turns of steering wheel lock to lock: 2.94.

BRAKES front disc, rear drum, dual circuit, servo; area rubbed by linings: total 399.6 sq in, 2,578 sq cm.

ELECTRICAL EQUIPMENT battery: 73 Ah; generator type: alternator, 42 A.

DIMENSIONS AND WEIGHT (see 280 hp power team).

OPTIONAL ACCESSORIES only limited slip final drive and air-conditioning system.

Delta 88 - Delta 88 Custom - Delta 88 Royale Series

PRICES IN USA:

Delta 88	Holiday Sedan	**$ 3,992**
Delta 88	Hardtop Coupé	**$ 4,048**
Delta 88	Town Sedan	**$ 4,110**
Delta 88 Custom	Holiday Sedan	**$ 4,209**
Delta 88 Custom	Hardtop Coupé	**$ 4,302**
Delta 88 Custom	Town Sedan	**$ 4,377**
Delta 88 Royale	Hardtop Sedan	**$ 4,560**
Delta 88 Royale	Convertible	**$ 4,568**

240 hp power team

(standard for Delta 88 Series; not available for Delta 88 Custom and Royale Series).

ENGINE front, 4 stroke; cylinders: 8, Vee-slanted at 90°; bore and stroke: 4.06 x 3.38 in, 103.1 x 85.8 mm; engine capacity: 350 cu in, 5,736 cu cm; compression ratio: 8.5; max power (SAE): 240 hp at 4,200 rpm; max torque (SAE): 350 lb ft, 48.3 kg m at 2,400 rpm; max engine rpm: 4,400; specific power: 41.8 hp/l; cylinder block: cast iron; cylinder head: cast iron; crankshaft bearings: 5; valves: 2 per cylinder, overhead, in line, push-rods and rockers, hydraulic tappets; camshafts: 1, at centre of Vee; lubrication: gear pump, full flow filter; lubricating system capacity: 8.3 imp pt, 9.9 US pt, 4.7 l; carburation: 1 Rochester 2GC downdraught twin barrel carburettor; fuel feed: mechanical pump; cooling system: water; cooling system capacity: 29.2 imp pt, 35.1 US pt, 16.6 l.

TRANSMISSION driving wheels: rear; gearbox: Turbo Hydramatic 350 automatic, hydraulic torque convertor and planetary gears with 3 ratios + reverse, max ratio of convertor at stall 2.25, possible manual selection; gearbox ratios: I 2.520, II 1.520, III 1, rev 1.930; selector lever: steering column; final drive: hypoid bevel; axle ratio: 3.080; width of rims: 6''; tyres: H78 x 15.

PERFORMANCE max speed: about 102 mph, 164 km/h; power-weight ratio: Delta 88 Holiday Sedan 17.6 lb/hp, 8 kg/hp; speed in direct drive at 1,000 rpm: 23.5 mph, 37.8 km/h; fuel consumption: 17 m/imp gal, 14.2 m/US gal, 16.6 l x 100 km.

CHASSIS channel section ladder frame; front suspension: independent, wishbones, coil springs, anti-roll bar, telescopic dampers; rear suspension: rigid axle, lower trailing radius arms, upper oblique torque arms, coil springs, telescopic dampers.

STEERING recirculating ball, servo; turns of steering wheel lock to lock: 2.97.

BRAKES front disc, rear drum, dual circuit, servo; area rubbed by linings: total 386.2 sq in, 2,491 sq cm.

ELECTRICAL EQUIPMENT voltage: 12 V; battery: 61 Ah; generator type: alternator, 42 A; ignition distributor: Delco-Remy; headlamps: 4.

DIMENSIONS AND WEIGHT wheel base: 124 in, 3,150 mm; front track: 64.10 in, 1,628 mm; rear track: 64 in, 1,636 mm; overall length: 220.20 in, 5,593 mm; overall width: 79.50 in, 2,019 mm; overall height: 53.40 in, 1,356 mm — holiday sedan 53.60 in, 1,361 mm — town sedan 54.30 in, 1,379 mm; ground clearance: 5.30 in, 135 mm; dry weight: Delta 88 Holiday Sedan 4,221 lb, 1,914 kg — Delta 88 Hardtop Coupé 4,165 lb, 1,889 kg — Delta 88 Town Sedan 4,198 lb, 1,904 kg; fuel tank capacity: 20 imp gal, 24 US gal, 91 l.

OPTIONAL ACCESSORIES limited slip final drive; air-conditioning system.

280 hp power team

(standard for Delta 88 Custom and Royale Series; optional for Delta 88 Series).

See 240 hp power team, except for:

ENGINE bore and stroke: 4.12 x 4.25 in, 104.6 x 107.9 mm;

engine capacity: 455 cu in, 7,456 cu cm; max power (SAE): 280 hp at 4,000 rpm; max torque (SAE): 445 lb ft, 61.4 kg m at 2,000 rpm; specific power: 37.6 hp/l.

TRANSMISSION axle ratio: 2.560.

PERFORMANCE max speed: about 109 mph, 175 km/h; power-weight ratio: Delta 88 Holiday Sedan 15 lb/hp, 6.8 kg/hp — Delta 88 Custom Holiday Sedan 15.6 lb/hp, 7.1 kg/hp; speed in direct drive at 1,000 rpm: 25.2 mph, 40.5 km/h; fuel consumption: 15.4 m/imp gal, 12.8 m/US gal, 18.4 l x 100 km.

STEERING turns of steering wheel lock to lock: 2.94.

ELECTRICAL EQUIPMENT battery: 73 Ah.

DIMENSIONS AND WEIGHT overall length: Delta 88 Royale Hardtop Coupé and Convertible 220 in, 5,588 mm; overall width: Delta 88 Royale Hardtop Coupé 79 in, 2,006 mm; dry weight: Delta 88 Custom Holiday Sedan 4,373 lb, 1,983 kg — Delta 88 Custom Hardtop Coupé 4,279 lb, 1,940 kg — Delta 88 Custom Town Sedan 4,328 lb, 1,963 kg — Delta 88 Royale Hardtop Coupé 4,357 lb, 1,976 kg — Delta 88 Royale Convertible 4,375 lb, 1,984 kg.

320 hp power team

(optional for all Series).

See 240 hp power team, except for:

ENGINE bore and stroke: 4.12 x 4.25 in, 104.6 x 107.9 mm; engine capacity: 455 cu in, 7,456 cu cm; max power (SAE): 320 hp at 4,400 rpm; max torque (SAE): 460 lb ft, 49.7 kg m at 2,800 rpm; max engine rpm: 4,800; specific power: 42.9 hp/l; carburation: 1 Rochester 4MC downdraught 4-barrel carburettor.

TRANSMISSION axle ratio: 2.730.

PERFORMANCE max speed: about 111 mph, 178 km/h; power-weight ratio: Delta 88 Holiday Sedan 13.2 lb/hp, 6 kg/hp — Delta 88 Custom Holiday Sedan 13.7 lb/hp, 6.2 kg/hp; speed in direct drive at 1,000 rpm: 25.3 mph, 40.7 km/h; fuel consumption: 14.6 m/imp gal, 12.2 m/US gal, 19.3 l x 100 km.

STEERING turns of steering wheel lock to lock: 2.94.

ELECTRICAL EQUIPMENT battery: 73 Ah.

DIMENSIONS AND WEIGHT (see 280 hp power team).

Ninety-Eight Series

PRICES IN USA:

Ninety-Eight	Holiday Sports Sedan	$ 4,890
Ninety-Eight	Hardtop Coupé	$ 4,828
Ninety-Eight	Luxury Sedan	$ 5,197
Ninety-Eight	Hardtop Sports Coupé	$ 5,103

320 hp power team

(standard for all models).

ENGINE front, 4 stroke; cylinders: 8, Vee-slanted at 90°; bore and stroke: 4.12 x 4.25 in, 104.6 x 107.9 mm; engine capacity: 455 cu in, 7,456 cu cm; compression ratio: 8.5; max power (SAE): 320 hp at 4,400 rpm; max torque (SAE): 460 lb ft, 49.7 kg m at 2,800 rpm; max engine rpm: 4,800; specific power: 42.9 hp/l; cylinder block: cast iron; cylinder head: cast iron; crankshaft bearings: 5; valves: 2 per cylinder, overhead, in line, push-rods and rockers hydraulic tappets; camshafts: 1, at centre of Vee; lubrication: gear pump, full flow filter; lubricating system capacity: 8.3 imp pt, 9.9 US pt, 4.7 l; carburation: 1 Rochester 4MC downdraught 4-barrel carburettor; fuel feed: mechanical pump; cooling system: water; cooling system capacity: 29.2 imp pt, 35.1 US pt, 16.6 l.

TRANSMISSION driving wheels: rear; gearbox: Turbo Hydramatic 400 automatic, hydraulic torque convertor and planetary gears with 3 ratios + reverse, max ratio of convertor at stall 2.20, possible manual selection; gearbox ratios: I 2.480, II 1.480, III 1, rev 2.080; selector lever: steering column; final drive: hypoid bevel; axle ratio: 2.730; width of rims: 6''; tyres: J78 x 15.

PERFORMANCE max speed: about 107 mph, 172 km/h; power-weight ratio: Ninety-Eight Luxury Sedan 14.3 lb/hp, 6.5 kg/hp; speed in direct drive at 1,000 rpm: 24 mph, 38.6 km/h; fuel consumption: 12.9 m/imp gal, 10.7 m/US gal, 21.9 l x 100 km.

CHASSIS box-type ladder frame; front suspension: independent, wishbones, coil springs, anti-roll bar, telescopic dampers; rear suspension: rigid axle, lower trailing radius arms, upper oblique torque arms, coil springs, telescopic dampers.

STEERING recirculating ball, servo; turns of steering wheel lock to lock: 2.94.

OLDSMOBILE Delta 88 Custom Hardtop Coupé

OLDSMOBILE Ninety-Eight Hardtop Coupé

OLDSMOBILE Ninety-Eight Luxury Sedan

320 HP POWER TEAM

BRAKES front disc, rear drum, dual circuit, servo; area rubbed by linings: total 386.2 sq in, 2,491 sq cm.

ELECTRICAL EQUIPMENT voltage: 12 V; battery: 74 Ah; generator type: alternator, 42 A; ignition distributor: Delco-Remy; headlamps: 4.

DIMENSIONS AND WEIGHT wheel base: 127 in, 3,226 mm; front track: 64.10 in, 1,628 mm; rear track: 64 in, 1,625 mm; overall length: 226.10 in, 5,743 mm; overall width: 79 in, 2,006 mm; overall height: 54.10 in, 1,374 mm — holiday sports sedan and luxury sedan 54.60 in, 1,387 mm; ground clearance: 5.30 in, 135 mm; dry weight: Ninety-Eight Holiday Sports Sedan 4,548 lb, 2,062 kg — Ninety-Eight Hardtop Coupé 4,482 lb, 2,032 kg — Ninety-Eight Luxury Sedan 4,582 lb, 2,078 kg; turning circle (between walls): 48 ft, 14.6 m; fuel tank capacity: 20.9 imp gal, 25 US gal, 95 l.

OPTIONAL ACCESSORIES limited slip final drive; air-conditioning system.

Toronado

PRICE IN USA:

Toronado   Custom Coupé   **$ 5,499**

350 hp power team

(standard).

ENGINE front, 4 stroke; cylinders: 8, Vee-slanted at 90°; bore and stroke: 4.12 x 4.25 in, 104.6 x 107.9 mm; engine capacity: 455 cu in, 7,456 cu cm; compression ratio: 10.2; max power (SAE): 350 hp at 4,400 rpm; max torque (SAE): 465 lb ft, 64.2 kg m at 2,800 rpm; max engine rpm: 4,800; specific power: 46.9 hp/l; cylinder block: cast iron; cylinder head: cast iron; crankshaft bearings: 5; valves: 2 per cylinder, overhead, in line, push-rods and rockers, hydraulic tappets; camshafts: 1, at centre of Vee; lubrication: gear pump, full flow filter; lubricating system capacity: 10 imp pt, 12 US pt, 5.7 l; carburation: 1 Rochester 4MC downdraught 4-barrel carburettor; fuel feed: mechanical pump; cooling system: water; cooling system capacity: 29.9 imp pt, 35.9 US pt, 17 l.

TRANSMISSION driving wheels: front; gearbox: Turbo Hydramatic 400 automatic, hydraulic torque convertor and planetary gears (chain torque by engine-mounted convertor) with 3 ratios + reverse, max ratio of convertor at stall 2.20, possible manual selection; gearbox ratios: I 2.480, II 1.480, III 1, rev 2.080; selector lever: steering column; final drive: spiral bevel; axle ratio: 3.070; width of rims: 6''; tyres: J78 x 15.

PERFORMANCE max speed: about 108 mph, 174 km/h; power-weight ratio: 13 lb/hp, 5.9 kg/hp; speed in direct drive at 1,000 rpm: 23.3 mph, 37.5 km/h; fuel consumption: 12.8 m/imp gal, 10.7 m/US gal, 22 l x 100 km.

CHASSIS perimeter box-type; front suspension: independent, wishbones, longitudinal torsion bars, anti-roll bar, telescopic dampers; rear suspension: rigid axle, lower trailing radius arms, upper oblique torque arms, coil springs, telescopic dampers.

STEERING recirculating ball, servo; turns of steering wheel lock to lock: 3.40.

BRAKES front disc, rear drum, dual circuit, servo; area rubbed by linings: total 364.4 sq in, 2,350 sq cm.

ELECTRICAL EQUIPMENT voltage: 12 V; battery: 74 Ah; generator type: alternator, 42 A; ignition distributor: Delco-Remy; headlamps: 4.

DIMENSIONS AND WEIGHT wheel base: 122.30 in, 3,106 mm; front track: 63.50 in, 1,613 mm; rear track: 63.60 in, 1,615 mm; overall length: 219.90 in, 5,585 mm; overall width: 79.80 in, 2,027 mm; overall height: 54.70 in, 1,389 mm; ground clearance: 5 in, 127 mm; dry weight: 4,577 lb, 2,076 kg; fuel tank capacity: 20 imp gal, 24 US gal, 91 l.

BODY seats: 5; front seats: separate.

OPTIONAL ACCESSORIES air-conditioning system.

PLYMOUTH   USA

Cricket

PRICE IN USA:

Cricket   Sedan   **$ —**

OLDSMOBILE Toronado Custom Coupé

PLYMOUTH Cricket Sedan

PLYMOUTH Duster 340 2-door Coupé

70 hp power team

(standard).

ENGINE front, 4 stroke; cylinders: 4, in line; bore and stroke: 3.39 x 2.53 in, 86 x 64.2 mm; engine capacity: 91.4 cu in, 1,498 cu cm; compression ratio: 8; max power (SAE): 70 hp at 5,200 rpm; max torque (SAE): 83 lb ft, 11.4 kg m at 3,000 rpm; max engine rpm: 5,400; specific power: 46.8 hp/l; cylinder block: cast iron; cylinder head: cast iron; crankshaft bearings: 5; valves: 2 per cylinder, overhead, in line, push-rods and rockers; camshafts: 1, overhead; lubrication: gear pump, full flow filter; lubricating system capacity: 7.9 imp pt, 9.5 US pt, 4.5 l; carburation: 1 downdraught single barrel carburettor; fuel feed: mechanical pump; cooling system: water; cooling system capacity: 16.7 imp pt, 20.1 US pt, 9.5 l.

TRANSMISSION driving wheels: rear; clutch: single dry plate; gearbox: mechanical; gears: 4 + reverse; synchromesh gears: I, II, III, IV; gearbox ratios: I 2.470, II 1.770, III 1.340, IV 1, rev 2.400; gear lever: central; final drive: hypoid bevel; axle ratio: 3.900; width of rims: 4.5''; tyres: 155 x 13.

PERFORMANCE max speed: about 86 mph, 138 km/h; power-weight ratio: 28 lb/hp, 12.7 kg/hp; carrying capacity: 882 lb, 400 kg; speed in direct drive at 1,000 rpm: 15.9 mph, 25.6 km/h; fuel consumption: 28.2 m/imp gal, 23.5 m/US gal, 10 l x 100 km.

CHASSIS integral; front suspension: independent, wishbones, coil springs, anti-roll bar, telescopic dampers; rear suspension: rigid axle, lower trailing radius arms, upper oblique torque arms, coil springs, telescopic dampers.

STEERING rack-and-pinion.

BRAKES front disc, rear drum, dual circuit, servo.

ELECTRICAL EQUIPMENT voltage: 12 V; battery: 46 Ah; generator type: alternator, 37 A; ignition distributor: Chrysler; headlamps: 4.

DIMENSIONS AND WEIGHT wheel base: 98 in, 2,489 mm; front track: 51 in, 1,295 mm; rear track: 51 in, 1,295 mm; overall length: 162 in, 4,115 mm; overall width: 62.50 in, 1,587 mm; overall height: 54.60 in, 1,387 mm; dry weight: 1,966 lb, 8°1 kg; turning circle (between walls): 31.9 ft, 9.7 m.

BODY saloon/sedan; doors: 4; seats: 5; front seats: separate, built-in headrests.

OPTIONAL ACCESSORIES Torqueflite automatic gearbox, hydraulic torque convertor and planetary gears with 3 ratios (I 2.450, II 1.450, III 1, rev 2.200), max ratio of convertor at stall 2.16, possible manual selection, 3.090 axle ratio.

Valiant - Valiant Duster - Duster 340 Series

PRICES IN USA:

Valiant	4-door Sedan	$ 2,392
Valiant Duster	2-door Coupé	$ 2,313
Duster 340	2-door Coupé	$ 2,703

For V8 engines add $ 124.

125 hp power team

(standard for Valiant and Valiant Duster; not available for Duster 340).

ENGINE front, 4 stroke; cylinders: 6, in line; bore and stroke: 3.40 x 3.64 in, 86.3 x 92.4 mm; engine capacity: 198 cu in, 3,245 cu cm; compression ratio: 8.4; max power (SAE): 125 hp at 4,400 rpm; max torque (SAE): 180 lb ft, 24.8 kg m at 2,000 rpm; max engine rpm: 4,600; specific power: 38.5 hp/l; cylinder block: cast iron; cylinder head: cast iron; crankshaft bearings: 4; valves: 2 per cylinder, overhead, in line, push-rods and rockers; camshafts: 1, side; lubrication: rotary pump, full flow filter; lubricating system capacity: 8.3 imp pt, 9.9 US pt, 4.7 l; carburation: 1 Carter BBS-4955S downdraught single barrel carburettor; fuel feed: mechanical pump; cooling system: water; cooling system capacity: 21.6 imp pt, 26 US pt, 12.3 l.

TRANSMISSION driving wheels: rear; clutch: single dry plate; gearbox: mechanical; gears: 3 + reverse; synchromesh gears: II and III; gearbox ratios: I 2.950, II 1.830, III 1, rev 3.800; gear lever: steering column; final drive: hypoid bevel; axle ratio: 3.230; width of rims: 4.5''; tyres: 6.45 x 14.

PERFORMANCE max speed: about 94 mph, 151 km/h; speed in direct drive at 1,000 rpm: 22.3 mph, 35.9 km/h; fuel consumption: 21.4 m/imp gal, 17.8 m/US gal, 13.2 l x 100 km.

OLDSMOBILE Toronado Custom Coupé (rear suspension)

PLYMOUTH Cricket Sedan

PLYMOUTH Duster 340 2-door Coupé

CHASSIS integral; front suspension: independent, wishbones, longitudinal torsion bars, telescopic dampers; rear suspension: rigid axle, semi-elliptic leafsprings, telescopic dampers.

STEERING recirculating ball; turns of steering wheel lock to lock: 5.30.

BRAKES drum, dual circuit; area rubbed by linings: total 254.5 sq in, 1,641 sq cm.

ELECTRICAL EQUIPMENT voltage: 12 V; battery: 40 Ah; generator type: alternator, 34 A; ignition distributor: Chrysler; headlamps: 2.

DIMENSIONS AND WEIGHT wheel base: 108 in, 2,743 mm; front track: 57.50 in, 1,460 mm — 4-door sedan 57.40 in, 1,458 mm; rear track: 55.50 in, 1,410 mm; overall length: 188.40 in, 4,785 mm; overall width: 71.10 in, 1,806 mm — 2-door coupé 71.60 in, 1,819 mm; overall height: 54 in, 1,371 mm — 2-door coupé 52.60 in, 1,336 mm; ground clearance: 5.10 in, 130 mm; turning circle (between walls): 40.5 ft, 12.3 m; fuel tank capacity: 14.1 imp gal, 17 US gal, 64 l.

OPTIONAL ACCESSORIES Torqueflite automatic gearbox with 3 ratios (I 2.450, II 1.450, III 1, rev 2.200), max ratio of convertor at stall 2.16, 2.760 axle ratio; limited slip final drive; power-assisted steering; front disc brakes with servo.

145 hp power team

(optional for Valiant and Valiant Duster; not available for Duster 340).

See 125 hp power team, except for:

ENGINE bore and stroke: 3.40 x 4.12 in, 86.4 x 104.6 mm; engine capacity: 225 cu in, 3,687 cu cm; max power (SAE): 145 hp at 4,000 rpm; max torque (SAE): 215 lb ft, 20.7 kg m at 2,400 rpm; max engine rpm: 4,500; specific power: 39.3 hp/l; carburation: 1 Holley R-4655 downdraught single barrel carburettor.

PERFORMANCE max speed: about 100 mph, 161 km/h; fuel consumption: 20.2 m/imp gal, 16.8 m/US gal, 14 l x 100 km.

230 hp power team

(standard for Valiant and Valiant Duster; not available for Duster 340).

See 125 hp power team, except for:

ENGINE cylinders: 8, Vee-slanted at 90°; bore and stroke: 3.91 x 3.31 in, 99.2 x 84 mm; engine capacity: 318 cu in, 5,211 cu cm; compression ratio: 8.8; max power (SAE): 230 hp at 4,400 rpm; max torque (SAE): 320 lb ft, 44.1 kg m at 2,000 rpm; max engine rpm: 5,000; specific power: 44.1 hp/l; crankshaft bearings: 5; valves: hydraulic tappets; camshafts: 1, at centre of Vee; carburation: 1 Carter BBD-4957S downdraught twin barrel carburettor; cooling system capacity: 26.6 imp pt, 31.9 US pt, 15.1 l.

TRANSMISSION synchromesh gears: I, II, III; gearbox ratios: I 3.080, II 1.700, III 1, rev 3.900; tyres: 6.95 x 14.

PERFORMANCE max speed: about 103 mph, 166 km/h; speed in direct drive at 1,000 rpm: 20.3 mph, 32.6 km/h; fuel consumption: 16.8 m/imp gal, 14 m/US gal, 16.8 l x 100 km.

BRAKES area rubbed by linings: total 251.4 sq in, 1,621 sq cm.

ELECTRICAL EQUIPMENT generator type: alternator, 37 A.

DIMENSIONS AND WEIGHT overall height: Valiant Duster 52.80 in, 1,341 mm.

275 hp power team

(standard for Duster 340; not available for Valiant and Valiant Duster).

See 125 hp power team, except for:

ENGINE cylinders: 8, Vee-slanted at 90°; bore and stroke: 4.04 x 3.31 in, 102.5 x 84 mm; engine capacity: 340 cu in, 5,572 cu cm; compression ratio: 10.5; max power (SAE): 275 hp at 5,000 rpm; max torque (SAE): 340 lb ft, 46.9 kg m at 3,200 rpm; max engine rpm: 5,300; specific power: 49.4 hp/l; crankshaft bearings: 5; valves: hydraulic tappets; camshafts: 1, at centre of Vee; carburation: 1 Carter TQ-4972S downdraught 4-barrel carburettor; cooling system capacity: 25 imp pt, 30 US pt, 14.2 l.

TRANSMISSION synchromesh gears: I, II, III; gearbox

275 HP POWER TEAM

ratios: I 2.550, II 1.490, III 1, rev 3.340; width of rims: 5.5''; tyres: E70 x 14.

PERFORMANCE max speed: about 106 mph, 170 km/h; speed in direct drive at 1,000 rpm: 20.1 mph, 32.3 km/h; fuel consumption: 15.6 m/imp gal, 13 m/US gal, 18.1 l x 100 km.

BRAKES area rubbed by linings: total 251.4 sq in, 1,621 sq cm.

ELECTRICAL EQUIPMENT generator type: alternator, 37 A.

DIMENSIONS AND WEIGHT overall height: 52.90 in, 1,344 mm.

OPTIONAL ACCESSORIES Torquefile automatic gearbox with 3.230 axle ratio; 4-speed fully synchronized mechanical gearbox (I 2.470, II 1.770, III 1.340, IV 1, rev 2.400).

Barracuda Coupé - Barracuda - Gran Coupé - 'Cuda - AAR 'Cuda Series

PRICES IN USA:

Barracuda Coupé	2-door Coupé	$ 2,633
Barracuda	2-door Hardtop	$ 2,745
Barracuda	2-door Convertible	$ 3,002
Gran Coupé	2-door Hardtop	$ 3,008
'Cuda	2-door Hardtop	$ 3,134
'Cuda	2-door Convertible	$ 3,391
AAR Cuda	2-door Hardtop	$ —

For V8 engines add $ 101 (Barracuda Coupé add $ 126).

125 hp power team

(standard for Barracuda Coupé Series; not available for other Series).

ENGINE front, 4 stroke; cylinders: 6, in line; bore and stroke: 3.40 x 3.64 in, 86.3 x 92.4 mm; engine capacity: 198 cu in, 3,245 cu cm; compression ratio: 8.4; max power (SAE): 125 hp at 4,400 rpm; max torque (SAE): 180 lb ft, 24.8 kg m at 2,000 rpm; max engine rpm: 4,600; specific power: 38.5 hp/l; cylinder block: cast iron; crankshaft bearings: 4; valves: 2 per cylinder, overhead, in line, push-rods and rockers; camshafts: 1, side; lubrication: rotary pump, full flow filter; lubricating system capacity: 8.3 imp pt, 9.9 US pt, 4.7 l; carburation: 1 Carter BBS-4955S downdraught single barrel carburettor; fuel feed: mechanical pump; cooling system: water; cooling system capacity: 21.6 imp pt, 26 US pt, 12.3 l.

TRANSMISSION driving wheels: rear; clutch: single dry plate; gearbox: mechanical; gears: 3 + reverse; synchromesh gears: I, II, III; gearbox ratios: I 3.080, II 1.700, III 1, rev 2.900; gear lever: central; final drive: hypoid bevel; axle ratio: 3.230; width of rims: 5''; tyres: 7.35 x 14.

PERFORMANCE max speed: about 94 mph, 151 km/h; power-weight ratio: 24.8 lb/hp, 11.2 kg/hp; speed in direct drive at 1,000 rpm: 22.4 mph, 36 km/h; fuel consumption: 20.9 m/imp gal, 17.4 m/US gal, 13.5 l x 100 km.

CHASSIS integral; front suspension: independent, wishbones, longitudinal torsion bars, telescopic dampers; rear suspension: rigid axle, semi-elliptic tealfsprings, telescopic dampers.

STEERING recirculating ball; turns of steering wheel lock to lock: 5.30.

BRAKES drum, dual circuit; area rubbed by linings: total 314.2 sq in, 2,026 sq cm.

ELECTRICAL EQUIPMENT voltage: 12 V; battery: 46 Ah; generator type: alternator, 37 A; ignition distributor: Chrysler; headlamps: 4.

DIMENSIONS AND WEIGHT wheel base: 108 in, 2,743 mm; front track: 59.70 in, 1,516 mm; rear track: 61.60 in, 1,565 mm; overall length: 186.60 in, 4,740 mm; overall width: 74.90 in, 1,902 mm; overall height: 50.60 in, 1,285 mm; ground clearance: 5.70 in, 145 mm; dry weight: 3,100 lb, 1,406 kg; turning circle (between walls): 41.3 ft, 12.6 m; fuel tank capacity: 15 imp gal, 18 US gal, 68 l.

OPTIONAL ACCESSORIES Torqueflite automatic gearbox with 3 ratios (I 2.450, II 1.450, III 1, rev 2.200), max ratio of convertor at stall 2.16, 2.760 axle ratio; limited slip final drive; anti-roll bar on front suspension; power-assisted steering; front disc brakes with servo.

PLYMOUTH Barracuda Coupé 2-door Coupé

PLYMOUTH 'Cuda 2-door Convertible

PLYMOUTH 300 hp engine

145 hp power team

(standard for Barracuda Series; optional for Barracuda Coupé Series; not available for other Series).

See 125 hp power team, except for:

ENGINE bore and stroke: 3.40 x 4.12 in, 86.3 x 104.6 mm; engine capacity: 225 cu in, 3,687 cu cm; max power (SAE): 145 hp at 4,000 rpm; max torque (SAE): 215 lb ft, 29.7 kg m at 2,400 rpm; max engine rpm: 4,500; specific power: 39.3 hp/l; carburation: 1 Holley R-4655A downdraught single barrel carburettor.

PERFORMANCE max speed: about 101 mph, 162 km/h; power-weight ratio: Barracuda 2-door Hardtop 21.5 lb/hp, 9.8 kg/hp — Barracuda Coupé 21.4 lb/hp, 9.7 kg/hp; fuel consumption: 19.3 m/imp gal, 16.1 m/US gal, 14.6 l x 100 km.

DIMENSIONS AND WEIGHT overall height: 50.80 in, 1,290 mm; dry weight: Barracuda 2-door Hardtop 3,125 lb, 1.417 kg — Barracuda 2-door Convertible 3,200 lb, 1,451 kg.

OPTIONAL ACCESSORIES air-conditioning system.

230 hp power team

(standard for Barracuda Coupé, Barracuda and Gran Coupé Series; not available for other Series).

See 125 hp power team, except for:

ENGINE cylinders: 8, Vee-slanted at 90°; bore and stroke: 3.91 x 3.31 in, 99.3 x 84 mm; engine capacity: 318 cu in, 5,211 cu cm; compression ratio: 8.6; max power (SAE): 230 hp at 4,400 rpm; max torque (SAE): 320 lb ft, 44.1 kg at 2,000 rpm; max engine rpm: 4,600; specific power: 44.1 hp/l; crankshaft bearings: 5; valves: hydraulic tappets; camshafts: 1, at centre of Vee; carburation: 1 Carter BBD-4957A downdraught twin barrel carburettor; cooling system capacity: 26.6 imp pt, 31.9 US pt, 15.1 l.

TRANSMISSION tyres: E78 x 14.

PERFORMANCE max speed: about 103 mph, 165 km/h; power-weight ratio: Barracuda Coupé 13.7 lb/hp, 6.1 kg/hp — Barracuda 2-door Hardtop 13.8 lb/hp, 6.2 kg/hp — Gran Coupé 2-door Hardtop 13.9 lb/hp, 6.3 kg/hp; speed in direct drive at 1,000 rpm: 22.5 mph, 36.2 km/h; fuel consumption: 16.4 m/imp gal, 13.7 m/US gal, 17.2 l x 100 km.

DIMENSIONS AND WEIGHT rear track: 60.70 in, 1,542 mm; overall height: 50.90 in, 1,293 mm; dry weight: Barracuda Coupé 3,160 lb, 1,433 kg — Barracuda 2-door Hardtop 3,180 lb, 1,442 kg — Barracuda 2-door Convertible 3,225 lb, 1,462 kg — Gran Coupé 2-door Hardtop 3,195 lb, 1,449 kg.

OPTIONAL ACCESSORIES air-conditioning system.

275 hp power team

(optional for 'Cuda and AAR Cuda Series; not available for other Series).

See 125 hp power team, except for:

ENGINE cylinders: 8, Vee-slanted at 90°; bore and stroke: 4.04 x 3.31 in, 102.5 x 84 mm; engine capacity: 340 cu in, 5,572 cu cm; compression ratio: 10.2; max power (SAE): 275 hp at 5,000 rpm; max torque (SAE): 340 lb ft, 46.9 kg m at 3,200 rpm; max engine rpm: 5,300; specific power: 49.4 hp/l; crankshaft bearings: 5; valves: hydraulic tappets; camshafts: 1, at centre of Vee; carburation: 1 Carter TQ-4972S downdraught 4-barrel carburettor; cooling system capacity: 25 imp pt, 30 US pt, 14.2 l.

TRANSMISSION gearbox ratios: I 2.550, II 1.490, III 1, rev 3.340; width of rims: 5.5''; tyres: F70 x 14.

PERFORMANCE max speed: about 109 mph, 175 km/h; power-weight ratio: 'Cuda 2-door Hardtop 12.6 lb/hp, 5.7 kg/hp; speed in direct drive at 1,000 rpm: 22.5 mph, 36.2 km/h; fuel consumption: 15 m/imp gal, 12.5 m/US gal, 18.8 l x 100 km.

CHASSIS front and rear suspension: anti-roll bar (standard).

BRAKES area rubbed by linings: total 380.1 sq in, 2,451 sq cm.

ELECTRICAL EQUIPMENT battery: 59 Ah.

DIMENSIONS AND WEIGHT front track: 'Cuda 60.20 in, 1,529 mm — AAR Cuda 60.70 in, 1,542 mm; rear track: 'Cuda 60.70 in, 1,542 mm — AAR Cuda 61.60 in, 1,554 mm; overall height: 'Cuda 51.20 in, 1,300 mm — AAR Cuda 51.70 in, 1,313 mm; dry weight: 'Cuda 2-door Hardtop 3,465 lb, 1,571 kg — 'Cuda 2-door Convertible 3,540 lb, 1,605 kg.

OPTIONAL ACCESSORIES Torqueflite automatic gearbox

PLYMOUTH Barracuda Coupé 2-door Coupé

PLYMOUTH Barracuda 2-door Convertible

PLYMOUTH 'Cuda 2-door Hardtop

with 3.230 axle ratio; 4-speed fully synchronized mechanical gearbox (I 2.470, II 1.770, III 1.340, IV 1, rev 2.400) central gear lever, 3.230 axle ratio; air-conditioning system.

275 hp power team

(optional for Barracuda Coupé, Barracuda and Gran Coupé Series; not available for other Series).

See 125 hp power team, except for:

ENGINE cylinders: 8, Vee-slanted at 90°; bore and stroke: 4.25 x 3.38 in, 107.9 x 85.8 mm; engine capacity: 383 cu in, 6,276 cu cm; compression ratio: 8.5; max power (SAE): 275 hp at 4,400 rpm; max torque (SAE): 375 lb ft, 51.8 kg m at 2,800 rpm; max engine rpm: 4,700; specific power: 43.8 hp/l; crankshaft bearings: 5; valves: hydraulic tappets; camshafts: 1, at centre of Vee; carburation: 1 Carter BBD-4962S downdraught twin barrel carburettor; cooling system capacity: 24.1 imp pt, 29 US pt, 13.7 l.

TRANSMISSION gearbox: Torqueflite automatic (standard), max ratio of convertor at stall 2.02; axle ratio: 2.760; width of rims: 5.5''; tyres: F78 x 14.

PERFORMANCE max speed: about 110 mph, 177 km/h; power-weight ratio: Barracuda Coupé 12.2 lb/hp, 5.4 kg/hp — Barracuda 2-door Hardtop 12.3 lb/hp, 5.5 kg/hp — Gran Coupé 2-door Hardtop 12.4 lb/hp, 5.6 kg/hp; speed in direct drive at 1,000 rpm: 24 mph, 38.6 km/h; fuel consumption: 15.4 m/imp gal, 12.8 m/US gal, 18.4 l x 100 km.

ELECTRICAL EQUIPMENT battery: 59 Ah.

DIMENSIONS AND WEIGHT (see 230 hp power team) dry weight: plus 211 lb, 96 kg.

OPTIONAL ACCESSORIES air-conditioning system.

290 hp power team

(standard for AAR Cuda; not available for other Series).

See 125 hp power team, except for.

ENGINE cylinders: 8, Vee-slanted at 90°; bore and stroke: 4.04 x 3.31 in, 102.5 x 84 mm; engine capacity: 340 cu in, 5.572 cu cm; compression ratio: 10.2; max power (SAE): 290 hp at 5,000 rpm; max torque (SAE): 340 lb ft, 46.9 kg m at 3,200 rpm; max engine rpm: 5,300; specific power: 52 hp/l; crankshaft bearings: 5; valves: hydraulic tappets; camshafts: 1, at centre of Vee; carburation: 3 Holley R-4789A-4790A-4791A downdraught twin barrel carburettors; cooling system capacity: 25 imp pt, 30 US pt, 14.2 l.

TRANSMISSION gears: 4 + reverse; synchromesh gears: I, II, III, IV; gearbox ratios: I 2.470, II 1.770, III 1.340, IV 1, rev 2.400; axle ratio: 3.550; width of rims: 7''; tyres: E60 x 15 front, G60 x 15 rear.

PERFORMANCE max speed: about 113 mph, 182 km/h; speed in direct drive at 1,000 rpm: 22.3 mph, 35.9 km/h; fuel consumption: 15.1 m/imp gal, 12.6 m/US gal, 18.7 l x 100 km.

CHASSIS front suspension: anti-roll bar (standard).

BRAKES area rubbed by linings: total 380.1 sq in, 2,451 sq cm.

ELECTRICAL EQUIPMENT battery: 59 Ah.

DIMENSIONS AND WEIGHT front track: 60.70 in, 1,542 mm; rear track: 61.20 in, 1,554 mm; overall height: 51.70 in, 1,313 mm.

OPTIONAL ACCESSORIES Torqueflite automatic gearbox with max ratio of convertor at stall 2.02, 3.550 axle ratio; air-conditioning system.

300 hp power team

(optional for Barracuda Coupé, Barracuda and Gran Coupé Series; not available for other Series).

See 125 hp power team, except for:

ENGINE cylinders: 8, Vee-slanted at 90°; bore and stroke: 4.25 x 3.38 in, 107.9 x 85.8 mm; engine capacity: 383 cu in, 6,276 cu cm; compression ratio: 8.5; max power (SAE): 300 hp at 4,800 rpm; max torque (SAE): 410 lb ft, 56.6 kg m at 3,400 rpm; max engine rpm: 5,200; specific power: 47.8 hp/l; crankshaft bearings: 5; valves: hydraulic tappets; camshafts: 1, at centre of Vee; corburation: 1 Holley R-4667A downdraught 4-barrel carburettor; cooling system capacity: 24.1 imp pt, 29 US pt, 13.7 l.

TRANSMISSION gearbox ratios: I 2.550, II 1.490, III 1, rev 3.340; width of rims: 5.5''; tyres: F78 x 14.

300 HP POWER TEAM

PERFORMANCE max speed: about 114 mph, 183 km/h; power-weight ratio: Barracuda Coupé 11.4 lb/hp, 5.1 kg/hp — Barracuda 2-door Hardtop and Gran Coupé 2-door Hardtop 11.5 lb/hp, 5.2 kg/hp; speed in direct drive at 1,000 rpm: 22.2 mph, 35.7 km/h; fuel consumption: 14.9 m/imp gal, 12.4 m/US gal, 18.9 l x 100 km.

CHASSIS front and rear suspension: anti-roll bar (standard).

BRAKES area rubbed by linings: total 380.1 sq in, 2,451 sq cm.

ELECTRICAL EQUIPMENT battery: 59 Ah.

DIMENSIONS AND WEIGHT (see 230 hp power team) dry weight: plus 268 lb, 122 kg.

OPTIONAL ACCESSORIES Torqueflite automatic gearbox with max ratio of convertor at stall 2.16, 2.760 axle ratio; 4-speed fully synchronized mechanical gearbox (I 2.470, II 1.770, III 1.340, IV 1, rev 2.400); air-conditioning system.

300 hp power team

(standard for 'Cuda and AAR Cuda Series; not available for other Series).

See 125 hp power team, except for:

ENGINE cylinders: 8, Vee-slanted at 90°; bore and stroke: 4.25 x 3.38 in, 107.9 x 85.8 mm; engine capacity: 383 cu in, 6,276 cu cm; compression ratio: 8.5; max power (SAE): 300 hp at 4,800 rpm; max torque (SAE): 410 lb ft, 56.6 kg m at 3,400 rpm; max engine rpm: 5,200; specific power: 47.8 hp/l; crankshaft bearings: 5; valves: hydraulic tappets; camshafts: 1, at centre of Vee; carburation: 1 Holley R-4667A downdraught 4-barrel carburettor; cooling system capacity: 24.1 imp pt, 29 US pt, 13.7 l.

TRANSMISSION gearbox ratios: I 2.550, II 1.490, III 1, rev 3.340; width of rims: 5.5''; tyres: F70 x 14.

PERFORMANCE max speed: about 115 mph, 185 km/h; power-weight ratio: 'Cuda 2-door Hardtop 11.9 lb/hp, 5.4 kg/hp; speed in direct drive at 1,000 rpm: 22.6 mph, 36.4 km/h; fuel consumption: 14.1 m/imp gal, 11.8 m/US gal, 20 l x 100 km.

BRAKES area rubbed by linings: total 380.1 sq in, 2,451 sq cm.

DIMENSIONS AND WEIGHT (see 275 hp power team) dry weight: plus 100 lb, 45 kg.

OPTIONAL ACCESSORIES Torqueflite automatic gearbox with max ratio of convertor at stall 2.16, 3.230 axle ratio; 4-speed fully synchronized mechanical gearbox (I 2.470, II 1.770, III 1.340, IV 1, rev 2.400), 3.230 axle ratio; air-conditioning system.

385 hp power team

(optional for 'Cuda and AAR Cuda Series; not available for other Series).

See 125 hp power team, except for:

ENGINE cylinders: 8, Vee-slanted at 90°; bore and stroke: 4.32 x 3.75 in, 109.7 x 95.2 mm; engine capacity: 440 cu in, 7,210 cu cm; compression ratio: 10.3; max power (SAE): 385 hp at 4,700 rpm; max torque (SAE): 490 lb ft, 67.6 kg m at 3,200 rpm; max engine rpm: 5,500; specific power: 53.4 hp/l; crankshaft bearings: 5; valves: hydraulic tappets; camshafts: 1, at centre of Vee; lubricating system capacity: 11.6 imp pt, 14 US pt, 6.6 l; carburation: 3 Holley R-4671A-4672A-4670A downdraught twin barrel carburettors; cooling system capacity: 27.5 imp pt, 33 US pt, 15.6 l.

TRANSMISSION gearbox: Torqueflite automatic (standard), max ratio of convertor at stall 2.02; axle ratio: 3.540; width of rims: 6''; tyres: F70 x 14.

PERFORMANCE max speed: about 122 mph, 196 km/h; power-weight ratio: 'Cuda 2-door Hardtop 9.4 lb/hp, 4.3 kg/hp; speed in direct drive at 1,000 rpm: 22.6 mph, 36.4 km/h; fuel consumption: 12.6 m/imp gal, 10.5 m/US gal, 22.4 l x 100 km.

CHASSIS front suspension: anti-roll bar (standard).

BRAKES area rubbed by linings: total 380.1 sq in, 2,451 sq cm.

ELECTRICAL EQUIPMENT battery: 70 Ah; ignition distributor: Prestolite.

DIMENSIONS AND WEIGHT (see 275 hp power team) dry weight: plus 148 lb, 67 kg.

PLYMOUTH Road Runner 2-door Hardtop

PLYMOUTH Satellite Custom 6-passenger Station Wagon

PLYMOUTH Satellite Brougham 4-door Sedan

OPTIONAL ACCESSORIES 4-speed fully synchronized mechanical gearbox (I 2.440, II 1.770, III 1.340, IV 1, rev 2.360), 3.540 axle ratio; air-conditioning system.

425 hp power team

(optional for 'Cuda and AAR Cuda Series; not available for other Series).

See 125 hp power team, except for:

ENGINE cylinders: 8, Vee-slanted at 90°; bore and stroke: 4.25 x 3.75 in, 107.9 x 95.2 mm; engine capacity: 426 cu in, 6,981 cu cm; compression ratio: 10.2; max power (SAE): 425 hp at 5,000 rpm; max torque (SAE): 490 lb ft, 67.6 kg m at 4,000 rpm; max engine rpm: 5,700; specific power: 60.9 hp/l; crankshaft bearings: 5; valves: hydraulic tappets; camshafts: 1, at centre of Vee; lubricating system capacity: 10 imp pt, 12 US pt, 5.7 l; carburation: 2 Carter AFB-4971S-4970S downdraught 4-barrel carburettors; cooling system capacity: 26.6 imp pt, 31.9 US pt, 15.1 l.

TRANSMISSION gearbox: Torqueflite automatic (standard), max ratio of convertor at stall 2.16; axle ratio: 3.230; width of rims: 7''; tyres: F60 x 15.

PERFORMANCE max speed: about 128 mph, 206 km/h; power-weight ratio: 'Cuda 2-door Hardtop 8.8 lb/hp, 4 kg/hp; speed in direct drive at 1,000 rpm: 22.7 mph, 36.5 km/h; fuel consumption: 12.3 m/imp gal, 10.2 m/US gal, 23 l x 100 km.

CHASSIS front suspension: anti-roll bar (standard).

BRAKES area rubbed by linings: total 380.1 sq in, 2,451 sq cm.

ELECTRICAL EQUIPMENT battery: 70 Ah; ignition distributor: Prestolite.

DIMENSIONS AND WEIGHT (see 275 hp power team) dry weight: plus 260 lb, 118 kg.

OPTIONAL ACCESSORIES 4-speed fully synchronized mechanical gearbox (I 2.440, II 1.770, III 1.340, IV 1, rev 2.360) 3.540 axle ratio; air-conditioning system.

Satellite Coupé - Satellite - Road Runner - Satellite Custom - Satellite Sebring - Satellite Brougham - Satellite Regent - Satellite Sebring Plus - GTX Series

PRICES IN USA:

Satellite Coupé	2-door Coupé	$ 2,663
Satellite	4-door Sedan	$ 2,734
Satellite	6-passenger Station Wagon	$ 3,032
Road Runner	2-door Hardtop	$ 3,120
Satellite Custom	4-door Sedan	$ 2,882
Satellite Custom	6-passenger Station Wagon	$ 3,253
Satellite Custom	9-passenger Station Wagon	$ 3,333
Satellite Sebring	2-door Hardtop	$ 2,905
Satellite Brougham	4-door Sedan	$ 3,162
Satellite Regent	6-passenger Station Wagon	$ 3,532
Satellite Regent	9-passenger Station Wagon	$ 3,612
Satellite Sebring Plus	2-door Hardtop	$ 3,153
GTX	2-door Hardtop	$ 3,707

For V8 engines add $ 95.

145 hp power team

(standard for Satellite Coupé. Satellite, Satellite Custom and Satellite Sebring Series; not available for other Series).

ENGINE front, 4 stroke; cylinders: 6, in line; bore and stroke: 3.40 x 4.12 in, 86.4 x 104.6 mm; engine capacity: 225 cu in, 3,687 cu cm; compression ratio: 8.4; max power (SAE): 145 hp at 4,000 rpm; max torque (SAE): 215 lb ft, 29.7 kg m at 2,400 rpm; max engine rpm: 4,500; specific power: 39.3 hp/l; cylinder block: cast iron; cylinder head: cast iron; crankshaft bearings: 4; valves: 2 per cylinder, overhead, in line, push-rods and rockers; camshafts: 1, side; lubrication: rotary pump, full flow filter; lubricating system capacity: 8.3 imp pt, 9.9 US pt, 4.7 l; carburation: 1 Holley R-4655A downdraught single barrel carburettor; fuel feed: mechanical pump; cooling system: water; cooling system capacity: 21.6 imp pt, 26 US pt, 12.3 l.

TRANSMISSION driving wheels: rear; clutch: single dry plate; gearbox: mechanical; gears: 3 + reverse; synchromesh gears: II and III; gearbox ratios: I 2.950, II 1.830, III 1, rev 3.800; gear lever: central or steering column; final drive: hypoid bevel; axle ratio: 3.230 — station wagons 3.550; width of rims: 5'' — station wagons 5.5''; tyres: E78 x 14 — station wagons H78 x 14.

PERFORMANCE max speed: about 92 mph, 148 km/h; power-

PLYMOUTH Road Runner 2-door Hardtop

PLYMOUTH Road Runner 2-door Hardtop

PLYMOUTH Satellite Brougham 4-door Sedan

weight ratio: Satellite 4-door Sedan and Satellite Custom 4-door Sedan 22.9 lb/hp, 10.4 kg/hp; speed in direct drive at 1,000 rpm: 21 mph, 33.8 km/h; fuel consumption: 19 m/imp gal, 15.8 m/US gal, 14.9 l x 100 km.

CHASSIS integral; front suspension: independent, wishbones, longitudinal torsion bars, telescopic dampers; rear suspension: rigid axle, semi-elliptic leafsprings, telescopic dampers.

STEERING recirculating ball; turns of steering wheel lock to lock: 5.30.

BRAKES drum, dual circuit; area rubbed by linings: total 314.2 sq in, 2,026 sq cm (station wagons 380.1 sq in, 2,451 sq cm).

ELECTRICAL EQUIPMENT voltage: 12 V; battery: 46 Ah; generator type: alternator, 37 A; ignition distributor: Chrysler; headlamps: 4.

DIMENSIONS AND WEIGHT wheel base: 2-door coupé and 2-door hardtop 115 in, 2,921 mm — 4-door sedans and station wagons 117 in, 2,972 mm; front track: 59.70 in, 1,516 mm — station wagons 60.10 in, 1,526 mm; rear track: 61.60 in, 1,565 mm — station wagons 63.40 in, 1,610 mm; overall length: 2-door coupé and 2-door hardtop 203.20 in, 5,161 mm — 4-door sedans 204.60 in, 5,197 mm — station wagons 210.90 in, 5,357 mm; overall width: 2-door coupé and 2-door hardtop 79.10 in, 2,009 mm — 4-door sedans 78.60 in, 1,996 mm — station wagons 79.20 in, 2,012 mm; overall height: 2-door coupé and 2-door hardtop 52 in, 1,321 mm — 4-door sedans 53.50 in, 1,359 mm — station wagons 56.40 in, 1,432 mm; ground clearance: 4.40 in, 112 mm; dry weight: Satellite 4-door Sedan 3,328 lb, 1,509 kg — Satellite 6-passenger Station Wagon 3,813 lb, 1,729 kg — Satellite Custom 4-door Sedan 3,328 lb, 1,509 kg — Satellite Custom 6-passenger Station Wagon 3,818 lb, 1,732 kg — Satellite Custom 9-passenger Station Wagon 3,888 lb, 1,763 kg — Satellite Sebring 2-door Hardtop 3,298 lb, 1,495 kg; fuel tank capacity: 17.4 imp gal, 21 US gal, 79 l.

OPTIONAL ACCESSORIES Torqueflite automatic gearbox with 3 ratios (I 2.450, II 1.450, III 1, rev 2.200), max ratio of convertor at stall 2.16, 2.940 axle ratio (station wagons 3.230); limited slip final drive; power-assisted steering; servo brake; front disc brakes with servo; air-conditioning system.

230 hp power team

(standard for Satellite Coupé, Satellite, Satellite Custom Satellite Sebring, Satellite Brougham, Satellite Regent and Satellite Sebring Plus Series; not available for other Series).

See 145 hp power team, except for:

ENGINE cylinders: 8, Vee-slanted at 90ª; bore and stroke: 3.91 x 3.31 in, 99.3 x 84 mm; engine capacity: 318 cu in, 5,211 cu cm; compression ratio: 8.6; max power (SAE): 230 hp at 4,400 rpm; max torque (SAE): 320 lb ft, 44.1 kg m at 2,000 rpm; max engine rpm: 5,000; specific power: 44.1 hp/l; crankshaft bearings: 5; valves: hydraulic tappets; camshafts: 1, at centre of Vee; carburation: 1 Carter BBD-4957S downdraught twin barrel carburettor; cooling system capacity: 26.6 imp pt, 31.9 US pt, 15.1 l.

TRANSMISSION synchromesh gears: I, II, III; gearbox ratios: I 3.080, II 1.700, III 1, rev 2.900; axle ratio: 2.940 — station wagons 3.230; tyres: F78 x 14 — station wagons H78 x 14.

PERFORMANCE max speed: about 101 mph, 162 km/h; power-weight ratio: Satellite 4-door Sedan, Satellite Custom 4-door Sedan and Satellite Brougham 4-door Sedan 15 lb/hp, 6.8 kg/hp; speed in direct drive at 1,000 rpm: 22 mph, 35.4 km/h; fuel consumption: 16.3 m/imp gal, 13.6 m/US gal, 17.3 l x 100 km.

DIMENSIONS AND WEIGHT rear track: 2-door hardtops and 4-door sedans 62 in, 1,575 mm; overall height: 2-door coupé 52.30 in, 1,328 mm — 2-door hardtops 52.70 in, 1,338 mm — 4-door sedans 53.80 in, 1,366 mm; dry weight: plus 128 lb, 58 kg — station wagons plus 93 lb, 42 kg — Satellite Brougham 4-door Sedan 3,470 lb, 1,574 kg — Satellite Regent 6-passenger Station Wagon 3,925 lb, 1,780 kg — Satellite Regent 9-passenger Station Wagon 3,995 lb, 1,812 kg — Satellite Sebring Plus 2-door Hardtop 3,440 lb, 1,559 kg.

OPTIONAL ACCESSORIES Torqueflite automatic gearbox with 2.710 axle ratio (station wagons 2.940).

275 hp power team

(optional for Satellite Coupé, Satellite, Satellite Custom, Satellite Sebring, Satellite Brougham, Satellite Regent and Satellite Sebring Plus Series; not available for other Series).

See 145 hp power team, except for:

ENGINE cylinders: 8, Vee-slanted at 90°; bore and stroke: 4.25 x 3.38 in, 107.9 x 85.8 mm; engine capacity: 383 cu in,

275 HP POWER TEAM

6,276 cu cm; compression ratio: 8.5; max power (SAE): 275 hp at 4,400 rpm; max torque (SAE): 375 lb ft, 51.8 kg m at 2,800 rpm; max engine rpm: 4,700; specific power: 43.8 hp/l; crankshaft bearings: 5; valves: hydraulic tappets; camshafts: 1, at centre of Vee; carburation: 1 Carter BBD-4962S downdraught twin barrel carburettor; cooling system capacity: 24.1 imp pt, 29 US pt, 13.7 l.

TRANSMISSION gearbox: Torqueflite automatic (standard), max ratio of convertor at stall 2.02; axle ratio: 2.450; — station wagons 2.760; tyres: F78 x 14 — station wagons H78 x 14.

PERFORMANCE max speed: about 103 mph, 165 km/h; power-weight ratio: Satellite 4-door Sedan and Satellite Custom 4-door Sedan 12.7 lb/hp, 5.8 kg/hp — Satellite Brougham 4-door Sedan 13.1 lb/hp, 5.9 kg/hp; speed in direct drive at 1,000 rpm: 24 mph, 38.6 km/h; fuel consumption: 15.3 m/imp gal, 12.7 m/US gal, 18.5 l x 100 km.

ELECTRICAL EQUIPMENT battery: 59 Ah.

DIMENSIONS AND WEIGHT (see 230 hp power team) dry weight: plus 155 lb, 70 kg.

300 hp power team

(standard for Road Runner; optional for Satellite Coupé, Satellite, Satellite Custom, Satellite Sebring, Satellite Brougham, Satellite Regent and Satellite Sebring Plus Series; not available for GTX).

See 145 hp power team, except for:

ENGINE cylinders: 8, Vee-slanted at 90°; bore and stroke: 4.25 x 3.38 in, 107.9 x 85.8 mm; engine capacity: 383 cu in, 6,276 cu cm; compression ratio: 8.5; max power (SAE): 300 hp at 4,800 rpm; max torque (SAE): 410 lb ft, 56.6 kg m at 3,400 rpm; max engine rpm: 5,200; specific power: 47.8 hp/l; crankshaft bearings: 5; valves: hydraulic tappets; camshafts: 1, at centre of Vee; carburation: 1 Holley R-4667A downdraught 4-barrel carburettor; cooling system capacity: 24.1 imp pt, 29 US pt, 13.7 l.

TRANSMISSION synchromesh gears: I, II, III; gearbox ratios: I 2.550, II 1.490, III 1, rev 3.340; axle ratio: 3.230; width of rims: 6'' — station wagons 5.5''; tyres: F70 x 14 — station wagons H78 x 14.

PERFORMANCE max speed: about 106 mph, 170 km/h; power-weight ratio: Satellite 4-door Sedan and Satellite Custom 4-door Sedan 11.8 lb/hp, 5.3 kg/hp — Satellite Brougham 4-door Sedan 12.3 lb/hp, 5.6 kg/hp — Road Runner 2-door Hardtop 12.5 lb/hp, 5.7 kg/hp; speed in direct drive at 1,000 rpm: 20.7 mph, 33.3 km/h; fuel consumption: 14.9 m/imp gal, 12.4 m/US gal, 19 l x 100 km.

BRAKES area rubbed by linings: total 380.1 sq in, 2,451 sq cm.

ELECTRICAL EQUIPMENT battery: 59 Ah.

DIMENSIONS AND WEIGHT (see 230 hp power team) dry weight: plus 224 lb, 102 kg — Road Runner 2-door Hardtop 3,750 lb, 1,619 kg.

OPTIONAL ACCESSORIES Torqueflite automatic gearbox with max ratio of convertor at stall 2.16, 3.230 axle ratio (station wagons 2.760); 4-speed fully synchronized mechanical gearbox (I 2.470, II 1.770, III 1.340, IV 1, rev 2.400).

370 hp power team

(standard for GTX; not available for other Series).

See 145 hp power team, except for:

ENGINE cylinders: 8, Vee-slanted at 90°; bore and stroke: 4.32 x 3.75 in, 109.7 x 95.2 mm; engine capacity: 440 cu in, 7,210 cu cm; compression ratio: 9.5; max power (SAE): 370 hp at 4,600 rpm; max torque (SAE): 480 lb ft, 66.2 kg m at 3,200 rpm; max engine rpm: 5,400; specific power: 51.3 hp/l; crankshaft bearings: 5; valves: hydraulic tappets; camshafts: 1, at centre of Vee; lubricating system capacity: 11.6 imp pt, 14 US pt, 6.6 l; carburation: 1 Carter AVS-4967S downdraught 4-barrel carburettor; cooling system capacity: 25.9 imp pt, 31.1 US pt, 14.7 l.

TRANSMISSION gearbox: Torqueflite automatic (standard), max ratio of convertor at stall 2.02; axle ratio: 3.230; width of rims: 6''; tyres: G70 x 14.

PERFORMANCE max speed: about 113 mph, 182 km/h; power-weight ratio: 10.2 lb/hp, 4.6 kg/hp; speed in direct drive at 1,000 rpm: 21.5 mph, 34.6 km/h; fuel consumption: 12.8 m/imp gal, 10.6 m/US gal, 22.1 l x 100 km.

CHASSIS front suspension: anti-roll bar.

PLYMOUTH Satellite Regent 6-passenger Station Wagon

PLYMOUTH Satellite Sebring Plus 2-door Hardtop

PLYMOUTH GTX 2-door Hardtop

BRAKES area rubbed by linings: total 380.1 sq in, 2,45 sq cm.

ELECTRICAL EQUIPMENT battery: 70 Ah.

DIMENSIONS AND WEIGHT rear track: 62 in, 1,575 mm; overall height: 53 in, 1,346 mm; dry weight: 3,785 lb, 1,71 kg.

OPTIONAL ACCESSORIES 4-speed fully synchronized mechanical gearbox (I 2.440, II 1.770, III 1.340, IV 1, rev 2.360) 3.540 axle ratio.

385 hp power team

(optional for Road Runner and GTX; not available for other Series).

See 145 hp power team, except for:

ENGINE cylinders: 8, Vee-slanted at 90°; bore and stroke: 4.32 x 3.75 in, 109.7 x 95.2 mm; engine capacity: 440 cu in, 7,210 cu cm; compression ratio: 10.3; max power (SAE): 385 hp at 4,700 rpm; max torque (SAE): 490 lb ft, 67.6 kg m at 3,200 rpm; max engine rpm: 5,600; specific power: 53.4 hp/l; crankshaft bearings: 5; valves: hydraulic tappets; camshafts: 1, at centre of Vee; lubricating system capacity: 11.6 imp pt, 14 US pt, 7 l; carburation: 3 Holley R-4671A-4672A-4669A downdraught twin barrel carburettor; cooling system capacity: 25.9 imp pt, 31.1 US pt, 14.7 l.

TRANSMISSION gearbox: Torqueflite automatic (standard), max ratio of convertor at stall 2.02; axle ratio: 3.230; width of rims: 6''; tyres: G70 x 14.

PERFORMANCE max speed: about 115 mph, 185 km/h; power-weight ratio: Road Runner 2-door Hardtop 9.7 lb/hp, 4.4 kg/hp — GTX 2-door Hardtop 9.9 lb/hp, 4.5 kg/hp; speed in direct drive at 1,000 rpm: 21.5 mph, 34.6 km/h; fuel consumption: 12.6 m/imp gal, 10.5 m/US gal, 22.5 l x 100 km.

CHASSIS front suspension: anti-roll bar.

BRAKES area rubbed by linings: total 380.1 sq in, 2,451 sq cm.

ELECTRICAL EQUIPMENT battery: 70 Ah.

DIMENSIONS AND WEIGHT (see 230 hp power team) rear track: 62 in, 1,575 mm; overall height: 53 in, 1,346 mm; dry weight: Road Runner 2-door Hardtop 3,750 lb, 1,700 kg — GTX 2-door Hardtop 3,813 lb, 1,729 kg.

OPTIONAL ACCESSORIES 4-speed fully synchronized mechanical gearbox (I 2.440, II 1.770, III 1.340, IV 1, rev 2.360), 3.540 axle ratio.

425 hp power team

(optional for Road Runner and GTX; not available for other Series).

See 145 hp power team, except for:

ENGINE cylinders: 8, Vee-slanted at 90°; bore and stroke: 4.25 x 3.75 in, 107.9 x 95.2 mm; engine capacity: 426 cu in, 6,981 cu cm; compression ratio: 10.2; max power (SAE): 425 hp at 5,000 rpm; max torque (SAE): 490 lb ft, 67.6 kg m at 4,000 rpm; max engine rpm: 5,700; specific power: 60.9 hp/l; crankshaft bearings: 5; valves: hydraulic tappets; camshafts: 1, at centre of Vee; lubricating system capacity: 11.6 imp pt, 14 US pt, 6.6 l; carburation: 2 Carter AFB-4971S-4969S downdraught 4-barrel carburettors; cooling system capacity: 26.6 imp pt, 31.9 US pt, 15.1 l.

TRANSMISSION gearbox: Torqueflite automatic (standard), max ratio of convertor at stall 2.16; axle ratio: 3.230; width of rims: 6''; tyres: G70 x 14.

PERFORMANCE max speed: about 123 mph, 198 km/h; power-weight ratio: Road Runner 2-door Hardtop 8.8 lb/hp, 4 kg/hp — GTX 2-door Hardtop 9.2 lb/hp, 4.2 kg/hp; speed in direct drive at 1,000 rpm: 21.5 mph, 34.6 km/h; fuel consumption: 12.1 m/imp gal, 10.1 m/US gal, 23.3 l x 100 km.

CHASSIS front suspension: anti-roll bar.

BRAKES area rubbed by linings: total 380.1 sq in, 2,451 sq cm.

ELECTRICAL EQUIPMENT battery: 70 Ah.

DIMENSIONS AND WEIGHT (see 230 hp power team) rear track: 62 in, 1,575 mm; overall height: 53 in, 1,346 mm; dry weight: Road Runner 2-door Hardtop 3,750 lb, 1,700 kg — GTX 2-door Hardtop 3,930 lb, 1,782 kg.

OPTIONAL ACCESSORIES 4-speed fully synchronized mechanical gearbox (I 2.440, II 1.770, III 1.340, IV 1, rev 2.360), 3.540 axle ratio.

PLYMOUTH Satellite Regent 6-passenger Station Wagon

PLYMOUTH Satellite Sebring Plus 2-door Hardtop

PLYMOUTH GTX 2-door Hardtop

Fury I - Fury II - Fury III - Sport Fury - Sport Fury GT - Suburban - Custom Suburban - Sport Suburban Series

PRICES IN USA:

Fury I	2-door Sedan	$ 2,781
Fury I	4-door Sedan	$ 2,814
Fury II	2-door Hardtop	$ 2,951
Fury II	4-door Sedan	$ 2,930
Fury III	2-door Hardtop	$ 3,102
Fury III	2-door Hardtop Special	$ 3,245
Fury III	4-door Sedan	$ 3,081
Fury III	4-door Hardtop	$ 3,257
Sport Fury	2-door Hardtop	$ 3,322
Sport Fury	2-door Hardtop Special	$ 3,355
Sport Fury	4-door Sedan	$ 3,301
Sport Fury	4-door Hardtop	$ 3,368
Sport Fury GT	2-door Hardtop	$ 3,975
Suburban	6-passenger Station Wagon	$ 3,399
Suburban	9-passenger Station Wagon	$ 3,510
Custom Suburban	6-passenger Station Wagon	$ 3,522
Custom Suburban	9-passenger Station Wagon	$ 3,598
Sport Suburban	6-passenger Station Wagon	$ 3,709
Sport Suburban	9-passenger Station Wagon	$ 3,784

For V8 engines add $ 110 (Fury III add $ 111).

145 hp power team

(standard for Fury I, Fury II, Fury III 2-door Hardtop and 4-door Sedan; not available for other models).

ENGINE front, 4 stroke; cylinders: 6, in line; bore and stroke: 3.40 x 4.12 in, 86.4 x 104.6 mm; engine capacity: 225 cu in, 3,687 cu cm; compression ratio: 8.4; max power (SAE): 145 hp at 4,000 rpm; max torque (SAE): 215 lb ft, 29.7 kg m at 2,400 rpm; max engine rpm: 4,500; specific power: 39.3 hp/l; cylinder block: cast iron; cylinder head: cast iron; crankshaft bearings: 4; valves: 2 per cylinder, overhead, in line, push-rods and rockers; camshafts: 1, side; lubrication: rotary pump, full flow filter; lubricating system capacity: 6.7 imp pt, 8 US pt, 3.8 l; carburation: 1 Holley R-4655 downdraught single barrel carburettor; fuel feed: mechanical pump; cooling system: water; cooling system capacity: 21.6 imp pt, 26 US pt, 12.3 l.

TRANSMISSION driving wheels: rear; clutch: single dry plate; gearbox: mechanical; gears: 3 + reverse; synchromesh gears: I, II, III; gearbox ratios: I 3.080, II 1.700, III 1, rev 2.900; gear lever: steering column; final drive: hypoid bevel; axle ratio: 3.550; width of rims: 5''; tyres: F78 x 15.

PERFORMANCE max speed: about 91 mph, 146 km/h; power-weight ratio: Fury I 4-door Sedan 26.4 lb/hp, 11.9 kg/hp — Fury II 4-door Sedan and Fury III 4-door Sedan 26.5 lb/hp, 12 kg/hp; speed in direct drive at 1,000 rpm: 20.6 mph, 33.1 km/h; fuel consumption: 18.8 m/imp gal, 15.7 m/US gal, 15 l x 100 km.

CHASSIS integral; front suspension: independent, wishbones, longitudinal torsion bars, telescopic dampers; rear suspension: rigid axle, semi-elliptic leafsprings, telescopic dampers.

STEERING recirculating ball; turns of steering wheel lock to lock: 5.80.

BRAKES drum, dual circuit; area rubbed by linings: total 362.9 sq in, 2,341 sq cm.

ELECTRICAL EQUIPMENT voltage: 12 V; battery: 46 Ah; generator type: alternator, 37 A; ignition distributor: Chrysler; headlamps: 4.

DIMENSIONS AND WEIGHT wheel base: 120 in, 3,048 mm; front track: 62.10 in, 1,577 mm; rear track 62 in, 1,575 mm; overall length: 215.10 in, 5,463 mm; overall width: 79.50 in, 2,019 mm — 4-door sedans 79.60 in, 2,022 mm; overall height: 55 in, 1,397 mm — 2-door hardtops 55.10 in, 1,399 mm; ground clearance: 6.10 in, 155 mm; dry weight: Fury I 2-door Sedan 3,797 lb, 1,722 kg — Fury I 4-door Sedan 3,832 lb, 1,738 kg — Fury II 2-door Hardtop 3,802 lb, 1,724 kg — Fury II 4-door Sedan 3,837 lb, 1,740 kg — Fury III 2-door Hardtop 3,807 lb, 1,726 kg — Fury III 4-door Sedan 3,842 lb, 1,742 kg; turning circle (between walls): 47.6 ft, 14.5 m; fuel tank capacity: 19.1 imp gal, 23 US gal, 87 l.

OPTIONAL ACCESSORIES Torqueflite automatic gearbox with 3 ratios (I 2.450, II 1.450, III 1, rev 2.200), max ratio of convertor at stall 2.16, 3.210 axle ratio; limited slip final drive; power-assisted steering; front disc brakes with servo

230 hp power team

(standard for Fury I, Fury II, Fury III, Sport Fury, Suburban, Custom Suburban and Sport Suburban Series; not available for Sport Fury GT).

See 145 hp power team, except for:

ENGINE cylinders: 8, Vee-slanted at 90°; bore and stroke: 3.91 x 3.31 in, 99.3 x 84 mm; engine capacity: 318 cu in, 5,211 cu cm; compression ratio: 8.6; max power (SAE): 230 hp at 4,400 rpm; max torque (SAE): 320 lb ft, 44.1 kg m

230 HP POWER TEAM

at 2,000 rpm; max engine rpm: 5,000; specific power: 44.1 hp/l; crankshaft bearings: 5; valves: hydraulic tappets; camshafts: 1, at centre of Vee; carburation: 1 Carter BBD-4957S downdraught twin barrel carburettor; cooling system capacity: 26.6 imp pt, 31.9 US pt, 15.1 l.

TRANSMISSION axle ratio: 3.210 — station wagons 3.230; width of rims: station wagons 6.5''; tyres: station wagons J78 x 15.

PERFORMANCE max speed: about 100 mph, 161 km/h; power-weight ratio: Fury I 4-door Sedan 17 lb/hp, 7.7 kg/hp — Fury II 4-door Sedan and Fury III 4-door Sedan 17.1 lb/hp, 7.8 kg/hp — Sport Fury 4-door Sedan 17.4 lb/hp, 7.9 kg/hp; speed in direct drive at 1,000 rpm: 21 mph, 33.8 km/h; fuel consumption: 15.8 m/imp gal, 13.1 m/US gal, 17.9 l x 100 km.

BRAKES area rubbed by linings: station wagons total 362.9 sq in, 2,341 sq cm.

DIMENSIONS AND WEIGHT wheel base: station wagons 122 in, 3,099 mm; rear track: station wagons 63.40 in, 1,610 mm; overall length: station wagons 220.20 in, 5,593 mm; overall height: station wagons 57.10 in, 1,450 mm; dry weight: Fury I 2-door Sedan 3,870 lb, 1,755 kg — Fury I 4-door Sedan 3,930 lb, 1,782 kg — Fury II 2-door Hardtop 3,870 lb, 1,755 kg — Fury II 4-door Sedan 3,935 lb, 1,784 kg — Fury III 2-door Hardtop 3,875 lb, 1,757 kg — Fury III 2-door Hardtop Special 3,870 lb, 1,755 kg — Fury III 4-door Sedan 3,940 lb, 1,787 kg — Fury III 4-door Hardtop 3,940 lb, 1,787 kg — Sport Fury 2-door Hardtop 3,925 lb, 1,780 kg — Sport Fury 2-door Hardtop Special 3,930 lb, 1,782 kg — Sport Fury 4-door Sedan 3,995 lb, 1,812 kg — Sport Fury 4-door Hardtop 3,985 lb, 1,807 kg — Suburban 6-passenger Station Wagon 4,365 lb, 1,980 kg — Suburban 9-passenger Station Wagon 4,410 lb, 2,000 kg — Custom Suburban 6-passenger Station Wagon 4,365 lb, 1,980 kg — Custom Suburban 9-passenger Station Wagon 4,420 lb, 2,004 kg — Sport Suburban 6-passenger Station Wagon 4,410 lb, 2,000 kg — Sport Suburban 9-passenger Station Wagon 4,490 lb, 2,036 kg; turning circle (between walls): station wagons 46.4 ft, 14.1 m.

OPTIONAL ACCESSORIES Torqueflite automatic gearbox with 2.710 axle ratio (station wagons 2.940); air-conditioning system.

255 hp power team

(optional for Fury I, Fury II, Fury III, Sport Fury, Suburban, Custom Suburban and Sport Suburban Series; not available for Sport Fury GT).

See 145 hp power team, except for:

ENGINE cylinders: 8, Vee-slanted at 90°; bore and stroke: 4 x 3.58 in, 101.6 x 90.9 mm; engine capacity: 360 cu in, 5,900 cu cm; compression ratio: 8.7; max power (SAE): 255 hp at 4,400 rpm; max torque (SAE): 360 lb ft, 49.7 kg m at 2,400 rpm; max engine rpm: 5,000; specific power: 43.2 hp/l; crankshaft bearings: 5; valves: hydraulic tappets; camshafts: 1, at centre of Vee; carburation: 1 Holley R-4665A downdraught twin barrel carburettor; cooling system capacity: 25 imp pt, 30 US pt, 14.2 l.

TRANSMISSION gearbox ratios: I 2.550, II 1.490, III 1, rev 3.340; axle ratio: 3.230; width of rims: station wagons 6.5''; tyres: station wagons J78 x 15.

PERFORMANCE max speed: about 101 mph, 162 km/h; power-weight ratio: Fury I 4-door Sedan, Fury II 4-door Sedan and Fury III 4-door Sedan 15.5 lb/hp, 7 kg/hp — Sport Fury 4-door Sedan 15.8 lb/hp, 7.2 kg/hp; speed in direct drive at 1,000 rpm: 21 mph, 33.8 km/h; fuel consumption: 15.4 m/imp gal, 12.9 m/US gal, 18.3 l x 100 km.

BRAKES area rubbed by linings: station wagons total 362.9 sq in, 2,341 sq cm.

ELECTRICAL EQUIPMENT battery: 59 Ah.

DIMENSIONS AND WEIGHT (see 230 hp power team) dry weight: plus 69 lb, 31 kg.

OPTIONAL ACCESSORIES Torqueflite automatic gearbox with 2.710 axle ratio (station wagons 2.760); air-conditioning system.

275 hp power team

(optional for Fury I, Fury II, Fury III, Sport Fury, Suburban, Custom Suburban and Sport Suburban Series; not available for Sport Fury GT).

See 145 hp power team, except for:

ENGINE cylinders: 8, Vee-slanted at 90°; bore and stroke: 4.25 x 3.38 in, 107.9 x 85.8 mm; engine capacity: 383 cu in, 6,276 cu cm; compression ratio: 8.5; max power (SAE): 275 hp at 4,400 rpm; max torque (SAE): 375 lb ft, 51.8 kg m at 2,800 rpm; marx engine rpm: 4,700; specific power: 43.7 hp/l; crankshaft bearings: 5; valves: hydraulic tappets; camshafts: 1, at centre of Vee; carburation: 1 Carter BBD-

PLYMOUTH Sport Fury 2-door Hardtop

PLYMOUTH Sport Fury 4-door Hardtop

PLYMOUTH Custom Suburban 6-passenger Station Wagon

961S downdraught twin barrel carburettor; cooling system capacity: 24.1 imp pt, 29 US pt, 13.7 l.

TRANSMISSION gearbox: mechanical (station wagons only, automatic standard); gearbox ratios: I 2.550, II 1.490, III ·, rev 3.340; axle ratio: 3.230; width of rims: 5.5'' — station wagons 6.5''; tyres: G78 x 15 — station wagons J78 x 15.

PERFORMANCE max speed: about 103 mph, 165 km/h; power-weight ratio: Fury I 4-door Sedan, Fury II 4-door Sedan and Fury III 4-door Sedan 14.8 lb/hp, 6.7 kg/hp — Sport Fury 4-door Sedan 15 lb/hp, 6.8 kg/hp; speed in direct drive at 1,000 rpm: 22 mph, 35.4 km/h; fuel consumption: 15.1 m/imp gal, 12.6 m/US gal, 18.7 l x 100 km.

CHASSIS front suspension: anti-roll bar.

ELECTRICAL EQUIPMENT battery: 59 Ah.

DIMENSIONS AND WEIGHT (see 230 hp power team) dry weight: 4-door sedans plus 163 lb, 74 kg.

OPTIONAL ACCESSORIES Torqueflite automatic gearbox with max ratio of convertor at stall 2.02, 2.760 axle ratio; air-conditioning system.

300 hp power team

(optional for Fury I, Fury II, Fury III, Sport Fury, Suburban, Custom Suburban and Sport Suburban Series; not available for Sport Fury GT).

See 145 hp power team, except for:

ENGINE cylinders: 8, Vee-slanted at 90°; bore and stroke: 4.25 x 3.38 in, 107.9 x 85.8 mm; engine capacity: 383 cu in, 6,276 cu cm; compression ratio: 8.5; max power (SAE): 300 hp at 4,800 rpm; max torque (SAE): 410 lb ft, 56.6 kg m at 3,400 rpm; max engine rpm: 5,200; specific power: 47.8 hp/l; crankshaft bearings: 5; valves: hydraulic tappets; camshafts: 1, at centre of Vee; carburation: 1 Holley R-4668A or Carter AVS-6125S downdraught 4-barrel carburettor; cooling system capacity: 24.1 imp pt, 29 US pt, 13.7 l.

TRANSMISSION gearbox: Torqueflite automatic (standard); axle ratio: 2.760; width of rims: 5.5'' — station wagons 6.5''; tyres: G78 x 15 — station wagons J78 x 15.

PERFORMANCE max speed: about 105 mph, 169 km/h; power-weight ratio: Fury I 4-door Sedan, Fury II 4-door Sedan and Fury III 4-door Sedan 13.7 lb/hp, 6.2 kg/hp — Sport Fury 4-door Sedan 13.9 lb/hp, 6.3 kg/hp; speed in direct drive at 1,000 rpm: 22.2 mph, 35.7 km/h; fuel consumption: 14.8 m/imp gal, 12.3 m/US gal, 19.1 l x 100 km.

CHASSIS front suspension: anti-roll bar.

ELECTRICAL EQUIPMENT battery: 59 Ah.

DIMENSIONS AND WEIGHT (see 230 hp power team) dry weight: 4-door sedans plus 215 lb, 98 kg.

OPTIONAL ACCESSORIES air-conditioning system.

335 hp power team

(standard for Sport Fury GT; optional for other Series).

See 145 hp power team, except for:

ENGINE cylinders: 8, Vee-slanted at 90°; bore and stroke: 4.32 x 3.75 in, 109.7 x 95.2 mm; engine capacity: 440 cu in, 7,210 cu cm; compression ratio: 8.8; max power (SAE): 335 hp at 4,400 rpm; max torque (SAE): 460 lb ft, 63.5 kg m at 3,200 rpm; max engine rpm: 5,000; specific power: 46.5 hp/l; crankshaft bearings: 5; valves: hydraulic tappets; camshafts: 1, at centre of Vee; carburation: 1 Carter AVS-6126S downdraught 4-barrel carburettor; cooling system capacity: 25.9 imp pt, 31.1 US pt, 14.7 l.

TRANSMISSION gearbox: Torqueflite automatic (standard), max ratio of convertor at stall 2.02; axle ratio: 2.760; width of rims: 6'' — station wagons 6.5''; tyres: H70 x 15 — station wagons J78 x 15.

PERFORMANCE max speed: about 108 mph, 174 km/h; power-weight ratio: Fury I 4-door Sedan, Fury II 4-door Sedan and Fury III 4-door Sedan 12.4 lb/hp, 5.6 kg/hp — Sport Fury GT 2-door Hardtop 11.7 lb/hp, 5.3 kg/hp — Sport Fury 4-door Sedan 12.6 lb/hp, 5.7 kg/hp; speed in direct drive at 1,000 rpm: 23 mph, 37 km/h; fuel consumption: 14.3 m/imp gal, 11.9 m/US gal, 19.7 l x 100 km.

CHASSIS front suspension: anti-roll bar.

BRAKES area rubbed by linings: total 393.6 sq in, 2,539 sq cm.

ELECTRICAL EQUIPMENT battery: 70 Ah.

DIMENSIONS AND WEIGHT (see 230 hp power team) overall height: Sport Fury GT 56.10 in, 1,425 mm; dry weight: 4-door sedans plus 261 lb, 118 kg — Sport Fury GT 2-door Hardtop 3,925 lb, 1,780 kg.

OPTIONAL ACCESSORIES air-conditioning system.

PLYMOUTH Sport Fury 2-door Hardtop

PLYMOUTH Sport Fury 4-door Hardtop

PLYMOUTH 440 cu in engine

385 hp power team

(optional for Sport Fury GT; not available for other Series).

See 145 hp power team, except for:

ENGINE cylinders: 8, Vee-slanted at 90°; bore and stroke: 4.32 x 3.75 in, 109.7 x 95.2 mm; engine capacity: 440 cu in, 7,210 cu cm; compression ratio: 9.5; max power (SAE): 385 hp at 4,700 rpm; max torque (SAE): 490 lb ft, 67.6 kg m at 3,200 rpm; max engine rpm: 5,500; specific power: 53.4 hp/l; crankshaft bearings: 5; valves: hydraulic tappets; camshafts: 1, at centre of Vee; lubricating system capacity: 10 imp pt, 12 US pt, 5.7 l; carburation: 3 Holley R-4671A-4672A-4670A downdraught twin barrel carburettors; cooling system capacity: 25.9 imp pt, 31.1 US pt, 14.7 l.

TRANSMISSION gearbox: Torqueflite automatic (standard), max ratio of convertor at stall 2.02; axle ratio: 2.760; width of rims: 6''; tyres: H70 x 15.

PERFORMANCE max speed: about 113 mph, 182 km/h; power-weight ratio: 10.2 lb/hp, 4.6 kg/hp; speed in direct drive at 1,000 rpm: 23 mph, 37 km/h; fuel consumption: 12.4 m/imp gal, 10.4 m/US gal, 22.7 l x 100 km.

CHASSIS front suspension: anti-roll bar.

BRAKES area rubbed by linings: total 380.1 sq in, 2,451 sq cm.

ELECTRICAL EQUIPMENT battery: 70 Ah.

DIMENSIONS AND WEIGHT overall height: 55.10 in, 1,399 mm; dry weight: 3,925 lb, 1,780 kg.

OPTIONAL ACCESSORIES air-conditioning system.

PONTIAC   USA

T-37 - Le Mans - Le Mans Sport - GTO Series

PRICES IN USA:

T-37	4-door Sedan	$ 2,795
T-37	Coupé	$ 2,747
T-37	Hardtop Coupé	$ 2,807
Le Mans	4-door Sedan	$ 2,925
Le Mans	4-door Hardtop	$ 3,064
Le Mans	Coupé	$ 2,877
Le Mans	Hardtop Coupé	$ 2,938
Le Mans	6-passenger Station Wagon	$ 3,353
Le Mans	9-passenger Station Wagon	$ 3,465
Le Mans Sport	4-door Hardtop	$ 3,255
Le Mans Sport	Hardtop Coupé	$ 3,125
Le Mans Sport	Convertible	$ 3,333
GTO	Hardtop Coupé	$ 3,446
GTO	Convertible	$ 3,676

For V8 engines add $ 121.

145 hp power team

(standard for T-37, Le Mans and Le Mans Sport Series; not available for GTO Series).

ENGINE front, 4 stroke; cylinders: 6, in line; bore and stroke: 3.87 x 3.52 in, 98.2 x 89.3 mm; engine capacity: 250 cu in, 4,097 cu cm; compression ratio: 8.5; max power (SAE): 145 hp at 4,200 rpm; max torque (SAE): 230 lb ft, 31.8 kg m at 1,600 rpm; max engine rpm: 4,400; specific power: 35.4 hp/l; cylinder block: cast iron; cylinder head: cast iron; crankshaft bearings: 7; valves: 2 per cylinder, overhead, in line, push-rods and rockers, hydraulic tappets; camshafts: 1, side; lubrication: gear pump, full flow filter; lubricating system capacity: 8.3 imp pt, 9.9 US pt, 4.7 l; carburation: 1 Rochester 7041017 downdraught single barrel carburettor; fuel feed: mechanical pump; cooling system: water; cooling system capacity: 21.6 imp pt, 26 US pt, 12.3 l.

TRANSMISSION driving wheels: rear; clutch: single dry plate; gearbox: mechanical; gears: 3 + reverse; synchromesh gears: I, II, III; gearbox ratios: I 2.850, II 1.680, III 1, rev 2.950; gear lever: steering column; final drive: hypoid bevel; axle ratio: 3.230; width of rims: T-37 5'' — Le Mans and Le Mans Sport 6''; tyres: E78 x 14 — Le Mans and Le Mans Sport F78 x 14 — Le Mans 9-passenger Station Wagon H78 x 14.

PERFORMANCE max speed: about 100 mph, 161 km/h; power-weight ratio: T-37 4-door Sedan and Le Mans 4-door Sedan 23.4 lb/hp, 10.6 kg/hp — Le Mans Sport 4-door Hardtop 24.3 lb/hp, 11 kg/hp; speed in direct drive at 1,000 rpm: 23 mph, 37 km/h; fuel consumption: 19.9 m/imp gal, 16.6 m/US gal, 14.2 l x 100 km.

CHASSIS perimeter (for convertible box-type); front suspension: independent, wishbones, coil springs, anti-roll bar, telescopic dampers; rear suspension: rigid axle, lower

145 HP POWER TEAM

trailing radius arms, upper oblique torque arms, coil springs, telescopic dampers.

STEERING recirculating ball; turns of steering wheel lock to lock: 5.60.

BRAKES drum (Le Mans Sport front disc, rear drum), dual circuit; area rubbed by linings: total 269.2 sq in, 1,739 sq cm (Le Mans Sport 350.9 sq in, 2,263 sq cm).

ELECTRICAL EQUIPMENT voltage: 12 V; battery: T-37 45 Ah — Le Mans 53 Ah — Le Mans Sport 61 Ah; generator type: alternator, 37 A; ignition distributor: Delco-Remy; headlamps: 4.

DIMENSIONS AND WEIGHT wheel base: 116 in, 2,946 mm — coupés, hardtop coupés and convertible 112 in, 2,845 mm; front track: 61 in, 1,549 mm; rear track: 60 in, 1,524 mm; overall length: 206.80 in, 5,253 mm — coupés, hardtop coupés and convertible 202.80 in, 5,151 mm — station wagons 210.90 in, 5,357 mm; overall width: 76.70 in, 1,948 mm; overall height: coupés and hardtop coupés 52 in, 1,321 mm — 4-door sedans and 4-door hardtops 52.60 in, 1,336 mm — convertible 52.30 in, 1,328 mm — station wagons 54.50 in, 1,384 mm; ground clearance: T-37 5.30 in, 135 mm — Le Mans and Le Mans Sport 4.30 in, 109 mm; dry weight: T-37 4-door Sedan 3,394 lb, 1,539 kg — T-37 Coupé 3,317 lb, 1,504 kg — T-37 Hardtop Coupé 3,324 lb, 1,507 kg — Le Mans 4-door Sedan 3,393 lb, 1,539 kg — Le Mans 4-door Hardtop 3,481 lb, 1,579 kg — Le Mans Coupé 3,320 lb, 1,505 kg — Le Mans Hardtop Coupé 3,327 lb, 1,509 kg — Le Mans 6-passenger Station Wagon 3,887 lb, 1,763 kg — Le Mans 9-passenger Station Wagon 3,949 lb, 1,791 kg — Le Mans Sport 4-door Hardtop 3,523 lb, 1,598 kg — Le Mans Sport Hardtop Coupé 3,360 lb, 1,524 kg — Le Mans Sport Convertible 3,428 lb, 1,554 kg; turning circle (between walls): 40.5 ft, 12.3 m — Le Mans Sport 41.7 ft, 12.7 m; fuel tank capacity: 16.7 imp gal, 20 US gal, 76 l (station wagons 19.1 imp gal, 23 US gal, 87 l).

OPTIONAL ACCESSORIES "Automatic" gearbox with 2 ratios (I 1.760, II 1, rev 1.760), max ratio of convertor at stall 2.2 3.080 axle ratio; Turbo Hydramatic automatic gearbox with 3 ratios (I 2.520, II 1.520, III 1, rev 1.920), max ratio of convertor at stall 2.2, 3.080 axle ratio; limited slip final drive; power-assisted steering; front disc brakes with servo; air-conditioning system.

250 hp power team

(optional for T-37, Le Mans and Le Mans Sport Series; not available for GTO Series).

See 145 hp power team, except for:

ENGINE cylinders: 8, Vee-slanted at 90°; bore and stroke: 3.87 x 3.75 in, 98.2 x 89.3 mm; engine capacity: 350 cu in, 5,736 cu cm; compression ratio: 8; max power (SAE): 250 hp at 4,400 rpm; max torque (SAE): 350 lb ft, 48.3 kg m at 2,400 rpm; max engine rpm: 4,600; specific power: 43.6 hp/l; crankshaft bearings: 5; camshafts: 1, at centre of Vee; lubricating system capacity: 10 imp pt, 12 US pt, 5.7 l; carburation: 1 Rochester 7041171 downdraught twin barrel carburettor; cooling system capacity: 33.6 imp pt, 40.4 US pt, 19.1 l.

TRANSMISSION gearbox ratios: I 2.540, II 1.500, III 1, rev 2.630.

PERFORMANCE max speed: about 106 mph, 170 km/h; power-weight ratio: T-37 4-door Sedan and Le Mans 4-door Sedan 14.6 lb/hp, 6.6 kg/hp — Le Mans Sport 4-door Hardtop 15.1 lb/hp, 6.8 kg/hp; speed in direct drive at 1,000 rpm: 25.1 mph, 40.4 km/h; fuel consumption: 17.2 m/imp gal, 14.3 m/US gal, 16.4 l x 100 km.

ELECTRICAL EQUIPMENT battery: 53 Ah.

DIMENSIONS AND WEIGHT dry weight: plus 256 lb, 116 kg.

OPTIONAL ACCESSORIES "Automatic" gearbox with 2.780 axle ratio (station wagons 3.080); Turbo Hydramatic automatic gearbox with 2.560 axle ratio (station wagons 2.780).

265 hp power team

(optional for T-37, Le Mans and Le Mans Sport Series; not available for GTO Series).

See 145 hp power team, except for:

ENGINE cylinders: 8, Vee-slanted at 90°; bore and stroke: 4.12 x 3.75 in, 104.6 x 95.2 mm; engine capacity: 400 cu in, 6,555 cu cm; compression ratio: 8.2; max power (SAE): 265 hp at 4,400 rpm; max torque (SAE): 400 lb ft, 55.2 kg m at 2,400 rpm; max engine rpm: 4,800; specific power: 40.4 hp/l; crankshaft bearings: 5; camshafts: 1, at centre of Vee; lubricating system capacity: 10 imp pt, 12 US pt, 5.7 l; carburation: 1 Rochester 7041060 downdraught twin barrel carburettor; cooling system capacity: 31 imp pt, 37.2 US pt, 17.6 l.

TRANSMISSION gearbox: Turbo Hydramatic automatic (standard), max ratio of convertor at stall 2; gearbox ratios:

PONTIAC Le Mans Sport Hardtop Coupé

PONTIAC GTO Convertible

PONTIAC Firebird Formula 400 Hardtop Coupé

I 2.480, II 1.480, III 1, rev 2.080; selector lever: steering column; axle ratio: 2.780.

PERFORMANCE max speed: about 107 mph, 172 km/h; power-weight ratio: T-37 4-door Sedan and Le Mans 4-door Sedan 14 lb/hp, 6.3 kg/hp — Le Mans Sport 4-door Hardtop 14.4 lb/hp, 6.5 kg/hp; speed in direct drive at 1,000 rpm: 23.7 mph, 38.1 km/h; fuel consumption: 17.1 m/imp gal, 14.3 m/US gal, 16.5 l x 100 km.

ELECTRICAL EQUIPMENT battery: 61 Ah.

DIMENSIONS AND WEIGHT dry weight: plus 308 lb, 140 kg.

OPTIONAL ACCESSORIES dual exhaust system; "Automatic" gearbox not available.

300 hp power team

(standard for GTO Series; optional for other Series).

See 145 hp power team, except for:

ENGINE cylinders: 8, Vee-slanted at 90°; bore and stroke: 4.12 x 3.75 in, 104.6 x 95.2 mm; engine capacity: 400 cu in, 6,555 cu cm; compression ratio: 8.2; max power (SAE): 300 hp at 4,800 rpm; max torque (SAE): 400 lb ft, 55.2 kg m at 2,400 rpm (at 3,600 rpm for T-37, Le Mans and Le Mans Sport); max engine rpm: 5,000; specific power: 45.8 hp/l; crankshaft bearings: 5; camshafts: 1, at centre of Vee; lubricating system capacity: 10 imp pt, 12 US pt, 5.7 l; carburation: 1 Rochester 7041263 downdraught 4-barrel carburettor; cooling system capacity: 31 imp pt, 37.2 US pt, 17.6 l.

TRANSMISSION gearbox ratios: I 2.420, II 1.580, III 1, rev 2.410; gear lever: central; axle ratio: 3.550; width of rims: GTO, Le Mans and Le Mans Sport 6''; tyres: GTO G70 x 14.

PERFORMANCE max speed: about 108 mph, 174 km/h; power-weight ratio: GTO Hardtop Coupé 12 lb/hp, 5.4 kg/hp — GTO Convertible 12.1 lb/hp, 5.5 kg/hp; speed in direct drive at 1,000 rpm: 22 mph, 35.4 km/h; fuel consumption: 15.1 m/imp gal, 12.6 m/US gal, 18.7 l x 100 km.

CHASSIS (for GTO only) rear suspension: anti-roll bar.

BRAKES (for GTO and Le Mans Sport) front disc, rear drum, dual circuit (servo standard for GTO only); area rubbed by linings: total 350.9 sq in, 2,263 sq cm.

ELECTRICAL EQUIPMENT battery: GTO 62 Ah.

DIMENSIONS AND WEIGHT overall length: 203.30 in, 5,164 mm; dry weight: plus 280 lb, 127 kg — GTO Hardtop Coupé 3,593 lb, 1,629 kg — GTO Convertible 3,642 lb, 1,652 kg.

OPTIONAL ACCESSORIES "Automatic" gearbox not available; 4-speed fully synchronized mechanical gearbox (not available for station wagons) (I 2.520, II 1.880, III 1.460, IV 1, rev 2.590), 3.900 axle ratio; Turbo Hydramatic automatic gearbox with 3 ratios (I 2.480, II 1.480, III 1, rev 2.080), max ratio of convertor at stall 2.3, 3.550 axle ratio.

325 hp power team

(optional for all Series).

See 145 hp power team, except for:

ENGINE cylinders: 8, Vee-slanted at 90°; bore and stroke: 4.15 x 4.21 in, 105.3 x 106.9 mm; engine capacity: 455 cu in, 7,456 cu cm; compression ratio: 8.2; max power (SAE): 325 hp at 4,400 rpm; max torque (SAE): 455 lb ft, 62.8 kg m at 3,200 rpm; max engine rpm: 5,000; specific power: 43.6 hp/l; crankshaft bearings: 5; camshafts: 1, at centre of Vee; lubricating system capacity: 10 imp pt, 12 US pt, 5.7 l; carburation: 1 Rochester 7041262 downdraught 4-barrel carburettor; cooling system capacity: 29.7 imp pt, 35.7 US pt, 16.9 l.

TRANSMISSION gearbox: Turbo Hydramatic automatic (standard), max ratio of convertor at stall 2.3; gearbox ratios: I 2.480, II 1.480, III 1, rev 2.080; selector lever: steering column; axle ratio: 3.070; width of rims: GTO, Le Mans and Le Mans Sport 6''; tyres: GTO G70 x 14.

PERFORMANCE max speed: about 109 mph, 175 km/h; power-weight ratio: T-37 4-door Sedan and Le Mans 4-door Sedan 11.4 lb/hp, 5.2 kg/hp — Le Mans Sport 4-door Hardtop 11.8 lb/hp, 5.3 kg/hp — GTO Hardtop Coupé 11.1 lb/hp, 5 kg/hp; speed in direct drive at 1,000 rpm: 22.3 mph, 35.9 km/h; fuel consumption: 14.8 m/imp gal, 12.3 m/US gal, 19.1 l x 100 km.

CHASSIS (for GTO only) rear suspension: anti-roll bar.

BRAKES (for GTO and Le Mans Sport) front disc, rear drum, dual circuit (servo standard for GTO only); area rubbed by linings: total 350.9 sq in, 2,263 sq cm.

ELECTRICAL EQUIPMENT battery: GTO 62 Ah.

DIMENSIONS AND WEIGHT overall length: 203.30 in, 5,164 mm; dry weight: plus 325 lb, 147 kg — GTO Hardtop Coupé 3,607 lb, 1,636 kg — GTO Convertible 3,656 lb, 1,658 kg.

OPTIONAL ACCESSORIES "Automatic" gearbox not available.

PONTIAC Le Mans Sport Hardtop Coupé

PONTIAC GTO Convertible

PONTIAC Firebird Formula 400 Hardtop Coupé

335 hp power team

(optional for all Series).

See 145 hp power team, except for:

ENGINE cylinders: 8, Vee-slanted at 90°; bore and stroke: 4.15 x 4.21 in, 105.3 x 106.9 mm; engine capacity: 455 cu in, 7,456 cu cm; compression ratio: 8.4; max power (SAE): 335 hp at 4,800 rpm; max torque (SAE): 480 lb ft, 66.2 kg m at 3,600 rpm; max engine rpm: 5,000; specific power: 44.9 hp/l; crankshaft bearings: 5; camshafts: 1, at centre of Vee; lubricating system capacity: 13.6 imp pt, 12 US pt, 5.7 l; carburation: 1 Rochester 7041267 downdraught 4-barrel carburettor; cooling system capacity: 29.7 imp pt, 35.7 US pt, 16.9 l.

TRANSMISSION gearbox ratios: I 2.420, II 1.580, III 1, rev 2.410; gear lever: central; axle ratio: 3.310; width of rims: GTO, Le Mans and Le Mans Sport 6''; tyres: GTO G70 x 14.

PERFORMANCE max speed: about 111 mph, 178 km/h; power-weight ratio: T-37 4-door Sedan and Le Mans 4-door Sedan 11.1 lb/hp, 5 kg/hp — Le Mans Sport 4-door Hardtop 11.5 lb/hp, 5.2 kg/hp — GTO Hardtop Coupé 10.8 lb/hp, 4.9 kg/hp; speed in direct drive at 1,000 rpm: 22.5 mph, 36.2 km/h; fuel consumption: 14.4 m/imp gal, 12 m/US gal, 19.6 l x 100 km.

CHASSIS (for GTO only) rear suspension: anti-roll bar.

BRAKES (for GTO and Le Mans Sport) front disc, rear drum, dual circuit (servo standard for GTO only); area rubbed by linings: total 350.9 sq in, 2,263 sq cm.

ELECTRICAL EQUIPMENT battery: 62 Ah.

DIMENSIONS AND WEIGHT overall length: 203.30 in, 5,164 mm; ground clearance: 4.70 in, 119 mm; dry weight: plus 320 lb, 145 kg — GTO Hardtop Coupé 3,606 lb, 1,635 kg — GTO Convertible 3,655 lb, 1,657 kg.

OPTIONAL ACCESSORIES "Automatic" gearbox not available; 4-speed fully synchronized mechanical gearbox (not available for station wagons) (I 2.200, II 1.640, III 1.280, IV 1, rev 2.270), 3.550 axle ratio; Turbo Hydramatic automatic gearbox with 3 ratios (I 2.480, II 1.480, III 1, rev 2.080), max ratio of convertor at stall 2.3, 3.310 axle ratio.

Firebird Series

PRICES IN USA:

Firebird	Hardtop Coupé	$ 3,042
Firebird Esprit	Hardtop Coupé	$ 3,411
Firebird Formula 400	Hardtop Coupé	$ 3,440
Firebird Trans Am	Hardtop Coupé	$ 4,590

For V8 engines add $ 121.

145 hp power team

(standard for Firebird; not available for other models).

ENGINE front, 4 stroke; cylinders: 6, in line; bore and stroke: 3.87 x 3.52 in, 98.2 x 89.3 mm; engine capacity: 250 cu in, 4,097 cu cm; compression ratio: 8.5; max power (SAE): 145 hp at 4,200 rpm; max torque (SAE): 230 lb ft, 31.8 kg m at 1,600 rpm; max engine rpm: 4,400; specific power: 35.4 hp/l; cylinder block: cast iron; cylinder head: cast iron; crankshaft bearings: 7; valves: 2 per cylinder, overhead, in line, push-rods and rockers, hydraulic tappets; camshafts: 1, side; lubrication: gear pump, full flow filter; lubricating system capacity: 8.3 imp pt, 9.9 US pt, 4.7 l; carburation: 1 Rochester 7041017 downdraught single barrel carburettor; fuel feed: mechanical pump; cooling system: water; cooling system capacity: 20.1 imp pt, 24.1 US pt, 11.4 l.

TRANSMISSION driving wheels: rear; clutch: single dry plate; gearbox: mechanical; gears: 3 + reverse; synchromesh gears: I, II, III; gearbox ratios: I 2.850, II 1.680, III 1, rev 2.950; gear lever: steering column; final drive: hypoid bevel; axle ratio: 3.080; width of rims: 6''; tyres: E78 x 14.

PERFORMANCE max speed: about 101 mph, 162 km/h; power-weight ratio: 22.3 lb/hp, 10.1 kg/hp; speed in direct drive at 1,000 rpm: 22.9 mph, 36.8 km/h; fuel consumption: 19.8 m/imp gal, 16.4 m/US gal, 14.3 l x 100 km.

CHASSIS integral with front ladder frame section; front suspension: independent, wishbones, coil springs, anti-roll bar, telescopic dampers; rear suspension: rigid axle, semi-elliptic leafsprings, anti-roll bar, telescopic dampers.

STEERING recirculating ball; turns of steering wheel lock to lock: 4.60.

BRAKES front disc, rear drum, dual circuit; area rubbed by linings: total 350.9 sq in, 2,263 sq cm.

ELECTRICAL EQUIPMENT voltage: 12 V; battery: 45 Ah; generator type: alternator, 37 A; ignition distributor: Delco-Remy; headlamps: 2.

DIMENSIONS AND WEIGHT wheel base: 108 in, 2,743 mm; front track: 61.30 in, 1,557 mm; rear track: 60 in, 1,524 mm; overall length: 191.60 in, 4,867 mm; overall width: 73.40 in, 1,864 mm; overall height: 50.40 in, 1,280 mm; ground clearance: 4.60 in, 117 mm; dry weight: 3,240 lb, 1,469 kg; turning circle (between walls): 39.8 ft, 12.1 m; fuel tank capacity: 14.1 imp gal, 17 US gal, 64 l.

OPTIONAL ACCESSORIES "Automatic" gearbox with 2 ratios (I 1.760, II 1, rev 1.760), max ratio of convertor at stall 2.20, 3.080 axle ratio; Turbo Hydramatic automatic gearbox with 3 ratios (I 2.520, II 1.520, III 1, rev 1.920), max ratio of convertor at stall 2.2, 3.080 axle ratio; limited slip final drive; power-assisted steering; servo brake.

250 hp power team

(standard for Firebird Esprit and Firebird Formula 400; optional for Firebird; not available for Firebird Trans Am).

See 145 hp power team, except for:

ENGINE cylinders: 8, Vee-slanted at 90°; bore and stroke: 3.87 x 3.75 in, 98.2 x 89.3 mm; engine capacity: 350 cu in, 5,736 cu cm; compression ratio: 8; max power (SAE): 250 hp at 4,400 rpm; max torque (SAE): 350 lb ft, 48.3 kg m at 2,400 rpm; max engine rpm: 4,600; specific power: 43.6 hp/l; crankshaft bearings: 5; camshafts: 1, at centre of Vee; lubricating system capacity: 10 imp pt, 12 US pt, 5.7 l; carburation: 1 Rochester 7041171 downdraught twin barrel carburettor; cooling system capacity: 32.4 imp pt, 38.9 US pt, 18.4 l.

TRANSMISSION gearbox ratios: I 2.540, II 1.500, III 1, rev 2.630; gear lever: central; axle ratio: 3.420; width of rims: 6'' — Firebird Formula 400 7''; tyres: E78 x 14 — Firebird Formula 400 F70 x 14.

PERFORMANCE max speed: about 110 mph, 177 km/h; power-weight ratio: Firebird 14.1 lb/hp, 6.4 kg/hp — Firebird Esprit 13.9 lb/hp, 6.3 kg/hp — Firebird Formula 400 14.8 lb/hp, 6.7 kg/hp; speed in direct drive at 1,000 rpm: 24 mph, 38.6 km/h; fuel consumption: 17.2 m/imp gal, 14.3 m/US gal, 16.4 l x 100 km.

STEERING turns of steering wheel lock to lock: 5.40.

ELECTRICAL EQUIPMENT battery: 53 Ah.

DIMENSIONS AND WEIGHT front track: 61.60 in, 1,565 mm; rear track: 60.30 in, 1,532 mm; dry weight: plus 277 lb, 126 kg — Firebird Esprit Hardtop Coupé 3,495 lb, 1,585 kg — Firebird Formula 400 Hardtop Coupé 3,595 lb, 1,630 kg.

OPTIONAL ACCESSORIES "Automatic" gearbox with 2.730 axle ratio; Turbo Hydramatic automatic gearbox with 2.730 axle ratio; 3-speed fully synchronized mechanical gearbox (I 2.420, II 1.580, III 1, rev 2.410), 3.420 axle ratio; air-conditioning system.

265 hp power team

(optional for Firebird Esprit; not available for other models).

See 145 hp power team, except for:

ENGINE cylinders: 8, Vee-slanted at 90°; bore and stroke: 4.12 x 3.75 in, 104.6 x 95.2 mm; engine capacity: 400 cu in, 6,555 cu cm; compression ratio: 8.2; max power (SAE): 265 hp at 4,400 rpm; max torque (SAE): 400 lb ft, 55.2 kg m at 2,400 rpm; max engine rpm: 4,800; specific power: 40.4 hp/l; crankshaft bearings: 5; camshafts: 1, at centre of Vee; lubricating system capacity: 10 imp pt, 12 US pt, 5.7 l; carburation: 1 Rochester 7041060 downdraught twin barrel carburettor; cooling system capacity: 31 imp pt, 37.2 US pt, 17.6 l.

TRANSMISSION gearbox: Turbo Hydramatic automatic (standard), max ratio of convertor at stall 2.04; gearbox ratios: I 2.480, II 1.480, III 1, rev 2.080; selector lever: steering column; axle ratio: 2.730.

PERFORMANCE max speed: about 112 mph, 180 km/h; power-weight ratio: 13.3 lb/hp, 6 kg/hp; speed in direct drive at 1,000 rpm: 23.8 mph, 38.3 km/h; fuel consumption: 17 m/imp gal, 14.2 m/US gal, 16.6 l x 100 km.

STEERING turns of steering wheel lock to lock: 5.40.

ELECTRICAL EQUIPMENT battery: 61 Ah.

DIMENSIONS AND WEIGHT front track: 61.60 in, 1,565 mm; rear track: 60.30 in, 1,532 mm; dry weight: 3,540 lb, 1,605 kg.

OPTIONAL ACCESSORIES "Automatic" gearbox not available; air-conditioning system.

PONTIAC Catalina Hardtop Coupé

PONTIAC Catalina Convertible

PONTIAC Safari 9-passenger Station Wagon

300 hp power team

(standard for Firebird Formula 400; not available for other models).

See 145 hp power team, except for:

ENGINE cylinders: 8, Vee-slanted at 90°; bore and stroke: 4.12 x 3.75 in, 104.6 x 95.2 mm; engine capacity: 400 cu in, 6,555 cu cm; compression ratio: 8.2; max power (SAE): 300 hp at 4,800 rpm; max torque (SAE): 400 lb ft, 55.2 kg m at 3,600 rpm; max engine rpm: 5,000; specific power: 45.8 hp/l; crankshaft bearings: 5; camshafts: 1, at centre of Vee; lubricating system capacity: 10 imp pt, 12 US pt, 5.7 l; carburation: 1 Rochester 7041263 downdraught 4-barrel carburettor; cooling system capacity: 31 imp pt, 37.2 US pt, 17.6 l.

TRANSMISSION gearbox ratios: I 2.420, II 1.580, III 1, rev 2.410; gear lever: central; axle ratio: 3.420; width of rims: 7''; tyres: F70 x 14.

PERFORMANCE max speed: about 115 mph, 185 km/h; power-weight ratio: 12 lb/hp, 5.4 kg/hp; speed in direct drive at 1,000 rpm: 23 mph, 37 km/h; fuel consumption: 15.1 m/imp gal, 12.6 m/US gal, 18.7 l x 100 km.

STEERING turns of steering wheel lock to lock: 5.40.

ELECTRICAL EQUIPMENT battery: 61 Ah.

DIMENSIONS AND WEIGHT front track: 61.60 in, 1,565 mm; rear track: 60.30 in, 1,532 mm; dry weight: 3,595 lb, 1,630 kg.

OPTIONAL ACCESSORIES "Automatic" gearbox not available; 4-speed fully synchronized mechanical gearbox (I 2.520, II 1.880, III 1.460, IV 1, rev 2.590), 3.730 axle ratio; Turbo Hydramatic automatic gearbox with 3 ratios (I 2.480, II 1.480, III 1, rev 2.080), max ratio of convertor at stall 2.3, 3.080 axle ratio; air-conditioning system.

325 hp power team

(standard for Firebird Formula 400; not available for other models).

See 145 hp power team, except for:

ENGINE cylinders: 8, Vee-slanted at 90°; bore and stroke: 4.15 x 4.21 in, 105.3 x 106.9 mm; engine capacity: 455 cu in, 7,456 cu cm; compression ratio: 8.2; max power (SAE): 325 hp at 4,400 rpm; max torque (SAE): 455 lb ft, 62.8 kg m at 3,200 rpm; max engine rpm: 5,000; specific power: 43.6 hp/l; crankshaft bearings: 5; camshafts: 1, at centre of Vee; lubricating system capacity: 10 imp pt, 12 US pt, 5.7 l; carburation: 1 Rochester 7041262 downdraught 4-barrel carburettor; cooling system capacity: 29.7 imp pt, 35.7 US pt, 16.9 l.

TRANSMISSION gearbox: Turbo Hydramatic automatic (standard), max ratio of convertor at stall 2.3; gearbox ratios: I 2.480, II 1.480, III 1, rev 2.080; selector lever: steering column; width of rims: 7''; tyres: F70 x 14.

PERFORMANCE max speed: about 120 mph, 193 km/h; power-weight ratio: 11.2 lb/hp, 5.1 kg/hp; speed in direct drive at 1,000 rpm: 24.2 mph, 39 km/h; fuel consumption: 14.6 m/imp gal, 12.2 m/US gal, 19.3 l x 100 km.

STEERING turns of steering wheel lock to lock: 5.40.

ELECTRICAL EQUIPMENT battery: 62 Ah.

DIMENSIONS AND WEIGHT front track: 61.60 in, 1,565 mm; rear track: 60.30 in, 1,532 mm; dry weight: 3,628 lb, 1,645 kg.

OPTIONAL ACCESSORIES "Automatic" gearbox not available; air-conditioning system.

335 hp power team

(standard for Firebird Trans Am; optional for Firebird Formula 400; not available for other models).

See 145 hp power team, except for:

ENGINE cylinders: 8, Vee-slanted at 90°; bore and stroke: 4.15 x 4.21 in, 105.3 x 106.9 mm; engine capacity: 455 cu in, 7,456 cu cm; compression ratio: 8.4; max power (SAE): 335 hp at 4,800 rpm; max torque (SAE): 480 lb ft, 66.2 kg m at 3,600 rpm; max engine rpm: 5,000; specific power: 44.9 hp/l; crankshaft bearings: 5; camshafts: 1, at centre of Vee; lubricating system capacity: 10 imp pt, 12 US pt, 5.7 l; carburation: 1 Rochester 7041267 downdraught 4-barrel carburettor; cooling system capacity: 29.7 imp pt, 35.7 US pt, 16.9 l.

TRANSMISSION gearbox ratios: I 2.420, II 1.580, III 1, rev 2.410; gear lever: central; axle ratio: 3.420; width of rims: 7''; tyres: F60 x 15 — Firebird Formula 400 F70 x 14.

PONTIAC Catalina Hardtop Coupé

PONTIAC Catalina Convertible

PONTIAC Safari 9-passenger Station Wagon

PERFORMANCE max speed: about 122 mph, 196 km/h; power-weight ratio: Firebird Trans Am 11 lb/hp, 5 kg/hp; speed in direct drive at 1,000 rpm: 24.5 mph, 39.4 km/h; fuel consumption: 14.3 m/imp gal, 11.9 m/US gal, 19.8 l x 100 km.

STEERING turns of steering wheel lock to lock: 5.40.

ELECTRICAL EQUIPMENT battery: 62 Ah.

DIMENSIONS AND WEIGHT front track: 61.70 in, 1,567 mm; rear track: 60.40 in, 1,534 mm; dry weight: Firebird Trans Am Hardtop Coupé 3,695 lb, 1,676 kg — Firebird Formula 400 Hardtop Coupé 3,608 lb, 1,636 kg.

OPTIONAL ACCESSORIES "Automatic" gearbox not available; Turbo Hydramatic automatic gearbox with 3 ratios (I 2.480, II 1.480, III 1, rev 2.080), max ratio of convertor at stall 2.3, 3.080 axle ratio; 4-speed fully synchronized mechanical gearbox (I 2.520, II 1.880, III 1.460, IV 1, rev 2.590), 3.420 axle ratio; air-conditioning system.

Catalina - Safari - Catalina Brougham - Bonneville - Grand Safari - Grand Ville Series

PRICES IN USA:

Catalina	4-door Sedan	$ 3,421
Catalina	4-door Hardtop	$ 3,590
Catalina	Hardtop Coupé	$ 3,521
Catalina	Convertible	$ 3,807
Safari	6-passenger Station Wagon	$ 3,892
Safari	9-passenger Station Wagon	$ 4,039
Catalina Brougham	4-door Sedan	$ 3,629
Catalina Brougham	4-door Hardtop	$ 3,783
Catalina Brougham	Hardtop Coupé	$ 3,713
Bonneville	4-door Sedan	$ 3,968
Bonneville	4-door Hardtop	$ 4,098
Bonneville	Hardtop Coupé	$ 4,030
Grand Safari	6-passenger Station Wagon	$ 4,401
Grand Safari	9-passenger Station Wagon	$ 4,548
Grand Ville	4-door Sedan	$ 4,324
Grand Ville	Hardtop Coupé	$ 4,255
Grand Ville	Convertible	$ 4,464

250 hp power team

(standard for Catalina and Safari Series; not available for other Series).

ENGINE front, 4 stroke; cylinders: 8, Vee-slanted at 90°; bore and stroke: 3.87 x 3.75 in, 98.2 x 89.3 mm; engine capacity: 350 cu in, 5,736 cu cm; compression ratio: 8; max power (SAE): 250 hp at 4,400 rpm; max torque (SAE): 350 lb ft, 48.3 kg m at 2,400 rpm; max engine rpm: 4,600; specific power: 43.6 hp/l; cylinder block: cast iron; cylinder head: cast iron; crankshaft bearings: 5; valves: 2 per cylinder, overhead, in line, push-rods and rockers, hydraulic tappets; camshafts: 1, at centre of Vee; lubrication: gear pump, full flow filter; lubricating system capacity: 10 imp pt, 12 US pt, 5.7 l; carburation: 1 Rochester 7041171 downdraught twin barrel carburettor; fuel feed: mechanical pump; cooling system: water; cooling system capacity: 33.6 imp pt, 40.4 US pt, 19.1 l.

TRANSMISSION driving wheels: rear; clutch: single dry plate; gearbox: mechanical; gears: 3 + reverse; synchromesh gears: I, II, III; gearbox ratios: I 2.420, II 1.610, III 1, rev 2.330; gear lever: steering column; final drive: hypoid bevel; axle ratio: 3.420 — station wagons 3.230; width of rims: 6''; tyres: G78 x 15 — station wagons L78 x 15.

PERFORMANCE max speed: about 100 mph, 161 km/h; power-weight ratio: Catalina 4-door Sedan 16.7 lb/hp, 7.6 kg/hp; speed in direct drive at 1,000 rpm: 21.9 mph, 35.3 km/h; fuel consumption: 16 m/imp gal, 13.4 m/US gal, 17.6 l x 100 km.

CHASSIS perimeter (box-type on convertible and station wagons); front suspension: independent, wishbones, coil springs, anti-roll bar, telescopic dampers; rear suspension: rigid axle (semi-elliptic leafsprings on station wagons), lower trailing radius arms, upper torque arms, coil springs, telescopic dampers.

STEERING recirculating ball; turns of steering wheel lock to lock: 5.60.

BRAKES front disc, rear drum, dual circuit; area rubbed by linings: total 374.7 sq in, 2,417 sq cm (station wagons 387.3 sq in, 2,498 sq cm).

ELECTRICAL EQUIPMENT voltage: 12 V; battery: 53 Ah; generator type: alternator, 37 A; ignition distributor: Delco-Remy; headlamps: 4.

DIMENSIONS AND WEIGHT wheel base: 123.50 in, 3,137 mm — station wagons 127 in, 3,226 mm; front track: 64 in, 1,625 mm; rear track: 64 in, 1,625 mm; overall length:

220.20 in, 5,593 mm — station wagons 230.20 in, 5,847 mm; overall width: 79.50 in, 2,019 mm; overall height: 4-door sedan 54.30 in, 1,379 mm — 4-door hardtop 53.60 in, 1,361 mm — hardtop coupé 53.40 in, 1,356 mm — convertible 53.70 in, 1,364 mm — station wagons 54.20 in, 1,377 mm; ground clearance: 4-door sedan and 4-door hardtop 5.20 in, 132 mm — hardtop coupé and convertible 5.10 in, 129 mm — station wagons 5.60 in, 142 mm; dry weight: Catalina 4-door Sedan Sedan 4,173 lb, 1,892 kg — Catalina 4-door Hardtop 4,240 lb, 1,923 kg — Catalina Hardtop Coupé 4,154 lb, 1,884 kg — Catalina Convertible 4,203 lb, 1,906 kg — Safari 6-passenger Station Wagon 4,856 lb, 2,202 kg — Safari 9-passenger Station Wagon 4,945 lb, 2,242 kg; turning circle (between walls): 46.4 ft, 14.1 m — station wagons 47.9 ft, 14.6 m; fuel tank capacity: 20.9 imp gal, 25 US gal, 95 l (station wagons 19.1 imp gal, 23 US gal, 87 l).

OPTIONAL ACCESSORIES only for Catalina Series "Automatic" gearbox with 2 ratios (I 1.760, II 1, rev 1.760), max ratio of convertor at stall 2.2, 3.080 axle ratio; Turbo Hydramatic automatic gearbox with 3 ratios (I 2.520, II 1.520, III 1, rev 1.920), max ratio of convertor at stall 2.2, 3.080 axle ratio; automatically or manually controlled levelling system on rear suspension; power-assisted steering; servo brake; air-conditioning system.

265 hp power team

(standard for Catalina Brougham Series; optional for Catalina and Safari Series; not available for other Series).

See 250 hp power team, except for:

ENGINE bore and stroke: 4.12 x 3.75 in, 104.6 x 95.2 mm; engine capacity: 400 cu in, 6,555 cu cm; compression ratio: 8.2; max power (SAE): 265 hp at 4,400 rpm; max torque (SAE): 400 lb ft, 55.2 kg m at 2,400 rpm; max engine rpm: 4,800; specific power: 40.4 hp/l; carburation: 1 Rochester 7041060 downdraught twin barrel carburettor.

TRANSMISSION gearbox: Turbo Hydramatic automatic (standard), max ratio of convertor at stall 2; gearbox ratios: I 2.480, II 1.480, III 1, rev 2.080; selector lever: steering column; axle ratio: 2.730.

PERFORMANCE max speed: about 102 mph, 164 km/h; power-weight ratio: Catalina 4-door Sedan 15.9 lb/hp, 7.2 kg/hp — Catalina Brougham 4-door Sedan 16 lb/hp, 7.3 kg/hp; speed in direct drive at 1,000 rpm: 23.6 mph, 38 km/h; fuel consumption: 15.7 m/imp gal, 13.1 m/US gal, 18 l x 100 km.

ELECTRICAL EQUIPMENT battery: 61 Ah.

DIMENSIONS AND WEIGHT dry weight: plus 54 lb, 24 kg — Catalina Brougham 4-door Sedan 4,237 lb, 1,921 kg — Catalina Brougham 4-door Hardtop 4,304 lb, 1,952 kg — Catalina Brougham Hardtop Coupé 4,218 lb, 1,913 kg.

OPTIONAL ACCESSORIES "Automatic" gearbox not available; only for Catalina Brougham Series 3-speed fully synchronized mechanical gearbox (I 2.420, II 1.610, III 1, rev 2.330), 3.230 axle ratio.

280 hp power team

(standard for Bonneville and Grand Safari Series; optional for Catalina, Safari and Catalina Brougham Series; not available for Grand Ville Series).

See 250 hp power team, except for:

ENGINE bore and stroke: 4.15 x 4.21 in, 105.3 x 106.9 mm; engine capacity: 455 cu in, 7,456 cu cm; compression ratio: 8.2; max power (SAE): 280 hp at 4,400 rpm; max torque (SAE): 455 lb ft, 62.8 kg m at 2,000 rpm; max engine rpm: 4,800; specific power: 37.6 hp/l; carburation: 1 Rochester 7041064 downdraught twin barrel carburettor; cooling system capacity: 29.7 imp pt, 35.7 US pt, 16.9 l.

TRANSMISSION gearbox: Turbo Hydramatic automatic (standard), max ratio of convertor at stall 2; gearbox ratios: I 2.480, II 1.480, III 1, rev 2.080; selector lever: steering column; axle ratio: 2.730 — station wagons 3.080; tyres: Bonneville H78 x 15 — station wagons L78 x 15.

PERFORMANCE max speed: about 105 mph, 169 km/h; power-weight ratio: Catalina 4-door Sedan 15.2 lb/hp, 6.9 kg/hp — Catalina Brougham 4-door Sedan 15.5 lb/hp, 7 kg/hp — Bonneville 4-door Sedan 15.8 lb/hp, 7.2 kg/hp; speed in direct drive at 1,000 rpm: 23.9 mph, 38.4 km/h; fuel consumption: 15.7 m/imp gal, 13.1 m/US gal, 18 l x 100 km.

ELECTRICAL EQUIPMENT battery: Bonneville 61 Ah.

DIMENSIONS AND WEIGHT wheel base: 126 in, 3,200 mm — station wagons 127 in, 3,226 mm; overall length: 224.20

PONTIAC Bonneville 4-door Hardtop

PONTIAC 455 cu in engine

PONTIAC Grand Prix Hardtop Coupé

in, 5,695 mm — station wagons 230.20 in, 5,847 mm; overall height: 4-door sedan 54.40 in, 1,382 mm — 4-door hardtop 53.70 in, 1,364 mm — hardtop coupé 53.50 in, 1,359 mm; ground clearance: 5.40 in, 137 mm — station wagons 5.60 in, 142 mm; dry weight: plus 86 lb, 39 kg — station wagons plus 60 lb, 27 kg — Bonneville 4-door Sedan 4,427 lb, 2,008 kg — Bonneville 4-door Hardtop 4,432 lb, 2,010 kg — Bonneville Hardtop Coupé 4,350 lb, 1,973 kg — Grand Safari 6-passenger Station Wagon 4,977 lb, 2,257 kg — Grand Safari 9-passenger Station Wagon 5,090 lb, 2,308 kg; turning circle (between walls): 47.5 ft, 14.5 m — station wagons 47.9 ft, 14.6 m.

OPTIONAL ACCESSORIES "Automatic" gearbox not available; only for Bonneville and Grand Safari Series 3-speed fully synchronized mechanical gearbox (I 2.420, II 1.610, III 1, rev 2.330), 3.230 axle ratio.

300 hp power team

(optional for Catalina, Safari and Catalina Brougham Series; not available for other Series).

See 250 hp power team, except for:

ENGINE bore and stroke: 4.12 x 3.75 in, 104.6 x 95.2 mm; engine capacity: 400 cu in, 6,555 cu cm; compression ratio: 8.2; max power (SAE): 300 hp at 4,800 rpm; max torque (SAE): 400 lb ft, 55.2 kg m at 3,600 rpm; max engine rpm: 5,000; specific power: 45.8 hp/l; carburation: 1 Rochester 7041264 downdraught 4-barrel carburettor.

TRANSMISSION gearbox: Turbo Hydramatic automatic (standard), max ratio of convertor at stall 2.3; gearbox ratios: I 2.480, II 1.480, III 1, rev 2.080; selector lever: steering column; axle ratio: 3.080.

PERFORMANCE max speed: about 108 mph, 174 km/h; power-weight ratio: Catalina 4-door Sedan 14.2 lb/hp, 6.4 kg/hp — Catalina Brougham 4-door Sedan 14.1 lb/hp, 6.3 kg/hp; speed in direct drive at 1,000 rpm: 22.7 mph, 36.5 km/h; fuel consumption: 14.3 m/imp gal, 11.9 m/US gal, 19.8 l x 100 km.

ELECTRICAL EQUIPMENT battery: 61 Ah.

DIMENSIONS AND WEIGHT dry weight: plus 89 lb, 40 kg — station wagons plus 61 lb, 28 kg — Catalina Brougham 4-door Sedan 4,237 lb, 1,921 kg — Catalina Brougham 4-door Hardtop 4,304 lb, 1,952 kg — Catalina Brougham Hardtop Coupé 4,218 lb, 1,913 kg.

OPTIONAL ACCESSORIES "Automatic" gearbox not available.

325 hp power team

(standard for Grand Ville Series; optional for Catalina, Safari, Catalina Brougham and Grand Safari Series; not available for Bonneville Series).

See 250 hp power team, except for:

ENGINE bore and stroke: 4.15 x 4.21 in, 105.3 x 106.9 mm; engine capacity: 455 cu in, 7,456 cu cm; compression ratio: 8.2; max power (SAE): 325 hp at 4,400 rpm; max torque (SAE): 455 lb ft, 62.8 kg m at 3,200 rpm; max engine rpm: 5,000; specific power: 43.6 hp/l; carburation: 1 Rochester 7041262 downdraught 4-barrel carburettor; cooling system capacity: 29.7 imp pt, 35.7 US pt, 16.9 l.

TRANSMISSION gearbox: Turbo Hydramatic automatic (standard), max ratio of convertor at stall 2.3; gearbox ratios: I 2.480, II 1.480, III 1, rev 2.080; selector lever: steering column; axle ratio: 3.080; tyres: Grand Ville H78 x 15 — station wagons L78 x 15.

PERFORMANCE max speed: about 109 mph, 175 km/h; power-weight ratio: Catalina 4-door Sedan 13 lb/hp, 5.8 kg/hp — Catalina Brougham 4-door Sedan 13.1 lb/hp, 5.9 kg/hp — Grand Ville 4-door Hardtop 13.7 lb/hp, 6.2 kg/hp; speed in direct drive at 1,000 rpm: 22.9 mph, 36.8 km/h; fuel consumption: 13.8 m/imp gal, 11.5 m/US gal, 20.4 l x 100 km.

STEERING servo.

ELECTRICAL EQUIPMENT battery: Grand Ville 62 Ah.

DIMENSIONS AND WEIGHT wheel base: 126 in, 3,200 mm; overall length: 224.20 in, 5,695 mm; overall height: 4-door hardtop and hardtop coupé 54.20 in, 1,377 mm — convertible 53.80 in, 1,366 mm; dry weight: Catalina plus 66 lb, 30 kg — station wagons plus 93 lb, 42 kg — Catalina Brougham plus 17 lb, 8 kg — Grand Ville 4-door Hardtop 4,455 lb, 2,020 kg — Grand Ville Hardtop Coupé 4,405 lb, 1,998 kg — Grand Ville Convertible 4,377 lb, 1,985 kg; turning circle (between walls): 47.5 ft, 14.5 m — station wagons 47.9 ft, 14.6 m.

OPTIONAL ACCESSORIES "Automatic" gearbox not available; only for Grand Ville Series 3-speed fully synchronized mechanical gearbox (I 2.420, II 1.610, III 1, rev 2.330), 3.230 axle ratio.

Middle East
Asia
Australasia

Models now in production
Illustrations and technical information

AUTOCARS   ISRAEL

Gilboa 1300

PRICE: —

ENGINE front, 4 stroke; cylinders: 4, vertical, in line; bore and stroke: 2.90 x 2.99 in, 73.7 x 76 mm; engine capacity: 79.1 cu in, 1,296 cu cm; compression ratio: 7.5; max power (DIN): 55.8 hp at 5,200 rpm; max torque (DIN): 63 lb ft, 8.7 kg m at 3,000 rpm; max engine rpm: 5,800; specific power: 43.1 hp/l; cylinder block: cast iron; cylinder head: cast iron; crankshaft bearings: 3; valves: 2 per cylinder, overhead, push-rods and rockers; camshafts: 1, side; lubrication: rotary pump, full flow filter; lubricating system capacity: 7.9 imp pt, 9.5 US pt, 4.5 l; carburation: 1 Solex B 30 PSEI downdraught single barrel carburetter; fuel feed: mechanical pump; cooling system: water; cooling system capacity: 8.4 imp pt, 10.1 US pt, 4.8 l.

TRANSMISSION driving wheels: rear; clutch: single dry plate; gearbox: mechanical; gears: 4 + reverse; synchromesh gears: II, III, IV; gearbox ratios: I 3.746, II 2.158, III 1.394, IV 1, rev 3.746; gear lever: central; final drive: hypoid bevel; axle ratio: 4.110; tyres: 5.60 x 13.

PERFORMANCE max speeds: 24 mph, 39 km/h in 1st gear; 42 mph, 68 km/h in 2nd gear; 65 mph, 105 km/h in 3rd gear; 85 mph, 136 km/h in 4th gear; power-weight ratio: 29.8 lb/hp, 13.5 kg/hp; carrying capacity: 882 lb, 400 kg; speed in direct drive at 1,000 rpm: 14.6 mph, 23.5 km/h; fuel consumption: 38.7 m/imp gal, 32.2 m/US gal, 7.3 l x 100 km.

CHASSIS box-type platform; front suspension: independent, wishbones, coil springs, telescopic dampers; rear suspension: rigid axle, semi-elliptic leafsprings, telescopic dampers.

STEERING rack-and-pinion; turns of steering wheel lock to lock: 2.50.

BRAKES front disc, rear drum; area rubbed by linings: total 205 sq in, 1,322 sq cm.

ELECTRICAL EQUIPMENT voltage: 12 V; battery: 53 Ah; generator type: dynamo, 240 W; ignition distributor: Lucas; headlamps: 2.

DIMENSIONS AND WEIGHT wheel base: 98.46 in, 2,501 mm; front track: 49.21 in, 1,250 mm; rear track: 49.21 in, 1,250 mm; overall length: 159.45 in, 4,050 mm; overall width: 61.42 in, 1,560 mm; overall height: 60.24 in, 1,530 mm; ground clearance: 6.30 in, 160 mm; dry weight: 1,665 lb, 755 kg; distribution of weight: 53% front axle, 47% rear axle; turning circle (between walls): 31.8 ft, 9.7 m; fuel tank capacity: 7.9 imp gal, 9.5 US gal, 36 l.

BODY saloon/sedan in plastic material; doors: 4; seats: 5; front seats: separate.

PRACTICAL INSTRUCTIONS fuel: 83 oct petrol; engine sump oil: 7 imp pt, 8.5 US pt, 4 l, SAE 20W-30, change every 5,000 miles, 8,000 km; gearbox oil: 1.8 imp pt, 2.1 US pt, 1 l, SAE 80, change every 5,000 miles, 8,000 km; final drive oil: 1.2 imp pt, 1.5 US pt, 0.7 l, SAE 90, change every 5,000 miles, 8,000 km; greasing: every 3,000 miles, 4,800 km, 4 points; normal tyre pressure: front 22 psi, 1.5 atm, rear 24 psi, 1.7 atm.

Ducas 1300

See Gilboa 1300, except for:

PRICE: —

BODY doors: 2.

Sussita 1300

See Gilboa 1300, except for:

PRICE: —

PERFORMANCE power-weight ratio: 31.5 lb/hp, 14.3 kg/hp.

DIMENSIONS AND WEIGHT overall height: 57.91 in, 1,471 mm; dry weight: 1,764 lb, 800 kg.

BODY estate car/station wagon; doors: 2+1.

AUTOCARS Gilboa 1300

OTOSAN Anadol A1

YLN 801A

OTOSAN   TURKEY

Anadol A1

PRICE: —

ENGINE front, 4 stroke; cylinders: 4, in line; bore and stroke: 3.19 x 2.48 in, 80.9 x 62.9 mm; engine capacity: 79.2 cu in, 1,298 cu cm; compression ratio: 8; max power (SAE): 57 hp at 5,000 rpm; max torque (SAE): 80 lb ft, 11 kg m at 3,600 rpm; max engine rpm: 5,500; specific power: 43.9 hp/l; cylinder block: light alloy, wet liners; cylinder head: light alloy; crankshaft bearings: 3; valves: 2 per cylinder, overhead, rockers; camshafts: 1, overhead; lubrication: eccentric pump, full flow filter; lubricating system capacity: 6.3 imp pt, 7.6 US pt, 3.6 l; carburation: 1 Ford GPD downdraught carburettor; fuel feed: mechanical pump; cooling system: water; cooling system capacity: 9 imp pt, 10.8 US pt, 5.1 l.

TRANSMISSION driving wheels: rear; clutch: single dry plate, hydraulically controlled; gearbox: mechanical; gears: 4 + reverse; synchromesh gears: I, II, III, IV; gearbox ratios: I 3.656, II 2.185, III 1.425, IV 1, rev 4.235; gear lever: central; final drive: hypoid bevel; axle ratio: 4.125; width of rims: 4.5''; tyres: 5.90 x 13.

PERFORMANCE max speeds: 22 mph, 35 km/h in 1st gear; 36 mph, 58 km/h in 2nd gear; 56 mph, 90 km/h in 3rd gear; 80 mph, 128 km/h in 4th gear; power-weight ratio: 30.1 lb/hp, 14 kg/hp; carrying capacity: 882 lb, 400 kg; speed in direct drive at 1,000 rpm: 16 mph, 25.8 km/h; fuel consumption: 37.7 m/imp gal, 31.4 m/US gal, 7.5 l x 100 km.

CHASSIS integral with reinforced platform; front suspension: independent, wishbones, coil springs, anti-roll bar, telescopic dampers; rear suspension: rigid axle, semi-elliptic leafsprings, telescopic dampers.

STEERING recirculating ball; turns of steering wheel lock to lock: 2.

BRAKES front disc, rear drum; area rubbed by linings: front 158.6 sq in, 1,023 sq cm, rear 72.6 sq in, 468 sq cm, total 231.2 sq in, 1,491 sq cm.

ELECTRICAL EQUIPMENT voltage: 12 V; battery: 55 Ah; generator type: dynamo, 264 W; ignition distributor: Lucas; headlamps: 2.

DIMENSIONS AND WEIGHT wheel base: 100.98 in, 2,565 mm; front track: 52.05 in, 1,322 mm; rear track: 49.41 in, 1,255 mm; overall length: 172.48 in, 4,381 mm; overall width: 64.72 in, 1,644 mm; overall height: 55.98 in, 1,422 mm; ground clearance: 6.30 in, 160 mm; dry weight: 1,764 lb, 800 kg; distribution of weight: 51.2% front axle, 48.8% rear axle; turning circle (between walls): 32.5 ft, 9.9 m; fuel tank capacity: 9.2 imp gal, 11.1 US gal, 42 l.

BODY saloon/sedan, in plastic material; doors: 2; seats: 5; front seats: separate.

PRACTICAL INSTRUCTIONS fuel: 90-96 oct petrol; engine sump oil: 5.6 imp pt, 6.8 US pt, 3.2 l, SAE 10W-20, change every 3,100 miles, 5,000 km; gearbox oil: 1.6 imp pt, 1.9 US pt, 0.9 l, SAE 80, change every 5,000 miles, 8,000 km; final drive oil: 1.9 imp pt, 2.3 US pt, 1.1 l, SAE 90, change every 18,600 miles, 30,000 km; greasing none; tappet clearances: inlet 0.010 in, 0.25 mm, exhaust 0.017 in, 0.43 mm; valve timing: inlet opens 17° before tdc and closes 51° after bdc, exhaust opens 51° before bdc and closes 17° after tdc; normal tyre pressure: front 24 psi, 1.7 atm, rear 24 psi, 1.7 atm.

YLN   CHINA (Taiwan)

801 A

PRICE: —

ENGINE front, 4 stroke; cylinders: 4, in line; bore and stroke: 3.43 x 3.27 in, 87.2 x 83 mm; engine capacity: 120.95 cu in, 1,982 cu cm; compression ratio: 8.2; max power (SAE): 99 hp at 5,000 rpm; max torque (SAE): 123 lb ft, 17 kg m at 3,600 rpm; max engine rpm: 5,200; specific power: 49.9 hp/l; cylinder block: cast iron; cylinder head: cast iron; crankshaft bearings: 3; valves: 2 per cylinder, overhead, push-rods and rockers; camshafts: 1, side; lubrication: rotary pump, full flow filter; lubricating system capacity: 5.8 imp pt, 7 US pt, 3.3 l; carburation: 1 Nihon-Kikaki downdraught twin barrel carburettor; fuel feed: mechanical pump; cooling system: water; cooling system capacity: 13.6 imp pt, 16.3 US pt, 7.7 l.

TRANSMISSION driving wheels: rear; clutch: single dry plate; gearbox: mechanical; gears: 3 + reverse; synchromesh gears: I, II, III; gearbox ratios: I 3.184, II 1.641, III 1, rev 2.922; gear lever: steering column; final drive: hypoid bevel; axle ratio: 4.111; tyres: 7.00 x 13.

AUTOCARS Gilboa 1300

OTOSAN Anadol A1

YLN 801A

PERFORMANCE max speeds: 25 mph, 40 km/h in 1st gear; 56 mph, 90 km/h in 2nd gear; 90 mph, 145 km/h in 3rd gear; power-weight ratio: 28.4 lb/hp, 12.9 kg/hp; carrying capacity: 1,058 lb, 480 kg; fuel consumption: 31.4 m/imp gal, 26.1 m/US gal, 9 l x 100 km.

CHASSIS integral; front suspension: independent, wishbones, coil springs, anti-roll bar, telescopic dampers; rear suspension: rigid axle, semi-elliptic leafsprings, telescopic dampers.

STEERING recirculating ball.

BRAKES drum; lining area: front 90.7 sq in, 585 sq cm, rear 71.9 sq in, 464 sq cm, total 162.6 sq in, 1,049 sq cm.

ELECTRICAL EQUIPMENT voltage: 12 V; battery: 50 Ah; generator type: alternator, 500 W; ignition distributor: Hitachi; headlamps: 4.

DIMENSIONS AND WEIGHT wheel base: 105.91 in, 2,690 mm; front track: 54.13 in, 1,375 mm; rear track: 54.13 in, 1,375 mm; overall length: 184.65 in, 4,690 mm; overall width: 66.54 in, 1,690 mm; overall height: 57.28 in, 1,455 mm; ground clearance: 7.28 in, 185 mm; dry weight: 2,825 lb, 1,281 kg; distribution of weight: 52.8% front axle, 47.2% rear axle; turning circle (between walls): 36.7 ft, 11.2 m; fuel tank capacity: 14.3 imp gal, 17.2 US gal, 65 l.

BODY saloon/sedan; doors: 4; seats: 6; front seats: bench.

PRACTICAL INSTRUCTIONS fuel: 90 oct petrol; engine sump oil: 5.8 imp pt, 7 US pt, 3.3 l, SAE 10W-30, change every 3,100 miles, 5,000 km; gearbox oil: 3.9 imp pt, 4.7 US pt, 2.2 l, SAE 140, change every 24,900 miles, 40,000 km; final drive oil: 1.6 imp pt, 1.9 US pt, 0.9 l, SAE 90, change every 24,900 miles, 40,000 km; greasing: every 6,200 miles, 10,000 km, 23 points; tappet clearances: inlet 0.017 in, 0.43 mm, exhaust 0.017 in, 0.43 mm; valve timing: inlet opens 16° before tdc and closes 52° after bdc, exhaust opens 54° before bdc and closes 20° after tdc; normal tyre pressure: front 21 psi, 1.5 atm, rear 21 psi, 1.5 atm.

HINDUSTAN INDIA

Ambassador Mk II

PRICE EX WORKS: 15,091 rupees.

ENGINE front, 4 stroke; cylinders: 4, in line; bore and stroke: 2.87 x 3.50 in, 73 x 88.9 mm; engine capacity: 90.9 cu in, 1,489 cu cm; compression ratio: 7.2; max power (SAE): 50 hp at 4,200 rpm; max torque (SAE): 75 lb ft, 10.2 kg m at 3,000 rpm; max engine rpm: 4,800; specific power: 33.6 hp/l; cylinder block: cast iron; cylinder head: cast iron; crankshaft bearings: 3; valves: 2 per cylinder, overhead, in line, push-rods and rockers; camshafts: 1, side; lubrication: gear pump, filter in sump; lubricating system capacity: 7.9 imp pt, 9.5 US pt, 4.5 l; carburation: 1 SU type H2 semi-downdraught carburettor; fuel feed: electric pump; cooling system: water; cooling system capacity: 13.9 imp pt, 16.7 US pt, 7.9 l.

TRANSMISSION driving wheels: rear; clutch: single dry plate; gearbox: mechanical; gears: 4 + reverse; synchromesh gears: II, III, IV; gearbox ratios: I 3.807, II 2.253, III 1.560, IV 1, rev 3.807; gear lever: steering column; final drive: hypoid bevel; axle ratio: 4.875; width of rims: 4''; tyres: 5.50 x 15.

PERFORMANCE max speeds: 19 mph, 31 km/h in 1st gear; 32 mph, 51 km/h in 2nd gear; 49 mph, 79 km/h in 3rd gear; 74 mph, 119 km/h in 4th gear; power-weight ratio: 49.2 lb/hp, 22.3 kg/hp; carrying capacity: 882 lb, 400 kg; acceleration: standing ¼ mile 25 sec, 0-50 mph (0-80 km/h) 19.8 sec; speed in direct drive at 1,000 rpm: 15.5 mph, 25 km/h; fuel consumption: 29.1 m/imp gal, 24.2 m/US gal, 9.7 l x 100 km.

CHASSIS integral; front suspension: independent, wishbones, longitudinal torsion bars, telescopic dampers; rear suspension: rigid axle, semi-elliptic leafsprings, telescopic dampers.

STEERING rack-and-pinion; turns of steering wheel lock to lock: 3.13.

BRAKES drum; lining area: total 96 sq in, 619 sq cm.

ELECTRICAL EQUIPMENT voltage: 12 V; battery: 62 Ah; generator type: dynamo, 297 W; ignition distributor: Lucas; headlamps: 2.

DIMENSIONS AND WEIGHT wheel base: 97.01 in, 2,464 mm; front track: 53.50 in, 1,359 mm; rear track: 52.99 in, 1,346 mm; overall length: 170.98 in, 4,343 mm; overall width: 65 in, 1,651 mm; overall height: 62.99 in, 1,600 mm; ground clearance: 6.26 in, 159 mm; dry weight: 2,456 lb, 1,114 kg; distribution of weight: 54.7% front axle, 45.3% rear axle; turning circle (between walls): 35.8 ft, 10.9 m; fuel tank capacity: 11.9 imp gal, 14.3 US gal, 54 l.

BODY saloon/sedan; doors: 4; seats: 5; front seats: bench.

OPTIONAL ACCESSORIES 5.90 x 15 tyres.

DAIHATSU   JAPAN

Fellow Max Sedan

PRICE EX WORKS: 315,000 yen.

ENGINE front, 2 stroke; cylinders: 2, in line; bore and stroke: 2.44 x 2.32 in, 62 x 59 mm; engine capacity: 21.7 cu in, 356 cu cm; compression ratio: 10; max power (DIN): 33 hp at 6,500 rpm; max torque (DIN): 27 lb ft, 3.7 kg m at 5,500 rpm; max engine rpm: 7,400; specific power: 92.7 hp/l; cylinder block: cast iron; cylinder head: light alloy; crankshaft bearings: 4; carburation: 1 Mikuni-Solex down-draught carburettor; fuel feed: mechanical pump; cooling system: water; cooling system capacity: 5.3 imp pt, 6.3 US pt, 3 l.

TRANSMISSION driving wheels: front; clutch: single dry plate (diaphragm); gearbox: mechanical; gears: 4 + reverse; synchromes gears: I, II, III, IV; gearbox ratios: I 4.727, II 2.823, III 1.809, IV 1.269, rev 4.865; gear lever: central; final drive: hypoid bevel; axle ratio: 4.450; width of rims: 3.5''; tyres: 5.20 x 10.

PERFORMANCE max speeds: 22 mph, 35 km/h in 1st gear; 34 mph, 55 km/h in 2nd gear; 53 mph, 85 km/h in 3rd gear; 65 mph, 105 km/h in 4th gear; power-weight ratio: 31.1 lb/hp, 14.1 kg/hp; carrying capacity: 706 lb, 320 kg; acceleration: standing ¼ mile 21.8 sec; speed in top at 1,000 rpm: 8.8 mph, 14.2 km/h; fuel consumption: 58.8 m/imp gal, 49 m/US gal, 4.8 l x 100 km.

CHASSIS integral; front suspension: independent, by Mc-Pherson, coil springs/telescopic damper struts, lower wishbones, lower trailing links; rear suspension: independent, semi-trailing arms, coil springs, telescopic dampers.

STEERING rack-and-pinion.

BRAKES drum; lining area: front 18.6 sq in, 120 sq cm, rear 18.6 sq in, 120 sq cm, total 37.2 sq in, 240 sq cm.

ELECTRICAL EQUIPMENT voltage: 12 V; battery: 26 Ah; generator type: alternator, 300 W; headlamps: 2.

DIMENSIONS AND WEIGHT wheel base: 82.28 in, 2,090 mm; front track: 44.09 in, 1,120 mm; rear track: 43.70 in, 1,110 mm; overall length: 117.91 in, 2,995 mm; overall width: 50.98 in, 1,295 mm; overall height: 51.38 in, 1,305 mm; ground clearance: 6.69 in, 170 mm; dry weight: 1,025 lb, 465 kg; distribution of weight: 63.5% front axle, 36.5% rear axle; turning circle (between walls): 26.9 ft, 8.2 m; fuel tank capacity: 5.7 imp gal, 6.9 US gal, 26 l.

BODY saloon/sedan; doors: 2; seats: 4; front seats: separate.

PRACTICAL INSTRUCTIONS fuel: mixture; engine sump oil: 5.3 imp pt, 6.3 US pt, 3 l, oil in separate tank; gearbox and final drive oil: 2.6 imp pt, 3.2 US pt, 1.5 l, SAE 90, change every 12,400 miles, 20,000 km; normal tyre pressure: front 28 psi, 2 atm, rear 23 psi, 1.6 atm.

OPTIONAL ACCESSORIES De Luxe, Custom and Hi Custom versions.

Fellow Max Station Wagon

See Fellow Max Sedan, except for:

PRICE: —

BODY estate car/station wagon; doors: 2 + 1.

Fellow Max SS Sedan

See Fellow Max Sedan, except for:

PRICE EX WORKS: 398,000 yen.

ENGINE compression ratio: 11; max power (DIN): 40 hp at 7,200 rpm; max torque (DIN): 30 lb ft, 4.1 kg m at 6,500 rpm; max engine rpm: 8,000; specific power: 112.4 hp/l; carburation: 2 Amal downdraught carburettors.

PERFORMANCE max speed: 75 mph, 120 km/h; power-weight ratio: 25.6 lb/hp, 11.6 kg/hp; acceleration: standing ¼ mile 19.8 sec.

DIMENSIONS AND WEIGHT overall height: 50.98 in, 1,295 mm; ground clearance: 6.30 in, 160 mm.

OPTIONAL ACCESSORIES only 135 x 10 tyres and S version.

Consorte Berlina

PRICE EX WORKS: 397,000 yen.

ENGINE front, 4 stroke; cylinders: 4, vertical, in line; bore and stroke: 2.68 x 2.60 in, 68 x 66 mm; engine capacity: 58.5 cu in, 958 cu cm; compression ratio: 9; max power (DIN):

DAIHATSU Fellow Max SS Sedan

DAIHATSU Consorte Berlina Super De Luxe

HONDA N III Town Custom Sedan

58 hp at 5,500 rpm; max torque (DIN): 58 lb ft, 8 kg m at 4,000 rpm; max engine rpm: 6,000; specific power: 60.5 hp/l; cylinder block: cast iron; cylinder head: light alloy; crankshaft bearings: 3; valves: 2 per cylinder, overhead, pushrods and rockers; camshafts: 1, side; lubrication: rotary pump, full flow filter; lubricating system capacity: 4.9 imp pt, 5.9 US pt, 2.8 l; carburation: 1 Aisan downdraught twin barrel carburettor; fuel feed: mechanical pump; cooling system: water; cooling system capacity: 7.2 imp pt, 8.7 US pt, 4.1 l.

TRANSMISSION driving wheels: rear; clutch: single dry plate (diaphragm); gearbox: mechanical; gears: 4 + reverse; synchromesh gears: I, II, III, IV; gearbox ratios: I 3.588, II 2.125, III 1.406, IV 1, rev 4.965; gear lever: central; final drive: hypoid bevel; axle ratio: 4.222; width of rims: 4''; tyres: 6.00 x 12.

PERFORMANCE max speeds: 25 mph, 40 km/h in 1st gear; 42 mph, 67 km/h in 2nd gear; 63 mph, 102 km/h in 3rd gear; 87 mph, 140 km/h in 4th gear; power-weight ratio: 25.6 lb/hp, 11.6 kg/hp; carrying capacity: 882 lb, 400 kg; acceleration: standing ¼ mile 19.5 sec; speed in direct drive at 1,000 rpm: 14.5 mph, 23.3 km/h; fuel consumption: 38.7 m/imp gal, 32.2 m/US gal, 7.3 l x 100 km.

CHASSIS integral; front suspension: independent, by McPherson, coil springs/telescopic dampers struts, lower wishbones, lower trailing links, anti-roll bar; rear suspension: rigid axle, semi-elliptic leafsprings, telescopic dampers.

STEERING screw and sector.

BRAKES front disc, rear drum; lining area: front 19.7 sq in, 127 sq cm, rear 35.7 sq in, 230 sq cm, total 55.4 sq in, 357 sq cm.

ELECTRICAL EQUIPMENT voltage: 12 V; battery: 32 Ah; generator type: alternator, 360 W; ignition distributor: Denso; headlamps: 2.

DIMENSIONS AND WEIGHT wheel base: 85.04 in, 2,160 mm; front track: 48.62 in, 1,235 mm; rear track: 47.24 in, 1,200 mm; overall length: 143.50 in, 3,645 mm; overall width: 57.09 in, 1,450 mm; overall height: 54.33 in, 1,380 mm; ground clearance: 6.69 in, 170 mm; dry weight: 1,477 lb, 670 kg; distribution of weight: 51% front axle, 49% rear axle; turning circle (between walls): 28.9 ft, 8.8 m; fuel tank capacity: 8.8 imp gal, 10.6 US gal, 40 l.

BODY saloon/sedan; doors: 2; seats: 4; front seats: separate.

PRACTICAL INSTRUCTIONS fuel: 90 oct petrol; engine sump oil: 4.9 imp pt, 5.9 US pt, 2.8 l, SAE 20W-30, change every 3,100 miles, 5,000 km; gearbox oil: 2.5 imp pt, 3 US pt, 1.4 l, SAE 80/90, change every 18,600 miles, 30,000 km; final drive oil: 1.8 imp pt, 2.1 US pt, 1 l, SAE 90, change every 18,600 miles, 30,000 km; tappet clearances: inlet 0.010 in, 0.25 mm, exhaust 0.010 in, 0.25 mm; valve timing: inlet opens 15° before tdc and closes 55° after bdc, exhaust opens 55° before bdc and closes 15° after tdc; normal tyre pressure: front 20 psi, 1.4 atm, rear 20 psi, 1.4 atm.

OPTIONAL ACCESSORIES De Luxe and Super De Luxe versions.

HONDA JAPAN

N III Town Custom Sedan

PRICE IN GB: £ 403.
PRICE EX WORKS: 425,000 yen.

ENGINE front, transverse, 4 stroke; cylinders: 2, in line; bore and stroke: 2.46 x 2.28 in, 62.5 x 57.8 mm; engine capacity: 21.6 cu in, 354 cu cm; compression ratio: 8.5; max power (DIN): 27 hp at 7,000 rpm; max torque (DIN): 22 lb ft, 3 kg m at 5,500 rpm; max engine rpm: 7,000; specific power: 76.3 hp/l; cylinder block: light alloy; cylinder head: light alloy; crankshaft bearings: 3, on roller bearings; valves: 2 per cylinder, overhead, rockers; camshafts: 1, overhead; lubrication: rotary pump, full flow filter; lubricating system capacity: 5.3 imp pt, 6.3 US pt, 3 l; carburation: 1 Keihin CV horizontal carburettor; fuel feed: electric pump; cooling system: aircooled.

TRANSMISSION driving wheels: front; clutch: single dry plate (diaphragm); gearbox: mechanical, in unit with engine; gears: 4 + reverse; synchromesh gears: I, II, III, IV; gearbox ratios: I 2.470, II 1.565, III 1, IV 0.648, rev 2.437; gear lever: central; final drive: helical spur gears, in unit with engine and gearbox; axle ratio: 3.739; width of rims: 3.5''; tyres: 5.20 x 10.

PERFORMANCE max speeds: 19 mph, 30 km/h in 1st gear; 30 mph, 48 km/h in 2nd gear; 47 mph, 76 km/h in 3rd gear; 65 mph, 105 km/h in 4th gear; power-weight ratio: 44.1 lb/hp, 20 kg/hp; carrying capacity: 706 lb, 320 kg; acceleration: standing ¼ mile 22 sec; speed in top at 1,000 rpm: 8.7 mph, 14 km/h; fuel consumption: 56.5 m/imp gal, 47 m/US gal, 5 l x 100 km.

CHASSIS integral, front auxiliary frame; front suspension: independent, by McPherson, coil springs/telescopic damper struts, lower wishbones, anti-roll bar; rear suspension: rigid axle, semi-elliptic leafsprings, telescopic dampers.

DAIHATSU Fellow Max SS Sedan

DAIHATSU Consorte Berlina Super De Luxe

HONDA N III Town Custom Sedan

STEERING rack-and-pinion; turns of steering wheel lock to lock: 3.10.

BRAKES drum; lining area: front 37.7 sq in, 243 sq cm, rear 37.7 sq in, 243 sq cm, total 75.4 sq in, 486 sq cm.

ELECTRICAL EQUIPMENT voltage: 12 V; battery: 32 Ah; generator type: dynamo, 20 A; ignition distributor: Nihon-Denso; headlamps: 2.

DIMENSIONS AND WEIGHT wheel base: 78.74 in, 2,000 mm; front track: 44.88 in, 1,140 mm; rear track: 43.90 in, 1,115 mm; overall length: 117.91 in, 2,995 mm; overall width: 50.98 in, 1,295 mm; overall height: 52.76 in, 1,340 mm; ground clearance: 6.70 in, 170 mm; dry weight: 1,191 lb, 540 kg; distribution of weight: 67% front axle, 33% rear axle; turning circle (between walls): 30.8 ft, 9.4 m; fuel tank capacity: 5.7 imp gal, 6.9 US gal, 26 l.

BODY saloon/sedan; doors: 2; seats: 4; front seats: bench.

PRACTICAL INSTRUCTIONS fuel: 88 oct petrol; engine sump, gearbox and final drive oil: 5.3 imp pt, 6.3 US pt, 3 l, SAE 20W-30, change every 3,100 miles, 5,000 km; tappet clearances: inlet 0.004 in, 0.10 mm, exhaust 0.004 in, 0.10 mm; valve timing: inlet opens 10° before tdc and closes 20° after bdc, exhaust opens 20° before bdc and closes 10° after tdc; normal tyre pressure: front 23 psi, 1.7 atm, rear 16 psi, 1.2 atm.

N III De Luxe Sedan

See N III Town Custom Sedan, except for:

PRICE EX WORKS: 346,000 yen.

ENGINE max power (DIN): 31 hp at 8,500 rpm; max engine rpm: 9,000; specific power: 87.6 hp/l.

PERFORMANCE max speed: 71 mph, 115 km/h; power-weight ratio: 35.3 lb/hp, 16 kg/hp.

DIMENSIONS AND WEIGHT dry weight: 1,091 lb, 495 kg.

PRACTICAL INSTRUCTIONS valve timing: inlet opens 0° before tdc and closes 30° after bdc, exhaust opens 30° before bdc and closes 0° after tdc.

N III 360 T Sedan

See N III Town Custom Sedan, except for:

PRICE EX WORKS: 361,000 yen.

ENGINE compression ratio: 9; max power (DIN): 36 hp at 9,000 rpm; max torque (DIN): 23 lb ft, 3.2 kg m at 7,000 rpm; max engine rpm: 9,000; specific power: 101.7 hp/l; carburation: 2 Keihin CV horizontal carburettors.

PERFORMANCE max speeds: 22 mph, 36 km/h in 1st gear; 35 mph, 57 km/h in 2nd gear; 56 mph, 90 km/h in 3rd gear; 75 mph, 120 km/h in 4th gear; power-weight ratio: 30.2 lb/hp, 13.7 kg/hp.

PRACTICAL INSTRUCTIONS valve timing: inlet opens 10° before tdc and closes 40° after bdc, exhaust opens 40° before bdc and closes 10° after tdc.

N III Automatic Sedan

See N III Town Custom Sedan, except for:

PRICE EX WORKS: 389,000 yen.

TRANSMISSION gearbox: Hondamatic automatic, hydraulic torque convertor with 3 ratios + reverse, constant-mesh; gearbox ratios: I 2.764, II 1.357, III 0.861, rev 3.538; axle ratio: 3.541.

PERFORMANCE max speed: 62 mph, 100 km/h.

Z Coupé PRO

See N III Town Custom Sedan, except for:

PRICE EX WORKS: 396,000 yen.

ENGINE max power (DIN): 31 hp at 8,500 rpm; max engine rpm: 9,000; specific power: 87.6 hp/l.

PERFORMANCE max speed: 71 mph, 115 km/h; power-weight ratio: 37.3 lb/hp, 16.9 kg/hp.

ELECTRICAL EQUIPMENT battery: 26 Ah.

DIMENSIONS AND WEIGHT overall height: 50.20 in, 1,275 mm; dry weight: 1,158 lb, 525 kg; distribution of weight: 64.8% front axle, 35.2% rear axle.

BODY coupé; seats: 2 + 2; front seats: separate.

Z COUPÉ PRO

PRACTICAL INSTRUCTIONS valve timing: inlet opens 0° before tdc and closes 30° after bdc, exhaust opens 30° before bdc and closes 0° after tdc.

Z TS Coupé

See Z Coupé PRO, except for:

PRICE EX WORKS: 386,000 yen.

ENGINE max power (DIN): 36 hp at 9,000 rpm; max torque (DIN): 23 lb ft, 3.2 kg m at 7,000 rpm; specific power: 101.7 hp/l; carburation: 2 Keihin horizontal carburettors.

TRANSMISSION axle ratio: 3.541.

PERFORMANCE max speeds: 21 mph, 33 km/h in 1st gear; 32 mph, 52 km/h in 2nd gear; 50 mph, 81 km/h in 3rd gear; 75 mph, 120 km/h in 4th gear; power-weight ratio: 32.2 lb/hp, 14.6 kg/hp.

PRACTICAL INSTRUCTIONS valve timing: inlet opens 10° before tdc and closes 40° after bdc, exhaust opens 40° before bdc and closes 10° after tdc.

Z GS Coupé

See Z Coupé PRO, except for:

PRICE EX WORKS: 463,000 yen.

TRANSMISSION gears: 5 + reverse; gearbox ratios: I 2.687, II 1.809, III 1.222, IV 0.870, V 0.648; axle ratio: 3.541.

PERFORMANCE max speeds: 19 mph, 30 km/h in 1st gear; 28 mph, 45 km/h in 2nd gear; 42 mph, 67 km/h in 3rd gear; 58 mph, 93 km/h in 4th gear; 75 mph, 120 km/h in 5th gear.

BRAKES front disc, rear drum, rear compensator, servo.

Vamos 4

PRICE EX WORKS: 345,000 yen.

ENGINE rear, 4 stroke; cylinders: 2, in line; bore and stroke: 2.46 x 2.28 in, 62.5 x 57.8 mm; engine capacity: 21.6 cu in, 354 cu cm; compression ratio: 8; max power (DIN): 30 hp at 8,000 rpm; max torque (DIN): 22 lb ft, 3 kg m at 5,500 rpm; specific power: 84.7 hp/l; cylinder block: light alloy; cylinder head: light alloy; crankshaft bearings: 4, on roller bearings; valves: 2 per cylinder, overhead, rockers; camshafts: 1, overhead; lubrication: plunger pump, full flow filter; lubricating system capacity: 5.3 imp pt, 6.3 US pt, 3 l; carburation: 1 Keihin CV horizontal carburettor; fuel feed: electric pump; cooling system: aircooled.

TRANSMISSION driving wheels: rear; clutch: single dry plate (diaphragm); gearbox: mechanical, in unit with engine; gears: 4 + reverse; synchromesh gears: I, II, III, IV; gearbox ratios: I 2.529, II 1.565, III 1, IV 0.615, rev 2.438; gear lever: central; final drive: hypoid bevel, in unit with engine and gearbox; axle ratio: 4.273; width of rims: 3.5''; tyres: 5.00 x 10.

PERFORMANCE max speeds: 16 mph, 25 km/h in 1st gear; 26 mph, 42 km/h in 2nd gear; 40 mph, 64 km/h in 3rd gear; 56 mph, 90 km/h in 4th gear; power-weight ratio: 38.1 lb/hp, 17.3 kg/hp; fuel consumption: 56.5 m/imp gal, 47 m/US gal, 5 l x 100 km.

CHASSIS platform; front suspension: independent, by McPherson, coil springs/telescopic damper struts, lower wishbones; rear suspension: de Dion rigid axle, semi-elliptic leafsprings, telescopic dampers.

STEERING rack-and-pinion.

BRAKES drum; lining area: front 37.7 sq in, 243 sq cm, rear 37.7 sq in, 243 sq cm, total 75.4 sq in, 486 sq cm.

ELECTRICAL EQUIPMENT voltage: 12 V; battery: 26 Ah; generator type: dynamo, 250 W; ignition distributor: Denso; headlamps: 2.

DIMENSIONS AND WEIGHT wheel base: 70.08 in, 1,780 mm; front track: 43.70 in, 1,110 mm; rear track: 44.09 in, 1,120 mm; overall length: 117.91 in, 2,995 mm; overall width: 50.98 in, 1,295 mm; overall height: 65.16 in, 1,655 mm; ground clearance: 8.27 in, 210 mm; dry weight: 1,147 lb, 520 kg; distribution of weight: 49% front axle, 51% rear axle; turning circle (between walls): 24.9 ft, 7.6 m; fuel tank capacity: 5.7 imp gal, 6.9 US gal, 26 l.

BODY open; doors: none; seats: 2-4; front seats: separate.

PRACTICAL INSTRUCTIONS fuel: 88 oct petrol; engine sump, gearbox and final drive oil: 5.3 imp pt, 6.3 US pt, 3 l, SAE 20W-30, change every 3,100 miles, 5,000 km; tappet clearances: inlet 0.004 in, 0.10 mm, exhaust 0.004 in, 0.10 mm; valve timing: inlet opens 5° before tdc and closes 25° after bdc, exhaust opens 40° before bdc and closes 5° after tdc; normal tyre pressure: front 24 psi, 1.7 atm, rear 24 psi, 1.7 atm.

HONDA Z TS Coupé

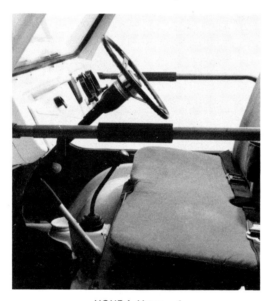

HONDA Vamos 4

HONDA "77" De Luxe Sedan

N 600 Sedan

PRICE: —

ENGINE front, 4 stroke; cylinders: 2, in line; bore and stroke: 2.91 x 2.74 in, 74 x 69.6 mm; engine capacity: 36.6 cu in, 599 cu cm; compression ratio: 8.5; max power (SAE): 36 hp at 6,000 rpm; max torque (SAE): 32 lb ft, 4.4 kg m at 2,500 rpm; max engine rpm: 8,000; specific power: 60.1 hp/l; cylinder block: light alloy; cylinder head: light alloy; crankshaft bearings: 3, on roller bearings; valves: 2 per cylinder, overhead, rockers; camshafts: 1, overhead; lubrication: gear pump, full flow filter; lubricating system capacity: 5.3 imp pt, 6.3 US pt, 3 l; carburation: 1 Keihin CV horizontal carburettor; fuel feed: electric pump; cooling system: aircooled.

TRANSMISSION driving wheels: front; clutch: single dry plate (diaphragm); gearbox: mechanical, in unit with engine; gears: 4 + reverse; synchromesh gears: I, II, III, IV; gearbox ratios: I 2.529, II 1.565, III 1, IV 0.714, rev 2.437; gear lever: central; final drive: helical spur gears; axle ratio: 3.037; width of rims: 3.5''; tyres: 5.20 x 10.

PERFORMANCE max speeds: 22 mph, 35 km/h in 1st gear; 35 mph, 56 km/h in 2nd gear; 54 mph, 87 km/h in 3rd gear; 75 mph, 120 km/h in 4th gear; power-weight ratio: 22.7 lb/hp, 10.3 kg/hp; carrying capacity: 706 lb, 320 kg; acceleration: standing ¼ mile 22.4 sec; speed in top at 1,000 rpm: 12.7 mph, 20.5 km/h; fuel consumption: 47.1 m/imp gal, 39.2 m/US gal, 6 l x 100 km.

CHASSIS integral; front suspension: independent, by McPherson, coil springs/telescopic damper struts, lower wishbones; rear suspension: rigid axle, semi-elliptic leafsprings, telescopic dampers.

STEERING rack-and-pinion; turns of steering wheel lock to lock: 3.10.

BRAKES front disc, rear drum.

ELECTRICAL EQUIPMENT voltage: 12 V; battery: 40 Ah; generator type: alternator, 300 W; ignition distributor: Denso; headlamps: 2.

DIMENSIONS AND WEIGHT wheel base: 78.74 in, 2,000 mm; front track: 45.28 in, 1,150 mm; rear track: 43.50 in, 1,105 mm; overall length: 122.05 in, 3,100 mm; overall width: 50.98 in, 1,295 mm; overall height: 52.36 in, 1,330 mm; ground clearance: 6.30 in, 160 mm; dry weight: 1,356 lb, 615 kg; distribution of weight: 64% front axle, 36% rear axle; turning circle (between walls): 31.2 ft, 9.5 m; fuel tank capacity: 5.7 imp gal, 6.9 US gal, 26 l.

BODY saloon/sedan; doors: 2; seats: 4; front seats: separate.

PRACTICAL INSTRUCTIONS fuel: 88 oct petrol; engine sump, gearbox and final drive oil: 5.3 imp pt, 6.3 US pt, 3 l, SAE 20W-30, change every 3,100 miles, 5,000 km; tappet clearances: inlet 0.003 in, 0.08 mm, exhaust 0.005 in, 0.12 mm; normal tyre pressure: front 24 psi, 1.7 atm, rear 21 psi, 1.5 atm.

N 600 Automatic Sedan

See N 600 Sedan, except for:

PRICE: —

ENGINE max power (SAE): 38 hp at 6,000 rpm; specific power: 63.4 hp/l.

TRANSMISSION gearbox: Hondamatic automatic, hydraulic torque convertor with 3 ratios + reverse, constant-mesh.

PERFORMANCE max speed: 71 mph, 115 km/h; power-weight ratio: 35.7 lb/hp, 16.2 kg/hp; acceleration: standing ¼ mile 23 sec.

"77" De Luxe Sedan

PRICE EX WORKS: 578,000 yen.

ENGINE front, 4 stroke; cylinders: 4, transverse, in line; bore and stroke: 2.91 x 2.97 in, 74 x 75.5 mm; engine capacity: 79.2 cu in, 1,298 cu cm; compression ratio: 9; max power (DIN): 95 hp at 7,000 rpm; max torque (DIN): 76 lb ft, 10.5 kg m at 4,000 rpm; max engine rpm: 8,000; specific power: 73.2 hp/l; cylinder block: light alloy, wet liners; cylinder head: light alloy; crankshaft bearings: 5; valves: 2 per cylinder, overhead, rockers; camshafts: 1, overhead; lubrication: gear pump, full flow filter, dry sump; lubricating system capacity: 7 imp pt, 8.5 US pt, 4 l; carburation: 1 Keihin CV horizontal carburettor; fuel feed: electric pump; cooling system: aircooled.

TRANSMISSION driving wheels: front; clutch: single dry plate (diaphragm); gearbox: mechanical; gears: 4 + reverse; synchromesh gears: I, II, III, IV; gearbox ratios: I 3.446, II 2.014, III 1.367, IV 1, rev 3.692; gear lever: central; final drive: helical spur gears; axle ratio: 3.500; width of rims: 4''; tyres: 6.20 x 13.

PERFORMANCE max speeds: 33 mph, 53 km/h in 1st gear; 54 mph, 87 km/h in 2nd gear; 79 mph, 127 km/h in 3rd gear; 106 mph, 170 km/h in 4th gear; power-weight ratio: 21.2 lb/hp, 9.6 kg/hp; carrying capacity: 882 lb, 400 kg;

HONDA Z TS Coupé

HONDA Vamos 4

HONDA "77" De Luxe Sedan

acceleration: standing ¼ mile 17.5 sec; speed in direct drive at 1,000 rpm: 14.3 mph, 23 km/h; fuel consumption: 35.3 m/imp gal, 29.4 m/US gal, 8 l x 100 km.

CHASSIS integral, front auxiliary frame; front suspension: independent, by McPherson, coil springs/telescopic damper struts, lower wishbones; rear suspension: independent, swinging semi-axles (cross beam system), semi-elliptic leafsprings, telescopic dampers.

STEERING rack-and-pinion; turns of steering wheel lock to lock: 3.80.

BRAKES front disc, rear drum, servo; lining area: front 16.1 sq in, 104 sq cm, rear 40 sq in, 258 sq cm, total 56.1 sq in, 362 sq cm.

ELECTRICAL EQUIPMENT voltage: 12 V; battery: 35 Ah; generator type: alternator; ignition distributor: Hitachi; headlamps: 2.

DIMENSIONS AND WEIGHT wheel base: 88.58 in, 2,250 mm; front track: 49.02 in, 1,245 mm; rear track: 47.05 in, 1,195 mm; overall length: 157.28 in, 3,995 mm; overall width: 57.68 in, 1,465 mm; overall height: 52.95 in, 1,345 mm; ground clearance: 6.89 in, 175 mm; dry weight: 2,007 lb, 910 kg; distribution of weight: 61.5% front axle, 38.5% rear axle; turning circle (between walls): 31.5 ft, 9.6 m; fuel tank capacity: 9.9 imp gal, 11.9 US gal, 45 l.

BODY saloon/sedan; doors: 4; seats: 5; front seats: separate.

PRACTICAL INSTRUCTIONS fuel: 90 oct petrol; engine sump oil: 7 imp pt, 8.5 US pt, 4 l, SAE 20W-30, change every 3,100 miles, 5,000 km; gearbox and final drive oil: 3.5 imp pt, 4.2 US pt, 2 l, SAE 80-90, change every 12,400 miles, 20,000 km; greasing: none; tappet clearances: inlet 0.004 in, 0.10 mm, exhaust 0.004 in, 0.10 mm; valve timing: inlet opens 10° before tdc and closes 20° after bdc, exhaust opens 40° before bdc and closes 10° after tdc; normal tyre pressure: front 23 psi, 1.6 atm, rear 20 psi, 1.4 atm.

OPTIONAL ACCESSORIES air-conditioning system.

"77" Automatic De Luxe Sedan

See "77" De Luxe Sedan, except for:

PRICE: —

ENGINE max power (DIN): 80 hp at 6,500 rpm; max torque (DIN): 74 lb ft, 10.2 kg m at 4,000 rpm; specific power: 61.6 hp/l.

TRANSMISSION gearbox: Hondamatic automatic, hydraulic torque convertor with 3 ratios + reverse; gearbox ratios: I 2.381, II 1.414, III 1, rev 3.214; selector lever: central.

PERFORMANCE max speeds: 42 mph, 67 km/h in 1st gear; 70 mph, 112 km/h in 2nd gear; 93 mph, 150 km/h in 3rd gear; power-weight ratio: 25.1 lb/hp, 11.4 kg/hp.

PRACTICAL INSTRUCTIONS gearbox oil: 10.6 imp pt, 12.7 US pt, 6 l, Automatic transmission fluid, change every 12,400 miles, 20,000 km; valve timing: inlet opens 10° before tdc and closes 20° after bdc, exhaust opens 40° before bdc and closes 10° after tdc.

"7" De Luxe Coupé

See "77" De Luxe Sedan, except for:

PRICE EX WORKS: 598,000 yen.

PERFORMANCE max speed: 109 mph, 175 km/h; power-weight ratio: 20.7 lb/hp, 9.4 kg/hp.

ELECTRICAL EQUIPMENT headlamps: 4.

DIMENSIONS AND WEIGHT overall length: 162.99 in, 4,140 mm; overall width: 58.86 in, 1,495 mm; overall height: 51.97 in, 1,320 mm; dry weight: 1,973 lb, 895 kg; distribution of weight: 63% front axle, 37% rear axle; turning circle (between walls): 35.4 ft, 10.8 m.

BODY coupé; doors: 2; seats: 4.

OPTIONAL ACCESSORIES air-conditioning system; S and Custom versions.

"7" Automatic De Luxe Coupé

See "7" De Luxe Coupé, except for:

PRICE EX WORKS: 636,000 yen.

ENGINE max power (DIN): 80 hp at 6,500 rpm; max torque (DIN): 74 lb ft, 10.2 kg m at 4,000 rpm; specific power: 61.6 hp/l.

TRANSMISSION gearbox: Hondamatic automatic, hydraulic torque convertor with 3 ratios + reverse; gearbox ratios: I 2.381, II 1.414, III 1, rev 3.214; selector lever: central.

PERFORMANCE max speeds: 42 mph, 67 km/h in 1st gear;

"7" AUTOMATIC DE LUXE COUPÉ

70 mph, 112 km/h in 2nd gear; 93 mph, 150 km/h in 3rd gear; power-weight ratio: 25.4 lb/hp, 11.5 kg/hp.

DIMENSIONS AND WEIGHT dry weight: 2,029 lb, 920 kg.

PRACTICAL INSTRUCTIONS gearbox oil: 10.6 imp pt, 12.7 US pt, 6 l, Automatic transmission fluid, change every 12,400 miles, 20,000 km; valve timing: inlet opens 10° before tdc and closes 20° after bdc, exhaust opens 40° before bdc and closes 10° after tdc.

"9" De Luxe Coupé

See "7" De Luxe Coupé, except for:

PRICE EX WORKS: 687,000 yen.

ENGINE compression ratio: 9.3; max power (SAE): 110 hp at 7,300 rpm; max torque (SAE): 83 lb ft, 11.5 kg m at 5,000 rpm; max engine rpm: 8,500; specific power: 84.7 hp/l; carburation: 4 Keihin horizontal carburettors.

PERFORMANCE max speeds: 34 mph, 55 km/h in 1st gear; 58 mph, 93 km/h in 2nd gear; 86 mph, 138 km/h in 3rd gear; 115 mph, 185 km/h in 4th gear; power-weight ratio: 18.1 lb/hp, 8.2 kg/hp.

PRACTICAL INSTRUCTIONS valve timing: inlet opens 5° before tdc and closes 40° after bdc, exhaust opens 40° before bdc and closes 5° after tdc.

OPTIONAL ACCESSORIES air-conditioning system and S and Custom versions.

ISUZU   JAPAN

Unicab KR80

PRICE: —

ENGINE front, 4 stroke; cylinders: 4, in line; bore and stroke: 2.95 x 2.95 in, 75 x 75 mm; engine capacity: 80.9 cu in, 1,325 cu cm; compression ratio: 7.5; max power (SAE): 58 hp at 5,000 rpm; max torque (SAE): 71 lb ft, 9.8 kg m at 1,800 rpm; max engine rpm: 5,000; specific power: 43.8 hp/l; cylinder block: cast iron; cylinder head: cast iron; crankshaft bearings: 5; valves: 2 per cylinder, overhead, push-rods and rockers; camshafts: 1, side; lubrication: rotary pump, full flow filter; lubricating system capacity: 5.6 imp pt, 6.8 US pt, 3.2 l; carburation: 1 Hitachi-Solex downdraught carburettor; fuel feed: mechanical pump; cooling system: water; cooling system capacity: 10.6 imp pt, 12.7 US pt, 6 l.

TRANSMISSION driving wheels: rear; clutch: single dry plate; gearbox: mechanical; gears: 4 + reverse; synchromesh gears: I, II, III, IV; gearbox ratios: I 4.314, II 2.842, III 1.630, IV 1, rev 4.469; gear lever: central; final drive: hypoid bevel; axle ratio: 5.125; tyres: 6.00 x 14.

PERFORMANCE max speeds: 17 mph, 27 km/h in 1st gear; 25 mph, 40 km/h in 2nd gear; 45 mph, 73 km/h in 3rd gear; 71 mph, 115 km/h in 4th gear; power-weight ratio: 36.4 lb/hp, 16.5 kg/hp; carrying capacity: 882 lb, 400 kg; speed in direct drive at 1,000 rpm: 14.3 mph, 23 km/h; fuel consumption: 35.3 m/imp gal, 29.4 m/US gal, 8 l x 100 km.

CHASSIS box-type ladder frame; front suspension: independent, wishbones, torsion bars, telescopic dampers; rear suspension: rigid axle, semi-elliptic leafsprings, telescopic dampers.

STEERING worm and roller.

BRAKES drum; area rubbed by linings: front 44.8 sq in, 289 sq cm, rear 44.8 sq in, 289 sq cm, total 89.6 sq in, 578 sq cm.

ELECTRICAL EQUIPMENT voltage: 12 V; battery: 40 Ah; generator type: alternator, 300 W; ignition distributor: Hitachi; headlamps: 2.

DIMENSIONS AND WEIGHT wheel base: 82.68 in, 2,100 mm; front track: 48.03 in, 1,220 mm; rear track: 47.24 in, 1,200 mm; overall length: 148.62 in, 3,775 mm; overall width: 59.05 in, 1,500 mm; overall height: 67.32 in, 1,710 mm; ground clearance: 8.07 in, 205 mm; dry weight: 2,117 lb, 960 kg; distribution of weight: 54.8% front axle, 45.2% rear axle; turning circle (between walls): 29.5 ft, 9 m; fuel tank capacity: 7.7 imp gal, 9.2 US gal, 35 l.

BODY open; doors: none; seats: 4; front seats: separate.

PRACTICAL INSTRUCTIONS fuel: 80-85 oct petrol; engine sump oil: 5.6 imp pt, 6.8 US pt, 3.2 l, SAE 20W-30, change every 1,900 miles, 3,000 km; gearbox oil: 3.3 imp pt, 4 US pt, 1.9 l, SAE 30, change every 11,200 miles, 18,000 km; final drive oil: 2.1 imp pt, 2.5 US pt, 1.2 l, SAE 90, change every 11,200 miles, 18,000 km; greasing: every 11,200 miles, 18,000 km, 8 points; tappet clearances: inlet 0.010 in, 0.25 mm, exhaust 0.014 in, 0.35 mm; valve timing inlet opens 15° before tdc and closes 73° after bdc, exhaust opens 55° before bdc and closes 29° after tdc; normal tyre pressure: front 24 psi, 1.7 atm, rear 24 psi, 1.7 atm.

HONDA "9" Custom Coupé

ISUZU Unicab KR80

ISUZU 4-door Bellett 1600 Sedan

Unicab KR85

ee Unicab KR80, except for:

RICE: —

NGINE bore and stroke: 3.11 x 2.95 in, 79 x 75 mm; engine apacity: 89.8 cu in, 1,471 cu cm; compression ratio: 8.2; nax power (SAE): 68 hp at 5,000 rpm; max torque (SAE): 2 lb ft, 11.3 kg m at 2,200 rpm; specific power: 46.2 hp/l; ubricating system capacity: 6.9 imp pt, 8.2 US pt, 3.9 l.

RANSMISSION axle ratio: 4.556.

ERFORMANCE max speeds: 19 mph, 30 km/h in 1st gear; 9 mph, 47 km/h in 2nd gear; 50 mph, 80 km/h in 3rd ear; 75 mph, 120 km/h in 4th gear; power-weight ratio: 2 lb/hp, 14.5 kg/hp; speed in direct drive at 1,000 rpm: 4.9 mph, 24 km/h; fuel consumption: 33.2 m/imp gal, 7.7 m/US gal, 8.5 l x 100 km.

DIMENSIONS AND WEIGHT overall height: 74.41 in, 1,890 mm; dry weight: 2,172 lb, 985 kg.

PTIONAL ACCESSORIES 5.125 axle ratio.

2-door Bellett 1500 Special Sedan

RICE EX WORKS: 545,000 yen.

ENGINE front, 4 stroke; cylinders: 4, in line; bore and stroke: 3.11 x 2.95 in, 79 x 75 mm; engine capacity: 89.8 cu in, 1,471 cu cm; compression ratio: 8.5; max power SAE): 78 hp at 5,200 rpm; max torque (SAE): 86 lb ft, 1.8 kg m at 2,600 rpm; max engine rpm: 5,800; specific power: 53 hp/l; cylinder block: cast iron; cylinder head: ight alloy; crankshaft bearings: 5; valves: 2 per cylinder, verhead, push-rods and rockers; camshafts: 1, side; ubrication: rotary pump, full flow filter; lubricating system apacity: 5.6 imp pt, 6.8 US pt, 3.2 l; carburation: 1 Nikki-Stromberg downdraught twin barrel carburettor; fuel feed: nechanical pump; cooling system: water; cooling system apacity: 13.2 imp pt, 15.9 US pt, 7.5 l.

TRANSMISSION driving wheels: rear; clutch: single dry late; gearbox: mechanical; gears: 4 + reverse, synchronesh gears: I, II, III, IV; gearbox ratios: I 3.507, II 2.175, II 1.418, IV 1, rev 3.927; gear lever: central; final drive: ypoid bevel; axle ratio: 4.100; width of rims: 4.5''; tyres: .60 x 13.

PERFORMANCE max speeds: 28 mph, 45 km/h in 1st gear; 45 mph, 72 km/h in 2nd gear; 69 mph, 111 km/h in 3rd ear; 93 mph, 150 km/h in 4th gear; power-weight ratio: 5.6 lb/hp, 11.6 kg/hp; carrying capacity: 882 lb, 400 kg; standing ¼ mile 18.9 sec; speed in direct drive at 1,000 pm: 16.9 mph, 27.2 km/h; fuel consumption: 31.7 m/imp gal, 26.4 m/US gal, 8.9 l x 100 km.

CHASSIS integral; front suspension: independent, wishbones, coil springs, anti-roll bar, telescopic dampers; rear suspension: independent, oblique swinging trailing arms, ransverse compensating leafspring (single), coil springs, anti-roll bar, telescopic dampers.

STEERING rack-and-pinion; turns of steering wheel lock to lock: 3.

BRAKES drum; area rubbed by linings: front 44.8 sq in, 289 sq cm, rear 44.8 sq in, 289 sq cm, total 89.6 sq in, 578 sq cm.

ELECTRICAL EQUIPMENT voltage: 12 V; battery: 35 Ah; generator type: alternator, 300 W; ignition distributor: Hitachi; headlamps: 4.

DIMENSIONS AND WEIGHT wheel base: 92.52 in, 2,350 mm; front track: 48.62 in, 1,235 mm; rear track: 47.64 in, 1,210 mm; overall length: 158.07 in, 4,015 mm; overall width: 58.86 in, 1,495 mm; overall height: 54.72 in, 1,390 mm; ground clearance: 8.07 in, 205 mm; dry weight: 1,996 lb, 905 kg; distribution of weight: 55% front axle, 45% rear axle; turning circle (between walls): 32.8 ft, 10 m; fuel tank capacity: 8.8 imp gal, 10.6 US gal, 40 l.

BODY saloon/sedan; doors: 2; seats: 5; front seats: separate.

PRACTICAL INSTRUCTIONS fuel: 90 oct petrol; engine sump oil: 5.6 imp pt, 6.8 US pt, 3.2 l, SAE 20W-30, change every 3,100 miles, 5,000 km; gearbox oil: 3.5 imp pt, 4.2 US pt, 2 l, SAE 30, change every 24,900 miles, 40,000 km; final drive oil: 1.2 imp pt, 1.5 US pt, 0.7 l, SAE 90/140, change every 24,900 miles, 40,000 km; greasing: every 9,600 miles, 18,000 km, 18 points; tappet clearances: inlet 0.008 in, 0.20 mm, exhaust 0.012 in, 0.30 mm; valve timing: inlet opens 15° before tdc and closes 73° after bdc, exhaust opens 55° before bdc and closes 29° after tdc; normal tyre pressure: front 20 psi, 1.4 atm, rear 20 psi, 1.4 atm.

4-door Bellett 1500 Special Sedan

See 2-door Bellett 1500 Special Sedan, except for:

PRICE EX WORKS: 575,000 yen.

PERFORMANCE power-weight ratio: 25.8 lb/hp, 11.7 kg/hp.

DIMENSIONS AND WEIGHT dry weight: 2,018 lb, 915 kg.

HONDA "9" Custom Coupé

ISUZU Unicab KR85

ISUZU Bellett 1600 Sedan

2-door Bellett 1600 Sedan

See 2-door Bellett 1500 Special Sedan, except for:

PRICE EX WORKS: 616,000 yen.

ENGINE bore and stroke: 3.23 x 2.95 in, 82 x 75 mm; engine capacity: 96.7 cu in, 1,584 cu cm; compression ratio: 8.7; max power (SAE): 90 hp at 5,400 rpm; max torque (SAE): 92 lb ft, 12.7 kg m at 3,000 rpm; max engine rpm: 6,000; specific power: 56.8 hp/l; valves: 2 per cylinder, overhead, rockers; camshafts: 1, overhead.

PERFORMANCE max speeds: 29 mph, 46 km/h in 1st gear; 45 mph, 73 km/h in 2nd gear; 70 mph, 112 km/h in 3rd gear; 96 mph, 155 km/h in 4th gear; power-weight ratio: 22.5 lb/hp, 10.2 kg/hp; speed in direct drive at 1,000 rpm: 16.2 mph, 26 km/h; fuel consumption: 31.4 m/imp gal, 26.1 m/US gal, 9 l x 100 km.

DIMENSIONS AND WEIGHT dry weight: 2,018 lb, 915 kg.

PRACTICAL INSTRUCTIONS valve timing: inlet opens 34° before tdc and closes 70° after bdc, exhaust opens 54° before bdc and closes 18° after tdc; normal tyre pressure: front 24 psi, 1.7 atm, rear 30 psi, 2.1 atm.

4-door Bellett 1600 Sedan

See 2-door Bellett 1600 Sedan, except for:

PRICE EX WORKS: 657,000 yen.

PERFORMANCE power-weight ratio: 22.7 lb/hp, 10.3 kg/hp.

DIMENSIONS AND WEIGHT dry weight: 2,040 lb, 925 kg.

2-door Bellett 1600 Sports Sedan

See 2-door Bellett 1600 Sedan, except for:

PRICE EX WORKS: 679,000 yen.

ENGINE compression ratio: 9.7; max power (SAE): 103 hp at 5,800 rpm; max torque (SAE): 99 lb ft, 13.6 kg m at 4,200 rpm; max engine rpm: 6,600; specific power: 65 hp/l; carburation: 2 Hitachi SU HJD42W-1 horizontal carburettors.

TRANSMISSION axle ratio: 3.727.

PERFORMANCE max speeds: 34 mph, 55 km/h in 1st gear; 56 mph, 90 km/h in 2nd gear; 81 mph, 130 km/h in 3rd gear; 103 mph, 165 km/h in 4th gear; power-weight ratio: 19.7 lb/hp, 8.9 kg/hp; acceleration: standing ¼ mile 17.7 sec; speed in direct drive at 1,000 rpm: 15.8 mph, 25.5 km/h; fuel consumption: 30.7 m/imp gal, 25.6 m/US gal, 9.2 l x 100 km.

BRAKES front disc, rear drum; lining area: front 16.7 sq in, 108 sq cm, rear 44.8 sq in, 289 sq cm, total 61.5 sq in, 397 sq cm.

DIMENSIONS AND WEIGHT front track: 49.02 in, 1,245 mm; rear track: 47.05 in, 1,195 mm; dry weight: 2,018 lb, 915 kg.

PRACTICAL INSTRUCTIONS fuel: 98-100 oct petrol; valve timing: inlet opens 31° before tdc and closes 67° after bdc, exhaust opens 59° after bdc and closes 23° after tdc.

4-door Bellett 1600 Sports Sedan

See 2-door Bellett 1600 Sports Sedan, except for:

PRICE EX WORKS: 720,000 yen.

PERFORMANCE power-weight ratio: 19.8 lb/hp, 9 kg/hp.

DIMENSIONS AND WEIGHT dry weight: 2,051 lb, 930 kg.

Bellett 1600 GT Coupé

See 2-door Bellett 1600 Sports Sedan, except for:

PRICE EX WORKS: 830.000 yen.

TRANSMISSION gearbox ratios: I 3.207, II 1.989, III 1.356, IV 1, rev 3.592; tyres: 6.45 x 13.

PERFORMANCE max speeds: 37 mph, 60 km/h in 1st gear; 60 mph, 97 km/h in 2nd gear; 87 mph, 140 km/h in 3rd gear; 106 mph, 170 km/h in 4th gear; power-weight ratio: 20.1 lb/hp, 9.1 kg/hp; carrying capacity: 617 lb, 280 kg; acceleration: standing ¼ mile 17.5 sec; speed in direct drive at 1,000 rpm: 16.5 mph, 26.5 km/h.

ELECTRICAL EQUIPMENT battery: 40 Ah.

DIMENSIONS AND WEIGHT front track: 49.61 in, 1,260 mm; rear track: 48.43 in, 1,230 mm; overall height: 52.55 in, 1,335 mm; dry weight: 2,073 lb, 940 kg.

BODY coupé; seats: 2 + 2.

PRACTICAL INSTRUCTIONS normal tyre pressure: front 26 psi, 1.8 atm, rear 31 psi, 2.2 atm.

Bellett 1600 GTR Coupé

See Bellett 1600 GT Coupé, except for:

PRICE EX WORKS: 1,110,000 yen.

ENGINE compression ratio: 10.3; max power (DIN): 120 hp at 6,400 rpm; max torque (DIN): 105 lb ft, 14.5 kg m at 5,000 rpm; max engine rpm: 7,000; specific power: 76 hp/l; valves: 2 per cylinder, overhead, thimble tappets; camshafts: 2, overhead; lubricating system capacity: 7.9 imp pt, 9.5 US pt, 4.5 l; carburation: 2 Mikuni-Solex 40 PHH downdraught twin barrel carburettors; fuel feed: electric pump.

TRANSMISSION clutch: single dry plate (diaphragm); gearbox ratios: I 3.467, II 1.989, III 1.356, IV 1, rev 3.592; final drive: hypoid bevel, limited slip; tyres: 165 x 13.

CHASSIS rear suspension: no anti-roll bar.

PERFORMANCE max speeds: 35 mph, 57 km/h in 1st gear; 64 mph, 103 km/h in 2nd gear; 91 mph, 147 km/h in 3rd gear; 118 mph, 190 km/h in 4th gear; power-weight ratio: 17.9 lb/hp, 8.1 kg/hp; acceleration: standing ¼ mile 16.6 sec; speed in direct drive at 1,000 rpm: 17.4 mph, 28 km/h; fuel consumption: 28.2 m/imp gal, 23.5 m/US gal, 10 l x 100 km.

ELECTRICAL EQUIPMENT generator type: alternator, 40 A.

DIMENSIONS AND WEIGHT rear track: 48.82 in, 1,240 mm; overall length: 157.68 in, 4,005 mm; overall height: 52.17 in, 1,325 mm; ground clearance: 7.68 in, 195 mm; dry weight: 2,139 lb, 970 kg.

PRACTICAL INSTRUCTIONS valve timing: inlet opens 40° before tdc and closes 44° after bdc, exhaust opens 57° before bdc and closes 15° after tdc.

Bellett 1800 GT Coupé

See Bellett 1600 GT Coupé, except for:

PRICE EX WORKS: 870,000 yen.

ENGINE bore and stroke: 3.31 x 3.23 in, 84 x 82 mm; engine capacity: 110.9 cu in, 1,817 cu cm; max power (DIN): 115 hp at 5,800 rpm; max torque (DIN): 112 lb ft, 15.5 kg m at 4,200 rpm; specific power: 63.3 hp/l; carburation: 2 Hitachi SU type HJD42W-5 horizontal carburettors.

PERFORMANCE max speed: 112 mph, 180 km/h; power-weight ratio: 18.1 lb/hp, 8.2 kg/hp; acceleration: standing ¼ mile 17.2 sec.

DIMENSIONS AND WEIGHT rear track: 48.82 in, 1,240 mm; overall height: 52.17 in, 1,325 mm; ground clearance: 7.68 in, 195 mm; dry weight: 1,863 lb, 845 kg; distribution of weight: 55.6% front axle, 44.4% rear axle.

117 Coupé

PRICE EX WORKS: 1,670,000 yen.

ENGINE front, 4 stroke; cylinders: 4, vertical, in line; bore and stroke: 3.23 x 2.95 in, 82 x 75 mm; engine capacity: 96.7 cu in, 1,584 cu cm; compression ratio: 10.3; max power (DIN): 120 hp at 6,400 rpm; max torque (DIN): 105 lb ft, 14.5 kg m at 5,000 rpm; max engine rpm: 7,000; specific power: 75.7 hp/l; cylinder block: cast iron; cylinder head: light alloy; crankshaft bearings: 5; valves: 2 per cylinder, overhead, thimble tappets; camshafts: 2, overhead; lubrication: rotary pump, full flow filter; lubricating system capacity: 8.8 imp pt, 10.6 US pt, 5 l; carburation: 2 Mikuni-Solex 40 PHH horizontal twin barrel carburettors; fuel feed: electric pump; cooling system: water; cooling system capacity: 11.4 imp pt, 13.7 US pt, 6.5 l.

TRANSMISSION driving wheels: rear; clutch: single dry plate; gearbox: mechanical; gears: 4 + reverse; synchromesh gears: I, II, III, IV; gearbox ratios: I 3.467, II 1.989, III 1.356, IV 1, rev 3.592; gear lever: central; final drive: hypoid bevel; axle ratio: 4.100; width of rims: 4.5''; tyres: 6.45 x 14.

PERFORMANCE max speeds: 30 mph, 48 km/h in 1st gear; 55 mph, 88 km/h in 2nd gear; 91 mph, 146 km/h in 3rd gear; 118 mph, 190 km/h in 4th gear; power-weight ratio: 20.1 lb/hp, 9.1 kg/hp; carrying capacity: 706 lb, 320 kg; acceleration: standing ¼ mile 16.8 sec; speed in direct drive at 1,000 rpm: 17.4 mph, 28 km/h; fuel consumption: 28.2 m/imp gal, 23.5 m/US gal, 10 l x 100 km.

CHASSIS integral with platform; front suspension: independent, wishbones, coil springs, anti-roll bar, telescopic dampers; rear suspension: rigid axle, semi-elliptic leaf-springs, torque arms, telescopic dampers.

STEERING worm and roller; turns of steering wheel lock to lock: 3.50.

BRAKES front disc, rear drum, servo; lining area: front 16.7 sq in, 108 sq cm, rear 57.5 sq in, 371 sq cm, total 74.2 sq in, 479 sq cm.

ISUZU Bellett 1800 GT Coupé

ISUZU 117 EC Coupé

ISUZU Florian 1800 TS Sedan

ELECTRICAL EQUIPMENT voltage: 12 V; battery: 35 Ah; generator type: alternator, 500 W; ignition distributor: Hitachi; headlamps: 4.

DIMENSIONS AND WEIGHT wheel base: 98.43 in, 2,500 mm; front track: 52.17 in, 1,325 mm, rear track: 51.57 in, 1,310 mm; overall length: 168.50 in, 4,280 mm; overall width: 62.99 in, 1,600 mm; overall height: 51.97 in, 1,320 mm; ground clearance: 7.09 in, 180 mm; dry weight: 2,403 lb, 1,090 kg; distribution of weight: 55% front axle, 45% rear axle; turning circle (between walls): 34.1 ft, 10.4 m; fuel tank capacity: 12.8 imp gal, 15.3 US gal, 58 l.

BODY coupé; doors: 2; seats: 4; front seats: separate.

PRACTICAL INSTRUCTIONS fuel: 100 oct petrol; engine sump oil: 8.8 imp pt, 10.6 US pt, 5 l, SAE 20W-30, change every 3,100 miles, 5,000 km; gearbox oil: 2.1 imp pt, 2.5 US pt, 1.2 l, SAE 30, change every 24,900 miles, 40,000 km; final drive oil: 1.8 imp pt, 2.1 US pt, 1 l, SAE 90/140, change every 24,900 miles, 40,000 km; valve timing: inlet opens 40° before tdc and closes 44° after bdc, exhaust opens 57° before bdc and closes 15° after tdc; normal tyre pressure: front 26 psi, 1.8 atm, rear 26 psi, 1.8 atm.

OPTIONAL ACCESSORIES air-conditioning system.

117 EC Coupé

See 117 Coupé, except for:

PRICE EX WORKS: 1,870,000 yen.

ENGINE max power (DIN): 130 hp at 6,600 rpm; max torque (DIN): 109 lb ft, 15 kg m at 5,000 rpm; specific power: 82.1 hp/l; carburation: Bosch electronically-controlled injection system.

PERFORMANCE max speeds: 34 mph, 55 km/h in 1st gear; 60 mph, 96 km/h in 2nd gear; 88 mph, 142 km/h in 3rd gear; 118 mph, 190 km/h in 4th gear; power-weight ratio: 18.5 lb/hp, 8.4 kg/hp.

117 1800 Coupé

See 117 Coupé, except for:

PRICE EX WORKS: 1,470,000 yen.

ENGINE bore and stroke: 3.31 x 3.23 in, 84 x 82 mm; engine capacity: 110.9 cu in, 1,817 cu cm; compression ratio: 9.7; max power (DIN): 115 hp at 5,800 rpm; max torque (DIN): 112 lb ft, 15.5 kg m at 4,200 rpm; specific power: 63.3 hp/l; valves: 2 per cylinder, overhead, rockers; camshafts: 1, overhead; carburation: 2 Hitachi SU type HJD42W-5 horizontal carburettors.

TRANSMISSION gearbox ratios: I 3.207, II 1.989, III 1.356, IV 1, rev 3.592; axle ratio: 3.727; tyres: 6.45 x 13.

PERFORMANCE max speeds: 34 mph, 55 km/h in 1st gear; 56 mph, 90 km/h in 2nd gear; 82 mph, 132 km/h in 3rd gear; 112 mph, 180 km/h in 4th gear; power-weight ratio: 20.5 lb/hp, 9.3 kg/hp; acceleration: standing ¼ mile 17.6 sec.

DIMENSIONS AND WEIGHT front track: 52.76 in, 1,340 mm; rear track: 51.77 in, 1,315 mm; overall height: 51.57 in, 1,310 mm; ground clearance: 6.69 in, 170 mm; dry weight: 2,359 lb, 1,070 kg.

PRACTICAL INSTRUCTIONS valve timing: inlet opens 31° before tdc and closes 67° after bdc, exhaust opens 59° before bdc and closes 23° after tdc.

Florian 1800 De Luxe Sedan

PRICE EX WORKS: 740,000 yen.

ENGINE front, 4 stroke; cylinders: 4, vertical, in line; bore and stroke: 3.31 x 3.23 in, 84 x 82 mm; engine capacity: 110.9 cu in, 1,817 cu cm; compression ratio: 8.7; max power (DIN): 100 hp at 5,400 rpm; max torque (DIN): 106 lb ft, 14.6 kg m at 3,000 rpm; max engine rpm: 6,300; specific power: 55 hp/l; cylinder block: cast iron; cylinder head: light alloy; crankshaft bearings: 5; valves: 2 per cylinder, overhead, rockers; camshafts: 1, overhead; lubrication: rotary pump, full flow filter; lubricating system capacity: 6.3 imp pt, 7.6 US pt, 3.6 l; carburation: 1 Hitachi Rochester DRJ340 downdraught twin barrel carburettor; fuel feed: mechanical pump; cooling system: water; cooling system capacity: 13.2 imp pt, 15.9 US pt, 7.5 l.

TRANSMISSION driving wheels: rear; clutch: single dry plate (diaphragm); gearbox: mechanical; gears: 4 + reverse; synchromesh gears: I, II, III, IV; gearbox ratios: I 3.507, II 2.175, III 1.418, IV 1, rev 3.927; gear lever: central; final drive: hypoid bevel; axle ratio: 3.727; width of rims: 4.5''; tyres: 6.45 x 13.

PERFORMANCE max speeds: 30 mph, 48 km/h in 1st gear;

ISUZU Bellett 1800 GT Coupé

ISUZU 117 EC Coupé

ISUZU Florian 1800 De Luxe Sedan

48 mph, 78 km/h in 2nd gear; 75 mph, 120 km/h in 3rd gear; 99 mph, 160 km/h in 4th gear; power-weight ratio: 21.2 lb/hp, 8.6 kg/hp; carrying capacity: 1,058 lb, 480 kg; acceleration: standing ¼ mile 18.1 sec; speed in direct drive at 1,000 rpm: 15.8 mph, 25.5 km/h; fuel consumption: 25.7 m/imp gal, 21.4 m/US gal, 11 l x 100 km.

CHASSIS integral; front suspension: independent, wishbones, coil springs, anti-roll bar, telescopic dampers; rear suspension: rigid axle, semi-elliptic leafsprings, telescopic dampers.

STEERING worm and roller; turns of steering wheel lock to lock: 3.50.

BRAKES drum, servo; lining area: front 51.9 sq in, 335 sq cm, rear 57.5 sq in, 371 sq cm, total 109.4 sq in, 706 sq cm.

ELECTRICAL EQUIPMENT voltage: 12 V; battery: 35 Ah; generator type: alternator, 35 A; ignition distributor: Hitachi; headlamps: 4.

DIMENSIONS AND WEIGHT wheel base: 98.43 in, 2,500 mm; front track: 52.17 in, 1,325 mm; rear track: 51.77 in, 1,315 mm; overall length: 169.49 in, 4,305 mm; overall width: 62.99 in, 1,600 mm; overall height: 56.89 in, 1,445 mm; ground clearance: 6.69 in, 170 mm; dry weight: 2,117 lb, 960 kg; distribution of weight: 55% front axle, 45% rear axle; turning circle (between walls): 34.1 ft, 10.4 m; fuel tank capacity: 10.1 imp gal, 12.1 US gal, 46 l.

BODY saloon/sedan; doors: 4; seats: 5; front seats: separate.

PRACTICAL INSTRUCTIONS fuel: 85-90 oct petrol; engine sump oil: 6.3 imp pt, 7.6 US pt, 3.6 l, SAE 20W-30, change every 3,100 miles, 5,000 km; gearbox oil: 2.1 imp pt, 2.5 US pt, 1.2 l, SAE 30, change every 24,900 miles, 40,000 km; final drive oil: 1.8 imp pt, 2.1 US pt, 1 l, SAE 90/140, change every 24,900 miles, 40,000 km; greasing: none; tappet clearances: inlet 0.004 in, 0.10 mm, exhaust 0.006 in, 0.15 mm; valve timing: inlet opens 34° before tdc and closes 70° after bdc, exhaust opens 54° before bdc and closes 18° after tdc; normal tyre pressure: front 20 psi, 1.4 atm, rear 20 psi, 1.4 atm.

OPTIONAL ACCESSORIES 165 x 13 tyres; air-conditioning system.

Florian 1800 Automatic Sedan

See Florian 1800 De Luxe Sedan, except for:

TRANSMISSION gearbox: automatic, hydraulic torque convertor and planetary gears with 3 ratios + reverse; gearbox ratios: I 2.393, II 1.450, III 1, rev 2.094.

PERFORMANCE max speed: 96 mph, 155 km/h.

Florian 1800 TS Sedan

See Florian 1800 De Luxe Sedan, except for:

PRICE EX WORKS: 800,000 yen.

ENGINE compression ratio: 9.7; max power (DIN): 115 hp at 5,800 rpm; max torque (DIN): 112 lb ft, 15.5 kg m at 4,200 rpm; specific power: 63.3 hp/l; carburation: 2 Hitachi SU type HJD42W-5 horizontal twin barrel carburettors.

TRANSMISSION gearbox ratios: I 3.207, II 1.989, III 1.356, IV 1, rev 3.592.

PERFORMANCE max speeds: 34 mph, 55 km/h in 1st gear; 56 mph, 90 km/h in 2nd gear; 82 mph, 132 km/h in 3rd gear; 109 mph, 175 km/h in 4th gear; power-weight ratio: 18.5 lb/hp, 8.4 kg/hp; acceleration: standing ¼ mile 17.6 sec; speed in direct drive at 1,000 rpm: 17.3 mph, 27.8 km/h.

DIMENSIONS AND WEIGHT dry weight: 2,128 lb, 965 kg.

PRACTICAL INSTRUCTIONS valve timing: inlet opens 31° before tdc and closes 67° after bdc, exhaust opens 59° before bdc and closes 23° after tdc.

MAZDA   JAPAN

2-door Carol 360 De Luxe Sedan

PRICE EX WORKS: 345,000 yen.

ENGINE rear, transverse, 4 stroke; cylinders: 4, in line; bore and stroke: 1.81 x 2.13 in, 46 x 54 mm; engine capacity: 21.8 cu in, 358 cu cm; compression ratio: 10; max power (SAE): 20 hp at 7,000 rpm; max torque (SAE): 17 lb ft, 2.4 kg m at 3,000 rpm; max engine rpm: 7,400;

2-DOOR CAROL 360 DE LUXE SEDAN

specific power: 55.9 hp/l; cylinder block: light alloy, wet liners; cylinder head: light alloy; crankshaft bearings: 5; valves: 2 per cylinder, overhead, push-rods and rockers; camshafts: 1, side; lubrication: gear pump, full flow filter; lubricating system capacity: 4.4 imp pt, 5.3 US pt, 2.5 l; carburation: 1 Hitachi-Stromberg DCA 240 downdraught twin barrel carburettor; fuel feed: electric pump; cooling system: water; cooling system capacity: 6.7 imp pt, 8 US pt, 3.8 l.

TRANSMISSION driving wheels: rear; clutch: single dry plate, hydraulically controlled; gearbox: mechanical; gears: 4 + reverse; synchromesh gears: I, II, III, IV; gearbox ratios: I 3.700, II 2.160, III 1.480, IV 1, rev 5.230; gear lever: central; final drive: spiral bevel; axle ratio: 4.870; width of rims: 3.5''; tyres: 5.20 x 10.

PERFORMANCE max speeds: 16 mph, 26 km/h in 1st gear; 27 mph, 43 km/h in 2nd gear; 39 mph, 63 km/h in 3rd gear; 59 mph, 95 km/h in 4th gear; power-weight ratio: 59.5 lb/hp, 27 kg/hp; carrying capacity: 706 lb, 320 kg; acceleration: standing 1/4 mile 27.8 sec; speed in direct drive at 1,000 rpm: 8.1 mph, 13 km/h; fuel consumption: 74.3 m/imp gal, 61.9 m/US gal, 3.8 l x 100 km.

CHASSIS integral; front suspension: independent, twin swinging longitudinal trailing arms, rubber springs (torsion), telescopic dampers; rear suspension: independent, swinging longitudinal trailing arms, rubber springs (torsion), telescopic dampers.

STEERING rack-and-pinion; turns of steering wheel lock to lock: 2.82.

BRAKES drum, 2 front leading shoes; lining area: front 25.1 sq in, 162 sq cm, rear 25.1 sq in, 162 sq cm, total 50.2 sq in, 324 sq cm.

ELECTRICAL EQUIPMENT voltage: 12 V; battery: 32 Ah; generator type: dynamo, 230 W; ignition distributor: Mitsubishi; headlamps: 2.

DIMENSIONS AND WEIGHT wheel base: 76 in, 1,930 mm; front track: 42.12 in, 1,070 mm; rear track: 43.70 in, 1,110 mm; overall length: 117.70 in, 2,990 mm; overall width: 51 in, 1,295 mm; overall height: 51.97 in, 1,320 mm; ground clearance: 7.30 in, 185 mm; dry weight: 1,191 lb, 540 kg; distribution of weight: 41.8% front axle, 58.2% rear axle; turning circle (between walls): 26.2 ft, 8 m; fuel tank capacity: 4.5 imp gal, 5.3 US gal, 20 l.

BODY saloon/sedan; doors: 2; seats: 4; front seats: separate.

PRACTICAL INSTRUCTIONS fuel: 98-100 oct petrol; engine sump oil: 4.4 imp pt, 5.3 US pt, 2.5 l, SAE 10W-20 (winter) 30W-40 (summer), change every 1,900 miles, 3,000 km; gearbox and final drive oil: 4 imp pt, 4.9 US pt, 2.3 l, SAE 80, change every 12,400 miles, 20,000 km; greasing: none; tappet clearances: inlet 0.002 in, 0.05 mm, exhaust 0.002 in, 0.05 mm; valve timing: inlet opens 12° before tdc and closes 40° after bdc, exhaust opens 46° before bdc and closes 6° after tdc; normal tyre pressure: front 20 psi, 1.4 atm, rear 24 psi, 1.7 atm.

4-door Carol 360 De Luxe Sedan

See 2-door Carol 360 De Luxe Sedan, except for:

PRICE EX WORKS: 370,000 yen.

PERFORMANCE power-weight ratio: 63.3 lb/hp, 28.7 kg/hp.

DIMENSIONS AND WEIGHT dry weight: 1,268 lb, 575 kg.

2-door Familia 1000 De Luxe Sedan

PRICE: —

ENGINE front, 4 stroke; cylinders: 4, in line; bore and stroke: 2.76 x 2.52 in, 70 x 64 mm; engine capacity: 60.1 cu in, 985 cu cm; compression ratio: 8.8; max power (DIN): 62 hp at 6,000 rpm; max torque (DIN): 59 lb ft, 8.1 kg m at 3,500 rpm; max engine rpm: 6,200; specific power: 62.9 hp/l; cylinder block: cast iron; cylinder head: light alloy; crankshafts bearings: 5; valves: 2 per cylinder, overhead, rockers; camshafts: 1, overhead; lubrication: rotary pump, full flow filter; lubricating system capacity: 6.5 imp pt, 7.8 US pt, 3.7 l; carburation: 1 Hitachi downdraught twin barrel carburettor; fuel feed: mechanical pump; cooling system: water; cooling system capacity: 10.4 imp pt, 12.5 US pt, 5.9 l.

TRANSMISSION driving wheels: rear; clutch: single dry plate; gearbox: mechanical; gears: 4 + reverse; synchromesh gears: I, II, III, IV; gearbox ratios: I 3.655, II 2.185, III 1.425, IV 1, rev 3.655; gear lever: central; final drive: hypoid bevel; axle ratio: 4.377; tyres: 6.00 x 13.

PERFORMANCE max speeds: 25 mph, 40 km/h in 1st gear; 40 mph, 65 km/h in 2nd gear; 65 mph, 105 km/h in 3rd gear; 87 mph, 140 km/h in 4th gear; power-weight ratio:

MAZDA 4-door Carol 360 De Luxe Sedan

MAZDA 4-door Familia 1000 De Luxe Sedan

MAZDA Familia 1300 De Luxe Coupé

7.3 lb/hp, 12.4 kg/hp; carrying capacity: 882 lb, 400 kg; acceleration: standing ¼ mile 19.3 sec; speed in direct drive at 1,000 rpm: 14.9 mph, 24 km/h; fuel consumption: 2.1 m/imp gal, 26.7 m/US gal, 8.8 l x 100 km.

CHASSIS integral; front suspension: independent, by McPherson, coil springs/telescopic damper struts, lower wishbones, lower trailing links, anti-roll bar; rear suspension: rigid axle, semi-elliptic leafsprings, telescopic dampers.

STEERING recirculating ball; turns of steering wheel lock to lock: 3.80.

BRAKES drum; lining area: front 39.7 sq in, 256 sq cm, rear 39.7 sq in, 256 sq cm, total 79.4 sq in, 512 sq cm.

ELECTRICAL EQUIPMENT voltage: 12 V; battery: 35 Ah; generator type: alternator, 280 W; ignition distributor: Mitubishi; headlamps: 2.

DIMENSIONS AND WEIGHT wheel base: 88.98 in, 2,260 mm; front track: 47.63 in, 1,210 mm; rear track: 42.91 in, 1,090 mm; overall length: 149.41 in, 3,795 mm; overall width: 58.27 in, 1,480 mm; overall height: 54.72 in, 1,390 mm; ground clearance: 6.30 in, 160 mm; dry weight: 1,698 lb, 770 kg; distribution of weight: 56% front axle, 44% rear axle; turning circle (between walls): 29.5 ft, 9 m; fuel tank capacity: 8.8 imp gal, 10.6 US gal, 40 l.

BODY saloon/sedan; doors: 2; seats: 5; front seats: separate.

PRACTICAL INSTRUCTIONS fuel: 85-90 oct petrol; engine sump oil: 6.5 imp pt, 7.8 US pt, 3.7 l, SAE 20W-30, change every 3,700 miles, 6,000 km; gearbox oil: 2.3 imp pt, 2.7 US pt, 1.3 l, SAE 80, change every 12,400 miles, 20,000 km; final drive oil: 2.1 imp pt, 2.5 US pt, 1.2 l, SAE 90, change every 12,400 miles, 20,000 km; greasing: none; tappet clearances: inlet 0.010 in, 0.25 mm, exhaust 0.012 in, 0.30 mm; valve timing: inlet opens 13° before tdc and closes 6° after tdc; normal tyre pressure: front 26 psi, 1.8 atm, rear 26 psi, 1.8 atm.

4-door Familia 1000 De Luxe Sedan

See 2-door Familia 1000 De Luxe Sedan, except for:

PRICE EX WORKS: 513,000 yen.

2-door Familia 1300 De Luxe Sedan

See 2-door Familia 1000 De Luxe Sedan, except for:

PRICE EX WORKS: 518,000 yen.

ENGINE bore and stroke: 2.87 x 2.99 in, 73 x 76 mm; engine capacity: 77.6 cu in, 1,272 cu cm; max power (DIN) 75 hp at 6,000 rpm; max torque (DIN) 76 lb ft, 10.5 kg m at 3,000 rpm; specific power: 59 hp/l.

TRANSMISSION axle ratio: 4.111.

PERFORMANCE max speeds: 26 mph, 42 km/h in 1st gear; 42 mph, 68 km/h in 2nd gear; 68 mph, 110 km/h in 3rd gear; 93 mph, 150 km/h in 4th gear; power-weight ratio: 22.9 lb/hp, 10.4 kg/hp; acceleration: standing ¼ mile 17.8 sec.

BRAKES front disc, rear drum; lining area: front 17.4 sq in, 112 sq cm, rear 39.7 sq in, 256 sq cm, total 57.1 sq in, 368 sq cm.

DIMENSIONS AND WEIGHT dry weight: 1,720 lb, 780 kg; distribution of weight: 56.4% front axle, 43.6% rear axle.

OPTIONAL ACCESSORIES 3-speed automatic gearbox.

4-door Familia 1300 De Luxe Sedan

See 2-door Familia 1300 De Luxe Sedan, except for:

PRICE EX WORKS: 538,000 yen.

Familia 1300 De Luxe Coupé

See 2-door Familia 1300 De Luxe Sedan, except for:

PRICE: —

TRANSMISSION tyres: 6.15 x 13.

PERFORMANCE max speed: 96 mph, 155 km/h.

DIMENSIONS AND WEIGHT: overall height: 52.95 in, 1,345 mm.

BODY coupé.

Capella 1500 De Luxe Sedan

PRICE EX WORKS: 618,000 yen.

ENGINE front, 4 stroke; cylinders: 4, vertical, in line; bore and stroke: 3.07 x 3.07 in, 78 x 78 mm; engine capacity: 90.9

MAZDA Carol 360 De Luxe Sedan

MAZDA Familia 1000 De Luxe Sedan

MAZDA Familia 1300 De Luxe Coupé

cu in, 1,490 cu cm; compression ratio: 8.6; max power (DIN): 92 hp at 5,800 rpm; max torque (DIN): 96 lb ft, 13.2 kg m at 4,000 rpm; max engine rpm: 6,000; specific power: 61.7 hp/l; cylinder block: cast iron; cylinder head: light alloy; crankshaft bearings: 5; valves: 2 per cylinder, overhead, rockers; camshafts: 1, overhead; lubrication: rotary pump, full flow filter; lubricating system capacity: 6.3 imp pt, 7.6 US pt, 3.6 l; carburation: 1 Nikki-Stromberg downdraught twin barrel carburettor; fuel feed: electric pump; cooling system: water; cooling system capacity: 12.3 imp pt, 14.8 US pt, 7 l.

TRANSMISSION driving wheels: rear; clutch: single dry plate (diaphragm); gearbox: mechanical; gears: 4 + reverse; synchromesh gears: I, II, III, IV; gearbox ratios: I 3.403, II 2.005, III 1.373, IV 1, rev 3.665; gear lever: central; final drive: hypoid bevel; axle ratio: 3.700; width of rims: 4''; tyres: 6.15 x 13.

PERFORMANCE max speeds: 30 mph, 48 km/h in 1st gear; 50 mph, 80 km/h in 2nd gear; 72 mph, 116 km/h in 3rd gear; 99 mph, 160 km/h in 4th gear; power-weight ratio: 21.8 lb/hp, 9.9 kg/hp; carrying capacity: 1,058 lb, 480 kg; speed in direct drive at 1,000 rpm: 16.6 mph, 26.7 km/h; fuel consumption: 31.4 m/imp gal, 26.1 m/US gal, 9 l x 100 km.

CHASSIS integral; front suspension: independent, by McPherson, coil springs/telescopic damper struts, lower wishbones, lower trailing links, anti-roll bar; rear suspension: rigid axle, lower radius arms, upper torque arms, transverse linkage bar, coil springs, telescopic dampers.

STEERING recirculating ball, variable ratio; turns of steering wheel lock to lock: 3.30.

BRAKES drum; lining area: front 54.6 sq in, 352 sq cm, rear 39.7 sq in, 256 sq cm, total 94.3 sq in, 608 sq cm.

ELECTRICAL EQUIPMENT voltage: 12 V; battery: 35 Ah; generator type: alternator, 40 A; headlamps: 2.

DIMENSIONS AND WEIGHT wheel base: 97.24 in, 2,470 mm; front track: 50.59 in, 1,285 mm; rear track: 50.39 in, 1,280 mm; overall length: 163.39 in, 4,150 mm; overall width: 62.20 in, 1,580 mm; overall height: 55.91 in, 1,420 mm; ground clearance: 6.30 in, 160 mm; dry weight: 2,018 lb, 915 kg; distribution of weight: 55.2% front axle, 44.8% rear axle; turning circle (between walls): 33.5 ft, 10.2 m; fuel tank capacity: 11 imp gal, 13.2 US gal, 50 l.

BODY saloon-sedan; doors: 4; seats: 5; front seats: separate.

PRACTICAL INSTRUCTIONS fuel: 85-90 oct petrol; engine sump oil: 6.3 imp pt, 7.6 US pt, 3.6 l, SAE 10W-20, change every 3,700 miles, 6,000 km; gearbox oil: 2.3 imp pt, 2.7 US pt, 1.3 l, SAE 80, change every 12,400 miles, 20,000 km; final drive oil: 2.1 imp pt, 2.5 US pt, 1.2 l, SAE 90, change every 12,400 miles, 20,000 km; greasing: none; tappet clearances: inlet 0.012 in, 0.30 mm, exhaust 0.012 in, 0.30 mm; valve timing: inlet opens 13° before tdc and closes 54° after bdc, exhaust opens 57° before bdc and closes 10° after tdc; normal tyre pressure: front 24 psi, 1.7 atm, rear 24 psi, 1.7 atm.

Capella 1500 De Luxe Coupé

See Capella 1500 De Luxe Sedan, except for:

PRICE: —

DIMENSIONS AND WEIGHT overall height: 54.92 in, 1,395 mm.

BODY coupé; doors: 2; seats: 4.

Capella 1600 De Luxe Sedan

See Capella 1500 De Luxe Sedan, except for:

PRICE EX WORKS: 658,000 yen.

ENGINE bore and stroke: 3.07 x 3.27 in, 78 x 83 mm; engine capacity: 96.8 cu in, 1,586 cu cm; max power (DIN): 100 hp at 6,000 rpm; max torque (DIN): 101 lb ft, 14 kg m at 3,500 rpm; specific power: 63 hp/l.

PERFORMANCE max speeds: 31 mph, 50 km/h in 1st gear; 52 mph, 83 km/h in 2nd gear; 76 mph, 123 km/h in 3rd gear; 103 mph, 165 km/h in 4th gear; power-weight ratio: 20.1 lb/hp, 9.1 kg/hp.

Capella 1600 Super De Luxe Sedan

See Capella 1600 De Luxe Sedan, except for:

PRICE EX WORKS: 698,000 yen.

BRAKES front disc, rear drum, servo.

Capella 1600 Super De Luxe Coupé

See Capella 1600 De Luxe Sedan, except for:

PRICE EX WORKS: 738,000 yen.

BRAKES front disc, rear drum, servo.

DIMENSIONS AND WEIGHT overall height: 54.92 in, 1,395 mm.

BODY coupé; doors: 2; seats: 4.

1800 De Luxe Sedan

PRICE EX WORKS: 715,000 yen.

ENGINE front, 4 stroke; cylinders: 4, in line; bore and stroke: 3.07 x 3.70 in, 78 x 94 mm; engine capacity: 109.6 cu in, 1,796 cu cm; compression ratio: 8.6; max power (DIN): 104 hp at 5,500 rpm; max torque (DIN): 112 lb ft, 15.5 kg m at 3,000 rpm; max engine rpm: 6,000; specific power: 57.9 hp/l; cylinder block: cast iron; cylinder head: light alloy; crankshaft bearings: 5; valves: 2 per cylinder, overhead, rockers; camshafts: 1, overhead; lubrication: gear pump, full flow filter; lubricating system capacity: 6.9 imp pt, 8.2 US pt, 3.9 l; carburation: 1 Hitachi HJN 42 horizontal carburettor; fuel feed: electric pump; cooling system: water; cooling system capacity: 13.4 imp pt, 16.1 US pt, 7.6 l.

TRANSMISSION driving wheels: rear; clutch: single dry plate; gearbox: mechanical; gears: 4 + reverse; synchromesh gears: I, II, III, IV; gearbox ratios: I 3.737, II 2.202, III 1.435, IV 1, rev 4.024; gear lever: central; final drive: hypoid bevel; axle ratio: 3.700; tyres: 6.45 x 14.

PERFORMANCE max speeds: 29 mph, 46 km/h in 1st gear; 51 mph, 82 km/h in 2nd gear; 78 mph, 125 km/h in 3rd gear; 103 mph, 165 km/h in 4th gear; power-weight ratio: 22.7 lb/hp, 10.3 kg/hp; carrying capacity: 1,058 lb, 480 kg; acceleration: standing ¼ mile 17.9 sec; speed in direct drive at 1,000 rpm: 18.6 mph, 30 km/h; fuel consumption: 28.2 m/imp gal, 23.5 m/US gal, 10 l x 100 km.

CHASSIS integral; front suspension: independent, wishbones, anti-roll bar, telescopic dampers; rear suspension: rigid axle, semi-elliptic leafsprings, telescopic dampers.

STEERING recirculating ball, variable ratio.

BRAKES front disc, rear drum; lining area: front 25.9 sq in, 167 sq cm, rear 65.9 sq in, 425 sq cm, total 91.8 sq in, 592 sq cm.

ELECTRICAL EQUIPMENT voltage: 12 V; battery: 35 Ah; generator type: dynamo, 450 W; ignition distributor: Mitsubishi; headlamps: 4.

DIMENSIONS AND WEIGHT wheel base: 98.43 in, 2,500 mm; front track: 52.36 in, 1,330 mm; rear track: 51.97 in, 1,320 mm; overall length: 172.05 in, 4,370 mm; overall width: 64.17 in, 1,630 mm; overall height: 56.30 in, 1,430 mm; ground clearance: 7.09 in, 180 mm; dry weight: 2,359 lb, 1,070 kg; distribution of weight: 56% front axle, 44% rear axle; turning circle (between walls): 32.1 ft, 9.8 m; fuel tank capacity: 11 imp gal, 13.2 US gal, 50 l.

BODY saloon/sedan; doors: 4; seats: 5; front seats: separate.

OPTIONAL ACCESSORIES Borg-Warner 35 automatic gearbox; electrically-controlled windows.

Familia Rotary SS Sedan

PRICE EX WORKS: 615,000 yen.

ENGINE front, 4 stroke, Wankel type; 2 co-axial 3-lobe rotors; engine capacity: 30 x 2 cu in, 491 x 2 cu cm; compression ratio: 9.4; max power (SAE): 110 hp at 7,000 rpm; max torque (SAE): 99 lb ft, 13.7 kg m at 4,000 rpm; max engine rpm: 7,000; engine block: light alloy, dual ignition; rotors: cast iron; crankshaft bearings: 3; lubrication: gear pump, full flow filter; lubricating system capacity: 7 imp pt, 8.5 US pt, 4 l; carburation: 1 Hitachi-Stromberg downdraught 4-barrel carburettor; fuel feed: electric pump; cooling system: water; cooling system capacity: 13.2 imp pt, 15.9 US pt, 7.5 l.

TRANSMISSION driving wheels: rear; clutch: single dry plate (diaphragm); gearbox: mechanical; gears: 4 + reverse; synchromesh gears: I, II, III, IV; gearbox ratios: I 3.737, II 2.202, III 1.435, IV 1, rev 4.024; gear lever: central; final drive: hypoid bevel; axle ratio: 3.700; tyres: 6.15 x 13.

PERFORMANCE max speeds: 32 mph, 51 km/h in 1st gear; 54 mph, 87 km/h in 2nd gear; 84 mph, 135 km/h in 3rd gear; 109 mph, 175 km/h in 4th gear; power-weight ratio: 16.5 lb/hp, 7.5 kg/hp; carrying capacity: 882 lb, 400 kg; acceleration: standing ¼ mile 16.8 sec; speed in direct drive at 1,000 rpm: 16.8 mph, 27 km/h; fuel consumption: 26.9 m/imp gal, 22.4 m/US gal, 10.5 l x 100 km.

MAZDA Familia Rotary SS Sedan

MAZDA 110S Cosmo Sport

MAZDA Capella RE GS Coupé

CHASSIS integral; front suspension: independent, wishbones, coil springs, anti-roll bar, telescopic dampers; rear suspension: rigid axle, semi-elliptic leafsprings, telescopic dampers.

STEERING recirculating ball; turns of steering wheel lock to lock: 3.73.

BRAKES front disc, rear drum; lining area: front 17.4 sq in, 112 sq cm, rear 39.7 sq in, 256 sq cm, total 57.1 sq in, 368 sq cm.

ELECTRICAL EQUIPMENT voltage: 12 V; battery: 45 Ah; generator type: alternator, 360 W; ignition distributor: Mitsubishi; headlamps: 2.

DIMENSIONS AND WEIGHT wheel base: 88.98 in, 2,260 mm; front track: 47.24 in, 1,200 mm; rear track: 46.85 in, 1,190 mm; overall length: 151.10 in, 3,838 mm; overall width: 58.27 in, 1,480 mm; overall height: 54.72 in, 1,390 mm; ground clearance: 6.30 in, 160 mm; dry weight: 1,819 lb, 825 kg; turning circle (between walls): 26.9 ft, 8.2 m; fuel tank capacity: 13.2 imp gal, 15.8 US gal, 60 l.

BODY saloon/sedan; doors: 4; seats: 4; front seats: separate.

PRACTICAL INSTRUCTIONS fuel: 85-90 oct petrol; engine sump oil: 7 imp pt, 8.5 US pt, 4 l, SAE 10W-30, change every 3,700 miles, 6,000 km; gearbox oil: 2.6 imp pt, 3.2 US pt, 1.5 l, SAE 90, change every 31,100 miles, 50,000 km; final drive oil: 2.1 imp pt, 2.5 US pt, 1.2 l, SAE 90, change every 31,100 miles, 50,000 km; greasing: every 2 years, 9 points; normal tyre pressure: front 20 psi, 1.4 atm, rear 20 psi, 1.4 atm.

OPTIONAL ACCESSORIES TSS version.

R100 De Luxe Coupé

See Familia Rotary SS Sedan, except for:

PRICE EX WORKS: 598,000 yen.

PERFORMANCE max speed: 112 mph, 180 km/h; power-weight ratio: 16.1 lb/hp, 7.3 kg/hp; carrying capacity: 706 lb, 320 kg; acceleration: standing ¼ mile 16.4 sec, 0-50 mph (0-80 km/h) 5.8 sec.

DIMENSIONS AND WEIGHT overall length: 150.79 in, 3,830 mm; overall height: 52.95 in, 1,345 mm; dry weight: 1,775 lb, 805 kg; distribution of weight: 56.5% front axle, 43.5% rear axle.

BODY coupé; doors: 2; seats: 2 + 2.

110S Cosmo Sport

PRICE EX WORKS: 1,580,000 yen.

ENGINE front, 4 stroke, Wankel type; 2 co-axial 3-lobe rotors; engine capacity: 30 x 2 cu in, 491 x 2 cu cm; compression ratio: 9.4; max power (SAE): 130 hp at 7,000 rpm; max torque (SAE): 102 lb ft, 14.2 kg m at 5,000 rpm; max engine rpm: 7,000; engine block: light alloy, dual ignition; rotors: cast iron; crankshaft bearings: 3; lubrication: gear pump, full flow filter, oil-water heat exchanger; lubricating system capacity: 6.7 imp pt, 8 US pt, 3.8 l; carburation: 1 Hitachi-Stromberg 4-barrel carburettor; fuel feed: electric pump; cooling system: engine block by water, rotors by oil; cooling system capacity: 8.4 imp pt, 10.1 US pt, 4.8 l.

TRANSMISSION driving wheels: rear; clutch: single dry plate (diaphragm); gearbox: mechanical; gears: 5 + reverse; synchromesh gears: I, II, III, IV, V; gearbox ratios: I 3.379, II 2.077, III 1.390, IV 1, V 0.841, rev 3.389; gear lever: central; final drive: hypoid bevel; axle ratio: 4.111; tyres: 155 x 15.

PERFORMANCE max speeds: 34 mph, 55 km/h in 1st gear; 56 mph, 90 km/h in 2nd gear; 84 mph, 135 km/h in 3rd gear; 115 mph, 185 km/h in 4th gear; 124 mph, 200 km/h in 5th gear; power-weight ratio: 16.3 lb/hp, 7.4 kg/hp; carrying capacity: 551 lb, 250 kg; acceleration: standing ¼ mile 15.8 sec; speed in top at 1,000 rpm: 18 mph, 29 km/h; fuel consumption: 26.9 m/imp gal, 22.4 m/US gal, 10.5 l x 100 km.

CHASSIS integral; front suspension: independent, wishbones, coil springs, anti-roll bar, telescopic dampers; rear suspension: de Dion rigid axle, semi-elliptic leafsprings, telescopic dampers.

STEERING rack-and-pinion; turns of steering wheel lock to lock: 2.98.

BRAKES front disc, rear drum, servo; lining area: front 20.8 sq in, 134 sq cm, rear 65.9 sq in, 425 sq cm, total 86.7 sq in, 559 sq cm.

ELECTRICAL EQUIPMENT voltage: 12 V; battery: 45 Ah; generator type: alternator, 360 W; ignition distributor: Mitsubishi; headlamps: 2.

MAZDA Familia Rotary SS Sedan

MAZDA 110S Cosmo Sport

MAZDA Capella RE GS Coupé

DIMENSIONS AND WEIGHT wheel base: 92.52 in, 2,350 mm; front track: 61 in, 1,260 mm; rear track: 49.21 in, 1,250 mm; overall length: 162.60 in, 4,130 mm; overall width: 62.80 in, 1,595 mm; overall height: 45.85 in, 1,165 mm; ground clearance: 4.92 in, 125 mm; dry weight: 2,117 lb, 960 kg; distribution of weight: 50.5% front axle, 49.5% rear axle; turning circle (between walls): 34.1 ft, 10.4 m; fuel tank capacity: 12.5 imp gal, 15 US gal, 57 l.

BODY coupé; doors: 2; seats: 2.

PRACTICAL INSTRUCTIONS fuel: 85-90 oct petrol; engine sump oil: 6.7 imp pt, 8 US pt, 3.8 l, SAE 10W-30, change every 3,700 miles, 6,000 km; gearbox oil: 3.5 imp pt, 4.2 US pt, 2 l, SAE 90, change every 31,100 miles, 50,000 km; final drive oil: 1.6 imp pt, 1.9 US pt, 0.9 l, SAE 90, change every 31,100 miles, 50,000 km; greasing: every 31,100 miles, 50,000 km, 13 points; normal tyre pressure: front 20 psi, 1.4 atm, rear 26 psi, 1.8 atm.

OPTIONAL ACCESSORIES air-conditioning system.

Capella RE De Luxe Sedan

PRICE EX WORKS: 748,000 yen.

ENGINE front, 4 stroke; 2 co-axial 3-lobe rotors; engine capacity: 35 x 2 cu in, 573 x 2 cu cm; compression ratio: 9.4; max power (DIN): 120 hp at 6,500 rpm; max torque (DIN): 116 lb ft, 16 kg m at 3,500 rpm; max engine rpm: 7,000; engine block: light alloy, dual ignition; rotors: cast iron; crankshaft bearings: 2; lubrication: rotary pump, full flow filter, oil-cooler; lubricating system capacity: 9.7 imp pt, 11.6 US pt, 5.5 l; carburation: 1 Nikki-Stromberg 4-barrel carburettor; fuel feed: electric pump; cooling system: water; cooling system capacity: 14.1 imp pt, 16.9 US pt, 8 l.

TRANSMISSION driving wheels: rear; clutch: single dry plate (diaphragm); gearbox: mechanical; gears: 4 + reverse; synchromesh gears: I, II, III, IV; gearbox ratios: I 3.683, II 2.263, III 1.397, IV 1, rev 3.692; gear lever: central; final drive: hypoid bevel; axle ratio: 3.700; width of rims: 4''; tyres: 155 x 13.

PERFORMANCE max speeds: 31 mph, 50 km/h 1st gear; 54 mph, 87 km/h in 2nd gear; 87 mph, 140 km/h in 3rd gear; 115 mph, 185 km/h in 4th gear; power-weight ratio: 17.6 lb/hp, 8 kg/hp; carrying capacity: 882 lb, 400 kg; speed in direct drive at 1,000 rpm: 16.5 mph, 26.5 km/h; fuel consumption: 25.7 m/imp gal, 21.4 m/US gal, 11 l x 100 km.

CHASSIS integral; front suspension: independent, by Mc-Pherson, coil springs/telescopic damper struts, lower wishbones, lower trailing links, anti-roll bar; rear suspension: rigid axle, lower trailing arms, upper torque arms, transverse linkage bar, coil springs, telescopic dampers.

STEERING recirculating ball, variable ratio; turns of steering wheel lock to lock: 3.30.

BRAKES front disc, rear drum, servo; lining area: front 24.8 sq in, 160 sq cm, rear 39.7 sq in, 256 sq cm, total 64.5 sq in, 416 sq cm.

ELECTRICAL EQUIPMENT voltage: 12 V; battery: 45 Ah; generator type: alternator, 40 A; ignition distributor: Mitsubishi; headlamps: 2.

DIMENSIONS AND WEIGHT wheel base: 97.24 in, 2,470 mm; front track: 50.59 in, 1,285 mm; rear track: 50.39 in, 1,280 mm; overall length: 163.39 in, 4,150 mm; overall width: 62.20 in, 1,580 mm; overall height: 55.91 in, 1,420 mm; ground clearance: 6.30 in, 160 mm; dry weight: 2,106 lb, 955 kg; distribution of weight: 53.6% front axle, 46.4% rear axle; turning circle (between walls): 33.5 ft, 10.2 m; fuel tank capacity: 14.3 imp gal, 17.2 US gal, 65 l.

BODY saloon/sedan; doors: 4; seats: 5; front seats: separate.

PRACTICAL INSTRUCTIONS fuel: 85-90 oct petrol; engine sump oil: 9.7 imp pt, 11.6 US pt, 5.5 l, SAE 10W-30, change every 3,700 miles, 6,000 km; gearbox oil: 4.4 imp pt, 5.3 US pt, 2.5 l, SAE 90, change every 29,800 miles, 48,000 km; final drive oil: 2.1 imp pt, 2.5 US pt, 1.2 l, SAE 90, change every 29,800 miles, 48,000 km; valve timing: inlet opens 32° before tdc and closes 40° after bdc, exhaust opens 80° before bdc and closes 48° after tdc; normal tyre pressure: front 24 psi, 1.7 atm, rear 24 psi, 1.7 atm.

Capella RE GS Coupé

See Capella RE De Luxe Sedan, except for:

PRICE EX WORKS: 845,000 yen.

PERFORMANCE max speed: 118 mph, 190 km/h.

DIMENSIONS AND WEIGHT overall height: 54.92 in, 1,395 mm; dry weight: 2,117 lb, 960 kg.

BODY coupé; doors: 2; seats: 4.

R130 De Luxe Coupé

PRICE EX WORKS: 1,450,000 yen.

ENGINE front, 4 stroke, Wankel type; 2 co-axial 3-lobe rotors; engine capacity: 40 x 2 cu in, 655 x 2 cu cm; compression ratio: 9; max power (SAE): 126 hp at 6,000 rpm; max torque (SAE): 127 lb ft, 17.5 kg m at 3,500 rpm; max engine rpm: 6,500; engine block: light alloy, dual ignition; rotors: cast iron; crankshaft bearings: 3; lubrication: gear pump, full flow filter, oil-water heat exchanger; lubricating system capacity: 8.8 imp pt, 10.6 US pt, 5 l; carburation: 1 Stromberg 4-barrel carburettor; fuel feed: electric pump; cooling system: engine block by water, rotors by oil; cooling system capacity: 15.5 imp pt, 18.6 US pt, 8.8 l.

TRANSMISSION driving wheels: front; clutch: single dry plate (diaphragm); gearbox: mechanical; gears: 4 + reverse; synchromesh gears: I, II, III, IV; gearbox ratios: I 3.727, II 2.176, III 1.391, IV 1.037, rev 3.727; gear lever: central; final drive: hypoid bevel; axle ratio: 3.900; width of rims: 4.5''; tyres: 165 x 15.

PERFORMANCE max speeds: 30 mph, 48 km/h in 1st gear; 55 mph, 88 km/h in 2nd gear; 87 mph, 140 km/h in 3rd gear; 118 mph, 190 km/h in 4th gear; power-weight ratio: 20.7 lb/hp, 9.4 kg/hp; carrying capacity: 882 lb, 400 kg; acceleration: standing ¼ mile 16.9 sec, 0-50 mph (0-80 km/h) 6.2 sec; fuel consumption: 23.5 m/imp gal, 19.6 m/US gal, 12 l x 100 km.

CHASSIS integral; front suspension: independent, wishbones, rubber springs (torsion), anti-roll bar, telescopic dampers; rear suspension: independent, semi-trailing arms, coil springs, telescopic dampers.

STEERING rack-and-pinion; turns of steering wheel lock to lock: 3.80.

BRAKES front disc, rear drum, servo.

ELECTRICAL EQUIPMENT voltage: 12 V; battery: 45 Ah; generator type: alternator, 560 W; ignition distributor: Mitsubishi; headlamps: 4.

DIMENSIONS AND WEIGHT wheel base: 101.57 in, 2,580 mm; front track: 52.36 in, 1,330 mm; rear track: 52.17 in, 1,325 mm; overall length: 180.51 in, 4,585 mm; overall width: 64.37 in, 1,635 mm; overall height: 54.53 in, 1,385 mm; ground clearance: 7.28 in, 185 mm; dry weight: 2,613 lb, 1,185 kg; distribution of weight: 62% front axle, 38% rear axle; turning circle (between walls): 34.8 ft, 10.6 m; fuel tank capacity: 14.3 imp gal, 17.2 US gal, 65 l.

BODY coupé; doors: 2; seats: 5; front seats: separate.

PRACTICAL INSTRUCTIONS fuel: 85-90 oct petrol; engine sump oil: 8.8 imp pt, 10.6 US pt, 5 l, SAE 10W-40, change every 3,700 miles, 6,000 km; gearbox and final drive oil: 6.2 imp pt, 7.4 US pt, 3.5 l, SAE 90, change every 31,100 miles, 50,000 km; greasing: every 31,100 miles, 50,000 km, 6 points; normal tyre pressure: front 28 psi, 2 atm, rear 23 psi, 1.6 atm.

R130 Super De Luxe Coupé

See R130 De Luxe Coupé, except for:

PRICE EX WORKS: 1,750,000 yen.

PERFORMANCE power-weight ratio: 22 lb/hp, 10 kg/hp.

STEERING servo; turns of steering wheel lock to lock: 3.50.

DIMENSIONS AND WEIGHT dry weight: 2,767 lb, 1,255 kg.

BODY details: electrically-controlled windows, air-conditioning system.

MITSUBISHI   JAPAN

Minica 70 Sedan

PRICE EX WORKS: 322,000 yen.

ENGINE front, 2 stroke; cylinders: 2, in line; bore and stroke: 2.44 x 2.35 in, 62 x 59.6 mm; engine capacity: 21.9 cu in, 359 cu cm; compression ratio: 8; max power (DIN): 30 hp at 6,000 rpm; max torque (DIN): 27 lb ft, 3.7 kg m at 5,000 rpm; max engine rpm: 6,800; specific power: 83.6 hp/l; cylinder block: cast iron; cylinder head: light alloy; crankshaft bearings: 3; lubrication: mechanical pump, injection to cylinders and crankshaft bearings, total loss system; carburation: 1 Solex horizontal carburettor; fuel feed: mechanical pump; cooling system: aircooled.

TRANSMISSION driving wheels: rear; clutch: single dry plate; gearbox: mechanical; gears: 4 + reverse; synchro-

MAZDA R130 De Luxe Coupé

MITSUBISHI Minica 70 GL Sedan

MITSUBISHI 4-door Colt 11 F De Luxe Sedan

mesh gears: I, II, III, IV; gearbox ratios: I 3.576, II 2.096, III 1.359, IV 1, rev 4.271; gear lever: central; final drive: hypoid bevel; axle ratio: 5.429; width of rims: 3.5''; tyres: 4.80 x 10.

PERFORMANCE max speeds: 19 mph, 31 km/h in 1st gear; 32 mph, 52 km/h in 2nd gear; 50 mph, 81 km/h in 3rd gear; 68 mph, 110 km/h in 4th gear; power-weight ratio: 34.2 lb/hp, 15.5 kg/hp; carrying capacity: 706 lb, 320 kg; speed in direct drive at 1,000 rpm: 10.3 mph, 16.5 km/h; fuel consumption: 70.6 m/imp gal, 58.8 m/US gal, 4 l x 100 km.

CHASSIS integral; front suspension: independent, by Mc-Pherson, coil springs/telescopic damper struts, anti-roll bar, lower wishbones, lower trailing links; rear suspension: rigid axle, lower trailing arms, upper torque arms, transverse linkage bar, coil springs, telescopic dampers.

STEERING recirculating ball.

BRAKES drum.

ELECTRICAL EQUIPMENT voltage: 12 V; battery: 24 Ah; generator type: alternator, 280 W; ignition distributor: Mitsubishi; headlamps: 4.

DIMENSIONS AND WEIGHT wheel base: 78.74 in, 2,000 mm; front track: 44.09 in, 1,120 mm; rear track: 42.52 in, 1,080 mm; overall length 117.91 in, 2,995 mm; overall width: 50.98 in, 1,295 mm; overall height: 52.95 in, 1,345 mm; ground clearance: 5.71 in, 145 mm; dry weight: 1,025 lb, 465 kg; turning circle (between walls): 24.9 ft, 7.6 m; fuel tank capacity: 5.5 imp gal, 6.6 US gal, 25 l.

BODY saloon/sedan; doors: 2; seats: 4; front seats: separate.

PRACTICAL INSTRUCTIONS fuel: mixture; engine sump oil: 5.3 imp pt, 6.3 US pt, 3 l, oil in separate tank; gearbox oil: 1.1 imp pt, 1.3 US pt, 0.6 l, SAE 80, change every 24,900 miles, 40,000 km; final drive oil: 1.1 imp pt, 1.3 US pt, 0.6 l, SAE 80, change every 24,900 miles, 40,000 km; normal tyre pressure: front 21 psi, 1.5 atm, rear 21 psi, 1.5 atm.

Minica 70 Station Wagon

See Minica 70 Sedan, except for:

PRICE: —

BODY estate car/station wagon; doors: 2 + 1.

Minica 70 GL Sedan

See Minica 70 Sedan, except for:

PRICE EX WORKS: 425,000 yen.

ENGINE compression ratio: 8.5; max power (DIN): 34 hp at 6,500 rpm; max torque (DIN): 28 lb ft, 3.8 kg m at 6,000 rpm; max engine rpm: 7,400; specific power: 94.7 hp/l.

PERFORMANCE max speed: 71 mph, 115 km/h; power-weight ratio: 30.2 lb/hp, 13.7 kg/hp.

Minica 70 GSS

See Minica 70 Sedan, except for:

PRICE EX WORKS: 415,000 yen.

ENGINE compression ratio: 10; max power (DIN): 38 hp at 7,000 rpm; max torque (DIN): 28 lb ft, 3.9 kg m at 6,500 rpm; max engine rpm: 8,000; specific power: 105.8 hp/l; cooling system: water.

TRANSMISSION axle ratio: 4.875; tyres: 145 x 10.

PERFORMANCE max speed: 78 mph, 125 km/h; power-weight ratio: 26.9 lb/hp, 12.2 kg/hp; fuel consumption: 51.4 m/imp gal, 42.8 m/US gal, 5.5 l x 100 km.

2-door Colt 11 F De Luxe Sedan

PRICE: —

ENGINE front, 4 stroke; cylinders: 4, in line; bore and stroke: 2.87 x 2.56 in, 73 x 65 mm; engine capacity: 66.4 cu in, 1,088 cu cm; compression ratio: 8.5; max power (DIN): 62 hp at 6,000 rpm; max torque (DIN): 63 lb ft, 8.7 kg m at 3,800 rpm; max engine rpm: 6,000; specific power: 57 hp/l; cylinder block: cast iron; cylinder head: light alloy; crankshaft bearings: 3; valves: 2 per cylinder, overhead, push-rods and rockers; camshafts: 1, side; lubrication: gear pump, full flow filter; lubricating system

MAZDA R130 De Luxe Coupé

MITSUBISHI Minica 70 GL Sedan

MITSUBISHI Colt 11 F De Luxe Sedan

capacity: 5.3 imp pt, 6.3 US pt, 3 l; carburation: 1 Aisan downdraught twin barrel carburettor; fuel feed: mechanical pump; cooling system: water; cooling system capacity: 7.6 imp pt, 9.1 US pt, 4.3 l.

TRANSMISSION driving wheels: rear; clutch: single dry plate; gearbox: mechanical; gears: 4 + reverse; synchromesh gears: I, II, III, IV; gearbox ratios: I 3.787, II 2.379, III 1.535, IV 1, rev 5.243; gear lever: central; final drive: hypoid bevel; axle ratio: 4.222; width of rims: 4''; tyres: 145 x 13.

PERFORMANCE max speeds: 23 mph, 37 km/h in 1st gear; 37 mph, 59 km/h in 2nd gear; 57 mph, 91 km/h in 3rd gear; 87 mph, 140 km/h in 4th gear; power-weight ratio: 26.9 lb/hp, 12.2 kg/hp; carrying capacity: 882 lb, 400 kg; speed in direct drive at 1,000 rpm: 14.5 mph, 23.3 km/h; fuel consumption: 35.3 m/imp gal, 29.4 m/US gal, 8 l x 100 km.

CHASSIS integral; front suspension: independent, wishbones, transverse semi-elliptic leafspring, telescopic dampers; rear suspension: rigid axle, semi-elliptic leafsprings, telescopic dampers.

STEERING recirculating ball.

BRAKES drum.

ELECTRICAL EQUIPMENT voltage: 12 V; battery: 32 Ah; generator type: alternator, 300 W; ignition distributor: Mitsubishi; headlamps: 2.

DIMENSIONS AND WEIGHT wheel base: 86.61 in, 2,200 mm; front track: 48.82 in, 1,240 mm; rear track: 46.65 in, 1,185 mm; overall length: 147.24 in, 3,740 mm; overall width: 57.09 in, 1,450 mm; overall height: 53.74 in, 1,365 mm; ground clearance: 6.42 in, 165 mm; dry weight: 1,665 lb, 755 kg; distribution of weight: 54.3% front axle, 45.7% rear axle; turning circle (between walls): 30.8 ft, 9.4 m; fuel tank capacity: 8.8 imp gal, 10.6 US gal, 40 l.

BODY saloon/sedan; doors: 2; seats: 5; front seats: separate.

PRACTICAL INSTRUCTIONS fuel: 98-100 oct petrol; engine sump oil: 5.3 imp pt, 6.3 US pt, 3 l, SAE 20W-30, change every 3,100 miles, 5,000 km; gearbox oil: 1.6 imp pt, 1.9 US pt, 0.9 l, SAE 90, change every 24,900 miles, 40,000 km; final drive oil: 1.1 imp pt, 1.3 US pt, 0.6 l, SAE 90, change every 24,900 miles, 40,000 km; greasing: every 12,400 miles, 20,000 km, 13 points; normal tyre pressure: front 21 psi, 1.5 atm, rear 21 psi, 1.5 atm.

3-door Colt 11 F De Luxe Sedan

See 2-door Colt 11 F De Luxe Sedan, except for:

PRICE: —

BODY doors: 2 + 1.

4-door Colt 11 F De Luxe Sedan

See 2-door Colt 11 F De Luxe Sedan, except for:

PRICE EX WORKS: 478,000 yen.

Colt 11 Station Wagon

See 2-door Colt 11 F De Luxe Sedan, except for:

PRICE: —

BODY estate car/station wagon; doors: 2 + 1.

Colt 11 Super Sports

See 2-door Colt 11 F De Luxe Sedan, except for:

PRICE EX WORKS: 555,000 yen.

ENGINE compression ratio: 10; max power (DIN): 73 hp at 6,300 rpm; max torque (DIN): 65 lb ft, 9 kg m at 4,500 rpm; max engine rpm: 6,600; specific power: 67.1 hp/l; carburation: 2 Hitachi SU horizontal carburettors.

PERFORMANCE max speeds: 26 mph, 42 km/h in 1st gear; 41 mph, 66 km/h in 2nd gear; 63 mph, 102 km/h in 3rd gear; 96 mph, 155 km/h in 4th gear; power-weight ratio: 22.7 lb/hp, 10.3 kg/hp; speed in direct drive at 1,000 rpm: 15.5 mph, 25 km/h; fuel consumption: 33.2 m/imp gal, 27.7 m/US gal, 8.5 l x 100 km.

BRAKES front disc, rear drum.

Colt Galant A I Sedan

PRICE EX WORKS: 518,000 yen.

ENGINE front, 4 stroke; cylinders: 4, in line; bore and stroke: 2.87 x 3.03 in, 73 x 77 mm; engine capacity: 78.7 cu in, 1,289 cu cm; compression ratio: 9; max power (DIN): 87 hp at 6,300 rpm; max torque (DIN): 80 lb ft, 11 kg m at 4,000 rpm; max engine rpm: 6,500; specific power: 67.5 hp/l; cylinder block: cast iron; cylinder head: light alloy; crankshaft bearings: 5; valves: 2 per cylinder, overhead, rockers; camshafts: 1, overhead; lubrication: rotary pump, full flow filter; lubricating system capacity: 6.2 imp pt, 7.4 US pt, 3.5 l; carburation: 1 Mikuni-Solex twin barrel carburettor; fuel feed: mechanical pump; cooling system: water; cooling system capacity: 10.6 imp pt, 12.7 US pt, 6 l.

TRANSMISSION driving wheels: rear; clutch: single dry plate; gearbox: mechanical; gears: 3 + reverse; synchromesh gears: I, II, III; gearbox ratios: I 3.198, II 1.635, III 1, rev 4.021; gear lever: steering column; final drive: hypoid bevel; axle ratio: 4.222; tyres: 6.15 x 13.

PERFORMANCE max speeds: 29 mph, 47 km/h in 1st gear; 57 mph, 92 km/h in 2nd gear; 93 mph, 150 km/h in 3rd gear; power-weight ratio: 20.9 lb/hp, 9.5 kg/hp; carrying capacity: 926 lb, 420 kg; acceleration: standing ¼ mile 18.3 sec; speed in direct drive at 1,000 rpm: 14.9 mph, 24 km/h; fuel consumption: 31.4 m/imp gal, 26.1 m/US gal, 9 l x 100 km.

CHASSIS integral; front suspension: independent, by McPherson, coil springs/telescopic damper struts, anti-roll bar, lower wishbones, lower trailing links; rear suspension: rigid axle, semi-elliptic leafsprings, telescopic dampers.

STEERING worm and roller; turns of steering wheel lock to lock: 3.50.

BRAKES drum.

ELECTRICAL EQUIPMENT voltage: 12 V; battery: 32 Ah; generator type: alternator, 400 W; ignition distributor: Mitsubishi; headlamps: 2.

DIMENSIONS AND WEIGHT wheel base: 95.28 in, 2,420 mm; front track: 50.59 in, 1,285 mm; rear track: 50.59 in, 1,285 mm; overall length: 159.84 in, 4,060 mm; overall width: 61.42 in, 1,560 mm; overall height: 54.53 in, 1,385 mm; ground clearance: 6.89 in, 175 mm; dry weight: 1,819 lb, 825 kg; distribution of weight: 53% front axle, 47% rear axle; turning circle (between walls): 30.2 ft, 9.2 m; fuel tank capacity: 9.9 imp gal, 11.9 US gal, 45 l.

BODY saloon/sedan; doors: 4; seats: 5; front seats: separate.

PRACTICAL INSTRUCTIONS fuel: 90 oct petrol; engine sump oil: 6.2 imp pt, 7.4 US pt, 3.5 l, SAE 20W-30, change every 3,100 miles, 5,000 km; gearbox oil: 3.2 imp pt, 3.8 US pt, 1.8 l, SAE 90, change every 24,900 miles, 40,000 km; final drive oil: 1.6 imp pt, 1.9 US pt, 0.9 l, SAE 80-90, change every 24,900 miles, 40,000 km; valve timing: inlet opens 18° before tdc and closes 50° after bdc, exhaust opens 48° before bdc and closes 20° after tdc; normal tyre pressure: front 20 psi, 1.4 atm, rear 23 psi, 1.6 atm.

OPTIONAL ACCESSORIES 4-speed mechanical gearbox (I 3.525, II 2.193, III 1.442, IV 1, rev 3.867), central gear lever; De Luxe version; Custom version.

Colt Galant A II Sedan

See Colt Galant A I Sedan, except for:

PRICE: —

ENGINE bore and stroke: 2.93 x 3.39 in, 74.5 x 86 mm; engine capacity: 91.5 cu in, 1,499 cu cm; max power (DIN): 95 hp at 6,300 rpm; max torque (DIN): 96 lb ft, 13.2 kg m at 4,000 rpm; specific power: 63.4 hp/l; carburation: 1 Stromberg downdraught twin barrel carburettor; cooling system capacity: 12 imp pt, 14.4 US pt, 6.8 l.

TRANSMISSION axle ratio: 3.889.

PERFORMANCE max speed: 99 mph, 160 km/h; power-weight ratio: 19.8 lb/hp, 9 kg/hp; fuel consumption: 29.7 m/imp gal, 24.8 m/US gal, 9.5 l x 100 km.

ELECTRICAL EQUIPMENT battery: 33 Ah.

DIMENSIONS AND WEIGHT overall length: 160.63 in, 4,080 mm; overall height: 53.94 in, 1,370 mm; ground clearance: 6.50 in, 165 mm; dry weight: 1,885 lb, 855 kg; distribution of weight: 52.6% front axle, 47.4% rear axle.

OPTIONAL ACCESSORIES only 4-speed mechanical gearbox (I 3.525, II 2.193, III 1.442, IV 1, rev 3.867), Borg-Warner automatic gearbox with 3 ratios (I 2.393, II 1.450, III 1, rev 2.094) and Custom version.

MITSUBISHI Colt Galant Hardtop Custom

MITSUBISHI Colt Galant GTO MR

MITSUBISHI Debonair Executive

Colt Galant Hardtop Custom

See Colt Galant A II Sedan, except for:

PRICE EX WORKS: 686,000 yen.

TRANSMISSION gears: 4 + reverse; gearbox ratio: I 3.525, II 2.193, III 1.442, IV 1, rev 3.867; gear lever: central.

PERFORMANCE max speed: 103 mph, 165 km/h; power-weight ratio: 20.5 lb/hp, 9.3 kg/hp.

DIMENSIONS AND WEIGHT front track: 50.98 in, 1,295 mm; overall width: 61.81 in, 1,570 mm; overall height: 52.76 in, 1,340 mm; dry weight: 1,940 lb, 880 kg.

BODY hardtop; doors: 2.

OPTIONAL ACCESSORIES only Borg-Warner automatic gearbox with 3 ratios (I 2.393, II 1.450, III 1, rev 2.094) and front disc brakes.

Colt Galant 1500 GS

See Colt Galant A II Sedan, except for:

PRICE EX WORKS: 711,000 yen.

ENGINE compression ratio: 10; max power (DIN): 105 hp at 6,700 rpm; max torque (DIN): 97 lb ft, 13.4 kg m at 4,800 rpm; max engine rpm: 7,000; specific power: 70 hp/l; carburation: 2 Aisan SU horizontal twin barrel carburettors.

TRANSMISSION gears: 4 + reverse; synchromesh gears: I, II, III, IV; gearbox ratios: I 3.525, II 2.193, III 1.442, IV 1, rev 3.867; gear lever: central.

PERFORMANCE max speeds: 33 mph, 53 km/h in 1st gear; 52 mph, 84 km/h in 2nd gear; 79 mph, 127 km/h in 3rd gear; 109 mph, 175 km/h in 4th gear; power-weight ratio: 17.9 lb/hp, 8.1 kg/hp; acceleration: standing ¼ mile 16.9 sec; fuel consumption: 28.2 m/imp gal, 23.5 m/US gal, 10 l x 100 km.

BRAKES front disc, rear drum.

OPTIONAL ACCESSORIES none.

Colt Galant Hardtop GS

See Colt Galant Hardtop Custom, except for:

PRICE EX WORKS: 761.000 yen.

ENGINE compression ratio: 10; max power (DIN): 105 hp at 6,700 rpm; max torque (DIN): 97 lb ft, 13.4 kg m at 4,800 rpm; max engine rpm: 7,000; specific power: 70 hp/l; carburation: 2 Aisan SU horizontal twin barrel carburettors.

PERFORMANCE max speeds: 33 mph, 53 km/h in 1st gear; 52 mph, 84 km/h in 2nd gear; 78 mph, 126 km/h in 3rd gear; 112 mph, 180 km/h in 4th gear; power-weight ratio: 18.5 lb/hp, 8.4 kg/hp; acceleration: standing ¼ mile 16.9 sec; fuel consumption: 28.2 m/imp gal, 23.5 m/US gal, 10 l x 100 km.

BRAKES front disc, rear drum.

OPTIONAL ACCESSORIES none.

Colt Galant GTO MI

PRICE EX WORKS: 786,000 yen.

ENGINE front, 4 stroke; cylinders: 4, vertical, in line; bore and stroke: 3.03 x 3.39 in, 76.9 x 86 mm; engine capacity: 97.4 cu in, 1,597 cu cm; compression ratio: 8.5; max power (DIN): 100 hp at 6,300 rpm; max torque (DIN): 101 lb ft, 14 kg m at 4,000 rpm; max engine rpm: 6,500; specific power: 62.6 hp/l; cylinder block: cast iron; cylinder head: light alloy; crankshaft bearings: 5; valves: 2 per cylinder, overhead, rockers; camshafts: 1, overhead; lubrication: rotary pump, full flow filter; lubricating system capacity: 6.2 imp pt, 7.4 US pt, 3.5 l; carburation: 1 Nikki-Stromberg downdraught twin barrel carburettor; fuel feed: mechanical pump; cooling system: water; cooling system capacity: 10.6 imp pt, 12.7 US pt, 6 l.

TRANSMISSION driving wheels: rear; clutch: single dry plate; gearbox: mechanical; gears: 4 + reverse; synchromesh gears: I, II, III, IV; gearbox ratios: I 3.525, II 2.193, III 1.442, IV 1, rev 3.867; gear lever: central; final drive: hypoid bevel; axle ratio: 3.889; width of rims: 4.5''; tyres: 6.15 x 13.

PERFORMANCE max speeds: 30 mph, 48 km/h in 1st gear; 48 mph, 77 km/h in 2nd gear; 73 mph, 118 km/h in 3rd gear; 106 mph, 170 km/h in 4th gear; power-weight ratio: 21.6 lb/hp, 9.8 kg/hp; carrying capacity: 882 lb, 400 kg; speed in direct drive at 1,000 rpm: 16.8 mph, 27 km/h; fuel consumption: 25.7 m/imp gal, 21.4 m/US gal, 11 l x 100 km.

CHASSIS integral; front suspension: independent, by McPherson, coil springs/telescopic damper struts, anti-roll bar, lower wishbones, lower trailing links; rear suspension: rigid axle, semi-elliptic leafsprings, telescopic dampers.

MITSUBISHI Colt Galant Hardtop Custom

STEERING recirculating ball, variable ratio; turns of steering wheel lock to lock: 3.50.

BRAKES front disc, rear drum, servo.

ELECTRICAL EQUIPMENT voltage: 12 V; battery: 35 Ah; generator type: alternator; ignition distributor: Mitsubishi; headlamps: 4.

DIMENSIONS AND WEIGHT wheel base: 95.28 in, 2,420 mm; front track: 50.98 in, 1,295 mm; rear track: 50.59 in, 1,285 mm; overall length: 162.40 in, 4,125 mm; overall width: 62.20 in, 1,580 mm; overall height: 51.57 in, 1,310 mm; ground clearance: 6.50 in, 165 mm; dry weight: 2,161 lb, 980 kg; turning circle (between walls): 30.2 ft, 9.2 m; fuel tank capacity: 12.1 imp gal, 14.5 US gal, 55 l.

BODY hardtop; doors: 2; seats: 5; front seats: separate.

PRACTICAL INSTRUCTIONS fuel: 100 oct petrol; engine sump oil: 6.2 imp pt, 7.4 US pt, 3.5 l, SAE 20W-30, change every 3,100 miles, 5,000 km; gearbox oil: 3.2 imp pt, 3.8 US pt, 1.8 l, SAE 90, change every 24,800 miles, 40,000 km; final drive oil: 1.6 imp pt, 1.9 US pt, 0.9 l, SAE 80-90, change every 24,800 miles, 40,000 km; normal tyre pressure: front 23 psi, 1.6 atm, rear 26 psi, 1.8 atm.

Colt Galant GTO MII

See Colt Galant GTO MI, except for:

PRICE EX WORKS: 843,000 yen.

ENGINE compression ratio: 9.5; max power (DIN): 110 hp at 6,700 rpm; max torque (DIN): 103 lb ft, 14.2 kg m at 4,800 rpm; max engine rpm: 7,000; specific power: 68.9 hp/l; carburation: 2 SU horizontal carburettors.

TRANSMISSION tyres: 165 x 13.

PERFORMANCE max speeds: 32 mph, 52 km/h in 1st gear; 52 mph, 84 km/h in 2nd gear; 80 mph, 128 km/h in 3rd gear; 115 mph, 185 km/h in 4th gear; power-weight ratio: 19.6 lb/hp, 8.9 kg/hp; speed in direct drive at 1,000 rpm: 16.4 mph, 26.4 km/h; fuel consumption: 24.6 m/imp gal, 20.5 m/US gal, 11.5 l x 100 km.

Colt Galant GTO MR

See Colt Galant GTO MI, except for·

PRICE: —

ENGINE compression ratio: 9.5; max power (DIN): 125 hp at 6,800 rpm; max torque (DIN): 105 lb ft, 14.5 kg m at 5,000 rpm; max engine rpm: 7,000; specific power: 78.3 hp/l; valves: 2 per cylinder, overhead, thimble tappets; camshafts: 2, overhead; carburation: 2 Mikuni-Solex 40 PHH horizontal carburettors.

TRANSMISSION gears: 5 + reverse; gearbox ratios: I 3.197, II 2.043, III 1.273, IV 1, V 0.845, rev 3.720; axle ratio: 4.222; tyres: 165 x 13.

PERFORMANCE max speeds: 34 mph, 55 km/h in 1st gear; 53 mph, 86 km/h in 2nd gear; 87 mph, 140 km/h in 3rd gear; 112 mph, 180 km/h in 4th gear; 124 mph, 200 km/h in 5th gear; power-weight ratio: 17.2 lb/hp, 7.8 kg/hp; speed in direct drive: 17.8 mph, 28.6 km/h; fuel consumption: 23.5 m/imp gal, 19.6 m/US gal, 12 l x 100 km.

CHASSIS rear suspension: twin trailing radius arms.

MITSUBISHI Colt Galant GTO MR

Debonair Executive

PRICE EX WORKS: 1,197,000 yen.

ENGINE front, 4 stroke; cylinders: 6, in line; bore and stroke: 2.87 x 3.13 in, 73 x 79.4 mm; engine capacity: 121.7 cu in, 1,994 cu cm; compression ratio: 10; max power (DIN): 130 hp at 6,000 rpm; max torque (DIN): 123 lb ft, 17 kg m at 4,000 rpm; max engine rpm: 5,500; specific power: 65.2 hp/l; cylinder block: cast iron; cylinder head: light alloy; crankshaft bearings: 7; valves: 2 per cylinder, overhead, rockers; camshafts: 1, overhead; lubrication: rotary pump, full flow filter; lubricating system capacity: 9.5 imp pt, 11.4 US pt, 5.4 l; carburation: 1 Nikki-Stromberg downdraught twin barrel carburettor; fuel feed: mechanical pump; cooling system: water; cooling system capacity: 15.8 imp pt, 19 US pt, 9 l.

TRANSMISSION driving wheels: rear; clutch: single dry plate (diaphragm); gearbox: mechanical; gears: 4 + reverse; synchromesh gears: I, II, III, IV; gearbox ratios: I 3.039, II 1.645, III 1, IV 0.797, rev 3.989; gear lever: steering column; final drive: hypoid bevel; axle ratio: 4.625; tyres: 6.95 x 14.

PERFORMANCE max speeds: 32 mph, 52 km/h in 1st gear; 59 mph, 95 km/h in 3rd gear; 98 mph, 157 km/h in 3rd gear; 106 mph, 170 km/h in 4th gear; power-weight ratio: 22.5 lb/hp, 10.2 kg/hp; acceleration: standing ¼ mile 17.8 sec; speed in top at 1,000 rpm: 17.6 mph, 28.3 km/h; fuel consumption: 22.6 m/imp gal, 18.8 m/US gal, 12.5 l x 100 km.

CHASSIS integral; front suspension: independent, wishbones, coil springs, anti-roll bar, telescopic dampers; rear

MITSUBISHI Debonair Executive

DEBONAIR EXECUTIVE

suspension: rigid axle, semi-elliptic leafsprings, telescopic dampers.

STEERING recirculating ball.

BRAKES front disc, rear drum, servo; lining area: total 75.3 sq in, 486 sq cm.

ELECTRICAL EQUIPMENT voltage: 12 V; battery: 35 Ah; generator type: alternator, 48 A; ignition distributor: Mitsubishi; headlamps: 4.

DIMENSIONS AND WEIGHT wheel base: 105.91 in, 2,690 mm; front track: 54.72 in, 1,390 mm; rear track: 54.72 in, 1,390 mm; overall length: 183.86 in, 4,670 mm; overall width: 66.54 in, 1,690 mm; overall height: 57.87 in, 1,470 mm; ground clearance: 7.09 in, 180 mm; dry weight: 2,923 lb, 1,330 kg; distribution of weight: 56% front axle, 44% rear axle; turning circle (between walls): 34.8 ft, 10.6 m; fuel tank capacity: 12.1 imp gal, 14.5 US gal, 55 l.

BODY saloon/sedan; doors: 4; seats: 6; front seats: bench.

PRACTICAL INSTRUCTIONS fuel: 98-100 oct petrol; engine sump oil: 9.5 imp pt. 11.4 US pt, 5.4 l, SAE 20W-30, change every 3,100 miles, 5,000 km; gearbox oil: 4.4 imp pt, 5.3 US pt, 2.5 l, SAE 90, change every 24,900 miles, 40,000 km; final drive oil: 2.3 imp pt, 2.7 US pt, 1.3 l, SAE 80-90, change every 24,900 miles, 40,000 km; greasing: every 12,400 miles, 20,000 km, 10 points; tappet clearances: inlet 0.006 in, 0.15 mm, exhaust 0.006 in, 0.15 mm; valve timing: inlet opens 23° before tdc and closes 63° after bdc, exhaust opens 63° before bdc and closes 23° after tdc; normal tyre pressure: front 21 psi, 1.5 atm, rear 21 psi, 1.5 atm.

VARIATIONS

ENGINE 9 compression ratio, max power (DIN) 120 hp at 6,000 rpm, max torque (DIN) 120 lb ft, 16.5 kg m at 4,000 rpm, 60.2 hp/l specific power.
PERFORMANCE max speed 103 mph, 165 km/h.

OPTIONAL ACCESSORIES Borg-Warner automatic gearbox with 3 ratios (I 2.393, II 1.450, III 1, rev 2.094), 4.222 axle ratio, max speed 96 mph, 155 km/h; electrically-controlled windows; air-conditioning system; separate front seats.

NISSAN   JAPAN

2-door Cherry Sedan

PRICE EX WORKS: 410,000 yen.

ENGINE front, transverse, 4 stroke; cylinders: 4, in line; bore and stroke: 2.87 x 2.32 in, 73 x 59 mm; engine capacity: 60.3 cu in, 988 cu cm; compression ratio: 9; max power (DIN): 58 hp at 6,000 rpm; max torque (DIN): 58 lb ft, 8 kg m at 4,000 rpm; max engine rpm: 6,200; specific power: 58.7 hp/l; cylinder block: cast iron; cylinder head: light alloy; crankshafts bearings: 3; valves: 2 per cylinder, overhead, push-rods and rockers; camshafts: 1, side; lubrication: rotary pump, full flow filter; lubricating system capacity: 5.8 imp pt, 7 US pt, 3.3 l; carburation: 1 Hitachi DCG286-4 downdraught twin barrel carburettor; fuel feed: mechanical pump; cooling system: water; cooling system capacity: 8.8 imp pt, 10.6 US pt, 5 l.

TRANSMISSION driving wheels: front; clutch: single dry plate (diaphragm); gearbox: mechanical; gears: 3 + reverse; synchromesh gears: I, II, III; gearbox ratios: I 3.358, II 1.687, III 1, rev 3.778; gear lever: central; final drive: helical spur gears; axle ratio: 4.429; width of rims: 4''; tyres: 6.00 x 12.

PERFORMANCE max speeds: 26 mph, 42 km/h in 1st gear; 52 mph, 83 km/h in 2nd gear; 87 mph, 140 km/h in 3rd gear; power-weight ratio: 24.9 lb/hp, 11.3 kg/hp; carrying capacity: 882 lb, 400 kg; acceleration: standing ¼ mile 19.2 sec; speed in direct drive at 1,000 rpm: 14.1 mph, 22.7 km/h; fuel consumption: 36.2 m/imp gal, 30.2 m/US gal, 7.8 l x 100 km.

CHASSIS integral, front auxiliary frame; front suspension: independent, by McPherson, coil springs/telescopic damper struts, lower wishbones, lower trailing links; rear suspension: independent, longitudinal trailing arms, coil springs, telescopic dampers.

STEERING rack-and-pinion; turns of steering wheel lock to lock: 3.20.

BRAKES drum.

ELECTRICAL EQUIPMENT voltage: 12 V; battery: 32 Ah; generator type: alternator, 25 A; ignition distributor: Hitachi; headlamps: 2.

DIMENSIONS AND WEIGHT wheel base: 91.93 in, 2,335 mm; front track: 50 in, 1,270 mm; rear track: 48.62 in, 1,235 mm; overall length: 142.13 in, 3,610 mm; overall width: 1,470 in, 57.87 mm; overall height: 54.33 in, 1,380 mm; ground clearance: 7.87 in, 200 mm; dry weight: 1,444 lb, 655 kg; distribu-

NISSAN 2-door Cherry X-1 Sedan

NISSAN 4-door Sunny 1200 Sedan

NISSAN Sunny 1200 Coupé

tion of weight: 63.4% front axle, 36.6% rear axle; turning circle (between walls): 32.8 ft, 10 m; fuel tank capacity: 7.9 imp gal, 9.5 US gal, 36 l.

BODY saloon/sedan; doors: 2; seats: 4; front seats: separate.

PRACTICAL INSTRUCTIONS fuel: 90 oct petrol; engine sump oil: 5.8 imp pt, 7 US pt, 3.3 l, SAE 20W-30, change every 3,100 miles, 5,000 km; gearbox and final drive oil: 4 imp pt, 4.9 US pt, 2.3 l, SAE 90, change every 31,000 miles, 50,000 km; tappet clearances: inlet 0.014 in, 0.35 mm, exhaust 0.014 in, 0.35 mm; valve timing: inlet opens 12° before tdc and closes 48° after bdc, exhaust opens 50° before bdc and closes 10° after tdc; normal tyre pressure: front 21 psi, 1.5 atm, rear 18 psi, 1.3 atm.

4-door Cherry GL Sedan

See 2-door Cherry Sedan, except for:

PRICE EX WORKS: 525,000 yen.

TRANSMISSION gears: 4 + reverse; gearbox ratios: I 3.673, II 2.217, III 1.448, IV 1, rev 4.093; axle ratio: 4.286.

PERFORMANCE max speeds: 24 mph, 38 km/h in 1st gear; 40 mph, 65 km/h in 2nd gear; 62 mph, 100 km/h in 3rd gear; 87 mph, 140 km/h in 4th gear.

BRAKES front disc, rear drum.

Cherry Station Wagon

See 2-door Cherry Sedan, except for:

PRICE: —

PERFORMANCE max speed: 84 mph, 135 km/h; power-weight ratio: 25.1 lb/hp, 11.4 kg/hp.

CHASSIS front suspension: rigid axle, semi-elliptic leafsprings, telescopic dampers.

DIMENSIONS AND WEIGHT front track: 49.80 in, 1,265 mm; overall width: 58.46 in, 1,485 mm; dry weight: 1,455 lb, 660 kg.

2-door Cherry X-1 Sedan

See 2-door Cherry Sedan, except for:

PRICE EX WORKS: 545,000 yen.

ENGINE bore and stroke: 2.87 x 2.76 in, 73 x 70 mm; engine capacity: 71.5 cu in, 1,171 mm; max power (DIN): 80 hp at 6,400 rpm; max torque (DIN): 71 lb ft, 9.8 kg m at 4,400 rpm; max engine rpm: 6,600; specific power: 68.3 hp/l; crankshaft bearings: 5; carburation: 2 Hitachi SU type HJE38W-5 horizontal carburettors.

TRANSMISSION gears: 4 + reverse; gearbox ratios: I 3.014, II 1.973, III 1.384, IV 1, rev 3.358; axle ratio: 4.067.

PERFORMANCE max speeds: 33 mph, 53 km/h in 1st gear; 51 mph, 82 km/h in 2nd gear; 73 mph, 117 km/h in 3rd gear; 99 mph, 160 km/h in 4th gear; power-weight ratio: 18.1 lb/hp, 8.2 kg/hp; acceleration: standing ¼ mile 17.3 sec; speed in direct drive at 1,000 rpm: 16.6 mph, 26.7 km/h; fuel consumption: 33.2 m/imp gal, 27.7 m/US gal, 8.5 l x 100 km.

BRAKES front disc, rear drum.

DIMENSIONS AND WEIGHT overall height: 54.13 in, 1,375 mm; ground clearance: 7.68 in, 195 mm; distribution of weight: 64% front axle, 36% rear axle.

PRACTICAL INSTRUCTIONS valve timing: inlet opens 20° before tdc and closes 56° after bdc, exhaust opens 58° before bdc and closes 18° after tdc.

4-door Cherry X-1 Sedan

See 2-door Cherry X-1 Sedan, except for:

PRICE EX WORKS: 569,000 yen.

PERFORMANCE power-weight ratio: 18.5 lb/hp, 8.4 kg/hp.

DIMENSIONS AND WEIGHT dry weight: 1,477 lb, 670 kg.

2-door Sunny 1200 Sedan

PRICE EX WORKS: 440,000 yen.

ENGINE front, 4 stroke; cylinders: 4, vertical, in line; bore and stroke: 2.87 x 2.76 in, 73 x 70 mm; engine capacity: 71.5 cu in, 1,171 cu cm; compression ratio: 9; max power (DIN): 68 hp at 6,000 rpm; max torque (DIN): 70 lb ft, 9.7 kg m at 3,600 rpm; max engine rpm: 6,250; specific power: 58.1 hp/l; cylinder block: cast iron; cylinder head: light alloy; crankshaft bearings: 5; valves: 2 per cylinder, overhead, push-rods and rockers; camshafts: 1, side; lubrication: rotary pump, full flow filter; lubricating system capacity: 4.8 imp pt, 5.7 US pt, 2.7 l; carburation: 1 Hitachi DCG306

NISSAN Cherry X-1 Sedan

NISSAN Sunny 1200 Sedan

NISSAN Sunny 1200 Coupé

downdraught twin barrel carburettor; fuel feed: mechanical pump; cooling system: water; cooling system capacity: 8.6 imp pt, 10.4 US pt, 4.9 l.

TRANSMISSION driving wheels: rear; clutch: single dry plate (diaphragm); gearbox: mechanical; gears: 3 + reverse; synchromesh gears: I, II, III; gearbox ratios: I 3.380, II 1.734, III 1, rev 3.380; gear lever: central; final drive: hypoid bevel; axle ratio: 3.900; width of rims: 6.00 x 12.

PERFORMANCE max speeds: 27 mph, 44 km/h in 1st gear; 52 mph, 86 km/h in 2nd gear; 93 mph, 150 km/h in 3rd gear; power-weight ratio: 22.7 lb/hp, 10.3 kg/hp; carrying capacity: 882 lb, 400 kg; acceleration: standing ¼ mile 18.6 sec; speed in direct drive at 1,000 rpm: 16.4 mph, 26.4 km/h; fuel consumption: 35.3 m/imp gal, 29.4 m/US gal, 8 l x 100 km.

CHASSIS integral; front suspension: independent. by McPherson, coil springs/telescopic damper struts, lower wishbones, lower trailing links; rear suspension: rigid axle, semi-elliptic leafsprings, telescopic dampers.

STEERING recirculating ball; turns of steering wheel lock to lock: 3.30.

BRAKES drum; lining area: front 42.3 sq in, 273 sq cm, rear 42.3 sq in, 273 sq cm, total 84.6 sq in, 546 sq cm.

ELECTRICAL EQUIPMENT voltage: 12 V; battery: 32 Ah; generator type: alternator; ignition distributor: Hitachi or Mitsubishi; headlamps: 2.

DIMENSIONS AND WEIGHT wheel base: 90.55 in, 2,300 mm; front track: 42.82 in, 1,240 mm; rear track: 49.02 in, 1,245 mm; overall length: 150.79 in, 3,830 mm; overall width: 58.86 in, 1,495 mm; overall height: 54.72 in, 1,390 mm; ground clearance: 6.69 in, 170 mm; dry weight: 1,544 lb, 700 kg; distribution of weight: 54.3% front axle, 45.7% rear axle; turning circle (between walls): 26.9 ft, 8.2 m; fuel tank capacity: 8.8 imp gal, 10.6 US gal, 40 l.

BODY saloon/sedan; doors: 2; seats: 4; front seats: separate.

PRACTICAL INSTRUCTIONS fuel: 90 oct petrol; engine sump oil: 4.8 imp pt, 5.7 US pt, 2.7 l, SAE 20W-30, change every 3,100 miles, 5,000 km; gearbox oil: 2.1 imp pt, 2.5 US pt, 1.2 l, SAE 90, change every 31,000 miles, 50,000 km; final drive oil: 1.6 imp pt, 1.9 US pt, 0.9 l, SAE 90, change every 31,000 miles, 50,000 km; tappet clearances: inlet 0.014 in, 0.35 mm, exhaust 0.014 in, 0.35 mm; valve timing: inlet opens 14° before tdc and closes 54° after bdc, exhaust opens 56° before bdc and closes 12° after tdc; normal tyre pressure: front 21 psi, 1.5 atm, rear 21 psi, 1.5 atm.

4-door Sunny 1200 Sedan

See 2-door Sunny 1200 Sedan, except for:

PRICE EX WORKS: 465,000 yen.

4-door Sunny 1200 De Luxe Sedan

See 2-door Sunny 1200 Sedan, except for:

PRICE EX WORKS: —

TRANSMISSION gears: 4 + reverse; gearbox ratios: I 3.757, II 2.169, III 1.404, IV 1, rev 3.640.

PERFORMANCE max speeds: 25 mph, 40 km/h in 1st gear; 45 mph, 72 km/h in 2nd gear; 70 mph, 112 km/h in 3rd gear; 93 mph, 150 km/h in 4th gear.

4-door Sunny 1200 GX Sedan

See 4-door Sunny 1200 De Luxe Sedan, except for:

PRICE EX WORKS: 605,000 yen.

ENGINE compression ratio: 10; max power (DIN): 83 hp at 6,400 rpm; max torque (DIN): 72 lb ft, 10 kg m at 4,400 rpm; max engine rpm: 6,600; specific power: 70.9 hp/l; lubricating system capacity: 6 imp pt, 7.2 US pt, 3.4 l; carburation: 2 Hitachi SU type HJE38W-5 horizontal carburettors.

PERFORMANCE max speeds: 28 mph, 45 km/h in 1st gear; 48 mph, 77 km/h in 2nd gear; 75 mph, 120 km/h in 3rd gear; 99 mph, 160 km/h in 4th gear; power-weight ratio: 18.7 lb/hp, 8.5 kg/hp; acceleration: standing ¼ mile 17.4 sec; fuel consumption: 32.1 m/imp gal, 26.7 m/US gal, 8.8 l x 100 km.

BRAKES front disc, rear drum; lining area: front 13 sq in, 84 sq cm, rear 42.2 sq in, 272 sq cm, total 55.2 sq in, 356 sq cm.

DIMENSIONS AND WEIGHT dry weight: 1,566 lb, 710 kg.

PRACTICAL INSTRUCTIONS valve timing: inlet opens 20° before tdc and closes 56° after bdc, exhaust opens 58° before bdc and closes 18° after tdc.

OPTIONAL ACCESSORIES automatic gearbox with 3 ratios (I 2.458, II 1.458, III 1, rev 2.182).

Sunny 1200 Coupé

See 4-door Sunny 1200 De Luxe Sedan, except for:

PRICE EX WORKS: 555,000 yen.

PERFORMANCE power-weight ratio: 22.5 lb/hp, 10.2 kg/hp.

DIMENSIONS AND WEIGHT overall length: 150.59 in, 3,825 mm; overall width: 59.65 in, 1,515 mm; overall height: 53.15 in, 1,350 mm; dry weight: 1,532 lb, 695 kg; distribution of weight: 53% front axle, 47% rear axle; fuel tank capacity: 8.4 imp gal, 10 US gal, 38 l.

BODY coupé; doors: 2.

Sunny 1200 GL Coupé

See Sunny 1200 Coupé, except for:

PRICE EX WORKS: 590,000 yen.

PERFORMANCE power-weight ratio: 22.7 lb/hp, 10.3 kg/hp.

BRAKES front disc, rear drum; lining area: front 13 sq in, 84 sq cm, rear 42.2 sq in, 272 sq cm, total 55.2 sq in, 356 sq cm.

DIMENSIONS AND WEIGHT dry weight: 1,544 lb, 700 kg.

Sunny 1200 GX Coupé

See Sunny 1200 Coupé, except for:

PRICE EX WORKS: 630,000 yen.

ENGINE compression ratio: 10; max power (DIN): 83 hp at 6,400 rpm; max torque (DIN): 72 lb ft, 10 kg m at 4,400 rpm; max engine rpm: 6,500; specific power: 70.9 hp/l; lubricating system capacity: 6 imp pt, 7.2 US pt, 3.4 l; carburation: 2 Hitachi SU type HJE38W-5 horizontal carburettors.

PERFORMANCE max speeds: 28 mph, 45 km/h in 1st gear; 48 mph, 77 km/h in 2nd gear; 75 mph, 120 km/h in 3rd gear; 99 mph, 160 km/h in 4th gear; power-weight ratio: 18.5 lb/hp, 8.4 kg/hp; acceleration: standing ¼ mile 17.4 sec; speed in direct drive at 1,000 rpm: 15 mph, 24.2 km/h; fuel consumption: 32.1 m/imp gal, 26.7 m/US gal, 8.8 l x 100 km.

BRAKES front disc, rear drum; lining area: front 13 sq in, 84 sq cm, rear 42.2 sq in, 272 sq cm, total 55.2 sq in, 356 sq cm.

DIMENSIONS AND WEIGHT dry weight: 1,544 lb, 700 kg.

PRACTICAL INSTRUCTIONS valve timing: inlet opens 40° before tdc and closes 56° after bdc, exhaust opens 58° before bdc and closes 18° after tdc.

OPTIONAL ACCESSORIES automatic gearbox with 3 ratios (I 2.458, II 1.458, III 1, rev 2.182).

2-door Datsun 1400 Sedan

PRICE EX WORKS: 525,000 yen.

ENGINE front, 4 stroke; cylinders: 4, in line; bore and stroke: 3.27 x 2.60 in, 83 x 66 mm; engine capacity: 87.1 cu in, 1,428 cu cm; compression ratio: 9; max power (DIN): 85 hp at 6,000 rpm; max torque (DIN): 86 lb ft, 11.8 kg m at 3,600 rpm; max engine rpm: 6,250; specific power: 59.5 hp/l; cylinder block: cast iron; cylinder head: light alloy; crankshaft bearings: 5; valves: 2 per cylinder, overhead, rockers; camshafts: 1, overhead; lubrication: rotary pump, full flow filter; lubricating system capacity: 8.1 imp pt, 9.7 US pt, 4.6 l; carburation: 1 Nikki downdraught twin barrel carburettor; fuel feed: mechanical pump; cooling system: water; cooling system capacity: 10.6 imp pt, 12.7 US pt, 6 l.

TRANSMISSION driving wheels: rear; clutch: single dry plate (diaphragm); gearbox: mechanical; gears: 3 + reverse; synchromesh gears: I, II, III; gearbox ratios: I 3.263, II 1.645, III 1, rev 3.355; gear lever: central; final drive: hypoid bevel; axle ratio: 4.375; width of rims: 4''; tyres: 5.60 x 13.

PERFORMANCE max speeds: 29 mph, 46 km/h in 1st gear; 57 mph, 91 km/h in 2nd gear; 93 mph, 150 km/h in 3rd gear; power-weight ratio: 22.9 lb/hp, 10.4 kg/hp; carrying capacity: 882 lb, 400 kg; speed in direct drive at 1,000 rpm: 14.9 mph, 24 km/h; fuel consumption: 33.2 m/imp gal, 27.7 m/US gal, 8.5 l x 100 km.

CHASSIS integral; front suspension: independent, by McPherson, coil springs/telescopic damper struts, lower wishbones, lower trailing links, anti-roll bar; rear suspension: independent, semi-trailing arms, coil springs, telescopic dampers.

STEERING recirculating ball; turns of steering wheel lock to lock: 3.30.

BRAKES drum; lining area: front 54 sq in, 348 sq cm, rear 54 sq in, 348 sq cm, total 108 sq in, 696 sq cm.

ELECTRICAL EQUIPMENT voltage: 12 V; battery: 35 Ah; generator type: alternator, 30 A; ignition distributor: Hitachi; headlamps: 4.

NISSAN Datsun 1600 Sedan

NISSAN Datsun 1800 SSS Coupé

NISSAN Skyline 1500 Sedan

DIMENSIONS AND WEIGHT wheel base: 95.28 in, 2,420 mm; front track: 50 in, 1,270 mm; rear track: 50 in, 1,270 mm; overall length: 162.20 in, 4,120 mm; overall width: 61.42 in, 1,560 mm; overall height: 55.91 in, 1,420 mm; ground clearance: 8.46 in, 215 mm; dry weight: 1,951 lb, 885 kg; distribution of weight: 55% front axle, 45% rear axle; turning circle (between walls): 33.5 ft, 10.2 m; fuel tank capacity: 10.1 imp gal, 12.1 US gal, 46 l.

BODY saloon/sedan; doors: 2; seats: 5; front seats: separate.

PRACTICAL INSTRUCTIONS fuel: 90 oct petrol; engine sump oil: 8.1 imp pt, 9.7 US pt, 4.6 l, SAE 20W-30, change every 3,100 miles, 5,000 km; gearbox oil: 3 imp pt, 3.6 US pt, 1.7 l, SAE 90, change every 31,000 miles, 50,000 km; final drive oil: 1.4 imp pt, 1.7 US pt, 0.8 l, SAE 90, change every 31,000 miles, 50,000 km; tappet clearances: inlet 0.010 in, 0.25 mm, exhaust 0.010 in, 0.25 mm; valve timing: inlet opens 8° before tdc and closes 44° after bdc, exhaust opens 50° before bdc and closes 10° after tdc; nromal tyre pressure: front 23 psi, 1.6 atm, rear 23 psi, 1.6 atm.

2-door Datsun 1400 De Luxe Sedan

See 2-door Datsun 1400 Sedan, except for:

PRICE EX WORKS: 609,000 yen.

TRANSMISSION gears: 4 + reverse; gearbox ratios: I 3.667, II 2.177, III 1.419, IV 1, rev 3.355.

PERFORMANCE max speeds: 25 mph, 40 km/h in 1st gear; 42 mph, 68 km/h in 2nd gear; 67 mph, 108 km/h in 3rd gear; 93 mph, 150 km/h in 4th gear; power-weight ratio: 23.8 lb/hp, 10.8 kg/hp.

DIMENSIONS AND WEIGHT dry weight: 2,018 lb, 915 kg.

4-door Datsun 1400 De Luxe Sedan

See 2-door Datsun 1400 De Luxe Sedan, except for:

PRICE EX WORKS: 629,000 yen.

PERFORMANCE power-weight ratio: 24 lb/hp, 10.9 kg/hp.

DIMENSIONS AND WEIGHT dry weight: 2,040 lb, 925 kg.

4-door Datsun 1400 GL Sedan

See 2-door Datsun 1400 De Luxe Sedan, except for:

PRICE EX WORKS: 669,000 yen.

PERFORMANCE power-weight ratio: 24.2 lb/hp, 11 kg/hp.

BRAKES front disc, rear drum, servo.

DIMENSIONS AND WEIGHT dry weight: 2,062 lb, 935 kg.

OPTIONAL ACCESSORIES automatic gearbox with 3 ratios (I 2.458, II 1.458, III 1, rev 2.182).

Datsun 1600 Sedan

PRICE: —

ENGINE front, 4 stroke; cylinders: 4, Vee-slanted at 12°, in line; bore and stroke: 3.27 x 2.90 in, 83 x 73.7 mm; engine capacity: 97.3 cu in, 1,595 cu cm; compression ratio: 8.5; max power (DIN): 96 hp at 5,600 rpm; max torque (DIN): 100 lb ft, 13.8 kg m at 3,600 rpm; max engine rpm: 5,600; specific power: 60.2 hp/l; cylinder block: cast iron; cylinder head: light alloy; crankshaft bearings: 5; valves: 2 per cylinder, overhead, rockers; camshafts: 1, overhead; lubrication: rotary pump, full flow filter; lubricating system capacity: 7 imp pt, 8.5 US pt, 4 l; carburation: 1 Hitachi downdraught twin barrel carburettor; fuel feed: mechanical pump; cooling system: water; cooling system capacity: 11.3 imp pt, 13.5 US pt, 6.4 l.

TRANSMISSION driving wheels: rear; clutch: single dry plate (diaphragm); gearbox: mechanical; gears: 4 + reverse; synchromesh gears: I, II, III, IV; gearbox ratios: I 3.382, II 2.013, III 1.312, IV 1, rev 3.364; gear lever: central; final drive: hypoid bevel; axle ratio: 3.700; width of rims: 4''; tyres: 5.60 x 13.

PERFORMANCE max speeds: 29 mph, 47 km/h in 1st gear; 51 mph, 82 km/h in 2nd gear; 78 mph, 125 km/h in 3rd gear; 99 mph, 160 km/h in 4th gear; power-weight ratio: 21.4 lb/hp, 9.7 kg/hp; carrying capacity: 882 lb, 400 kg; acceleration: standing ¼ mile 19.5 sec; speed in direct drive at 1,000 rpm: 18 mph, 29 km/h; fuel consumption: 28.2 m/imp gal, 23.5 m/US gal, 10 l x 100 km.

CHASSIS integral, front and rear auxiliary frames; front suspension: independent, by McPherson, coil springs/tele-

NISSAN Datsun 1600 Sedan

NISSAN Datsun 1800 SSS Coupé

NISSAN Skyline 1500 Sedan

scopic damper struts, lower wishbones, lower trailing links, anti-roll bar; rear suspension: independent, semi-trailing arms, coil springs, telescopic dampers.

STEERING recirculating ball; turns of steering wheel lock to lock: 3.20.

BRAKES drum; lining area: front 54.4 sq in, 351 sq cm, rear 54.4 sq in, 351 sq cm, total 108.8 sq in, 702 sq cm.

ELECTRICAL EQUIPMENT voltage: 12 V; battery: 40 Ah; generator type: alternator, 30 A; ignition distributor: Hitachi; headlamps: 4.

DIMENSIONS AND WEIGHT wheel base: 95.28 in, 2,420 mm; front track: 50 in, 1,270 mm; rear track: 50 in, 1,270 mm; overall length: 162.20 in, 4,120 mm; overall width: 61.42 in, 1,560 mm; overall height: 55.51 in, 1,410 mm; ground clearance: 8.27 in, 210 mm; dry weight: 2,051 lb, 930 kg; distribution of weight: 55% front axle, 45% rear axle; turning circle (between walls): 34.1 ft, 10.4 m; fuel tank capacity: 10.1 imp gal, 12.1 US gal, 46 l.

BODY saloon/sedan; doors: 4; seats: 5; front seats: separate.

PRACTICAL INSTRUCTIONS fuel: 90 oct petrol; engine sump oil: 7 imp pt, 8.5 US pt, 4 l, SAE 20W-30, change every 3,100 miles, 5,000 km; gearbox oil: 3 imp pt, 3.6 US pt, 1.7 l, SAE 90, change every 31,000 miles, 50,000 km; final drive oil: 1.4 imp pt, 1.7 US pt, 0.8 l, SAE 90, change every 31,000 miles, 50,000 km; greasing: every 31,000 miles, 50,000 km, 5 points; tappet clearances: inlet 0.010 in, 0.25 mm, exhaust 0.014 in, 0.35 mm; valve timing: inlet opens 8° before tdc and closes 44° after bdc, exhaust opens 50° before bdc and closes 10° after tdc; normal tyre pressure: front 24 psi, 1.7 atm, rear 28 psi, 2 atm.

OPTIONAL ACCESSORIES 3-speed mechanical gearbox; 3-speed automatic gearbox.

Datsun 1600 Coupé

See Datsun 1600 Sedan, except for:

PRICE: —

DIMENSIONS AND WEIGHT overall height: 54.92 in, 1,395 mm.

BODY coupé; doors: 2; seats: 4.

OPTIONAL ACCESSORIES none.

Datsun 1600 Station Wagon

See Datsun 1600 Sedan, except for:

PRICE IN GB: £ 832.

TRANSMISSION gearbox ratios: I 3.657, II 2.177, III 1.419, IV 1, rev 3.637.

PERFORMANCE power-weight ratio: 21.6 lb/hp, 9.8 kg/hp.

DIMENSIONS AND WEIGHT front track: 50.20 in, 1,275 mm; rear track: 49.61 in, 1,260 mm; overall length: 163.19 in, 4,145 mm; overall height: 56.50 in, 1,435 mm; ground clearance: 6.50 in, 165 mm; dry weight: 2,084 lb, 945 kg; fuel tank capacity: 9.9 imp gal, 11.9 US gal, 45 l.

BODY estate car/station wagon; doors: 4+1.

OPTIONAL ACCESSORIES 3-speed automatic gearbox not available.

Datsun 1600 SSS Sedan

See Datsun 1600 Sedan, except for:

PRICE: —

ENGINE compression ratio: 9.5; max power (DIN): 109 hp at 6,000 rpm; max torque (DIN): 104 lb ft, 14.3 kg m at 4,000 rpm; max engine rpm: 6,400; specific power: 68.3 hp/l; carburation: 2 SU HJL38W-3 horizontal carburettors.

PERFORMANCE max speeds: 34 mph, 55 km/h in 1st gear; 57 mph, 92 km/h in 2nd gear; 88 mph, 142 km/h in 3rd gear; 103 mph, 165 km/h in 4th gear; power-weight ratio: 18.7 lb/hp, 8.5 kg/hp; fuel consumption: 26.9 m/imp gal, 22.4 m/US gal, 10.5 l x 100 km.

BRAKES front disc, rear drum; lining area: front 17.7 sq in, 114 sq cm.

PRACTICAL INSTRUCTIONS valve timing: inlet opens 16° before tdc and closes 52° after bdc, exhaust opens 54° before bdc and closes 14° after tdc.

OPTIONAL ACCESSORIES none.

Datsun 1600 SSS Coupé

See Datsun 1600 SSS Sedan, except for:

PRICE: —

TRANSMISSION axle ratio: 3.900.

PERFORMANCE max speeds: 29 mph, 47 km/h in 1st gear; 47 mph, 76 km/h in 2nd gear; 73 mph, 118 km/h in 3rd gear; 103 mph, 165 km/h in 4th gear; speed in direct drive at 1,000 rpm: 16.8 mph, 27 km/h.

DIMENSIONS AND WEIGHT overall height: 54.92 in, 1,395 mm.

BODY coupé; doors: 2; seats: 4.

Datsun 1800 SSS Sedan

See Datsun 1600 Sedan, except for:

PRICE EX WORKS: 738,000 yen.

ENGINE bore and stroke: 3.35 x 3.07 in, 85 x 78 mm; engine capacity: 108 cu in, 1,770 cu cm; compression ratio: 9.5; max power (DIN): 115 hp at 6,000 rpm; max torque (DIN): 112 lb ft, 15.5 kg m at 4,000 rpm; max engine rpm: 7,000; specific power: 65 hp/l; lubricating system capacity: 8.1 imp pt, 9.7 US pt, 4.6 l; carburation: 2 Hitachi SU type HJL38W horizontal carburettors; cooling system capacity: 10.6 imp pt, 12.7 US pt, 6 l.

PERFORMANCE max speeds: 35 mph, 56 km/h in 1st gear; 60 mph, 96 km/h in 2nd gear; 89 mph, 143 km/h in 3rd gear; 109 mph, 175 km/h in 4th gear; power-weight ratio: 18.1 lb/hp, 8.2 kg/hp; acceleration: standing ¼ mile 17.5 sec; speed in direct drive at 1,000 rpm: 16.2 mph, 26 km/h; fuel consumption: 23.5 m/imp gal, 19.6 m/US gal, 12 l x 100 km.

STEERING turns of steering wheel lock to lock: 3.30.

BRAKES front disc, rear drum, servo; lining area: front 17.4 sq in, 112 sq cm, rear 54 sq in, 348 sq cm, total 71.4 sq in, 460 sq cm.

ELECTRICAL EQUIPMENT battery: 45 Ah.

DIMENSIONS AND WEIGHT overall length: 161.22 in, 4,095 mm; overall height: 55.91 in, 1,420 mm; ground clearance: 8.46 in, 215 mm.

PRACTICAL INSTRUCTIONS valve timing: inlet opens 16° before tdc and closes 52° after bdc, exhaust opens 54° before bdc and closes 14° after tdc; normal tyre pressure: front 23 psi, 1.6 atm, rear 23 psi, 1.6 atm.

VARIATIONS

ENGINE 8.5 compression ratio, max power (DIN) 100 hp at 6,000 rpm, max torque (DIN) 109 lb ft, 15 kg m at 4,000 rpm, 62.1 hp/l specific power.
PERFORMANCE max speed 106 mph, 170 km/h, power-weight ratio 19 lb/hp, 8.6 kg/hp.

OPTIONAL ACCESSORIES 165 x 13 tyres; automatic gearbox with 3 ratios (I 2.458, II 1.458, III 1, rev 2.182), 3.900 axle ratio, max speed 103 mph, 165 km/h.

Datsun 1800 SSS Coupé

See Datsun 1800 SSS Sedan, except for:

PRICE EX WORKS: 813,000 yen.

PERFORMANCE power-weight ratio: 18.3 lb/hp, 8.3 kg/hp.

DIMENSIONS AND WEIGHT overall height: 55.31 in, 1,405 mm; dry weight: 2,095 lb, 950 kg.

BODY coupé; doors: 2; seats: 4.

Skyline 1500 Sedan

PRICE: —

ENGINE front, 4 stroke; cylinders: 4, slanted at 12°, in line; bore and stroke: 3.23 x 2.76 in, 82 x 70.2 mm; engine capacity: 90.5 cu in, 1,483 cu cm; compression ratio: 8.5; max power (DIN): 94 hp at 6,000 rpm; max torque (DIN): 96 lb ft, 13.2 kg m at 4,000 rpm; max engine rpm: 6,000; specific power: 63.4 hp/l; cylinder block: cast iron; cylinder head: light alloy; crankshaft bearings: 5; valves: 2 per cylinder, overhead, rockers; camshafts: 1, overhead; lubrication: gear pump, full flow filter; lubricating system capacity: 6.5 imp pt, 7.8 US pt, 3.7 l; carburation: 1 Nihon Kikaki downdraught twin barrel carburettor; fuel feed: electric pump; cooling system: water; cooling system capacity: 13.6 imp pt, 16.3 US pt, 7.7 l.

NISSAN Skyline 1800 Hardtop

NISSAN Skyline 2000 GT Sedan

NISSAN Laurel 1800 GL Sedan

TRANSMISSION driving wheels: rear; clutch: single dry plate (diaphragm); gearbox: mechanical; gears: 4 + reverse; synchromesh gears: I, II, III, IV; gearbox ratios: I 3.657, II 2.177, III 1.419, IV 1, rev 3.638; gear lever: central; final drive: hypoid bevel; axle ratio: 4.111; width of rims: 4''; tyres: 5.60 x 13.

PERFORMANCE max speeds: 28 mph, 45 km/h in 1st gear; 47 mph, 75 km/h in 2nd gear; 71 mph, 115 km/h in 3rd gear; 99 mph, 160 km/h in 4th gear; power-weight ratio: 22.5 lb/hp, 10.2 kg/hp; carrying capacity: 882 lb, 400 kg; acceleration: standing ¼ mile 18.9 sec, 0-50 mph (0-80 km/h) 10.7 sec; speed in direct drive at 1,000 rpm: 16.8 mph, 27 km/h; fuel consumption: 29.7 m/imp gal, 24.8 m/US gal, 9.5 l x 100 km.

CHASSIS integral; front suspension: independent, by McPherson, coil springs/telescopic damper struts, lower wishbones, lower trailing links, anti-roll bar; rear suspension: rigid axle, semi-elliptic leafsprings, telescopic dampers.

STEERING recirculating ball; turns of steering wheel lock to lock: 3.30.

BRAKES drum; lining area: front 54.4 sq in, 351 sq cm, rear 54.4 sq in, 351 sq cm, total 108.8 sq in, 702 sq cm.

ELECTRICAL EQUIPMENT voltage: 12 V; battery: 40 Ah; generator type: alternator, 420 W; ignition distributor: Mitsubishi; headlamps: 4.

DIMENSIONS AND WEIGHT wheel base: 92.13 in, 2,490 mm; front track: 52.17 in, 1,325 mm; rear track: 51.97 in, 1,320 mm; overall length: 166.73 in, 4,235 mm; overall width: 62.80 in, 1,595 mm; overall height: 55.31 in, 1,405 mm; ground clearance: 6.90 in, 175 mm; dry weight: 2,117 lb, 960 kg; distribution of weight: 56% front axle, 44% rear axle; turning circle (between walls): 32.8 ft, 10 m; fuel tank capacity: 11 imp gal, 13.2 US gal, 50 l.

BODY saloon/sedan; doors: 4; seats: 5; front seats: bench.

PRACTICAL INSTRUCTIONS fuel: 88 oct petrol; engine sump oil: 6.5 imp pt, 7.8 US pt, 3.7 l, SAE 20W-30, change every 3,100 miles, 5,000 km; gearbox oil: 3 imp pt, 3.6 US pt, 1.7 l, SAE 90, change every 37,300 miles, 60,000 km; final drive oil: 1.9 imp pt, 2.3 US pt, 1.1 l, SAE 90, change every 37,300 miles, 60,000 km; greasing: every 37,300 miles, 60,000 km, 4 points; tappet clearances: inlet 0.008 in, 0.20 mm, exhaust 0.008 in, 0.20 mm; valve timing: inlet opens 15° before tdc and closes 55° after bdc, exhaust opens 55° before bdc and closes 15° after tdc; normal tyre pressure: front 20 psi, 1.4 atm, rear 23 psi, 1.6 atm.

OPTIONAL ACCESSORIES 3-speed mechanical gearbox (I 3.263, II 1.645, III 1), steering column gear lever; limited slip final drive; 165 x 14 tyres; front disc brakes, servo; air-conditioning system.

Skyline 1800 Hardtop

See Skyline 1500 Sedan, except for:

PRICE EX WORKS: 772,000 yen.

ENGINE bore and stroke: 3.35 x 3.15 in, 85 x 80 mm; engine capacity: 110.8 cu in, 1,815 cu cm; compression ratio: 8.3; max power (DIN): 100 hp at 5,600 rpm; max torque (DIN): 109 lb ft, 15 kg m at 3,600 rpm; max engine rpm: 6,400; specific power: 55.1 hp/l; carburation: 1 Nikki downdraught twin barrel carburettor; cooling system capacity: 15 imp pt, 18 US pt, 8.5 l.

TRANSMISSION gearbox ratios: I 3.382, II 2.013, III 1.312, IV 1, rev 3.365; axle ratio: 3.889; tyres: 6.15 x 14.

PERFORMANCE max speeds: 31 mph, 50 km/h in 1st gear; 52 mph, 83 km/h in 2nd gear; 79 mph, 127 km/h in 3rd gear; 103 mph, 165 km/h in 4th gear; power-weight ratio: 20.9 lb/hp, 9.5 kg/hp; acceleration: standing ¼ mile 17.8 sec; speed in direct drive at 1,000 rpm: 17.4 mph, 28 km/h; fuel consumption: 26.2 m/imp gal, 21.8 m/US gal, 10.8 l x 100 km.

BRAKES front disc, rear drum, servo (standard); lining area: front 17.7 sq in, 114 sq cm.

DIMENSIONS AND WEIGHT wheel base: 95.28 in, 2,420 mm; overall length: 162.79 in, 4,135 mm; overall height: 54.72 in, 1,390 mm; dry weight: 2,128 lb, 965 kg.

BODY hardtop; doors: 2; seats: 4; front seats: separate.

OPTIONAL ACCESSORIES only 164 x 14 tyres and automatic gearbox with 3 ratios (I 2.458, II 1.458, III 1, rev 2.182), max speed 99 mph, 160 km/h.

Skyline 2000 GT Sedan

See Skyline 1500 Sedan, except for:

PRICE: —

ENGINE bore and stroke: 4.07 x 2.74 in, 78 x 69.7 mm; engine capacity: 121.9 cu in, 1,998 cu cm; compression ratio: 9;

NISSAN Skyline 1800 Hardtop

NISSAN Skyline 2000 GT Sedan

NISSAN Laurel 1800 GL Sedan

max power (DIN): 120 hp at 6,000 rpm; max torque (DIN): 123 lb ft, 17 kg m at 4,000 rpm; specific power: 60.1 hp/l; lubricating system capacity: 8.1 imp pt, 9.7 US pt, 4.6 l; carburation: 1 Hitachi downdraught twin barrel carburettor; cooling system capacity: 15.8 imp pt, 19 US pt, 9 l.

TRANSMISSION gearbox ratios: I 3.549, II 2.197, III 1.420, IV 1, rev 3.164; axle ratio: 3.889; tyres: 6.45 x 14.

PERFORMANCE max speeds: 30 mph, 49 km/h in 1st gear; 50 mph, 80 km/h in 2nd gear; 76 mph, 123 km/h in 3rd gear; 109 mph, 175 km/h in 4th gear; power-weight ratio: 20.1 lb/hp, 9.1 kg/hp; speed in direct drive at 1,000 rpm: 17.9 mph, 28.8 km/h; fuel consumption: 25.7 m/imp gal, 21.4 m/US gal, 11 l x 100 km.

CHASSIS rear suspension: independent, oblique trailing arms, coil springs, telescopic dampers.

BRAKES front disc, rear drum, servo.

ELECTRICAL EQUIPMENT battery: 35 Ah; generator type: alternator, 40 A.

DIMENSIONS AND WEIGHT wheel base: 103.94 in, 2,640 mm; overall length: 174.41 in, 4,430 mm; overall height: 54.72 in, 1,390 mm; ground clearance: 6.69 in, 170 mm; dry weight: 2,403 lb, 1,090 kg; turning circle (between walls): 37.4 ft, 11.4 m.

Laurel 1800 Sedan

PRICE: —

ENGINE front, 4 stroke; cylinders: 4, in line; bore and stroke: 3.35 x 3.15 in, 85 x 80 mm; engine capacity: 110.8 cu in, 1,815 cu cm; compression ratio: 8.3; max power (DIN): 100 hp at 5,600 rpm; max torque (DIN): 109 lb ft, 15 kg m at 3,600 rpm; max engine rpm: 5,600; specific power: 55.1 hp/l; cylinder block: cast iron; cylinder head: light alloy; crankshaft bearings: 5; valves: 2 per cylinder, overhead, rockers; camshafts: 1, overhead; lubrication: gear pump, full flow filter; lubricating system capacity: 6.7 imp pt, 8 US pt, 3.8 l; carburation: 1 Hitachi downdraught twin barrel carburettor; fuel feed: electric pump; cooling system: water; cooling system capacity: 15.1 imp pt, 18.2 US pt, 8.6 l.

TRANSMISSION driving wheels: rear; clutch: single dry plate (diaphragm); gearbox: mechanical; gears: 4 + reverse; synchromesh gears: I, II, III, IV; gearbox ratios: I 3.382, II 2.013, III 1.312, IV 1, rev 3.364; gear lever: central; final drive: hypoid bevel; axle ratio: 3.700; width of rims: 4.5''; tyres: 6.50 x 13.

PERFORMANCE max speeds: 30 mph, 49 km/h in 1st gear; 52 mph, 84 km/h in 2nd gear; 83 mph, 134 km/h in 3rd gear; 103 mph, 165 km/h in 4th gear; power-weight ratio: 21.7 lb/hp, 9.8 kg/hp; carrying capacity: 992 lb, 450 kg; acceleration: standing ¼ mile 18.1 sec, 0-50 mph (0-80 km/h) 8.1 sec; speed in direct drive at 1,000 rpm: 17.4 mph, 28 km/h; fuel consumption: 25.7 m/imp gal, 21.4 m/US gal, 11 l x 100 km.

CHASSIS integral; front suspension: independent, by McPherson, coil springs/telescopic damper struts, lower trailing links, anti-roll bar; rear suspension: independent, semi-trailing arms, coil springs, telescopic dampers.

STEERING rack-and-pinion; turns of steering wheel lock to lock: 3.30.

BRAKES front disc, rear drum; lining area: front 17.4 sq in, 112 sq cm, rear 54 sq in, 348 sq cm, total 71.4 sq in, 460 sq cm.

ELECTRICAL EQUIPMENT voltage: 12 V; battery: 35 Ah; generator type: alternator, 45 A; ignition distributor: Hitachi; headlamps: 4.

DIMENSIONS AND WEIGHT wheel base: 103.50 in, 2,620 mm; front track: 51.38 in, 1,305 mm; rear track: 51.18 in, 1,300 mm; overall length: 171.26 in, 4,350 mm; overall width: 63.19 in, 1,605 mm; overall height: 55.32 in, 1,405 mm; ground clearance: 7.29 in, 185 mm; dry weight: 2,172 lb, 985 kg; distribution of weight: 53% front axle, 47% rear axle; turning circle (between walls): 32.1 ft, 9.8 m; fuel tank capacity: 11.2 imp gal, 13.5 US gal, 51 l.

BODY saloon/sedan; doors: 4; seats: 5; front seats: separate.

PRACTICAL INSTRUCTIONS fuel: 90 oct petrol; engine sump oil: 6.7 imp pt, 8 US pt, 3.8 l, SAE 20W-30, change every 3,100 miles, 5,000 km; gearbox oil: 3 imp pt, 3.6 US pt, 1.7 l, SAE 90, change every 31,100 miles, 50,000 km; final drive oil: 1.8 imp pt, 2.1 US pt, 1 l, SAE 90, change every 31,100 miles, 50,000 km; greasing: none; tappet clearances: inlet 0.008 in, 0.20 mm, exhaust 0.008 in, 0.20 mm; valve timing: inlet opens 18° before tdc and closes 52° after bdc, exhaust opens 58° before bdc and closes 12° after tdc; normal tyre pressure: front 23 psi, 1.6 atm, rear 23 psi, 1.6 atm.

OPTIONAL ACCESSORIES 3.900 axle ratio; 3-speed mechanical gearbox; automatic gearbox with 3 ratios (I 2.458, II 1.458, III 1, rev 2.182); air-conditioning system; electrically-controlled windows; GL version.

Laurel 1800 Hardtop

See Laurel 1800 Sedan, except for:

PRICE EX WORKS: 795,000 yen.

TRANSMISSION tyres: 6.45 x 14.

PERFORMANCE power-weight ratio: 21.6 lb/hp, 9.8 kg/hp.

DIMENSIONS AND WEIGHT front track: 51.77 in, 1,315 mm; rear track: 51.57 in, 1,310 mm; overall length: 170.47 in, 4,330 mm; overall height: 54.33 in, 1,380 mm; ground clearance: 70.87 in, 180 mm; dry weight: 2,249 lb, 1,020 kg; turning circle (between walls): 34.8 ft, 10.6 m.

BODY hardtop; doors: 2.

Laurel 2000 Hardtop

See Laurel 1800 Hardtop, except for:

PRICE EX WORKS: 825,000 yen.

ENGINE bore and stroke: 3.50 x 3.15 in, 89 x 80 mm; engine capacity: 121.4 cu in, 1,990 cu cm; max power (DIN): 110 hp at 5,600 rpm; max torque (DIN): 120 lb ft, 16.5 kg m at 3,200 rpm; specific power: 55.3 hp/l; cooling system capacity: 14.1 imp pt, 16.9 US pt, 8 l x 100 km.

TRANSMISSION gearbox ratios: I 3.549, II 2.197, III 1.420, IV 1, rev 3.164.

PERFORMANCE max speed: 106 mph, 170 km/h; power-weight ratio: 22.5 lb/hp, 10.2 kg/hp; acceleration: standing ¼ mile 17.6 sec; fuel consumption: 24.6 m/imp gal, 20.5 m/US gal, 11.5 l x 100 km.

PRACTICAL INSTRUCTIONS tappet clearances: inlet 0.010 in, 0.25 mm, exhaust 0.010 in, 0.25 mm; valve timing: inlet opens 12° before tdc and closes 48° after bdc, exhaust opens 48° before bdc and closes 12° after tdc.

Laurel 2000 GX Hardtop

See Laurel 2000 Hardtop, except for:

PRICE EX WORKS: 875,000 yen.

ENGINE compression ratio: 9.7; max power (DIN): 125 hp at 5,800 rpm; max torque (DIN): 127 lb ft, 17.5 kg m at 3,600 rpm; max engine rpm: 6,300; specific power: 62.8 hp/l; carburation: 2 Hitachi SU type HJM42W horizontal carburettors.

TRANSMISSION gearbox ratios: I 3.278, II 2.029, III 1.311, IV 1, rev 2.922.

PERFORMANCE max speeds: 34 mph, 55 km/h in 1st gear; 56 mph, 90 km/h in 2nd gear; 85 mph, 137 km/h in 3rd gear; 112 mph, 180 km/h in 4th gear; power-weight ratio: 18.1 lb/hp, 8.2 kg/hp; acceleration: standing ¼ mile 17.2 sec.

OPTIONAL ACCESSORIES only air-conditioning system and electrically-controlled windows.

Skyline 2000 GT-R Hardtop

PRICE EX WORKS: 1,540,000 yen.

ENGINE front, 4 stroke; cylinders: 6, in line; bore and stroke: 3.23 x 2.47 in, 82 x 62.8 mm; engine capacity: 121.4 cu in, 1,989 cu cm; compression ratio: 9.5; max power (DIN): 160 hp at 7,000 rpm; max torque (DIN): 130 lb ft, 18 kg m at 5,600 rpm; max engine rpm: 7,400; specific power: 80.4 hp/l; cylinder block: cast iron; cylinder head: light alloy; crankshaft bearings: 7; valves: 4 per cylinder, overhead, Vee-slanted, thimble tappets; camshafts: 2, overhead; lubrication: gear pump, full flow filter; lubricating system capacity: 10.6 imp pt, 12.7 US pt, 6 l; carburation: 3 Mikuni-Solex N 40 PHH horizontal twin barrel carburettors; fuel feed: electric pump; cooling system: water; cooling system capacity: 11.8 imp pt, 14.2 US pt, 6.7 l.

TRANSMISSION driving wheels: rear; clutch: single dry plate (diaphragm); gearbox: mechanical; gears: 5 + reverse; synchromesh gears: I, II, III, IV, V; gearbox ratios: I 2.957, II 1.858, III 1.311, IV 1, V 0.852, rev 2.922; gear lever: central; final drive: hypoid bevel; axle ratio: 4.444; width of rims: 4.5''; tyres: 6.45H x 14.

PERFORMANCE max speeds: 40 mph, 65 km/h in 1st gear; 66 mph, 106 km/h in 2nd gear; 94 mph, 152 km/h in 3rd gear; 115 mph, 185 km/h in 4th gear; 124 mph, 200 km/h in 5th gear; power-weight ratio: 15.4 lb/hp, 7 kg/hp; carrying capacity: 882 lb, 400 kg; acceleration: standing ¼ mile 16.3 sec, 0-50 mph (0-80 km/h) 6.7 sec; speed in direct drive at 1,000 rpm: 15.5 mph, 25 km/h; fuel consumption: 23.5 m/imp gal, 19.6 m/US gal, 12 l x 100 km.

CHASSIS integral; front suspension: independent, by McPherson, coil springs/telescopic damper struts, lower wishbones, lower trailing links, anti-roll bar; rear suspension: independent, semi-trailing arms, coil springs, telescopic dampers.

NISSAN Laurel 2000 GX Hardtop

NISSAN Skyline 2000 GT-R Hardtop

NISSAN Datsun 240 Z Sports

STEERING recirculating ball; turns of steering wheel lock to lock: 3.30.

BRAKES front disc, rear drum; lining area: front 20.8 sq in, 134 sq cm, rear 54.4 sq in, 351 sq cm, total 75.2 sq in, 485 sq cm.

ELECTRICAL EQUIPMENT voltage: 12 V; battery: 35 Ah; generator type: alternator, 30 A; ignition distributor: Mitsubishi (full-transistor); headlamps: 4.

DIMENSIONS AND WEIGHT wheel base: 101.18 in, 2,570 mm; front track: 53.94 in, 1,370 mm; rear track: 53.74 in, 1,365 mm; overall length: 170.47 in, 4,330 mm; overall width: 65.55 in, 1,665 mm; overall height: 53.94 in, 1,370 mm; ground clearance: 6.30 in, 160 mm; dry weight: 2,426 lb, 1,100 kg; distribution of weight: 55% front axle, 45% rear axle; turning circle (between walls): 36.7 ft, 11.2 m; fuel tank capacity: 22 imp gal, 26.4 US gal, 100 l.

BODY hardtop; doors: 2; seats: 5; front seats: separate.

PRACTICAL INSTRUCTIONS fuel: 98-100 oct petrol; engine sump oil: 10.6 imp pt, 12.7 US pt, 6 l, SAE 20W-30, change every 3,100 miles, 5,000 km; gearbox oil: 3 imp pt, 3.6 US pt, 1.7 l, SAE 90, change every 37,300 miles, 60,000 km; final drive oil: 2.3 imp pt, 4.9 US pt, 1.3 l, SAE 90, change every 37,300 miles, 60,000 km; greasing: none; tappet clearances: inlet 0.013 in, 0.32 mm, exhaust 0.013 in, 0.32 mm; valve timing: inlet opens 25° before tdc and closes 45° after bdc, exhaust opens 45° before bdc and closes 25° after tdc; normal tyre pressure: front 28 psi, 2 atm, rear 28 psi, 2 atm.

VARIATIONS

ENGINE 9 compression ratio, max power (DIN) 155 hp at 7,000 rpm, max torque (DIN) 128 lb ft, 17.6 kg m at 5,600 rpm, 77.9 hp/l specific power.

PERFORMANCE max speed 121 mph, 195 km/h, power-weight ratio 15.6 lb/hp, 7.1 kg/hp.

OPTIONAL ACCESSORIES limited slip final drive; 165 x 14 tyres: air-conditioning system.

Datsun Z 432 Sports

PRICE: —

ENGINE front, 4 stroke; cylinders: 6, in line; bore and stroke: 3.23 x 2.47 in, 82 x 62.8 mm; engine capacity: 121.4 cu in, 1,989 cu cm; compression ratio: 9.5; max power (SAE): 160 hp at 7,000 rpm; max torque (SAE): 130 lb ft, 18 kg m at 5,600 rpm; max engine rpm: 7,500; specific power: 80.4 hp/l; cylinder block: cast iron; cylinder head: light alloy; crankshaft bearings: 7; valves: 4 per cylinder, overhead, thimble tappets; camshafts: 2, overhead; lubrication: gear pump, full flow filter; lubricating system capacity: 10.6 imp pt, 12.7 US pt, 6 l; carburation: 3 Mikuni-Solex horizontal twin barrel carburettors; fuel feed: electric pump; cooling system: water; cooling system capacity: 17.6 imp pt, 21.1 US pt, 10 l.

TRANSMISSION driving wheels: rear; clutch: single dry plate; gearbox: mechanical; gears: 5 + reverse; synchromesh gears: I, II, III, IV, V; gearbox ratios: I 2.957, II 1.858, III 1.311, IV 1, V 0.852, rev 2.922; gear lever: central; final drive: hypoid bevel; axle ratio: 4.444; width of rims: 5.5''; tyres: 6.95H x 14.

PERFORMANCE max speeds: 37 mph, 60 km/h in 1st gear; 61 mph, 98 km/h in 2nd gear; 85 mph, 137 km/h in 3rd gear; 114 mph, 183 km/h in 4th gear; 130 mph, 210 km/h in 5th gear; power-weight ratio: 14.3 lb/hp, 6.5 kg/hp; carrying capacity: 397 lb, 180 kg; acceleration: standing ¼ mile 15.8 sec; speed in top at 1,000 rpm: 15.5 mph, 25 km/h; fuel consumption: 23.5 m/imp gal, 19.6 m/US gal, 12 l x 100 km.

CHASSIS integral, front auxiliary frame; front suspension: independent, by McPherson, coil springs/telescopic damper struts, lower trailing links, anti-roll bar; rear suspension: independent, semi-trailing arms, coil springs/telescopic dampers.

STEERING rack-and-pinion; turns of steering wheel lock to lock: 2.50.

BRAKES front disc, rear drum, servo; lining area: front 12.6 sq in, 81 sq cm, rear 54.4 sq in, 351 sq cm, total 67 sq in, 432 sq cm.

ELECTRICAL EQUIPMENT voltage: 12 V; battery: 35 Ah; generator type: alternator, 600 W; ignition distributor: Mitsubishi; headlamps: 2.

DIMENSIONS AND WEIGHT wheel base: 90.75 in, 2,305 mm; front track: 53.35 in, 1,355 mm; rear track: 52.95 in, 1,345 mm; overall length: 162.01 in, 4,115 mm; overall width: 64.17 in, 1,630 mm; overall height: 50.79 in, 1,290 mm; ground clearance: 6.50 in, 165 mm; dry weight: 2,293 lb, 1,040 kg; distribution of weight: 52.4% front axle, 47.6% rear axle; turning circle (between walls): 31.5 ft, 9.6 m; fuel tank capacity: 13.2 imp gal, 15.8 US gal, 60 l.

NISSAN Laurel 2000 GX Hardtop

NISSAN Skyline 2000 GT-R Hardtop

NISSAN Datsun 240 Z Sports

BODY coupé; doors: 2; seats: 2.

PRACTICAL INSTRUCTIONS fuel: 98-100 oct petrol; engine sump oil: 10.6 imp pt, 12.7 US pt, 6 l, SAE 20W-30, change every 3,100 miles, 5,000 km; gearbox oil: 2.6 imp pt, 3.2 US pt, 1.5 l, SAE 90, change every 31,100 miles, 50,000 km; final drive oil: 2.3 imp pt, 2.7 US pt, 1.3 l, SAE 90, change every 31,100 miles, 50,000 km; greasing: every 31,100 miles, 50,000 km, 5 points; tappet clearances: inlet 0.009 in, 0.23 mm, exhaust 0.015 in, 0.37 mm; valve timing: inlet opens 30° before tdc and closes 50° after bdc, exhaust opens 50° before bdc and closes 30° after tdc; normal tyre pressure: front 33 psi, 2.3 atm, rear 33 psi, 2.3 atm.

VARIATIONS

Competition version.

Datsun 240 Z Sports

See Datsun Z 432 Sports, except for:

PRICE: —

ENGINE bore and stroke: 3.27 x 2.90 in, 83 x 73.7 mm; engine capacity: 146 cu in, 2,393 cu cm; compression ratio: 9; max power (SAE): 161 hp at 5,600 rpm; max torque (SAE): 146 lb ft, 20.1 kg m at 4,400 rpm; max engine rpm: 6,000; specific power: 63.1 hp/l; valves: 2 per cylinder, overhead, rockers; camshafts: 1, overhead; lubrication: rotary pump; lubricating system capacity: 7.2 imp pt, 8.7 US pt, 4.1 l; carburation: 2 Hitachi HJG46W horizontal twin barrel carburettors; fuel feed: mechanical pump; cooling system capacity: 10.6 imp pt, 12.7 US pt, 6 l.

TRANSMISSION clutch: single dry plate (diaphragm); axle ratio: 3.900; width of rims: 4.5''; tyres: 6.45H x 14.

PERFORMANCE max speeds: 36 mph, 58 km/h in 1st gear; 57 mph, 92 km/h in 2nd gear; 81 mph, 130 km/h in 3rd gear; 106 mph, 170 km/h in 4th gear; 130 mph, 210 km/h in 5th gear; power-weight ratio: 15 lb/hp, 6.8 kg/hp; acceleration: standing ¼ mile 16.2 sec; speed in direct drive at 1,000 rpm: 17.6 mph, 28.4 km/h.

STEERING turns of steering wheel lock to lock: 3.

ELECTRICAL EQUIPMENT battery: 40 Ah; generator type: alternator, 500 W; ignition distributor: Hitachi.

DIMENSIONS AND WEIGHT front track: 53.39 in, 1,356 mm; rear track: 53.03 in, 1,347 mm; overall length: 162.83 in, 4,136 mm; overall height: 50.63 in, 1,286 mm; dry weight: 2,260 lb, 1,025 kg.

PRACTICAL INSTRUCTIONS engine sump oil: 7.2 imp pt, 8.7 US pt, 4.1 l; final drive oil: 1.8 imp pt, 2.1 US pt, 1 l; tappet clearances: inlet 0.010 in, 0.25 mm, exhaust 0.014 in, 0.35 mm; valve timing: inlet opens 16° before tdc and closes 52° after bdc, exhaust opens 54° before bdc and closes 14° after tdc; normal tyre pressure: front 28 psi, 2 atm, rear 28 psi, 2 atm.

VARIATIONS

(Export model).

TRANSMISSION 4-speed mechanical gearbox (I 3.549, II 2.197, III 1.420, IV 1, rev 3.164), 3.364 axle ratio, 175x 14 tyres.
PERFORMANCE max speeds (I) 35 mph, 56 km/h, (II) 56 mph, 90 km/h, (III) 86 mph, 139 km/h, (IV) 127 mph, 205 km/h, power-weight ratio 15.2 lb/hp, 6.9 kg/hp.
DIMENSIONS AND WEIGHT dry weight 2,302 lb, 1,044 kg.

Datsun 2000 Sedan

PRICE IN GB: £ 1,077.

ENGINE front, 4 stroke; cylinders: 6, in line; bore and stroke: 3.07 x 2.74 in, 78 x 69.7 mm; engine capacity: 121.9 cu in, 1,998 cu cm; compression ratio: 8.6; max power (SAE): 115 hp at 5,600 rpm; max torque (SAE): 120 lb ft, 16.5 kg m at 3,600 rpm; max engine rpm: 6,000; specific power: 57.9 hp/l; cylinder block: cast iron; cylinder head: light alloy; crankshaft bearings: 7; valves: 2 per cylinder, overhead, rockers; camshafts: 1, overhead; lubrication: rotary pump, full flow filter; lubricating system capacity: 7 imp pt, 8.5 US pt, 4 l; carburation: 1 Hitachi downdraught twin barrel carburettor; fuel feed: mechanical pump; cooling system: water; cooling system capacity: 15.8 imp pt, 19 US pt, 9 l.

TRANSMISSION driving wheels: rear; clutch: single dry plate (diaphragm); gearbox: mechanical; gears: 4 + reverse; synchromesh gears: I, II, III, IV; gearbox ratios: I 3.549, II 2.198, III 1.420, IV 1, rev 3.169; gear lever: steering column; final drive: hypoid bevel; axle ratio: 3.889; width of rims: 5''; tyres: 6.95 x 14.

PERFORMANCE max speeds: 32 mph, 52 km/h in 1st gear; 47 mph, 76 km/h in 2nd gear; 73 mph, 117 km/h in 3rd

DATSUN 2000 SEDAN

gear; 103 mph, 165 km/h in 4th gear; power-weight ratio: 24.9 lb/hp, 11.3 kg/hp; carrying capacity: 1,058 lb, 480 kg; acceleration: standing ¼ mile 19.2 sec; speed in direct drive at 1,000 rpm: 17.4 mph, 28 km/h; fuel consumption: 23.5 m/imp gal, 19.6 m/US gal, 12 l x 100 km.

CHASSIS integral; front suspension: independent, wishbones, coil springs, anti-roll bar, telescopic dampers; rear suspension: rigid axle, semi-elliptic leafsprings, telescopic dampers.

STEERING recirculating ball; turns of steering wheel lock to lock: 4.30.

BRAKES front disc, rear drum, servo; lining area: front 15.8 sq in, 102 sq cm, rear 71.9 sq in, 464 sq cm, total 87.7 sq in, 566 sq cm.

ELECTRICAL EQUIPMENT voltage: 12 V; battery: 50 Ah; generator type: alternator, 500 W; ignition distributor: Hitachi; headlamps: 4.

DIMENSIONS AND WEIGHT wheel base: 105.91 in, 2,690 mm; front track: 54.13 in, 1,375 mm; rear track: 54.13 in, 1,375 mm; overall length: 184.65 in, 4,690 mm; overall width: 66.54 in, 1,690 mm; overall height: 57.28 in, 1,455 mm; ground clearance: 7.28 in, 185 mm; dry weight: 2,867 lb, 1,300 kg; distribution of weight: 52.6% front axle, 47.4% rear axle; turning circle (between walls): 36.7 ft, 11.2 m; fuel tank capacity: 14.3 imp gal, 17.2 US gal, 65 l.

BODY saloon/sedan; doors: 4; seats: 6; front seats: bench.

PRACTICAL INSTRUCTIONS fuel: 98-100 oct petrol; engine sump oil: 7 imp pt, 8.5 US pt, 4 l, SAE 20W-30, change every 3,100 miles, 5,000 km; gearbox oil: 2.6 imp pt, 3.2 US pt, 1.5 l, SAE 90, change every 31,100 miles, 50,000 km; final drive oil: 1.6 imp pt, 1.9 US pt, 0.9 l, SAE 90, change every 31,100 miles, 50,000 km; greasing: every 31,100 miles, 50,000 km, 5 points; tappet clearances: inlet 0.010 in, 0.25 mm, exhaust 0.012 in, 0.30 mm; valve timing: inlet opens 8° before tdc and closes 44° after bdc, exhaust opens 50° before bdc and closes 10° after tdc; normal tyre pressure: front 21 psi, 1.5 atm, rear 30 psi, 2.1 atm.

OPTIONAL ACCESSORIES 3-speed automatic gearbox.

Datsun 2000 Station Wagon

See Datsun 2000 Sedan, except for:

PRICE IN GB: £ 1,146.

TRANSMISSION axle ratio: 4.111.

PERFORMANCE power-weight ratio: 26 lb/hp, 11.8 kg/hp

BRAKES drum.

DIMENSIONS AND WEIGHT overall height: 57.87 in, 1,470 mm; dry weight: 2,999 lb, 1,360 kg.

BODY estate car/station wagon; doors: 4 + 1.

Datsun 2000 Diesel Sedan

See Datsun 2000 Sedan, except for:

PRICE: —

ENGINE Diesel; cylinders: 4, in line; bore and stroke: 3.27 x 3.94 in, 83 x 100 mm; engine capacity: 132 cu in, 2,164 cu cm; compression ratio: 22; max power (SAE): 70 hp at 4,000 rpm; max torque (SAE): 107 lb ft, 14.8 kg m at 1,800 rpm; specific power: 32.3 hp/l; crankshaft bearings: 3; valves: 2 per cylinder, overhead, push-rods and rockers; camshafts: 1, side; carburation: injection pump.

TRANSMISSION tyres: 6.40 x 14.

PERFORMANCE max speeds: 24 mph, 38 km/h in 1st gear; 34 mph, 55 km/h in 2nd gear; 53 mph, 86 km/h in 3rd gear; 78 mph, 125 km/h in 4th gear; power-weight ratio: 40.6 lb/hp, 18.4 kg/hp.

DIMENSIONS AND WEIGHT dry weight: 2,833 lb, 1,285 kg.

Datsun 2400 Sedan

See Datsun 2000 Sedan, except for:

PRICE: —

ENGINE bore and stroke: 3.27 x 2.90 in, 83 x 73.7 mm; engine capacity: 146 cu in, 2,393 cu cm; compression ratio: 8.5; max power (SAE): 130 hp at 5,600 rpm; max torque

NISSAN Datsun 2400 Sedan

NISSAN Gloria Super De Luxe Sedan

NISSAN President A Sedan

(SAE): 145 lb ft, 20 kg m at 3,600 rpm; specific power: 54.3 hp/l.

PERFORMANCE max speed: 109 mph, 175 km/h; power-weight ratio: 22.5 lb/hp, 10.2 kg/hp; acceleration: standing ¼ mile 18.4 sec; speed in direct drive at 1,000 rpm: 18.6 mph, 29.9 km/h; fuel consumption: 22.6 m/imp gal, 18.8 m/US gal, 12.5 l x 100 km.

DIMENSIONS AND WEIGHT dry weight: 2,933 lb, 1,330 kg.

Gloria Super De Luxe Sedan

PRICE: —

ENGINE front, 4 stroke; cylinders: 6, in line; bore and stroke: 3.07 x 2.74 in, 78 x 69.7 mm; engine capacity: 121.9 cu in, 1,998 cu cm; compression ratio: 9.4; max power (SAE): 125 hp at 6,000 rpm; max torque (SAE): 123 lb ft, 17 kg m at 4,000 rpm; max engine rpm: 6,000; specific power: 62.6 hp/l; cylinder block: cast iron; cylinder head: light alloy; crankshaft bearings: 7; valves: 2 per cylinder, overhead, rockers; camshafts: 1, overhead; lubrication: rotary pump, full flow filter (cartridge); lubricating system capacity: 7 imp pt, 8.5 US pt, 4 l; carburation: 1 Nikki downdraught 4-barrel carburettor; fuel feed: mechanical pump; cooling system: water; cooling system capacity: 18.5 imp pt, 22.2 US pt, 10.5 l.

TRANSMISSION driving wheels: rear; clutch: single dry plate (diaphragm); gearbox: mechanical; gears: 4 + reverse; synchromesh gears: I, II, III, IV; gearbox ratios: I 2.957, II 1.572, III 1, IV 0.785, rev 2.922; gear lever: steering column; final drive: hypoid bevel; axle ratio: 4.875; width of rims: 5''; tyres: 6.95 x 14.

PERFORMANCE max speeds: 29 mph, 47 km/h in 1st gear; 55 mph, 89 km/h in 2nd gear; 87 mph, 140 km/h in 3rd gear; 103 mph, 165 km/h in 4th gear; power-weight ratio: 22.3 lb/hp, 10.1 kg/hp; carrying capacity: 1,058 lb, 480 kg; acceleration: standing ¼ mile 19.2 sec; speed in direct drive at 1,000 rpm: 17.7 mph, 28.5 km/h; fuel consumption: 21.7 m/imp gal, 18.1 m/US gal, 13 l x 100 km.

CHASSIS integral; front suspension: independent, wishbones, coil springs, anti-roll bar, telescopic dampers; rear suspension: rigid axle, semi-elliptic leafsprings, telescopic dampers.

STEERING recirculating ball; turns of steering wheel lock to lock: 4.30.

BRAKES front disc, rear drum, servo; lining area: front 26.5 sq in, 171 sq cm, rear 67.6 sq in, 436 sq cm, total 94.1 sq in, 607 sq cm.

ELECTRICAL EQUIPMENT voltage: 12 V; battery: 50 Ah; generator type: alternator, 30 A; ignition distributor: Hitachi; headlamps: 4.

DIMENSIONS AND WEIGHT wheel base: 105.91 in, 2,690 mm; front track: 54.53 in, 1,385 mm; rear track: 54.72 in, 1,390 mm; overall length: 184.65 in, 4,690 mm; overall width: 66.34 in, 1,695 mm; overall height: 57.28 in, 1,455 mm; ground clearance: 6.89 in, 175 mm; dry weight: 2,778 lb, 1,260 kg; distribution of weight: 53.5% front axle, 46.5% rear axle; turning circle (between walls): 36.1 ft, 11 m; fuel tank capacity: 14.3 imp gal, 17.2 US gal, 65 l.

BODY saloon/sedan; doors: 4; seats: 5; front seats: separate.

PRACTICAL INSTRUCTIONS fuel: 98-100 oct petrol; engine sump oil: 7 imp pt, 8.5 US pt, 4 l, SAE 20W-30, change every 3,100 miles, 5,000 km; gearbox oil: 4.4 imp pt, 5.3 US pt, 2.5 l, SAE 90, change every 37,300 miles, 60,000 km; final drive oil: 2.1 imp pt, 2.5 US pt, 1.2 l, SAE 90, change every 37,300 miles, 60,000 km; greasing: every 37,300 miles, 60,000 km, 5 points; tappet clearances: inlet 0.010 in, 0.25 mm, exhaust 0.012 in, 0.30 mm; valve timing: inlet opens 8° before tdc and closes 44° after bdc, exhaust opens 50° before bdc and closes 10° after tdc; normal tyre pressure: front 24 psi, 1.7 atm, rear 24 psi, 1.7 atm.

OPTIONAL ACCESSORIES 3-speed automatic gearbox.

Gloria Station Wagon

See Gloria Super De Luxe Sedan, except for:

PRICE: —

TRANSMISSION tyres: 7.00 x 13.

PERFORMANCE max speed: 99 mph, 160 km/h; power-weight ratio: 23.1 lb/hp, 10.5 kg/hp.

DIMENSIONS AND WEIGHT overall height: 58.86 in, 1,495 mm; dry weight: 2,900 lb, 1,315 kg.

BODY estate car/station wagon; doors: 4 + 1; seats: 6; front seats: bench.

NISSAN Datsun 2400 Sedan

NISSAN Gloria Super De Luxe Sedan

NISSAN President A Sedan

President A Sedan

PRICE: —

ENGINE front, 4 stroke; cylinders: 6, in line; bore and stroke: 3.43 x 3.27 in, 87.2 x 83 mm; engine capacity: 181.5 cu in, 2,974 cu cm; compression ratio: 8.7; max power (SAE): 130 hp at 4,400 rpm; max torque (SAE): 174 lb ft, 24 kg m at 3,200 rpm; max engine rpm: 4,400; specific power: 43.7 hp/l; cylinder block: cast iron; cylinder head: light alloy; crankshaft bearings: 7; valves: 2 per cylinder, overhead, rockers; camshafts: 1, overhead; lubrication: gear pump; lubricating system capacity: 8.3 imp pt, 9.9 US pt, 4.7 l; carburation: 1 Hitachi downdraught 4-barrel carburettor; fuel feed: mechanical pump; cooling system: water; cooling system capacity: 28.2 imp pt, 33.8 US pt, 16 l.

TRANSMISSION driving wheels: rear; clutch: single dry plate (diaphragm); gearbox: mechanical; gears: 3 + reverse; synchromesh gears: I, II, III; gearbox ratios: I 3.184, II 1.641, III 1, rev 2.922; gear lever: steering column; final drive: hypoid bevel; axle ratio: 3.900; width of rims: 5''; tyres: 7.50 x 14.

PERFORMANCE max speeds: 46 mph, 74 km/h in 1st gear; 76 mph, 122 km/h in 2nd gear; 99 mph, 160 km/h in 3rd gear; power-weight ratio: 26 lb/hp, 11.8 kg/hp; carrying capacity: 1,058 lb, 480 kg; speed in direct drive at 1,000 rpm: 23 mph, 37 km/h; fuel consumption: 20.2 m/imp gal, 16.8 m/US gal, 14 l x 100 km.

CHASSIS integral; front suspension: independent, wishbones, coil springs, anti-roll bar, telescopic dampers; rear suspension: rigid axle, semi-elliptic leafsprings, anti-roll bar, telescopic dampers.

STEERING recirculating ball.

BRAKES front disc, rear drum, servo; lining area: front 15.8 sq in, 102 sq cm, rear 71.9 sq in, 464 sq cm, total 87.7 sq in, 566 sq cm.

ELECTRICAL EQUIPMENT voltage: 12 V; battery: 50 Ah; generator type: alternator, 600 W; ignition distributor: Hitachi; headlamps: 4.

DIMENSIONS AND WEIGHT wheel base: 112.20 in, 2,850 mm; front track: 58.46 in, 1,485 mm; rear track: 58.07 in, 1,475 mm; overall length: 198.62 in, 5,045 mm; overall width: 70.67 in, 1,795 mm; overall height: 58.46 in, 1,485 mm; ground clearance: 7.68 in, 195 mm; dry weight: 3,374 lb, 1,530 kg; distribution of weight: 51% front axle, 49% rear axle; turning circle (between walls): 38 ft, 11.6 m; fuel tank capacity: 16.5 imp gal, 19.8 US gal, 75 l.

BODY saloon/sedan; doors: 4; seats: 6; front seats: bench.

PRACTICAL INSTRUCTIONS fuel: 90 oct petrol; engine sump oil: 7.2 imp pt, 8.7 US pt, 4.1 l, SAE 10W-30, change every 3,100 miles, 5,000 km; gearbox oil: 4.4 imp pt, 5.3 US pt, 2.5 l, SAE 90, change every 24,900 miles, 40,000 km; final drive oil: 2.6 imp pt, 3.2 US pt, 1.5 l, SAE 90, change every 24,900 miles, 40,000 km; greasing: every 12,400 miles, 20,000 km, 19 points; normal tyre pressure: front 24 psi, 1.7 atm, rear 24 psi, 1.7 atm.

OPTIONAL ACCESSORIES power-assisted steering; separate front seats; electrically-controlled windows; air-conditioning system.

President D Sedan

See President A Sedan, except for:

PRICE: —

ENGINE cylinders: 8, Vee-slanted at 90°; bore and stroke: 3.62 x 2.95 in, 92 x 75 mm; engine capacity: 243.3 cu in, 3,988 cu cm; compression ratio: 9; max power (SAE): 195 hp at 5,000 rpm; max torque (SAE): 238 lb ft, 32.8 kg m at 3,200 rpm; max engine rpm: 5,000; specific power: 48.9 hp/l; crankshaft bearings: 5; valves: 2 per cylinder, overhead, push-rods and rockers, hydraulic tappets; camshafts: 1, at centre of Vee.

TRANSMISSION gearbox: automatic, hydraulic torque convertor and planetary gears with 3 ratios + reverse; gearbox ratios: I 2.393, II 1,450, III 1, rev 2.094; selector lever: steering column; axle ratio: 3.154.

PERFORMANCE max speeds: 47 mph, 75 km/h in 1st gear; 78 mph, 125 km/h in 2nd gear; 115 mph, 185 km/h in 3rd gear; power-weight ratio: 18.1 lb/hp, 8.2 kg/hp; acceleration: standing ¼ mile 18.4 sec; speed in direct drive at 1,000 rpm: 24.9 mph, 40 km/h; fuel consumption: 17.7 m/imp gal, 14.7 m/US gal, 16 l x 100 km.

STEERING servo.

DIMENSIONS AND WEIGHT dry weight: 3,539 lb, 1,605 kg.

BODY details: electrically-controlled windows.

PRACTICAL INSTRUCTIONS gearbox oil: 13.6 imp pt, 16.3 US pt, 7.7 l, automatic transmission fluid; valve timing: inlet opens 22° before tdc and closes 62° after bdc, exhaust opens 62° before bdc and closes 22° after tdc.

OPTIONAL ACCESSORIES only separate front seats and air-conditioning system.

SUBARU   JAPAN

360 Sedan

PRICE EX WORKS: 309,000 yen.

ENGINE rear, transverse, 2 stroke; cylinders: 2, in line; bore and stroke: 2.42 x 2.36 in, 61.5 x 60 mm; engine capacity: 21.7 cu in, 356 cu cm; compression ratio: 6.7; max power (DIN): 25 hp at 5,500 rpm; max torque (DIN): 25 lb ft, 3.5 kg m at 4,500 rpm; max engine rpm: 5,800; specific power: 70.2 hp/l; cylinder block: cast iron; cylinder head: light alloy; crankshaft bearings: 5; carburation: 1 Hitachi HAB 28 horizontal carburettor; fuel feed: gravity; cooling system: air-cooled.

TRANSMISSION driving wheels: rear; clutch: single dry plate (diaphragm); gearbox: mechanical; gears: 4 + reverse; synchromesh gears: II, III, IV; gearbox ratios: I 3.130, II 1.601, III 1, IV 0.806, rev 4.248; gear lever: central; final drive: spiral bevel; axle ratio: 3.667; width of rims: 3''; tyres: 4.80 x 10.

PERFORMANCE max speeds: 22 mph, 35 km/h in 1st gear; 32 mph, 52 km/h in 2nd gear; 57 mph, 92 km/h in 3rd gear; 68 mph, 110 km/h in 4th gear; power-weight ratio: 37 lb/hp, 16.8 kg/hp; carrying capacity: 706 lb, 320 kg; acceleration: standing 1/4 mile 22.9 sec; speed in top at 1,000 rpm: 11.4 mph, 18.4 km/h; fuel consumption: 78.5 m/imp gal, 65.3 m/US gal, 3.6 l x 100 km.

CHASSIS integral; front suspension: independent, swinging trailing arms, torsion bars, coil springs, telescopic dampers; rear suspension: independent, swinging semi-axles, swinging trailing arms, torsion bars, telescopic dampers.

STEERING rack-and-pinion; turns of steering wheel lock to lock: 3.60.

BRAKES drum; lining area: front 33.5 sq in, 216 sq cm, rear 33.5 sq in, 216 sq cm, total 67 sq in, 432 sq cm.

ELECTRICAL EQUIPMENT voltage: 12 V; battery: 26 Ah; generator type: dynamo, 200 W; ignition distributor: Nihon-Denso or Hitachi; headlamps: 2.

DIMENSIONS AND WEIGHT wheel base: 70.87 in, 1,800 mm; front track: 44.88 in, 1,140 mm; rear track: 42.13 in, 1,070 mm; overall length: 117.91 in, 2,995 mm; overall width: 51.18 in, 1,300 mm; overall height: 53.54 in, 1,360 mm; ground clearance: 6.30 in, 160 mm; dry weight: 926 lb, 420 kg; distribution of weight: 37% front axle, 63% rear axle; turning circle (between walls): 26.2 ft, 8 m; fuel tank capacity: 5.5 imp gal, 6.6 US gal, 25 l.

BODY saloon/sedan; doors: 2; seats: 4; front seats: separate.

PRACTICAL INSTRUCTIONS fuel: mixture; engine sump oil: 4.4 imp pt, 5.3 US pt, 2.5 l, oil in separate tank; gearbox and final drive oil: 2.8 imp pt, 3.4 US pt, 1.6 l, change every 24,900 miles, 40,000 km; greasing: every 6,200 miles, 10,000 km, 5 points; normal tyre pressure: front 13 psi, 0.9 atm, rear 26 psi, 1.8 atm.

OPTIONAL ACCESSORIES electromagnetic clutch; De Luxe version.

R-2 Sedan

PRICE EX WORKS: 315,000 yen.

ENGINE rear, transverse, 2 stroke; cylinders: 2, in line; bore and stroke: 2.42 x 2.36 in, 61.5 x 60 mm; engine capacity: 21.7 cu in, 356 cu cm; compression ratio: 6.5; max power (DIN): 30 hp at 5,500 rpm; max torque (DIN): 27 lb ft, 3.7 kg m at 5,500 rpm; max engine rpm: 7,000; specific power: 84.3 hp/l; cylinder block: light alloy; cylinder head: light alloy; crankshaft bearings: 5; carburation: 1 Hitachi HAB 28 horizontal carburettor; fuel feed: mechanical pump; cooling system: air-cooled.

TRANSMISSION driving wheels: rear; clutch: single dry plate (diaphragm); gearbox: mechanical; gears: 4 + reverse; synchromesh gears: I, II, III, IV; gearbox ratios: I 3.688, II 2.204, III 1.476, IV 1, rev 3.663; gear lever: central; final drive: spiral bevel; axle ratio: 3.238; width of rims: 3''; tyres: 4.80 x 10.

PERFORMANCE max speeds: 20 mph, 32 km/h in 1st gear; 33 mph, 53 km/h in 2nd gear; 50 mph, 80 km/h in 3rd gear; 71 mph, 115 km/h in 4th gear; power-weight ratio: 32.6 lb/hp, 14.8 kg/hp; carrying capacity: 706 lb, 320 kg; acceleration: standing 1/4 mile 21.9 sec, 0-50 mph (0-80 km/h) 14.4 sec; speed in direct drive at 1,000 rpm: 10.4 mph, 16.8 km/h; fuel consumption: 78.5 m/imp gal, 65.3 m/US gal, 3.6 l x 100 km.

CHASSIS integral; front suspension: independent, semi-trailing arms, torsion bars, telescopic dampers; rear suspension: independent, semi-trailing arms, torsion bars, telescopic dampers.

SUBARU 360 De Luxe Sedan

SUBARU R-2 SS Sedan

SUBARU FF-1 1300 GL Sedan

STEERING rack-and-pinion; turns of steering wheel lock to lock: 2.90.

BRAKES drum; lining area: front 33.2 sq in, 214 sq cm, rear 33.6 sq in, 217 sq cm, total 66.8 sq in, 431 sq cm.

ELECTRICAL EQUIPMENT voltage: 12 V; battery: 26 Ah; generator type: dynamo, 200 W; ignition distributor: Nihon-Denso; headlamps: 2.

DIMENSIONS AND WEIGHT wheel base: 75.59 in, 1,920 mm; front track: 44.09 in, 1,120 mm; rear track: 43.50 in, 1,105 mm; overall length: 117.91 in, 2,995 mm; overall width: 50.98 in, 1,295 mm; overall height: 52.95 in, 1,345 mm; ground clearance: 6.69 in, 170 mm; dry weight: 981 lb, 445 kg; distribution of weight: 40% front axle, 60% rear axle; turning circle (between walls): 26.2 ft, 8 m; fuel tank capacity: 5.5 imp gal, 6.6 US gal, 25 l.

BODY saloon/sedan; doors: 2; seats: 4; front seats: separate.

PRACTICAL INSTRUCTIONS fuel: mixture; engine sump oil: 4.4 imp pt, 5.3 US pt, 2.5 l, oil in separate tank; gearbox and final drive oil: 2.8 imp pt, 3.4 US pt, 1.6 l, SAE 80-90, change every 24,900 miles, 40,000 km; greasing: none; normal tyre pressure: front 13 psi, 0.9 atm, rear 26 psi, 1.8 atm.

OPTIONAL ACCESSORIES electromagnetic clutch; Super De Luxe version.

R-2 Custom Station Wagon

See R-2 Sedan, except for:

PRICE: —

BODY estate car/station wagon; doors: 2 + 1.

R-2 GL Sedan

See R-2 Sedan, except for:

PRICE EX WORKS: 410,000 yen.

ENGINE max power (DIN): 32 hp at 6,500 rpm; max torque (DIN): 28 lb ft, 3.8 kg m at 5,500 rpm; specific power: 89.9 hp/l.

PERFORMANCE power-weight ratio: 31.7 lb/hp, 14.4 kg/hp; acceleration: standing 1/4 mile 21.7 sec.

R-2 SS Sedan

See R-2 Sedan, except for:

PRICE EX WORKS: 395,000 yen.

ENGINE compression ratio: 7.5; max power (DIN): 36 hp at 7,000 rpm; max torque (DIN): 28 lb ft, 3.8 kg m at 6,400 rpm; max engine rpm: 7,500; specific power: 101.1 hp/l; carburation: 1 Solex 36 PHH horizontal carburettor.

TRANSMISSION tyres: 135 x 10.

PERFORMANCE max speed: 75 mph, 120 km/h; power-weight ratio: 27.6 lb/hp, 12.5 kg/hp; acceleration: standing 1/4 mile 19.9 sec.

DIMENSIONS AND WEIGHT front track: 44.29 in, 1,125 mm; rear track: 43.70 in, 1,110 mm; overall height: 52.56 in, 1,335 mm; ground clearance: 6.30 in, 160 mm; dry weight: 992 lb, 450 kg.

2-door FF-1 Sedan

PRICE EX WORKS: 449,000 yen.

ENGINE front, 4 stroke; cylinders: 4, horizontally opposed; bore and stroke: 2.99 x 2.36 in, 76 x 60 mm; engine capacity: 66.4 cu in, 1,088 cu cm; compression ratio: 9; max power (DIN): 62 hp at 6,000 rpm; max torque (DIN): 63 lb ft, 8.7 kg m at 3,200 rpm; max engine rpm: 6,000; specific power: 57 hp/l; cylinder block: light alloy; cylinder head: light alloy; crankshaft bearings: 3; valves: 2 per cylinder, overhead, push-rods and rockers; camshafts: 1, side; lubrication: rotary pump, full flow filter; lubricating system capacity: 5.6 imp pt, 6.8 US pt, 3.2 l; carburation: 1 Hitachi DCG 286 downdraught twin barrel carburettor; fuel feed: electric pump; cooling system: water; cooling system capacity: 9.9 imp pt, 11.8 US pt, 5.6 l.

TRANSMISSION driving wheels: front; clutch: single dry plate (diaphragm); gearbox: mechanical; gears: 4 + reverse; synchromesh gears: I, II, III, IV; gearbox ratios: I 3.540, II 2.235, III 1.542, IV 1.033, rev 4.100; gear lever: central; final drive: hypoid bevel; axle ratio: 4.125; width of rims: 4''; tyres: 6.15 x 13.

PERFORMANCE max speeds: 28 mph, 45 km/h in 1st gear; 43 mph, 70 km/h in 2nd gear; 62 mph, 100 km/h in 3rd

SUBARU 360 De Luxe Sedan

SUBARU R-2 SS Sedan

SUBARU 4-door FF-1 1300 GL Sedan

gear; 90 mph, 145 km/h in 4th gear; power-weight ratio: 24.7 lb/hp, 11.2 kg/hp; carrying capacity: 882 lb, 400 kg; acceleration: standing ¼ mile 18.7 sec, 0-50 mph (0-80 km/h) 9.6 sec; speed in top at 1,000 rpm: 14.3 mph, 23 km/h; fuel consumption: 35.3 m/imp gal, 29.4 m/US gal, 8 l x 100 km.

CHASSIS integral; front suspension: independent, wishbones, longitudinal torsion bars, telescopic dampers; rear suspension: independent, semi-trailing arms, torsion bars, coil springs, telescopic dampers.

STEERING rack-and-pinion; turns of steering wheel lock to lock: 3.30.

BRAKES drum; lining area: front 54.6 sq in, 352 sq cm, rear 30.5 sq in, 197 sq cm, total 85.1 sq in, 549 sq cm.

ELECTRICAL EQUIPMENT voltage: 12 V; battery: 32 Ah; generator type: alternator, 360 W; ignition distributor: Hitachi; headlamps: 2.

DIMENSIONS AND WEIGHT wheel base: 95.28 in, 2,420 mm; front track: 48.23 in, 1,225 mm; rear track: 47.64 in, 1,210 mm; overall length: 154.72 in, 3,930 mm; overall width: 58.27 in, 1,480 mm; overall height: 54.72 in, 1,390 mm; ground clearance: 7.09 in, 180 mm; dry weight: 1,532 lb, 695 kg; distribution of weight: 65.5% front axle, 34.5% rear axle; turning circle (between walls): 31.5 ft, 9.6 m; fuel tank capacity: 7.9 imp gal, 9.5 US gal, 36 l.

BODY saloon/sedan; doors: 2; seats: 5; front seats: separate.

PRACTICAL INSTRUCTIONS fuel: 90 oct petrol; engine sump oil: 4.8 imp pt, 5.7 US pt, 2.7 l, SAE 20W-30, change every 3,100 miles, 5,000 km; gearbox and final drive oil: 4.4 imp pt, 5.3 US pt, 2.5 l, SAE 80-90, change every 24,900 miles, 40,000 km; greasing: none; tappet clearances: inlet 0.009 in, 0.22 mm, exhaust 0.011 in, 0.27 mm; valve timing: inlet opens 20° before tdc and closes 60° after bdc, exhaust opens 60° before bdc and closes 20° after tdc; normal tyre pressure: front 23 psi, 1.6 atm, rear 17 psi, 1.2 atm.

4-door FF-1 Sedan

See 2-door FF-1 Sedan, except for:

PRICE EX WORKS: 534,000 yen.

FF-1 Station Wagon

See 2-door FF-1 Sedan, except for:

PRICE: —

TRANSMISSION gearbox ratios: I 4.000, II 2.438, III 1.542, IV 1.033, rev 4.100; axle ratio: 4.100.

PERFORMANCE max speeds: 25 mph, 40 km/h in 1st gear; 40 mph, 64 km/h in 2nd gear; 62 mph, 100 km/h in 3rd gear; 90 mph, 145 km/h in 4th gear; power-weight ratio: 26.5 lb/hp, 12 kg/hp; acceleration: standing ¼ mile 20 sec.

DIMENSIONS AND WEIGHT rear track: 48.62 in, 1,235 mm; overall length: 152.76 in, 3,880 mm; overal height: 55.71 in, 1,415 mm; dry weight: 1,643 lb, 745 kg.

BODY estate car/station wagon; doors: 2 + 1.

OPTIONAL ACCESSORIES steering column gear lever.

2-door FF-1 1300 G Sedan

See 2-door FF-1 Sedan, except for:

PRICE EX WORKS: 474,000 yen.

ENGINE bore and stroke: 3.23 x 2.36 in, 82 x 60 mm; engine capacity: 77.3 cu in, 1,267 cu cm; max power (DIN): 80 hp at 6,400 rpm; max torque (DIN): 73 lb ft, 10.1 kg m at 4,000 rpm; specific power: 63.1 hp/l; lubricating system capacity: 5.8 imp pt, 7 US pt, 3.3 l; carburation: 1 Hitachi DCG 306 downdraught carburettor; cooling system: electric thermostatic fan; cooling system capacity: 10.6 imp pt, 12.7 US pt, 6 l.

TRANSMISSION gearbox ratios: I 3.307, II 2.176, III 1.480, IV 1.033, rev 3.636; axle ratio: 3.889.

PERFORMANCE max speeds: 33 mph, 53 km/h in 1st gear; 47 mph, 76 km/h in 2nd gear; 71 mph, 115 km/h in 3rd gear; 99 mph, 160 km/h in 4th gear; power-weight ratio: 20.1 lb/hp, 9.1 kg/hp; acceleration: standing ¼ mile 17.9 sec; speed in top at 1,000 rpm: 15.3 mph, 24.6 km/h; fuel consumption: 31.4 m/imp gal, 26.1 m/US gal, 9 l x 100 km.

STEERING turns of steering wheel lock to lock: 3.60.

BRAKES front disc, rear drum; lining area: front 19.8 sq in, 128 sq cm, rear 26.2 sq in, 169 sq cm, total 46 sq in, 297 sq cm.

2-DOOR FF-1 1300 G SEDAN

ELECTRICAL EQUIPMENT battery: 35 Ah; generator type: alternator, 30 A.

DIMENSIONS AND WEIGHT rear track: 47.44 in, 1,205 mm; overall length: 153.54 in, 3,900 mm; ground clearance: 6.89 in, 175 mm; dry weight: 1,599 lb, 725 kg; distribution of weight: 64.8% front axle, 35.2% rear axle; turning circle (between walls): 34.8 ft, 10.6 m; fuel tank capacity: 9.9 imp gal, 11.9 US gal, 45 l.

PRACTICAL INSTRUCTIONS valve timing: inlet opens 24° before tdc and closes 64° after bdc, exhaust opens 70° before bdc and closes 18° after tdc; normal tyre pressure: front 24 psi, 1.7 atm, rear 21 psi, 1.5 atm.

4-door FF-1 1300 G De Luxe Sedan

See 2-door FF-1 Sedan, except for:

PRICE EX WORKS: 559,000 yen.

2-door FF-1 1300 GL Sedan

See 2-door FF-1 Sedan, except for:

PRICE EX WORKS: 574,000 yen.

4-door FF-1 1300 GL Sedan

See 2-door FF-1 Sedan, except for:

PRICE EX WORKS: 599,000 yen.

FF-1 1300 G Sports

See 2-door FF-1 1300 G Sedan, except for:

PRICE EX WORKS: 639,000 yen.

ENGINE compression ratio: 10; max power (DIN): 93 hp at 7,000 rpm; max torque (DIN): 76 lb ft, 10.5 kg m at 5,000 rpm; specific power: 73.4 hp/l; carburation: 2 Hitachi DCG 306 downdraught twin barrel carburettors.

TRANSMISSION tyres: 145 x 13.

PERFORMANCE max speeds: 35 mph, 56 km/h in 1st gear; 51 mph, 82 km/h in 2nd gear; 75 mph, 120 km/h in 3rd gear; 106 mph, 170 km/h in 4th gear; power-weight ratio: 18.2 lb/hp, 8.2 kg/hp; acceleration: standing ¼ mile 16.8 sec; speed in top at 1,000 rpm: 16.2 mph, 26.1 km/h.

DIMENSIONS AND WEIGHT overall height: 54.13 in, 1,375 mm; ground clearance: 6.50 in, 165 mm; dry weight: 1,676 lb, 760 kg; distribution of weight: 65.7% front axle, 34.3% rear axle.

PRACTICAL INSTRUCTIONS valve timing: inlet opens 40° before tdc and closes 76° after bdc, exhaust opens 76° before bdc and closes 40° after tdc.

FF-1 1300 G Super Touring

See FF-1 1300 G Sports, except for:

PRICE EX WORKS: 690,000 yen.

BODY doors: 4.

SUZUKI   JAPAN

Fronte 71 Super De Luxe Sedan

PRICE EX WORKS: 394,000 yen.

ENGINE rear, transverse, 2 stroke; cylinders: 3, in line; bore and stroke: 2.05 x 2.20 in, 52 x 56 mm; engine capacity: 21.7 cu in, 356 cu cm; compression ratio: 6.8; max power (DIN): 31 hp at 6,000 rpm; max torque (DIN): 27 lb ft, 3.7 kg m at 5,000 rpm; max engine rpm: 6,000; specific power: 87 hp/l; cylinder block: cast iron; cylinder head: light alloy; crankshaft bearings: 7, on ball bearings; lubrication: mechanical pump, injection to cylinders and crankshaft bearings, total loss system; carburation: 3 Mikuni-Villiers VM 22 semi-downdraught carburettors; fuel feed: mechanical pump; cooling system: aircooled.

TRANSMISSION driving wheels: rear; clutch: single dry plate (diaphragm); gearbox: mechanical; gears: 4 + reverse; synchromesh gears: I, II, III, IV; gearbox ratios: I 3.182, II 1.875, III 1.238, IV 0.880, rev 2.727; gear lever: central; final drive: spiral bevel; axle ratio: 4.385; width of rims: 3.5''; tyres: 5.20 x 10.

PERFORMANCE max speeds: 21 mph, 34 km/h in 1st gear; 33 mph, 53 km/h in 2nd gear; 50 mph, 80 km/h in 3rd gear; 71 mph, 115 km/h in 4th gear; power-weight ratio: 32.6

SUBARU FF-1 1300 G Sports

SUZUKI Fronte 71 Super De Luxe Sedan

SUZUKI Jimny

lb/hp, 14.8 kg/hp; carrying capacity: 706 lb, 320 kg; acceleration: standing 1/4 mile 21.5 sec; speed in top at 1,000 rpm: 10.4 mph, 16.8 km/h; fuel consumption: 78.5 m/imp gal, 65.3 m/US gal, 3.6 l x 100 km.

CHASSIS integral; front suspension: independent, wishbones, coil springs, anti-roll bar, telescopic dampers; rear suspension: independent, semi-trailing arms, coil springs, telescopic dampers.

STEERING rack-and-pinion; turns of steering wheel lock to lock: 2.75.

BRAKES drum; lining area: front 31.6 sq in, 204 sq cm, rear 31.6 sq in, 204 sq cm, total 63.2 sq in, 408 sq cm.

ELECTRICAL EQUIPMENT voltage: 12 V; battery: 24 Ah; generator type: dynamo, 300 W; ignition distributor: Mitsubishi or Nihon-Denso; headlamps: 2.

DIMENSIONS AND WEIGHT wheel base: 79.13 in, 2,010 mm; front track: 44.09 in, 1,120 mm; rear track: 42.72 in, 1,085 mm; overall length: 117.91 in, 2,995 mm; overall width: 50.98 in, 1,295 mm; overall height: 50.98 in, 1,295 mm; ground clearance: 7.68 in, 195 mm; dry weight: 1,014 lb, 460 kg; distribution of weight: 36% front axle, 64% rear axle; turning circle (between walls): 25.6 ft, 7.8 m; fuel tank capacity: 5.9 imp gal, 7.1 US gal, 27 l.

BODY saloon/sedan; doors: 2; seats: 4; front seats: separate.

PRACTICAL INSTRUCTIONS fuel: mixture; engine sump oil: 7 imp pt, 8.5 US pt, 4 l, oil in separate tank; gearbox and final drive oil: 1.8 imp pt, 2.1 US pt, 1 l, SAE 90, change every 6 months; greasing: none; normal tyre pressure: front 14 psi, 1 atm, rear 24 psi, 1.7 atm.

VARIATIONS

ENGINE 7.1 compression ratio, max power (DIN) 34 hp at 6,500 rpm, 95.5 hp/l specific power.
PERFORMANCE max speed 75 mph, 120 km/h, power-weight ratio 29.8 lb/hp, 13.5 kg/hp, fuel consumption 56.5 m/imp gal, 47 m/US gal, 5 l x 100 km.

Fronte 71 SSS Sedan

See Fronte 71 Super De Luxe Sedan, except for:

PRICE EX WORKS: 405,000 yen.

ENGINE compression ratio: 6.9; max power (DIN): 36 hp at 7,000 rpm; max torque (DIN): 27 lb ft, 3.7 kg m at 6,500 rpm; max engine rpm: 8,000 specific power: 101.1 hp/l; cylinder block: light alloy; carburation: 3 Mikuni-Villiers VM 24 horizontal carburettors.

PERFORMANCE max speeds: 22 mph, 35 km/h in 1st gear; 35 mph, 56 km/h in 2nd gear; 54 mph, 87 km/h in 3rd gear; 75 mph, 120 km/h in 4th gear; power-weight ratio: 28 lb/hp, 12.7 kg/hp; acceleration: standing 1/4 mile 19.9 sec; fuel consumption: 62.8 m/imp gal, 52.3 m/US gal, 4.5 l x 100 km.

DIMENSIONS AND WEIGHT front track: 44.49 in, 1,130 mm; rear track: 43.70 in, 1,110 mm; overall height: 49.61 in, 1,260 mm; ground clearance: 6.30 in, 160 mm.

VARIATIONS

None.

OPTIONAL ACCESSORIES 135 x 10 tyres.

Fronte 360 Hi-Custom Station Wagon

See Fronte 71 Super De Luxe Sedan, except for:

PRICE EX WORKS: 394,000 yen.

ENGINE front; max power (SAE): 30 hp at 6,500 rpm; max torque (SAE): 23 lb ft, 3.2 kg m at 5,000 rpm; max engine rpm: 7,500; specific power: 84.3 hp/l.

TRANSMISSION gearbox ratios: I 3.683, II 2.218, III 1.418, IV 1, rev 3.683; final drive: hypoid bevel; axle ratio: 5.667; tyres: 4.50 x 10.

PERFORMANCE max speeds: 19 mph, 30 km/h in 1st gear; 30 mph, 48 km/h in 2nd gear; 48 mph, 77 km/h in 3rd gear; 68 mph, 110 km/h in 4th gear; power-weight ratio: 36.8 lb/hp, 16.7 kg/hp; speed in direct drive at 1,000 rpm: 8.7 mph, 14 km/h.

CHASSIS front suspension: independent, by McPherson, coil springs/telescopic damper struts, anti-roll bar; rear suspension: rigid axle, semi-elliptic leafsprings, telescopic dampers.

STEERING recirculating ball.

DIMENSIONS AND WEIGHT wheel base: 78.54 in, 1,995 mm; front track: 44.02 in, 1,118 mm; rear track: 42.52 in, 1,080 mm; overall height: 54.33 in, 1,380 mm; ground clearance: 5.51 in, 140 mm; dry weight: 1,103 lb, 500 kg; distribution of weight: 54% front axle, 46% rear axle; fuel tank capacity: 5.5 imp gal, 6.6 US gal, 25 l.

BODY estate car/station wagon; doors: 2 + 1.

PRACTICAL INSTRUCTIONS engine sump oil: 6.2 imp pt, 7.4

SUBARU FF-1 1300 G Sports

SUZUKI Fronte 71 SSS Sedan

SUZUKI Jimny

US pt, 3.5 l, oil in separate tank; gearbox oil: 2.1 imp pt, 2.5 US pt, 1.2 l, SAE 90, change every 6 months; final drive oil: 1.4 imp pt, 1.7 US pt, 0.8 l, SAE 90, change every 6 months; normal tyre pressure: front 20 psi, 1.4 atm, rear 24 psi, 1.7 atm.

VARIATIONS

None.

Jimny

PRICE EX WORKS: 484,000 yen.

ENGINE front, 2 stroke; cylinders: 2, horizontal, in line; bore and stroke: 2.40 x 2.42 in, 61 x 61.5 mm; engine capacity: 21.9 cu in, 359 cu cm; compression ratio: 7.3; max power (DIN): 25 hp at 6,000 rpm; max torque (DIN): 25 lb ft, 3.4 kg m at 5,000 rpm; max engine rpm: 7,000; specific power: 69.6 hp/l; cylinder block: light alloy; cylinder head: light alloy; crankshaft bearings: 3, on ball bearings; lubrication: mechanical pump, injection to cylinders and crankshaft bearings, total loss system; carburation: 1 Mikuni 30 PHD horizontal carburettor; fuel feed: mechanical pump; cooling system: aircooled.

TRANSMISSION driving wheels: front and rear; clutch: single dry plate (diaphragm); gearbox: mechanical; gears: 4 + reverse and 2-ratio transfer box; synchromesh gears: I, II, III, IV; gearbox ratios: I 3.683, II 2.218, III 1.477, IV 1, rev 3.683; transfer box ratios: I 1.744, II 2.975; gear lever: central; final drive: hypoid bevel; axle ratio: 5.667; width of rims: 4.5''; tyres: 6.00 x 16.

PERFORMANCE max speeds: 14 mph, 22 km/h in 1st gear; 22 mph, 35 km/h in 2nd gear; 35 mph, 56 km/h in 3rd gear; 47 mph, 75 km/h in 4th gear; power-weight ratio: 52.9 lb/hp, 24 kg/hp; carrying capacity: 551 lb, 250 kg; fuel consumption: 56.5 m/imp gal, 47 m/US gal, 5 l x 100 km.

CHASSIS box-type ladder frame; front suspension: rigid axle, semi-elliptic leafsprings, telescopic dampers; rear suspension: rigid axle, semi-elliptic leafsprings, telescopic dampers.

STEERING recirculating ball; turns of steering wheel lock to lock: 3.20.

BRAKES drum; lining area: front 42.2 sq in, 272 sq cm, rear 42.2 sq in, 272 sq cm, total 84.4 sq in, 544 sq cm.

ELECTRICAL EQUIPMENT voltage: 12 V; battery: 24 Ah; generator type: dynamo, 300 W; headlamps: 2.

DIMENSIONS AND WEIGHT wheel base: 75.98 in, 1,930 mm; front track: 42.91 in, 1,090 mm; rear track: 43.31 in, 1,100 mm; overall length: 117.91 in, 2,995 mm; overall width: 50.98 in, 1,295 mm; overall height: 65.75 in, 1,670 mm; ground clearance: 9.25 in, 235 mm; dry weight: 1,323 lb, 600 kg; distribution of weight: 54.2% front axle, 45.8% rear axle; turning circle (between walls): 28.9 ft, 8.8 m; fuel tank capacity: 5.7 imp gal, 6.9 US gal, 26 l.

BODY open; doors: none; seats: 3; front seats: separate.

PRACTICAL INSTRUCTIONS fuel: mixture; engine sump oil: 6.2 imp pt, 7.4 US pt, 3.5 l, oil in separate tank; gearbox and final drive oil: 1.4 imp pt, 1.7 US pt, 0.8 l, SAE 90, change every 6 months; transfer box oil: 1.2 imp pt, 1.5 US pt, 0.7 l, change every 6 months; greasing: none; normal tyre pressure: front 16 psi, 1.1 atm, rear 16 psi, 1.1 atm.

TOYOTA JAPAN

Publica 800 Sedan

PRICE EX WORKS: 365,000 yen.

ENGINE front, 4 stroke; cylinders: 2, horizontally opposed; bore and stroke: 3.27 x 2.87 in, 83 x 73 mm; engine capacity: 48.2 cu in, 790 cu cm; compression ratio: 8.2; max power (DIN): 40 hp at 5,000 rpm; max torque (DIN): 46 lb ft, 6.4 kg m at 3,000 rpm; max engine rpm: 5,400; specific power: 50.6 hp/l; cylinder block: light alloy; cylinder head: light alloy; crankshaft bearings: 2; valves: 2 per cylinder, overhead, push-rods and rockers; camshafts: 1, side; lubrication: rotary pump, full flow filter; lubricating system capacity: 5.3 imp pt, 6.3 US pt, 3 l; carburation: 1 Aisan downdraught twin barrel carburettor; fuel feed: mechanical pump; cooling system: aircooled.

TRANSMISSION driving wheels: rear; clutch: single dry plate; gearbox: mechanical; gears: 4 + reverse; synchromesh gears: I, II, III, IV; gearbox ratios: I 4.200, II 2.400, III 1.684, IV 1.125, rev 4.333; gear lever: central; final drive: hypoid bevel; axle ratio: 3.890; width of rims: 4''; tyres: 6.00 x 12.

PERFORMANCE max speeds: 19 mph, 30 km/h in 1st gear; 32 mph, 52 km/h in 2nd gear; 47 mph, 75 km/h in 3rd gear; 75 mph, 120 km/h in 4th gear; power-weight ratio: 35.1 lb/hp, 15.9 kg/hp; carrying capacity: 706 lb, 320 kg; acceleration: standing 1/4 mile 22.1 sec; speed in top at 1,000 rpm: 14.3 mph, 23 km/h; fuel consumption: 56.5 m/imp gal, 47 m/US gal, 5 l x 100 km.

CHASSIS integral; front suspension: independent, by Mc-

PUBLICA 800 SEDAN

Pherson, coil springs/telescopic damper struts, lower wishbones (trailing links) anti-roll bar; rear suspension: rigid axle, semi-elliptic leafsprings, telescopic dampers.

STEERING worm and roller.

BRAKES drum; lining area: front 35.7 sq in, 230 sq cm, rear 35.7 sq in, 230 sq cm, total 71.4 sq in, 460 sq cm.

ELECTRICAL EQUIPMENT voltage: 12 V; battery: 32 Ah; generator type: alternator, 360 W; ignition distributor: Nihon-Denso; headlamps: 2.

DIMENSIONS AND WEIGHT wheel base: 85.04 in, 2,160 mm; front track: 48.62 in, 1,235 mm; rear track: 47.24 in, 1,200 mm; overall length: 143.50 in, 3,645 mm; overall width: 57.09 in, 1,450 mm; overall height: 54.33 in, 1,380 mm; ground clearance: 6.69 in, 170 mm; dry weight: 1,400 lb, 635 kg; distribution of weight: 50% front axle, 50% rear axle; turning circle (between walls): 28.9 ft, 8.8 m; fuel tank capacity: 8.8 imp gal, 10.6 US gal, 40 l.

BODY saloon/sedan; doors: 2; seats: 4; front seats: separate.

PRACTICAL INSTRUCTIONS fuel: 90 oct petrol; engine sump oil: 5.3 imp pt, 6.3 US pt, 3 l, SAE 20W-30, change every 3,100 miles, 5,000 km; gearbox oil: 1.8 imp pt, 2.1 US pt, 1 l, SAE 80, change every 18,600 miles, 30,000 km; final drive oil: 1.1 imp pt, 1.3 US pt, 0.6 l, SAE 90, change every 18,600 miles, 30,000 km; greasing: none; valve timing: inlet opens 24° before tdc and closes 64° after bdc, exhaust opens 64° before bdc and closes 24° after tdc; normal tyre pressure: front 14 psi, 1 atm, rear 14 psi, 1 atm.

Publica 800 Station Wagon

See Publica 800 Sedan, except for:

PRICE: —

BODY estate car/station wagon; doors: 2 + 1.

Publica 1000 Sedan

See Publica 800 Sedan, except for:

PRICE EX WORKS: 395,000 yen.

ENGINE cylinders: 4, in line; bore and stroke: 2.83 x 2.40 in, 72 x 61 mm; engine capacity: 60.6 cu in, 993 cu cm; compression ratio: 9; max power (DIN): 58 hp at 6,000 rpm; max torque (DIN): 57 lb ft, 7.9 kg m at 4,500 rpm; max engine rpm: 6,200; specific power: 58.4 hp/l; cylinder block: cast iron; crankshaft bearings: 5; lubricating system capacity: 5.8 imp pt, 7 US pt, 3.3 l; cooling system: water; cooling system capacity: 8.3 imp pt, 9.9 US pt, 4.7 l.

TRANSMISSION gearbox ratios: I 3.684, II 2.050, III 1.383, IV 1, rev 4.316; axle ratio: 4.222.

PERFORMANCE max speeds: 24 mph, 38 km/h in 1st gear; 42 mph, 68 km/h in 2nd gear; 62 mph, 100 km/h in 3rd gear; 87 mph, 140 km/h in 4th gear; power-weight ratio: 25.8 lb/hp, 11.7 kg/hp; acceleration: standing ¼ mile 19.5 sec; fuel consumption: 36.7 m/imp gal, 30.5 m/US gal, 7.7 l x 100 km.

DIMENSIONS AND WEIGHT dry weight: 1,499 lb, 680 kg.

PRACTICAL INSTRUCTIONS engine sump oil: 5.8 imp pt, 7 US pt, 3.3 l; gearbox oil: 3 imp pt, 3.6 US pt, 1.7 l; final drive oil: 1.8 imp pt, 2.1 US pt, 1 l; valve timing: inlet opens 16° before tdc and closes 50° after bdc, exhaust opens 50° before bdc and closes 16° after tdc; normal tyre pressure: front 17 psi, 1.2 atm, rear 17 psi, 1.2 atm.

Publica 1200 Hi-De Luxe Sedan

See Publica 1000 Sedan, except for:

PRICE EX WORKS: 475,000 yen.

ENGINE bore and stroke: 2.87 x 2.60 in, 75 x 66 mm; engine capacity: 71.1 cu in, 1,166 cu cm; compression ratio: 9; max power (DIN): 68 hp at 6,000 rpm; max torque (DIN): 69 lb ft, 9.5 kg m at 3,800 rpm; max engine rpm: 6,000; specific power: 58.3 hp/l.

PERFORMANCE max speeds: 25 mph, 40 km/h in 1st gear; 43 mph, 70 km/h in 2nd gear; 65 mph, 104 km/h in 3rd gear; 93 mph, 150 km/h in 4th gear; power weight ratio: 22 lb/hp, 10 kg/hp; acceleration: standing ¼ mile 18.5 sec; speed in direct drive at 1,000 rpm: 15.5 mph, 25 km/h; fuel consumption: 34.4 m/imp gal, 28.7 m/US gal, 8.2 l x 100 km.

OPTIONAL ACCESSORIES 3-speed automatic gearbox.

Publica 1200 SL Sedan

See Publica 1000 Sedan, except for:

PRICE EX WORKS: 495,000 yen.

ENGINE bore and stroke: 2.95 x 2.60 in, 75 x 66 mm; engine capacity: 71.1 cu in, 1,166 cu cm; compression ratio: 10;

TOYOTA Publica 1000 Sedan

TOYOTA Corolla 1200 De Luxe Sedan

TOYOTA Corolla 1400 SL Coupé

max power (DIN): 77 hp at 6,600 rpm; max torque (DIN): 70 lb ft, 9.6 kg m at 4,600 rpm; max engine rpm: 6,800; specific power: 66 hp/l; carburation: 2 Aisan downdraught twin barrel carburettors.

PERFORMANCE max speed: 99 mph, 160 km/h; power-weight ratio: 19.8 lb/hp, 9 kg/hp; fuel consumption: 31.4 m/imp gal, 26.1 m/US gal, 9 l x 100 km.

BRAKES front disc, rear drum.

DIMENSIONS AND WEIGHT overall length: 144.49 in, 3,670 mm; dry weight: 1,521 lb, 690 kg.

2-door Corolla 1200 De Luxe Sedan

PRICE EX WORKS: 501,500 yen.

ENGINE front, 4 stroke; cylinders: 4, in line; bore and stroke: 2.95 x 2.60 in, 75 x 66 mm; engine capacity: 71.1 cu in, 1,165 cu cm; compression ratio: 9; max power (DIN): 68 hp at 6,000 rpm; max torque (DIN): 68 lb ft, 9.5 kg m at 3,800 rpm; max engine rpm: 6,300; specific power: 58.3 hp/l; cylinder block: cast iron; cylinder head: light alloy; crankshaft bearings: 5; valves: 2 per cylinder, overhead, push-rods and rockers; camshafts: 1, side; lubrication: rotary pump, full flow filter; lubricating system capacity: 6.2 imp pt, 7.4 US pt, 3.5 l; carburation: 1 Aisan 3K downdraught twin barrel carburettor; fuel feed: mechanical pump; cooling system: water; cooling system capacity: 8.4 imp pt, 10.1 US pt, 4.8 l.

TRANSMISSION driving wheels: rear; clutch: single dry plate; gearbox: mechanical; gears: 4 + reverse; synchromesh gears: I, II, III, IV; gearbox ratios: I 3.684, II 2.050, III 1.383, IV 1, rev 4.316; gear lever: central; final drive: hypoid bevel; axle ratio: 4.222; width of rims: 4''; tyres: 6.00 x 12.

PERFORMANCE max speeds: 25 mph, 40 km/h in 1st gear; 45 mph, 72 km/h in 2nd gear; 66 mph, 107 km/h in 3rd gear; 90 mph, 145 km/h in 4th gear; power-weight ratio: 24.9 lb/hp, 11.3 kg/hp; carrying capacity: 706 lb, 320 kg; acceleration: standing ¼ mile 18.5 sec; speed in direct drive at 1,000 rpm: 15 mph, 24.2 km/h; fuel consumption: 35.3 m/imp gal, 29.4 m/US gal, 8 l x 100 km.

CHASSIS integral; front suspension: independent, by McPherson, coil springs/telescopic damper struts, lower wishbones (trailing links) anti-roll bar; rear suspension: rigid axle, semi-elliptic leafsprings, telescopic dampers.

STEERING recirculating ball; turns of steering wheel lock to lock 3.30.

BRAKES drum; lining area: front 47.1 sq in, 304 sq cm, rear 41.6 sq in, 268 sq cm, total 88.7 sq in, 572 sq cm.

ELECTRICAL EQUIPMENT voltage: 12 V; battery: 35 Ah; generator type: alternator, 30 A; ignition distributor: Nihon-Denso; headlamps: 2.

DIMENSIONS AND WEIGHT wheel base: 91.93 in, 2,335 mm; front track: 49.41 in, 1,255 mm; rear track: 49.02 in, 1,245 mm; overall length: 155.31 in, 3,945 mm; overall width: 59.25 in, 1,505 mm; overall height: 54.13 in, 1,375 mm; ground clearance: 6.69 in, 170 mm; dry weight: 1,698 lb, 770 kg; distribution of weight: 54.5% front axle, 45.5% rear axle; turning circle (between walls): 32.1 ft, 9.8 m; fuel tank capacity: 9.9 imp gal, 11.9 US gal, 45 l.

BODY saloon/sedan; doors: 2; seats: 4; front seats: separate.

PRACTICAL INSTRUCTIONS fuel: 90 oct petrol; engine sump oil: 6.2 imp pt, 7.4 US pt, 3.5 l, SAE 20W-30, change every 3,100 miles, 5,000 km; gearbox oil: 1.8 imp pt, 2.1 US pt, 1 l, SAE 90, change every 18,600 miles, 30,000 km; final drive oil: 1.4 imp pt, 1.7 US pt, 0.8 l, SAE 90, change every 18,600 miles, 30,000 km; greasing: none; tappet clearances: inlet 0.003 in, 0.08 mm, exhaust 0.007 in, 0.18 mm; valve timing: inlet opens 16° before tdc and closes 50° after bdc, exhaust opens 50° before bdc and closes 16° after tdc; normal tyre pressure: front 20 psi, 1.4 atm, rear 20 psi, 1.4 atm.

OPTIONAL ACCESSORIES Toyoglide automatic gearbox with 2 ratios, max speed 87 mph, 140 km/h.

4-door Corolla 1200 De Luxe Sedan

See 2-door Corolla 1200 De Luxe Sedan, except for:

PRICE: —

Corolla 1200 Coupé

See 2-door Corolla 1200 De Luxe Sedan, except for:

PRICE EX WORKS: 537,000 yen.

PERFORMANCE power-weight ratio: 26.9 lb/hp, 12.2 kg/hp.

DIMENSIONS AND WEIGHT front track: 49.61 in, 1,260 mm; overall height: 52.95 in, 1,345 mm; ground clearance: 6.10 in, 155 mm; dry weight: 1,830 lb, 830 kg; distribution of weight: 57.8% front axle, 42.2% rear axle.

BODY coupé.

TOYOTA Publica 1000 Sedan

TOYOTA 2-door Corolla 1200 De Luxe Sedan

TOYOTA Corolla 1400 SL Coupé

4-door Corolla 1200 Hi-De Luxe Sedan

See 2-door Corolla 1200 De Luxe Sedan, except for:

PRICE EX WORKS: 555,000 yen.

ENGINE compression ratio: 10; max power (DIN): 73 hp at 6,600 rpm; max torque (DIN): 70 lb ft, 9.6 kg m at 4,200 rpm; specific power: 62.6 hp/l.

PERFORMANCE max speed: 93 mph, 150 km/h; power-weight ratio: 23.1 lb/hp, 10.5 kg/hp.

BRAKES front disc, rear drum.

2-door Corolla 1200 SL Sedan

See 2-door Corolla 1200 De Luxe Sedan, except for:

PRICE EX WORKS: 564,000 yen.

ENGINE compression ratio: 10; max power (DIN): 77 hp at 6,600 rpm; max torque (DIN): 70 lb ft, 9.6 kg m at 4,600 rpm; specific power: 66 hp/l; carburation: 2 Aisan downdraught twin barrel carburettors.

PERFORMANCE max speed: 99 mph, 160 km/h; power-weight ratio: 22 lb/hp, 10 kg/hp.

BRAKES front disc, rear drum.

Corolla 1200 SL Coupé

See 2-door Corolla 1200 SL Sedan, except for:

PRICE EX WORKS: 594,000 yen.

PERFORMANCE power-weight ratio: 23.8 lb/hp, 10.8 kg/hp.

DIMENSIONS AND WEIGHT front track: 49.61 in, 1,260 mm; overall height: 52.95 in, 1,345 mm; ground clearance: 6.10 in, 155 mm; dry weight: 1,830 lb, 830 kg; distribution of weight: 57.8% front axle, 42.2% rear axle.

BODY coupé.

2-door Corolla 1400 Hi-De Luxe Sedan

See 2-door Corolla 1200 De Luxe Sedan, except for:

PRICE EX WORKS: 590,000 yen.

ENGINE bore and stroke: 3.15 x 2.76 in, 80 x 70 mm; engine capacity: 85.9 cu in, 1,407 cu cm; compression ratio: 8.5; max power (DIN): 86 hp at 6,000 rpm; max torque (DIN): 85 lb ft, 11.7 kg m at 3,800 rpm; max engine rpm: 6,300; specific power: 61.1 hp/l.

TRANSMISSION gearbox ratios: I 3.587, II 2.022, III 1.384, IV 1, rev 3.484; axle ratio: 4.111; tyres: 6.15 x 13.

PERFORMANCE max speeds: 27 mph, 43 km/h in 1st gear; 47 mph, 76 km/h in 2nd gear; 68 mph, 110 km/h in 3rd gear; 99 mph, 160 km/h in 4th gear; power-weight ratio: 21.8 lb/hp, 9.9 kg/hp; acceleration: standing ¼ mile 17.5 sec; speed in direct drive at 1,000 rpm: 14 mph, 22.5 km/h; fuel consumption: 31.4 m/imp gal, 26.1 m/US gal, 9 l x 100 km.

BRAKES front disc, rear drum; lining area: front 24.2 sq in, 156 sq cm, rear 60.2 sq in, 388 sq cm, total 84.4 sq in, 544 sq cm.

DIMENSIONS AND WEIGHT front track: 49.61 in, 1,260 mm; dry weight: 1,874 lb, 850 kg; distribution of weight: 56.4% front axle, 43.6% rear axle

PRACTICAL INSTRUCTIONS tappet clearances: inlet 0.007 in, 0.18 mm, exhaust 0.013 in, 0.33 mm; valve timing: inlet opens 16° before tdc and closes 54° after bdc, exhaust opens 58° before bdc and closes 12° after tdc.

VARIATIONS

ENGINE (export) bore and stroke 3.35 x 2.76 in, 85 x 70 mm, engine capacity 96.9 cu in, 1,588 cu cm, max power (DIN) 100 hp at 6,000 rpm, max torque (DIN) 99 lb ft, 13.7 kg m at 3,800 rpm, 63 hp/l specific power.
PERFORMANCE max speed about 106 mph, 170 km/h, power-weight ratio 18.7 lb/hp, 8.5 kg/hp.

4-door Corolla 1400 Hi-De Luxe Sedan

See 2-door Corolla 1400 Hi-De Luxe Sedan, except for:

PRICE: —

Corolla 1400 Hi-De Luxe Coupé

See 2-door Corolla 1400 Hi-De Luxe Sedan, except for:

PRICE EX WORKS: 595,000 yen.

PERFORMANCE power-weight ratio: 21.2 lb/hp, 9.6 kg/hp.

DIMENSIONS AND WEIGHT overall height: 52.95 in, 1,345 mm; ground clearance: 6.10 in, 155 mm; dry weight: 1,830 lb, 830 kg; distribution of weight: 57.8% front axle, 42.2% rear axle.

BODY coupé.

2-door Corolla 1400 SL Sedan

See 2-door Corolla 1400 Hi-De Luxe Sedan, except for:

PRICE EX WORKS: 604,000 yen.

ENGINE compression ratio: 9.6; max power (DIN): 90 hp at 6,000 rpm; max torque (DIN): 87 lb ft, 12 kg m at 3,800 rpm; specific power: 64 hp/l.

PERFORMANCE power-weight ratio: 20.7 lb/hp, 9.4 kg/hp; acceleration: standing ¼ mile 17.3 sec.

4-door Corolla 1400 SL Sedan

See 2-door Corolla 1400 SL Sedan, except for:

PRICE: —

Corolla 1400 SL Coupé

See 2-door Corolla 1400 SL Sedan, except for:

PRICE EX WORKS: 634,000 yen.

PERFORMANCE power-weight ratio: 20.3 lb/hp, 9.2 kg/hp.

DIMENSIONS AND WEIGHT overall height: 76.57 in, 1,945 mm; ground clearance: 6.10 in, 155 mm; dry weight: 1,830 lb, 830 kg; distribution of weight: 57.8% front axle, 42.2% rear axle.

BODY coupé.

2-door Carina 1400 De Luxe Sedan

PRICE EX WORKS: 579,000 yen.

ENGINE front, 4 stroke; cylinders: 4, in line; bore and stroke: 3.15 x 2.76 in, 80 x 70 mm; engine capacity: 85.9 cu in, 1,407 cu cm; compression ratio: 8.5; max power (DIN): 86 hp at 6,000 rpm; max torque (DIN): 85 lb ft, 11.7 kg m at 3,800 rpm; max engine rpm: 6,300; specific power: 61.1 hp/l; cylinder block: cast iron; cylinder head: light alloy; crankshaft bearings: 5; valves: 2 per cylinder, overhead, push-rods and rockers; camshafts: 1, side; lubrication: rotary pump, full flow filter; lubricating system capacity: 6.2 imp pt, 7.4 US pt, 3.5 l; carburation: 1 Aisan downdraught twin barrel carburettor; fuel feed: mechanical pump; cooling system: water; cooling system capacity: 8.4 imp pt, 10.1 US pt, 4.8 l.

TRANSMISSION driving wheels: rear; clutch: single dry plate; gearbox: mechanical; gears: 3 + reverse; synchromesh gears: I, II, III; gearbox ratios: I 3.337, II 1.653, III 1, rev 4.449; gear lever: central; final drive: hypoid bevel; axle ratio: 4.375; width of rims: 4; tyres: 6.00 x 12.

PERFORMANCE max speeds: 29 mph, 46 km/h in 1st gear; 58 mph, 94 km/h in 2nd gear; 96 mph, 155 km/h in 3rd gear; power-weight ratio: 23.1 lb/hp, 10.5 kg/hp; carrying capacity: 882 lb, 400 kg; acceleration: standing ¼ mile 17.7 sec; speed in direct drive at 1,000 rpm: 15.5 mph, 25 km/h; fuel consumption: 31.4 m/imp gal, 26.1 m/US gal, 9 l x 100 km.

CHASSIS integral; front suspension: independent, by McPherson, coil springs/telescopic damper struts, lower wishbones (trailing links) anti-roll bar; rear suspension: rigid axle, twin trailing radius arms, transverse linkage bar, coil springs, telescopic dampers.

STEERING recirculating ball; turns of steering wheel lock to lock: 3.30.

BRAKES drum; lining area: front 47.1 sq in, 304 sq cm, rear 41.6 sq in, 268 sq cm, total 88.7 sq in, 572 sq cm.

ELECTRICAL EQUIPMENT voltage: 12 V; battery: 35 Ah; generator type: alternator, 30 A; ignition distributor: Nihon-Denso; headlamps: 4.

DIMENSIONS AND WEIGHT wheel base: 95.47 in, 2,425 mm;

TOYOTA 2-door Carina 1600 Super De Luxe Sedan

TOYOTA Corona 1700 SL Hardtop

TOYOTA Corona 1900 Sedan

front track: 50.39 in, 1,280 mm; rear track: 50.59 in, 1,285 mm; overall length: 162.79 in, 4,135 mm; overall width: 61.81 in, 1,570 mm; overall height: 54.53 in, 1,385 mm; ground clearance: 6.89 in, 175 mm; dry weight: 1,985 lb, 900 kg; distribution of weight: 57.3% front axle, 42.7% rear axle; turning circle (between walls): 31.5 ft, 9.6 m; fuel tank capacity: 9.9 imp gal, 11.9 US gal, 45 l.

BODY saloon/sedan; doors: 2; seats: 5; front seats: separate.

PRACTICAL INSTRUCTIONS fuel: 90 oct petrol; engine sump oil: 6.2 imp pt, 7.4 US pt, 3.5 l, SAE 20W-30, change every 3,100 miles, 5,000 km; gearbox oil: 2.6 imp pt, 3.2 US pt, 1.5 l, SAE 80, change every 18,600 miles, 30,000 km; final drive oil: 1.8 imp pt, 2.1 US pt, 1 l, SAE 90, change every 18,600 miles, 30,000 km; tappet clearances: inlet 0.007 in, 0.18 mm, exhaust 0.013 in, 0.33 mm; valve timing: inlet opens 16° before tdc and closes 54° after bdc, exhaust opens 58° before bdc and closes 12° after tdc; normal tyre pressure: front 20 psi, 1.4 atm, rear 20 psi, 1.4 atm.

OPTIONAL ACCESSORIES 4-speed mechanical gearbox; 2-speed automatic gearbox.

4-door Carina 1400 De Luxe Sedan

See 2-door Carina 1400 De Luxe Sedan, except for:

PRICE: —

2-door Carina 1600 Super De Luxe Sedan

See 2-door Carina 1400 De Luxe Sedan, except for:

PRICE EX WORKS: 644,000 yen.

ENGINE bore and stroke: 3.35 x 2.76 in, 85 x 70 mm; engine capacity: 96.9 cu in, 1,588 mm; max power (DIN): 100 hp at 6,000 rpm; max torque (DIN): 99 lb ft, 13.7 kg m at 3,800 rpm; max engine rpm: 6,400; specific power: 63 hp/l; lubricating system capacity: 6.5 imp pt, 7.8 US pt, 3.7 l; carburation: 1 Aisan 2T downdraught twin barrel carburettor; cooling system capacity: 11.4 imp pt, 13.7 US pt, 6.5 l.

TRANSMISSION clutch: single dry plate (diaphragm); gears: 4 + reverse; gearbox ratios: I 3.587, II 2.022, III 1.384, IV 1, rev 3.484; axle ratio: 3.900; tyres: 5.60 x 13.

PERFORMANCE max speeds: 29 mph, 46 km/h in 1st gear; 51 mph, 82 km/h in 2nd gear; 74 mph, 119 km/h in 3rd gear; 103 mph, 165 km/h in 4th gear; power-weight ratio: 19.8 lb/hp, 9 kg/hp; speed in direct drive at 1,000 rpm: 16.2 mph, 26 km/h; fuel consumption: 29.7 m/imp gal, 24.8 m/US gal, 9.5 l x 100 km.

STEERING turns of steering wheel lock to lock: 3.50.

BRAKES front disc, rear drum; lining area: front 28.5 sq in, 184 sq cm, rear 35.3 sq in, 228 sq cm, total 63.8 sq in, 412 sq cm.

ELECTRICAL EQUIPMENT generator: alternator, AX 40 A.

DIMENSIONS AND WEIGHT fuel tank capacity: 11 imp gal, 13.2 US gal, 50 l.

PRACTICAL INSTRUCTIONS normal tyre pressure: front 24 psi, 1.7 atm, rear 24 psi, 1.7 atm.

OPTIONAL ACCESSORIES 5-speed mechanical gearbox and 3-speed Toyoglide automatic gearbox.

4-door Carina 1600 Super De Luxe Sedan

See 2-door Carina 1600 Super De Luxe Sedan, except for:

PRICE: —

2-door Carina 1600 ST Sedan

See 2-door Carina 1600 Super De Luxe Sedan, except for:

PRICE EX WORKS: 700,000 yen.

ENGINE compression ratio: 9.4; max power (DIN): 105 hp at 6,000 rpm; max torque (DIN): 105 lb ft, 14.5 kg m at 4,200 rpm; specific power: 66.1 hp/l; carburation: 2 Aisan 2TB downdraught twin barrel carburettors.

TRANSMISSION gears: 5 + reverse; gearbox ratios: I 3.587, II 2.022, III 1.384, IV 1, V 0.861, rev 3.484; axle ratio: 4.111; width of rims: 4.5''; tyres: 6.45 x 13.

PERFORMANCE max speeds: 25 mph, 41 km/h in 1st gear; 53 mph, 86 km/h in 2nd gear; 66 mph, 106 km/h in 3rd gear; 91 mph, 147 km/h in 4th gear; 109 mph, 175 km/h in 5th

TOYOTA Carina 1600 Super De Luxe Sedan

TOYOTA Corona 1700 SL Hardtop

TOYOTA Corona 1900 Sedan

gear; power-weight ratio: 19 lb/hp, 8.6 kg/hp; speed in top at 1,000 rpm: 16.8 mph, 27 km/h; fuel consumption: 28.2 m/imp gal, 23.5 m/US gal, 10 l x 100 km.

OPTIONAL ACCESSORIES none.

4-door Carina 1600 ST Sedan

See 2-door Carina 1600 ST Sedan, except for:

PRICE: —

Corona 1500 De Luxe Sedan

PRICE EX WORKS: 592,000 yen.

ENGINE front, 4 stroke; cylinders: 4, in line; bore and stroke: 3.07 x 3.07 in, 78 x 78 mm; engine capacity: 90.9 cu in, 1,490 cu cm; compression ratio: 8.3; max power (DIN): 77 hp at 5,200 rpm; max torque (DIN): 80 lb ft, 11 kg m at 2,800 rpm; max engine rpm: 5,500; specific power: 51.7 hp/l; cylinder block: cast iron; cylinder head: light alloy; crankshaft bearings: 3; valves: 2 per cylinder, overhead, push-rods and rockers; camshafts: 1, side; lubrication: rotary pump, full flow filter; lubricating system capacity: 8.8 imp pt, 10.6 US pt, 5 l; carburation: 1 Aisan downdraught twin barrel carburettor; fuel feed: mechanical pump; cooling system: water; cooling system capacity: 13 imp pt, 15.6 US pt, 7.4 l.

TRANSMISSION driving wheels: rear; clutch: single dry plate (diaphragm); gearbox: mechanical; gears: 3 + reverse; synchromesh gears: I, II, III; gearbox ratios: I 3.337, II 1.653, III 1, rev 4.449; gear lever: central; final drive: hypoid bevel; axle ratio: 4.111; width of rims: 4''; tyres: 5.60 x 13.

PERFORMANCE max speeds: 27 mph, 43 km/h in 1st gear; 55 mph, 88 km/h in 2nd gear; 90 mph, 145 km/h in 3rd gear; power-weight ratio: 28.7 lb/hp, 13 kg/hp; speed in direct drive at 1,000 rpm: 16.5 mph, 26.5 km/h; fuel consumption: 31.4 m/imp gal, 26.1 m/US gal, 9 l x 100 km.

CHASSIS integral; front suspension: independent, wishbones, coil springs, anti-roll bar, telescopic dampers; rear suspension: rigid axle, semi-elliptic leafsprings, telescopic dampers.

STEERING recirculating ball; turns of steering wheel lock to lock: 3.50.

BRAKES drum; lining area: front 58.3 sq in, 376 sq cm, rear 58.3 sq in, 376 sq cm. total 116.6 sq in, 752 sq cm.

ELECTRICAL EQUIPMENT voltage: 12 V; battery: 35 Ah; generator type: alternator, 40 A; ignition distributor: Denso; headlamps: 4.

DIMENSIONS AND WEIGHT wheel base: 95 in, 2,413 mm; front track: 50.79 in, 1,290 mm; rear track: 50.39 in, 1,280 mm; overall length: 164.02 in, 4,166 mm; overall width: 61.81 in, 1,570 mm; overall height: 55.12 in, 1,400 mm; ground clearance: 7.09 in, 180 mm; dry weight: 2,215 lb, 1,005 kg; distribution of weight: 57% front axle, 43% rear axle; turning circle (between walls): 31.5 ft, 9.6 m; fuel tank capacity: 11 imp gal, 13.2 US gal, 50 l.

BODY saloon/sedan; doors: 4; seats: 5; front seats: separate.

PRACTICAL INSTRUCTIONS fuel: 91 oct petrol; engine sump oil: 8.8 imp pt, 10.6 US pt, 5 l, SAE 20W-30, change every 3,100 miles, 5,000 km; gearbox oil: 3.5 imp pt, 4.2 US pt, 2 l, SAE 80, change every 18,600 miles, 30,000 km; final drive oil: 1.8 imp pt, 2.1 US pt, 1 l, SAE 90, change every 18,600 miles, 30,000 km; tappet clearances: inlet 0.007 in, 0.18 mm, exhaust 0.013 in, 0.33 mm; valve timing: inlet opens 16° before tdc and closes 54° after bdc, exhaust opens 54° before bdc and closes 16° after tdc; normal tyre pressure: front 21 psi, 1.5 atm, rear 21 psi, 1.5 atm.

OPTIONAL ACCESSORIES 4-speed mechanical gearbox; 2-speed automatic gearbox.

Corona 1700 De Luxe Sedan

See Corona 1500 De Luxe Sedan, except for:

PRICE EX WORKS: 652,000 yen.

ENGINE bore and stroke: 3.39 x 2.89 in, 86 x 73.5 mm; engine capacity: 104.2 cu in, 1,707 cu cm; compression ratio: 8.5; max power (DIN): 95 hp at 5,500 rpm; max torque (DIN): 101 lb ft, 14 kg m at 3,800 rpm; max engine rpm: 5,800; specific power: 55.6 hp/l.

TRANSMISSION gears: 4 + reverse; gearbox ratios: I 3.673, II 2.114, III 1.403, IV 1, rev 4.183; axle ratio: 4.111.

CORONA 1700 DE LUXE SEDAN

PERFORMANCE max speeds: 27 mph, 44 km/h in 1st gear; 47 mph, 76 km/h in 2nd gear; 71 mph, 114 km/h in 3rd gear; 99 mph, 160 km/h in 4th gear; power-weight ratio: 23.3 lb/hp, 10.6 kg/hp; speed in direct drive at 1,000 rpm: 17.4 mph, 28 km/h; fuel consumption: 29.7 m/imp gal, 24.8 m/US gal, 9.5 l x 100 km.

BRAKES front disc, rear drum; lining area: front 24.2 sq in, 156 sq cm, rear 60.2 sq in, 388 sq cm, total 84.4 sq in, 544 sq cm.

PRACTICAL INSTRUCTIONS valve timing: inlet opens 15° before tdc and closes 45° after bdc, exhaust opens 50° before bdc and closes 10° after tdc.

OPTIONAL ACCESSORIES 6.45 x 13 tyres; 3-speed automatic gearbox; electronically-controlled automatic gearbox.

Corona 1700 Hardtop

See Corona 1700 De Luxe Sedan, except for:

PRICE: —

TRANSMISSION width of rims: 4.5''; tyres: 6.45 x 13.

PERFORMANCE power-weight ratio: 22.5 lb/hp, 10.2 kg/hp.

DIMENSIONS AND WEIGHT wheel base: 95.67 in, 2,430 mm; overall length: 164.17 in, 4,170 mm; overall height: 54.53 in, 1,385 mm; dry weight: 2,139 lb, 970 kg.

BODY hardtop.

Corona 1700 SL Hardtop

See Corona 1700 Hardtop, except for:

PRICE EX WORKS: 768,000 yen.

ENGINE compression ratio: 9.5; max power (DIN): 105 hp at 6,000 rpm; max torque (DIN): 105 lb ft, 14.5 kg m at 4,000 rpm; max engine rpm: 6,400; specific power: 61.5 hp/l; carburation: 2 SU type GR-B horizontal carburettors.

TRANSMISSION axle ratio: 3.900.

PERFORMANCE max speeds: 29 mph, 46 km/h in 1st gear; 52 mph, 84 km/h in 2nd gear; 78 mph, 125 km/h in 3rd gear; 106 mph, 170 km/h in 4th gear; power-weight ratio: 20.3 lb/hp, 9.2 kg/hp; speed in direct drive at 1,000 rpm: 16.8 mph, 27 km/h; fuel consumption: 28.8 m/imp gal, 24 m/US gal, 9.8 l x 100 km.

Corona 1900 Sedan

(Export model)

See Corona 1500 De Luxe Sedan, except for:

PRICE: —

ENGINE bore and stroke: 3.39 x 3.15 in, 86 x 80 mm; engine capacity: 113.4 cu in, 1,858 cu cm; compression ratio: 9; max power (SAE): 108 hp at 5,500 rpm; max torque (SAE): 117 lb ft, 16.2 kg m at 3,600 rpm; max engine rpm: 6,000; specific power: 58.1 hp/l; cylinder head: cast iron; valves: 2 per cylinder, overhead, rockers; camshafts: 1, overhead.

TRANSMISSION gears: 4 + reverse; synchromesh gears: I, II, III, IV; gearbox ratios: I 3.673, II 2.114, III 1.403, IV 1, rev 4.183; axle ratio: 3.700; tyres: 6.00 x 13.

PERFORMANCE max speeds: 26 mph, 42 km/h in 1st gear; 46 mph, 74 km/h in 2nd gear; 69 mph, 111 km/h in 3rd gear; 98 mph, 157 km/h in 4th gear; power-weight ratio: 20.5 lb/hp, 9.3 kg/hp; speed in direct drive at 1,000 rpm: 16.5 mph, 26.5 km/h; fuel consumption: 28.2 m/imp gal, 23.5 m/US gal, 10 l x 100 km.

BRAKES front disc, rear drum, servo; lining area: front 24.2 sq in, 156 sq cm, rear 60.2 sq in, 388 sq cm, total 84.4 sq in, 544 sq cm.

OPTIONAL ACCESSORIES 3-speed automatic gearbox.

Corona Mk II 1900 Sedan

PRICE: —

ENGINE front, 4 stroke; cylinders: 4, in line; bore and stroke: 3.39 x 3.15 in, 86 x 80 mm; engine capacity: 113.4 cu in, 1,858 cu cm; compression ratio: 9; max power (SAE): 108 hp at 5,500 rpm; max torque (SAE): 117 lb ft, 16.2 kg m at 3,600 rpm; max engine rpm: 6,000; specific power: 58.1 hp/l; cylinder block: cast iron; cylinder head: cast

TOYOTA Corona Mk II 1900 GL Sedan

TOYOTA Corona Mk II 1900 GSL Hardtop

TOYOTA Celica 1600 GT

iron; crankshaft bearings: 5; valves: 2 per cylinder, overhead, rockers; camshafts: 1, overhead; lubrication: rotary pump, full flow filter; lubricating system capacity: 8.8 imp pt, 10.6 US pt, 5 l; carburation: 1 Aisan downdraught twin barrel carburettor; fuel feed: mechanical pump; cooling system: water; cooling system capacity: 13 imp pt, 15.6 US pt, 7.4 l.

TRANSMISSION driving wheels: rear; clutch: single dry plate (diaphragm); gearbox: mechanical; gears: 4 + reverse; synchromesh gears: I, II, III, IV; gearbox ratios: I 3.673, II 2.114, III 1.403, IV 1, rev 4.183; gear lever: central; final drive: hypoid bevel; axle ratio: 3.700; width of rims: 4.5''; tyres: 6.45 x 13.

PERFORMANCE max speeds: 28 mph, 45 km/h in 1st gear; 50 mph, 80 km/h in 2nd gear; 75 mph, 120 km/h in 3rd gear; 103 mph, 165 km/h in 4th gear; power-weight ratio: 19.4 lb/hp, 8.8 kg/hp; carrying capacity: 882 lb, 400 kg; speed in direct drive at 1,000 rpm: 17.4 mph, 28 km/h; fuel consumption: 31.4 m/imp gal, 26.1 m/US gal, 9 l x 100 km.

CHASSIS integral; front suspension: independent, wishbones, coil springs, anti-roll bar, telescopic dampers; rear suspension: rigid axle, semi-elliptic leafsprings, telescopic dampers.

STEERING recirculating ball.

BRAKES front disc, rear drum, servo; lining area: front 24.2 sq in, 156 sq cm, rear 60.2 sq in, 388 sq cm, total 84.4 sq in, 544 sq cm.

ELECTRICAL EQUIPMENT voltage: 12 V; battery: 40 Ah; generator type: alternator, 480 W; ignition distributor: Denso; headlamps: 4.

DIMENSIONS AND WEIGHT wheel base: 98.82 in, 2,510 mm; front track: 52.17 in, 1,325 mm; rear track: 51.97 in, 1,320 mm; overall length: 169.09 in, 4,295 mm; overall width: 63.19 in, 1,605 mm; overall height: 55.31 in, 1,405 mm; ground clearance: 7.09 in, 180 mm; dry weight: 2,095 lb, 950 kg; distribution of weight: 56.3% front axle, 43.7% rear axle; turning circle (between walls): 31.8 ft, 9.7 m; fuel tank capacity: 11.4 imp gal, 13.7 US gal, 52 l.

BODY saloon/sedan; doors: 4; seats: 5; front seats: separate.

PRACTICAL INSTRUCTIONS fuel: 90 oct petrol; engine sump oil: 8.8 imp pt, 10.6 US pt, 5 l, SAE 20W-30, change every 3,100 miles, 5,000 km; gearbox oil: 3.5 imp pt, 4.2 US pt, 2 l, SAE 80, change every 18,600 miles, 30,000 km; final drive oil: 1.8 imp pt, 2.1 US pt, 1 l, SAE 90, change every 18,600 miles, 30,000 km; greasing: none; tappet clearances: inlet 0.007 in, 0.18 mm, exhaust 0.013 in, 0.33 mm; valve timing: inlet opens 15° before tdc and closes 45° after bdc, exhaust opens 50° before bdc and closes 10° after tdc; normal tyre pressure: front 27 psi, 1.9 atm, rear 27 psi, 1.9 atm.

OPTIONAL ACCESSORIES 3-speed automatic gearbox; GL version.

Corona Mk II 1900 Hardtop

See Corona Mk II 1900 Sedan, except for:

PRICE: —

TRANSMISSION tyres: 165 x 13.

PERFORMANCE power-weight ratio: 20.7 lb/hp, 9.4 kg/hp.

DIMENSIONS AND WEIGHT overall height: 54.92 in, 1,395 mm; dry weight: 2,249 lb, 1,020 kg.

BODY hardtop; doors: 2.

Corona Mk II 1900 SL Hardtop

See Corona Mk II 1900 Hardtop, except for:

PRICE EX WORKS: 912,500 yen.

ENGINE compression ratio: 10; max power (SAE): 120 hp at 6,000 rpm; max torque (SAE): 120 lb ft, 16.6 kg m at 4,000 rpm; max engine rpm: 6,200; specific power: 64.6 hp/l; carburation: 2 SU horizontal carburettors.

PERFORMANCE max speeds: 30 mph, 48 km/h in 1st gear; 52 mph, 84 km/h in 2nd gear; 79 mph, 127 km/h in 3rd gear; 109 mph, 175 km/h in 4th gear; power-weight ratio: 18.7 lb/hp, 8.5 kg/hp; acceleration: standing ¼ mile 17.9 sec; speed in direct drive at 1,000 rpm: 17.8 mph, 28.7 km/h.

ELECTRICAL EQUIPMENT battery: 45 Ah.

PRACTICAL INSTRUCTIONS fuel: 100 oct petrol; valve timing: inlet opens 16° before tdc and closes 60° after bdc, exhaust opens 56° before bdc and closes 20° after tdc.

OPTIONAL ACCESSORIES GSL version.

TOYOTA Corona Mk II 1900 GL Sedan

TOYOTA Corona Mk II 1900 GSL Hardtop

TOYOTA Celica 1600 GT

Corona Mk II 1900 GSS Hardtop

See Corona Mk II 1900 Hardtop, except for:

PRICE EX WORKS: 1,055,000 yen.

ENGINE compression ratio: 9.7; max power (SAE): 140 hp at 6,400 rpm; max torque (SAE): 101 lb ft, 14 kg m at 5,200 rpm; max engine rpm: 7,000; specific power: 75.3 hp/l; valves: 2 per cylinder, overhead, thimble tappets; camshafts: 2, overhead; carburation: 2 Mikuni-Solex 40 PHH horizontal twin barrel carburettors; fuel feed: electric pump.

TRANSMISSION gears: 5 + reverse; synchromesh gears: I, II, III, IV, V; gearbox ratios: I 3.074, II 1.838, III 1.256, IV 1, V 0.856; final drive: limited slip; axle ratio: 4.375; width of rims: 5''; tyres: 165 x 14.

PERFORMANCE max speeds: 31 mph, 50 km/h in 1st gear; 52 mph, 84 km/h in 2nd gear; 78 mph, 125 km/h in 3rd gear; 101 mph, 162 km/h in 4th gear; 124 mph, 200 km/h in 5th gear; power-weight ratio: 16.5 lb/hp, 7.5 kg/hp; acceleration: standing 1/4 mile 16.6 sec; speed in top at 1,000 rpm: 18 mph, 29 km/h; fuel consumption: 26.9 m/imp gal, 22.4 m/US gal, 10.5 l x 100 km.

ELECTRICAL EQUIPMENT battery: 60 Ah.

DIMENSIONS AND WEIGHT overall height: 54.53 in, 1,385 mm; dry weight: 2,315 lb, 1,050 kg; turning circle (between walls): 35.8 ft, 10.9 m.

PRACTICAL INSTRUCTIONS valve timing: inlet opens 18° before tdc and closes 58° after bdc, exhaust opens 58° before bdc and closes 18° after tdc.

OPTIONAL ACCESSORIES 4.625 4.875 axle ratios; electrically-controlled windows; air-conditioning system.

Celica 1600 GT

PRICE EX WORKS: 875,000 yen.

ENGINE front, 4 stroke; cylinders: 4, in line; bore and stroke: 3.35 x 2.76 in, 85 x 70 mm; engine capacity: 96.9 cu in, 1,588 cu cm; compression ratio: 9.8; max power (DIN): 115 hp at 6,400 rpm; max torque (DIN): 105 lb ft, 14.5 kg m at 5,200 rpm; max engine rpm: 6,800; specific power: 72.4 hp/l; cylinder block: cast iron; cylinder head: light alloy; crankshaft bearings: 5; valves: 2 per cylinder, overhead, Vee-slanted, thimble tappets; camshafts: 2, overhead; lubrication: rotary pump, full flow filter; lubricating system capacity: 6.7 imp pt, 8 US pt, 3.8 l; carburation: 2 Mikuni-Solex N 40 PHH3 horizontal carburettors; fuel feed: mechanical pump; cooling system: water; cooling system capacity: 13 imp pt, 15.6 US pt, 7.4 l.

TRANSMISSION driving wheels: rear; clutch: single dry plate (diaphragm); gearbox: mechanical; gears: 5 + reverse; synchromesh gears: I, II, III, IV, V; gearbox ratios: I 3.587, II 2.022, III 1.384, IV 1, V 0.861; gear lever: central; final drive: hypoid bevel; axle ratio: 4.111; width of rims: 4.5''; tyres: 6.45 H x 13.

PERFORMANCE max speeds: 30 mph, 48 km/h in 1st gear; 56 mph, 90 km/h in 2nd gear; 85 mph, 136 km/h in 3rd gear; 112 mph, 180 km/h in 4th gear; 118 mph, 190 km/h in 5th gear; power-weight ratio: 18.1 lb/hp, 8.2 kg/hp; carrying capacity: 706 lb, 320 kg; acceleration: standing 1/4 mile 16.5 sec; speed in top at 1,000 rpm: 17.4 mph, 28 km/h; fuel consumption: 26.9 m/imp gal, 22.4 m/US gal, 10.5 l x 100 km.

CHASSIS integral; front suspension: independent, by Mc-Pherson, coil springs/telescopic damper struts, lower wishbones (trailing links) anti-roll bar; rear suspension: rigid axle, lower trailing arms, upper torque arms, transverse linkage bar, coil springs, telescopic dampers.

STEERING recirculating ball; turns of steering wheel lock to lock: 3.50.

BRAKES front disc, rear drum, servo; lining area: front 24.2 sq in, 156 sq cm, rear 54 sq in, 348 sq cm, total 78.2 sq in, 504 sq cm.

ELECTRICAL EQUIPMENT voltage: 12 V; battery: 35 Ah; generator type: alternator, 40 A; ignition distributor: Denso; headlamps: 4.

DIMENSIONS AND WEIGHT wheel base: 95.47 in, 2,425 mm; front track: 50.39 in, 1,280 mm; rear track: 50.59 in, 1,285 mm; overall length: 163.98 in, 4,165 mm; overall width: 62.99 in, 1,600 mm; overall height: 51.57 in, 1,310 mm; ground clearance: 6.89 in, 175 mm; dry weight: 2,073 lb, 940 kg; distribution of weight: 57.4% front axle, 42.6% rear axle; turning circle (between walls): 34.1 ft, 10.4 m; fuel tank capacity: 11 imp gal, 13.2 US gal, 50 l.

BODY coupé; doors: 2; seats: 4; front seats: separate.

PRACTICAL INSTRUCTIONS fuel: 100 oct petrol; engine sump oil: 6.7 imp pt, 8 US pt, 3.8 l, SAE 20W-30, change every

CELICA 1600 GT

3,100 miles, 5,000 km; gearbox oil: 2.6 imp pt, 3.2 US pt, 1.5 l, SAE 80, change every 18,600 miles, 30,000 km; final drive oil: 1.8 imp pt, 2.1 US pt, 1 l, SAE 90, change every 18,600 miles, 30,000 km; tappet clearances: inlet 0.011 in, 0.29 mm, exhaust 0.013 in, 0.34 mm; valve timing: inlet opens 20° before tdc and closes 40° after bdc, exhaust opens 52° before bdc and closes 16° after tdc; normal tyre pressure: front 26 psi, 1.8 atm, rear 26 psi, 1.8 atm.

VARIATIONS

ENGINE 9.4 compression ratio, max power (DIN) 105 hp at 6,000 rpm, max torque (DIN) 101 lb ft, 14 kg m at 4,200 rpm, 66.1 hp/l specific power, 2 Aisan downdraught twin barrel carburettors.
TRANSMISSION gears 4 + reverse, gearbox ratios I 3.587, II 2.022, III 1.384, IV 1, rev 3.484, 3.900 axle ratio, 6.45 x 13 tyres (on request 5-speed mechanical gearbox and automatic gearbox with 3 ratios I 2.400, II 1.479, III 1, rev 1.920, 4.111 axle ratio).
PERFORMANCE max speed about 112 mph, 180 km/h, power-weight ratio 19.6 lb/hp, 8.9 kg/hp.

ENGINE 8.5 compression ratio, max power (DIN) 100 hp at 6,000 rpm, max torque (DIN) 99 lb ft, 13.7 kg m at 3,800 rpm, 63 hp/l specific power, 1 Aisan downdraught twin barrel carburettor.
TRANSMISSION gears 4 + reverse, 3.900 axle ratio, 5.60 x 13 tyres (on request 5-speed mechanical gearbox and 3-speed automatic gearbox, 4.111 axle ratio).
PERFORMANCE max speed about 109 mph, 175 km/h, power-weight ratio 20.7 lb/hp, 9.4 kg/hp.

ENGINE bore and stroke 3.15 x 2.76 in, 80 x 70 mm, engine capacity 85.9 cu in, 1,407 cu cm, 8.5 compression ratio, max power (DIN) 86 hp at 6,000 rpm, max torque (DIN) 85 lb ft, 11.7 kg m at 3,800 rpm, 61.1 hp/l specific power, 2 valves per cylinder, overhead, push-rods and rockers, 1 side camshaft, 1 Aisan downdraught twin barrel carburettor.
TRANSMISSION gears 4 + reverse, 5.60 x 13 tyres.
PERFORMANCE max speed about 103 mph, 165 km/h, power-weight ratio 24 lb/hp, 10.9 kg/hp.

OPTIONAL ACCESSORIES 165 x 13 tyres; limited slip final drive.

Crown SL Hardtop

PRICE: —

ENGINE front, 4 stroke; cylinders: 6, in line; bore and stroke: 2.95 x 2.95 in, 75 x 75 mm; engine capacity: 121.3 cu in, 1,988 cu cm; compression ratio: 8.8; max power (DIN) 125 hp at 5,800 rpm; max torque (DIN): 120 lb ft, 16.5 kg m at 3,800 rpm; max engine rpm: 6,000; specific power: 62.9 hp/l; cylinder block: cast iron; cylinder head: light alloy; crankshaft bearings: 7; valves: 2 per cylinder, overhead, rockers; camshafts: 1, overhead; lubrication: gear pump, full flow filter; lubricating system capacity: 7.9 imp pt, 9.5 US pt, 4.5 l; carburation: 2 SU horizontal carburettors; fuel feed: mechanical pump; cooling system: water; cooling system capacity: 17.1 imp pt, 20.5 US pt, 9.7 l.

TRANSMISSION driving wheels: rear; clutch: single dry plate; gearbox: mechanical; gears: 4 + reverse; synchromesh gears: I, II, III, IV; gearbox ratios: I 3.673, II 2.114, III 1.403, IV 1, rev 4.183; gear lever: central; final drive: hypoid bevel; axle ratio: 4.111; width of rims: 5''; tyres: 6.95 x 14.

PERFORMANCE max speeds: 29 mph, 46 km/h in 1st gear; 49 mph, 79 km/h in 2nd gear; 75 mph, 120 km/h in 3rd gear; 103 mph, 165 km/h in 4th gear; power-weight ratio: 22.9 lb/hp, 10.4 kg/hp; carrying capacity: 882 lb, 400 kg; speed in direct drive at 1,000 rpm: 17.4 mph, 28 km/h; fuel consumption: 31.4 m/imp gal, 26.1 m/US gal, 9 l x 100 km.

CHASSIS box-type ladder frame; front suspension: independent, wishbones, coil springs, anti-roll bar, telescopic dampers; rear suspension: rigid axle, lower radius arms, upper torque arm, transverse linkage bar, coil springs, telescopic dampers.

STEERING recirculating ball.

BRAKES front disc, rear drum, servo; lining area: front 20.8 sq in, 134 sq cm, rear 63.4 sq in, 409 sq cm, total 84.2 sq in, 543 sq cm.

ELECTRICAL EQUIPMENT voltage: 12 V; battery: 35 Ah; generator type: alternator, 540 W; ignition distributor: Nihon-Denso; headlamps: 2.

DIMENSIONS AND WEIGHT wheel base: 105.91 in, 2,690 mm; front track: 53.94 in, 1,370 mm; rear track: 54.33 in, 1,380 mm; overall length: 181.50 in, 4,610 mm; overall width: 66.54 in, 1,690 mm; overall height: 55.91 in, 1,420 mm; ground clearance: 7.28 in, 185 mm; dry weight:

TOYOTA Crown De Luxe Sedan

TOYOTA Crown Hardtop

TOYOTA Century D Sedan

2,885 lb, 1,295 kg; distribution of weight: 52.5% front axle, 47.5% rear axle; turning circle (between walls): 36.1 ft, 11 m; fuel tank capacity: 13.2 imp gal, 15.8 US gal, 60 l.

BODY hardtop; doors: 2; seats: 5; front seats: separate.

PRACTICAL INSTRUCTIONS fuel: 90 oct petrol; engine sump oil: 7.9 imp pt, 9.5 US pt, 4.5 l, SAE 20W-30, change every 3,100 miles, 5,000 km; gearbox oil: 3.7 imp pt, 4.4 US pt, 2.1 l, SAE 90, change every 18,600 miles, 30,000 km; final drive oil: 2.1 imp pt, 2.5 US pt, 1.2 l, SAE 90, change every 18,600 miles, 30,000 km; greasing: none; tappet clearances: inlet 0.006 in, 0.15 mm, exhaust 0.009 in, 0.23 mm; valve timing: inlet opens 20° before tdc and closes 48° after bdc, exhaust opens 56° before bdc and closes 12° after tdc; normal tyre pressure: front 23 psi, 1.6 atm, rear 23 psi, 1.6 atm.

OPTIONAL ACCESSORIES Toyoglide automatic gearbox with 3 ratios; power-assisted steering.

Crown De Luxe Sedan

See Crown SL Hardtop, except for:

PRICE IN GB: £ 1,145.

ENGINE bore and stroke: 2.95 x 3.35 in, 75 x 85 mm; engine capacity: 137.5 cu in, 2,253 cu cm; max power (SAE): 115 hp at 5,200 rpm; max torque (SAE): 128 lb ft, 17.6 kg m at 3,600 rpm; max engine rpm: 5,200; specific power: 51 hp/l; lubricating system capacity: 9.2 imp pt, 11 US pt, 5.2 l; carburation: 1 Aisan downdraught twin barrel carburettor; cooling system capacity: 19.4 imp pt, 23.3 US pt, 11 l.

TRANSMISSION gearbox ratios: I 3.059, II 1.645, III 1, IV 0.700, rev 4.079; gear lever: steering column; axle ratio: 4.875.

PERFORMANCE max speeds: 25 mph, 40 km/h in 1st gear; 46 mph, 74 km/h in 2nd gear; 75 mph, 121 km/h in 3rd gear; 96 mph, 155 km/h in 4th gear; power-weight ratio: 24 lb/hp, 10.9 kg/hp; acceleration: standing ¼ mile 19.4 sec; speed in direct drive at 1,000 rpm: 14.7 mph, 23.6 km/h; fuel consumption: 26.9 m/imp gal, 22.4 m/US gal, 10.5 l x 100 km.

ELECTRICAL EQUIPMENT battery: 40 Ah; headlamps: 4.

DIMENSIONS AND WEIGHT front track: 53.54 in, 1,360 mm; overall length: 183.66 in, 4,665 mm; overall height: 56.89 in, 1,445 mm; dry weight: 2,767 lb, 1,255 kg; distribution of weight: 53.9% front axle, 46.1% rear axle; fuel tank capacity: 14.3 imp gal, 17.2 US gal, 65 l.

BODY saloon/sedan; doors: 4; seats: 6; front seats: bench.

PRACTICAL INSTRUCTIONS engine sump oil: 9.2 imp pt, 11 US pt, 5.2 l; tappet clearances: inlet 0.004 in, 0.10 mm, exhaust 0.007 in, 0.18 mm; valve timing: inlet opens 16° before tdc and closes 48° after bdc, exhaust opens 56° before bdc and closes 8° after tdc.

Crown Hardtop

See Crown SL Hardtop, except for:

PRICE: —

ENGINE bore and stroke: 2.95 x 3.35 in, 75 x 85 mm; engine capacity: 137.5 cu in, 2,253 cu cm; max power (SAE): 115 hp at 5,200 rpm; max torque (SAE): 128 lb ft, 17.6 kg m at 3,600 rpm; max engine rpm: 5,200; specific power: 51 hp/l; lubricating system capacity: 9.2 imp pt, 11 US pt, 5.2 l; carburation: 1 Aisan downdraught twin barrel carburettor; cooling system capacity: 19.4 imp pt, 23.3 US pt, 11 l.

PERFORMANCE max speed: 99 mph, 160 km/h; power-weight ratio: 24.9 lb/hp, 11.3 kg/hp; acceleration: standing ¼ mile 19 sec; speed in direct drive at 1,000 rpm: 17.1 mph, 27.6 km/h.

PRACTICAL INSTRUCTIONS engine sump oil: 9.2 imp pt, 11 US pt, 5.2 l; tappet clearances: inlet 0.004 in, 0.10 mm, exhaust 0.007 in, 0.18 mm; valve timing: inlet opens 16° before tdc and closes 48° after bdc, exhaust opens 56° before bdc and closes 8° after tdc.

Century D Sedan

PRICE EX WORKS: 2,761,000 yen.

ENGINE front, 4 stroke; cylinders: 8, Vee-slanted at 90°; bore and stroke: 3.07 x 3.07 in, 78 x 78 mm; engine capacity: 181.9 cu in, 2,981 cu cm; compression ratio: 9.8; max power (DIN): 170 hp at 5,600 rpm; max torque (DIN): 181 lb ft, 25 kg m at 3,600 rpm; max engine rpm: 5,600;

TOYOTA Crown De Luxe Sedan

TOYOTA Crown Hardtop

TOYOTA Century D Sedan

specific power: 57 hp/l; cylinder block: light alloy; cylinder head: light alloy; crankshaft bearings: 5; valves: 2 per cylinder, overhead, push-rods and rockers; camshafts: 1, at centre of Vee; lubrication: gear pump, full flow filter; lubricating system capacity: 8.8 imp pt, 10.6 US pt, 5 l; carburation: 1 Rochester downdraught 4-barrel carburettor; fuel feed: electric pump; cooling system: water; cooling system capacity: 23.6 imp pt, 28.3 US pt, 13.4 l.

TRANSMISSION driving wheels: rear; gearbox: Toyoglide automatic, hydraulic torque convertor and planetary gears with 3 ratios + reverse, max ratio of convertor at stall 2, possible manual selection; gearbox ratios: I 2.400, II 1.479, III 1, rev 1.920; selector lever: steering column; final drive: hypoid bevel; axle ratio: 3.900; tyres: 7.35 x 14.

PERFORMANCE max speeds: 40 mph, 65 km/h in 1st gear; 62 mph, 100 km/h in 2nd gear; 106 mph, 170 km/h in 3rd gear; power-weight ratio: 23.4 lb/hp, 10.6 kg/hp; carrying capacity: 1,058 lb, 480 kg; speed in direct drive at 1,000 rpm: 19.1 mph, 30.8 km/h; fuel consumption: 23.5 m/imp gal, 19.6 m/US gal, 12 l x 100 km.

CHASSIS integral; front suspension: independent, by McPherson, air bellows/telescopic damper struts, lower wishbones (trailing links), anti-roll bar; rear suspension: rigid axle, lower radius arms, upper torque arm, transverse linkage bar, coil springs, telescopic dampers.

STEERING recirculating ball, servo.

BRAKES drum, servo; lining area: front 92.7 sq in, 598 sq cm, rear 75 sq in, 484 sq cm, total 167.7 sq in, 1,082 sq cm.

ELECTRICAL EQUIPMENT voltage: 12 V; battery: 45 Ah; generator type: alternator, 780 W; ignition distributor: Nihon-Denso; headlamps: 2, iodine.

DIMENSIONS AND WEIGHT wheel base: 112.60 in, 2,860 mm; front track: 59.84 in, 1,520 mm; rear track: 60.63 in, 1,540 mm; overall length: 196.06 in, 4,980 mm; overall width: 74.41 in, 1,890 mm; overall height: 57.09 in, 1,450 mm; ground clearance: 6.89 in, 175 mm; dry weight: 3,969 lb, 1,800 kg; distribution of weight: 53.9% front axle, 46.1% rear axle; turning circle (between walls): 37.4 ft, 11.4 m; fuel tank capacity: 19.8 imp gal, 23.6 US gal, 90 l.

BODY saloon/sedan; doors: 4; seats: 6; front seats: bench.

PRACTICAL INSTRUCTIONS fuel: 98-100 oct petrol; engine sump oil: 8.8 imp pt, 10.6 US pt, 5 l, SAE 30, change every 3,100 miles, 5,000 km; gearbox oil: 12.3 imp pt, 14.8 US pt, 7 l, automatic transmission fluid; final drive oil: 3.3 imp pt, 4 US pt, 1.9 l, SAE 90, change every 18,600 miles, 30,000 km; valve timing: inlet opens 15° before tdc and closes 57° after bdc, exhaust opens 57° before bdc and closes 15° after tdc; normal tyre pressure: front 34 psi, 2.4 atm, rear 34 psi, 2.4 atm.

OPTIONAL ACCESSORIES limited slip final drive.

Century A Sedan

See Century D Sedan, except for:

PRICE EX WORKS: 2,703,000 yen.

TRANSMISSION gearbox: mechanical; gears: 4 + reverse; synchromesh gears: I, II, III, IV; gearbox ratios: I 3.673, II 2.114, III 1.403, IV 1, rev 4.183; gear lever: central; axle ratio: 3.545.

PERFORMANCE max speeds: 30 mph, 48 km/h in 1st gear; 52 mph, 84 km/h in 2nd gear; 78 mph, 126 km/h in 3rd gear; 106 mph, 170 km/h in 4th gear; speed in direct drive at 1,000 rpm: 19.8 mph, 31.8 km/h.

Century B Sedan

See Century D Sedan, except for:

PRICE EX WORKS: 2,356,000 yen.

TRANSMISSION gearbox: mechanical; gears: 3 + reverse; synchromesh gears: I, II, III; gearbox ratios: I 3.059, II 1.645, III 1, rev 4.079; gear lever: steering column; axle ratio: 3.545.

PERFORMANCE max speeds: 36 mph, 58 km/h in 1st gear; 67 mph, 108 km/h in 2nd gear; 106 mph, 170 km/h in 3rd gear; speed in direct drive at 1,000 rpm: 19.8 mph, 31.8 km/h.

Century C Sedan

See Century B Sedan, except for:

PRICE EX WORKS: 2,556,000 yen.

HOLDEN AUSTRALIA

Torana 2-door Saloon

PRICE EX WORGS: 1,909 Aust. $.

ENGINE front, 4 stroke; cylinders: 4, in line; bore and stroke: 3.06 x 2.40 in, 77.7 x 61 mm; engine capacity: 70.7 cu in, 1,159 cu cm; compression ratio: 8.5; max power (SAE): 56.2 hp at 5,400 rpm; max torque (SAE): 66 lb ft, 9.1 kg m at 3,000 rpm; max engine rpm: 6,000; specific power: 48.5 hp/l; cylinder block: cast iron; cylinder head: cast iron; crankshaft bearings: 3; valves: 2 per cylinder, overhead, in line, push-rods and rockers; camshafts: 1, side; lubrication: gear pump, full flow filter; lubricating system capacity: 5.5 imp pt, 6.6 US pt, 3.1 l; carburation: 1 Zenith 30 IZ downdraught single barrel carburettor; fuel feed: mechanical pump; cooling system: water; cooling system capacity: 7.9 imp pt, 9.5 US pt, 4.5 l.

TRANSMISSION driving wheels: rear; clutch: single dry plate (diaphragm); gearbox: mechanical; gears: 4 + reverse; synchromesh gears: I, II, III, IV; gearbox ratios: I 3.765, II 2.213, III 1.404, IV 1, rev 3.707; gear lever: central; final drive: hypoid bevel; axle ratio: 3.899; width of rims: 4''; tyres: 5.50 x 12.

PERFORMANCE max speeds: 25 mph, 40 km/h in 1st gear; 43 mph, 69 km/h in 2nd gear; 67 mph, 108 km/h in 3rd gear; 83 mph, 133 km/h in 4th gear; power-weight ratio: 31.5 lb/hp, 14.3 kg/hp; carrying capacity: 882 lb, 400 kg; speed in direct drive at 1,000 rpm: 15.8 mph, 25.4 km/h; fuel consumption: 34.4 m/imp gal, 28.7 m/US gal, 8.2 l x 100 km.

CHASSIS integral; front suspension: independent, wishbones, coil springs, telescopic dampers; rear suspension: rigid axle, 2 trailing lower radius arms, 2 upper oblique radius arms, coil springs, telescopic dampers.

STEERING rack-and-pinion; turns of steering wheel lock to lock: 3.40.

BRAKES drum; area rubbed by linings: total 126 sq in, 813 sq cm.

ELECTRICAL EQUIPMENT voltage: 12 V; battery: 38 Ah; generator type: alternator, 470 W; ignition distributor: AC Delco; headlamps: 2.

DIMENSIONS AND WEIGHT wheel base: 95.80 in, 2,433 mm; front track: 51 in, 1,295 mm; rear track: 51 in, 1,295 mm; overall length: 162.20 in, 4,120 mm; overall width: 63 in, 1,600 mm; overall height: 53.20 in, 1,351 mm; ground clearance: 4.90 in, 124 mm; dry weight: 1,768 lb, 802 kg; turning circle (between walls): 33.8 ft, 10.3 m; fuel tank capacity: 8 imp gal, 9.5 US gal, 36 l.

BODY saloon/sedan; doors: 2; seats: 4; front seats: separate.

PRACTICAL INSTRUCTIONS fuel: 98 oct petrol; engine sump oil: 4.9 imp pt, 5.9 US pt, 2.8 l, SAE 10W-20, change every 6,000 miles, 9,700 km; gearbox oil: 0.9 imp pt, 1.1 US pt, 0.5 l, SAE 90, change every 6,000 miles, 9,700 km; final drive oil: 1.2 imp pt, 1.5 US pt, 0.7 l, SAE 90, change every 6,000 miles, 9,700 km; greasing: every 12,000 miles, 19,300 km, 4 points; tappet clearances: inlet 0.006 in, 0.15 mm, exhaust 0.010 in, 0.25 mm; valve timing: inlet opens 39° before tdc and closes 93° after bdc, exhaust opens 65° before bdc and closes 45° after tdc; normal tyre pressure: front 24 psi, 1.7 atm, rear 24 psi, 1.7 atm.

VARIATIONS

ENGINE 9 compression ratio, max power (SAE) 68.9 hp, 59.4 hp/l specific power.
TRANSMISSION 6.20 x 12 tyres (standard).
PERFORMANCE max speed 90 mph, 145 km/h.
BRAKES disc (standard).

OPTIONAL ACCESSORIES Trimatic automatic gearbox with 3 ratios; 4.125 axle ratio; 6.20 x 12 tyres; front disc brakes.

Torana S 2-door Saloon

See Torana 2-door Saloon, except for:

PRICE EX WORKS: 2,013 Aust. $.

PERFORMANCE power-weight ratio: 31.7 lb/hp, 14.4 kg/hp.

DIMENSIONS AND WEIGHT dry weight: 1,779 lb, 807 kg.

Torana S 4-door Saloon

See Torana 2-door Saloon, except for:

PRICE EX WORKS: 2,147 Aust. $.

PERFORMANCE power-weight ratio: 32.6 lb/hp, 14.8 kg/hp.

DIMENSIONS AND WEIGHT dry weight: 1,828 lb, 829 kg.

HOLDEN Torana 2250 SL 4-door Saloon

HOLDEN Torana GTR XU-1 Coupé

HOLDEN Torana GTR-X Coupé

Torana SL 2-door Saloon

See Torana 2-door Saloon, except for:

PRICE EX WORKS: 2,180 Aust. $.

PERFORMANCE power-weight ratio: 32 lb/hp, 14.5 kg/hp.

DIMENSIONS AND WEIGHT dry weight: 1,797 lb, 815 kg.

Torana 2250 S 2-door Saloon

PRICE EX WORKS: 2,322 Aust. $.

ENGINE front, 4 stroke; cylinders: 6, in line; bore and stroke: 3.12 x 3 in, 79.2 x 76.2 mm; engine capacity: 138 cu in, 2,262 cu cm; compression ratio: 9.2; max power (SAE): 95 hp at 4,600 rpm; max torque (SAE): 120 lb ft, 16.5 kg m at 1,600 rpm; max engine rpm: 5,200; specific power: 42 hp/l; cylinder block: cast iron; cylinder head: cast iron; crankshaft bearings: 7; valves: 2 per cylinder, overhead, push-rods and rockers, hydraulic tappets; camshafts: 1, side; lubrication: gear pump, full flow filter; lubricating system capacity: 7.5 imp pt, 8.9 US pt, 4.2 l; carburation: 1 Bendix-Stromberg downdraught single barrel carburettor; fuel feed: mechanical pump; cooling system: water; cooling system capacity: 18 imp pt, 21.6 US pt, 10.2 l.

TRANSMISSION driving wheels: rear; clutch: single dry plate; gearbox: mechanical; gears: 3 + reverse; synchromesh gears: I, II, III; gearbox ratios: I 3.070, II 1.680, III 1, rev 3.590; gear lever: steering column; final drive: hypoid bevel; axle ratio: 3.080; width of rims: 4.5''; tyres: A 78 L x 13.

PERFORMANCE max speeds: 37 mph, 59 km/h in 1st gear; 68 mph, 109 km/h in 2nd gear; 114 mph, 183 km/h in 3rd gear; power-weight ratio: 22.9 lb/hp, 10.4 kg/hp; carrying capacity: 882 lb, 400 kg; speed in direct drive at 1,000 rpm: 21.9 mph, 35.2 km/h.

CHASSIS integral; front suspension: independent, wishbones, coil springs, telescopic dampers; rear suspension: rigid axle, 2 trailing lower radius arms, 2 upper oblique radius arms, coil springs, telescopic dampers.

STEERING rack-and-pinion; turns of steering wheel lock to lock: 3.30.

BRAKES drum; area rubbed by linings: front 99 sq in, 638 sq cm, rear 99 sq in, 638 sq cm, total 198 sq in, 1,276 sq cm.

ELECTRICAL EQUIPMENT voltage: 12 V; battery: 44 Ah; generator type: alternator, 470 W; ignition distributor: Bosch or Lucas; headlamps: 2.

DIMENSIONS AND WEIGHT wheel base: 100 in, 2,540 mm; front track: 51.80 in, 1,316 mm; rear track: 50.80 in, 1,290 mm; overall length: 172.70 in, 4,386 mm; overall width: 63 in, 1,600 mm; overall height: 53.30 in, 1,354 mm; ground clearance: 5.40 in, 137 mm; dry weight: 2,172 lb, 985 kg; turning circle (between walls): 36.5 ft, 11.1 m; fuel tank capacity: 10 imp gal, 11.9 US gal, 45 l.

BODY saloon/sedan; doors: 2; seats: 4; front seats: separate.

PRACTICAL INSTRUCTIONS fuel: 97 oct petrol; engine sump oil: 7.5 imp pt, 8.9 US pt, 4.2 l, SAE 5W-20 (winter) 10W-40 (summer), change every 6,000 miles, 9,700 km; gearbox oil: 3.7 imp pt, 4.4 US pt, 2.1 l, HN-1046, change every 12,000 miles, 19,300 km; final drive oil: 2.5 imp pt, 3 US pt, 1.4 l, SAE 90 EP, change every 6,000 miles, 9,700 km; greasing: every 12,000 miles, 19,300 km or 6 months, 4 points; valve timing: inlet opens 35° before tdc and closes 75° after bdc, exhaust opens 70° before bdc and closes 40° after tdc; normal tyre pressure: front 20 psi, 1.4 atm, rear 20 psi, 1.4 atm.

OPTIONAL ACCESSORIES Trimatic automatic gearbox with 3 ratios, steering column or central gear selector lever; 4-speed mechanical gearbox with central gear lever; limited slip final drive; 3.550 2.780 3.360 axle ratios; 5.5'' wide rims; front disc brakes; servo brake.

Torana 2250 S 4-door Saloon

See Torana 2250 S 2-door Saloon, except for:

PRICE EX WORKS: 2,368 Aust. $.

PERFORMANCE power-weight ratio: 23.4 lb/hp, 10.6 kg/hp.

DIMENSIONS AND WEIGHT dry weight: 2,220 lb, 1,007 kg.

HOLDEN Torana 2250 SL 4-door Saloon

HOLDEN Torana GTR XU-1 Coupé

HOLDEN Torana GTR-X Coupé

Torana 2250 SL 4-door Saloon

See Torana 2250 S 2-door Saloon, except for:

PRICE EX WORKS: 2,623 Aust. $.

PERFORMANCE power-weight ratio: 23.6 lb/hp, 10.7 kg/hp.

DIMENSIONS AND WEIGHT dry weight: 2,234 lb, 1,013 kg.

Torana 2600 S 2-door Saloon

See Torana 2250 S 2-door Saloon, except for:

PRICE: —

ENGINE capacity: 161 cu in, 2,638 cu cm; max power (SAE): 114 hp; specific power: 69.6 hp/l.

PERFORMANCE power-weight ratio: 18.4 lb/hp, 8.3 kg/hp.

Torana 2600 S 4-door Saloon

See Torana 2600 S 2-door Saloon, except for:

PRICE: —

Torana 2600 SL 4-door Saloon

See Torana 2600 S 2-door Saloon, except for:

PRICE: —

Torana GTR Coupé

See Torana 2600 S 2-door Saloon, except for:

PRICE EX WORKS: 2,883 Aust. $.

ENGINE max power (SAE): 125 hp; specific power: 47.4 hp/l; carburation: 1 downdraught twin barrel carburettor.

TRANSMISSION gears: 4 + reverse (standard); gear lever: central; width of rims: 5.5'' (standard).

CHASSIS front and rear suspensions: anti-roll bar.

BRAKES front disc (standard).

BODY coupé.

Torana GTR XU-1 Coupé

See Torana GTR Coupé, except for:

PRICE EX WORKS: 3,149 Aust. $.

ENGINE bore and stroke: 3.63 x 3 in, 92.1 x 76.2 mm; engine capacity: 186 cu in, 3,049 cu cm; compression ratio: 10; max power (SAE): 160 hp at 5,200 rpm; max torque (SAE): 190 lb ft, 26.2 kg m at 3,600 rpm; specific power: 52.5 hp/l; carburation: 3 Stromberg 150 CDS horizontal carburettors; cooling system capacity: 14.1 imp pt, 16.9 US pt, 8 l.

TRANSMISSION gearbox ratios: I 3.430, II 2.160, III 1.370, IV 1, rev 3.320; gear lever: central; axle ratio: 3.360; tyres: B 70 H x 13.

PERFORMANCE max speed: 118 mph, 190 km/h; power-weight ratio: 14.2 lb/hp, 6.4 kg/hp.

DIMENSIONS AND WEIGHT front track: 52.20 in, 1,321 mm; rear track: 51.20 in, 1,296 mm; overall height: 53 in, 1,346 mm; ground clearance: 5 in, 127 mm; dry weight: 2,275 lb, 1,032 kg; fuel tank capacity: 17 imp gal, 20.3 US gal, 77 l.

Torana GTR-X Coupé

See Torana GTR XU-1 Coupé, except for:

PRICE: —

TRANSMISSION tyres: C70 x 13.

PERFORMANCE max speed: 124 mph, 200 km/h; power-weight ratio: 14.4 lb/hp, 6.5 kg/hp.

DIMENSIONS AND WEIGHT wheel base: 94 in, 2,387 mm; front track: 54 in, 1,371 mm; rear track: 55 in, 1,397 mm; overall length: 164.50 in, 4,178 mm; overall width: 68.20 in, 1,732 mm; overall height: 44.70 in, 1,135 mm; dry weight: 2,300 lb, 1,043 kg; fuel tank capacity: 13 imp gal, 15.6 US gal, 59 l.

BODY: seats: 2.

Belmont Saloon

PRICE EX WORKS: 2,435 Aust. $.

ENGINE front, 4 stroke; cylinders: 6, in line; bore and stroke: 3.37 x 3 in, 85.7 x 76.2 mm; engine capacity: 161 cu in, 2,638 cu cm; compression ratio: 9.2; max power (SAE): 114 hp at 4,400 rpm; max torque (SAE): 157 lb ft, 21.7 kg m at 2,000 rpm; max engine rpm: 5,200; specific power: 43.2 hp/l; cylinder block: cast iron; cylinder head: cast iron; crankshaft bearings: 7; valves: 2 per cylinder, overhead, push-rods and rockers, hydraulic tappets; camshafts: 1, side; lubrication: gear pump, full flow filter; lubricating system capacity: 7.5 imp pt, 8.9 US pt, 4.2 l; carburation: 1 Bendix-Stromberg downdraught single barrel carburettor; fuel feed: mechanical pump; cooling system: water; cooling system capacity: 14 imp pt, 16.7 US pt, 7.9 l.

TRANSMISSION driving wheels: rear; clutch: single dry plate; gearbox: mechanical; gears: 3 + reverse; synchromesh gears: I, II, III; gearbox ratios: I 3.070, II 1.680, III 1, rev 3.590; gear lever: steering column; final drive: hypoid bevel; axle ratio: 3.550; width of rims: 5''; tyres: 6.95 x 14.

PERFORMANCE max speeds: 33 mph, 53 km/h in 1st gear; 61 mph, 98 km/h in 2nd gear; 103 mph, 165 km/h in 3rd gear; power-weight ratio: 23.4 lb/hp, 10.6 kg/hp; speed in direct drive at 1,000 rpm: 19.9 mph, 32 km/h.

CHASSIS integral; front suspension: independent, wishbones, coil springs, telescopic dampers; rear suspension: rigid axle, semi-elliptic leafsprings, telescopic dampers.

STEERING recirculating ball.

BRAKES drum; area rubbed by linings: front 141.4 sq in, 912 sq cm, rear 110 sq in, 709 sq cm, total 251.4 sq in, 1,621 sq cm.

ELECTRICAL EQUIPMENT voltage: 12 V; battery: 44 Ah; generator type: alternator, 470 W; ignition distributor: Bosch or Lucas; headlamps: 2.

DIMENSIONS AND WEIGHT wheel base: 111 in, 2,819 mm; front track: 58.12 in, 1,476 mm; rear track: 58.12 in, 1,476 mm; overall length: 184.80 in, 4,694 mm; overall width: 71.80 in, 1,824 mm; overall height: 55.60 in, 1,412 mm; ground clearance: 7.20 in, 183 mm; dry weight: 2,675 lb, 1,213 kg; fuel tank capacity: 16.5 imp gal, 19.8 US gal, 75 l.

BODY saloon/sedan; doors: 4; seats: 6; front seats: bench.

PRACTICAL INSTRUCTIONS fuel: 97 oct petrol; engine sump oil: 7.5 imp pt, 8.9 US pt, 4.2 l, SAE 5W-20 (winter) 10W-40 (summer), change every 6,000 miles, 9,700 km; gearbox oil: 3.7 imp pt, 4.4 US pt, 2.1 l, HN-1046, change every 12,000 miles, 19,300 km; final drive oil: 2.5 imp pt, 3 US pt, 1.4 l, SAE 90 EP, change every 6,000 miles, 9,700 km; greasing: every 12,000 miles, 19,300 km or 6 months, 10 points; valve timing: inlet opens 35° before tdc and closes 70° after bdc, exhaust opens 75° before bdc and closes 40° after tdc; normal tyre pressure: front 24 psi, 1.7 atm, rear 24 psi, 1.7 atm.

VARIATIONS

ENGINE capacity 186 cu in, 3,049 cu cm, max power (SAE) 130 hp, 42.6 hp/l specific power, 1 downdraught single barrel carburettor.

ENGINE capacity 186 cu in, 3,049 cu cm, max power (SAE) 145 hp, 47.6 hp/l specific power, 1 downdraught twin barrel carburettor.

ENGINE 8 Vee-slanted cylinders, engine capacity 253 cu in, 4,147 cu cm, max power (SAE) 185 hp, 44.6 hp/l specific power, 1 twin barrel carburettor.

ENGINE 8 Vee-slanted cylinders, engine capacity 308 cu in, 5,048 cu cm, max power (SAE) 240 hp, 47.5 hp/l specific power, 1 4-barrel carburettor.
TRANSMISSION Trimatic automatic gearbox (standard).

OPTIONAL ACCESSORIES Trimatic automatic gearbox; 4-speed mechanical gearbox; limited slip final drive; 2.780 3.080 3.360 3.900 axle ratios; 185 x 14, 7.35 x 14, D70 x 14 or ER70 x 14 tyres; power-assisted steering; front disc brakes; servo brake; air-conditioning system.

Belmont Estate Car

See Belmont Saloon, except for:

PRICE EX WORKS: 2,643 Aust. $.

TRANSMISSION tyres: 7.35 x 14.

PERFORMANCE power-weight ratio: 24.9 lb/hp, 11.3 kg/hp.

DIMENSIONS AND WEIGHT overall height: 56.81 in, 1,443 mm; ground clearance: 7.48 in, 190 mm; dry weight: 2,836 lb, 1,286 kg.

BODY estate car/station wagon; doors: 4 + 1.

HOLDEN Kingswood Saloon

HOLDEN Premier Saloon

HOLDEN Brougham

Kingswood Saloon

See Belmont Saloon, except for:

PRICE EX WORKS: 2,607 Aust. $.

PERFORMANCE power-weight ratio: 23.6 lb/hp, 10.7 kg/hp.

DIMENSIONS AND WEIGHT dry weight: 2,695 lb, 1,222 kg.

Kingswood Estate Car

See Kingswood Saloon, except for:

PRICE EX WORKS: 2,815 Aust. $.

TRANSMISSION tyres: 7.35 x 14.

PERFORMANCE power-weight ratio: 25 lb/hp, 11.3 kg/hp.

DIMENSIONS AND WEIGHT ground clearance: 7.52 in, 191 mm; dry weight: 2,853 lb, 1,294 kg.

BODY estate car/station wagon; doors: 4 + 1.

Premier Saloon

See Belmont Saloon, except for:

PRICE EX WORKS: 3,135 Aust. $.

ENGINE bore and stroke: 3.62 x 3 in, 92.1 x 76.2 mm; engine capacity: 186 cu in, 3,049 cu cm; max power (SAE): 130 hp at 4,400 rpm; max torque (SAE): 181 lb ft, 25 kg m at 2,000 rpm; specific power: 42.7 hp/l.

PERFORMANCE power-weight ratio: 21.1 lb/hp, 9.6 kg/hp.

DIMENSIONS AND WEIGHT dry weight: 2,752 lb, 1,248 kg.

VARIATIONS

ENGINE capacity 186 cu in, 3,049 cu cm, max power (SAE) 145 hp, 47.6 hp/l specific power, 1 downdraught twin barrel carburettor.

ENGINE 8 Vee-slanted cylinders, engine capacity 253 cu in, 4,147 cu cm, max power (SAE) 185 hp, 44.6 hp/l specific power, 1 twin barrel carburettor.

ENGINE 8 Vee-slanted cylinders, engine capacity 308 cu in, 5,048 cu cm, max power (SAE) 240 hp, 47.5 hp/l specific power, 1 4-barrel carburettor.
TRANSMISSION Trimatic automatic gearbox (standard).

Premier Estate Car

See Premier Saloon, except for:

PRICE EX WORKS: 3,256 Aust. $.

TRANSMISSION tyres: 7.35 x 14.

PERFORMANCE power-weight ratio: 19.8 lb/hp, 9 kg/hp.

DIMENSIONS AND WEIGHT overall height: 56.61 in, 1,438 mm; ground clearance: 7.28 in, 185 mm; dry weight: 2,591 lb, 1,175 kg.

BODY estate car/station wagon; doors: 4 + 1.

Monaro GTS Coupé

PRICE EX WORKS: 3,335 Aust. $.

ENGINE front, 4 stroke; cylinders: 6, in line; bore and stroke: 3.62 x 3 in, 92.1 x 76.2 mm; engine capacity: 186 cu in, 3,049 cu cm; compression ratio: 9.2; max power (SAE): 145 hp at 4,600 rpm; max torque (SAE): 184 lb ft, 25.4 kg m at 2,200 rpm; max engine rpm: 5,200; specific power: 47.6 hp/l; cylinder block: cast iron; cylinder head: cast iron; crankshaft bearings: 7; valves: 2 per cylinder, overhead, in line, push-rods and rockers, hydraulic tappets; camshafts: 1, side; lubrication: gear pump, full flow filter; lubricating system capacity: 7.5 imp pt, 8.9 US pt, 4.2 l; carburation: 1 Bendix-Stromberg downdraught twin barrel carburettor; fuel feed: mechanical pump; cooling system: water; cooling system capacity: 14 imp pt, 16.7 US pt, 7.9 l.

TRANSMISSION driving wheels: rear; clutch: single dry plate; gearbox: mechanical; gears: 4 + reverse; synchromesh gears: I, II, III, IV; gearbox ratios: I 3.430, II 2.160, III 1.370, IV 1, rev 3.320; gear lever: central; final drive: hypoid bevel; axle ratio: 3.360; width of rims: 5''; tyres: 6.95 S x 14.

PERFORMANCE max speeds: 32 mph, 51 km/h in 1st gear; 51 mph, 82 km/h in 2nd gear; 80 mph, 128 km/h in 3rd gear; 109 mph, 177 km/h in 4th gear; power-weight ratio: 19.4 lb/hp, 8.8 kg/hp; speed in direct drive at 1,000 rpm: 21.1 mph, 33.9 km/h.

HOLDEN Kingswood Saloon

HOLDEN Premier Saloon

HOLDEN Monaro GTS Coupé (350 cu in)

CHASSIS integral; front suspension: independent, wishbones, coil springs, telescopic dampers; rear suspension: rigid axle, semi-elliptic leafsprings, telescopic dampers.

STEERING recirculating ball.

BRAKES front disc, rear drum, servo; area rubbed by linings: rear 110 sq in, 709 sq cm.

ELECTRICAL EQUIPMENT generator type: alternator, 470 W; ignition distributor: Bosch or Lucas; headlamps: 2.

DIMENSIONS AND WEIGHT wheel base: 111 in, 2,819 mm; front track: 58.12 in, 1,476 mm; rear track: 58.12 in, 1,476 mm; overall length: 184.80 in, 4,694 mm; overall width: 71.80 in, 1,824 mm; overall height: 54.90 in, 1,394 mm; ground clearance: 7.30 in, 185 mm; dry weight: 2,800 lb, 1,270 kg; fuel tank capacity: 16.5 imp gal, 19.8 US gal, 75 l.

BODY coupé; seats: 4; front seats: separate, bucket seats.

VARIATIONS

ENGINE 8 Vee-slanted cylinders, engine capacity 253 cu in, 4,147 cu cm, max power (SAE) 185 hp, 44.6 hp/l specific power, 1 twin barrel carburettor.

ENGINE 8 Vee-slanted cylinders, engine capacity 308 cu in, 5,048 cu cm, max power (SAE) 240 hp, 47.5 hp/l specific power, 1 4-barrel carburettor.

ENGINE 8 Vee-slanted cylinders, engine capacity 350 cu in, 5,736 cu cm.

OPTIONAL ACCESSORIES Trimatic automatic gearbox; 4-speed mechanical gearbox (I 2.540, II 1.800, III 1.440, IV 1, rev 2.540) only for V8 engines; limited slip final drive; 2.780 3.080 3.550 3.360 3.900 axle ratios; 185 R x 14, ER 70 x 14 or D 70 H x 14 tyres; power-assisted steering.

Brougham

PRICE EX WORKS: 4,081 Aust. $.

ENGINE front, 4 stroke; cylinders: 8, Vee-slanted; bore and stroke: 4 x 3.06 in, 101.5 x 77.6 mm; engine capacity: 308 cu in, 5,047 cu cm; compression ratio: 9; max power (SAE): 240 hp at 4,800 rpm; max torque (SAE): 315 lb ft, 43.5 kg m at 3,000 rpm; max engine rpm: 5,200; specific power: 47.6 hp/l; cylinder block: cast iron; cylinder head: cast iron; crankshaft bearings: 5; valves: 2 per cylinder, overhead, push-rods and rockers, hydraulic tappets; camshafts: 1, at centre of Vee; lubrication: gear pump, full flow filter; lubricating system capacity: 8 imp pt, 9.5 US pt, 4.5 l; carburation: 1 Rochester downdraught 4-barrel carburettor; fuel feed: mechanical; cooling system: water; cooling system capacity: 20 imp pt, 23.9 US pt, 11.3 l.

TRANSMISSION driving wheels: rear; gearbox: Trimatic automatic, hydraulic torque convertor and planetary gears with 3 ratios + reverse, max ratio of convertor at stall 2.2, possible manual selection; gearbox ratios: I 2.400, II 1.480, III 1, rev 1.290; selector lever: steering column; final drive: hypoid bevel; axle ratio: 2.780; width of rims: 5''; tyres: 7.35 L x 14.

PERFORMANCE max speeds: 52 mph, 83 km/h in 1st gear; 84 mph, 135 km/h in 2nd gear; 124 mph, 200 km/h in 3rd gear; power-weight ratio: 12.8 lb/hp, 5.8 kg/hp; speed in direct drive at 1,000 rpm: 25.5 mph, 41 km/h.

CHASSIS integral; front suspension: independent, wishbones, coil springs, telescopic dampers; rear suspension: rigid axle, semi-elliptic leafsprings, telescopic dampers.

STEERING recirculating ball, servo.

BRAKES front disc, rear drum; area rubbed by linings: rear 110 sq in, 709 sq cm.

ELECTRICAL EQUIPMENT voltage: 12 V; battery: 53 Ah; generator type: alternator, 470 W; ignition distributor: Bosch; headlamps: 4.

DIMENSIONS AND WEIGHT wheel base: 111 in, 2,819 mm; front track: 58.12 in, 1,476 mm; rear track: 58.12 in, 1,476 mm; overall length: 192.10 in, 4,879 mm; overall width: 71.70 in, 1,821 mm; overall height: 55.40 in, 1,407 mm; ground clearance: 6.60 in, 168 mm; dry weight: 3,083 lb, 1,398 kg; fuel tank capacity: 16.5 imp gal, 19.8 US gal, 75 l.

BODY saloon/sedan; doors: 4; seats: 6; front seats: bench.

PRACTICAL INSTRUCTIONS fuel: 97 oct petrol; engine sump oil: 8 imp pt, 9.5 US pt, 4.5 l, SAE 5W-20 (winter) 10W-40 (summer), change every 6,000 miles, 9,700 km; gearbox oil: 14.1 imp pt, 16.9 US pt, 8 l, Dexron, change every 12,000 miles, 19,300 km; final drive oil: 2.5 imp pt, 3 US pt, 1.4 l, SAE 90 EP, change every 6,000 miles, 9,700 km; greasing: every 12,000 miles, 19,300 km or 6 months, 10 points; valve timing: inlet opens 43° before tdc and closes 91° after bdc, exhaust opens 87° before bdc and closes 47° after tdc; normal tyre pressure: front 24 psi, 1.7 atm, rear 24 psi, 1.7 atm.

OPTIONAL ACCESSORIES limited slip final drive; 3.360 axle ratio; air-conditioning system.

Car manufacturers
and coachbuilders

An outline of their history, structure and activities

CAR MANUFACTURERS

ABARTH & C. S.p.A. **Italy**

Founded in 1949. President: A. Scagliarini. Managing Directors: C. Abarth, C. Scagliarini. Head office, press office and works: c. Marche 38, Turin. Employees: 350. Cars produced in 1969: 1,760. Most important models: Berlinetta 204 (1950); Biposto 1500 (1952); Abarth Alfa 2000, 208 A and 209 A (1954); Fiat Abarth 750 and Spider 210 A (1956); Fiat Abarth 500 (1957); 500 Abarth Record (1958); Fiat Abarth 750, 750 Bialbero and 850 (1959); Fiat Abarth 1000 Bialbero (1960); Fiat Abarth 850 TC, 1000 TC, 1000 Sport, 1450 Sport, 1600, 2200, Abarth Simca 1300, Porsche Abarth Carrera (1961-62); Fiat Abarth 1000 SP, 1300 OT, 2000 Gruppo 4, 3000 (1965-1969). Numerous endurance records from 1956 on in 500, 750, 1000, 1100 categories. Makers World Championship from 1962 to 1966. European Touring Challenge Cup in 1965, 1966, 1967 and 1969.

AB VOLVO **Sweden**

Founded in 1926. Chairman: F. Hartmann. Deputy Chairman: Hadar H:son Hallström. Managing Director: G. Engellau. Head office, press office and works: Box 382, S-405 08, Göteborg. Employees: 15,759. Cars produced in 1969: 181,500. Most important models: Volvo P4 (1927); Volvo 53-56 (1939); PV 50 (1944); PV 444 (1947); P 1900 (1954-57); 122S Amazon (1957); P 544 (1958-62); P 1800 (1961); 144 (1966); 164 (1968). Entries and wins in numerous competitions.

ASSEMBLY IN OTHER COUNTRIES — **Belgium**: Volvo Europa N.V. (subsidiary), Postbus 237, Ghent (assem. 140 series). **Canada**: Volvo (Canada) Ltd Manufacturing Division (subsidiary), P.O. Box 2027, Halifax (assem. 140 series). **Malaysia**: Swedish Motor Assemblies Sdn. Bhd. (subsidiary), Batu Tiga, Industrial Estate, Selangor (assem. 140 and 160 series). **South Africa**: Motor Assemblies Lawson Motors Pty Ltd (concessionaire), P.O. Box 30, Durban (assem. 120, 140 and 160 series). Cars assembled in other countries in 1969: about 135,000.

ACADIAN - see GENERAL MOTORS OF CANADA Ltd

A.C. CARS Ltd **Great Britain**

Founded in 1900 by Portwine & Weller, assumed title Autocarriers (A.C.) Ltd in 1907, transferred from London to Thames Ditton in 1911. Present title since 1930. Chairman and Managing Director: W.D. Hurlock. Directors: A.D. Turner, L.E.K. Vines. Works Manager: R. Alsop. Head office and works. The High Street, Thames Ditton, Surrey. Press office: P. Garnett-Keeler, 50 Mayfair Ave, Worcester Park, Surrey. Employees: about 150. Models: ACE Bristol 2 l Le Mans (1959); ACE Cobra Le Mans (1963). Entries and wins in numerous competitions (Monte Carlo Rally, Le Mans, etc.).

ADAM OPEL AG **Germany (Federal Republic)**

Founded in 1862. Owned by General Motors Corp. USA since 1929. Chairman: L.R. Mason. Directors: C.S. Chapman, A.A. Cunningham, dr. R. Hoenicke, dr. K. Kartzke, R.A. Lutz, J.P. McCormack, H. Mersheimer, E. Rohde, F. Schwenger. Head office and press office: 6090 Rüsselsheim am Main. Works: Berlin, Bochum, Kaiserslautern, Rüsselsheim, Strasbourg. Employees: 57,765. Cars produced in 1969: 801,205. Car production begun in 1898. Most important models: Opel 10/18 (1908); 4/8 (1909); 6/16 (1910); 8/25 (1920); 4/12 (1924); 4/14 (1925-29); Olympia (1936); Super Six, Admiral (1938); Kapitän (1939); Rekord (1961); Kadett (1962); Admiral, Diplomat (1967); Olympia, Commodore (1968); GT (1969).

ASSEMBLY IN OTHER COUNTRIES — **Belgium**: General Motors Continental S.A. (associated company), Noorderlaan 75, Antwerp (assem. Kadett, Olympia, Rekord, Kapitän, Admiral, Diplomat, Commodore). **Chile**. Alberto Avayu y Cia. (associated company), Casilla 13503, Santiago (assem. Kadett, Rekord). **Costa Rica**: Distribuidores Lachner & Saenz S.A. (concessionaire), Apartado 14, San José (assem. Kadett, Rekord). **Denmark**: General Motors International A/S (associated company), Aldersrogade 20, Copenhagen (assem. Kadett, Olympia, Rekord, Commodore). **Indonesia**: P.N. Gaja Motor (concessionaire), Djl. Hajan Wuruk 48, Djakarta (assem. Kadett, Rekord). **Ireland**: Reg. Armstrong Motors Ltd (concessionaire), South Dock Works, Ringsend Rd, Dublin 4 (assem. Kadett, Rekord, Commodore). **Mexico**: General Motors de México S.A. de C.V. (associated company), Avda. Ejercito Nacional 185, Mexico City 1, D.F. (assem. Rekord). **Pakistan**: Gandhava Industries Ltd (concessionaire), Karachi (assem. Kadett, Rekord). **Peru**: General Motors del Perú S.A. (associated company), Avda. Alfonso Ugarte 1140, Apartado 1612, Lima (assem. Kadett, Rekord). **Philippines**: Yutivo Sons Hardware Co. (concessionaire), Yutivo Bldg, P.O. Box 159, 404 Dasmarinas, Manila (assem. Kadett, Rekord). **Portugal**: General Motors de Portugal Ltda (associated company), Rua Particular n. 1 de Rafinaria Colonial 26, Lisbon 3 (assem. Kadett, Rekord). **South Africa**: General Motors South Africa Pty Ltd (associated company), Kempston Rd, Port Elizabeth (assem. Kadett, Rekord). **Switzerland**: General Motors Suisse S.A. (associated company), Salzhausstrasse 21, Bienne (manuf. Ascona; assem. Kadett, Olympia, Rekord, Kapitän, Admiral, Commodore). **Uruguay**: General Motors Uruguaya S.A. (associated company), Casilla de Correo 234, Montevideo (assem. Kadett, Rekord). **Venezuela**: General Motors de Venezuela C.A. (associated company), Mail Apartado 666, Caracas (assem. Kadett, Rekord).

ALFA ROMEO S.p.A. **Italy**

Founded in 1910 under the name of Anonima Lombarda Fabbrica Automobili, became Accomandita Semplice Ing. Nicola Romeo in 1915, Società Anonima Italiana Ing. Nicola Romeo & C. in 1918, S.A. Alfa Romeo in 1930. Became part of the IRI Group in 1933 and assumed the name of S.A. Alfa Romeo Milano-Napoli in 1939. Present title since 1946. For volume of production it holds the second place in the Italian motor industry. President: G. Luraghi. Managing Director: R. di Nola. General Manager: A. Bardini. Head office and press office: v. Gattamelata 45, 20149 Milan. Works: Milan-Arese, Naples-Pomigliano d'Arco. Employees: about 20,000. Cars produced in 1969: 105,000. Most important models: 24 hp (1910); 40-60 hp (1913); RL Targa Florio (1923); P2 (1924); 6C-1500 (1926); 6C-1750 (1929); 8C-2300 (1930); P3 (1932); 8C-2600 (1933); 8C-2900 (1935); 158 (1938); 6C-2500 SS (1939); 2500 Freccia d'Oro (1947); 1900 (1950); Giulietta (1954); 2000 (1959); 2600 (1962); Giulia TI (1962); Giulia 1300 (1964); Giulia Super, GTA (1965); Junior (1966). Entries and wins in numerous competitions. European Mountain Championship and European Touring Challenge Cup in 1967. In 1968 the 33/2 l was classified first at Daytona, in the Targa Florio and the Nürburgring 1000 km. In 1969 Alfa Romeo won, among others, the European Touring Challenge Cup, the National Championship for Makes in Brazil, three American National Drivers Championships, in 1970 it won the principal races of the European Touring Championship.

MANUFACTURE AND ASSEMBLY IN OTHER COUNTRIES — **Brazil**: Fabrica Nacional de Motores (associated company), Av. Presidente Vargas 542, Rio de Janeiro (manuf. 2150 Berlina). **Malaysia**: Citi Motors (concessionaire), Ipooh Perak (assem. 1300 TI, 1750 Berlina). **Malta**: Muscat's Garage (concessionaire), rue d'Argens, Msida (assem. Giulia Super). **Portugal**: Mocar Ltda (concessionaire), Av. A.A. de Aguiar 19/a, Lisbon (assem. 1750 Berlina, GT 1300 Junior). **South Africa**: Alfa Romeo Sud-Africa (Pty) Ltd (associated company), P.O. Box 2435, Johannesburg (assem. Giulia 1300 TI, Giulia Super, 1300 Junior, 1750 Berlina, GT 1750). **Uruguay**: Mauser S.A. (concessionaire), Sierra 2271/79, Montevideo (assem. 1300 TI, 1750 Berlina). **Yugoslavia**: Cosmos (concessionaire), (assem. 1750 Berlina, 1300 TI).

ALPINE - see AUTOMOBILES ALPINE S.A.

AMERICAN MOTORS CORP. **USA**

Established in 1954 as a result of the merger between Nash-Kelvinator Corp. and Hudson Motor Car Co. Chairman and Chief Executive Officer: R.D. Chapin jr. President and Chief Operating Officer: W.V. Luneburg. Head office and press office: 14250 Plymouth Rd, Detroit, Michigan 48232. Works: 5626 - 25th Ave, Kenosha, Wisconsin; 3880 N. Richards, Milwaukee, Wisconsin. Employees: 16,000. Cars produced in 1969: 242,898.

MANUFACTURE AND ASSEMBLY IN OTHER COUNTRIES — **Argentina**: Industrias Kaiser Argentina-Renault S.A. (associated company), Sarmiento 1230, Buenos Aires (Ambassador, American, Classic). **Australia**: Australian Motor Industries Ltd (associated company), G.P.O. Box 2006S, Cook St, Port Melbourne, Victoria (AMX, Javelin, Rebel). **Canada**: American Motors (Canada) Ltd (subsidiary), Brampton, Ontario (Ambassador, Rambler, Rebel). **Costa Rica**: Ecasa (concessionaire), Apartado 2884, San José (Rambler, Rebel). **Germany (F.R.)**: Wilhelm Karmann G.m.b.H. (concessionaire), Osnabrück (Javelin). **Iran**: Sherkate Sahami Jeep (concessionaire), Jeep Bldg, Ekbatan Ave, Teheran (Arya). **Mexico**: Vehículos Automotores Mexicanos (associated company), Norte 65, No. 1099, Industrial Vallejo, Mexico City 16, D.F. (American, Classic, Javelin). **New Zealand**: Campbell Motor Imports Ltd (concessionaire), 438 Queen St, Auckland (Rebel). **Peru**: Industria Automotriz Peruana S.A. (associated company), Casilla 3841, Lima (Rambler, Rebel). **Philippines**: Luzon Machineries Inc. (concessionaire), 741 Rizal Ave Ext. Caloocan City (Ambassador, Rambler, Rebel). **South Africa**: American Motors South Africa Pty Ltd (subsidiary), P.O. Box 36, President and Catlin Sts, Germiston, Transvaal. **Venezuela**: Constructora Venezolana de Vehículos C.A. (associated company), Edificio Gran Avenida, 2° Piso, Plaza Venezuela, Caracas (Javelin, Rambler, Rebel). Cars produced or assembled in other countries in 1969: 25,700.

ANDINO - see AUTOMOTORES 9 DE JULIO S.A.

ASTON MARTIN LAGONDA Ltd **Great Britain**

Founded in 1913 under the name of Bamford & Martin, is one of the greatest names in the world of touring and competition cars. Present title since 1947 when it was taken over by D. Brown. Chairman: Sir David Brown. Managing Director: A.S. Heggie. Directors: D. Gershon, A.G. Pilkington, R.M. Bamford. Head office: David Brown Corp., 96/97 Piccadilly, London W.1. Press office: Image Ltd, 35 Great Peter St, London S.W.1. Works: Tickford St, Newport, Pagnell, Bucks. Employees: 850. Cars produced in 1969: 750. Most important models: Lion Martin series (1921-25); first series 1.5 l (1927-32); second series 1.5 l (1932-34); third series 1.5 l (1934-36); 2 l series with single overhead camshaft (1936-40); 2 l DB1 series (1948-50); 2.6 l DB2 series (1950-53); 2.6 and 2.9 l DB3 series (1952-53); 2.6 and 2.9 l DB2/4 series (1953-55); 2.9 l DB3S series (1955-56); 2.9 l DB2/4 Mk II series (1955-57); 2.9 l DB Mk III series (1957-59); 3.7 l DB4 series (1959-63); 3.7 l DB4 GT series (1959-63). Entries in numerous competitions (Le Mans, Spa, Tourist Trophy, Nürburgring, Aintree).

AUDI NSU AUTO UNION AG **Germany (Federal Republic)**

(Makes: Audi, NSU)

Established in 1969 as a result of the merger between Auto Union GmbH (founded in Zwickau in 1932 and transferred to Ingolstadt in 1948 when the Zwickau company was nationalised) and NSU Motorenwerke AG (founded in 1873 at Riedlingen, moved to Neckarsulm in 1880; changed its name to Neckarsulmer Fahrzeugwerke AG in 1919 and became NSU Motorenwerke AG in 1960). Board of Directors: G.S. von Heydekampf (Chairman); V. Frankenberger, F.W. Pollmann (Vice Chairmen); H. Kialka, L. Kraus, Ph. Wesp, A. Zimmermann, G. Henn, H.-E. Schönbeck (members). Head and press office: 7107 Neckarsulm. Works: as above, Postfach 220, 807 Ingolstadt. Employees: 27,100. Cars produced in 1969: 264,400. Most important models: NSU Prinz 4 (1961); NSU 1000 (1963); NSU 1200 (1965); NSU TT and NSU TTS (1965-67); Audi Super 90 (1966); NSU Ro 80 (1967); Audi 60 and Audi 60 L, Audi 75 L and Audi 75 Variant (1968); Audi 100 and Audi 100 LS (1969).

ASSEMBLY IN OTHER COUNTRIES — **South Africa**: VW of South Africa Ltd (associated company), P.O. Box 80, Uitenhage (assem. Audi Super 90). Cars produced in other countries in 1968: 1,254.

AUSTIN - see BLMC

AUSTIN HEALEY - see BLMC

AUTOBIANCHI **Italy**

(belonging to Fiat S.p.A.)

Created in 1955 by collaboration between the Edoardo Bianchi firm, Fiat and Pirelli, on 30 March 1968 it was incorporated into Fiat under the title of the Autobianchi Company; however, both on the Italian and on foreign markets it retains its own maker's marks, sales organisation and maintenance services. Offices: v. Fabio Filzi 24, 20124 Milan. Employees: about 4,000. Cars produced in 1969: 76,000. For further information see Fiat S.p.A.

AUTOCARS COMPANY Ltd **Israel**

Founded in 1958 as private company. In 1966 Standard-Triumph Motor Co. England (associated of Leyland Motor Corp.) entered in partnership with it. Managing Director: Y. Shubinsky. Head office and press office: P.O. Box 444, Tirat Hacarmel, Haifa. Works: Tirat Hacarmel, Haifa; T.I.L., Nesher, Haifa (assem. Triumph 1300, 1500, Kaiser Jeep). Employees: 2,000. Cars produced in 1968: 5,000. Most important models: Sussita, Carmel, Gilboa, all with fibreglass bodywork.

AUTOMOBILE MONTEVERDI **Switzerland**

Oberwilerstrasse 14-20, 4102 Binningen.

AUTOMOBILES ALPINE S.A. **France**

Founded in 1955. President: J. Rédélé. Head office and press office: 3 bd. Foch, Epinay s/Seine (93). Works: 40 av. Pasteur, Dieppe (76). Employees: 143. Cars produced in 1969: 360. Most important models: Mille Miles (1955); Coupé Sport and Sport Convertible (1959-60); Berlinette Tour de France (1961); A110 956 and 1108 cu cm series (1962); M. 63 (1963); M. 64 and F2, F3 (1964). Entries and wins in numerous competitions (Rallies, Le Mans, etc.).

• The information given in these descriptions refers specifically to cars and therefore does not cover the activities in which any of the car manufacturers are engaged in other fields of industry.

MANUFACTURE IN OTHER COUNTRIES — **Brazil**: Willys Overland do Brasil (associated company), São Paulo (manuf. Interlagos). **Bulgaria**: Bullet (associated company), Sofia. **Mexico**: Diesel Nacional (associated company), Mexico City. **Spain**: Fasa (associated company), Valladolid. Cars produced in other countries in 1969: 1,640.

AUTOMOBILES PEUGEOT S.A. — **France**

Founded in 1890 under the name of Les Fils Peugeot Fres. Present title since 1966. President and General Manager: F. Gautier. Vice-Presidents: M. Jordan, R. Peugeot. Head office and press office: 75 av. de la Grande-Armée, Paris 16e. Works: Dijon, Lille, Montbéliard, Mulhouse, Sochaux, St. Etienne, Vesoul. Employees: about 48,000. Cars produced in 1969: 489,078. Most important models: Bébé Peugeot (1911); 201, 301, 302, 402, 203 (1929-60); 403 (1955); 404 (1960); 204 (1965); 504 (1968). First place in ACF (1912-13, 1923-24).

MANUFACTURE AND ASSEMBLY IN OTHER COUNTRIES — **Argentina**: Safrar (subsidiary), Buenos Aires (manuf. 404, 504). **Australia**: Renault (wholesale) Pty Ltd, West Heidelberg (assem. 404, 504). **Belgium**: S.A.B.A.P.-Bruxelles (subsidiary) Usines Ragheno-Mechelen (assem. 304, 404, 204). **Chile**: Franco Chilena, Los Andes (assem. 404). **Colombia**: L. Lara (concessionaire), Bogotá (assem. 404). **Ireland**: Peugeot Sales, Dublin (assem. 404, 204). **Malaysia**: Asia Automobiles Industries, Petaling-Jaya (assem. 404). **New Zealand**: Campbell Motors, Auckland (assem. 404). **Nigeria**: Scoa, Lagos (assem. 404). **Peru**: Iapsa, Lima (assem. 404). **Portugal**: Movauto, Setúbal (assem. 204, 304, 404, 504). **South Africa**: P.A.A. Pty Ltd (subsidiary), Johannesburg (assem. 304, 404, 504). **Uruguay**: S.A.D.A.R., Montevideo (assem. 404, 504).

AUTOMOBILI FERRUCCIO LAMBORGHINI S.p.A. — **Italy**

Founded in 1962 under the name Automobili Ferruccio Lamborghini Sas. Present title since 1965. Manager: Ing. h.c. F. Lamborghini. Head office, press office and works: v. Modena 1b, 40019 S. Agata Bolognese (Bologna). Employees: 240. Cars produced in 1969: 411. Models: 350 GT (1963); 400 GT (1966); Miura (1967); Espada, Islero (1968).

AUTOMOTORES 9 DE JULIO S.A. — **Argentina**

(Make: Andino)

Founded in 1967. President: R. Lui. Head office, press office and works: Calle Libertad 200, 9 de Julio, Buenos Aires. Employees: 15. Cars produced in 1969: 15. Models: Lui-Varela 850 GT (1968); Andino GT (1969).

AVANTI MOTOR CORP. — **USA**

Founded in 1965. President: N.D. Altman. Vice-Presidents: F. Baer, A.D. Altman. Secretary and Treasurer: L. Newman. Head office and works: 765 S. Lafayette Blvd, South Bend, Indiana 46623. Press office: Donald Landy Inc., 25755 Southfield Rd, Southfield, Mich. 48075. Employees: 81. Cars produced in 1969: 167.

AZLK-AVTOMOBILNY ZAVOD IMENI LENINSKOGO KOMSOMOLA — **USSR**

Avtoexport, Ul. Volkhonka 14, Moscow G. 512. Works: Moscow.

BAYERISCHE MOTOREN WERKE AG — **Germany (Federal Republic)**

Established in 1916 as Bayerische Flugzeugwerke AG. Present title since 1918. Chairman: E. von Kuenheim. Vice-Presidents: W. Gieschen, P.G. Hahnemann, K. Monz, B. Osswald. Head office and press office: Lerchenauerstrasse 76, 8 Munich 13. Works: Munich, Berlin, Landshut, Dingolfing. Employees: 21,300. Cars produced in 1969: 147,841. Most important models: 3/15 hp Saloon (1928); 326, 327, 328 (1936); 501 6 cyl. (1951); BMW V8 (1954); 503 and 507 Sport (1955); 700 (1959); 1500 (1962); 1800 (1963); 2000 (1966); 2002, 2500, 2800 (1968). Entries and wins in numerous competitions (Mille Miglia, Monza 12 hour, Hockenheim, Nürburgring, Friburg Mountain Record, Brands Hatch, European Mountain Championship; winner 1968 and 1969 European Cup for Touring Cars, Francorchamps 24 hour, Formula 2).

ASSEMBLY IN OTHER COUNTRIES — **Belgium**: Ets Moorkens S.A. (concessionaire), Kontich-Antwerp (assem. 1600, 1800, 2000, 2002). **Portugal**: Soc. Com. e Ind. de Automoveis Francisco Batista Russo & Irmao Sarl, Lisbon (assem. 1600, 2002). **South Africa**: Euro Republic Automobile Distr. (Pty) Ltd, Pretoria (assem. 1800 SA, 2000 SA). **Uruguay**: Convex S.A., Montevideo (assem. 1600).

BEDFORD - see VAUXHALL MOTORS Ltd

BENTLEY MOTORS (1931) Ltd — **Great Britain**

Taken over by Rolls-Royce Ltd in 1931, specializing in high-class vehicles. Head office: Nightingale Rd, Derby. Press office: 14-15 Conduit St., London W.1. Works: Pym's Lane, Crewe, Cheshire. Most important models: first Bentley 3.5 l manufactured by Rolls-Royce (1933); 4.5 l Mk VI (1946); Continental (1951); "R" Type (1952); S1 (1955); S2 (1959); S3 (1962); "T" series (1965).

BLMC BRITISH LEYLAND MOTOR CORP. Ltd — **Great Britain**

(Makes: Austin, Austin-Healey, MG, Mini, Morris, Vanden Plas, Wolseley)

British Leyland is Britain's largest producer of motor vehicles. Formed in May, 1968, following a merger between British Motor Holdings (BMC and Jaguar) and the Leyland Motor Corporation (incorporating Leyland Motors, Rover and Triumph) the new group employs 200,000 people throughout the world and current annual sales exceed £ 900 million. Head office: Berkeley Square House, Berkeley Sq., London W.1. Chairman and Managing Director: Lord Stokes. Deputy Chairmen: Sir William Lyons, L. Whyte. Deputy Managing Directors: A. Fogg, J. Plane, G. Turnbull. British Leyland has five operating divisions covering all aspects of its operations. Responsible for car production is the Austin Morris and Manufacturing Group (makes: Austin, Austin-Healey, MG, Mini, Morris, Vanden Plas, Wolseley). This group incorporates the Pressed Steel Fisher and the former British Motor Corp. which designs and produces a wide range of cars under the above marque names. BMC was formed in 1952 following a merger between the Austin Motor Company and the Nuffield Organisation, two companies who had energetically competed with each other since the early days of motoring. It was Britain's largest vehicle manufacturer prior to the formation of British Leyland. Chairman: Lord Stokes. Group Managing Director: G. Turnbull. Deputy Managing Director: H.R. Barber. Head office and press office: Longbridge, Birmingham, Works: as above, Oxford, South Wales, Swindon, Abingdon, Coventry, Scotland. Employees: 93,000. Cars produced in 1969: 779,000.

MANUFACTURE AND ASSEMBLY IN OTHER COUNTRIES — **Australia**: BMC (Australia) Pty Ltd, Joynton Ave, Zetland N.S.W. (manuf. and assem. Austin and Nuffield models). **Belgium**: S.A. Bruxelloise d'Auto Transports, Division Morris-MG, av. de Baume et Marpent, Haine-Saint-Pierre, Hainaut (assem. Nuffield models). **Chile**: Equipos Mecánicos Salfa Siam S.A., Arica (assem. Austin and Nuffield models). **Colombia**: Fábrica Colombiana de Automotores S.A., Apartado Aéreo 73-79, Bogotá (assem. Austin models). **France**: Sté Willems S.A., rue Noël Pons, Nanterre, Seine (assem. Nuffield models). **Holland**: J.J. Molenaar's Automobielbedrijf N.V., Barchman Wuytierslaan 2, Amersfoort (assem. Austin and Nuffield models). **India**: Hindustan Motors Ltd, 15 India Exchange Pl., Calcutta (manuf. Nuffield models). **Indonesia**: P.T. Tjahja Sakti Motor Corp. c/o Indonesia Service Co., P.O. Box 121, Djil. Lodan, Djakarta-Kota (assem. Nuffield models). **Ireland**: Lincoln & Nolan Ltd, 57-58 Lower Baggot St, Dublin 2 (assem. Austin models); Brittain Dublin Ltd, Portobello, Dublin (assem. Nuffield models); Booth Pool & Co. Ltd, Liffey Bank Islandbridge, Dublin (assem. Nuffield models). **Italy**: Innocenti Società Generale per l'Industria Metallurgica e Meccanica, v. Pitteri 81, Milan (manuf. Austin and Nuffield models). **New Zealand**: Austin Distributors Federation N.Z. Ltd, Western Hutt Rd, P.O. Box 114, Petone (assem. Austin models); Dominion Motors Ltd, Courtenay Pl., P.O. Box 599, Wellington C.3 (assem. Nuffield models). **Philippines**: Faber Inc., P.O. Box 3172, Manila (assem. Nuffield models). **Portugal**: Industria de Montagem de Automoveis, Setúbal (assem. Austin and Nuffield models). **Rhodesia**: BMC (Rhodesia) Pty Ltd, P.O. Box 631, Umtali (assem. Austin and Nuffield models). **South Africa**: BMC (S.A.) Pty Ltd, P.O. Box 1, Black Heath, Cape Province (assem. Austin and Nuffield models). **Spain**: Sociedad Anónima Vehiculos Automóviles, Apartado 131, Valladolid (assem. Austin models).

BRISTOL CARS PARTNERSHIP — **Great Britain**

Established in 1946 as "Car Division" of the British Aeroplane Co., became affiliated company of British Aeroplane Co. in 1955, and subsidiary of Bristol Siddeley Engines in 1959. Became a privately owned company in 1960 and owned by a partnership from 1966. Partners: Sir George White B.T., F.S. Derham, T.A.D. Crook. Head office, press office and works: Filton, Bristol. Most important models: 400 (1947); 401 and 402 (1949); 403 and 404 (1953-55); 405 (1954-58); 406 (1958); 407 (1961); 408 (1963); 409 (1965); 410 (1967); 411 (1969). Entries and first places in numerous competitions with Bristol 400 (14th Polish International Rally, Monte Carlo Rally, Targa Florio, Mille Miglia) with F1 and F2 (British Grand Prix, Grand Prix of Europe, Sebring, Reims, Montlhéry, Le Mans, etc.).

BUICK - see GENERAL MOTORS CORP.

CADILLAC - see GENERAL MOTORS CORP.

CARROSSERIE CHAPPE FRÈRES & GESSALIN S.r.l. — **France**

(Make: CG)

Founded in 1946. Manager: A. Chappe. Head office, press office and works: rue du Coq Gaulois 77, Brie-Comte-Robert (S. et M.). Employees: 30. Cars produced in 1968: 40.

CG - see CARROSSERIE CHAPPE FRÈRES & GESSALIN S.r.l.

CHECKER MOTORS CORP. — **USA**

Founded in 1922. Chairman and President: David Markin. Executive Vice-President: R.E. Oakland. Head office, press office and works: 2016 N. Pitcher St, Kalamazoo, Michigan 49007. Employees: 800. Cars produced in 1969: 5,494.

CHEVROLET (USA, Argentina, Brazil) - see GENERAL MOTORS CORP.

CHRYSLER CORP. — **USA**

(Makes: Chrysler, Dodge, Imperial, Plymouth)

Founded in 1925 as successor to Maxwell Motors Corp. It holds third place in the world's motor industry. It is in a period of expansion, having set new sales records in each of the past five years. Chrysler Corp. is made up of two "divisions": Chrysler-Plymouth Division (1220 East Jefferson Ave, Detroit 48231, Mich.) and Dodge Division (7900 Joseph Campau, Detroit 48231, Mich.). Chairman: L.A. Townsend. President Chrysler International: P.N. Buckminster. Vice President-International: I.J. Minett. Vice President Far East and African Operations: C.B. Gorey jr. Vice President Europe: P.N. Buckminster. Vice President Latin and South America: G.E. White. Direction for all operations outside the United States and Canada: Chrysler International S.A. (P.O. Box 158, 1211 Geneva 24, Switzerland), formed in 1958. Head office and press office Chrysler Corp.: 341 Massachusetts Ave, Box 1919, Detroit 48231, Mich. Works: Detroit area, Michigan; Los Angeles, Calif.; New Castle, Ind.; Kokomo, Ind.; Indianapolis, Ind.; Twinsburg, Ohio; Syracuse, N.Y.; Newark, Delaware and others. Employees: about 235,000. Cars produced in 1969: 1,593,641. Most important models: Chrysler (1924); Imperial (1926); Plymouth and Dodge (1928). Entries in various national competitions with recent first places in Constructor's Trophy of U.S. Auto Club, NASCAR Circuit (National Association for Stock Car Automobile Racing) and other Championships conducted by the Sports Club of America, Automobile Racing Club of America and International Motor Contest Association. In 1958 the Chrysler Corp. acquired 25% of Chrysler France shares; in 1963 it increased its holding in this company to 64%, in 1965 to 69% and in 1966 to 77%. In 1967 acquired 77% of Chrysler United Kingdom Ltd shares and in 1969, 86% of Chrysler España S.A. shares.

MANUFACTURE AND ASSEMBLY IN OTHER COUNTRIES — **Argentina**: Chrysler Fevre Argentina Saic (subsidiary), Casilla de Correo 444, Buenos Aires (manuf. Dodge, Coronado, GTX, Polara, Valiant). **Australia**: Chrysler Australia Ltd (subsidiary), G.P.O. Box 1320 F, Adelaide (manuf. Valiant, Hillman, Hunter). **Brazil**: Chrysler do Brasil (subsidiary), Caixa Postal 30358, São Paulo (manuf. Dodge). **Colombia**: Chrysler Colmotores (associated company), Diagonal 38 Sur Con Carreta 33, Apartado Aéreo 7329, Bogotá (assem. Simca, Dart). **Holland**: Chrysler International S.A., P.O. Box 832, Rotterdam (assem. Dodge, Dart, Plymouth, Valiant). **Mexico**: Fábricas Auto-Mex S.A. (associated company), P.O. Box 53951, Mexico City D.F. (manuf. Duster, Monaco, Coronet, Dart; Valiant). **Peru**: Chrysler Perú S.A. (subsidiary), Apartado 5037, Lima (assem. Dart, Coronet; Hillman Minx De Luxe). **Philippines**: Chrysler Philippines Corp. (subsidiary), P.O. Box 4592, Manila (assem. Coronet, Dart, Hillman). **South Africa**: Chrysler South Africa (Pty) Ltd (subsidiary), P.O. Box 411, Pretoria (manuf. Valiant; assem. Chrysler, United Kingdom Arrow). **Spain**: Chrysler España S.A. (associated company), Apartado 140 Villaverde, Madrid 14 (manuf. Dodge Dart; Simca 1000). **Venezuela**: Chrysler de Venezuela S.A. (subsidiary), Apartado 62362-Chacao, Edificio Torre Phelps, Plaza Venezuela, Caracas (assem. Valiant, Dart, Belvedere, Coronet, Chrysler; Chrysler U.K. Imp, Hunter, Humber, Sceptre).

CHRYSLER FRANCE — **France**

(Make: Simca)

Founded in 1934 under the name of Sté Industrielle de Mécanique et de Carrosserie Automobile. Assumed title Société Simca Automobiles in 1960. In 1964 the controlling interest passed to the Chrysler Motors Corp. Present title since 1970. President and Chairman of the Board: G. Héreil. General Manager: G. Gillespie. Vice-Presidents: H. Chardon, J. Forgeot. Executives: J. Faure, L.B. Warren, I.J. Minett, P. Grezel, J. Terray, G.G. Cittadini Cesi, E.H. Graham, G. Hunt. Head office and press office: 136 av. des Champs Elysées, Paris 8e. Works: Poissy (Yvelines); La Rochelle-Perigny (C.M.); Sully-sur-Loire (Loiret); Sept Fons (Allier); Vieux Condé (Nord); Bondy (Seine-Saint-Denis). Employees: about 30,000. Cars produced in 1969: 351,000. Most important models: Fiat cars 508 Balilla (1932-34); 527 Ardita (1935); 500 Topolino (1936); 508 Nuova Balilla (1937); Six (1949); 1200 Sports (1950); Huit (Nuova-Balilla 1100), Neuf, Aronde (1951); Ariane, Etoile Six (1961); Simca 1000 (1961-65); 1300, 1500 (1963); 1200 S, 1100, 1301, 1501 (1967); 1100 (1968).

MANUFACTURE AND ASSEMBLY IN OTHER COUNTRIES — **Chile**: Nun y Guzman (concessionaire), Saldo 444, Santiago (assem. 1000). **Morocco**: Somaca (associated company), km 12 Autoroute Rabat-Casablanca (assem. 1000, 1100, 1301, 1501). **New Zealand**: Concord Motors Ltd, Auckland (assem. 1000). **Portugal**: Somave (concessionaria), Vendao Novao (assem. 1000, 1100, 1301). **Spain**: Ets. Barreiros Diesel S.A. (associated company), Alcalá 32, Madrid 14 (manuf. 1000, 1100).

CHRYSLER UNITED KINGDOM Ltd — **Great Britain**

(Makes: Hillman, Humber, Sunbeam)

Founded in 1917 under the name of Rootes Motors Ltd. In 1967 it became a member of the Chrysler Group. Present title since 1970. Chairman: Lord Rootes. Managing Director: G.A. Hunt, C.B.E. Directors: B. Boxall, C.B.E., P.N. Buckminster, G. Hereil, T. Killefer, I.J. Minett, Lord Inchyra, A.F. Murray, Sir Eric Roll, W.J. Tate, L.B. Warren. Head office and press office: Quadrant House, Dunstable, Beds. Works: Chrysler Scotland Ltd, Linwood, nr. Paisley, Renfrewshire, Scotland; Ryton on Dunsmore Stoke, nr. Coventry, Warwickshire; Dunstable, Luton, Bedfordshire. Employees: 25,400. Cars produced in 1969: 204,609.

MANUFACTURE AND ASSEMBLY IN OTHER COUNTRIES — **Australia**: Chrysler Australia Ltd (associated company), P.O. Box 1320 F, Adelaide (manuf. and assem. Hunter, Estate, Minx). **Costa Rica**: Almacén Electra S.A. (concessionaire), San José (assem. Vogue). **Iran**: Iran National Industrial Manufacturing Co. Ltd (associated company), Ekbatan Ave, Teheran (manuf. and assem. Hunter, Paykaan, Minx). **Ireland**: Chrysler Ireland Ltd (associated company), Shanowen Rd, Whitehall, Dublin 9 (assem. Hunter, Vogue, Minx, Sceptre). **Malaysia**: Associated Motor Industries (concessionaire), P.O. Box 763, Kuala Lumpur (assem. Hunter). **Malta**: Industrial Motor Co. Ltd (concessionaire), National Rd, Blata-il-Badia (assem. Minx, Estate, Hunter). **New Zealand**: Todd Motors Ltd (concessionaire), P.O. Box 2295, Wellington (assem. Hunter, Estate, Vogue, Avenger). **Peru**: Chrysler Perú S.A. (associated company), Apartado 5057, Lima (manuf. Minx). **Philippines**: Chrysler Philippines Co. (associated company), P.O. Box 4592, Manila (assem. Hunter, Minx, Imp). **Portugal**: Chrysler de Portugal Ltda (associated company), Av. de Roma 15B, Lisbon 5 (assem. Vogue, Imp). **South Africa**: Chrysler South Africa (Pty) Ltd (associated company), Chrysler Park, P.O. Box 411, Pretoria (manuf. and assem. Hunter, Estate, Sceptre, Vogue). **Trinidad**: H.E. Robinson Co. (concessionaire), 4 Edward St, Port of Spain, Trinidad W.1 (assem. Hunter, Minx, Vogue). **Venezuela**: Chrysler Venezuela S.A. (associated company), Apartado 621, Valencia, Estado Carabobo (assem. Hunter, Estate, Sceptre). Cars produced in other countries in 1969: 51,000.

CITROËN S.A. — **France**

Founded in 1919 by André Citroën, became S.A. André Citroën in 1927. Present title since 1968. Honorary Chairman: F. Rollier. President and Managing Director: R. Ravenel. Vice-President: A. Brueder. Executives: R. Marais, P. Berliet. Head office and press office: 133 quai André Citroën, Paris 15e. Works: as above, Issy-les-Moulineaux, Puteaux, Levallois-Perret, Clichy, Saint-Ouen, Asnières, Aubervilliers, Gennevilliers, Saint-Denis, Nanterre, Rennes-La-Barre-Thomas, Rennes-La-Janais, Strasbourg, Caen, Froncle, Saint-Etienne, Mulhouse, Reims, Metz, Venissieux et Bourg (Berliet). Employees: 81,500. Cars produced in 1969: 505,997. Most important models: Torpedo A Type (1919); B2 10 CV (1921); 5 CV (1922); B12 10 CV (1925); B14 (1926); C6 (1928); 7A, 7 and 11 CV (1934); 15 Six (1938); 2 CV (1948); 2 CV 425 cu cm (1954); DS 19 (1955); ID 19 (1957); 2 CV 4 x 4 (1958); Ami 6 3 CV (1961); Ami 6 Break, DS Pallas (1964); DS 21 (1965); Dyane (1967); Mehari (1968); Ami 8 (1969). Entries and first places in numerous competitions: World distance and speed record at Montlhéry (1932-33), 28th Monte Carlo Rally and Constructor's Cup (1959), Liège-Sofia-Liège Road Marathon (1961), Norwegian Snow and Ice Winter Rally, Lyon-Charbonnière-Solitude, Alpine Trophy, Thousand Lakes Rally, Constructors' Cup, Trophy of Nations (1962), Finnish Snow Rally, Northern Roads, Lyon-Charbonnière-Solitude, Norwegian Winter Rally, International Alpine Criterium, Constructors' Cup in Monte Carlo Rally and Liège-Sofia-Liège Marathon, Tour of Corsica (1963), Spa-Sofia-Liège Marathon (1964), Rallie Neige et Glace, Mobil Economy Run, Coupe des Alpes, Monte Carlo (1966), Constructors' Cup (1967), Neige et Glace, Mobil Economy Run (1968), Morocco Rally (1969 and 1970).

MANUFACTURE AND ASSEMBLY IN OTHER COUNTRIES — **Argentina**: Citroën Argentine (subsidiary), Zemita 3220, Buenos Aires (assem. 2 CV). **Belgium**: Sté Belge de Automobiles Citroën S.A. (subsidiary), 82 rue Saint-Denis, Brussels (assem. 2 CV, Ami 6). **Chile**: Sociedad Importadora e Industrial José Lhorente y Cia. Ltda. (subsidiary), Arica Lote 26, Chinthorre (manuf. 2 CV). **Dahomey**: Cotonou (assem. 2 CV, Ami 8). **Iran**: Teheran (assem. Dyane). **Madagascar**: Enterprise de Construction Auto-Malgache (concessionaire), Route de Majunga, Tananarive (assem. 2 CV Dyane, Ami 8). **Portugal**: Sociedad Citroën Lusitania S.a.r.l. (subsidiary), Estrada de Nelas, Beira Alta, Mangualde (Dyane 6, Ami 8, DS). **South Africa**: Stanley Motors Ltd (concessionaire), Natalspruit, Johannesburg (assem. ID 19). **Spain**: Citroën Hispania (subsidiary), free zone of Vigo (manuf. 2 CV, Ami 6, Dyane, Mehari). **Yugoslavia**: Tovarna Motornih Vozil (Tomos) (concessionaire), Koper (manuf. 2 CV, Ami 8, DS).

DAF - see VAN DOORNE'S AUTOMOBIELFABRIEKEN NV

DAIHATSU KOGYO COMPANY Ltd — **Japan**

Established in 1907 as Hatsudoki Seizo Kabushiki Kaisha, assumed title of Daihatsu Kogyo Co. Ltd in 1951. Now consists of Daihatsu Motor Co. Ltd and Daihatsu Motor Sales Co. Ltd, and belongs to the Toyota Group. Chairman: Y. Koishi. President: Y. Ise. Executive Director: S. Hara. Directors: I. Takaoka, Y. Murai. Head office and works: 1-1 Daihatsu-cho, Ikeda City, Osaka. Press office: Daihatsu Motor Sales Co. Ltd, 2-7 Nihonbashi-Honcho, Chuo-ku, Tokyo. Employees: 9,600. Cars produced in 1969: 19,774. Production of 4-wheeled vehicles begun in 1958. Most important models: Compagno Station Wagon (1963); Compagno 800 Sedan (1964); Compagno Spider and Sedan (1965); Fellow 360 (1966).

DAIMLER (THE DAIMLER COMPANY Ltd) - see JAGUAR CARS Ltd

DAIMLER-BENZ AG — **Germany (Federal Republic)**

(Make: Mercedes-Benz)

Established in 1926 as a result of the merger between Daimler-Motorengesellschaft and Benz & Cie, it is the best-known German manufacturer of highclass cars. Board of Directors: J. Zahn (Chairman); O. Jacob, W. Langheck, U. Raue, H. Scherenberg, H.M. Schleyer, H. Schmidt, R.P.G. Staelin, A. Wychodil (members). Head office and press office: Mercedes-Strasse 136, 7 Stuttgart-Untertürkheim. Works: as above, Sindelfingen, Mannheim, Gaggenau, Berlin-Marienfelde, Düsseldorf, Bad Homburg, Wörth/Rhein. Employees: 90,000. Cars produced in 1969: 256,713. Most important models: Stuttgart 200, Mannheim (1926); Stuttgart 260, Mannheim 350 and Sportwagen SSK (1928); Grosser Mercedes (1930); Nürburg 500 (1931); 170 V (1935); 260 D, first Diesel car (1935); Grosser Mercedes (1938); 170 V (1946); 300 SL (1954); 190 SL (1955); 180 b/Db and 220 Sb (1959); 190 c/Dc and 300 SE (1961); 230 SL and 600 (1963); 250 (1966); 200, 220, 230, 250, 280 S, 280 SE, 300 SEL 6.3, 250 C, 250 CE (1968); 280 SE 3.5, 300 SEL 3.5 (1969). First places in numerous international competitions (1894-1955).

ASSEMBLY IN OTHER COUNTRIES — **Belgium**: S.A. pour l'Importation de Moteurs et d'Automobiles (concessionaire), 14 Rode Kruisplein, Malines (assem. 200, 200 D, 220, 220 D, 230, 250). **Ireland**: Ballsbridge Motors Ltd, Wholesale Division (concessionaire), Naas Road Factory, Dublin 12 (assem. 200, 200 D, 220, 220 D, 230, 250, 280 S). **Malaysia**: The Cycle & Carriage Industries Sdn. Bhd. (concessionaire), Lot 9, Jalan 219, Federal Highway, Petaling Jaya (assem. 200, 200 D, 220, 220 D, 230, 250, 280 S). **Philippines**: Universal Motors Corp. (concessionaire), 2232 Pasong Tamo Ave, P.O. Box 3250, Manila, Makati Rizal (assem. 200, 200 D, 220, 220 D, 230, 250). **Peru**: Srs. Autec S.A., Automotores y Equipos S.A. (concessionaire), Avda. Panamericana 1080, Apartado 5592, Lima (assem. 200, 200 D, 220, 220 D, 230, 250). **Portugal**: Movauto, Montagem de Vehiculos, Automoveis Ltd, Setúbal (assem. 200, 200 D, 220, 220 D, 230, 250, 280 S). **Singapore**: Cycle & Carriage Co. (Industries) Ltd (concessionaire), 164-168 Hill View Ave, P.O. Box 12, Singapore 23 (assem. 200, 200 D, 220, 220 D, 230, 250, 280 S). **South Africa**: Car Distributors Assembly Ltd (associated company), P.O. Box 671, East London (assem. 200, 200 D, 220, 220 D, 230, 250, 280 S). **Venezuela**: Consorcio Inversionista Fabril S.A., Diversión Industrial Automotriz (concessionaire), Apartado de Correo 2085, Caracas (assem. 200, 200 D, 220, 220 D, 230, 250, 280 S). Cars produced in other countries in 1969: 15,900.

DE TOMASO AUTOMOBILI S.p.A. — **Italy**

Founded in 1959. President: A. de Tomaso. General Manager: N. Ugolini. Head office, press office and works: v. Jacopo Peri 68, Modena. Employees: 70. Cars produced in 1969: 300. Most important models: OSCA 1500 monocoque; Sport with OSCA 1100 engine, Berlinetta Vallelunga with Ford Cortina 1500 engine (two-seater); Sport Prototype 5 litre (1965); Mangusta with Ford V8 4700 engine (1966).

DODGE (USA and Argentina) - see CHRYSLER CORP.

Dr. Ing. h.c. F. PORSCHE KG — **Germany (Federal Republic)**

Founded in 1948. Proprietor and General Manager: F. Porsche. Head office and press office: Porschestrasse 42, 7000 Stuttgart-Zuffenhausen. Works: Schwieberdingerstrasse, 7000 Stuttgart-Zuffenhausen. Employees: 3,900. Cars produced in 1969: 15,575. Most important models: Porsche 1100 (1950-55); 1300 Normal (1951-57); 1500 Normal (1951-54); 1500 Super (1952-54); 1300 Super (1954-57); 1600 Normal, 1600 Super, Carrera 1500 (1955); Carrera 1600 (1958); 1600 Super 90 (1959); 911 Type (1963); 912 (1965). First places in numerous international competitions: Le Mans 24 hour with 1100 Coupé (1959), Sebring, European Mountain Championship (1958-59-60-61), Targa Florio and Nürburgring (1959 and 1967), Constructors' Cup for F2 cars (1960), European Rally Championship with Carrera (1961), GT World Championship up to 2000 cu cm (1962-63-64-65), World Cup for speed and endurance, European Touring Car Trophy, 32 national Championships. Has taken part in the most importat Grand Prix with F1 cars (France G.P., Solitude G.P.).

EXCALIBUR - see SS AUTOMOBILES Inc.

FABRYKA SAMOCHODÓW OSOBOWYCH — **Poland**

(Makes: Polski-Fiat, Syrena, Warszawa)

Founded in 1949. State-owned Company. Chairman: W. Dryll. Vice-Presidents: J. Bielecki, Y. Bialkowski, Z. Drodzda, Y. Burchard, Z. Chorazy. Head office, press office and works: ul. Stalingradzka 50, Warsaw. Employees: 14,000. Cars produced in 1969: 41,000. Most important models: Warszawa 223 and 224 (1964); Syrena 104 (1958); Polski-Fiat 125 P (1968). Entries in Rallies (Monte Carlo, Jadransky, Peace and Friendship, etc.).

FAIRTHORPE Ltd — **Great Britain**

Founded in 1955. Proprietor: D.C.T. Bennett. General Manager: T. Bennett. Head office: Deepwood House, Farnham Royal, Bucks. Press office and works: Denham Green Lane, Denham, Bucks. Most important models: Electron Minor, Electron, Zeta, Mk IV EM, TXI, TX-GT, TX-S, TX-SS.

FERRARI S.p.A.
ESERCIZIO FABBRICHE AUTOMOBILI E CORSE — **Italy**

Founded in 1929 under the name of Scuderia Ferrari, became Società Auto-Avio Costruzioni Ferrari in 1940. Present legal form and title since 1960. As from 1 July 1969, is associated with Fiat. Its name is bound up with superb technical achievements in the field of racing and GT cars. President: E. Ferrari. Managing Director: F. Bellicardi. General Manager: G. Dondo. Directors: A. Fiorelli, O. Montabone, C. Pelloni, S. Pininfarina, P. Lardi. Head office: vl. Trento e Trieste 31, 41100 Modena. Press office and works: v. Abetone Inferiore 2, 41053 Maranello (Modena). Employees: 640. Cars produced in 1969: 730. Most important GT models: 125 (1947); 166 Inter (1949); 340 America (1952); 250 GT (1961); V12 250 GT (1961); Superfast (1961); 275 GTB 4 Berlinetta (1963); Dino 206 GT Berlinetta, 365 Coupé GT 2 + 2 (1967); 365 GTB 4 Berlinetta, 246 GT Dino (1969). Entries, in various categories, in world competitions and most important championships.

FIAT S.p.A. — **Italy**

Founded in July 1899 under the name of Società Anonima Fabbrica Italiana di Automobili Torino. With the statutary modification of the shareholders' meeting in 1918, it assumed the title of FIAT and the initials may be written with either capital or small letters. In 1968 Fiat incorporated Autobianchi and OM which are still produced as a separate make with their own sales organisation and maintenance. In 1969 it has taken over Lancia & Co. and has acquired 50% of Ferrari shares. President: G. Agnelli. Vice-President: G. Nasi. Vice-President: G. Bono. Managing Directors: U. Agnelli, G. Bono. General Manager: N. Gioia. Joint General Manager: F. Rota. Head office and press office: c. Marconi 10, 10125 Turin. Works: Automobili Mirafiori, c. Giovanni Agnelli 200, 10135 Turin; Officine Rivalta, Strada Provinciale Orbassano-Piossasco 81, 10040 Rivalta; Azienda Autobianchi, vl. Lombardia, 20033 Desio; Sezione OSA, v. Nizza 250, 10126 Turin; Stabilimento Officine di Stura, lungo Stura Lazio 45, 10156 Turin; Sezione Officine di Marina di Pisa, v. F. Barbolani 17, 56013 Marina di Pisa; Sezione Officine di Firenze, v. A. Guidoni 7, 50127 Florence; Sezione Ricambi, lungo Stura Lazio 15, 10156 Turin. Employees: over 170,000 (Fiat Group including OM and Autobianchi). Cars produced in 1969: 1,293,000. Most important models: Fiat 3½ HP (1899-1900); 6 HP and 8 HP, 12 HP, 24-32 HP (1900-04); 16-24 HP (1903-04); Brevetti and 60 HP (1905-06); 18-24 (1908); Fiacre mod. 1 (1908-10); Fiat 1, 2, 3, 4, 5 (1910-16); Zero and 3 Ter (1912-15); 3A and 2B (1912-20); 70 (1915-20); 501 (1919-26); 505 and 510 (1919-25); Superfiat (1921-22); 519 (1922-24); 502 (1923-26); 509 (1925-27); 503 and 507 (1926-27); 512 (1926-28); 520 (1927-29); 521 (1928-31); 525 (1928-29); 525 SS (1929-31); 514 and 514 MM (1929-32); 515, 522 C and 524 C (1931-34); 508 Balilla and 508 S Balilla Sport (1932-37); 518 (1933-38); Ardita 2500 (1934-36); 1500 (1935-48); 500 (1936-48); 508 C Balilla 1100 (1937-39); 2800 (1938-44); 1100 (1939-48); 500 B and Giardiniera (1948-49); 1100 B and 1500 D (1948-49); 1500 E (1949-50); 1100 E (1949-53); 500 C (1949-54); 500 C Giardiniera (1949-52); 1100 ES (1950-51); 1400, 1400 A and 1400 B (1950-58); 500 C Belvedere (1951-55); 1900, 1900 A and 1900 B (1952-58); 8V (1952-54); Nuova 1100 and Nuova 1100 Familiare (1953-56); 1100 TV (1953-56); 600 (1955-60); 1100/103 E (1956-57); Nuova 500 Trasformabile (1957-60); 1100/103 D (1957-60); Nuova 500 Sport (1958-60); 1200 Gran Luce (1957-60); 1200 Trasformabile (1958-59); 1100/103 H (1959-60); 1800 and 1800 Familiare (1959-61); 1100 Special (1960-62); 500 D Tetto Apribile, 600 D Multipla, 500 Giardiniera (1960); 1300, 1500, 1800 B, 1800 B Familiare, 1300 Speciale, 1300 Familiare, 2300 Coupé, 2300 S Coupé (1961); 1100 D, 1100 D Familiare (1962); 2300 Lusso, 2300 Lusso Familiare, 1500 L, 1500 Cabriolet, 1600 S Cabriolet (1963); 850 (1964); 124 and 124 Sport Spider (1966); Dino Spider (1966); 125, Dino Coupé, 124 Sport Coupé, 850 Idroconvert (1967); 850 Special, Sport Coupé, Sport Spider, 500 L, 124 Special, 125 Special (1968); 128, 130 (1969). It has been entering competitions since 1900, when the true racing car was not yet born. First national wins, followed by many others, in the Automobile Tour of Italy with the 6-8 HP, a car with two horizontal rear cylinders. Since 1904 numerous first places in the international field. In the 1927 officially retired from motor racing.

MANUFACTURE AND ASSEMBLY IN OTHER COUNTRIES — **Argentina**: Concord Automóviles S.A. (subsidiary), Cerrito 740, Buenos Aires (manuf. 600 E, 1500, 1600). **Austria**: Steyr-Daimler-Puch AG (concessionaire), Puchstrasse 8011, Graz, Thondorf (assem. 500). **Bulgaria**: Autoprom (concessionaire), B.d. Totleben 34, Sofia (assem. 850, 124). **Chile**: Samafa (subsidiary), Rancagua (assem. 600, 125). **Costa Rica**: Sava (concessionaire), Apartado 696, San José (assem. 850, 124). **Egypt**: El Nasr Automotive Mfg Co. (associated company), Wadi-Hof, Helwan-Cairo (assem. 1100 R). **Germany**: Deutsche FIAT AG (subsidiary), 140 Salzstrasse, Heilbronn (assem. 600, 124, 125). **India**: The Premier Automobiles Ltd (associated company), Shastri Marg, Kurla, Bombay (manuf. 1100 D). **Iran**: Saica (subsidiary), 40 Khiabane Khoshbine, Teheran (assem. 1100 R). **Ireland**: Fiat (Ireland) Ltd (subsidiary), Ind. Garden Estate, Chapelizod, Dublin (assem. 600, 850, 124, 1100 R). **Korea**: Asia Motors Co. Inc. (concessionaire), Kwang Ju Plant, Seoul (assem. 124). **Malaysia**: Sharikat Fiat Distributors (concessionaire), Alexandra Rd 281, Singapore (assem. 600, 850, 1100 R, 124, 125). **Morocco:** Somaca (concessionaire), km 12 Autoroute Rabat-Casablanca (assem. 600, 850, 124, 125). **New Zealand**: Torino Motors Ltd (concessionaire), 19/29 Nelson St, Auckland C1 (assem. 500, 850, 125). **Paraguay**: Nicolas Bo S.A. (concessionaire), Montevideo y Piribebuy, Asunción (assem. 850, 124, 125). **Peru**: Fiat Perú S.A. (subsidiary), Pr. Javier Prado 1050, Lima (assem. 850, 124, 125). **Poland**: Pol-Mot (concessionaire), Warsaw (manuf. 125 P). **Portugal**: Somave S.r.l. (subsidiary), 15 Av. Eng. Duarte Pacheco, Lisbon (assem. 600, 850, 124, 125). **South Africa**: Fiat South Africa Ltd (subsidiary), 2 Bosworth St Alrode Extension, Alberton, Transvaal (assem. 850, 124, 125). **Spain**: Seat (associated company), Apartado 740, Barcelona (manuf. 600, 850, 124). **Thailand**: Karnasuta Gen. Assembly Co. (concessionaire), P.O. Box 1421, Bangkok (assem. 1100 R, 124, 125). **Turkey**: Tofas (concessionaire), Buyudere Caddesi 8/9, Istanbul (manuf. 124). **Uruguay**: Automotora Basso S.A. (concessionaire), Avda. Rondeau 1751, Montevideo (assem. 850, 124). **Venezuela**: Fiav (concessionaire), Alcabala de Candelaria à Urapal 8, Caracas (assem. 124, 125). **Yugoslavia**: Zavodi Crvena Zastava (associated company), Kragujevac, Belgrade (manuf. 600, 1300, 1500; assem. 850, 124, 125, 125 P). Cars produced in other countries in 1969: 330,000.

FNM - FABRICA NACIONAL DE MOTORES S.A. — Brazil

Established in 1942. It is the oldest motor manufacturing company in Brazil. Has been manufacturing Alfa Romeo industrial vehicles under licence since 1956. In October 1968 Alfa Romeo acquired 85% of the shares, thus gaining control of the company. President: M.A. Santos. Superintendent: R. Vio. General Manager: M. Savoia. Head office: Av. Presidente Vargas 542 - 20°, Rio de Janeiro. Press office and works: Rodovia Washington Luiz, km 23, Duque de Caxias, Rio de Janeiro. Employees: 3,000. Cars produced in 1969: 1,646. Models: 2000 (1960).

FORD MOTOR COMPANY — USA

(Makes: Ford USA, Lincoln, Mercury)

Founded in 1903, it is second largest of the American motor manufacturers. Chairman: Henry Ford II. President North America Automotive Operations: L.A. Iacocca. President International Automotive Operations: R. Stevenson. It is made up of the Ford Division (Rotunda Drive at Southfield Rd, Dearborn, Mich. General Manager J.B. Naughton, 3,850 employees, 1,743,462 cars produced in 1969), the Lincoln-Mercury Division (3000 Schaefer Rd, Dearborn, Mich. General Manager B.E. Bidwell, 1,280 employees, 419,676 cars produced in 1969). Head office and press office: The American Rd, Dearborn, Mich. Works: Dearborn; Atlanta, Ga.; Chicago, Ill.; Dallas, Tex.; Kansas City, Mo.; Lorain, Ohio; Los Angeles, Calif.; Louisville, Ky.; Mahwah, N.J.; Metuchen, N.J.; Norfolk, Va.; San José, Calif.; St. Paul, Minn.; Wayne, Mich.; Vixhom, Mich. Employees: 244,840. Cars produced in North America in 1969: 2,554,074.

MANUFACTURE AND ASSEMBLY IN OTHER COUNTRIES (excluding models of Ford Motor Company Ltd, Great Britain, of Ford Motor Company of Canada, of Ford Werke AG, Germany and of Ford-Willys do Brasil S.A.). — **Argentina**: Ford Motor Argentina S.A. (subsidiary), Casilla Correo Central 696, Buenos Aires 32/1 (manuf. and assem. Fairlane, Falcon). **Australia**: Ford Motor Company of Australia Ltd (subsidiary), Private Bag 6, Campbellfield, Victoria (manuf. Falcon). **Chile**: Ford Motor Company (subsidiary), Casilla 54-D, Santiago (assem. Falcon). **Mexico**: Ford Motor Company S.A. (subsidiary), Apartado Postal 39 bis, Mexico City (manuf. and assem. Ford, Mustang). **New Zealand**: Ford Motor Company of New Zealand Ltd (subsidiary), P.O. Box 12, Lower Hutt (assem. Falcon). **Philippines**: Ford Philippines Inc. (subsidiary), P.O. Box 415, Commercial Center, Makati Rizal (assem. Ford). **Singapore**: Ford Motor Company Private Ltd (subsidiary), Bukit Timah P.O. Box 4075, Singapore (assem. Falcon). **South Africa**: Ford Motor Co. of South Africa (Pty) Ltd (subsidiary), P.O. Box 788, Port Elizabeth (assem. Fairlane, Fairmont, Ranchero). **Venezuela**: Ford Motor de Venezuela S.A. (subsidiary), Apartado 5131 del Este, Caracas (assem. Fairlane, Falcon, Mustang, Maverick, Ford).

FORD MOTOR COMPANY Ltd — Great Britain

Founded in 1911, owned by the Ford Motor Company USA, it had its first head office at Trafford Park (Manchester). In 1925, construction of the Dagenham works was begun where production was started in 1931. Chairman: Sir Leonard Crossland. Managing Director: W.B. Batty. Head office and press office: Eagle Way, Warley Brentwood, Essex. Works: Dagenham, Essex; Halewood (near Liverpool) and others. Employees: 66,000. Cars produced in 1969: 524,003. Most important models: 8 hp "Y", 10 hp "C", 14.9 hp "B.F.", 24 hp "B", 30 hp "V8" (all prior to 2nd World War); Prefect (1938); Anglia (1939); Pilot (1947); Consul, Zephyr (1951); Anglia 100E, Popular, Zodiac (1953); Mk II Consul, Zephyr, Zodiac (1956); Anglia 105E (1959); Consul Classic 315, Capri (1961); Mk III Zephyr, Zodiac, Cortina (1962); Corsair (1963); Mk IV Zephyr, Zodiac (1966); Mk II Cortina (1966); Escort (1968); Capri (1969). Entries and wins in numerous competitions.

ASSEMBLY IN OTHER COUNTRIES — **Australia**: Ford Motor Company of Australia Ltd (associated company), 1735 Sidney Rd, Campbellfield, Victoria (assem. Cortina, Escort, Capri). **Costa Rica**: Anglofores Ltda. (concessionaire), Apartado 1768, San José (assem. Escort). **Holland**: N.V. Nederlandsche Ford Automobiel Fabriek (associated company), P.O. Box 795, Amsterdam (assem. Cortina). **Ireland**: Henry Ford and Son Ltd (associated company), Cork (assem. Cortina). **Israel**: Palestina Automobile Corp. Ltd (concessionaire), P.O. Box 975, Tel Aviv (assem. Escort). **Korea**: Hyundai Motor Co. (concessionaire), 55 Chrongro 3KA, Seoul (assem. Cortina). **Malaysia**: Associated Motor Industries, Malaysian Sendirian Berhad (concessionaire), 109 Jalan Pudu, Kuala Lumpur (assem. Cortina, Escort). **New Zealand**: Ford Motor Company of New Zealand Ltd (associated company), P.O. 30012, Lower Hutt (assem. Escort, Cortina, Zephyr, Zodiac). **Pakistan**: Ali Autos Ltd (concessionaire), P.O. Box 4206, Karachi (assem. Cortina). **Peru**: Ford Motor Co. Perú S.A. (associated company), Apartado 4130, Lima (assem. Escort). **Philippines**: Ford Philipp. Inc. (associated company), P.O. Box 415, Makati Commercial Centre, Makati Rizal (assem. Cortina, Escort). **Portugal**: Ford Lusitana (associated company), Apartado 2248, R. Rosa Arajo 2, Lisbon (assem. Escort, Cortina). **Singapore**: Ford Motor Co. Private Ltd (associated company), Bukit Timah P.O. Box 4047, Bukit Timah Rd, Singapore (assem. Cortina, Escort, Capri). **South Africa**: Ford Motor Company of South Africa (Pty) Ltd (associated company), P.O. Box 788 Port Elizabeth (assem. Escort, Cortina, Capri). **Thailand**: Anglo-Thai Motor Industries Ltd (concessionaire), P.O. Box 33, Bangkok (assem. Escort, Cortina, Capri). **Venezuela**: Ford Motor Company Venezuela S.A. (associated company), Apartado 61131 Del Este, Caracas (assem. Cortina). Cars produced in other countries in 1969: 126,296.

FORD MOTOR COMPANY OF CANADA Ltd — Canada

Founded in 1904 in Windsor, Ontario. Over the years it has built approximately 40 per cent of all cars and trucks produced by the Canadian automotive industry. President: K.E. Scott. Vice Presidents: R.F. Bennett, D.H.E. Carlson, K. Hallsworth, R.F. McNulty, S.A. Skillman. Head office and press office: The Canadian Road, Oakville, Ontario. Works: Oakville, Ontario; St. Thomas, Ontario. Employees: 16,183. Vehicles produced in 1969: 556,700 (including trucks and cars assembled for Ford USA).

MANUFACTURE AND ASSEMBLY IN OTHER COUNTRIES — **Australia**: Ford Motor Company of Australia Ltd (subsidiary), Broadmeadows (manufacture). **New Zealand**: Ford Motor Company of New Zealand Ltd (subsidiary), Lower Hutt, Auckland (assembly). **Singapore**: Ford Motor Company Private Ltd (associated company), Singapore (assembly). **South Africa**: Ford Motor Company of South Africa (Pty) Ltd (associated company), Port Elizabeth (assembly).

FORD WERKE AG — Germany (Federal Republic)

Founded in 1925. Owned by Ford Motor Company USA. Chairman and Managing Director: J.A. Banning. Directors: K.B. Amedick, H.A. Barthelmeh, H. Bergemann, H.J. Lehmann, W. Inden, P.H. Kuhn, H. Miller, H. Schmidt. Head office and press office: Ottoplatz 2, Köln-Deutz. Works: Henry Ford-Strasse 1, Köln-Niehl. Employees: 45,430. Cars produced in 1969: 613,579. Most important models: Köln 1 l, Rheinland 3 l (1933); Eifel 1.2 l (1935); Taunus (1938); Taunus (since 1948); 12M (1952); 15M (1955); 17M (1957); 17M (1960); 12M (1962); 17M and 20M (1964); 12M and 15M (1966); 17M, 20M and 20M 2.3 l (1967); Escort (1968); Capri (1969). Winner of East African Safari in 1969.

MANUFACTURE AND ASSEMBLY IN OTHER COUNTRIES — **Belgium**: Ford Werke AG Fabrieken (subsidiary), Genk (manuf. 12M, 15M, Transit, Escort). **Costa Rica**: Anglofores Ltda. (concessionaire), Apartado 1768, San José (assem. 17M). **Peru**: Ford Motor Company del Perú, S.A. (associated company), Jh. Antonio Miro Quesada 260, Casilla 4407, Lima (assem. 12M, 15M, 17M, 20M). **Philippines**: Manila Trading & Supply Co. (concessionaire), P.O. Box 7444, Port Area, Manila (assem. 12M, 15M, 17M, 20M). **Portugal**: Ford Lusitana Sarl (associated company), Apartado 2248, Lisbon 2 (assem. 12M, 15M, 17M, 20M). **South Africa**: Ford Motor Company of South Africa Pty Ltd (associated company), P.O. Box 788, Port Elizabeth (assem. 17M, 20M). Cars produced in other countries in 1969: 14,107.

FORD-WILLYS DO BRASIL S.A. — Brazil

Established in 1967 as a result of the merger between Willys Overland do Brasil and Ford Motor do Brasil S.A. President: E.S. Knutson. Ford directors: J.D. Collins, N. Chiaparini, R.T. Lindgren; Willys directors: P.L. Yriati, F.A. Erdman, J.P. Dias, W.M. Pearce, E.A. Neto. Head office and press office: Av. Rudge Ramos, 1501 Cidade, São Bernardo do Campo, São Paulo. Works: Av. Henry Ford 1787, Estrada do Taboão 899, São Bernardo do Campo, São Paulo. Employees: 18,000. Cars produced in 1969: 88,550. Most important models: Ford T (1924); Willys Jeep (1954); Rural Jeep (1958); Renault Dauphine (1959); Aero Willys (1960); Itamaraty (1965); Ford Galaxie (1966); Ford Corcel, LTD (1968). Entries in numerous competitions from 1962 to 1968. Brazilian Makers Championship in 1967-68.

FUJI HEAVY INDUSTRIES Ltd — Japan

(Make: Subaru)

Founded in 1945 under the name of Fuji Sangyo Co. Present title since 1963. Member of Nissan Group. Chairman: N. Yokota. President: E. Ohhara. Directors: T. Yamada, Y. Inoue. Head office and press office: 1-7-2 (Subaru Bld), Nishi-Shinjuku, Shinjukuku, Tokyo. Works: Gumma Works, 9-6 Oshawa 3-chome, Mitaka-shi, Tokyo. Employees: 7,964. Cars produced in 1969: 135,069. Most important models: Subaru 360 Sedan (1958); Subaru 1000 (1966); Subaru 1000 Sports (1967).

GAZ - GORKOVSKY AVTOMOBILNY ZAVOD — USSR

Avtoexport, Ul. Volkhonka 14, Moscow G 512. Works: Gorki.

GENERAL MOTORS CORP. — USA

(Makes: Buick, Cadillac, Chevrolet, Oldsmobile, Pontiac)

Founded in 1908, it is the largest motor manufacturer in the world with a production range which extends from the most economical and popular cars to the most costly. Chairman: J.M. Roche. President: E.N. Cole. GM has brought together five American motor manufacturing factories, transforming them into the following divisions: Buick Motor Division (1051 East Hamilton Ave, Flint, Mich. 48550), General Manager L.N. Mays, 22,500 employees, 713,894 cars produced in 1969; Cadillac Motor Car Division (2860 Clark Ave, Detroit, Mich. 48232), General Manager G.R. Elges, 11,500 employees, 266,489 cars produced in 1969; Chevrolet Motor Division (3044 West Grand Blvd, Detroit, Mich. 48202), General Manager G.Z. De Lorean, 129,000 employees, 2,002,074 cars produced in 1969; Oldsmobile Division (920 Townsend St, Lansing, Mich. 48921), General Manager J.B. Beltz, 16,000 employees, 668,108 cars produced in 1969; Pontiac Motor Division (196 Oakland Ave, Pontiac, Mich. 48053), General Manager F.J. McDonald, 20,000 employees, 774,707 cars produced in 1969. The GM also owns General Motors - Holden's Pty Ltd (Australia), Adam Opel AG (Germany) and Vauxhall Motors Ltd (Great Britain). Head office: 3044 West Grand Blvd, Detroit, Mich. 48202.

MANUFACTURE AND ASSEMBLY IN OTHER COUNTRIES (excluding non-American GM makes) — **Argentina**: General Motors Argentina S.A. (subsidiary), Rodriguez Pena 256, San Martin, Buenos Aires (manuf. Chevy II). **Belgium**: General Motors Continental (subsidiary), Noorderlaan 75, Antwerp (assem. Buick, Electra, Riviera; Chevrolet Chevelle, Impala). **Brazil**: General Motors do Brasil S.A. (subsidiary), São Caetano do Sul, São Paulo (manuf. Chevrolet Opala). **Denmark**: General Motors International A.S. (subsidiary), Aldersrogade 20, Copenhagen (assem. Buick Skylark). **South Africa**: General Motors South African Pty Ltd (subsidiary), Kempston Rd, Port Elizabeth (assem. Pontiac Parisienne). **Switzerland**: General Motors Suisse S.A. (subsidiary), Salzhausstrasse 21, Bienne (assem. Chevrolet Chevy II, Chevelle, Camaro).

GENERAL MOTORS - HOLDEN'S Pty Ltd — Australia

Established in 1931 as a result of the merger between General Motors (Australia) Pty Ltd and Holden's Motor Body Builders Ltd. Affiliate of the General Motors Corp. USA. Managing Director: A.G. Gibbs. Head office and press office: 241 Salmon St, Fishermans Bend, Melbourne, Victoria. Works: as above; Dandenong, Victoria; Woodville, Elizabeth, South Australia; Pagewood, New South Wales; Acacia Ridge, Queensland; Mosman Pk, Perth, West Australia. Employees: 26,000. Cars produced in 1969: 174,476.

ASSEMBLY IN OTHER COUNTRIES — **New Zealand**: General Motors News Zealand Ltd (subsidiary), Trantham Plant No. 1,

Private Bag, Upper Hutt (assem. Sedan, Premier). **South Africa**: General Motors South Africa Pty Ltd (subsidiary), Kempston Rd, Port Elizabeth (assem. Sedan).

GENERAL MOTORS OF CANADA Ltd **Canada**

(Make: Acadian, Pontiac)

Established in 1918 as a result of the merger between McLaughlin Motor Car Company and Chevrolet Motor Car Company, it is a whollyowned subsidiary of General Motors Corp. Chairman: R.S. McLaughlin. President and Chief Executive Officer: R.S. Withers. Executive Vice President and General Manufacturing Manager: E.J. Barbeau. Vice President and Comptroller: J.D. Mintline. Vice Presidents: E.V. Rippingille Jr, F.W. Walker Jr. Head office and press office: William St, Oshawa, Ontario. Works: Oshawa, Ste. Therese, P.Q. Employees: 30,000. Cars produced in 1969: 391,561 (including cars assembled for GM Corp. USA).

GIANNINI AUTOMOBILI S.p.A. **Italy**

Founded in 1920 under the name of F.lli Giannini A. & D., it later became Giannini Automobili S.p.A. President: M. Recchi Franceschini. Managing Director: V. Polverelli. Head office, press office and works: v. Tiburtina 97, Rome. Employees: 65. Cars produced in 1969: 1,200. Most important models: 750 Berlinetta San Remo (1949); Fiat 750 TV and 850 GT (1963); 850 Coupé Gazzella, Fiat 500 TV and TVS, 590 GT and GTS (1964); Fiat Berlina 500 S, 850 SL and 950, Fiat Coupé 850 and 1000, Fiat 1300 Super and 1500 GL, Fiat 500 TVS Montecarlo (1965). It is engaged above all producing variations of Fiat cars. Entries in various competitions and first places in category in various Italian championships.

GILBERN CARS Ltd **Great Britain**

Founded in 1959 under the name of Gilbern Sports Cars & Components. Changed to Gilbern Sports Car (Components) Ltd in 1962. Present title since 1968. Board of Directors: M.M. Collings, M.C. Collings, R.A. Collings, M.J. Leather. Head office, press office and works: Llantwit Fardre, nr. Pontypridd, Glam. Employees: 50. Cars produced in 1968: 200. Models: GT Mk 1 (1959-61); GT 1622 (1962-63); GT 1800 (1964-67); Genie 3 I (1966-69); Invader (1969).

GINETTA CARS Ltd **Great Britain**

Founded in 1958. Managing Director: K.R. Walklett. Directors: T.G. Walklett, D.J. Walklett, I.A. Walklett. Head office, press office and works: West End Works, Witham, Essex. Employees: 42. Cars produced in 1969: 250.

GLASSIC INDUSTRIES Inc. **USA**

Founded in 1964. President: J.W. Faircloth. Vice-President and General Manager: E.V.J. Faircloth. Head office, press office and works: 3125 Belvedere Rd, West Palm Beach, Florida 33406. Employees: 15. Cars produced in 1969: 50. Models: Sport Phaeton and Sports Roadster.

GROUP LOTUS CARS COMPANIES Ltd **Great Britain**

Founded in 1952. Chairman: A.C.B. Chapman. Group Board: A.C.B. Chapman, F.R. Bushell, P.R. Kirwan-Taylor, D.A. Austin. Managing Director: D.A. Austin. Head office, press office and works: Norwich, NOR 92W. Employees: 1,000. Cars produced in 1969: 4,500. Most important models: Mk Six (1952); Mk Eight, Mk Nine, Mk Ten, Elite (1957); Eleven (1960); Elan (1962); Elan + 2 (1967); Europa (1968). Entries and first places in numerous international competitions with F1, F2, F3, F5 cars (Indianapolis, Le Mans, Monte Carlo Grand Prix, United States Grand Prix, Pacific Grand Prix at Laguna Seca, etc.).

HILLMAN - see CHRYSLER UNITED KINGDOM Ltd

HINDUSTAN MOTORS Ltd **India**

Founded in 1942. Chairman: B.M. Birla. President: S.L. Bhatter. Head office: 15 India Exchange Pl., Calcutta 1. Press office: 11 RN Mukherjee Rd, Calcutta 1. Works: P.O. Uttarpara, Dist. Hooghly, W. Bengal. Employees: 12,000. Cars produced in 1968: 22,687. Car production begun in 1951. Most important models: Hindustan 10, Hindustan 14, Landmaster (1954); Ambassador (1957); Ambassador O.H.V. (1959); Ambassador Mk II (1963).

HOLDEN - see GENERAL MOTORS - HOLDEN'S Pty Ltd

HONDA MOTOR COMPANY Ltd **Japan**

Founded in 1946 as Honda Gijitsu Kenkyujo. Present title since 1948. President: S. Honda. Executive Vice-President: T. Fujisawa. Executive Directors: S. Isobe, Kiyoshi Kawashima, K. Kawashima, T. Shirai, M. Nishida. Head office and press office: 5 Yaesu, 5-chome, Chuo-ku, Tokyo. Works: Saitama, 8-1 Honcho, Wako-shi, Saitamaken; Suzuka, 1907 Hirata-cho, Suzuka-shi, Mie-ken; Hamamatsu, 34 Oi-machi, Hamamatsu-shi, Shizuoka-ken; Sayama, 1-10 Shin-Sayama, Sayama-shi, Saitama-ken. Employees: 18,550. Cars produced in 1969: 281,568. Models: Honda Sports 500 (1962); Honda Sports 600 (1964); LM 700 Estate Car, S800 (1965); N360 (1967); N600 (1968); 1300 (1969). Entries and wins in F1 and F2 racings (Mexican G.P. (1965), Italian G.P. (1967), French G.P. and G.P. USA (1968).

HUMBER - see CHRYSLER UNITED KINGDOM Ltd

IKA - RENAULT S.A.I.C. y F. **Argentina**

Founded in 1955 under the name of Industrias Kaiser Argentina S.A.I.C. y F. Present title since 1968. President and General Manager: Y. Lavaud. Vice-President: J. Leroy. Managing Director: C. Gruau. Head office and press office: Sarmiento 1230, Buenos Aires. Works: Barrio Santa Isabel, Prov. Cordoba. Employees: 9,000.

ASSEMBLY IN OTHER COUNTRIES — **Chile**: Renault Chile S.A. (filiale), José Miguel de la Barra 480, 5° Piso - DPTO 501, Santiago (assem. Renault 4). **Uruguay**: Santa Rosa Automotores S.A. (concessionaire), Cerro Largo 888, Montevideo (assem. Renault, Gordini, 4L, 4, Parisienne; Torino S, 300, 380, S 380).

IMPERIAL - see CHRYSLER CORP.

INNOCENTI SOCIETÀ GENERALE PER L'INDUSTRIA METALLURGICA E MECCANICA S.p.A. **Italy**

Founded in 1933 under the name of Società Anonima Fratelli Innocenti, became Innocenti Anonima per Applicazioni Tubolari Acciaio before assuming present title. Collaborates with BLMC. President: L. Innocenti. Vice-President: C. Fumagalli. Managing Director: M. Fusaia. General Manager: G. Rodocanachi. Head office, press office and works: v. Pitteri 81, Milan. Employees: 6,334. Cars produced in 1969: 50,540. Manufacture of Innocenti Austin A40 (Berlina and Combinata) begun in 1960, of Innocenti Morris IM-3S in 1963, Innocenti Austin J4 in 1964, Innocenti Mini Minor in 1965, S Spider in 1966, of Mini T in 1967 and of Innocenti Mini Mk 2 and Mini Cooper Mk 2 in 1968.

INTERNATIONAL HARVESTER COMPANY **USA**

Founded in 1902. Principal products agricultural machinery construction equipment and trucks exported all over the world. Chairman: H.O. Bercher. President: B. McCormick. Executive Vice-Presidents: W.E. Callahan, O.G. Voss. Head office and press office: 401 N. Michigan Ave, Chicago, Illinois 60611.

ASSEMBLY IN OTHER COUNTRIES — **Australia**: International Harvester Company of Australia Pty Ltd (subsidiary), G.P.O. Box 4305, Melbourne, C.1, Victoria (assem. Travelall, Scout). **Philippines**: International Harvester MacLeod Inc. (subsidiary), P.O. Box 308, Manila (assem. Travelall, Scout). **South Africa**: International Harvester Company S.A. Pty Ltd (subsidiary), P.O. Box 12 Isando, Transvaal (assem. Travelall, Scout). **Turkey**: Turk Otomotiv Endustrileri A.S. (associated company), Cayirova, Gebze (assem. Scout, Travelall). **Venezuela**: Industria Venezolana de Maquinarias C.A. (associated company), Apartado 50956, Sabana Grande, Caracas (assem. Scout, Travelall).

ISO S.p.A. AUTOMOTOVEICOLI **Italy**

Founded in 1939 under the name of Isothermos. Present title since 1949. President: Maria A. Rivolta Barberi. Managing Directors: E. Staffico, P. Rivolta Barberi. Head office: c. Venezia 16, Milan. Press office and works: v. Vittorio Veneto 66, Bresso (Milan). Employees: 150. Cars produced in 1969: 370. At first (1952) produced the Isetta, since 1964 has produced the Iso Rivolta GT, Iso Grifo and Iso Grifo 7 l, Fidia with Chevrolet engines and Lele.

ISUZU MOTORS Ltd **Japan**

Established in 1937 as a result of the merger between the Ishikawajima motor manufacturing factory, which held the Wolseley manufacturing licence from 1918 to 1927, and the Tokyo Gas & Electric, which began the manufacture of military trucks in 1916. Chairman: N. Kusunoki. President: T. Aramaki. Executive Vice-Presidents: T. Okamoto, H. Okamura. Head office and press office: 22-10 Miami-oi, 6-chome, Shinagawa-ku, Tokyo. Works: Kawasaki Factory, 5931 Shimodono-machi, Daishi Kawasaki City, Kanagawa Pref.; Fujisawa Factory, 8 Tsuchitana, Fujisawa City, Kanagawa Pref. Employees: 12,000. Cars produced in 1969: 36,429. Most important models: Bellel (1962); Bellett, Bellett Standard (1963); Florian (1967); 117 Coupé (1968). Took part in 1969 in the 1000 Lakes Rally.

JAGUAR CARS Ltd **Great Britain**

Founded in 1922 under the name of Swallow Sidecar Co., became SS. Cars Ltd and then Jaguar Cars Ltd in 1945. In 1960 it acquired the Daimler Co., founded in 1896, in 1961 Guy Motors Ltd, in 1963 Coventry Climax Engines Ltd. Recently it became part of BLMC Ltd. Chairman and Chief Executive: Sir William Lyons. Managing Director and Deputy Chairman: F.R.W. England. Joint Managing Director: R.W. Grice. Head office, press office and works: Browns Lane, Allesley, Coventry, CV5 9DR. Employees: about 7,500. Cars produced in 1969: about 30,000. Most important models: SS I, SS II (1931-36); SS Jaguar (1935-49); SS Jaguar 100 (1935-40); Jaguar Mk V (1948-51); XK 120 (1948-54); Mk VII (1950-56); C-Type (1951-53); D-Type (1954-57); 2.4 (240) (1955); E-Type (1961); Mk 10 (1961-66); 420 G (1966). Victories in various competitions (Liège-Rome-Liège, Alpine Rally, Monte Carlo Rally, Tour de France, Sebring, Reims). First place at Le Mans (1951-53-55-56-57), in German Touring Car Championship and in European Touring Challenge Cup (1963).

ASSEMBLY IN OTHER COUNTRIES — **South Africa**: Biritish Leyland Factory, Blackheat, Capetown. Cars assembled in 1969: about 1,000.

JEEP CORP. **USA**

Founded in 1903 under the name of Standard Wheel Co. at Terre Haute (Indiana), assumed the title of Overland Automobile Co. in 1907 and Willys-Overland Co. in 1908 when it transferred to Toledo (Ohio). In 1919, it merged with Electric Auto-Lite, New Process Gear and Duesenberg Motors, taking the title of Willys Corp., later changed to Willys Motors Inc. (1953) and to Kaiser Jeep Corp. (1963). On 4 February 1970 the American Motors Corp. approved the agreement by which AM acquired Kaiser Jeep Corp. Press office: 14250 Plymouth Rd, Detroit, Mich. 48232. First Overland "Runabout" model in 1903. Production of Jeep Universal CJ-5 begun in 1955, of Jeep Wagoneer and Gladiator in 1962, of Jeepster series in 1967.

MANUFACTURE AND ASSEMBLY IN OTHER COUNTRIES — **Australia**: Jeep Corp. of Australia Pty Ltd, P.O. Box 75, Salisbury North 4107; Evans Rd, Salisbury North, Brisbane (assem. Jeep Universal and Wagoneer). **Belgium**: Anciens Etablissements Berg S.A., 538 Chaussée de Waterloo, Brussels (assem. Jeep Universal). **Ceylon**: United Motors, P.O. Box 697, 100 Hyde Park Corner, Colombo 2 (assem. Jeep Universal). **Chile**: Divema S.A., Avda. Blanco Encalada 1737, Casilla 3657, Santiago (assem. Jeep Universal). **Colombia**: Leónidas Lara e Hijos, Plaza de San Victorino, Bogotá (assem. Jeep Universal and Wagoneer). **Costa Rica**: Auto Técnica S.A., Apartado 2028, San José (assem. Jeep Universal and Wagoneer). **France**: Sofia, 71 av. des Termes, Paris 17e (assem. Jeep Universal). **Holland**: Kemper en Van Twist Diesel N.V., Mijlweg 33, P.O. Box 156, Dordrecht (assem. Jeep Universal and Wagoneer). **India**: Mahindra & Mahindra Ltd, Gateway Bldg, Apollo Bunder, Bombay (assem. Jeep Universal and Wagoneer). **Indonesia**: N.V. Indonesian Service Co. Ltd, Trommol Pos Djak. 121, Djalan Lodan, Djakarta-Kota (assem. Jeep Universal). **Iran**: Sherkate Sahami Jeep, Ekbatan Ave, Jeep Bldg, Teheran (assem. Jeep Universal and Wagoneer). **Israel**: Autocars Co. Ltd, P.O. Box 444, Haifa (assem. Jeep Universal and Wagoneer). **Japan**: Mitsubishi Heavy-Industries Ltd, No. 10, 2-chome, Marunouchi, Chiyoda-ku, Tokyo (manuf. Jeep Universal). **Korea**: Shin Jin Motor Co. Ltd, No. 91 Suh So Moon Dong, Suh Dae Moon Ku, Seoul (assem. Jeep Universal). **Mexico**: Vehiculos Automotores Mexicanos S.A., Calle Norte 65, No. 1099, Mexico City 16, DF. (assem. Jeep Universal and Wagoneer; Rambler). **Morocco**: Société d'Importation & Distribution Automobile, 84 av. Lalla Yacoute, Casablanca (assem. Jeep Universal). **Pakistan**: Kandawalla Industries, Kandawalla Bldg, M.A. Jinnah Rd, Karachi 3 (assem. Jeep Universal and Wagoneer). **Philippines**: U.S. Automotive Co. Inc., 1000-1020 United Nations Ave, corner San Marcelino St., P.O. Box 3399, Manila (assem. Jeep and Wagoneer). **Portugal**: C. Santos Commercio Industria S.A.R.L. (concessionaire), Av. de Liberdade 29-41, Lisbon 2 (assem. Jeep Universal). **Singapore**: The Cycle & Carriage Co. (Malayan) Ser. Ber., P.O. Box 1149, 41/43 Orchard Rd, Singapore (assem. Jeep Universal). **South Africa**: Praetor Assemblers (Pty) Ltd, P.O. 60, Rosslyn Frans du Toit St, Pretoria (assem. Jeep Universal and Wagoneer). **Spain**: Material Movil y Construcciones S.A., V.I.A.S.A. Division, Apartado 279, Zaragoza (manuf. Jeep Universal). **Taiwan**: Yue Loong Motor Co. Ltd, 15 Sin Yang St, Taipei (assem. Jeep Universal). **Thailand**: Thai Yarnyon Co. Ltd, 388/3 Petchburi Rd, Bangkok (assem. Jeep Universal). **Turkey**: Türk Willys-Overland Fabrikalari A.S., Cumhuriyet Caddesi, Pegasus Evi, Harblye, Istanbul (assem. Jeep Universal and Wagoneer). **Venezuela**: Willys de Venezuela S.A., Apartado 41-42. Tejerias, Edo Uragua (assem. Jeep Universal and Wagoneer).

JENSEN MOTORS Ltd **Great Britain**

Founded in 1934. President: K.H. Quale. Chairman: D.N. Healey. Managing Director: A.W. Vickers. Directors: D.K.R. Beattle, A.B.N. Good, G.C. Healey, F.R. Welsh, L.H.N. Wilkinson, R.A. Graves. Head office and works: Kelvin Way, West Bromwich, Staffordshire. Press office: Good Relations Ltd, 23 Sloane St, London S.W.1. Employees: 550. Cars produced in 1969: 512. Most important models: Jensen Interceptor (1950-58); 541 "R" (1957-60); 541 "S" (1960-62); C-V8 (1962-66); Interceptor and FF (1966-69).

LAMBORGHINI - see AUTOMOBILI FERRUCCIO LAMBORGHINI S.p.A.

LANCIA & C. - FABBRICA AUTOMOBILI S.p.A. **Italy**

Founded in 1906, this company has always been noted for the production of extremely well-finished prestige cars.

President: A. Canonica. Vice-President: A. Fiorelli. General Manager: G. Calbiani. Head office and press office: v. Vincenzo Lancia 27, Turin. Works: as above; Strada Statale 26, Chivasso (Turin); v. Volta 6, Bolzano. Employees: about 12,000. Cars produced in 1969: 45,000. Most important models: First car 14 hp (1907); Alfa and Dialfa (1908); Beta (1909); Gamma (1910); Delta, Didelta, Epsilon, Eta (1911); Theta (1913); Kappa (1919); Dikappa (1921); Trikappa (1922); Lambda (1923); Dilambda (1928); Artena, Astura (1931); Augusta (1933); Aprilia (1937); Ardea (1939); Aurelia (1950); Aurelia B20 (1951); Appia (1953); Flaminia (1957); Flavia (1960); Flavia Coupé and Convertible (1962); Flavia Sport (1963); Fulvia (1963); Fulvia Coupé (1965); Fulvia Sport (1965); Fulvia Coupé 1.3 HF (1966); Flavia 819 (1967); Fulvia Coupé 1.6 HF (1968). Entries in numerous competitions (Montecarlo, Tulipe, Finland Rallies; Daytona, Sebring, Targa Florio, Nürburgring, etc.).

ASSEMBLY IN OTHER COUNTRIES — **South Africa**: Trans-African Continental Motors Co. Pty Ltd (concessionaire), 174 Anderson St, Johannesburg (assem. Flavia, Fulvia).

LINCOLN - see FORD MOTOR COMPANY

LMX AUTOMOBILE S.r.l. — **Italy**

Founded in 1968, produces sport cars with Ford engines. Technical Manager: M. Liprandi. Head office and press office: v. Bigli 19, 20121 Milan. Works: c.so Casale 313, Turin.

LOTUS - see GROUP LOTUS CARS COMPANIES Ltd

MARCOS CARS Ltd — **Great Britain**

Managing Director and Chairman: J.G.W. Marsh. Directors: W.N.R. Harrison, R.C. Shutter. Head office, press office and works: Greeland Mills, Bradford-on-Avon, Wiltshire. Employees: 120. Cars produced in 1968: 114. Models: Marcos 1 l (1960-64); 1800 (1964-65); 1500 (1965-67); 1600 (1967). Entries and wins in numerous competitions.

MASERATI - see OFFICINE ALFIERI MASERATI S.p.A.

MATRA SPORTS S.A. — **France**

Founded in 1932 under the name of Deutch-Bonnet, given title of René Bonnet in 1961. Present title since 1964. At the extraordinary general meeting on 12 November 1968 a merger was decided with Engins Matra S.A. as "Motoring Division" of the latter. President: M. Chassagny. Vice-President: S. Floirat. Managing Director: J.L. Lagardère. Head office: 4, rue de Presbourg, Paris 8e. Press office: av. Louis Bréguet, B.P. 1, 78 Velizy. Works: 1, av. Saint-Exupéry, Romorantin; 1, av. Louis Bréguet, 78 Velizy. Employees: 450. Cars produced in 1969: 1,800. Models: Deutch-Bonnet (1932-40); René Bonnet (1961-64); Matra-Bonnet (1965); Matra M530 (1966). Entries and wins in numerous competitions with F2 and F3 cars (Reims, Albi, Magny-Cours in 1965, Monaco, Rouen, Grand Prix de Monaco, 24 hour Le Mans, Palmarès in 1966-67-68). World Champion in 1969.

MAZDA - see TOYO KOGYO COMPANY Ltd

MERCEDES-BENZ - see DAIMLER-BENZ AG

MERCURY - see FORD MOTOR COMPANY

MG - see BLMC

MINI - see BLMC

MITSUBISHI MOTORS CORP. — **Japan**

Established in October 1917 as Mitsubishi Shipbuilding & Engineering Co. Ltd and later changed its name to Mitsubishi Heavy Industries Ltd. After the Second World War it split into three companies under the Enterprise Reorganisation Law, but these again reunited in June 1964 as Mitsubishi Heavy Industries Ltd. Products include ships and other vessels, railway vehicles, aircraft, space equipment, missiles, atomic equipment, heavy machinery. The Automobile Division became an indipendent company in June 1970 under the name of Mitsubishi Motors Corp. President: Y. Satoh. Executive Vice-President: T. Fuwa. Directors: T. Miyahara, M. Tauji, K. Furuhata, S. Ohtsuka. Head office and press office: No. 33-8 Shiba 5-chome, Minatoku, Tokyo. Works: Mizushima Motor Vehicle Works: No. 1, 1-chome, Mizushima Kanigandori, Kuraishi, Okoyama-Pref.; Nagoya Motor Vehicle Works: No. 2, Oye-cho, Minato-ku, Nagoya. Employees: 21,000. Cars produced in 1969: 157,929.

MONTEVERDI - see AUTOMOBILE MONTEVERDI

MORGAN MOTOR COMPANY Ltd — **Great Britain**

Founded in 1910. Governing Director: P.H.G. Morgan. Head office, press office and works: Pickersleigh Rd, Malvern Link, Worcestershire. Employees: 96. Cars produced in 1969: 473. Production of 4-wheeled vehicles begun in 1936. Most important models: Morgan 4/4, Morgan Plus 8. Entries and wins in numerous competitions since 1911.

MORRIS - see BLMC

NISSAN MOTOR COMPANY Ltd — **Japan**

Founded in 1933 under the name of Jidosha Seizo Co. Ltd. Present title since 1934. In 1966 it took over Prince Motors Ltd. President: K. Kawamata. Executive Vice-Presidents: T. Iwakoshi, T. Igarashi. Head office and press office: 17-1, 6-chome, Ginza-Higashi, Chuo-ku, Tokyo. Works: Mitaka, 8-1, 5-chome, Shimo-Renjaku, Mitaka, Tokyo; Murayama, 6000 Nakafuji, Murayama, Kitatama-gun, Tokyo; Agikubo, 5-1, 3-chome, Momoi, Suginami-ku, Tokyo; Oppama, 1, Natsushima-cho, Yokosuka; Tochigi, 2500, Kaminokawa, Tochigi-ken; Yokohama 2, Takara-cho, Kanagawa-ku, Yokohama; Yoshiwara, 1-1, Takara-cho, Yoshiwara Fuji, Shizuoka-ken; Zama, 5070, Nagakubo, Zama, Kanagawa-ken. Employees: 48,000. Cars produced in 1969: 697,691. Most important models: Datsun (1958); Datsun Bluebird (1959); Datsun 1600 Sports, 2000, Cedric (1960); Nissan Gloria (1962); Datsun Coupé 1600 (1964); Nissan President (1965); Datsun 1000, Nissan Prince Royal (1966). First places in Round Australia Rally (1958); East African Safari Rally and Kenya Rally (1966); Shell 4000 Canada Rally (1967-68); South Africa's Moonlight Rally and Beira Rally (1967); Zacateca Race, Malaysian Race, Anssie Race, Southern Cross Rally (1968); South African Castrol 2000 Rally, East African Safari Rally (1969-70).

MANUFACTURE AND ASSEMBLY IN OTHER COUNTRIES — **Australia**: Nissan Motor Co. (Australia) Pty Ltd (subsidiary), 210-218 Victoria St, Carlton, 3053 Melbourne, Victoria. **Chile**: Industrias Nissan Motor Chile S.A. (associated company), Alameda B. O'Higgins 1460, 7° Piso, Casilla 144-D, Santiago. **Costa Rica**: Agencia Datsun Cia. Comercial Aizenman Ltda. (associated company), Apartado Postal 3219, San José. **Malaysia**: Tan Chong & Sons Co. (associated company), Kuala Lumpur. **Mexico**: Nissan Mexicana S.A. de C.V. (associated company), Avda. Insurgentes Sur No. 1457, Piso del 1° al 5°, Mexico City 19, D.F. **New Zealand**: Nissan Motor Distributors (New Zealand) Co. Ltd (associated company), P.O. Box 1072, Auckland; Croydon Motors Ltd (associated company), Christchurch. **Peru**: Nissan Motor del Perú S.A. (associated company), P.O. Box 6107, Lima. **Philippines**: Wellington Motors Corp. (associated company), Wellington Bldg, Plaza Calderón de la Barca, Binondo, Manila. **Portugal**: Entreposto Commercial de Automóveis (associated company), Lisbon. **South Africa**: Datsun Motor Vehicle Distributors (associated company), Pretoria. **Taiwan**: Yue Loong Motor Co. Ltd (associated company), 16 Sin Yang St, Taipei. **Thailand**: Siam Motors and Nissan Co. Ltd (associated company), 865, Rama 1 Rd, Bangkok. Cars produced in other countries in 1969: 136,180.

NSU - see AUDI NSU AUTO UNION AG

OFFICINE ALFIERI MASERATI S.p.A. — **Italy**

Founded in 1926, it is famous for its GT and racing cars. In 1968 signed a collaboration agreement with Citroën S.A. Honorary Chairman: A. Orsi. President: P. Bercot. Managing Director and General Manager: G. Malleret. Head office, press office and works: v. Ciro Menotti 322, Modena. Employees: about 700. Most important models: A 6/1500 (1948); A6G/2000 (1954); 3500 GT (1956); 5000 GT (1958); 3500 GTI and 5000 GTI (1960); Mistral, Quattroporte (1964); Mexico, Ghibli (1966); Indy (1969). Up to 1957, entered all motor races (Targa Florio 1926, 500 Miles Indianapolis 1938-40, European Mountain Championship 1956-57) and obtained, among others, the title of world racing drivers championship.

OLDSMOBILE - see GENERAL MOTORS CORP.

OPEL - see ADAM OPEL AG

OTAS COSTRUZIONI AUTOMOBILISTICHE — **Italy**

Founded in 1969. Proprietor F. Giannini. Head office and works: Ozegna Canavese, Turin. Cars produced in 1969: 300. Most important models: Grand Prix America and Iniezione (1969).

OTOSAN A.S. — **Turkey**

Founded in 1959. It is part of the large Koç Group-Koç Holding and produces cars with fibreglass body works and Ford engines. General Manager: A. Binbir. Head office and press office: P.K. 102, Kadiköy, Istanbul.

PEUGEOT - see AUTOMOBILES PEUGEOT S.A.

PLYMOUTH - see CHRYSLER CORP.

POLSKI-FIAT - see FABRIKA SAMOCHODÓW OSOBOWYCH

PONTIAC - see GENERAL MOTORS (USA and Canada)

PORSCHE - see Dr. Ing. h.c. F. PORSCHE KG

PUMA VEÍCULOS E MOTORES Ltda. — **Brazil**

Founded in 1964 under the name of Sociedade de Automóveis Lumimari Ltda. Present title since 1966. Directors: J.L. Fernandes, G. Malzoni, L.R. Alves da Costa, M. Masteguin. Head office, press office and works: Av. Presidente Wilson 4413, Caixa Postal 42649, São Paulo. Employees: 125. Cars produced in 1968: 151. Models: Malzoni GT with DKW engine (1964-65); Puma GT with DKW engine (1966-67); Puma 1500 GT with VW engine (1968).

RÉGIE NATIONALE DES USINES RENAULT — **France**

Founded in 1898 under the name of Société Anonyme des Usines Renault. Present title since 1945 when it was nationalized. It is today the largest motor manufacturer in France. President: P. Dreyfus. Vice-President: A. Giraud. Head office and press office: 8-10 av. Emile Zola, Boulogne-Billancourt, 92 (Seine). Works: as above; Pierre Lefaucheux, Flins (Seine-et-Oise); Usine de Cléon, Cléon (Seine-Maritime); Usine du Mans, Pierre-Piffault (Sarthe); Usine de Choisy, Choisy-le-Roy (Seine); Usine d'Orléans, St. Jean de la Ruelle; Usine du Havre, Sandouville (Seine-Maritime). Employees: 83,000. Cars produced in 1969: 1,009,372. Most important models: 1.75 CV (1898); 2 cylinder (1904); 35 CV (1912); Marne Taxi, Type AG, Type TT (1923); 45 hp (1923-27); Celtaquatre (1934); Viva Grand Sport (1938); 4 CV (1947); Fregate (1951); Dauphine (1957); Floride (1959); Floride S, Caravelle, R8 (1962); Caravelle 1100 (1963); R8 Major (1964); R16 (1965); 4 Parisienne (1966); R16 TS, 6 (1968); R12 (1969). Entries and wins in numerous competitions (Monte Carlo Rally, Alpine Rally, Tour de Corse, Liège-Rome-Liège, Sebring, Reims, Nürburgring, Mobil Economy Run, etc.).

MANUFACTURE AND ASSEMBLY IN OTHER COUNTRIES — **Algeria**: Caral Renault Algérie (subsidiary), El Harrach, BP 57, Algiers (assem. R4, R8, R16, R16 TS). **Argentina**: Industrias Kaiser Argentina S.A. (subsidiary), Avda. Santa Maria, Casilla Correo 8, Cordoba (manuf. R4). **Australia**: Renault Australia Pty Ltd (subsidiary), Melbourne (assem. R6, R10, R16, R16 TS). **Belgium**: Régie Renault (subsidiary), Schaarbeeklei, Vilvoorde 1 (assem. R4, R6, R8, R10). **Bulgaria**: Bulgarenault (concessionaire), Plovdiv (assem. R8, R10). **Canada**: Soma Inc. (associated company), Saint-Bruno de Montarville, Comté Chambly, Quebec (assem. R8, R10, R12, R16). **Chile**: Renault de Chile (subsidiary), Casilla 585, Arica (assem. R4). **Colombia**: Sofasa (associated company), Carrera 5, Nr. 15/91, Apartado Aereo 18 248, Bogotá (assem. R4). **Costa Rica**: Auto Ensembladora S.A. Ltda. (concessionaire), Avda. 10 Calle 14, Apartado 2424, San José (assem. R8, R10). **Ireland**: Smith Engineering Ltd, Wexford (R4, R6, R8, R10, R12, R16). **Ivory Coast**: Safar (subsidiary), BP 2764, Abidjan (assem. R4, R6, R8, R10, R12, R16, R16 TS). **Madagascar**: Somacoa (associated company), PB 796, Tananarive (assem. R4, R6, R12, R16, R16 TS). **Malaysia**: Associated Motor Industries, Sendirian Berhad, 109 Jalan Pudu, Kuala Lumpur (assem. R10, R16). **Mexico**: Diesel Nacional S.A. (concessionaire), Ciudad Sahagun, Hidalgo (assem. R4, R8, R10). **Morocco**: Somaca, km 12 Autoroute Rabat-Casablanca (assem. R4, R6, R8, R12, R16, R16 TS). **New Zealand**: Campbell Industries (concessionaire), Thames (assem. R10). **Peru**: I.A.P. S.A. (associated company), Apartado 3841, Lima (assem. R4, R10). **Philippines**: Renault Philippines Inc. (subsidiary), 978 Marques de Comillas, P.O. Box 143, Manila (assem. R10, R16, R16 TS). **Portugal**: Industrias Lusitanas Renault (associated company), Guarda (assem. R4, R6, R8 S, R10, R12, R16, R16 TS). **Rumania**: Uzina de Autoturismo Pitesti (concessionaire), Colibasi (assem. R8, R12). **Singapore**: AMI (concessionaire), Taman Jurong, P.O. Box 19, Singapore 22 (assem. R10). **South Africa**: Rosslyn Motor Assembly (associated company), 35-39 Ernest Oppenheimer St, Rosslyn Industrial Township, Pretoria (R4, R6, R10, R12, R16 TS). **Spain**: Fasa-Renault (associated company), Apartado 198, Valladolid (assem. R4, R6, R8, R12). **Trinidad**: Henry Pain Ltd, Port of Spain (assem. R10, R16). **Tunisia**: Stia (associated company), Route de Monastir, Sousse (assem. R4). **Turkey**: Ordu Yarkimlasma Kurumu (associated company), Bursa (R12). **Venezuela**: Constructora Venezolana de Vehiculos (associated company), Mariara, Estado Carabobo (assem. R10, R16). **Yugoslavia**: Titovi Zavodi Litostroj (concessionaire), Ljubljana (assem. R4, R6, R8, R10, R12).

RELIANT - see THE RELIANT MOTOR COMPANY Ltd

RENAULT - see RÉGIE NATIONALE DES USINES RENAULT

ROLLS-ROYCE Ltd — **Great Britain**

Founded in 1904, has specialized in the production of exceptionally high-class and aristocratic cars. Chairman: F. Llewellyn Smith, CBE. Managing Director: G. Fawn. Directors: J.H. Craig, R.E. Garner, J.S. Hollings, I.D. Nelson, T. Neville, D.A.S. Plastow, L.S. Poulton. Head office: Moor Lane, Derby. Press office: 14-15 Conduit St, London W.1. Works: Pym's Lane, Crewe, Cheshire. Employees: 5,500. Most important models: first Rolls-Royce in 1904; Silver Ghost (1906-25); Twenty (1911); Phantom I (1925-29); Phantom II (1929-36); Phantom III (1936); Silver Wraith (1946); Phantom IV (1950); Silver Cloud I (1955); Silver Cloud II, Phantom V (1959); Silver Cloud III (1962); Silver Shadow (1965); Phantom VI (1968).

ROVER - see THE ROVER COMPANY Ltd

SAAB AKTIEBOLAG Ltd **Sweden**

Founded in 1937 under the name of Svenska Aeroplan AB. Present title since 1965. President: C. Mileikowsky. Chairman: E. Boheman. Vice-Chairman: M. Wallenberg. Head office and press office: 58188 Linköping. Car works: 46101 Trollhättan, Linköping, Gothenburg, Nyköping. Employees: about 10,900. Cars produced in 1969: 45,073. Motor manufacture begun in 1950. Most important models: Saab 92 (1950); Saab 93 (1956); Saab GT 748 cu cm (1958); Saab 95 (1959); Saab Sport (1962); Saab 96 (1966); Saab 99 (1967). First places in various competitions (RAC Rally, Monte Carlo Rally, Tulip Rally, Rally of the Thousand Lakes, etc.).

SEAT - SOCIEDAD ESPAÑOLA DE AUTOMOVILES DE TURISMO S.A. **Spain**

Founded in 1950. President: D.J. Sánchez-Cortés y Dávila. Vice-President: D.F. Urquijo de Federico. Managing Director: D.F. Lozano Aguirre. Head office and press office: Avda. Generalísimo 146, Madrid 16. Works: Zona Franca, Barcelona. Employees: 17,000. Cars produced in 1969: 222,218. Most important models: 600 D (1963); 850 (1966); 850 Coupé (1967); 850 Special (1968); 124 (1968); 1500/69 (1968); 850 Spider (1969); 1430 (1969).

SIMCA - see CHRYSLER FRANCE

ŠKODA - AUTOMOBILOVÉ ZÁVODY NÁRODNI PODNIK **Czechoslovakia**

Founded in 1894 by Laurin and Klement for the construction of velocipedes, assumed title of Laurin & Klement Co. Ltd in 1907, Škoda in 1925, and in 1945 became national corporation (AZNP). Director: M. Zapadlo. Deputy Directors: J. Muller, L. Sobotka. Head office, press office and works: Trída Rudé armady, Mladá Boleslav. Employees: 15,000. Cars produced in 1969: 124,300. Car production begun in 1905 (2 cylinder cars). Most important models: Laurin & Klement (1905); E 4 cyl. (1907); "S" Type (1911); 100, 105, 110, 120 Type (1923); 4R, 6R (1924); 420, 422 (1934); Popular, Rapid (1935-39); S 1101, S 1102 (1945-51); S 440 (1956); Octavia, Felicia (1958); Octavia Combi, S 1202 (1962); S 1000 MB (1964); S 100 L, S 110 L, S 1203 (1969).

ASSEMBLY IN OTHER COUNTRIES — **Chile**: Imcoda, Importación y Comercio Ltd, Cienfuegos 67, Santiago (assem. Octavia Combi). **New Zealand**: Motor Lines Ltd, 8 Fort Richard Rd, Otahuhu, Auckland (assem. S 110, Jeep Trekka). **Pakistan**: Haroon Industries Ltd, Part Division D-2, S.I.T.E., Manghopir Rd, Karachi 16 (assem. Octavia, Skopak). **Turkey**: Oto Celik Kollektif Sirketi, Mr. Kamila Yazici ve Izzet Ozilkam, Emirler Sokak 3/1, Sirkecia, Istanbul (assem. 1202, Pick-up).

SS AUTOMOBILES Inc. **USA**

(Make: Excalibur)

Founded in 1964. Chairman: B. Stevens. President: D.B. Stevens. Vice-President and Treasurer: W.C. Stevens. Head office and works: 1735 South 106th St, Milwaukee, Wisc. 53214. Press office: R.C. Auletta & Co., 59 East 54th St, New York, N.Y. 10022. Employees: 22. Cars produced in 1969: 87. Models: Roadster SSK, Phaeton SS.

STEYR-DAIMLER-PUCH AG **Austria**

Founded in 1864, assumed the title of Steyr-Werke AG in 1926, merged with Austro-Daimler-Puchwerke AG in 1934. Present title since 1935. Managing Director: K. Rabus. Vice Managing Director: H. Roesler. Head office and press office: Kärntnerring 7, Vienna 1. Works: Steyr, Graz, Vienna. Employees: about 18,000. Cars produced in 1969: about 1,200. In 1948 signed an assembly contract with Fiat; in 1953 it manufactured the 2000 cu cm 65 hp engine, mounted between 1953 and 1958 on Fiat bodywork; in 1957 began production in Graz of a low horsepower car basically corresponding to the Fiat 500. Most important models: 12/16 hp 4 cyl. (1901); 9 hp Double-Phaeton-Wagen (1903); DV 30/35 hp 4 cyl. (1910); SI VI 45/50 hp 4 cyl. (1911); G III 18/20 hp 4 cyl. (1911-12); VIII Alpenwagen 14/38 hp 4 cyl. (1913-23); 6/25 hp 4 cyl. (1919-20); Waffenauto Typ II 12/40 hp 6 cyl. (1920-24); Typ IV 7/23 hp 4 cyl. (1921-24); 45 hp Daimler Sascha (1922); Typ V 12/40 hp 6 cyl. (1924-25); Typ XII 6/30 hp 6 cyl. (1926-29); Typ XX 8/40 hp 6 cyl. (1928-29); Austria 8 cyl. 5.3 l 100 hp (1929); Daimler 100 hp ADR 8 8 cyl. (1932-33); Steyr 100 32 hp 4 cyl. (1934-36); 50/55 22 hp 4 cyl. (1936-40); 220 55 hp 6 cyl. (1937-41); 500 (1957).

SUBARU - see FUJI HEAVY INDUSTRIES Ltd

SUNBEAM - see CHRYSLER UNITED KINGDOM Ltd

SUZUKI MOTOR COMPANY Ltd **Japan**

Founded in 1909 under the name of Suzuki Shokkuku Seisakusho. Present title since 1954. President: S. Suzuki. Executive Vice-President: J. Suzuki. Head office and press office: No. 300 Kamimura-Takatsuka, Hamana-gun, Shizuoka-ken. Works: Kosai, Shirasuka 4520, Kosai-cho, Hamana-gun, Shizuoka-ken, Iwata, Iwai 2500, Iwata-shi, Shizuoka-ken. Employees: 9,544. Cars produced in 1969: 162,571. Most important models: Suzulight 360 (1955); Suzuki Fronte 360 LC10 (1967); Fronte 500 (1968).

SYRENA - see FABRIKA SAMOCHODÓW OSOBOWYCH

TATRA NÁRODNI PODNIK **Czechoslovakia**

Tatra is one of the oldest European motor manufacturers. In the second half of the 19th century de luxe coaches were being built in the little Nesselsdorf workshop. Production of railway carriages was begun in 1892 and the first motor-car, called the "President", was produced in 1897. General Manager: M. Kopec. Head office and press office: Kopřivnice. Works: Tatra Kopřivnice, okres Nový Jičin. Cars produced in 1969: 1,500. Most important models: President (1897); B Type (1902); E Type 12 hp (1905); K Type (1906); T 14/15 (1914); Tatra 4/12 (1923); Twelver (1925); 17/31 (1926-30); Tatra 30 (1927-29); Tatra 24/30 (1930-34); Tatra 52 (1930-38); Tatra 57 (1932); Tatra 75 (1933-37); Tatra 77 (1934); Tatra 87 (1936-38); Tatraplan (1949); Tatra 603 (1957); Tatra 2-603 (1964). It has been entering competitions since 1900 (Targa Florio, Leningrad-Moscow-Tbilisi-Moscow, Alpine Rally, Polsky Rally, Vltava Rally, Marathon de la Route, etc.).

TECHNICAL EXPONENTS Ltd. **Great Britain**

Managing Director: T.P. Bennett. Director: L.A.L. Fuller. Head office and press office: 74-75 Waterford Rd, London SW6. Works: Denham Green Lane, Denham, Bucks. Employees: 22.

THE RELIANT MOTOR COMPANY Ltd **Great Britain**

Founded in 1934 under the name of Reliant Engineering Co. (Tamworth) Ltd. Present title since 1962. Acquired Bond Cars Ltd in 1969. Chairman: J.S. Hodge, FACCA. Deputy Chairman: F.D. Walters. Managing Director: R.W. Wiggin. Directors: T.H. Scott, T.W. Snowdon, N.C. Crighton. Head office and works: Two Gates, Tamworth, Staffordshire. Press office: Adrian Ball & Associated Ltd, 113-114 Fleet St, London E.C.4. Employees: 1,600. Cars produced in 1969: 20,000. Most important models: first sport car Sabre (1960); Sabre 6 (1961); Scimitar GT, Rebel 700 (1964); Rebel 700 Estate (1967); Scimitar GTE (1968), all with glassfibre bodywork. Entries from 1962 to 1964 in numerous competitions (Tulip Rally, RAC Rally of Great Britain, Monte Carlo Rally, Circuit of Ireland, Alpine Rally, Spa-Sofia-Liège Rally).

MANUFACTURE IN OTHER COUNTRIES — **Turkey**: Otosan A.S. (associated company), P.K. 102, Kadiköy, Istanbul (manuf. Anadol).

THE ROVER COMPANY Ltd **Great Britain**

Founded in 1877 by J. Starley, became J.K. Starley and Co. Ltd in 1888 and The Rover Cycle Company in 1896. Present title since 1906. It is now part of the British Leyland Motor Corp. Ltd. Chairman: Sir George Farmer. Managing Director: A.B. Smith. General Manager and Production Director: B.G.L. Jackman. Head office, press office and works: Meteor Works, Lode Lane, Solihull, Warwickshire. Employees: 13,994. Cars produced in 1969: 67,896. Motor manufacturing begun in 1904. Most important models: 8 hp (1904-10); 6 hp (1906-10); 12 hp (1910-23); 8 hp Twin Air-cooled (1920-24); 10, 12, 14 and 16 hp range (1934-47); P3 models 60 and 75 (1948-49); P4 models 60, 75, 80, 90, 95, 100, 105, 110 (1950-64); 3 l (1958); Rover 2000 (1963); 3.5 l Saloon and Coupé (1967); Rover 3500 (1968).

MANUFACTURE AND ASSEMBLY IN OTHER COUNTRIES — **Angola**: Uniao Commercial de Automoviles Ltda (concessionaire), Caixa Postal 1236, Luanda (assem. Land Rover, 88" and 109" Regular). **Australia:** BLMC of Australia, Rover Division (associated company), P.O. Box 6, 893-931 South Dowling St, Waterloo (manuf. Land Rover). **Cameroons**: Ciacam-King (concessionaire), B.P. 4022, Douala (assem. Land Rover). **Costa Rica**: Almacén Electra S.A. (concessionaire), P.O. Box 730, San José (assem. Land Rover). **Ecuador**: B. Aviles Alfaro and Cia. (concessionaire), P.O. Box 354, Avda. de las Americas, Guayaquil (assem. Land Rover). **Ghana**: Africa Motors Ltd (concessionaire), P.O. Box 1642, Accra (assem. Land Rover, 109" Regular and 88" Estate Car). **Indonesia**: Java Motor Import. Corp. N.V. (concessionaire), P.O. Box 161, 17 Djalah Raya Kramat, Djakarta (assem. Land Rover). **Iran**: Sherkat Sahami Sanaati Towlidi Morratab (concessionaire), P.O. Box 1508, Teheran (manuf. Land Rover). **Ireland**: British Leyland Ireland (Jaguar, Rover, Triumph) Ltd (associated company), Cashel Rd, Dublin 12 (assem. Land Rover). **Kenya**: Leyland Albion (E. Africa) Ltd (associated company), P.O. Box 18502, Nairobi (assem. Land Rover). **Madagascar**: Landis Madagascar (distributor), 5 rue Robert Ducrocq, Behoririka (P.O. Box 633), Tananarive (assem. Land Rover). **Malta:** Muscat's Garage Ltd (concessionaire), rue d'Argens, Msida (assem. Land Rover). **Morocco**: Aetco-Lever Moroc (concessionaire), B.P. 519, Casablanca (assem. Land Rover). **New Zealand**: The British Leyland Motor Corp. of New Zealand Ltd (associated company), P.O. Box 2179, Auckland (manuf. Land Rover and Rover cars). **Nigeria**: Bewac Ltd (concessionaire), 1 Commercial Rd, Apapa (assem. Land Rover, 88" and 109" Regular and Estate Car). **Philippines**: Liberty Motors Inc. (concessionaire), P.O. Box 1826, Manila (manuf. Land Rover). **Singapore**: Champion Motors Singapore Ltd (concessionaire), P.O. Box 627, Singapore 9 (assem. Land Rover). **South Africa**: Leykor Manufacturing Pty Ltd (associated company), P.O. Box 1, Blackheat, Cape Town (manuf. Land Rover and Rover cars). **Spain**: Metalúrgica de Santa Ana S.A. (concessionaire), Apartado 13170, Madrid (manuf. Land Rover). **Tanzania**: Leyland Albion (Tanzania) Ltd (associated company), P.O. Box 2388, Dar-es-Salam (assem. Land Rover). **Trinidad**: H.E. Robinson & Co. Ltd (concessionaire), P.O. Box 641, Port of Spain, B.W.1 (assem. Land Rover). **Turkey**: Matas Trading Corp. (concessionaire), Halaskargazi Cad, 133 Pangalti, Istanbul (manuf. Land Rover, 88" and 109" Regular). **Uruguay**: Horacio Torrendett S.A., Cuareim 20-52, Montevideo (assem. Land Rover). **Venezuela**: Mack de Venezuela C.A. (concessionaire), Apartado 158, Caracas (assem. Land Rover). **Zambia**: Rover Zambia Ltd (associated company), P.O. Box Sk 6, Skyways, Ndola (assem. Land Rover). Cars produced in other countries in 1969: 24,218.

TOYO KOGYO COMPANY Ltd **Japan**

(Make: Mazda)

Founded in 1920 under the name of Toyo Cork Kogyo Co. Ltd. Present title since 1927. President: K. Matsuda. Vice-President: T. Murao. Director: S. Takebayashi. Head office, press office and works: 6047, Fuchumachi, Aki-gun, Hiroshima. Employees: 27,000. Cars produced in 1969: 223,000. Car production begun in 1930 with Mazda (3-speed). Most important models: 360 Coupé (1960); 360 and 600 (1962); 800 Sedan (1964); 1000 Coupé (1965); 1500 Sedan (1966); 1500 SS, 110 S, 1000 Sedan (1967); 1200 Coupé and Sedan, R100 Coupé, 1800 Sedan (1968); Rotary SS, R100 Coupé E Type (1969). Entries in numerous competitions: Singapore GP, Macao GP (1966); Macao GP (1967); 84 hour Marathon (1968); Singapore GP, Francorchamps (1969).

TOYOTA MOTOR COMPANY Ltd **Japan**

Founded in 1937. President: E. Toyoda. Executive Vice-Presidents: S. Ohno, S. Saito. Chairman of the Board: T. Ishida. Head office and press office: 1, Toyota-cho, Toyota City, Aichi-ken. Works: as above; Moto-machi Works, 1 Moto-machi, Toyota City, Aichi-ken; Kamigo Works, 1 Taiseicho, Toyota City; Takaoka Works, 1 Aza-Kanayama, Ohaza Tsutsumi, Toyota City, Aichi-ken; Miyoshi Works, Miyoshimachi, Nishikamo-gun, Aichi-ken; Honsha Works, 1, Toyotacho, Toyota City, Aichi-ken. Employees: 38,500. Cars produced in 1969: 964,088. Most important models: Toyo Ace (1954); Toyopet Crown (1955); Toyopet Corona (1957); Toyopet Crown Deluxe (1958); Toyopet Crown Diesel (1959); Toyopet New Corona and Publica (1960); Toyopet New Crown (1962); Crown Eight (1963); Toyota Corolla 1100 (1966); Toyota Century (1967); Toyota Corona Mk II, Toyota 1000 (1968).

ASSEMBLY IN OTHER COUNTRIES — **Australia**: Australian Motor Industries Ltd (associated company), Cook St, Port Melbourne, Victoria (assem. Corolla, Corona, Crown). **Brazil**: Toyota do Brasil S.A. (subsidiary), Estrada de Piraporinha km 23, São Bernardo do Campo, São Paulo (assem. Land Cruiser). **Costa Rica**: Purdy Motor Co. Ltd (concessionaire), El Paseo Colón, San José (assem. Corolla, Corona, Land Cruiser). **Ghana**: Fattal Brothers Ltd (concessionaire), Ring Road West Industrial Area, Ghana (assem. Corona). **Korea**: Shinjin Motor Co. Ltd (concessionaire), Nr. 91 Shu So Moon Dong, Shu Dae Moon Ku, Seoul (Toyota 800, Corona, Crown, Land Cruiser). **Malaysia**: Borneo Motors (Malaysia) Sdn. Berhad (concessionaire), 76-78 Ampang Rd, Kuala Lumpur (assem. Corolla, Corona, Crown). **New Zealand**: Consolidated Motor Industries Ltd (concessionaire), Hume House, 152 The Terrace, Wellington (assem. Corolla, Corona, Land Cruiser). **Peru**: Toyota del Peru S.A. (subsidiary), Avda. Arica 571, Breña, Lima (assem. Corona, Land Cruiser, Stout). **Philippines**: Delta Motor Corp. (concessionaire), 2285 Pasong Tamo, Makati Rizal (assem. Corolla, Corona, Crown). **Portugal**: Salvador Caetano Industrias Metalurgicas e Veiculos de Transporte SARL (concessionaire), Vila Nova de Gaia (assem. Corolla, Dyna). **South Africa**: Toyota South Africa Ltd (subsidiary), Veka Bldg, Cor. Lilian & Commercial Roads, Fordsburg, Johannesburg (assem. Corona, Stout, Dyna). **Thailand**: Toyota Motor Thailand Co. Ltd (subsidiary), 180 Suriwongse Rd, Bangkok (assem. Corolla, Corona). **Venezuela**: Compañía Anónima Tocars (concessionaire), Edificio Tocars-Chacao, Av. Francisco de Miranda, Caracas (assem. Land Cruiser).

TRABANT - see VEB SACHSENRING AUTOMOBILWERKE ZWICKAU

TRIUMPH MOTOR COMPANY Ltd **Great Britain**

Founded in 1903 under the name of Standard Motor Co.; incorporated Triumph Motor Co. in 1945; in 1968 became part of the Specialist Car Division of the British Leyland Motor Corp. Chairman: W.H. Davis. Director and General Manager: M.W.J. Sanders. Directors: C.S. King, A.C.L. Mills, M.P. Graham White, W.A. Robinson. Head office and works: Canley, Coventry CV4 9DB. Press office: Fletchamstead, Coventry CV4 9DB, Warwickshire. Employees: about 12,000. Cars produced in 1969: 122,160. Most important models: 6 hp (1903); 24/30 hp (1906); 11.4 hp (1920); Eight (1939); Eight, Twelve, Fourteen (1945); Triumph 1800 Saloon and Roadster (1946); Vanguard (1947); Mayflower (1951); Standard 8, TR2 (1953); Herald (1958); TR4, Spitfire, Vitesse (1962); Triumph 2000, 12/50 Herald (1963); 1300, TR4A (1965); TR5 PI (1967); Herald 13/60 (1968). Entries in numerous competitions. First place in Jabbekke Highway, in 1954 RAC Rally, etc.

ASSEMBLY IN OTHER COUNTRIES — **Australia**: Australian Motor Industries Ltd (associated company), Box 2006S G.P.O., Port Melbourne, Victoria (assem. 2000, 2.5 P.I.). **Belgium**: Leyland-Triumph S.A. (associated company), 1 Eggestraat, Malines (assem. 2000, 2.5 P.I., Toledo, Herald 13/60, Vitesse, Spitfire Mk IV, GT6 Mk III). **Ireland**: British Leyland Ireland (Jaguar, Rover, Triumph) Ltd (subsidiary), Cashel Rd, Dublin (assem. 2000, 2.5. P.I., 1300, Herald 13/60, Toledo, Spitfire). **Israel**: Autocars Co. Ltd (concessionaire), Tirat Hacarmel, Haifa (assem. 1300, 1500). **Malta**: Muscat's Garage Ltd (concessionaire), rue d'Argens, Msida (assem. Herald 13/60, 1300). **New Zealand**: British Leyland Motor Corporation of New Zealand Ltd (subsidiary), P.O. Box 2179, Auckland (assem. Herald 13/60, 2000, 2.5 P.I., Toledo). **Portugal**: Stampor - Sociedade Anglo-Portuguese de Automoveis Sarl (associated company), rua Cova da Moura No. 2, 2°-E, Lisbon 3 (assem. 2000, 2.5 P.I., 1300, Toledo, Spitfire). **South Africa**: Leykor Distributors (Pty) Ltd (associated company), P.O. Box 2179, Johannesburg (assem. 2000, 2.5 P.I.).

TVR ENGINEERING Ltd **Great Britain**

Established in 1954 as Grantura Engineering Ltd. Present title since 1966. Chairman: A. Lilley. Managing Director: M.A. Lilley. Director: J. W. Wishart. Head office, press office and works: Fielding's Industrial Estate, Bispham Rd, Layton, Blackpool, Lancs. Employees: 70. Cars produced in 1969: 350. Most important models: TVR Mk I (1954-60); TVR Mk II (1960); TVR Mk II A (1962); TVR Mk III (1963-64); TVR Mk III 1800 (1963); TVR Griffith series 200 (1964); TVR Griffith 400 (1965); TVR 200 V8 (1966); TVR Tuscan SE, Vixen 1600 (1967); Vixen S2 (1968); Tuscan V6 (1969). Entries and wins in numerous competitions.

ASSEMBLY IN OTHER COUNTRIES — **Ireland**: Marlborough Assemblers (concessionaire), 4-5 Westmoreland St, Dublin 2 (assem. Tuscan V6, Vixen S2).

VANDEN PLAS - see BLMC

VAN DOORNE'S AUTOMOBIELFARIEKEN NV **Holland**

(Make: Daf)

Founded in 1928. Chairman: W.A.V. van Doorne. Deputy Chairman: M.P.J.H. van Doorne. Head office, press office and works: Geldropseweg 303, Eindhoven. Employees: 10,000. Cars produced in 1969: 65,000. Production of commercial vehicles started in 1950 and fully automatic cars in 1959. Most important models: Daf 600 (1959); Daf 750 and Daffodil (1961); Daf 44 (1966); Daf 33, Daf 55 (1967). Entries with passenger models in various minor and major international rallies since 1961 with overall and category wins. From 1965 to 1968 competed with an automatic transmission F3 racing car with remarkable results on twisty circuits.

VAUXHALL MOTORS Ltd **Great Britain**

(Makes: Bedford, Vauxhall)

Founded in 1903. Transferred from Vauxhall District of London to Luton in 1905. Present title since 1907. Taken over by General Motors Corp. in 1925. Chairman and Managing Director: A.D. Rhea. Directors: J. Alden, L.F. Coyle, R. Hopkins, L.R. Mason, P.G.H. Newton, R. May, G.E. Moore, J.E. Rhame, C.F.P. Waller, D.A. West, L. Wright. Head office, press office and works: Kimpton Rd, Luton, Beds. Employees: 34,156. Cars produced in 1969: 169,456. Most important models: Velox (1949); Cresta (1954); Victor (1957); Viva (1963). Entries in various competitions from 1909 to 1924.

ASSEMBLY IN OTHER COUNTRIES — **Belgium**: General Motors Continental S.A. (associated company), P.B. 549, Antwerp (assem. Victor, Viva). **Denmark**: General Motors International A.S. (associated company), Aldersrogade 20, Copenhagen (assem. Victor). **Ireland**: McCairns Motors (concessionaire), Alexandra Rd, East Wall, Dublin (assem. Viva). **Malaysia**: Champion Motors (M), Sdn. Bhd. (concessionaire), P.O.B. 814, Kuala Lumpur (assem. Victor, Viva). **New Zealand**: General Motors New Zealand Ltd (associated company), Trentham Plant 1, Alexandra Rd, Private Bag, Upper Hutt. (assem. Victor, Viva). **Pakistan**: Ghandhara Industries Ltd (concessionaire), P.O. Box 2706, Hab Chauki Rd, S.I.T.E., Karachi 13 (assem. Victor); Ghandhara Industries Ltd (concessionaire), P.O.B. 73, 2. Golpahar, Chittagong (assem. Viva). **Philippines**: Yutivo Corp. (concessionaire), P.O. Box 159, Manila (assem. Victor, Viva). **Portugal**: General Motors de Portugal Ltda (associated company), Caixa Postal 2484, Lote 408 - 2a Circular - Av. Marechal Gomes da Çosta, Lisbon 6 (assem. Victor, Viva). **Singapore**: Associated Motors Industries Ltd (concessionaire), P.O. Box 19, Tamar Jurong, Singapore 22 (assem. Victor, Viva). **South Africa**: General Motors South Africa (associated company), P.O. Box 1137, Kempston Rd, Port Elizabeth (manuf. Viva). **Switzerland**: General Motors Suisse S.A. (associated company), Postfach 2501, Salzhausstrasse 21, Bienne (assem. Viva, Victor). **Trinidad**: Neal & Massy Industries Ltd (concessionaire), P.O. Box 1298, Port of Spain, Trinidad W.1 (assem. Victor, Viva). Cars assembled in other countries in 1969: 35,808.

VAZ - VOLZHSKY AVTOMOBILNY ZAVOD **USSR**

Avtoexport, Ul. Volkhonka 14, Moscow G. 512. Works: Togliatti.

VEB AUTOMOBILWERKE EISENACH **Germany (Democratic Republic)**

(Make: Wartburg)

Friedrich-Naumann-Strasse, Postschliessfach 218-219, 59 Eisenach.

VEB SACHSENRING AUTOMOBILWERKE ZWICKAU **Germany (Democratic Republic)**

(Make: Trabant)

Founded in 1904 under the name of A. Horch Motorwagenwerke AG Zwickau, became Audi-Mobilwagenwerke AG Zwickau in 1909, merged with Auto Union in 1932, nationalized in 1946. Present title since 1958. Head office and press office: W. Rathenau Strasse, Zwickau. Employees: 9,000. Cars produced in 1969: 73,800. Most important models: world record 500 hp 16 cyl-rear-engined car (1937-38); DKW 3.5-5 I, F2, F3, F4, F5, F6, F7, F8 (two stroke front drive engine up to 1945); F8 (1949-55); F9 (1949-52); P70, S 240 (1955-59); Trabant (1958-62); Trabant 600 (1962-63); Trabant 601 (1964). Entries in numerous competitions Rally Munich-Vienna-Budapest, Semperit-Rally, Thousand Lakes Rally, Tour de Belgique, Tulip Rally, Monte Carlo Rally).

VOLKSWAGENWERK AG **Germany (Federal Republic)**

Founded in 1937 under the name of Gesellschaft zur Vorbereitung des Deutschen Volkswagen mbH, became Volkswagenwerk GmbH in 1938. Present title since 1960. For volume of production it is the foremost German motor manufacturer. President: K. Lotz. Directors: H. Backsmann, C.H. Hahn, O. Höhne, H. Münzner, F. Novotny, G. Prinz, F. Thomée, W. Holste. Head office and press office: 3180 Wolfsburg. Works: as above, Braunschweig, Emden, Hannover, Kassel. Employees: 104,975. Cars produced in 1969: 1,639,630. Most important models: VW Limousine 1200 (1945); VW 1200 Export and VW Convertible (1949); 1200 Karmann-Ghia Coupé (1955); 1200 Karmann-Ghia Convertible (1957); VW 1500 and 1500 Karmann-Ghia Coupé (1961); VW 1500 N Limousine, VW 1500 S Limousine, 1500 S Karmann-Ghia Coupé (1963); VW 1600 TL (1965); VW 411 (1968); VW 411 E and 411 LE (1969).

MANUFACTURE AND ASSEMBLY IN OTHER COUNTRIES — **Australia**: Motor Producers Ltd (associated company), Melbourne (assem. VW 1500, 1600). **Brazil**: Volkswagen do Brasil S.A. (associated company), São Bernardo do Campo (manuf. VW 1200, 1300, 1600). **Mexico**: Volkswagen de México S.A. de C.V. (associated company), Mexico City (manuf. VW 1500). **South Africa**: Volkswagen of South Africa Ltd (associated company), Uitenhage (assem. VW 1500, 1600). Cars produced in other countries in 1969: 251,234.

VOLVO - see AB VOLVO Ltd

VW-PORSCHE VERTRIEBSGESELLSCHAFT mbH **Germany (Federal Republic)**

Founded in 1969. General Managers: O.E. Filius, K. Schneider. PR Manager: H. von Hanstein. Head office and press office: Heilbronner Str. 67, Stuttgart. Employees: about 390.

WARSZAWA - see FABRYKA SAMOCHODÓW OSOBOWYCH

WARTBURG - see VEB AUTOMOBILWERKE EISENACH

WOLSELEY - see BLMC

YLN - YUE LOONG MOTOR COMPANY Ltd **Taiwan**

Founded under the name of Yue Loong Engineering Co. Ltd. Present title since 1953. President: T.L. Yen. Vice-Presidents: C.C. Yen, D. Yen, V.Z. Faung, C.L. Chu. Head office and press office: 16 Sing Yang St, Taipei. Works: Hsen Tien, Taipei. Employees: 2,200. Cars produced in 1969: 6,000. Under licence of Nissan Motor Co. and American Motors Corp. manufactures various types of sedans and jeeps including the YL-1 and the YL-2. Models: YLN 706 Bluebird (1960); YLN 801 Cedric (1964).

ZAZ - ZAPOROZHSKY AVTOMOBILNY ZAVOD **USSR**

Avtoexport, Ul. Volkhonka 14, Moscow G. 512. Works: Zaporozhje.

ZIL **USSR**

Avtoexport, Ul. Volkhonka 14, Moscow G. 512. Works: Moscow.

COACHBUILDERS

BERTONE (Carrozzeria) S.a.s. **Italy**

Founded in 1957. Produces small and medium series of car bodies; bespoke production for car manufacturing firms and construction of prototypes. General partner: N. Bertone. Head office: c.so Canonico Allamano 201, 10095 Grugliasco, Turin.

FRANCIS LOMBARDI S.a.s. **Italy**

Founded in 1947. Produces car bodies; at present specialized in construction of sports and medium-powered cars. Has specialised for twenty years in cars with folding seats. Owner: F. Lombardi. Head office: strada Trino 200, 13100 Vercelli.

GHIA S.p.A. **Italy**

Founded in 1915. Produces car bodies. President and Managing Director: A. de Tomaso. Members of Board: V. Bonica, H. DeGraw, A. Maserati. Head office: v. A. da Montefeltro 5, 10134 Turin.

ITAL DESIGN SIRP S.p.A. **Italy**

Founded in 1968. Styling and design of cars in small, medium and large series; construction of models and prototypes. Directors: L. Bosio, G. Giugiaro, A. Mantovani. Head office and press office: v. Tepice 16, 10126 Turin.

MORETTI S.A.S. FABBRICA AUTOMOBILI & STABILIMENTI CARROZZERIE **Italy**

Founded in 1926, began motor manufacturing in 1946. Since 1960 no longer produces mechanical parts but is engaged exclusively in production of car bodies. Uses chassis produced by Fiat with whom it has been collaborating for about eighteen years. General partner: G. Moretti. Holders of powers of attorney: G. Moretti and S. Moretti. Head office, press office and works: v. Monginevro 278-282, 10142 Turin.

PININFARINA (Carrozzeria) S.p.A. **Italy**

Founded in 1930. Produces special and de luxe bodies. President: S. Pininfarina. Managing Director: R. Carli. Member of Board: E. Carbonato. Head office: v. Lesna 78-80, 10095 Grugliasco, Turin.

SAVIO GIUSEPPE CARROZZERIA AUTOMOBILI **Italy**

Founded in 1919. Produces bodies for cars and special Fiat motor vehicles. Owners: I. Savio and T. Savio in Caracciolo. Head office: v. C. Corradino 8, Borgo San Pietro, 10047 Moncalieri, Turin.

VIGNALE (Carrozzeria) S.p.A. **Italy**

Founded in 1946. Produces special car bodies. President: A. de Tomaso. Head office: strada del Portone 177, 10095 Grugliasco, Turin.

ZAGATO (Carrozzeria) S.p.A. **Italy**

Founded in 1919. Produces car bodies. President: E. Zagato. Managing Director: G. Zagato. Head office: v. Arese, Terrazzano, 20017 Rho, Milan.

Indexes

NAME OF CAR

Cars called by names (in alphabetical order)

Model	Make
AAR CUDA	PLYMOUTH
ADMIRAL	OPEL
AERO WILLYS	FORD (BR)
ALPINE	SUNBEAM
AMBASSADOR	AMERICAN MOTORS, HINDUSTAN
AMI 8	CITROËN
ANADOL	OTOSAN
ASCONA	OPEL
AUSTIN J5	INNOCENTI
AVENGER	HILLMAN
BARRACUDA	PLYMOUTH
BEAGLE	BEDFORD
BEL AIR	CHEVROLET (USA)
BELLETT	ISUZU
BELMONT	HOLDEN
BELVEDERE	PLYMOUTH
BERLINETTE TOUR DE FRANCE	ALPINE
BIANCHINA	AUTOBIANCHI
BISCAYNE	CHEVROLET (USA)
BONNEVILLE	PONTIAC (USA)
BREAK	CITROËN
BROOKWOOD	CHEVROLET (USA)
BROUGHAM	HOLDEN, MERCURY
CALAIS	CADILLAC
CAMARO	CHEVROLET (USA)
CAMPAGNOLA	FIAT (I)
CAPELLA	MAZDA
CAPRI	FORD (D, GB)
CAPRICE	CHEVROLET (USA)
CARINA	TOYOTA
CAROL	MAZDA
CATALINA	PONTIAC (CDN, USA)
CELICA	TOYOTA
CENTURION	BUICK
CENTURY	TOYOTA
CHALLENGER	DODGE (USA)
CHARGER	DODGE (USA)
CHERRY	NISSAN
CHEVELLE	CHEVROLET (USA)
CHEVY	CHEVROLET (RA)
CHRYSLER 160	CHRYSLER FRANCE
CHRYSLER 180	CHRYSLER FRANCE
CLUBMAN	MINI (BRITISH LEYLAND)
COLONY PARK	MERCURY
COLT	MITSUBISHI
COMET	MERCURY
COMMERCIALE	CITROËN
COMMODORE	OPEL
CONCOURS	CHEVROLET (USA)
CONSORTE	DAIHATSU
CONTINENTAL	LINCOLN
COOPER	MINI (BRITISH LEYLAND)
CORCEL	FORD (BR)
COROLLA	TOYOTA
CORONA	TOYOTA
CORONADO	DODGE (RA)
CORONET	DODGE (USA)
CORTINA	FORD (GB)
CORVETTE	CHEVROLET (USA)
COUGAR	MERCURY
COUNTRY SEDAN	FORD (USA)
COUNTRY SQUIRE	FORD (USA)
COUPÉ GRAND PRIX	GIANNINI
CRESTA	VAUXHALL

Model	Make
CRICKET	PLYMOUTH
CROWN	IMPERIAL, TOYOTA
'CUDA	PLYMOUTH
CUSTOM	FORD (USA)
CUSTOM SUBURBAN	PLYMOUTH
CUTLASS	OLDSMOBILE
CYCLONE	MERCURY
DART	DODGE (USA)
DATSUN	NISSAN
DEAUVILLE	DE TOMASO
DEBONAIR	MITSUBISHI
DEMON	DODGE (USA)
DELTA	OLDSMOBILE
DE VILLE	CADILLAC
DINO	FERRARI, FIAT
DIPLOMAT	OPEL
DUCAS	AUTOCARS
DYANE	CITROËN
ELAN	LOTUS
ELECTRA	BUICK
ESCORT	FORD (D, GB)
ESPADA	LAMBORGHINI
ESTATE WAGON	BUICK
EUROPA	LOTUS
FAMILIA	MAZDA
FAMILIALE	CITROËN
FELLOW	DAIHATSU
FIDIA	ISO
FIREBIRD	PONTIAC (USA)
FLAVIA	LANCIA
FLEETWOOD	CADILLAC
FLORIAN	ISUZU
FRONTE	SUZUKI
FULVIA	LANCIA
FURY	PLYMOUTH
GALAXIE	FORD (BR, USA)
GHIBLI	MASERATI
GILBOA	AUTOCARS
GIULIA	ALFA ROMEO
GLORIA	NISSAN
GRAND PRIX	PONTIAC (USA)
GRAND SAFARI	PONTIAC (USA)
GRAND VILLE	PONTIAC (USA)
GREENBRIER	CHEVROLET (USA)
GREMLIN	AMERICAN MOTORS
GRIFO	ISO
HAI	MONTEVERDI
HERALD	TRIUMPH
HIGH SPEED	MONTEVERDI
HORNET	AMERICAN MOTORS
HUNTER	HILLMAN
IMP	HILLMAN
IMPALA	CHEVROLET (USA)
INDY	MASERATI
INTERCEPTOR II	JENSEN
INVADER	GILBERN
ITAMARATY	FORD (BR)
JARAMA	LAMBORGHINI
JAVELIN	AMERICAN MOTORS
JEEP	JEEP CORPORATION
JEEPSTER	JEEP CORPORATION
JIMNY	SUZUKI
KADETT	OPEL
KARMANN-GHIA	VOLKSWAGEN
KINGSWOOD	CHEVROLET (USA), HOLDEN

Model	Make
LAND ROVER	ROVER
LAUREL	NISSAN
LAURENTIAN	PONTIAC (CDN)
LE BARON	IMPERIAL
LELE	ISO
LE MANS	PONTIAC (USA)
LE SABRE	BUICK
LIMOUSINE	DAIMLER
MALIBU	CHEVROLET (USA)
MANGUSTA	DE TOMASO
MANTA	OPEL
MANTIS	MARCOS
MARATHON	CHECKER
MARQUIS	MERCURY
MATADOR	AMERICAN MOTORS
MAVERICK	FORD (USA)
MAXI	AUSTIN
MEHARI	CITROËN
METEOR	FORD (CDN)
MEXICO	MASERATI
MIDGET	MG
MINI	INNOCENTI
MINICA	MITSUBISHI
MINOR	MORRIS
MIURA S	LAMBORGHINI
MONARO	HOLDEN
MONTE CARLO	CHEVROLET (USA)
MONTEGO	MERCURY
MONTEREY	MERCURY
MONTREAL	ALFA ROMEO
MOSKVICH	AZLK
MUSTANG	FORD (USA)
NEWPORT	CHRYSLER
NEW YORKER	CHRYSLER
NINETY-EIGHT	OLDSMOBILE
NOMAD	CHEVROLET (USA)
NOVA	CHEVROLET (USA)
OPALA	CHEVROLET (BR)
OXFORD	MORRIS
PARISIENNE	PONTIAC (CDN)
PHANTOM	ROLLS-ROYCE
PINTO	FORD (USA)
POLARA	DODGE (RA, USA)
PREMIER	HOLDEN
PRESIDENT	NISSAN
PRINCESS	VANDEN PLAS
PRINZ	NSU
PUBLICA	TOYOTA
RANCH WAGON	FORD (USA)
RANGE ROVER	ROVER
RAPIER	SUNBEAM
REBEL	RELIANT
REKORD	OPEL
RIVIERA	BUICK
SAFARI	PONTIAC (USA)
SATELLITE	PLYMOUTH
SCEPTRE	HUMBER
SCIMITAR	RELIANT
SCORPIONE	ABARTH
SCOUT	INTERNATIONAL HARVESTER
SEVEN	LOTUS
SILVER SHADOW	ROLLS-ROYCE
SIMCA	CHRYSLER FRANCE
SIM'4	CHRYSLER FRANCE
SIREX	LMX
SIXTEEN-SIXTY	WOLSELEY
SKYLARK	BUICK
SKYLINE	NISSAN

Model	Make
SOVEREIGN	DAIMLER
SPITFIRE	TRIUMPH
SPORT	SUNBEAM
SPORT FURY	PLYMOUTH
SPORT PHAETON	GLASSIC
SPORTS ROADSTER	GLASSIC
SPORT SUBURBAN	PLYMOUTH
SPORTWAGON	BUICK
SPRITE	AUSTIN-HEALEY
STAG	TRIUMPH
STILETTO	SUNBEAM
SUBURBAN	PLYMOUTH
SUNNY	NISSAN
SUSSITA	AUTOCARS
TAUNUS	FORD (D)
THE EXECUTIVE	FORD (GB)
THUNDERBIRD	FORD (USA)
TOLEDO	TRIUMPH
TORANA	HOLDEN
TORINO	FORD (USA), IKA
TORONADO	OLDSMOBILE
TOWN	
AND COUNTRY	CHRYSLER
TOWNSMAN	CHEVROLET (USA)
TUSCAN	TVR
UNICAB	ISUZU
URRACO	LAMBORGHINI
VALIANT	DODGE (RA), PLYMOUTH
VAMOS	HONDA
VARIANT	VOLKSWAGEN
VEGA	CHEVROLET (USA)
VENTORA	VAUXHALL
VICTOR	VAUXHALL
VISCOUNT	VAUXHALL
VISTA CRUISER	OLDSMOBILE
VITESSE	TRIUMPH
VIVA	VAUXHALL
VIXEN	TVR
VOLGA	GAZ
ZAPOROZHETS	ZAZ
ZEPHYR	FORD (GB)
ZODIAC	FORD (GB)

Cars called by letters (in alphabetical order)

Model	Make
A 111	AUTOBIANCHI
A 112	AUTOBIANCHI
A 112 KL	OTAS
DB6 Mk II	ASTON MARTIN
DBS	ASTON MARTIN
DS	CITROËN
F-85	OLDSMOBILE
FF II	JENSEN
FF-1	SUBARU
G15	GINETTA
G21	GINETTA
GS	BUICK, CITROËN
GT	ANDINO, DODGE (RA), HILLMAN, ISO, OPEL
GT6	TRIUMPH
GT 1300 JUNIOR	ALFA ROMEO

Model	Make
GTA 1300 JUNIOR	ALFA ROMEO
GTE 1600	PUMA
GTO	PONTIAC
GTX	DODGE (RA), PLYMOUTH
K 70	VOLKSWAGEN
LTD	FORD (BR, USA)
MARK V EM	FAIRTHORPE
MGB	MG
N III	HONDA
N 600	HONDA
PLUS 8	MORGAN
R-2	SUBARU
R100	MAZDA
R130	MAZDA
Ro 80	NSU
SS	EXCALIBUR
SSK	EXCALIBUR
T 2-603	TATRA
T-37	PONTIAC (USA)
T SERIES	BENTLEY
TR6 P.I.	TRIUMPH
TT	NSU
TTS	NSU
TX-GT	FAIRTHORPE
TX-S	FAIRTHORPE
TX-SS	FAIRTHORPE
TX TRIPPER	TECHNICAL EXPONENTS
VX 4/90	VAUXHALL
XJ6	JAGUAR
XL	FORD (USA)
Z	HONDA

Cars called by numbers (in numerical order)

Model	Make
2 CV	CITROËN
2-LITRE	MARCOS
2.5-LITRE P.I.	TRIUMPH
3-LITRE	AUSTIN, MARCOS
3.5-LITRE	ROVER
4	RENAULT
4.2-LITRE E TYPE	JAGUAR
4/4 1600	MORGAN
4-4-2	OLDSMOBILE
6	RENAULT
"7"	HONDA
8	RENAULT
"9"	HONDA
10	RENAULT
12	RENAULT
16	RENAULT
17M	FORD (D)
18/85 Mk II	WOLSELEY
20M	FORD (D)
26M	FORD (D)
33	DAF
44	DAF
55	DAF
60	AUDI
69 AM	GAZ
75	AUDI
"77"	HONDA
90	AUDI
95 V4	SAAB
96 V4	SAAB
99	SAAB
100	AUDI, ŠKODA
104	SYRENA
110	ŠKODA

Model	Make
110 S	HONDA
114	ZIL
117	ISUZU
124	FIAT (I)
125	FIAT (I)
125 P	POLSKI-FIAT
128	FIAT (I), GIANNINI
130	FIAT (I)
142	VOLVO
144	VOLVO
145	VOLVO
164	VOLVO
181	VOLKSWAGEN
200	MERCEDES-BENZ
204	PEUGEOT
220	MERCEDES-BENZ
223	WARSZAWA
230	MERCEDES-BENZ
250	MERCEDES-BENZ
280	MERCEDES-BENZ
300	CHRYSLER
300 SEL	MERCEDES-BENZ
304	PEUGEOT
360	SUBARU
365	FERRARI
404	PEUGEOT
411	BRISTOL, VOLKSWAGEN
420 G	JAGUAR
428	AC
500	FIAT (I), GIANNINI
500 S	STEYR-PUCH
504	PEUGEOT
530 LX	MATRA SPORTS
590	GIANNINI
595	ABARTH
600	MERCEDES-BENZ
601	TRABANT
650	GIANNINI
695 SS	ABARTH
801 A	YLN
850	FIAT (I), MINI (BRITISH LEYLAND), SEAT
850 TC CORSA	ABARTH
911	PORSCHE
914	VOLKSWAGEN-PORSCHE
914/6	VOLKSWAGEN-PORSCHE
1000	ABARTH, MINI (BRITISH LEYLAND), NSU
1000-353	WARTBURG
1100	AUSTIN, MORRIS
1200	NSU, VOLKSWAGEN
1200 S	CG
1275 GT	MINI (BRITISH LEYLAND)
1300	AUSTIN, MG, MORRIS, TRIUMPH, VOLKSWAGEN, WOLSELEY
1302	VOLKSWAGEN
1430	SEAT
1500	TRIUMPH, VOLKSWAGEN
1600	BMW, FIAT (RA), VOLKSWAGEN
1750	ALFA ROMEO
1800	AUSTIN, BMW, MAZDA, MORRIS
1800 E	VOLVO
2000	BMW, TRIUMPH
2000 AUTOMATIC	ROVER
2000 SC	ROVER
2000 TC	ROVER
2002	BMW
2101	VAZ
2150	FNM
2500	BMW
2800	BMW
3500	ROVER

MAXIMUM SPEED

Up to 65 mph

	mph
SUZUKI Jimny	47
HONDA Vamos 4	56
AUTOBIANCHI Bianchina Giardiniera	59
FIAT Campagnola C	59
GAZ 69AM	59
MAZDA Carol 360 De Luxe Sedan	59
TRABANT 601 Universal	61
CITROËN Mehari 2+2	62
FIAT 850 Familiare	62
HONDA N III Automatic Sedan	62
TRABANT 601 Limousine	62
CITROËN 2 CV 4	63
FIAT 500 Berlina	63
CITROËN Dyane	65
DAIHATSU Fellow Max	65
HONDA N III Town Custom	65
STEYR-PUCH 500 S	65

From 66 mph to 80 mph

	mph
RELIANT Rebel 700 Estate Car	66
ROVER Land Rover 88'' Regular	66
ROVER Land Rover 109'' Estate Car	66
CITROËN 2 CV 6	68
FIAT Campagnola A	68
MITSUBISHI Minica 70	68
RELIANT Rebel 700 Saloon	68
RENAULT 4	68
SUBARU 360 Sedan	68
SUZUKI Fronte 360 Hi-Custom Station Wagon	68
DAF 33 De Luxe Saloon	70
VOLKSWAGEN 181	70
GIANNINI Fiat Giannini 500 TV	71
HONDA N III De Luxe Sedan	71
HONDA Z Coupé PRO	71
HONDA N 600 Automatic Sedan	71
ISUZU Unicab KR80	71
MITSUBISHI Minica 70 GL Sedan	71
SUBARU R-2	71
SUZUKI Fronte 71 Super De Luxe Sedan	71
VOLKSWAGEN 1200 Standard	71
VOLKSWAGEN 1300 (1.2-litre)	71
BEDFORD Beagle	73
CITROËN Dyane 6	73
MINI (BRITISH LEYLAND) 850 Saloon	73
MINI (BRITISH LEYLAND) Clubman	73
HINDUSTAN Ambassador Mk II	74
ABARTH Fiat Abarth 595	75
CHRYSLER FRANCE Sim'4	75
DAIHATSU Fellow Max SS Sedan	75
FIAT 850 Berlina	75
HONDA N III 360 T Sedan	75
HONDA Z Coupé	75
HONDA N 600 Sedan	75
ISUZU Unicab KR85	75
MINI (BRITISH LEYLAND) 1000 Saloon	75
NSU Prinz 4L	75
RENAULT 6 (850)	75
SUBARU R-2 SS Sedan	75
SUZUKI Fronte 71 SS Sedan	75
SYRENA 104	75
TOYOTA Publica 800	75
ZAZ Zaporozhets 966 Limousine	75
CITROËN Ami 8	76
DAF 44	76
GLASSIC Glassic Series (111 hp power team)	76
PEUGEOT 204 Break Grand Luxe Diesel	76
FIAT 850 Super Berlina	78
GIANNINI Fiat Giannini 590 GT	78
INNOCENTI Mini Matic	78
JEEP CORPORATION Jeepster Commando Series (75 hp power team)	78
JEEP CORPORATION Jeep Universal (75 hp power team)	78
MITSUBISHI Minica 70 GSS	78
NISSAN Datsun 2000 Diesel Sedan	78

	mph
OPEL Kadett	78
ŠKODA 100 Saloon	78
VOLKSWAGEN 1200 (1.3-litre)	78
VOLKSWAGEN 1300	78
VOLKSWAGEN 1302 Limousine	78
VOLKSWAGEN 1600 A (1.5-litre)	78
VOLKSWAGEN 1600 (1.5-litre)	78
WARTBURG 1000-353 Tourist	78
AUSTIN 1100 Mk II De Luxe Saloon	79
HILLMAN Hunter GT	79
MORRIS 1100 Mk II De Luxe Saloon	79
HILLMAN Imp	80
MORRIS Minor 1000 Saloon	80
OTOSAN Anadol	80
VAUXHALL Viva	80

From 81 mph to 100 mph

	mph
ABARTH Fiat Abarth 595 SS	81
HILLMAN Hunter De Luxe Estate Car	81
MERCEDES-BENZ 200 D	81
AZLK Moskvich 408	81
AZLK Moskvich 426	81
NSU 1000 C	81
OPEL Kadett Coupé	81
VOLKSWAGEN 1302 S Limousine	81
VOLKSWAGEN 1302 LS Cabriolet	81
WARSZAWA 223 K	81
WARTBURG 1000-353	81
CHRYSLER FRANCE Simca 1301 Berline	82
FORD Escort 1100	82
FORD Pinto 2-door Sedan (75 hp power team)	82
PEUGEOT 404 Berline Diesel	82
RENAULT 6L (1100)	82
RENAULT 8 Automatic	82
RENAULT 10 Automatic	82
FORD Corcel	83
FORD Capri 1300 (Germany)	83
HILLMAN Hunter De Luxe Saloon	83
HOLDEN Torana Saloon	83
OPEL Rekord Caravan	83
PEUGEOT 504 Berline Diesel	83
RENAULT 8 Major	83
TRIUMPH Herald 13/60 Estate Car	83
AUTOBIANCHI A 112 Berlina	84
CHRYSLER FRANCE Simca 1100 LS Berline (5 CV)	84
FIAT 850 Special Berlina	84
FIAT 128 Berlina	84
FORD Taunus	84
FORD 17M	84
GIANNINI Fiat Giannini 650 NP	84
HILLMAN Avenger	84
INNOCENTI Mini Minor Mk 3	84
INNOCENTI Mini T	84
MERCEDES-BENZ 220 D	84
MORRIS Oxford Series VI Saloon	84
NISSAN Cherry Station Wagon	84
RENAULT 10	84
ŠKODA 100 L Saloon	84
VOLKSWAGEN 1600	84
WARSZAWA 223	84
WOLSELEY Sixteen-Sixty	84
AUSTIN 1300 Countryman	85
AUTOCARS Gilboa 1300	85
AUTOCARS Ducas 1300	85
AUTOCARS Sussita 1300	85
DAF 55	85
FORD Cortina 1300	85
GAZ Volga 21	85
SEAT 4-door 850 Especial	85
TRIUMPH Herald 13/60	85
TRIUMPH Toledo	85
TRIUMPH 1300	85
VAUXHALL Viva SL	85

Model	mph
AUDI 60	86
FIAT 128 Familiare	86
FORD Aero Willys	86
FORD Capri 1300 (Great Britain)	86
PLYMOUTH Cricket (70 hp power team)	86
VOLKSWAGEN 1600 Karmann-Ghia	86
ABARTH Fiat Abarth 695 SS	87
AUSTIN 1300 Super De Luxe Saloon	87
CHRYSLER FRANCE Simca 1000	87
CHRYSLER FRANCE Simca 1100	87
DAF 55 T Coupé	87
DAIHATSU Consorte Berlina	87
FIAT 124	87
FORD Capri 1500 (Germany)	87
MAZDA Familia 1000 De Luxe Sedan	87
MINI (BRITISH LEYLAND) 1275 G.T.	87
MITSUBISHI Colt 11 F De Luxe Sedan	87
MITSUBISHI Colt 11 F Station Wagon	87
MORRIS 1300 Super De Luxe Saloon	87
OPEL Rekord Limousine	87
PEUGEOT 204	87
POLSKI-FIAT 125 P/1300	87
SAAB 95 V4	87
TOYOTA Publica 1000 Sedan	87
TRIUMPH 1500	87
VAZ 2101	87
CHEVROLET Vega 2300 Series (90 hp power team)	88
DODGE Polara Series (145 hp power team)	88
FORD Corcel GT Coupé	88
FORD Zephyr	88
FORD Maverick and Maverick Grabber Series (100 hp power team)	88
JEEP CORPORATION Jeep Wagoneer Series (135 hp power team)	88
DODGE Challenger Coupé (125 hp power team)	89
HILLMAN Hunter Super	89
OPEL Kadett LS Rallye Coupé	89
OPEL Rekord L	89
RENAULT 12	89
AUSTIN Maxi 1500	90
CHEVROLET Opala 2500	90
FIAT 850 Sport Coupé	90
FORD Escort 1300 L	90
GAZ Volga 24	90
GIANNINI Fiat Giannini 500 Montecarlo	90
HILLMAN Avenger GL	90
HILLMAN Hunter GL	90
MITSUBISHI Colt Galant A II Sedan	90
NSU 1200	90
OPEL Ascona 16	90
PEUGEOT 404 Familiale	90
RENAULT 8S	90
SAAB 96 V4	90
ŠKODA 110	90
SUBARU FF-1	90
SUNBEAM Sport	90
SUNBEAM Stiletto	90
TOYOTA Corolla 1200	90
TOYOTA Corona 1500 De Luxe Sedan	90
VANDEN PLAS Princess 1300	90
WOLSELEY 1300 Mk II	90
WOLSELEY 18/85 Mk II	90
YLN 801 A	90
AUSTIN 1800 Mk II De Luxe Saloon	91
CHEVROLET Biscayne - Bel Air - Impala 2-door Sport Coupé and 4-door Sedan models (145 hp power team)	91
CHRYSLER FRANCE Simca 1000 Special	91
CHRYSLER FRANCE Simca 1000 Rallye	91
CHRYSLER FRANCE Simca 1301 Special	91
CITROËN GS	91
FORD Itamaraty	91
FORD Cortina 1600	91
MORRIS 1800 Mk II De Luxe Saloon	91
OLDSMOBILE Cutlass (145 hp power team)	91
PLYMOUTH Fury I, Fury II, Fury III 2-door Hardtop and 4-door Sedan models (145 hp power team)	91

Model	mph
AMERICAN MOTORS Matador Series (135 hp power team)	92
AUSTIN 1300 G.T. Saloon	92
AUSTIN Maxi 1750	92
CHECKER Marathon Series (155 hp power team)	92
DODGE Dart - Demon - Dart Swinger and Dart Custom Series (125 hp power team)	92
FORD Capri 1600 (Great Britain)	92
FORD Custom - Custom 500 and Galaxie 500 Series (140 hp power team)	92
FORD Torino and Torino 500 Series (145 hp power team)	92
MORRIS 1300 G.T. Saloon	92
OPEL Kadett Rallye Coupé	92
PEUGEOT 404 Berline Grand Tourisme	92
PLYMOUTH Satellite Coupé - Satellite - Satellite Custom and Satellite Sebring Series (145 hp power team)	92
PONTIAC Laurentian Series (145 hp power team)	92
SUNBEAM Alpine	92
TRIUMPH 1300 TC	92
VOLKSWAGEN K 70 (75 hp)	92
ACADIAN Acadian Series (145 hp power team)	93
AMERICAN MOTORS Javelin and Javelin SST (135 hp power team)	93
AUDI 75	93
AZLK Moskvich 412	93
AZLK Moskvich 427	93
CHEVROLET Chevelle - Malibu - Nomad - Greenbrier - Concours - Concours Estate Series (145 hp power team)	93
FIAT 124 Special Berlina	93
FORD Galaxie 500	93
FORD LTD	93
FORD 17M Hardtop	93
FORD Capri 1300 GT (Great Britain)	93
GIANNINI Fiat Giannini 590 Vallelunga	93
HONDA "77" Automatic De Luxe Sedan	93
HONDA "7" Automatic De Luxe Coupé	93
INNOCENTI Mini Cooper Mk 3	93
ISUZU Bellett 1500 Special Sedan	93
MAZDA Familia 1300 De Luxe Sedan	93
MITSUBISHI Colt Galant A I Sedan	93
NISSAN Sunny 1200	93
NISSAN Datsun 1400 Sedan	93
PEUGEOT 304	93
POLSKI-FIAT 125 P/1500	93
RENAULT 16 L	93
TOYOTA Publica 1200 Hi-De Luxe Sedan	93
TOYOTA 4-door Corolla 1200 Hi-De Luxe Sedan	93
VOLKSWAGEN 411 E	93
AMERICAN MOTORS Hornet - Hornet SST and Hornet Sportabout Series (135 hp power team)	94
DODGE Challenger Series (145 hp power team)	94
DODGE Charger Coupé - Coronet and Charger Series and all Coronet Custom Series except 9-passenger Station Wagon (145 hp power team)	94
PEUGEOT 304 Coupé	94
PEUGEOT 304 Cabriolet	94
PLYMOUTH Barracuda Coupé Series (125 hp power team)	94
PLYMOUTH Valiant and Valiant Duster (125 hp power team)	94
VAUXHALL Victor Super Estate Car	94
AUSTIN-HEALEY Sprite Mk IV	95
BUICK Skylark Series (145 hp power team)	95
CHEVROLET Nova and Nova SS Series (145 hp power team)	95
FIAT 850 Sport Spider	95
MERCURY Comet - Comet GT Series (100 hp power team)	95
MG Midget Mk III	95
OLDSMOBILE Cutlass and Vista Cruiser Series (240 hp power team)	95

Model	mph
VOLVO 145 Station Wagon	95
ALFA ROMEO Giulia 1300	96
AUTOBIANCHI A 111 Berlina	96
CHRYSLER FRANCE Simca 1100 Special Berline	96
FORD Capri GT 1700 (Germany)	96
FORD 20M	96
FORD Zephyr V6	96
ISUZU Bellett 1600 Sedan	96
ISUZU Bellett 1800 Automatic Sedan	96
MAZDA Familia 1300 De Luxe Coupé	96
MITSUBISHI Colt 11 Super Sports	96
NSU TT	96
OPEL Manta	96
OPEL GT 1100 Coupé	96
ROVER Range Rover	96
SAAB 99 Saloon	96
SEAT 1430	96
TOYOTA Carina 1400 De Luxe Sedan	96
TOYOTA Crown De Luxe Sedan	96
VAUXHALL Victor Super Saloon	96
VAUXHALL Victor 2000 SL Estate Car	96
AMERICAN MOTORS Ambassador DPL Series (150 hp power team)	97
AUDI 100 Limousine	97
HUMBER Sceptre	97
MG 1300 Mk II	97
TRIUMPH Spitfire Mk II	97
CHRYSLER FRANCE Chrysler 160	98
FORD Escort GT Saloon	98
HILLMAN Avenger GT	98
MINI (BRITISH LEYLAND) Cooper 'S' Saloon	98
OPEL Rekord Coupé	98
TOYOTA Corona 1900 Sedan	98
VAUXHALL Victor 2000 SL Saloon	98
VOLKSWAGEN K 70 (90 hp)	98
VOLVO 142 Saloon	98
VOLVO 144 Saloon	98
ALFA ROMEO Giulia 1300 TI	99
BMW 1600	99
BMW 1800	99
CHEVROLET Chevy Super Sport	99
CHEVROLET Camaro Series (145 hp power team)	99
CITROËN DSpecial Berline	99
CITROËN Familiale 20	99
DODGE Dodge	99
FIAT 1600 Sport	99
FIAT 124 Special T Berlina	99
FIAT 125 Berlina	99
FORD 17M RS	99
FORD Capri 1600 GT (Great Britain)	99
FORD Mustang and Mustang Grandé (145 hp power team)	99
GIANNINI Fiat Giannini 650 Coupé/Cabriolet	99
GIANNINI 2-door Fiat Giannini 128 NP Berlina	99
ISUZU Florian 1800 De Luxe Sedan	99
LANCIA Fulvia Berlina 2ª Serie	99
LOTUS Seven S4	99
MAZDA Capella 1500 De Luxe	99
MERCEDES-BENZ 200	99
MERCURY Montego - Montego MX - Montego MX Brougham and Montego MX Villager (145 hp power team)	99
NISSAN Cherry X-1 Sedan	99
NISSAN Sunny 1200 GX	99
NISSAN Datsun 1600	99
NISSAN Skyline 1500 Sedan	99
NISSAN Gloria Station Wagon	99
NISSAN President A Sedan	99
NSU TTS	99
OTAS A 112 KL	99
PONTIAC Laurentian - Catalina - Parisienne Brougham Series (145 hp power team)	99
RENAULT 16 TS	99
SUBARU FF-1 1300 G Sedan	99
TATRA T2-603	99
TOYOTA Publica 1200 SL Sedan	99
TOYOTA Corolla 1200 SL	99
TOYOTA Corolla 1400	99
TOYOTA Corona 1700	99

	mph
TOYOTA Crown Hardtop	99
AUSTIN 1800 Mk II S De Luxe Saloon	100
CHRYSLER FRANCE Simca 1501	100
FORD Escort Mexico 1600 GT	100
FORD Torino GT - Torino Brougham - Torino Ranch Wagon and Torino Squire Series (210 hp power team)	100
MORRIS 1800 Mk II 'S' De Luxe Saloon	100
PLYMOUTH Fury I - Fury II - Fury III - Sport Fury - Suburban - Custom Suburban and Sport Suburban Series (230 hp power team)	100
PONTIAC T-37 (145 hp power team)	100
PONTIAC Catalina and Safari Series (250 hp power team)	100
ROLLS-ROYCE Phantom VI 7-passenger Limousine	100
ROVER 2000 SC	100
ROVER 2000 Automatic	100
TRIUMPH 2000 Mk II	100
VAUXHALL Viscount	100
WOLSELEY 18/85 Mk II S	100

From 101 mph to 120 mph

	mph
AUDI Super 90 Limousine	101
FORD Taunus GT	101
FORD Taunus GXL	101
FORD Cortina 1600 GT Saloon	101
FORD Cortina 1600 GXL Saloon	101
GINETTA G15	101
PEUGEOT 504 Berline	101
PLYMOUTH Barracuda Series (145 hp power team)	101
PLYMOUTH Satellite Coupé - Satellite - Satellite Custom - Satellite Sebring - Satellite Brougham - Satellite Regent and Satellite Sebring Plus Series (230 hp power team)	101
PONTIAC Firebird (145 hp power team)	101
VAUXHALL VX 4/90	101
AMERICAN MOTORS Gremlin Series (135 hp power team)	102
CHEVROLET Nova and Nova SS Series (200 hp power team)	102
FORD LTD - LTD Brougham and Station Wagons Series (240 hp power team)	102
FORD Meteor Rideau - Meteor Rideau 500 - Meteor Montcalm Series (260 hp power team)	102
MERCURY Cyclone GT (210 hp power team)	102
OLDSMOBILE Delta 88 Series (240 hp power team)	102
OLDSMOBILE Custom Cruiser Series (280 hp power team)	102
PONTIAC Catalina Brougham Series (265 hp power team)	102
OPEL Manta SR	102
ALFA ROMEO Giulia 1300 Super	103
AUDI 100 S Limousine	103
BMW 2002 Automatic	103
DODGE Polara	103
DODGE Coronado Automatic	103
DODGE Polara and Polara Custom Series (230 hp power team)	103
FNM 2150	103
FORD Capri GT 2000 (Germany)	103
FORD Cortina 2000	103
FORD Zodiac	103
FORD The Executive	103
GIANNINI Fiat Giannini 1000 Coupé Grand Prix	103
HOLDEN Belmont	103
HOLDEN Kingswood	103
HOLDEN Premier	103
IKA Torino	103
ISUZU Bellett 1600 Sports Sedan	103
LANCIA Flavia Berlina 1.8	103
MARCOS 2-litre	103
MAZDA Capella 1600	103
MAZDA 1800 De Luxe Sedan	103
MITSUBISHI Colt Galant Hardtop Custom	103
NISSAN Datsun 1600 SSS	103
NISSAN Skyline 1800 Hardtop	103
NISSAN Laurel 1800	103
NISSAN Datsun 2000	103
NISSAN Gloria Super De Luxe Sedan	103
OLDSMOBILE F-85 - Cutlass and Cutlass 'S' Series (145 hp power team)	103
PLYMOUTH Barracuda Coupé - Barracuda and Grand Coupé Series (230 hp power team)	103
PLYMOUTH Valiant and Valiant Duster Series (230 hp power team)	103
PUMA GTE 1600	103
SUNBEAM Rapier	103
TOYOTA Carina 1600 Super De Luxe Sedan	103
TOYOTA Corona Mk II 1900	103
TRIUMPH Spitfire Mk III	103
TRIUMPH 2-litre Mk II Vitesse	103
VOLVO 145 S Station Wagon	103
AMERICAN MOTORS Ambassador SST and Ambassador Brougham Series (210 hp power team)	104
AUDI 100 LS Automatic Limousine	104
BMW 2000 Limousine	104
FAIRTHORPE Mark IV EM	104
FORD Capri 3000 (Great Britain)	104
MERCEDES-BENZ 220	104
CHEVROLET Biscayne - Bel Air - Impala - Brookwood - Townsman - Kingswood Series (245 hp power team)	105
DODGE Challenger Coupé and Challenger Series (230 hp power team)	105
MORGAN 4/4 1600	105
PONTIAC Bonneville and Grand Safari Series (280 hp power team)	105
VAUXHALL Ventora 2	105
VAUXHALL Victor 3300 SL Estate Car	105
ACADIAN Acadian Series (200 hp power team)	106
ALFA ROMEO GT 1300 Junior	106
ALFA ROMEO Spider 1300 Junior	106
ALFA ROMEO GT 1300 Junior Z	106
ANDINO GT 1100	106
AUDI 100 LS Limousine	106
BMW 2002	106
BUICK Skylark and Skylark Custom Series (230 hp power team)	106
BUICK Sportwagon 6-passenger (230 hp power team)	106
CHEVROLET Caprice and Kingswood Estate Series (255 hp power team)	106
CHRYSLER Newport - Newport Custom - Town and Country Series (275 hp power team)	106
CHRYSLER FRANCE Chrysler 160 GT	106
CHRYSLER FRANCE Chrysler 180	106
CITROËN DSuper Berline	106
CITROËN DS 20	106
CITROËN Familiale 21	106
DODGE GTX	106
DODGE Charger Coupé - Coronet - Coronet Custom - Charger - Charger 500 - Charger S.E. - Coronet Brougham and Coronet Crestwood Series (230 hp power team)	106
DODGE Polara and Polara Custom Series (255 hp power team)	106
FIAT 124 Sport Coupé	106
FIAT 124 Sport Spider	106
FIAT 125 Special Berlina	106
FORD 20M RS	106
FORD Capri 2000 GT (Great Britain)	106
HONDA "77" De Luxe Sedan	106
ISUZU Bellett 1600 GT Coupé	106
LANCIA Fulvia Coupé 1.3 S 2ª Serie	106
GIANNINI 2-door Fiat Giannini 128 NP-S Berlina	106
MG MGB GT	106
MG MGB Sports	106
MITSUBISHI Colt Galant GTO MI	106
MITSUBISHI Debonair Executive	106
NISSAN Laurel 2000 Hardtop	106
OPEL Rekord Sprint Coupé	106
PLYMOUTH Duster 340 (275 hp power team)	106
PLYMOUTH Road Runner (300 hp power team)	106
SUBARU FF-1 1300 G Sports	106
SUBARU FF-1 1300 G Super Touring	106
TOYOTA Corona 1700 SL Hardtop	106
TOYOTA Century Sedan	106
VOLVO 142 S Saloon	106
VOLVO 144 S Saloon	106
MARCOS 3-litre	107
OLDSMOBILE Ninety-Eight Series (320 hp power team)	107
OLDSMOBILE F-85 - Cutlass and Cutlass 'S' Series (240 hp power team)	108
OLDSMOBILE Toronado (350 hp power team)	108
PLYMOUTH Sport Fury GT (335 hp power team)	108
PONTIAC GTO Series (300 hp power team)	108
TECHNICAL EXPONENTS TX Tripper 1300	108
ALFA ROMEO GTA 1300 Junior	109
ALFA ROMEO Giulia Super	109
DODGE Dart - Demon - Dart Swinger and Dart Custom Series (230 hp power team)	109
FORD 26M	109
HOLDEN Monaro GTS Coupé	109
HONDA "7" De Luxe Coupé	109
ISUZU Florian 1800 TS Sedan	109
LANCIA Flavia Berlina 2000	109
MATRA SPORTS 530 LX	109
MAZDA Familia Rotary SS Sedan	109
MERCEDES-BENZ 230	109
MITSUBISHI Colt Galant 1500 GS	109
NISSAN Datsun 1800 SSS	109
NISSAN Skyline 2000 GT Sedan	109
NISSAN Datsun 2400 Sedan	109
OLDSMOBILE Delta 88 Custom and Royale Series (280 hp power team)	109
OPEL Admiral	109
PONTIAC Grand Prix (300 hp power team)	109
PONTIAC Grand Ville Series (325 hp power team)	109
TOYOTA Carina 1600 ST Sedan	109
TOYOTA Corona Mk II 1900 SL Hardtop	109
BUICK G.S. Series (260 hp power team)	110
CHRYSLER FRANCE Simca 1200 S Coupé	110
DODGE Polara Brougham and Monaco Series (275 hp power team)	110
FORD Torino Cobra (285 hp power team)	110
OPEL Commodore Limousine	110
PONTIAC Firebird Esprit and Firebird Formula 400 (250 hp power team)	110
SUNBEAM Rapier H120	110
TRIUMPH 2.5-litre P.I. Mk II	110
TRIUMPH GT6 Mk II	110
VAUXHALL Cresta	110
BUICK Centurion - Electra 225 - Electra 225 Custom - Riviera Series (315 hp power team)	111
CHEVROLET Opala 3800	111
CHEVROLET Monte Carlo Series (245 hp power team)	111
FORD Capri GT 2300 (Germany)	111
MERCURY Monterey 4-door Saloon, 2- and 4-door Hardtop (240 hp power team)	111
PEUGEOT 504 Coupé	111
PEUGEOT 504 Cabriolet	111
VOLKSWAGEN-PORSCHE 914	111
ABARTH Fiat Abarth 850 TC Corsa Gr. 2	112
ABARTH Fiat Abarth Scorpione 1300 S	112
ALFA ROMEO 1750 Berlina	112
ALPINE Berlinette 85 Tour de France	112
CITROËN DS 21	112
FAIRTHORPE TX-GT	112
FIAT 124 Sport Coupé 1600	112
FIAT 124 Sport Spider 1600	112
FORD Mustang Mach 1 (210 hp power team)	112

	mph
ISUZU Bellett 1800 GT Coupé	112
ISUZU 117 1800 Coupé	112
LANCIA Fulvia Sport 1.3 S 2ª Serie	112
LANCIA Fulvia Coupé 1600 HF 2ª Serie	112
LINCOLN Continental - Continental Mk III Series (365 hp power team)	112
LOTUS Europa	112
MAZDA R100 De Luxe Coupé	112
MERCEDES-BENZ 250 Limousine	112
MERCEDES-BENZ 250 C Coupé	112
MITSUBISHI Colt Galant Hardtop GS	112
NISSAN Laurel 2000 GX Hardtop	112
NSU Ro 80	112
ROVER 2000 TC	112
TRIUMPH GT6 Mk III	112
CHEVROLET Camaro (200 hp power team)	113
DODGE Challenger T/A (290 hp power team)	113
FORD Escort RS 1600	113
MERCURY Monterey Station Wagon - Colony Park Station Wagon and Monterey Custom Series (260 hp power team)	113
MERCURY Cyclone Series (285 hp power team)	113
OPEL Commodore Coupé	113
OPEL Commodore GS Limousine	113
OPEL Admiral 2800 S	113
PLYMOUTH AAR Cuda (290 hp power team)	113
PLYMOUTH GTX (370 hp power team)	113
BMW 2500 Automatic Limousine	114
DODGE Challenger R/T (300 hp power team)	114
DODGE Charger Super Bee (300 hp power team)	114
HOLDEN Torana 2250 Saloon	114
HOLDEN Torana 2600 S Saloon	114
HOLDEN Torana GTR Coupé	114
IMPERIAL Le Baron Series (335 hp power team)	114
AMERICAN MOTORS Javelin AMX (245 hp power team)	115
AUDI 100 Coupé S	115
BMW 2002 TI	115
BMW 2000 TII Limousine	115
BUICK Estate Wagon Series (315 hp power team)	115
DAIMLER Limousine	115
FAIRTHORPE TX-S	115
FIAT 130 Berlina	115
FORD Escort Twin Cam Saloon	115
HONDA "9" De Luxe Coupé	115
LANCIA Flavia Coupé 2000	115
MAZDA Capella RE De Luxe Sedan	115
MERCEDES-BENZ 280 S Limousine	115
MERCURY Cougar - Cougar XR-7 - Cougar GT Series (240 hp power team)	115
MITSUBISHI Colt Galant GTO MII	115
NISSAN President D Sedan	115
OLDSMOBILE Cutlass Supreme Series (260 hp power team)	115
OPEL GT 1900 Coupé	115
PLYMOUTH 'Cuda and AAR Cuda Series (300 hp power team)	115
PONTIAC Firebird Formula 400 (300 hp power team)	115
RENAULT 12 Gordini	115
ROVER 3.5-litre	115
TVR Vixen S2	115
VOLVO 164 Saloon	115
AMERICAN MOTORS Hornet SC/360 Series (245 hp power team)	116
CHEVROLET Camaro SS (270 hp power team)	116
CHRYSLER 300 and New Yorker Series (335 hp power team)	116
DAIMLER Sovereign 2.8-litre	116
DODGE Demon 340 (275 hp power team)	116
MERCURY Marquis and Marquis Brougham Series (380 hp power team)	116
OPEL Commodore GS Coupé	116
VOLVO 142 Grand Luxe Saloon	116
VOLVO 144 Grand Luxe Saloon	116

	mph
CG 1200 S Coupé	117
CG 1200 S Spider	117
CHEVROLET Chevelle SS and Malibu SS (365 hp power team)	117
DODGE Charger R/T (370 hp power team)	117
RELIANT Scimitar GTE	117
ALFA ROMEO 1750 GT Veloce	118
ALFA ROMEO 1750 Spider Veloce	118
BMW 2500 Limousine	118
FORD Capri GT 2600 (Germany)	118
HOLDEN Torana GTR XU-1 Coupé	118
ISUZU Bellett 1600 GTR Coupé	118
ISUZU 117 Coupé	118
JAGUAR XJ6 2.8-litre Saloon	118
MAZDA Capella RE GS Coupé	118
MAZDA R130 De Luxe Coupé	118
MERCEDES-BENZ 250 CE Coupé	118
MERCEDES-BENZ 280 SE Limousine	118
MERCEDES-BENZ 280 SEL Limousine	118
MERCEDES-BENZ 280 SE Coupé	118
MERCEDES-BENZ 280 SE Cabriolet	118
MERCURY Cyclone Spoiler (370 hp power team)	118
OPEL Admiral 2800 E	118
OPEL Diplomat E	118
ROVER 3500	118
TOYOTA Celica 1600 GT	118
TRIUMPH Stag	118
ZIL 114 Limousine	118
BENTLEY T Series 4-door Saloon	119
BENTLEY T Series H.J. Mulliner 2-door Saloon	119
BENTLEY T Series H.J. Mulliner Drophead Coupé	119
OLDSMOBILE 4-4-2 Series (340 hp power team)	119
OPEL Commodore GS/E Limousine	119
ROLLS-ROYCE Silver Shadow 4-door Saloon	119
ROLLS-ROYCE Silver Shadow H.J. Mulliner 2-door Saloon	119
ROLLS-ROYCE Silver Shadow H.J. Mulliner Drophead Coupé	119
TECHNICAL EXPONENTS TX Tripper 1600	119
BMW 2800 Automatic Coupé	120
CADILLAC Calais - De Ville - Fleetwood Series (345 hp power team)	120
CHEVROLET Corvette Series (270 hp power team)	120
JAGUAR 420 G	120
LOTUS Elan + 2 'S'	120
MARCOS 3-litre (Volvo)	120
PONTIAC Firebird Formula 400 (325 hp power team)	120
ROLLS-ROYCE Silver Shadow Long Wheelbase 4-door Saloon	120

Over 120 mph

	mph
CADILLAC Fleetwood Eldorado Series (365 hp power team)	121
CHEVROLET Camaro Z28 (330 hp power team)	121
VOLVO 1800 E Coupé	121
CHEVROLET Monte Carlo SS (365 hp power team)	122
LOTUS Elan S4 Drophead Coupé	122
LOTUS Elan S4 Coupé	122
OPEL Commodore GS/E Coupé	122
PONTIAC Firebird Trans Am (335 hp power team)	122
BMW 2800 CS Automatic Coupé	123
ABARTH Fiat Abarth 1000 Berlina Corsa Gr. 2	124
BMW 2800 Limousine	124
DAIMLER Sovereign 4.2-litre	124
FORD Thunderbird - Thunderbird Landau (360 hp power team)	124

	mph
HOLDEN Torana GTR-X Coupé	124
HOLDEN Brougham	124
IKA Torino GS Coupé	124
JAGUAR XJ6 4.2-litre De Luxe Saloon	124
LMX Sirex 2300 HCS Coupé	124
LMX Sirex 2300 HCS Spider	124
MAZDA 110S Cosmo Sport	124
MERCEDES-BENZ 280 SL Roadster	124
MITSUBISHI Colt Galant GTO MR	124
NISSAN Skyline 2000 GT-R Hardtop	124
TOYOTA Corona Mk II 1900 GSS Hardtop	124
TRIUMPH TR6 P.I.	125
TVR Tuscan V6	125
ALPINE Berlinette 1300 G Tour de France	127
BMW 2800 CS Coupé	127
FIAT Dino Coupé 2400	127
MERCEDES-BENZ 300 SEL 3.5 Coupé	127
MERCEDES-BENZ 280 SE 3.5 Cabriolet	127
MERCEDES-BENZ 600 Limousine	127
MERCEDES-BENZ 600 Pullman-Limousine	127
OPEL Diplomat V8	127
PORSCHE 911 T Coupé	127
PORSCHE 911 T Targa	127
GINETTA G21	128
VOLKSWAGEN-PORSCHE 914/6	128
GILBERN Invader	129
AVANTI Avanti II Coupé (270 hp power team)	130
FAIRTHORPE TX-SS	130
FIAT Dino Spider 2400	130
LOTUS Elan "Sprint"	130
MERCEDES-BENZ 280 SE 3.5 Coupé	130
MORGAN Plus 8 2-seater	130
NISSAN Datsun Z 432 Sports	130
NISSAN Datsun 240 Z Sports	130
MARCOS Mantis	132
ALPINE Berlinette 1300 S Tour de France	134
ALPINE Berlinette 1600 S Tour de France	134
JENSEN Interceptor II	135
JENSEN FF II	135
ALFA ROMEO Montreal	137
CITROËN SM	137
ISO Fidia	137
MERCEDES-BENZ 300 SEL 6.3 Limousine	137
PORSCHE 911 E Coupé	137
PORSCHE 911 E Targa	137
BRISTOL 411	140
ASTON MARTIN DBS	141
DE TOMASO 4-door Deauville	143
ISO Lele	143
ISO Grifo GL	143
ISO Grifo Spider	143
PORSCHE 911 S Coupé	143
PORSCHE 911 S Targa	143
FERRARI Dino 246 GT	146
LAMBORGHINI Urraco	149
MASERATI Mexico	149
AC 428 Convertible	150
AC 428 Fastback	150
FERRARI 365 GT 2 + 2	152
JAGUAR 4.2-litre E Type Coupé	153
JAGUAR 4.2-litre E Type Convertible	153
JAGUAR 4.2-litre E Type 2 + 2	153
DE TOMASO Mangusta	155
EXCALIBUR SSK-SS Series (300 hp power team)	155
LAMBORGHINI Espada	155
MASERATI Indy	155
MONTEVERDI High Speed 375 L	155
ASTON MARTIN DB6 Mk II	157
ASTON MARTIN DBS V8	161
LAMBORGHINI Jarama	162
MONTEVERDI High Speed 375 S	162
MASERATI Ghibli Coupé	168
MASERATI Ghibli SS Spider	168
ISO Grifo 7-litre	171
FERRARI 365 GTB 4 Berlinetta	174
LAMBORGHINI Miura S	174
MASERATI Ghibli SS Coupé	174
MONTEVERDI Hai 450 SS	180

MAKES, MODELS AND PRICES

Page	MAKE AND MODEL	Price in GB £	Price in USA $	Price ex Works
	ABARTH (Italy)			
230	Fiat Abarth 595			720,000
	Luxury version			760,000
	Competition version			830,000
	Luxury Competition version			865,000
230	Fiat Abarth 595 SS			830,000
	Luxury version			870,000
	Competition version			930,000
	Luxury Competition version			970,000
230	Fiat Abarth 695 SS			905,000
	Luxury version			945,000
	Competition version			1,010,000
	Luxury Competition version			1,050,000
231	Fiat Abarth 695 SS Assetto Corsa			1,040,000
	light alloy wheels			167,000
	semi-axles with cardan joints			122,000
231	Fiat Abarth 850 TC Corsa Gr. 2			2,690,000
231	Fiat Abarth 1000 Berlina Corsa Gr. 2			3,710,000
231	Fiat Abarth Scorpione 1300 S			1,840,000
232	Fiat Abarth Scorpione 1300 SS			2,050,000
	AC (Great Britain)			
164	428 Convertible	5,800		
164	428 Fastback	5,800		
	ACADIAN (Canada)			
283	Acadian 2-door Coupé	—		
283	Acadian 4-door Sedan	—		
	ALFA ROMEO (Italy)			
232	Giulia 1300			1,310,000
232	Giulia 1300 TI	993		1,515,000
232	Giulia 1300 Super			1,595,000
232	GT 1300 Junior	1,414		1,845,000
233	GTA 1300 Junior			2,385,000
233	Spider 1300 Junior	1,338		1,940,000
233	GT 1300 Junior Z			2,335,000
234	Giulia Super	1,223		1,795,000
234	1750 Berlina	1,480	3,595	
235	1750 GT Veloce	1,860	4,546	
235	1750 Spider Veloce	1,683	4,298	
235	Montreal			—
	ALPINE (France)			
102	Berlinette 85 Tour de France			21,960
102	Berlinette 1300 G Tour de France			28,760
102	Berlinette 1300 S Tour de France			32,400
102	Berlinette 1600 S Tour de France			30,840
	Berlinette Series:			
	larger sump (except for 1300 S and 1600 S)			392
	electric pump			280
	limited slip final drive			1,960
	5-speed mechanical gearbox (except for 1300 G, 1300 S and 1600 S)			1,110
	165 x 13 tyres			892
	servo brake			660
	larger fuel tank			1,920
	AMERICAN MOTORS (USA)			
286	Gremlin 2-passenger Sedan		1,899	
286	Gremlin 4-passenger Sedan		1,999	
	Gremlin Series:			
	automatic gearbox		200	
	power-assisted steering		100	
	servo brake		45	
287	Hornet 2-door Sedan		2,174	
287	Hornet 4-door Sedan		2,234	
	Hornet Series:			
	automatic gearbox		210	
	power-assisted steering		100	
	servo brake		45	
287	Hornet SST 2-door Sedan		2,274	
287	Hornet SST 4-door Sedan		2,334	
287	Hornet Sportabout Station Wagon		2,594	
	Hornet SST and Hornet Sportabout Series:			
	automatic gearbox		210	
	power-assisted steering		100	
	servo brake		45	
	V8 engine		129	
	automatic gearbox		216	
287	Hornet SC/360 2-door Sedan		2,663	
	automatic gearbox		238	
288	Javelin 2-door Hardtop		2,879	
288	Javelin SST 2-door Hardtop		2,999	
	Javelin and Javelin SST models:			
	automatic gearbox		217	
	power-assisted steering		111	
	servo brake		49	
	V8 engine		101	
288	Javelin AMX 2-door Hardtop		3,432	
	automatic gearbox		246	
289	Matador 2-door Hardtop		2,799	
289	Matador 4-door Sedan		2,770	
289	Matador Station Wagon		3,163	
	Matador Series:			
	automatic gearbox		217	
	power-assisted steering		111	
	servo brake		49	
	V8 engine		101	
291	Ambassador DPL 4-door Sedan		3,616	
	V8 engine		101	
291	Ambassador SST 2-door Hardtop		3,870	
291	Ambassador SST 4-door Sedan		3,852	
291	Ambassador SST Station Wagon		4,253	
291	Ambassador Brougham 2-door Hardtop		3,999	
291	Ambassador Brougham 4-door Sedan		3,983	
291	Ambassador Brougham Station Wagon		4,430	
	Ambassador DPL, Ambassador SST and Ambassador Brougham Series:			
	power-assisted steering		111	
	servo brake		49	
	ANDINO (Argentina)			
276	GT 1100			1,850,000
	ASTON MARTIN (Great Britain)			
164	DB6 Mk II	4,212		
	9.4 compression ratio engine	203		
165	DBS	4,755	17,900	
166	DBS V8	5,744		
	AUDI (Germany, F.R.)			
125	2-door 60 Limousine			7,990
126	4-door 60 Limousine			8,290

The prices refer to all the models listed in the volume, to the "Optional Accessories" and to the "Variations".
The first column shows the prices of cars produced in or imported into the United Kingdom; the second, the prices of cars produced in or imported into the United States of America; and the third, the prices of cars not imported into the United Kingdom or the United States, expressed in the currency of the country of origin.
All prices in the U.S.A. do not include U.S. transportation fees, state and local taxes; prices of the cars imported into the United States (East Coast) include ocean freight, U.S. excise tax and import duty.

Page	MAKE AND MODEL	Price in GB £	Price in USA $	Price ex Works
126	2-door 60 L Limousine			8,290
126	4-door 60 L Limousine			8,590
126	60 Variant			8,590
126	2-door 75 L Limousine			8,690
127	4-door 75 L Limousine			8,990
127	75 Variant	1,107		8,890
127	2-door Super 90 Limousine	1,047	2,995	
127	4-door Super 90 Limousine	1,082	3,095	
	60, 75 and 90 Series:			
	central gear lever			*95*
	6.45 x 13 tyres			*150*
	reclining backrests			*150*
	sunshine roof (except for			
	Variant models)			*400*
127	2-door 100 Limousine			10,190
127	4-door 100 Limousine			10,190
127	2-door 100 S Limousine			10,590
127	4-door 100 S Limousine			10,590
127	2-door 100 LS Limousine	1,192	3,695	
128	4-door 100 LS Limousine	1,220	3,795	
128	2-door 100 LS Automatic Limousine	1,342		12,090
128	4-door 100 LS Automatic Limousine	1,370		
128	100 Coupé S			14,400
	100 Series:			
	central gear lever			*95*
	sunshine roof			*440*
	AUSTIN (Great Britain)			
166	1100 Mk II 2-door De Luxe Saloon	612		
167	1100 Mk II 4-door Super De Luxe Saloon	657		
167	1300 2-door Super De Luxe Saloon	653		
167	1300 4-door Super De Luxe Saloon	678		
167	1300 Countryman	733		
167	1300 G.T. Saloon	761		
	1100 and 1300 Series:			
	automatic gearbox (except for 1300 G.T. Saloon)	*75*		
	reclining backrests	*13*		
	electrically-heated rear window (except for 1300 Countryman)	*8*		
	servo brake (only for 1300 G.T. Saloon)	*8*		
167	Maxi 1500	808		
168	Maxi 1750	843		
	Maxi Series:			
	electrically-heated rear window	*15*		
168	1800 Mk II De Luxe Saloon	891		
168	1800 Mk II S De Luxe Saloon	940		
	1800 Series:			
	automatic gearbox	*80*		
	power-assisted steering	*35*		
	reclining backrests	*15*		
	electrically-heated rear window	*15*		
169	3-litre De Luxe Saloon	1,388		
	overdrive	*45*		
	automatic gearbox	*80*		
	electrically-heated rear window	*15*		
	AUSTIN-HEALEY (Great Britain)			
169	Sprite Mk IV	692	2,081	
	oil cooler	*10*		
	wire wheels	*25*		
	anti-roll bar	*3*		
	hardtop	*50*		
	AUTOBIANCHI (Italy)			
235	Bianchina Giardiniera	442		660,000
	reclining backrests			*8,000*
236	A 112 Berlina			980,000
	rev counter			*17,500*
236	A 111 Berlina			1,440,000
	electrically-heated rear window			*8,000*

Page	MAKE AND MODEL	Price in GB £	Price in USA $	Price ex Works
	AUTOCARS (Israel)			
360	Gilboa 1300			—
360	Ducas 1300			—
360	Sussita 1300			—
	AVANTI (USA)			
292	Avanti II Coupé		7,645	
	power-assisted steering		*100*	
	electrically-controlled windows		*100*	
	AZLK (USSR)			
270	Moskvich 408	572		
271	Moskvich 426			—
271	Moskvich 412			
271	Moskvich 427	610		
	BEDFORD (Great Britain)			
170	Beagle	556		
	BENTLEY (Great Britain)			
171	T Series 4-door Saloon	7,005	20,500	
171	T Series H.J. Mulliner 2-door Saloon	8,800	29,000	
171	T Series H.J. Mulliner Drophead Coupé	9,200	31,400	
	T Series:			
	iodine headlamps	*11*		
	BMW (Germany, F.R.)			
128	1600 Limousine	1,184	2,899	
128	1600 Cabriolet			13,253
129	2002	1,358	3,159	
129	2002 Automatic	1,495	3,475	
129	2002 TI			11,988
	1600 and 2002 Series:			
	mechanical gearbox			*899*
	anti-roll bar (except for 2002 Series)			*71*
	limited slip final drive			*411*
	sunshine roof (except for 1600 Cabriolet)			*472*
	rev counter			*122*
129	1800	1,375		11,577
130	1800 Automatic	1,512		12,798
130	2000 Limousine	1,528		12,676
131	2000 Automatic Limousine	1,665		13,897
131	2000 TII Limousine			14,286
	1800 and 2000 Series:			
	anti-roll bar (except for 2000 TII)			*82*
	sunshine roof			*583*
	rev counter (except for 2000 TII)			*239*
131	2500 Limousine	2,294	5,637	
131	2500 Automatic Limousine	2,446	6,002	
131	2800 Limousine	2,639	6,663	
131	2800 Automatic Limousine	2,791	7,027	
131	2800 CS Coupé	3,558	7,973	
132	2800 CS Automatic Coupé	3,710	8,337	
	2500 and 2800 Series:			
	limited slip final drive			*411*
	Nivomats units			*388*
	sunshine roof			*583*
	power-assisted steering			*710*
	BRISTOL (Great Britain)			
171	411	5,358		
	BUICK (USA)			
292	Skylark 2-door Coupé		2,846	
292	Skylark 2-door Hardtop Coupé		2,917	
292	Skylark 4-door Sedan		2,896	
	Skylark Series:			

Page	MAKE AND MODEL	Price in GB £	Price in USA $	Price ex Works
	automatic gearbox		*211*	
	V8 engine		*121*	
292	Skylark Custom 2-door Hardtop Coupé		3,316	
292	Skylark Custom 4-door Hardtop Sedan		3,396	
292	Skylark Custom 2-door Convertible		3,437	
292	Skylark Custom 4-door Sedan		3,287	
292	G.S. 2-door Hardtop Coupé		3,284	
292	G.S. 2-door Convertible		3,475	
	Skylark, Skylark Custom and G.S. Series:			
	automatic gearbox		*222*	
	power-assisted steering		*111*	
	servo brake		*47*	
294	Sportwagon 6-passenger		3,514	
	automatic gearbox		*222*	
	power-assisted steering		*111*	
294	Estate Wagon 6-passenger		4,403	
294	Estate Wagon 9-passenger		4,549	
	Estate Wagon Series:			
	automatic gearbox		*243*	
295	Le Sabre 4-door Hardtop Sedan		3,904	
295	Le Sabre 2-door Hardtop Coupé		3,846	
295	Le Sabre 4-door Sedan		3,777	
295	Le Sabre Custom 4-door Hardtop Sedan		3,998	
295	Le Sabre Custom 2-door Hardtop Coupé		3,934	
295	Le Sabre Custom 2-door Convertible		4,127	
295	Le Sabre Custom 4-door Sedan		3,870	
	Le Sabre and Le Sabre Custom Series:			
	automatic gearbox		*222*	
296	Centurion 4-door Hardtop Sedan		4,332	
296	Centurion 2-door Hardtop Coupé		4,407	
296	Centurion 2-door Convertible		4,416	
296	Electra 225 2-door Hardtop Coupé		4,839	
296	Electra 225 4-door Hardtop Sedan		4,953	
296	Electra 225 Custom 2-door Hardtop Coupé		5,018	
296	Electra 225 Custom 4-door Hardtop Sedan		5,131	
296	Riviera 2-door Hardtop Coupé		5,290	
	Centurion, Electra 225 and Electra 225 Custom Series:			
	automatic gearbox			
	(only for Centurion Series)		*243*	
	CADILLAC (USA)			
296	Calais Coupé		5,934	
296	Calais Hardtop Sedan		6,110	
296	De Ville Coupé		6,299	
296	De Ville Hardtop Sedan		6,533	
296	Fleetwood Sixty Special Brougham		7,821	
296	Fleetwood Seventy-Five Sedan		11,955	
296	Fleetwood Seventy-Five Limousine		12,094	
297	Fleetwood Eldorado Coupé		7,416	
297	Fleetwood Eldorado Convertible		7,784	
	CG (France)			
102	1200 S Coupé			23,400
103	1200 S Spider			23,950
	CHECKER (USA)			
298	Marathon Sedan		—	
298	Marathon 6-passenger De Luxe Sedan		—	
298	Marathon 8-passenger De Luxe Sedan		—	
298	Marathon De Luxe Limousine		—	

Page	MAKE AND MODEL	Price in GB £	Price in USA $	Price ex Works
298	Marathon 6-passenger Station Wagon		—	
298	Marathon 8-passenger Station Wagon		—	
	CHEVROLET (Argentina)			
276	Chevy Super Sport			—
	CHEVROLET (Brazil)			
279	Opala 2500			—
279	Opala 2500 De Luxo			—
279	Opala 3800			—
279	Opala 3800 De Luxo			—
	CHEVROLET (USA)			
299	Vega 2300 2-door Sedan		2,091	
299	Vega 2300 2-door Coupé		2,197	
299	Vega 2300 Station Wagon		2,329	
	Vega 2300 Series:			
	semi-automatic gearbox		*111*	
	automatic gearbox		*168*	
	power-assisted steering		*95*	
299	Nova 2-door Coupé		2,378	
299	Nova 4-door Sedan		2,407	
299	Nova SS 2-door Coupé		—	
	Nova and Nova SS Series:			
	semi-automatic gearbox		*115*	
	automatic gearbox		*174*	
	power-assisted steering		*103*	
	servo brake		*47*	
	V8 engine		*95*	
	automatic gearbox		*206*	
300	Monte Carlo 2-door Sport Coupé		3,304	
300	Monte Carlo SS 2-door Sport Coupé		—	
	Monte Carlo and Monte Carlo SS Series:			
	automatic gearbox		*190*	
	automatic gearbox		*217*	
	power-assisted steering		*111*	
302	Chevelle 2-door Sport Coupé		2,707	
302	Chevelle 4-door Sedan		2,672	
302	Malibu 2-door Sport Coupé		2,880	
302	Malibu 4-door Sport Sedan		3,047	
302	Malibu 2-door Convertible		3,245	
302	Malibu 4-door Sedan		2,846	
302	Nomad 6-passenger Station Wagon		2,997	
302	Greenbrier 6-passenger Station Wagon		3,223	
302	Greenbrier 9-passenger Station Wagon		3,335	
302	Concours 6-passenger Station Wagon		3,332	
302	Concours 9-passenger Station Wagon		3,445	
302	Concours Estate 6-passenger Station Wagon		3,509	
302	Concours Estate 9-passenger Station Wagon		3,621	
	Chevelle, Malibu, Nomad, Greenbrier, Concours and Concours Estate Series:			
	automatic gearbox		*190*	
	automatic gearbox (only for Chevelle, Malibu and Nomad Series)		*180*	
	V8 engine		*95*	
302	Chevelle SS 2-door Sport Coupé		—	
302	Malibu SS 2-door Sport Coupé		—	
	Chevelle, Chevelle SS, Malibu, Malibu SS, Nomad, Greenbrier, Concours, Concours Estate			

Page	MAKE AND MODEL	Price in GB £	Price in USA $	Price ex Works
	Series:			
	automatic gearbox		217	
	power-assisted steering		111	
	servo brake		47	
304	Camaro 2-door Sport Coupé		2,916	
	automatic gearbox		180	
	V8 engine		95	
304	Camaro SS 2-door Sport Coupé		—	
304	Camaro Z28 2-door Sport Coupé		—	
	Camaro, Camaro SS and			
	Camaro Z28 Series:			
	automatic gearbox		217	
	power-assisted steering		111	
	servo brake		47	
305	Biscayne 4-door Sedan		2,985	
305	Bel Air 4-door Sedan		3,122	
305	Impala 2-door Sport Coupé		3,297	
305	Impala 4-door Sedan		3,280	
	Biscayne, Bel Air and			
	Impala models:			
	automatic gearbox		180	
	V8 engine		121	
305	Impala 2-door Custom Coupé		3,484	
305	Impala 4-door Sport Sedan		3,472	
305	Impala 2-door Convertible		3,680	
305	Caprice 4-door Sedan		3,793	
305	Caprice 2-door Coupé		3,740	
305	Brookwood 6-passenger Station Wagon		3,587	
305	Townsman 6-passenger Station Wagon		3,679	
305	Townsman 9-passenger Station Wagon		3,794	
305	Kingswood 6-passenger Station Wagon		3,771	
305	Kingswood 9-passenger Station Wagon		3,885	
305	Kingswood Estate 6-passenger Station Wagon		4,042	
305	Kingswood Estate 9-passenger Station Wagon		4,157	
	Biscayne, Bel Air, Impala, Caprice, Brookwood, Townsman, Kingswood, Kingswood Estate Series:			
	automatic gearbox		190	
	automatic gearbox		217	
	power-assisted steering		111	
308	Corvette 2-door Sport Coupé		5,536	
308	Corvette 2-door Convertible		5,299	
	Corvette Series:			
	power-assisted steering		111	
	servo brake		47	
	CHRYSLER (USA)			
308	Newport 2-door Hardtop		3,779	
308	Newport 4-door Sedan		3,704	
308	Newport 4-door Hardtop		3,842	
308	Newport Custom 2-door Hardtop		3,905	
308	Newport Custom 4-door Sedan		3,833	
308	Newport Custom 4-door Hardtop		3,985	
308	300 2-door Hardtop		4,378	
308	300 4-door Hardtop		4,457	
308	New Yorker 2-door Hardtop		4,923	
308	New Yorker 4-door Sedan		4,872	
308	New Yorker 4-door Hardtop		5,003	
308	Town and Country 6-passenger Station Wagon		4,921	
308	Town and Country 9-passenger Station Wagon		5,007	
	Newport, Newport Custom, 300, New Yorker, Town and Country			

Page	MAKE AND MODEL	Price in GB £	Price in USA $	Price ex Works
	Series:			
	automatic gearbox (only for Newport and Newport Custom Series)		241	
	power-assisted steering		125	
	front disc brakes with servo		76	
	CHRYSLER FRANCE (France)			
103	Sim' 4			7,695
104	Simca 1000	534		7,995
104	Simca 1000 GL	572		8,745
104	Simca 1000 Special	625		9,515
104	Simca 1000 Rallye			8,995
	1000 Series:			
	semi-automatic gearbox (except for 1000 Special and Rallye)	68		763
104	2-door Simca 1100 LS Berline (5 CV)			9,595
104	4-door Simca 1100 LS Berline (5 CV)			9,995
104	2-door Simca 1100 LS Berline	625		9,895
105	4-door Simca 1100 LS Berline			10,295
105	4-door Simca 1100 GLS Berline	687		11,195
105	4-door Simca 1100 LS Break			10,995
105	4-door Simca 1100 GLS Break	687		11,895
105	2-door Simca 1100 Special Berline	763	1,875	
106	4-door Simca 1100 Special Berline	794	1,960	
	1100 Series:			
	semi-automatic gearbox			893
	servo brake			153
	electrically-heated rear window (only for GLS models)			112
106	Simca 1200 S Coupé	1,220		17,195
106	Simca 1301 Berline	802		10,845
107	Simca 1301 Special Berline			11,995
107	Simca 1301 Special Break			12,745
107	Simca 1501 GL Berline	863		
107	Simca 1501 GL Break			13,645
107	Simca 1501 Special Berline			—
107	Simca 1501 Special Break	1,008		
	1301 and 1501 Series:			
	automatic gearbox			1,406
	electrically-heated rear window			118
107	Chrysler 160			13,760
108	Chrysler 160 GT			14,690
108	Chrysler 180			15,590
	Chrysler Series:			
	automatic gearbox			1,500
	electrically-heated rear window			118
	CITROËN (France)			
108	2 CV 4			6,640
108	2 CV 6			7,180
	2 CV Series:			
	centrifugal clutch			128
	separate front seats			88
108	Dyane	436		6,832
109	Dyane 6	477		7,980
	Dyane Series:			
	centrifugal clutch			128
	back seat folding down to luggage table			100
	commercial version			60
109	Mehari 2 + 2		1,795	8,692
	centrifugal clutch			128
110	Ami 8 Berline Confort	508		8,940
110	Ami 8 Berline Club	574		9,420
111	Ami 8 Break Confort	585		9,420
111	Ami 8 Commerciale			9,420
	Ami 8 Series:			
	centrifugal clutch			128

Page	MAKE AND MODEL	Price in GB £	Price in USA $	Price ex Works
	separate front seats			*176*
111	GS Confort			11,380
111	GS Club			12,200
	GS Series:			
	electrically-heated rear window			*96*
111	DSpecial Berline	1,126		14,800
111	DSuper Berline	1,241		16,240
112	DS 20 Berline	1,436		19,200
112	DS 20 Pallas			21,340
112	DS 20 Prestige			23,600
112	Familiale Luxe 20	1,446		19,820
112	Familiale Confort 20			20,220
112	Break Luxe 20			19,400
112	Break Confort 20			20,440
112	Commerciale 20			19,180
	DS and 20 Series:			
	power-assisted steering			*496*
	4 headlamps automatically adjustable in height			*332*
	headlamps automatically adjustable in height			*252*
	boosted heating for temperatures below — 15°C, 5°F			*348*
	electrically-heated rear window (only for DSpecial, DSuper and DS models)			*96*
	5-speed gearbox (except for DSpecial Berline)			*300*
112	DS 21 Berline	1,585	4,066	
112	DS 21 Pallas	1,812	4,329	
113	DS 21 Prestige			25,280
113	DS 21 Cabriolet			37,000
113	Familiale Luxe 21	1,598	3,934	21,420
113	Familiale Confort 21		4,175	20,600
113	Break Luxe 21			21,640
113	Break Confort 21			20,380
113	Commerciale 21			
	DS 21 and 21 Series:			
	injection engine			*2,460*
	4 headlamps automatically adjustable in height			*204*
	boosted heating for temperatures below — 15°C, 5°F			*348*
	electrically-heated rear window (except for 21 Series)			*96*
113	SM			46,000
	air-conditioning system			*1,900*
	DAF (Holland)			
228	33 De Luxe Saloon	534		
228	44 De Luxe Saloon	611		
229	44 C Estate Car	695		
	33 and 44 models:			
	sunshine roof	*37*		
229	55 De Luxe Saloon	672		
229	55 T Coupé	764		
229	55 C Estate Car	740		
	55 Series:			
	sunshine roof	*50*		
	DAIHATSU (Japan)			
362	Fellow Max Sedan			315,000
362	Fellow Max Station Wagon			—
362	Fellow Max SS Sedan			398,000
	Fellow Series:			
	De Luxe version			*35,000*
	Custom version			*65,000*
	Hi Custom version			*80,000*
	S version (only for Max SS)			*— 18,000*
362	Consorte Berlina			397,000
	De Luxe version			*447,000*
	Super De Luxe version			*462,000*

Page	MAKE AND MODEL	Price in GB £	Price in USA $	Price ex Works
	DAIMLER (Great Britain)			
172	Sovereign 2.8-litre	1,958		
	automatic gearbox	*38*		
172	Sovereign 4.2-litre	2,194		
	automatic gearbox	*71*		
	Sovereign Series:			
	air-conditioning system	*193*		
	electrically-controlled windows	*45*		
172	Limousine	3,824		
	DE TOMASO (Italy)			
237	Deauville 4-door			—
237	Mangusta			6,845,000
	DODGE (Argentina)			
276	Dodge			—
276	Polara			—
277	Coronado Automatic			—
277	GTX			—
	DODGE (USA)			
310	Dart 4-door Sedan		2,450	
310	Demon 2-door Coupé		2,343	
310	Dart Swinger 2-door Hardtop		2,561	
310	Dart Custom 4-door Sedan		2,609	
	Dart, Demon, Dart Swinger and Dart Custom Series:			
	automatic gearbox		*183*	
	V8 engine		*124*	
311	Demon 340 2-door Coupé		2,721	
	Dart, Demon, Demon 340, Dart Swinger, Dart Custom Series:			
	automatic gearbox		*191*	
	power-assisted steering		*100*	
	servo brake		*42*	
311	Challenger Coupé 2 door Coupé		2,706	
311	Challenger 2-door Hardtop		2,827	
311	Challenger 2-door Convertible		3,084	
	Challenger Coupé and Challenger Series:			
	automatic gearbox		*209*	
	V8 engine		*102*	
	V8 engine (only for Challenger Coupé)		*126*	
311	Challenger T/A 2-door Hardtop		—	
311	Challenger R/T 2-door Hardtop		3,252	
	automatic gearbox		*229*	
	Challenger Coupé, Challenger, Challenger T/A, Challenger R/T Series:			
	power-assisted steering		*97*	
	servo brake		*42*	
314	Charger Coupé 2-door Coupé		2,707	
314	Coronet 4-door Sedan		2,777	
314	Coronet 6-passenger Station Wagon		3,075	
314	Coronet Custom 4-door Sedan		2,925	
314	Coronet Custom 6-passenger Station Wagon		3,296	
314	Charger 2-door Hardtop		2,948	
	Charger Coupé, Coronet, Coronet Custom and Charger models:			
	automatic gearbox		*216*	
	V8 engine		*95*	
314	Charger Super Bee 2-door Hardtop		3,245	
	automatic gearbox		*238*	
314	Coronet Custom 9-passenger Station Wagon		3,472	
314	Charger 500 2-door Hardtop		3,196	
314	Charger S.E. 2-door Hardtop		3,096	
314	Coronet Brougham 4-door Sedan		3,206	
314	Coronet Crestwood 6-passenger Station Wagon		3,575	

Page	MAKE AND MODEL	Price in GB £	Price in USA $	Price ex Works
314	Coronet Crestwood 9-passenger Station Wagon		3,655	
314	Charger R/T 2-door Hardtop		3,750	
	Charger Coupé, Coronet, Charger Super Bee, Coronet Custom, Charger, Charger 500, Charger S.E., Coronet Brougham, Coronet Crestwood, Charger R/T Series:			
	automatic gearbox		*238*	
	power-assisted steering		*111*	
	servo brake		*45*	
316	Polara 2-door Hardtop		2,987	
316	Polara 4-door Sedan		2,966	
	Polara Series:			
	V8 engine		*111*	
316	Polara Custom 2-door Hardtop		3,259	
316	Polara Custom 4-door Sedan		3,238	
316	Polara Custom 4-door Hardtop		3,326	
316	Polara Custom 6-passenger Station Wagon		3,660	
316	Polara Custom 9-passenger Station Wagon		3,766	
316	Polara Brougham 2-door Hardtop		3,463	
316	Polara Brougham 4-door Hardtop		3,529	
316	Monaco 2-door Hardtop		3,855	
316	Monaco 4-door Sedan		3,780	
316	Monaco 4-door Hardtop		3,919	
316	Monaco 6-passenger Station Wagon		4,310	
316	Monaco 9-passenger Station Wagon		4,442	
	Polara, Polara Custom, Polara Brougham and Monaco Series:			
	automatic gearbox		*216*	
	power-assisted steering		*111*	
	front disc brakes with servo		*70*	
	EXCALIBUR (USA)			
319	SSK Roadster		12,000	
319	SS Roadster		12,000	
319	SS Phaeton		12,900	
	FAIRTHORPE (Great Britain)			
173	Mark V EM	734		
	servo brake	*14*		
	electrically-heated rear window	*15*		
	supercharger	*75*		
173	TX-S	1,329		
174	TX-SS	1,426		
174	TX-GT	1,284		
	TX Series:			
	servo brake	*14*		
	FERRARI (Italy)			
238	Dino 246 GT			5,500,000
239	365 GT 2 + 2	6,700	21,700	
239	365 GTB 4 Berlinetta	7,020	20,500	
	FIAT (Argentina)			
277	1600 Sport			17,950
	FIAT (Italy)			
239	500 Berlina	380		545,000
240	500 L Berlina	411		595,000
240	850 Berlina			820,000
240	850 Super Berlina	502	1,504	
240	850 Special Berlina	572		870,000
	850 Super and Special:			
	semi-automatic gearbox	*60*		*110,000*
240	850 Sport Coupé	717	1,988	
	light alloy wheels			*50,000*
241	850 Sport Spider		2,168	1,200,000
	light alloy wheels			*50,000*
	hardtop			*120,000*

Page	MAKE AND MODEL	Price in GB £	Price in USA $	Price ex Works
241	850 Familiare			1,130,000
	500 and 850 Series:			
	reclining backrests			*8,000*
242	2-door 128 Berlina	636		1,000,000
243	4-door 128 Berlina	669		1,060,000
243	128 Familiare	721		1,115,000
	128 Series:			
	reclining backrests			*14,000*
243	124 Berlina	718	2,015	
	reclining backrests			*14,000*
	electrically-heated rear window			*10,000*
243	124 Familiare	798	2,273	
	reclining backrests			*14,000*
243	124 Special Berlina	783		1,340,000
	automatic gearbox			*150,000*
	electrically-heated rear window			*10,000*
244	124 Special T Berlina			1,390,000
	automatic gearbox			*150,000*
	electronic ignition			*55,000*
	rev counter			*21,000*
	electrically-heated rear window			*10,000*
244	124 Sport Coupé	1,260	2,999	
244	124 Sport Spider		3,304	1,790,000
244	124 Sport Coupé 1600	1,335		1,825,000
245	124 Sport Spider 1600			1,870,000
	124 Sport Series:			
	electronic ignition (only for 1600 models)			*55,000*
	light alloy wheels	*60*		*50,000*
	electrically-heated rear window (only for Coupé models)			*10,000*
	headrests			*25,000*
	hardtop (only for Spider models)			*170,000*
	electronic ignition (only for 1600 models)			*55,000*
245	125 Berlina	925		1,480,000
246	125 Special Berlina	1,030		1,590,000
	electronic ignition			*55,000*
	air-conditioning system			*200,000*
	light alloy wheels	*60*		*50,000*
	125 Series:			
	automatic gearbox			*150,000*
	rev counter			*21,000*
	electrically-heated rear window			*10,000*
246	Dino Coupé 2400			4,450,000
247	Dino Spider 2400			4,300,000
	electrically-controlled windows			*98,000*
	hardtop			*300,000*
	headrests			*20,000*
247	130 Berlina			3,400,000
	mechanical gearbox			*— 80,000*
	air-conditioning system			*235,000*
	electrically-controlled windows			*87,000*
247	Campagnola A			2,050,000
248	Campagnola C			2,450,000
	Campagnola Series:			
	power take-off			*21,000*
	limited slip final drive			*25,000*
	FNM (Brazil)			
280	2150			20,000
280	2150 Luxo			22,000
	FORD (Brazil)			
280	4-door Corcel Sedan			—
280	4-door Corcel Sedan Luxo			—
280	Corcel Coupé			—
280	Corcel Coupé Luxo			—
281	Corcel GT Coupé			—
281	Corcel Station Wagon			—
281	Aero Willys			—
282	Itamaraty			—

Page	MAKE AND MODEL	Price in GB £	Price in USA $	Price ex Works
282	Galaxie 500			—
283	LTD			—
	FORD (Canada)			
284	Meteor Rideau 4-door Pillared Hardtop			—
284	Meteor Rideau 500 2-door Hardtop			—
284	Meteor Rideau 500 4-door Hardtop			—
284	Meteor Rideau 500 Station Wagon			—
284	Meteor Montcalm 2-door Hardtop			—
284	Meteor Montcalm 4-door Hardtop			—
284	Meteor Montcalm Station Wagon			—
284	Meteor Montcalm 4-door Pillared Hardtop			—
	FORD (Germany, F.R.)			
132	2-door Taunus Limousine			7,093
132	4-door Taunus Limousine			7,393
132	5-door Taunus Turnier			7,848
132	2-door Taunus L Limousine			7,304
132	4-door Taunus L Limousine			7,592
132	Taunus L Coupé			7,703
133	5-door Taunus L Turnier			8,059
133	2-door Taunus XL Limousine			8,103
133	4-door Taunus XL Limousine			8,403
133	Taunus XL Coupé			8,380
133	5-door Taunus XL Turnier			8,858
	Taunus models:			
	automatic gearbox			799
	165 x 13 tyres			119
	175 x 13 tyres, 5.5" wide rims			251
	servo brake			113
	sunshine roof			340
133	2-door Taunus GT Limousine			8,824
134	4-door Taunus GT Limousine			9,124
134	Taunus GT Coupé			9,180
134	2-door Taunus GXL Limousine			9,490
134	4-door Taunus GXL Limousine			9,790
134	Taunus GXL Coupé			9,846
	Taunus GT and GXL models:			
	automatic gearbox			799
	185/70 HR x 13 tyres with 5.5" wide rims			60
134	2-door 17M Limousine	964		8,658
135	4-door 17M Limousine			9,013
135	17M Hardtop			9,413
135	3-door 17M Turnier			9,046
135	5-door 17M Turnier			9,402
	17M models:			
	103.7 cu in, 1,699 cu cm engine	9		60
	110.6 cu in, 1,812 cu cm engine	38		292
	121.9 cu in, 1,998 cu cm engine (113 hp)	65		464
	139.8 cu in, 2,293 cu cm engine	39		957
	central gear lever	12		102
	automatic gearbox	124		959
	175 x 14 tyres	18		150
	power-assisted steering	77		
	sunshine roof	55		454
135	2-door 17M RS Limousine			10,329
136	4-door 17M RS Limousine			10,684
136	17M RS Hardtop			10,562
	17M RS models:			
	139.8 cu in, 2,293 cu cm engine			404
	sunshine roof			454
136	Capri 1300			7,781
136	Capri 1500			8,125
136	Capri GT 1700			8,902
137	Capri GT 2000			9,435
137	Capri GT 2300			9,979
137	Capri GT 2600			10,501
	Capri Series:			

Page	MAKE AND MODEL	Price in GB £	Price in USA $	Price ex Works
	automatic gearbox			799
	5" wheels			119
	165 x 13 tyres			139
	servo brake			113
	alternator			60
	L equipment			124
	XL equipment			315
	XLR equipment (only for GT models)			635
137	2-door 20M Limousine	1,127		10,112
139	4-door 20M Limousine			10,467
139	20M Hardtop			10,501
139	3-door 20M Turnier			10,501
139	5-door 20M Turnier			10,856
139	2-door 20M XL Limousine			10,933
139	4-door 20M XL Limousine			11,289
139	20M XL Hardtop			11,167
	20M models:			
	139.9 cu in, 2,293 cu cm engine	39		404
	155.5 cu in, 2,548 cu cm engine (except for Turnier models)	85		801
	central gear lever	12		102
	175 x 14 tyres	16		134
	power-assisted steering	77		
	sunshine roof	55		454
139	2-door 20M RS Limousine			11,605
139	4-door 20M RS Limousine			11,960
139	20M RS Hardtop			11,838
	20M RS models:			
	power-assisted steering	77		
	sunshine roof	55		454
139	4-door 26M Limousine			14,774
140	26M Hardtop			14,774
	26M Series:			
	mechanical gearbox			—733
	electrically-controlled sunshine roof			107
	FORD (Great Britain)			
175	Escort 1100 Standard 2-door Saloon	583		
175	Escort 1100 Standard 4-door Saloon	608		
175	Escort 1100 2-door Saloon	618		
175	Escort 1100 4-door Saloon	643		
175	Escort 1100 Estate Car	692		
	Escort 1100 models:			
	4.5" wide rims with 6.00 x 12 tyres	13		
	front disc brakes	13		
	automatic gearbox (except for Standard models)	92		
	L equipment (only for Estate Car)	19		
175	Escort 1300 L 2-door Saloon	661		
176	Escort 1300 L 4-door Saloon	686		
	Escort 1300 models:			
	automatic gearbox	68		
	XL equipment	28		
176	Escort 1300 Estate Car	727		
	L equipment	19		
	XL equipment	47		
176	Escort GT 2-door Saloon	740		
176	Escort GT 4-door Saloon	765		
	Escort GT models:			
	centre console	4		
176	Escort Twin Cam Saloon	1,042		
176	Escort Mexico 1600 GT	881		
176	Escort RS 1600	1,108		
177	Cortina 1300 2-door Saloon	700		
177	Cortina 1300 4-door Saloon	725		
178	Cortina 1300 Estate Car	811		
178	Cortina 1600 2-door Saloon	736		
178	Cortina 1600 4-door Saloon	761		
178	Cortina 1600 Estate Car	847		

Page	MAKE AND MODEL	Price in GB £	Price in USA $	Price ex Works
	Cortina 1300 and 1600 models:			
	5.5" sport road wheels with			
	175 x 13 tyres	26		
	servo brake	9		
	reclining backrests	16		
	L equipment	21		
	XL equipment	77		
	automatic gearbox (only for			
	1600 models)	68		
178	Cortina 1600 GT 2-door Saloon	852		
179	Cortina 1600 GT 4-door Saloon	877		
179	Cortina 1600 GXL 2-door Saloon	964		
179	Cortina 1600 GXL 4-door Saloon	989		
	Cortina 1600 GT and GXL models:			
	automatic gearbox	68		
179	Cortina 2000 2-door Saloon	787		
179	Cortina 2000 4-door Saloon	812		
179	Cortina 2000 Estate Car	898		
179	Cortina 2000 GT 2-door Saloon	888		
179	Cortina 2000 GT 4-door Saloon	913		
179	Cortina 2000 GXL 2-door Saloon	1,000		
179	Cortina 2000 GXL 4-door Saloon	1,025		
	Cortina 2000 Series:			
	automatic gearbox	68		
	185 x 13 tyres	25		
	L equipment	21		
	XL equipment	77		
179	Capri 1300	769		
180	Capri 1300 GT	860		
	Capri 1300 Series:			
	5" wide rims with 165 x 13 tyres	26		
	servo brake	9		
	reclining backrests	16		
	sunshine roof	32		
	sport roads wheels	16		
	electrically-heated rear window			
	and alternator	15		
	L equipment	13		
	XL equipment	37		
180	Capri 1600	823		
180	Capri 1600 GT	901		
	sunshine roof	32		
	sport road wheels	16		
	XLR equipment	68		
	Capri 1600 models:			
	automatic gearbox	68		
	L equipment	13		
	XL equipment	37		
180	Capri 2000 GT	935		
181	Capri 3000 GT	1,070		
181	Capri 3000 E	1,207		
	Capri 2000 and 3000 models:			
	automatic gearbox	68		
	reclining backrests (except for			
	Capri 3000 E)	16		
	sunshine roof	32		
	sport road wheels	16		
	L equipment	12		
	XL equipment	36		
	XLR equipment	68		
	electrically-heated rear window			
	(only for Capri 3000 models)	10		
181	Zephyr Saloon	870		
182	Zephyr Estate Car	1,239		
183	Zephyr De Luxe Saloon	941		
183	Zephyr De Luxe Estate Car	1,310		
	Zephyr Series:			
	automatic gearbox	85		
	5" wide rims with 185 x 14 tyres	16		
	reclining backrests	16		
	electrically-heated rear window	15		
183	Zephyr V6 Saloon	936		

Page	MAKE AND MODEL	Price in GB £	Price in USA $	Price ex Works
183	Zephyr V6 Estate Car	1,306		
183	Zephyr V6 De Luxe Saloon	1,007		
183	Zephyr V6 De Luxe Estate Car	1,376		
	Zephyr V6 Series:			
	overdrive	52		
	power-assisted steering	42		
183	Zodiac Saloon	1,238		
183	Zodiac Estate Car	1,607		
	Zodiac Series:			
	overdrive	52		
	automatic gearbox	85		
183	The Executive	1,496		
	mechanical gearbox	— 35		
	FORD (USA)			
319	Pinto 2-door Sedan		1,919	
	automatic gearbox		175	
	air-conditioning system		374	
319	Maverick 2-door Sedan		2,175	
319	Maverick 4-door Sedan		2,235	
319	Maverick Grabber 2-door Sports			
	Sedan		2,354	
	Maverick and Maverick Grabber			
	Series:			
	automatic gearbox		183	
	power-assisted steering		95	
320	Mustang 2-door Hardtop		2,911	
320	Mustang 2-door Fastback		2,973	
320	Mustang 2-door Convertible		3,227	
320	Mustang Grandé 2-door Hardtop		3,117	
	Mustang models:			
	V8 engine		95	
320	Mustang Mach 1 2-door Fastback		3,268	
	Mustang Series:			
	automatic gearbox		217	
	power-assisted steering		110	
	front disc brakes with servo		70	
322	Torino 2-door Hardtop		2,706	
322	Torino 4-door Sedan		2,672	
322	Torino 500 2-door Hardtop		2,887	
322	Torino 500 2-door Fastback		2,943	
322	Torino 500 4-door Sedan		2,855	
322	Torino 500 4-door Hardtop		2,959	
322	Torino 500 Station Wagon		3,170	
	Torino, Torino 500 Series:			
	V8 engine		95	
322	Torino Ranch Wagon			
	Station Wagon		3,560	
322	Torino Squire Station Wagon		3,023	
322	Torino GT 2-door Hardtop		3,150	
322	Torino GT 2-door Convertible		3,408	
322	Torino Brougham 2-door Hardtop		3,175	
322	Torino Brougham 4-door Hardtop		3,248	
322	Torino Cobra 2-door Hardtop		3,295	
	automatic gearbox		222	
	Torino, Torino Ranch Wagon,			
	Torino Squire, Torino 500, Torino			
	GT, Torino Brougham, Torino			
	Cobra Series:			
	automatic gearbox		217	
	power-assisted steering		110	
	servo brake		70	
324	Custom 4-door Sedan		2,940	
324	Custom 500 4-door Sedan		3,078	
324	Galaxie 500 4-door Sedan		3,246	
324	Galaxie 500 2-door Hardtop		3,280	
324	Galaxie 500 4-door Hardtop		3,317	
	Custom, Custom 500 Series:			
	V8 engine		75	
	Galaxie 500 Series:			
	V8 engine		121	
324	LTD 2-door Hardtop		3,575	

Page	MAKE AND MODEL	Price in GB £	Price in USA $	Price ex Works
324	LTD 2-door Convertible		3,746	
324	LTD 4-door Sedan		3,583	
324	LTD 4-door Hardtop		3,621	
324	LTD Brougham 4-door Sedan		3,746	
324	LTD Brougham 2-door Hardtop		3,749	
324	LTD Brougham 4-door Hardtop		3,792	
324	4-door Ranch Wagon		—	
324	4-door Custom Ranch Wagon		3,542	
324	4-door Country Sedan		3,726	
324	4-door Country Squire		4,032	
	Custom, Custom 500, Galaxie 500, LTD, LTD Brougham, Station Wagon Series:			
	automatic gearbox		217	
	power-assisted steering		110	
	front disc brakes with servo		52	
326	Thunderbird 2-door Hardtop		5,295	
326	Thunderbird Landau 2-door Hardtop		5,438	
326	Thunderbird Landau 4-door Hardtop		5,516	
	GAZ (USSR)			
271	Volga 21			—
271	Volga 22 G			—
272	Volga 24			—
272	69AM			—
	GIANNINI (Italy)			
248	Fiat Giannini 500 TV			645,000
248	Fiat Giannini 500 TVL			700,000
248	Fiat Giannini 500 Montecarlo			795,000
248	Fiat Giannini 590 GT			705,000
249	Fiat Giannini 590 GTL			760,000
249	Fiat Giannini 590 Vallelunga			795,000
249	Fiat Giannini 650 NP			725,000
249	Fiat Giannini 650 NPL			780,000
250	Fiat Giannini 650 Coupé/Cabriolet			—
250	Fiat Giannini 1000 Coupé Grand Prix			1,640,000
251	2-door Fiat Giannini 128 NP Berlina			1,250,000
251	2-door Fiat Giannini 128 NP-S Berlina			1,380,000
	GILBERN (Great Britain)			
184	Invader Saloon	1,649		
184	Invader Estate Car	—		
	Invader Series:			
	overdrive	69		
	automatic gearbox	110		
	sunshine roof	50		
	GINETTA (Great Britain)			
184	G15	849		
	light alloy wheels	35		
184	G21	1,845		
	overdrive/top	95		
	automatic gearbox	120		
	electrically-heated rear window	25		
	sunshine roof	39		
	GLASSIC (USA)			
327	Glassic Sport Phaeton		5,995	
327	Glassic Sports Roadster		5,995	
	HILLMAN (Great Britain)			
185	Imp	513		
186	Imp De Luxe	554		
186	Super Imp	588		
186	Avenger De Luxe	690		
187	Avenger Super	719		
	Avenger De Luxe and ·Super models:			
	engine 91.4 cu in, 1,498 cu cm	28		

Page	MAKE AND MODEL	Price in GB £	Price in USA $	Price ex Works
187	Avenger GL	806		
	automatic gearbox	70		
187	Avenger GT	869		
	automatic gearbox	70		
187	Hunter De Luxe Saloon	754		
188	Hunter De Luxe Estate Car	855		
	1.7-litre engine	28		
	Hunter De Luxe models:			
	automatic gearbox	103		
188	Hunter Super	812		
188	Hunter GL Saloon	880		
188	Hunter GL Estate Car	981		
188	Hunter GT	890		
	Hunter Super, GL and GT models:			
	overdrive	48		
	automatic gearbox (except for Hunter GT)	75		
	HINDUSTAN (India)			
361	Ambassador Mk II			15,091
	HOLDEN (Australia)			
400	Torana 2-door Saloon			1,909
400	Torana S 2-door Saloon			2,013
400	Torana S 4-door Saloon			2,147
400	Torana SL 2-door Saloon			2,180
400	Torana 2250 S 2-door Saloon			2,322
400	Torana 2250 S 4-door Saloon			2,368
401	Torana 2250 SL 4-door Saloon			2,623
401	Torana 2600 S 2-door Saloon			—
401	Torana 2600 S 4-door Saloon			—
401	Torana 2600 SL 4-door Saloon			—
401	Torana GTR Coupé			2,883
401	Torana GTR XU-1 Coupé			3,149
401	Torana GTR-X Coupé			—
401	Belmont Saloon			2,435
402	Belmont Estate Car			2,643
403	Kingswood Saloon			2,607
403	Kingswood Estate Car			2,815
403	Premier Saloon			3,135
403	Premier Estate Car			3,256
403	Monaro GTS Coupé			3,335
403	Brougham			4,081
	HONDA (Japan)			
363	N III Town Custom Sedan	403		425,000
363	N III De Luxe Sedan			346,000
363	N III 360 T Sedan			361,000
363	N III Automatic Sedan			389,000
363	Z Coupé PRO			396,000
364	Z TS Coupé			386,000
364	Z GS Coupé			463,000
364	Vamos 4			345,000
364	N 600 Sedan			—
364	N 600 Automatic Sedan			—
364	"77" De Luxe Sedan			578,000
365	"77" Automatic De Luxe Sedan			
365	"7" De Luxe Coupé			598,000
	S version			645,000
	Custom version			675,000
365	"7" Automatic De Luxe Coupé			636,000
366	"9" De Luxe Coupé			687,000
	S version			729,000
	Custom version			759,000
	HUMBER (Great Britain)			
189	Sceptre	1,075		
	automatic gearbox	40		
	IKA (Argentina)			
278	Torino L			17,412

Page	MAKE AND MODEL	Price in GB £	Price in USA $	Price ex Works
279	Torino S			19,950
279	Torino TS Berlina			22,000
279	Torino TS Coupé			23,561
279	Torino GS Coupé			25,679
	IMPERIAL (USA)			
327	Le Baron 2-door Hardtop		6,005	
327	Le Baron 4-door Hardtop		6,237	
	INNOCENTI (Italy)			
251	Mini Minor Mk 3			998,000
251	Mini T (all-metal body)			1,005,000
251	Mini T (wood-trimmed body)			1,065,000
252	Mini Matic			1,194,000
252	Mini Cooper Mk 3			1,307,000
252	Austin J5			1,216,000
	INTERNATIONAL HARVESTER (USA)			
328	Scout 800A		—	
328	Scout 800B		—	
328	Travelall 1000D		—	
	ISO (Italy)			
252	Fidia	5,436	14,800	
253	Lele	5,704		7,000,000
253	Grifo GL	5,589	13,448	
254	Grifo Spider			7,650,000
254	Grifo 7-litre	6,815	15,500	
	ISUZU (Japan)			
366	Unicab KR80			—
367	Unicab KR85			—
367	2-door Bellett 1500 Special Sedan			545,000
367	4-door Bellett 1500 Special Sedan			575,000
367	2-door Bellett 1600 Sedan			616,000
367	4-door Bellett 1600 Sedan			657,000
367	2-door Bellett 1600 Sports Sedan			679,000
367	4-door Bellett 1600 Sports Sedan			720,000
367	Bellett 1600 GT Coupé			830,000
368	Bellett 1600 GTR Coupé			1,110,000
368	Bellett 1800 GT Coupé			870,000
368	117 Coupé			1,670,000
368	117 EC Coupé			1,870,000
368	117 1800 Coupé			1,470,000
368	Florian 1800 De Luxe Sedan			740,000
369	Florian 1800 Automatic Sedan			—
369	Florian 1800 TS Sedan			800,000
	JAGUAR (Great Britain)			
190	XJ6 2.8-litre Standard Saloon	1,745		
191	XJ6 2.8-litre De Luxe Saloon	1,823		
191	XJ6 4.2-litre De Luxe Saloon	2,059		
	automatic gearbox	113		
	XJ6 Series:			
	overdrive/top	48		
	automatic gearbox	80		
	power-assisted steering	57		
	electrically-heated rear window	15		
	electrically-controlled windows			
	(only for De Luxe models)	45		
	air-conditioning system			
	(only for De Luxe models)	193		
191	420 G Saloon	2,090		
191	420 G Limousine	2,259		
	420 G Series:			
	overdrive/top	53		
	automatic gearbox	123		
	air-conditioning system	202		
	electrically-controlled windows	50		
	electrically-heated rear window	15		
191	4.2-litre E Type Coupé	1,886	5,725	
192	4.2-litre E Type Convertible	1,799	5,534	

Page	MAKE AND MODEL	Price in GB £	Price in USA $	Price ex Works
192	4.2-litre E Type 2 + 2	2,073	5,907	
	automatic gearbox	123	238	
	4.2-litre Series:			
	chrome-plated pressed steel wheels			
		24		
	rack-and-pinion steering with variable ratio servo			
		57		
	JEEP CORPORATION (USA)			
329	Jeep Wagoneer Standard		4,447	
329	Jeep Wagoneer Custom		4,697	
330	Jeepster Commando Convertible		3,291	
330	Jeepster Commando Roadster		3,197	
330	Jeepster Commando Station Wagon		3,446	
	Jeepster Commando Series:			
	V6 engine		201	
331	Jeep Universal		2,886	
	V6 engine		100	
	JENSEN (Great Britain)			
192	Interceptor II	4,470		
192	FF II	5,900		
	LAMBORGHINI (Italy)			
254	Urraco			—
255	Espada	8,450		8,300,000
	wire wheels			100,000
255	Jarama			8,000,000
	wire wheels			100,000
	air-conditioning system			250,000
255	Miura S	8,340		8,150,000
	air-conditioning system			350,000
	LANCIA (Italy)			
256	Fulvia Berlina 2ª Serie	1,079	2,950	
256	Fulvia Coupé 1.3 S 2ª Serie	1,432	3,440	
256	Fulvia Sport 1.3 S 2ª Serie	1,723	4,150	
256	Fulvia Coupé 1600 HF 2ª Serie	2,064		2,580,000
257	Flavia Berlina 1.8			2,100,000
258	Flavia Berlina 1.8 LX	1,586		2,275,000
	Flavia 1.8 Series:			
	injection engine			210,000
	ZF hydraulic power-assisted steering			140,000
	separate front seats with central gear lever			45,000
258	Flavia Berlina 2000	1,651		2,470,000
259	Flavia Berlina 2000 LX	1,763	4,305	
259	Flavia Coupé 2000	2,288	5,380	
	Flavia 2000 Series:			
	injection engine			210,000
	ZF hydraulic power-assisted steering			140,000
	LINCOLN (USA)			
331	Continental 4-door Sedan		7,213	
331	Continental 2-door Hardtop Coupé		6,966	
331	Continental Mk III 2-door Hardtop		8,421	
	LMX (Italy)			
259	Sirex 2300 HCS Coupé			3,580,000
259	Sirex 2300 HCS Spider			3,780,000
	LOTUS (Great Britain)			
193	Europa	1,399	4,295	
	servo brake	15		
193	Elan S4 Drophead Coupé	1,498	4,795	
194	Elan S4 Coupé	1,498	4,795	
194	Elan "Sprint"	—		
195	Elan + 2 'S'	2,002		
	Elan Series:			
	3.550 axle ratio	23		

Page	MAKE AND MODEL	Price in GB £	Price in USA $	Price ex Works
	light alloy wheels	*29*		
	servo brake	*15*		
195	*Seven S4*	*945*		
	MARCOS (Great Britain)			
195	2-litre	1,675		
195	3-litre	1,895		
196	3-litre (Volvo)	1,950		
	2- and 3-litre models:			
	sunshine roof	*45*		
	light alloy wheels (except for 3-litre model)	*55*		
196	Mantis	2,438		
	MASERATI (Italy)			
260	Mexico	5,965		7,390,000
260	Indy	6,271	17,500	
	Mexico and Indy:			
	288 cu in, 4,719 cu cm engine	*379*		*400,000*
260	Ghibli Coupé	6,727	18,900	
260	Ghibli Spider	7,117	19,400	
261	Ghibli SS Coupé			8,690,000
261	Ghibli SS Spider			8,990,000
	Mexico, Indy and Ghibli models:			
	limited slip final drive			*250,000*
	power-assisted steering			*130,000*
	automatic gearbox			*400,000*
	hardtop (only for spiders)			*450,000*
	MATRA SPORTS (France)			
114	530 LX			21,500
	light alloy wheels			*1,250*
	fixed top version			*20,500*
	MAZDA (Japan)			
369	2-door Carol 360 De Luxe Sedan			345,000
370	4-door Carol 360 De Luxe Sedan			370,000
370	2-door Familia 1000 De Luxe Sedan			—
371	4-door Familia 1000 De Luxe Sedan			513,000
371	2-door Familia 1300 De Luxe Sedan			518,000
371	4-door Familia 1300 De Luxe Sedan			538,000
371	Familia 1300 De Luxe Coupé			—
371	Capella 1500 De Luxe Sedan			618,000
371	Capella 1500 De Luxe Coupé			—
371	Capella 1600 De Luxe Sedan			658,000
371	Capella 1600 Super De Luxe Sedan			698,000
372	Capella 1600 Super De Luxe Coupé			738,000
372	1800 De Luxe Sedan			715,000
372	Familia Rotary SS Sedan			615,000
372	R100 De Luxe Coupé			598,000
372	110S Cosmo Sport			1,580,000
373	Capella RE De Luxe Sedan			748,000
373	Capella RE GS Coupé			845,000
374	R130 De Luxe Coupé			1,450,000
374	R130 Super De Luxe Coupé			1,750,000
	MERCEDES-BENZ (Germany, F.R.)			
140	200			12,743
140	200 D			13,264
140	220	1,971	4,961	
140	220 D	2,124	5,067	
140	230			14,619
141	250 Limousine	2,292	5,539	
141	250 C Coupé			18,426
141	250 CE Coupé	2,793	6,625	
	200, 220, 230 and 250 Series:			
	automatic gearbox	*169*		*1,443*
	power-assisted steering			*516*
	sunshine roof			*599*
141	280 S Limousine	2,599	6,588	
142	280 SE Limousine	2,828	6,866	
142	280 SEL Limousine		7,657	23,421
142	280 SE Coupé		11,612	29,137
143	280 SE Cabriolet		12,444	31,302
143	280 SL Roadster	3,419	7,244	
	280 Series:			
	mechanical gearbox	*169*		*1,443*
	power-assisted steering			*566*
	sunshine roof (except for Roadster)			*805*
143	300 SEL 3.5 Limousine	5,203		31,024
	sunshine roof			*805*
143	280 SE 3.5 Coupé	5,187		32,023
	automatic gearbox	*169*		*1,443*
144	280 SE 3.5 Cabriolet	5,551		35,631
144	300 SEL 6.3 Limousine	6,214	15,122	
144	600 Limousine	7,654	24,600	
145	600 Pullman-Limousine	8,538	28,120	
	MERCURY (USA)			
332	Comet 2-door Sedan		2,217	
332	Comet 4-door Sedan		2,276	
332	Comet GT 2-door Sedan		2,396	
	Comet and Comet GT Series:			
	automatic gearbox		*184*	
	power-assisted steering		*95*	
	V8 engine		*163*	
	automatic gearbox		*222*	
332	Montego 2-door Hardtop		2,777	
332	Montego 4-door Sedan		2,772	
332	Montego MX 2-door Hardtop		2,891	
332	Montego MX 4-door Sedan		2,878	
332	Montego MX Station Wagon		3,215	
332	Montego MX Brougham 2-door Hardtop		3,085	
332	Montego MX Brougham 4-door Sedan		3,073	
332	Montego MX Brougham 4-door Hardtop		3,157	
332	Montego MX Villager Station Wagon		3,456	
	Montego, Montego MX, Montego MX Brougham and Montego MX Villager Series:			
	automatic gearbox		*214*	
	V8 engine		*116*	
332	Cyclone 2-door Hardtop		3,369	
332	Cyclone GT 2-door Hardtop		3,680	
332	Cyclone Spoiler 2-door Hardtop		3,801	
	Montego, Montego MX, Montego MX Brougham, Montego MX Villager, Cyclone, Cyclone GT, Cyclone Spoiler Series:			
	automatic gearbox		*222*	
	power-assisted steering		*110*	
	front disc brakes with servo		*70*	
335	Cougar 2-door Hardtop		3,289	
335	Cougar 2-door Convertible		3,681	
335	Cougar XR-7 2-door Hardtop		3,629	
335	Cougar XR-7 2-door Convertible		3,877	
335	Cougar GT 2-door Hardtop		3,398	
	Cougar, Cougar XR-7 and Cougar GT Series:			
	automatic gearbox		*222*	
	power-assisted steering		*110*	
	front disc brakes with servo		*70*	
335	Monterey 4-door Sedan		3,423	
335	Monterey 2-door Hardtop		3,465	

Page	MAKE AND MODEL	Price in GB £	Price in USA $	Price ex Works
335	Monterey 4-door Hardtop		3,533	
335	Monterey Station Wagon		4,283	
335	Monterey Custom 4-door Sedan		3,958	
335	Monterey Custom 2-door Hardtop		4,041	
335	Monterey Custom 4-door Hardtop		4,113	
335	Marquis 4-door Sedan		4,474	
335	Marquis 2-door Hardtop		4,557	
335	Marquis 4-door Hardtop		4,624	
335	Marquis Station Wagon		4,547	
335	Marquis Brougham 4-door Sedan		4,880	
335	Marquis Brougham 2-door Hardtop		4,963	
335	Marquis Brougham 4-door Hardtop		5,033	
335	Colony Park Station Wagon		4,806	
	Monterey, Monterey Custom,			
	Marquis, Marquis Brougham,			
	Colony Park Series:			
	automatic gearbox		*223*	
	power-assisted steering		*121*	
	front disc brakes with servo		*70*	
	MG (Great Britain)			
196	Midget Mk III	692	2,279	
	oil cooler	*10*		
	wire wheels	*25*		
	anti-roll bar	*3*		
	hardtop	*50*		
	tonneau cover	*9*		
197	1300 Mk II	740		
	reclining backrests	*13*		
	electrically-heated rear window	*8*		
197	MGB GT	1,037		
	overdrive	*50*		
	servo brake	*8*		
	electrically-heated rear window	*15*		
198	MGB Sports	932		
	MINI (Great Britain)			
199	850 Saloon	487		
199	1000 Saloon	552		
199	Cooper 'S' Saloon	770		
	4.5" wide rims	*5*		
	protective cap for oil sump	*6*		
199	Clubman Saloon	589		
200	Clubman Estate Car	634		
200	1275 G.T.	683		
	850, 1000, Cooper, Clubman			
	and 1275 models:			
	automatic gearbox	*75*		
	reclining backrests	*13*		
	electrically-heated rear window			
	(except for Estate Car)	*7*		
	MITSUBISHI (Japan)			
374	Minica 70 Sedan			322,000
375	Minica 70 Station Wagon			—
375	Minica 70 GL Sedan			425,000
375	Minica 70 GSS			415,000
375	2-door Colt 11 F De Luxe Sedan			—
375	3-door Colt 11 F De Luxe Sedan			—
375	4-door Colt 11 F De Luxe Sedan			—
375	Colt 11 Station Wagon			—
375	Colt 11 Super Sports			555,000
376	Colt Galant A I Sedan			518,000
376	Colt Galant A II Sedan			—
376	Colt Galant Hardtop Custom			686,000
376	Colt Galant 1500 GS			711,000
376	Colt Galant Hardtop GS			761,000
376	Colt Galant GTO M I			786,000
377	Colt Galant GTO M II			843,000
377	Colt Galant GTO MR			—
377	Debonair Executive			1,197,000

Page	MAKE AND MODEL	Price in GB £	Price in USA $	Price ex Works
	MONTEVERDI (Switzerland)			
269	High Speed 375 S			71,000
269	High Speed 375 L			73,000
269	Hai 450 SS			—
	MORGAN (Great Britain)			
200	4/4 1600 2-seater	915		
200	4/4 1600 4-seater	945		
200	Plus 8 2-seater	1,300		
	dual exhaust system	*13*		
	MORRIS (Great Britain)			
201	Minor 1000 2-door Saloon	566		
202	Minor 1000 2-door De Luxe Saloon	588		
202	Minor 1000 4-door Saloon	592		
202	Minor 1000 4-door De Luxe Saloon	614		
202	Minor 1000 Traveller De Luxe	696		
	Minor Series:			
	reclining backrests	*13*		
202	1100 Mk II 2-door De Luxe Saloon	612		
203	1100 Mk II 4-door Super			
	De Luxe Saloon	657		
203	1300 2-door Super De Luxe Saloon	653		
203	1300 4-door Super De Luxe Saloon	678		
203	1300 Traveller	733		
203	1300 G.T. Saloon	761		
	servo brake	*8*		
	1100 and 1300 Series:			
	automatic gearbox	*75*		
	reclining backrests	*13*		
	electrically-heated rear window			
	(except for 1300 Traveller)	*8*		
203	Oxford Series VI Saloon	738		
204	Oxford Series VI De Luxe Saloon	769		
	Oxford Series:			
	Diesel engine	*95*		
	automatic gearbox	*68*		
	reclining backrests	*13*		
	electrically-heated rear window	*15*		
204	1800 Mk II De Luxe Saloon	891		
204	1800 Mk II 'S' De Luxe Saloon	940		
	1800 Series:			
	automatic gearbox	*80*		
	power-assisted steering	*35*		
	reclining backrests	*15*		
	electrically-heated rear window	*15*		
	NISSAN (Japan)			
378	2-door Cherry Sedan			410,000
379	4-door Cherry GL Sedan			525,000
379	Cherry Station Wagon			—
379	2-door Cherry X-1 Sedan			545,000
379	4-door Cherry X-1 Sedan			569,000
379	2-door Sunny 1200 Sedan			440,000
379	4-door Sunny 1200 Sedan			465,000
379	4-door Sunny 1200 De Luxe Sedan			—
379	4-door Sunny 1200 GX Sedan			605,000
380	Sunny 1200 Coupé			555,000
380	Sunny 1200 GL Coupé			590,000
380	Sunny 1200 GX Coupé			630,000
380	2-door Datsun 1400 Sedan			525,000
380	2-door Datsun 1400 De Luxe Sedan			609,000
380	4-door Datsun 1400 De Luxe Sedan			629,000
380	4-door Datsun 1400 GL Sedan			669,000
380	Datsun 1600 Sedan			—
381	Datsun 1600 Coupé			—
381	Datsun 1600 Station Wagon	832		
381	Datsun 1600 SSS Sedan			—
382	Datsun 1600 SSS Coupé			—
382	Datsun 1800 SSS Sedan			738,000
382	Datsun 1800 SSS Coupé			813,000
382	Skyline 1500 Sedan			—

Page	MAKE AND MODEL	Price in GB £	Price in USA $	Price ex Works
383	Skyline 1800 Hardtop			772,000
383	Skyline 2000 GT Sedan			—
383	Laurel 1800 Sedan			—
384	Laurel 1800 Hardtop			795,000
384	Laurel 2000 Hardtop			825,000
384	Laurel 2000 GX Hardtop			875,000
384	Skyline 2000 GT-R Hardtop			1,540,000
384	Datsun Z 432 Sports			—
385	Datsun 240 Z Sports			—
385	Datsun 2000 Sedan	1,077		
386	Datsun 2000 Station Wagon	1,146		
386	Datsun 2000 Diesel Sedan			—
386	Datsun 2400 Sedan			—
387	Gloria Super De Luxe Sedan			—
387	Gloria Station Wagon			—
387	President A Sedan			—
387	President D Sedan			—
	NSU (Germany, F.R.)			
145	Prinz 4L	503		4,990
146	1000 C	595	1,979	
146	TTS	857		8,500
147	1200			6,210
147	1200 C	648	2,252	
147	1200 C Automatic	723		6,990
147	TT	725	2,352	
147	Ro 80	1,981		16,500
	light alloy wheels			775
	sunshine roof			600
	Prinz 4L, 1000 C, TTS, 1200,			
	1200 C, 1200 C Automatic, TT:			
	front disc brakes			150
	sunshine roof			310
	145 x 12 tyres (except for			
	Prinz 4L, 1200 Series)			140
	OLDSMOBILE (USA)			
336	F-85 Town Sedan		2,884	
336	F-85 Sports Coupé		—	
336	Cutlass Town Sedan		2,998	
336	Cutlass Sports Coupé		2,900	
336	Cutlass 'S' Sports Coupé		2,957	
336	Cutlass 'S' Hardtop Coupé		3,020	
	F-85, Cutlass and Cutlass 'S'			
	Series:			
	automatic gearbox		211	
	V8 engine		121	
336	Cutlass Supreme Hardtop Sedan		3,397	
336	Cutlass Supreme Hardtop Coupé		3,322	
336	Cutlass Supreme Convertible		3,506	
	F-85, Cutlass, Cutlass 'S',			
	Cutlass Supreme Series:			
	automatic gearbox		222	
	power-assisted steering		111	
	front disc brakes with servo		47	
338	4-4-2 Hardtop Coupé		3,551	
338	4-4-2 Convertible		3,742	
	4-4-2 Series:			
	automatic gearbox		243	
	power-assisted steering		111	
	front disc brakes with servo		70	
339	Cutlass 6-passenger Station Wagon		3,453	
	automatic gearbox		211	
	V8 engine		121	
339	Vista Cruiser 6-passenger Station Wagon		3,865	
339	Vista Cruiser 9-passenger Station Wagon		4,007	
339	Custom Cruiser 6-passenger Station Wagon		4,539	
339	Custom Cruiser 9-passenger Station Wagon		4,680	

Page	MAKE AND MODEL	Price in GB £	Price in USA $	Price ex Works
	Cutlass, Vista Cruiser and			
	Custom Cruiser Series:			
	automatic gearbox		222	
	automatic gearbox			
	(only for Cutlass model)		243	
	power-assisted steering		111	
	servo brake		47	
340	Delta 88 Holiday Sedan		3,992	
340	Delta 88 Hardtop Coupé		4,048	
340	Delta 88 Town Sedan		4,110	
340	Delta 88 Custom Holiday Sedan		4,209	
340	Delta 88 Custom Hardtop Coupé		4,302	
340	Delta 88 Custom Town Sedan		4,377	
340	Delta 88 Rolaye Hardtop Sedan		4,560	
340	Delta 88 Royale Convertible		4,568	
	air-conditioning system		437	
341	Ninety-Eight Holiday Sports Sedan		4,890	
341	Ninety-Eight Hardtop Coupé		4,828	
341	Ninety-Eight Luxury Sedan		5,197	
341	Ninety-Eight Hardtop Sports Coupé		5,103	
342	Toronado Custom Coupé		5,499	
	OPEL (Germany, F.R.)			
148	2-door Kadett Limousine	643	1,925	
148	4-door Kadett Limousine	674		6,466
148	2-door Kadett L Limousine			6,682
148	4-door Kadett L Limousine			7,015
148	2-door Kadett LS Limousine	715		
148	4-door Kadett LS Limousine	751		
	Kadett models:			
	1.1-litre S engine			347
	automatic gearbox			640
	front disc brakes	24		
	sunshine roof	45		317
	electrically-heated rear window			81
148	Kadett Coupé		2,098	7,110
149	Kadett LS Coupé	777	2,197	
149	3-door Kadett Caravan	718	2,218	
149	3-door Kadett L Caravan	760		7,148
	Kadett models:			
	1.1-litre SR engine			439
149	Kadett Rallye Coupé		2,446	8,388
150	Kadett LS Rallye Coupé	913		
	Kadett Rallye models:			
	1.9-litre S engine			716
150	2-door Ascona 16 Limousine			7,365
151	4-door Ascona 16 Limousine			7,764
151	2-door Ascona 16 L Limousine			7,964
151	4-door Ascona 16 L Limousine			8,364
151	Ascona 16 Voyage			8,580
151	Manta			8,269
151	Manta L	1,015		8,719
151	Manta SR	1,128		9,718
	Ascona and Manta Series:			
	9.5 compression ratio engine			
	(only for Ascona Series)			267
	115.8 cu in, 1,897 cu cm engine	35		272
	automatic gearbox	99		799
	sunshine roof	50		388
	limited slip final drive			
	(only for Manta Series)	31		
151	2-door Rekord Limousine	995		8,097
152	4-door Rekord Limousine	1,032		8,414
152	3-door Rekord Caravan	1,055		8,486
152	5-door Rekord Caravan			8,886
152	2-door Rekord L Limousine			8,408
152	4-door Rekord L Limousine	1,076		8,797
152	Rekord Coupé	1,177		9,402
152	Rekord L Caravan	1,161		9,346
	Rekord Series:			
	1.7-litre S engine			88
	1.9-litre S engine			148

Page	MAKE AND MODEL	Price in GB £	Price in USA $	Price ex Works
	automatic gearbox	105		799
	limited slip final drive			213
	sunshine roof			424
	electrically-heated rear window			92
152	Rekord Sprint Coupé	1,319		11,104
153	GT 1100 Coupé			11,100
154	GT 1900 Coupé	1,574	3,440	
	GT Series:			
	limited slip final drive			213
	165 x 13 tyres			118
	automatic gearbox	105		799
	anti-roll bar			58
	44 Ah battery			16
	electrically-heated rear window	10		81
154	2-door Commodore Limousine			11,572
155	4-door Commodore Limousine	1,320		11,905
155	Commodore Coupé	1,375		12,160
155	2-door Commodore GS Limousine			12,813
155	4-door Commodore GS Limousine	1,514		13,146
155	Commodore GS Coupé	1,569		13,401
155	2-door Commodore GS/E Limousine			14,005
155	4-door Commodore GS/E Limousine			14,338
155	Commodore GS/E Coupé			14,593
	Commodore Series:			
	automatic gearbox	117		999
	limited slip final drive	31		213
	power-assisted steering	73		592
	sunshine roof	54		424
	electrically-heated rear window	18		92
155	Admiral			15,429
156	Admiral 2800 S			15,856
156	Admiral 2800 E			18,026
156	Diplomat E			20,352
156	Diplomat V8			23,016
	Admiral and Diplomat Series:			
	central gear lever			111
	automatic gearbox (except for Diplomat Series)			999
	limited slip final drive			400
	power-assisted steering (except for Diplomat Series)			649
	55 Ah battery			22
	electrically-controlled windows			672
	electrically-heated rear window (except for Diplomat Series)			124
	sunshine roof			522
	OTAS (Italy)			
261	A 112 KL			1,400,000
	OTOSAN (Turkey)			
360	Anadol A1			—
	PEUGEOT (France)			
115	204 Berline Luxe			10,080
115	204 Berline Grand Luxe	837		11,250
	sunshine roof	19		210
115	204 Break Grand Luxe	878		11,740
115	204 Break Grand Luxe Diesel			13,740
115	304 Berline	913		12,180
116	304 Coupé			14,150
116	304 Cabriolet			13,550
116	304 Break Super-Luxe			12,900
	304 Series:			
	sunshine roof (except for Cabriolet)	19		210
	hardtop (only for Cabriolet)			1,150
116	404 Berline Grand Tuorisme	1,013		12,720
	automatic gearbox			1,710
	sunshine roof	19		210
117	404 Berline Diesel			14,770
	sunshine roof	19		210

Page	MAKE AND MODEL	Price in GB £	Price in USA $	Price ex Works
117	404 Familiale Grand Luxe	1,146		13,830
	Diesel engine			2,050
117	404 Break Super-Luxe			14,630
118	404 Commerciale Grand Luxe	1,139		12,580
	Diesel engine			1,270
118	504 Berline	1,219	3,195	
119	504 Berline Diesel			17,750
119	504 Coupé			25,880
119	504 Cabriolet			24,730
	504 Series:			
	injection engine	85		2,800
	automatic gearbox	93	200	
	sunshine roof (except for Coupé)	27		250
	PLYMOUTH (USA)			
342	Cricket Sedan		—	
343	Valiant 4-door Sedan		2,392	
343	Valiant Duster 2-door Coupé		2,313	
	Valiant and Valiant Duster Series:			
	automatic gearbox		183	
	V8 engine		124	
343	Duster 340 2-door Coupé		2,703	
	Valiant, Valiant Duster and Duster 340 Series:			
	automatic gearbox		214	
	power-assisted steering		100	
	front disc brakes with servo		42	
344	Barracuda Coupé 2-door Coupé		2,633	
344	Barracuda 2-door Hardtop		2,745	
344	Barracuda 2-door Convertible		3,002	
	Barracuda Coupé and Barracuda Series:			
	automatic gearbox		209	
	V8 engine		101	
	V8 engine (only for Barracuda Coupé)		126	
344	Gran Coupé 2-door Hardtop		3,008	
344	'Cuda 2-door Hardtop		3,134	
344	'Cuda 2-door Convertible		3,391	
344	AAR Cuda 2-door Hardtop		—	
	Barracuda Coupé, Barracuda, Gran Coupé, 'Cuda and AAR Cuda Series:			
	automatic gearbox		229	
	power-assisted steering		97	
	front disc brakes with servo		42	
347	Satellite Coupé 2-door Coupé		2,663	
347	Satellite 4-door Sedan		2,734	
347	Satellite 6-passenger Station Wagon		3,032	
347	Satellite Custom 4-door Sedan		2,882	
347	Satellite Custom 6-passenger Station Wagon		3,253	
347	Satellite Custom 9-passenger Station Wagon		3,333	
347	Satellite Sebring 2-door Hardtop		2,905	
	Satellite Coupé, Satellite, Satellite Custom and Satellite Sebring Series:			
	V8 engine		95	
347	Road Runner 2-door Hardtop		3,120	
	automatic gearbox		238	
347	Satellite Brougham 4-door Sedan		3,162	
347	Satellite Regent 6-passenger Station Wagon		3,532	
347	Satellite Regent 9-passenger Station Wagon		3,612	
347	Satellite Sebring Plus 2-door Hardtop		3,153	
347	GTX 2-door Hardtop		3,707	

Page	MAKE AND MODEL	Price in GB £	Price in USA $	Price ex Works
	Satellite Coupé, Satellite, Road Runner, Satellite Custom, Satellite Sebring, Satellite Brougham, Satellite Regent, Satellite Sebring Plus and GTX Series:			
	automatic gearbox (except for Road Runner)		*216*	
	power-assisted steering		*111*	
	servo brake		*45*	
349	Fury I 2-door Sedan		2,781	
349	Fury I 4-door Sedan		2,814	
349	Fury II 2-door Hardtop		2,951	
349	Fury II 4-door Sedan		2,930	
349	Fury III 2-door Hardtop		3,102	
349	Fury III 4-door Sedan		3,081	
	Fury I, Fury II and Fury III Series:			
	V8 engine		*110*	
349	Fury III 2-door Hardtop Special		3,245	
349	Fury III 4-door Hardtop		3,257	
349	Sport Fury 2-door Hardtop		3,322	
349	Sport Fury 2-door Hardtop Special		3,355	
349	Sport Fury 4-door Sedan		3,301	
349	Sport Fury 4-door Hardtop		3,368	
349	Sport Fury GT 2-door Hardtop		3,975	
349	Suburban 6-passenger Station Wagon		3,399	
349	Suburban 9-passenger Station Wagon		3,510	
349	Custom Suburban 6-passenger Station Wagon		3,522	
349	Custom Suburban 9-passenger Station Wagon		3,598	
349	Sport Suburban 6-passenger Station Wagon		3,709	
349	Sport Suburban 9-passenger Station Wagon		3,784	
	Fury I, Fury II, Fury III, Sport Fury, Sport Fury GT, Suburban, Custom Suburban, Sport Suburban Series:			
	automatic gearbox		*216*	
	power-assisted steering		*111*	
	front disc brakes with servo		*70*	
	POLSKI-FIAT (Poland)			
262	125 P/1300			—
262	125 P/1500			—
	PONTIAC (Canada)			
285	Laurentian 2-door Hardtop			—
285	Laurentian 4-door Hardtop			—
285	Laurentian 4-door Sedan			—
285	Catalina 2-door Hardtop			—
285	Catalina 4-door Hardtop			—
285	Catalina 4-door Sedan			—
285	Parisienne Brougham 2-door Hardtop			—
235	Parisienne Brougham 4-door Hardtop			—
285	Parisienne Brougham 4-door Sedan			—
	PONTIAC (USA)			
351	T-37 4-door Sedan		2,795	
351	T-37 Coupé		2,747	
351	T-37 Hardtop Coupé		2,807	
351	Le Mans 4-door Sedan		2,925	
351	Le Mans 4-door Hardtop		3,064	
351	Le Mans Coupé		2,877	
351	Le Mans Hardtop Coupé		2,938	
351	Le Mans 6-passenger Station Wagon		3,353	
351	Le Mans 9-passenger			

Page	MAKE AND MODEL	Price in GB £	Price in USA $	Price ex Works
	Station Wagon		3,465	
351	Le Mans Sport 4-door Hardtop		3,255	
351	Le Mans Sport Hardtop Coupé		3,125	
351	Le Mans Sport Convertible		3,333	
	T-37, Le Mans and Le Mans Sport Series:			
	automatic gearbox		*180*	
	automatic gearbox		*211*	
	V8 engine		*121*	
351	GTO Hardtop Coupé		3,446	
351	GTO Convertible		3,676	
	T-37, Le Mans, Le Mans Sport and GTO Series:			
	automatic gearbox		*190*	
	automatic gearbox		*222*	
	automatic gearbox		*243*	
	power-assisted steering		*111*	
	front disc brakes		*47*	
353	Firebird Hardtop Coupé		3,042	
	automatic gearbox		*180*	
	automatic gearbox		*211*	
	V8 engine		*121*	
353	Firebird Esprit Hardtop Coupé		3,411	
353	Firebird Formula 400 Hardtop Coupé		3,440	
353	Firebird Trans Am Hardtop Coupé		4,590	
	Firebird Series:			
	automatic gearbox		*190*	
	automatic gearbox		*222*	
	power-assisted steering		*111*	
	servo brake		*47*	
355	Catalina 4-door Sedan		3,421	
355	Catalina 4-door Hardtop		3,590	
355	Catalina Hardtop Coupé		3,521	
355	Catalina Convertible		3,807	
355	Safari 6-passenger Station Wagon		3,892	
355	Safari 9-passenger Station Wagon		4,039	
355	Catalina Brougham 4-door Sedan		3,629	
355	Catalina Brougham 4-door Hardtop		3,783	
355	Catalina Brougham Hardtop Coupé		3,713	
355	Bonneville 4-door Sedan		3,968	
355	Bonneville 4-door Hardtop		4,098	
355	Bonneville Hardtop Coupé		4,030	
355	Grand Safari 6-passenger Station Wagon		4,401	
355	Grand Safari 9-passenger Station Wagon		4,548	
355	Grand Ville 4-door Hardtop		4,324	
355	Grand Ville Hardtop Coupé		4,255	
355	Grand Ville Convertible		4,464	
	Catalina, Safari, Catalina Brougham, Bonneville, Grand Safari, Grand Ville Series:			
	automatic gearbox		*190*	
	automatic gearbox		*222*	
	automatic gearbox (only for Safari Series)		*243*	
	power-assisted steering		*121*	
357	Grand Prix Hardtop Coupé		4,314	
	automatic gearbox		*243*	
	PORSCHE (Germany, F.R.)			
156	911 T Coupé	2,810	6,430	
157	911 T Targa	3,120	7,105	
157	911 E Coupé	3,510	7,895	
157	911 E Targa	3,820	8,570	
158	911 S Coupé	3,990	8,675	
158	911 S Targa	4,300	9,350	
	911 Series:			
	mechanical gearbox		*100*	
	semi-automatic gearbox (except for 911 S models)	*130*	*315*	

Page	MAKE AND MODEL	Price in GB £	Price in USA $	Price ex Works
	PUMA (Brazil)			
283	GTE 1600			22,310
	RELIANT (Great Britain)			
204	Rebel 700 Saloon	588		
205	Rebel 700 Estate Car	642		
205	Scimitar GTE	1,641		
	overdrive	*55*		
	automatic gearbox	*106*		
	light alloy wheels	*52*		
	electrically-heated rear window	*25*		
	RENAULT (France)			
119	4	457		7,128
119	4 Export	495		7,990
119	6 (850)	572		8,990
120	6 L (1100)			9,990
120	6 TL (1100)	626		
120	8 Major	556		8,920
120	8 Automatic			—
121	8 S	615		9,840
121	10	610	1,725	
122	10 Automatic	686		10,660
122	12 L Berline	683		10,780
123	12 TL Berline	725		11,580
123	12 Break			11,990
123	12 Gordini			16,500
123	16 L	786		12,600
123	16 TL	839	2,395	
123	16 L Commerciale			12,800
124	16 TS	978		15,200
124	16 TS Commerciale			15,340
	16 Series:			
	sunshine roof	*78*		
	automatic (electronic) gearbox	*129*		*1,600*
	ROLLS-ROYCE (Great Britain)			
206	Silver Shadow 4-door Saloon	7,100	20,700	
207	Silver Shadow Long Wheelbase 4-door Saloon	8,150	24,500	
207	Silver Shadow Long Wheelbase 4-door Saloon with division	8,690	26,800	
207	Silver Shadow H.J. Mulliner 2-door Saloon	8,850	29,200	
207	Silver Shadow H.J. Mulliner Drophead Coupé	9,250	31,600	
207	Phantom VI 7-passenger Limousine	10,050		
	ROVER (Great Britain)			
207	2000 SC	1,281		
208	2000 Automatic	1,379	4,198	
208	2000 TC	1,360	4,198	
	2000 Series:			
	electric immersion heater for cylinder block	*6*		
	headrests on front and rear seats	*10*		
	sunshine roof	*95*		
	electrically-heated rear window	*11*		
	oil cooler (only for 2000 TC)	*16*		
208	3500	1,568	5,398	
	headrests on front and rear seats	*10*		
	sunshine roof	*95*		
208	3.5-litre Saloon	1,883		
209	3.5-litre Coupé	1,964		
	3.5-litre Series:			
	headrests on front and rear seats	*11*		
209	Land Rover 88" Regular	889		
210	Land Rover 109" Estate Car	1,019		
210	Range Rover	1,529		

Page	MAKE AND MODEL	Price in GB £	Price in USA $	Price ex Works
	SAAB (Sweden)			
264	96 V4	780	2,545	
265	95 V4	860	2,799	
265	99 2-door Saloon	1,086	3,100	
266	99 4-door Saloon	1,143		
	99 Series:			
	112.9 cu in, 1,850 cu cm engine		*165*	
	SEAT (Spain)			
263	4-door 850 Especial			94,000
264	1430			136,600
	ŠKODA (Czechoslovakia)			
100	100 Saloon	511		
101	100 L Saloon	542		
101	110 L Saloon	565		
101	110 LS Saloon			—
101	110 R Coupé			—
	STEYR-PUCH (Austria)			
100	500 S			29,700
	SUBARU (Japan)			
388	360 Sedan			309,000
	De Luxe version			*338,000*
388	R-2 Sedan			315,000
388	R-2 Custom Station Wagon			—
388	R-2 GL Sedan			410,000
388	R-2 SS Sedan			395,000
	R-2 Series:			
	Super De Luxe version			*65,000*
388	2-door FF-1 Sedan			449,000
389	4-door FF-1 Sedan			534,000
389	FF-1 Station Wagon			—
389	2-door FF-1 1300 G Sedan			474,000
390	4-door FF-1 1300 G De Luxe Sedan			559,000
390	2-door FF-1 1300 GL Sedan			574,000
390	4-door FF-1 1300 GL Sedan			599,000
390	FF-1 1300 G Sports			639,000
390	FF-1 1300 G Super Touring			690,000
	SUNBEAM (Great Britain)			
211	Sport	666		
211	Stiletto	720		
211	Rapier	1,090		
212	Rapier H120	1,268		
	Rapier Series:			
	automatic gearbox	*40*		
212	Alpine	955		
	overdrive	*48*		
	automatic gearbox	*75*		
	SUZUKI (Japan)			
390	Fronte 71 Super De Luxe Sedan			394,000
391	Fronte 71 SSS Sedan			405,000
391	Fronte 360 Hi-Custom Station Wagon			394,000
391	Jimny			484,000
	SYRENA (Poland)			
262	104			—
	TATRA (Czechoslovakia)			
101	T2-603			—
	TECHNICAL EXPONENTS (Great Britain)			
212	TX Tripper 1300	780		
212	TX Tripper 1600	845		
	TOYOTA (Japan)			
391	Publica 800 Sedan			365,000
392	Publica 800 Station Wagon			—

Page	MAKE AND MODEL	Price in GB £	Price in USA $	Price ex Works
392	Publica 1000 Sedan			395,000
392	Publica 1200 Hi-De Luxe Sedan			475,000
392	Publica 1200 SL Sedan			495,000
392	2-door Corolla 1200 De Luxe Sedan			501,500
392	4-door Corolla 1200 De Luxe Sedan			—
392	Corolla 1200 Coupé			537,000
393	4-door Corolla 1200 Hi-De Luxe Sedan			555,000
393	2-door Corolla 1200 SL Sedan			564,000
393	Corolla 1200 SL Coupé			594,000
393	2-door Corolla 1400 Hi-De Luxe Sedan			590,000
393	4-door Corolla 1400 Hi-De Luxe Sedan			—
394	Corolla 1400 Hi-De Luxe Coupé			595,000
394	2-door Corolla 1400 SL Sedan			604,000
394	4-door Corolla 1400 SL Sedan			—
394	Corolla 1400 SL Coupé			634,000
394	2-door Carina 1400 De Luxe Sedan			579,000
395	4-door Carina 1400 De Luxe Sedan			—
395	2-door Carina 1600 Super De Luxe Sedan			644,000
395	4-door Carina 1600 Super De Luxe Sedan			—
395	2-door Carina 1600 ST Sedan			700,000
395	4-door Carina 1600 ST Sedan			—
395	Corona 1500 De Luxe Sedan			592,000
395	Corona 1700 De Luxe Sedan			652,000
395	Corona 1700 Hardtop			—
396	Corona 1700 SL Hardtop			768,000
396	Corona 1900 Sedan			—
396	Corona Mk II 1900 Sedan			—
396	Corona Mk II 1900 Hardtop			—
396	Corona Mk II 1900 SL Hardtop			912,500
397	Corona Mk II 1900 GSS Hardtop			1,055,000
397	Celica 1600 GT			875,000
398	Crown SL Hardtop			—
399	Crown De Luxe Sedan	1,145		
399	Crown Hardtop			—
399	Century D Sedan			2,761,000
399	Century A Sedan			2,703,000
399	Century B Sedan			2,356,000
399	Century C Sedan			2,556,000
	TRABANT (Germany, D.R.)			
124	601 Limousine			—
124	601 Universal			—
	TRIUMPH (Great Britain)			
213	Herald 13/60 Saloon	648		
213	Herald 13/60 Convertible	695		
	tonneau cover	10		
214	Herald 13/60 Estate Car	717		
214	Toledo	679		
215	1300	760		
215	1300 TC	754		
215	Spitfire Mk III	669	2,295	
	overdrive	48		
	hardtop	38	150	
	tonneau cover	10		
215	Spitfire Mk IV	735		
216	1500	851		
216	2-litre Mk II Vitesse Saloon	827		
	overdrive	48		
216	2-litre Mk II Vitesse Convertible	865		
	tonneau cover	10		
216	2000 Mk II Saloon	1,185		
216	2000 Mk II Estate Car	1,400		
217	2.5-litre P.I. Mk II Saloon	1,360		
218	2.5-litre P.I. Mk II Estate Car	1,575		
	2000 and 2.5-litre Series: overdrive	50		

Page	MAKE AND MODEL	Price in GB £	Price in USA $	Price ex Works
	automatic gearbox	78		
	175 SR x 13 tyres	9		
	power-assisted steering	40		
218	GT6 Mk II	925	2,995	
219	GT6 Mk III	970		
	GT6 Series: overdrive	48		
219	TR6 P.I.	1,111	3,275	
	overdrive	48		
	wire wheels	38		
	hardtop	37	220	
	tonneau cover	10		
219	Stag	1,650		
	overdrive	50		
	automatic gearbox	80		
	hardtop	37		
	TVR (Great Britain)			
220	Vixen S2	1,242		
	light alloy wheels	48		
220	Tuscan V6	1,558		
	VANDEN PLAS (Great Britain)			
220	Princess 1300	919		
	automatic gearbox	75		
	sunshine roof	40		
	electrically-heated rear window	12		
	VAUXHALL (Great Britain)			
221	Viva	598		
222	Viva De Luxe 2-door Saloon	650		
222	Viva De Luxe 4-door Saloon	675		
222	Viva De Luxe Estate Car	725		
	Viva De Luxe models: 9 compression ratio engine	31		
	automatic gearbox	80		
	6.20 x 13 tyres	4		
	front disc brakes	13		
	electrically-heated rear window	8		
	heavy-duty suspension (only for Estate Car)	9		
222	Viva SL 2-door Saloon	736		
223	Viva SL 4-door Saloon	761		
223	Viva SL Estate Car	806		
	Viva SL models: 97.6 cu in, 1,599 cu cm engine	24		
	automatic gearbox	80		
	electrically-heated rear window	8		
	heavy-duty suspension (only for Estate Car)	9		
223	Victor Super Saloon	796		
223	Victor Super Estate Car	884		
	Victor models: mechanical gearbox	12		
	overdrive	48		
	automatic gearbox	101		
	6.90 x 13 or 165 x 13 tyres	10		
	front disc brakes	13		
	reclining backrests	7		
	electrically-heated rear window	8		
223	Victor 2000 SL Saloon	881		
224	Victor 2000 SL Estate Car	975		
	Victor 2000 models: mechanical gearbox	12		
	overdrive	48		
	automatic gearbox	80		
224	VX 4/90	1,019		
	automatic gearbox	60		
	175/70 HR x 13 tyres	17		
	electrically-heated rear window	7		
224	Ventora 2	1,113		
	overdrive	48		
	automatic gearbox	85		

Page	MAKE AND MODEL	Price in GB £	Price in USA $	Price ex Works
224	*power-assisted steering*	*55*		
	Victor 3300 SL Estate Car	1,085		
	175 HR x 13 tyres	*17*		
	with overdrive 175 HR x 13 tyres	*48*		
	heavy-duty rear suspension	*1*		
	reclining backrests	*7*		
225	Cresta	1,042		
	automatic gearbox	*85*		
	7.00 x 14 tyres	*10*		
	power-assisted steering	*55*		
	reclining backrests	*30*		
	leather upholstery	*18*		
	electrically-heated rear window	*7*		
225	Cresta De Luxe	1,131		
226	Viscount	1,325		
	mechanical gearbox	*— 70*		
	VAZ (USSR)			
272	2101			—
	VOLKSWAGEN (Germany, F.R.)			
158	1200 Standard	534	1,839	
	sunshine roof	*36*	*90*	
	12 V voltage			38
	independent heating			353
159	1200 (1.3-litre)			4,795
	semi-automatic gearbox		*139*	495
159	1300 (1.2-litre)			5,395
159	1300			5,495
	1300 Series:			
	headrests on front seats			45
	front disc brakes (only for 1300)			144
	L equipment			195
159	1302 Limousine	611		5,745
159	1302 S Limousine			5,945
160	1302 LS Cabriolet		2,249	7,490
	1302 Series:			
	semi-automatic gearbox			495
	limited slip final drive			435
	front disc brakes			144
	sunshine roof (except for Cabriolet)	*36*		295
	L equipment (except for Cabriolet)			195
	independent heating			353
160	1600 Karmann-Ghia Coupé		2,399	7,990
160	1600 Karmann-Ghia Cabriolet		2,609	8,790
160	181			8,500
160	1600 A (1.5-litre)			6,725
161	1600 (1.5-litre)			6,980
161	1600 L (1.5-litre)			7,380
161	1600 TA (1.5-litre)			6,725
161	1600 T (1.5-litre)			6,980
161	1600 TL (1.5-litre)			7,380
162	1600 Variant (1.5-litre)			7,180
162	1600 Variant L (1.5-litre)			7,680
	1600 (1.5-litre) Series:			
	sunshine roof	*56*		295
	headrests on front seats			45
	independent heating			353
161	1600 A			6,845
161	1600			7,100
161	1600 L			7,500
161	1600 TA	748	2,339	
161	1600 T			7,100
161	1600 TL			7,500
162	1600 Variant	849	2,750	
162	1600 Variant L			7,800
	1600 Series:			
	electronically-controlled fuel injection system	*102*		485
	automatic gearbox	*90*	*197*	

Page	MAKE AND MODEL	Price in GB £	Price in USA $	Price ex Works
162	K 70 (75 hp)			9,450
163	K 70 L (75 hp)			9,790
163	K 70 (90 hp)			9,645
163	K 70 L (90 hp)			9,985
163	2-door 411 E			8,390
163	4-door 411 E			8,735
163	2-door 411 LE	1,022		8,810
163	4-door 411 LE	1,068		9,155
163	411 E Variant			8,770
163	411 LE Variant	1,094		9,190
	411 Series:			
	automatic gearbox	*90*		800
	sunshine roof	*55*		423
	VOLKSWAGEN-PORSCHE (Germany, F.R.)			
163	914			11,955
164	914 S	1,730	3,595	
164	914/6	2,660	5,999	
	914 Series:			
	semi-automatic gearbox		*315*	
	VOLVO (Sweden)			
266	142 Saloon		3,095	
267	142 De Luxe Saloon			—
267	142 S Saloon			—
267	142 S De Luxe Saloon			—
267	142 Grand Luxe Saloon			—
267	144 Saloon		3,195	
267	144 De Luxe Saloon	1,241		
267	144 S Saloon			—
267	144 S De Luxe Saloon			—
267	144 Grand Luxe Saloon	1,476		
267	145 Station Wagon		3,495	
268	145 De Luxe Station Wagon	1,382		
268	145 S Station Wagon			—
268	145 S De Luxe Station Wagon	1,437		
	142, 144 and 145 Series:			
	automatic gearbox	*85*	*180*	
268	1800 E Coupé		4,495	
268	164 Saloon	1,720	4,070	
	automatic gearbox	*55*		
	WARSZAWA (Poland)			
263	223			—
263	223 K			—
	WARTBURG (Germany, D.R.)			
124	1000-353	572		
125	1000-353 Tourist	611		
	WOLSELEY (Great Britain)			
226	1300 Mk II	740		
	automatic gearbox	*75*		
	reclining backrests	*13*		
	electrically-heated rear window	*8*		
227	Sixteen-Sixty	827		
	automatic gearbox	*68*		
	reclining backrests	*13*		
	electrically-heated rear window	*15*		
227	18/85 Mk II	1,009		
227	18/85 Mk II S	1,058		
	18/85 Series:			
	automatic gearbox	*80*		
	electrically-heated rear window	*15*		
	YLN (China, Taiwan)			
360	801 A			—
	ZAZ (USSR)			
272	Zaporozhets 966 Limousine			—
	ZIL (USSR)			
273	114 Limousine			—